Warman's

THIRTEENTH ANTIQUES
AND THEIR PRICES

by
Edwin G. Warman

A Check List and Guide of
Comparative Prices for
Antique Dealers and Collectors

Published by
E. G. Warman Publishing Inc.
Uniontown, Pennsylvania 15401

Revised
1977

INTRODUCTION

"Antiques and Their Prices," the first and foremost price guide on antiques published in America, celebrates another birthday. It was purely coincidental that the "13th Antiques and Their Prices" publication date corresponded with the birthday celebration of our nation. America had its beginning with 13 states, 13 stripes and 13 stars. It was not intentional!

Prices on all antiques and collectibles continue to rise. More and more people are buying antiques for use, investment purposes, potential appreciation and pleasure. They realize that there is a limited supply of old things available and they are either holding on to what they own or trying to acquire what they can while the supply lasts. Record auction prices are being recorded all over the world. Collectors are buying what they want or need with what seems to be little regard for cost.

Some categories in the collecting field have increased more in value than others. Art glass, cut glass, period furnishings, early china and other 'true' antiques have escalated so in price that they are relatively out of reach to the average buyer. Consequently renewed interests, later periods, neglected areas and recent collectibles are taking a strong hold. Pressed glasswares are experiencing a revival. Objects made of metal such as silver, gold and bronze have always been desirable; but the high cost of the raw material has influenced the price of the finished art works considerably. Folk art, semi-modern porcelains and pottery, prints, late furniture and memorabilia are being eagerly sought out today. The law of supply and demand reigns. The field of new and modern collectibles, such as plates, spoons, and bicentennial items, is one of today's most profitable and major industries. When purchasing these current, new collectibles, consider them first for their aesthetic value rather than as an investment potential. In all probability, it will take several years for a secondary collectors' market to develop.

The prices listed in this book are average retail prices. They were compiled personally with the assistance of an experienced staff. Information was gained by attending antique shows, sales and auctions; from private sources, shops, dealers and collectors. Prices vary from region to region due to availability, demand, condition and interest; they will not always correspond with the prices listed herein. The primary purpose of this book is to be regarded as A GUIDE TO PRICES and NOT THE FINAL AUTHORITY!

It is virtually impossible and impractical to list and cover in depth all the various items deemed important to the many diversified collectors in the antique world. I have attempted to give representative listings of today's most desirable antiques and collectibles.

Every effort has been made to record accurate prices and correct information. However, in the event of clerical, typographical or any other errors, I decline to assume any and all responsibility for loss or losses incurred by the purchasers or users of this book.

Regretfully, I am personally unable to reply to the many requests I receive for information and prices from individuals. I suggest additional information can be obtained by attending antique shows and sales, consulting private dealers, reference books and trade publications. These are all invaluable aids for becoming a more knowledgeable and advanced collector.

Happy Antiquing!

Edwin G. Warman

ACKNOWLEDGMENTS

Allen, Mary Jane, Pittsburgh, Pa.
Ann's Antiques, Butler, Pa.
Antique Cellar, The, Vanderbilt, Pa.
Antique Lady, The, Allison Park, Pa.
Apt, Bette M., Pittsburgh, Pa.
Back Door Antiques, New Castle, Pa.
Blair, Elsie, Hopwood, Pa.
Boden, Julia Antiques, McKeesport, Pa.
Bowen's Antiques, Kensington, Md.
Brandywine Valley Antiques, Chadds Ford, Pa.
Brass Lantern Antiques, Willey Ford, W.Va.
Briar Hill Manor Antiques, Kittanning, Pa.
Brighton House Antiques, Beaver, Pa.
Brown, T. & R.
Burroughs Antiques, Washington, Pa.
Candlewood Antiques & Gifts, Monroeville, Pa.
Chillingworth, Peter, Scenery Hill, Pa.
Country Store, The, Laughlintown, Pa.
Decker, Sally Ann, Morgantown, W.Va.
Dell's Antiques, Denver, N.C.
Dematteo, Nancy, Troy, Ohio
Don & Shirley's Antiques, McMurray, Pa.
Donavan's, Norvelt, Pa.
Double "O", The, Washington, Pa.
Downer, Albert, Ruffs Creek, Pa.
Dryfoos, Leon, Antiques, Erie, Pa.
Economy Village Antiques, Ambridge, Pa.
Eller, E. R., Pittsburgh, Pa.
Feeny, Bill, Antiques, Ligonier, Pa.
Fischer & Strassler, Mt. Lebanon, Pa.
Frank, Hilda & Lou, Pittsburgh, Pa.
Free, Faye C., New Stanton, Pa.
Frost, Jean, Columbus, Ohio
Gaines, Betty, Mt. Lebanon, Pa.
Gates, John F., Photographer, Uniontown, Pa.
Gazing Ball, The, Lundhurst, Ohio
George, Majory, Fox Chapel, Pa.
Glentiques Ltd., Glenford, N.Y.
Goldian's Antiques, Colver, Pa.
Gould, Barbara, New Kensington, Pa.
Hallmark House, Barnesville, Ohio
Hawkin's Antiques, Willoughby, Ohio
Helmick, D. K., Photographer, Uniontown, Pa.
Herr, Charlotte, Beech Creek, Pa.
Hevener, Neil, Charlottesville, Va.
Hi-Wheel Antiques, Cumberland, Md.
Hodges, Charles A., Miamisburg, Ohio
Imperial Antiques, Shadyside, Ohio
Johnson, Betty, Glassport, Pa.
Kay's Antique Shop, New Stanton, Pa.

Kent House Antiques, Magadore, Ohio
King of Crystal, Cedar Grove, N.J.
Kinzle's Antiques, Duncansville, Pa.
Kocevar's Antiques, Manheim, Pa.
Kraybill's, Sewickley, Pa.
Laura's Antiques & Curios, Coraopolis, Pa.
Lloyd's Antiques, Wellsburg, W.Va.
Lohmann, Davis Ltd., Salem, W.Va.
Lou-Ral Antique, Pittsburgh, Pa.
Mac's Antiques, Terra Alta, W.Va.
Marshall's Antiques, Brockway, Pa.
Matzie's, H., Huntingdon, Pa.
McMillan, Marge, Pittsburgh, Pa.
Mohney, Mary S., Washington, Pa.
Neville, Thomas, Quincy, Illinois
New Strom Antiques, Hartford, Connecticut
Old Company Store, The, Ursina, Pa.
Old Pike Antiques, Addison, Pa.
Olstad, Rose, Bar Harbor, Me.
Our Family Tree, Colerain, Ohio
Our House, Belmont, Ohio
Palmer, Frank R., Mt. Vernon, Ohio
Palmer, H. Meredith, Uniontown, Pa.
Plain & Fancy, Columbus, Ohio
Resh's Antiques, Lancaster, Pa.
Reed, Patricia Anne, Newcastle, Maine
Richardson, Pick, Reynoldsburg, Ohio
Rivera, Sergio, Philadelphia, Pa.
Rizzoto, Michael, York Springs, Va.
Ross Antiques, Fairmont, W.Va.
Rush House Antiques, Farmington, Pa.
Saul, M. & L., Washington, Pa.
Schmunk, Joan, Beaver, Pa.
Shanaberger's, Farmington, Pa.
Shoestring Antiques, Wexford, Pa.
Stout, June, Prosperity, Pa.
Vallos, Ethel, Youngstown, Ohio
Village Antiques, Columbus, Ohio
Wainright, W. Allen, Medina, Ohio
Walker, Dorothy, Pittsburgh, Pa.
We Two Antiques, Wheeling, W.Va.
Webb, Dorothy, Ambridge, Pa.
Westco Antiques, Hosletter, Pa.
Whales's Tale, The, Cridens Corner, Pa.
White House Antiques, Pittsburgh, Pa.
Wilson's, Hickory, Pa.
Woodring, Jane, Seville, Ohio
Wright, Richard, Spring City, Pa.
Wyatt, Betty, Bridgeport, W.Va.
Ye Ole Mill Antiques, Pittsburgh, Pa.

If I have overlooked anyone who so kindly permitted me to photograph items or assisted me in any way to compile the "13th Antiques and Their Prices," it was not intentional; and my sincerest apologies. Thank you for your generosity and interest in helping to make this book possible.

PATTERN GLASS

SECTION ONE

CLEAR GLASS PATTERNS

Quotations listed on Pattern Glass are retail prices for pieces in perfect condition. All prices are on clear glass. The Colored Glass Section follows this group and is designated as "Section Two." Each pattern is illustrated with an original drawing or photograph. Items marked with an asterisk (*), have been, or are now being reproduced.

ACTRESS
[Theatrical, Goddess of Liberty, Annie]

Made by Labelle Glass Co., Bridgeport, Ohio, C 1872.

ALABAMA
[Beaded Bull's Eye and Drape]

Made by U. S. Glass Co., C 1898.

Bowl, footed, 6" ....$	40.00
Butter dish........................	65.00
Cake stand	62.50
Celery	60.00
Cheese dish, covered	100.00
Compote	
Covered, high standard	100.00
Covered, low standard	85.00
Open, 7"	30.00
Open, 10"	60.00
Creamer	55.00
Goblet	67.50
Honey dish, covered	60.00
Marmalade jar	55.00
*Pickle	22.50
Pitcher	
Pinafore, 9¼ x 12¾", oval	42.00
Miss Nielson center.............	52.50
Sauce	
Flat...........................	12.50
Footed	15.00
Shakers, pair.....................	50.00
Spooner	45.00
Sugar bowl	60.00
Tray, bread	50.00

*Reproduced Item

Butter dish, covered...............$	23.00
Compote, open, 5"	20.00
Creamer	22.00
Honey dish	12.00
Pickle	12.00
Pitcher, water	40.00
Spooner.........................	13.50
Sugar bowl, covered	22.50
Syrup	29.50

ALMOND THUMBPRINT
[Pointed Thumbprint, Finger Print]

Made by Bryce Bros., Pittsburgh, Pa., C 1890.

Butter dish........................$	78.00
Celery	60.00
Champagne.......................	60.00

Compote, covered
    4¾", high standard 42.00
    7", high standard 55.00
    10", high standard 75.00
    4¾", low standard 36.00
    7", low standard 42.50
Cordial 60.00
Creamer 65.00
Cruet, footed 65.00
Decanter 50.00
Egg cup 30.00
Goblet 42.50
Punch bowl 125.00
Salt
    Individual 10.00
    Large, flat 12.00
    Footed, covered 30.00
Sugar bowl 55.00
Sweetmeat jar, covered, 6" 90.00
Tumbler 36.50

AMAZON
[Sawtooth Band]

Banana stand . . . . $ 35.00
Bowl, open 18.50
Butter dish 28.00
Cake stand 30.00
Celery 20.00
Champagne 17.50
Claret 15.00
Compote
    Jelly, 5½" 22.00
    Open, high standard 37.50
Cordial 16.50
Flower vase 19.50
Goblet 16.00
Pitcher
    Syrup 22.50
    Water 38.00
Sauce, flat, 4½" 9.00
Shakers, pair 24.00
Spooner 18.00
Sugar bowl 28.00

Tumbler 12.00
Wine 12.50

AMBERETTE
[See Colored Glass Section]

ANTHEMION

Made by Model Flint Glass Co., Findlay, Ohio, 1890 period.

Bowl, berry, 7" . . . . $ 22.50
Butter dish 27.50
Cake plate, 9¼" 30.00
Celery 16.50
Creamer 20.00
Marmalade jar 15.00
Pitcher 35.00
Plate, 10" 30.00
Sauce 10.00
Spooner 30.00
Sugar bowl 27.50
Tumbler 22.50

APOLLO

Made first by Adams & Co., C. 1875; secondly, by McKee Bros., about 1895. Both of Pittsburgh, Pa.

Bowl . . . . $ 12.00
Butter dish 32.50
Cake stand 28.50
Celery 23.50
Compote
    Covered, high standard 45.00
    Open, low standard 32.50
Creamer 28.00
Goblet 20.00

Pickle	12.50
Pitcher, water	37.50
Sauce	
Flat	6.50
Footed	10.00
Spooner	16.50
Sugar bowl	32.00
Tray, water	25.00
Tumbler	11.50
Wine	12.50

ARABESQUE

Produced by Bakewell, Pears & Co., Pittsburgh, Pa. C. 1862-64.

Butter dish	$ 40.00
Celery	25.00
Compote	
Covered, 6", high standard	40.00
Covered, 8", low standard	40.00
Covered, 8", high standard	45.00
Creamer	42.50
Goblet	22.50
Pitcher	37.50
Sauce	10.00
Spooner	35.00
Sugar bowl	45.00

ARCHED GRAPE

Produced by Sandwich Glass Co. in 1870's.

Butter dish	$ 42.50
Celery	35.00

Compote	
Covered, high standard	48.50
Covered, low standard	42.00
Cordial	15.00
Creamer	35.00
Goblet	25.00
Pitcher	50.00
Sauce	10.00
Spooner	30.00
Sugar bowl	40.00
Wine	22.50

ARGUS

Bakewell, Pears & Co. made this thumbprint-type pattern in flint glass at Pittsburgh in the early 1870's.

Ale glass	$ 35.00
Bitters bottle	38.50
Bowl, 5½"	32.00
Butter dish	50.00
Celery	60.00
Champagne	55.00
Cordial	20.00
Creamer	55.00
Decanter	
Pint	55.00
Quart	65.00
Egg cup	22.50
Goblet	40.00
Lamp, footed	50.00
Mug, applied handle [scarce]	65.00
Salt, open	16.50
Sauce	17.50
Spooner	35.00
Sugar bowl	65.00
Tumbler	
Footed	30.00
Jelly	22.50
Water	27.50
Wine	50.00

ART
[Teardrop, Diamond Block, Job's Tears]

Produced by Adams & Co., Pittsburgh, Pa., in the 1870's.

Banana dish [scarce]	$ 85.00

Basket, fruit	45.00
Bowl, berry, 8"	25.00
Butter dish......................	37.50
Cake stand, 10"	35.00
Celery	30.00
Compote	
Covered, 7", footed	42.50
Open, 7½", footed	35.00
Open, 10"	40.00
Cracker jar	25.00
Creamer	30.00
Cruet	25.00
Goblet	27.50
Mug	17.50
Pickle	15.00
Pitcher, water	45.00
Sauce	8.50
Spooner	18.50
Sugar bowl	35.00
Tumbler	13.50
Vinegar jug	
½ pint	20.00
3 pints	25.00

ASHBURTON

A popular pattern in large thumbprint, in the mid 1850's to 1860. Made by New England Glass Co., Cambridge, Mass., Sandwich Glass Co., in Mass., and McKee Bros., Pittsburgh, Pa.

Ale glass	$	40.00
Bitters bottle		42.50
Butter dish......................		95.00

Celery		
Plain top		65.00
Scalloped top		85.00
Champagne.....................		55.00
*Cordial........................		50.00
Creamer [Scarce]................		145.00
Decanter		
Pint...........................		62.50
Quart.........................		75.00
3 pints		80.00
Egg cup		23.50
Goblet		
*Flaring sides		60.00
Straight sides		50.00
Jug		
Pint...........................		75.00
*Quart........................		90.00
3 pints		100.00
Lamp		65.00
*Lemonade glass		45.00
Mug		50.00
Sauce		18.50
Spooner.......................		37.50
*Sugar bowl		100.00
Toddy jar, covered [rare]		225.00
Tumbler		
Jelly		25.00
Water.........................		35.00
Whiskey		45.00
Wine bottle, with tumble-up		135.00
*Wine.........................		45.00

*Reproduced Item

ATLANTA
[Clear Lion Head]

Produced C. 1898, by Fostoria Glass Co., Moundsville, W. Va.

Bowl, berry	$	17.50
Butter dish, covered..............		39.50
Cake stand		40.00
Celery		35.00
Compote		
Covered, 5", square stem........		45.00
Open, 5", square stem		35.00
Creamer		30.00
Goblet		28.50

Marmalade jar	22.50
Pickle	14.00
Salt	12.00
Sauce	10.00
Spooner	22.50
Sugar bowl, covered	37.50
Toothpick	14.50

BABY FACE

Butter dish	$ 110.00
Cake stand	
Large	63.50
Small	86.00
Celery vase	60.00
Compote	
*Covered, small	110.00
Open, large	100.00
Cordial	75.00
Creamer	100.00
*Goblet	85.00
Lamp	85.00
Pitcher	160.00
Salt dip	27.50
Sauce, footed	22.50
Spooner	65.00
*Sugar bowl	110.00
*Wine	44.50

*Reproduced Item

BABY THUMBPRINT, See Dakota

BALL AND SWIRL

Bowl, finger	$ 11.50
Butter dish	37.50
Cake stand	25.50

Compote	
Covered, high standard	40.00
Open, high standard	25.00
Cordial	17.50
Creamer	25.00
Decanter	26.00
Goblet	14.00
Mug	
Large	13.50
Small	11.50
Pitcher	
Tankard	46.00
Water	32.50
Sauce, footed	10.00
Spooner	14.50
Sugar bowl	37.50
Tumbler	11.50
Wine	14.50

BALTIMORE PEAR
[Gypsy, Double Pear, Twin Pear]

Bowl	
Berry	$ 28.00
Covered	40.00
*Butter dish	46.00
*Cake stand	55.00
*Celery	40.00
Compote	
Covered, 6", high standard	69.00
Covered, 7", high standard	78.00
Covered, 8", high standard	84.00
Covered, 8¼", low standard	75.00
Open, large	48.50
*Creamer	40.00
*Goblet	34.50
Pickle	17.50
*Pitcher, water	69.00
Plate, 10"	42.50
Sauce	
Flat	9.50
Footed, large	13.50
*Footed, small	15.50
Spooner	30.00
*Sugar bowl	46.00

*Reproduced Item

BAMBOO
[Notched Rib]

Made in the middle 1880's by Labelle Glass Co., Bridgeport, Ohio.

Butter dish ....$	23.00
Celery	17.50
Compote	
Covered, 7"......................	32.50
Covered, 8"......................	37.00
Covered, 9"......................	43.50
Creamer	21.00
Dish	
Oblong, 7"	9.00
Oblong, 8"	10.50
Oblong, 9"	13.50
Pitcher, water	30.50
Sauce, 4"	7.00
Shakers, pair.....................	21.00
Spooner	13.50
Sugar bowl, covered	23.00
Tumbler	14.00

BARBERRY

Bowl, 8", covered ....$	23.00
Butter dish......................	45.00
Cake plate......................	29.00
Celery	45.00
Compote	
Covered, high standard	52.00
Covered, 8", low standard	40.00
Cordial.........................	30.00
Creamer	45.00
Dish, oval, 8x5½"	22.50

Egg cup	25.00
Goblet	25.00
Honey dish, 3½"	11.50
Pickle	28.00
Pitcher	55.00
Plate	
6"	25.00
Cup plate size.................	17.50
Salt, footed	15.00
Sauce	
Flat..........................	12.00
Footed	13.00
Spooner	42.50
Sugar bowl	55.00
Syrup jug, pewter top	65.00
Wine...........................	11.50

BARLEY

Butter dish......................$	29.00
Cake stand, 9"	29.00
Celery	30.00
Compote, covered, 8½"	46.00
Cordial	17.50
Creamer	25.00
Dish, oval, 6½x9½"	17.00
Goblet	22.50
Marmalade jar	27.50
Pickle, open handles	17.50
Pitcher	34.00
Plate, 6"........................	21.00
Platter	32.00
Sauce	
Flat..........................	9.00
Footed, 4"	10.50
Footed, 5"	12.00
Spooner........................	27.50
Sugar bowl	31.00
Wine...........................	14.00

BARRED FORGET-ME-NOT
[See Colored Glass Section]

BASKETWEAVE
[See Colored Glass Section]

BEADED ACORN MEDALLION

Butter dish ....$	28.00
Compote	
Covered, high standard	44.00
Covered, low standard	34.50
Creamer	42.50
Dish, oval.......................	13.50
Egg cup	16.00
Goblet	25.00
Honey dish	10.50
Pickle	11.00
Pitcher	37.00
Plate, 6"..........................	22.50
Salt, footed	15.00
Sauce	6.50
Spooner..........................	27.50
Sugar bowl	29.00
Wine.............................	9.50

BEADED BAND

Butter dish......................$	26.00
Cake stand	21.00
Celery	20.00
Compote, covered	55.00
Cordial..........................	22.50
Creamer	21.00
Goblet	25.00
Marmalade jar	19.00
Pickle	24.50
Pitcher	
Syrup	40.00
Water...........................	42.50
Platter	16.50
Sauce	12.00
Shakers, pair....................	16.50

Spooner	35.00
Sugar bowl	26.00

BEADED DEWDROP
[Wisconsin]

Made in 1898-99 by U. S. Glass Co., Gas City, Indiana.

Bowl	
Covered, oblong, 6", 8" ....$	15.00
Covered, round, 7", 8"	19.00
Butter dish	
Handled.......................	45.00
Large	55.00
Small	45.00
Cake plate, 9½" standard	42.00
Celery	45.00
Celery tray	35.00
Compote	
Covered, 6", 7", 8"............	46.00
Open, 8½", 9½", 10½"	32.00
Condiment set. 4 pieces in holder ...	55.00
Creamer	
Individual	35.00
Large	45.00
Cruet	16.00
Cup and saucer...................	19.00
Dish	
Candy	15.00
Handled, oval, 6", covered.......	42.50
Handled, oval, 6", open	13.50
Sweetmeat	21.00
Goblet	42.50
Mug	35.00
Pitcher	
3 pints	55.00
½ gallon	60.00
Sauce	
Handled, 5½"..................	12.00
Flat, 4".......................	10.00
Shakers	
Squatty, pair...................	30.00
Tall, pair	35.00
Spooner.........................	18.50
Sugar bowl	
Large, covered	50.00
Small, covered	42.50
Syrup	45.00
Toothpick holder	25.00

| Tumbler | 35.00 |
| Wine | 35.00 |

BEADED GRAPE
[See Colored Glass Section]

BEADED GRAPE MEDALLION

Made by Boston Silver Glass Co., C. 1867-68, at Cambridge, Mass.

Butter dish	$ 45.00
Castor bottle	10.50
Celery	55.00
Compote	
Covered, 7¼", 8¼", large, high standard	55.00
Covered, low standard	50.00
Covered, oval, collared base, 10 x 7"	44.50
Cordial	35.00
Creamer, applied handle [scarce]	70.00
Dish, oval, large	60.00
Egg cup	27.50
Goblet	30.00
Honey dish	9.50
Lamp, handled	29.00
Pickle	11.50
Pitcher	80.00
Plate, 6"	17.50
Salt	
Footed	16.00
Oval, flat	12.00
Round, flat	12.00
Celery dip	6.00
Sauce	10.50
Spooner	30.00
Sugar bowl	52.50

BEADED LOOP
[Oregon]

Made C. 1906-08 by U. S. Glass Co., one of the States' series.

Bowl, berry, covered	$ 18.50
Butter dish	28.00
Cake stand	35.00

Celery	32.50
Compote, open	23.00
Cordial	14.00
Creamer	25.00
Dish, oval	20.00
Goblet	25.00
Mug	15.50
Pickle	18.00
Pitcher	
Milk	28.00
Syrup	23.00
Water	35.00
Sauce	8.00
Shakers	
Salt and pepper	21.00
Sugar	19.00
Spooner	30.00
Sugar bowl	28.00
Toothpick holder	9.00
Tray, bread	18.50
Tumbler	22.50
Wine	22.50

BEADED OVAL AND SCROLL
[Dot]

Made by Bryce Bros., Pittsburgh, Pa. C. 1878-90.

Bowl, 6¼"	$ 13.50
Butter dish	30.00
Cake stand	22.50
Compote, high standard	35.00
Cordial	22.50
Creamer	30.00
Dish, oval	30.00
Goblet	22.50
Pickle	16.00

Pitcher	42.50
Sauce	12.00
Shakers, pair	18.50
Spooner	30.00
Sugar bowl	40.00

BEADED TULIP
[Andes]

Bowl	$ 17.50
Butter dish	37.50
Compote, covered, high standard	34.50
Cake stand	40.00
Cordial	27.00
Creamer	23.00
Dish, oval, 9½" long	14.00
Goblet	30.00
Lamp	21.00
Marmalade jar	17.50
Pickle	11.50
Pitcher	
Milk	27.50
Water	32.00
Plate, 6"	25.00
Sauce	
Flat	9.50
Footed	12.00
Spooner	27.50
Sugar bowl	34.00
Tray, water	35.00
Wine	17.50

BEARDED MAN
[Old Man of the Woods, Neptune, Santa Claus, Old Man, Queen Anne]

First made by La Belle Glass Co., Bridgeport, Ohio in the late 1870's. Later reissued in the 1912-1915 period.

Butter dish	$ 37.50
Celery	28.50
Compote, covered, 7", 8"	42.00
Creamer	25.00
Pitcher, water	50.00
Sauce, 4½", footed	19.00

Spooner	25.00
Sugar bowl	35.00

BELLFLOWER
[Ribbed Leaf]

First made by Sandwich Glass Co., C. 1850. Later produced by McKee Bros., Pittsburgh, Pa. C. 1870. At present time the single vine goblet is being reproduced. The old has a crystal clear resonant ring common to flint glass when tapped. The new does not have this tone.

SINGLE VINE   DOUBLE VINE

Bowl	
Berry, flat, scalloped edge	$ 82.50
Flat, 8"	90.00
Deep	75.00
Butter dish	
Beaded edge	72.00
Plain edge	62.50
Scalloped edge	75.00
Cake stand [rare]	---------
Castor bottle	30.00
Celery	
Clear marginal band	125.00
Ribbed top	140.00
Champagne	65.00
Compote	
Covered, 8", high standard	160.00
Covered, 8", low standard	140.00
Open, 8", high standard, scalloped top	75.00
Open, low standard, scalloped top	67.50
Open, 9¾" diam., 8½" high	69.50
Open, low standard, small	65.00
Cordial	65.00

Creamer		
Double vine		95.00
Single vine		100.00
Decanter		
Double vine, quart		105.00
Single vine, pint		97.50
Single vine, quart		92.50
Dish, oval, large		70.00
Egg cup		35.00
*Goblet, single vine		37.50
Honey dish		20.00
Lamp		
All glass		85.00
Bracket lamp		80.00
Marble base		95.00
Mug, applied handle		110.00
Pickle, 5x7" [scarce]		85.00
Pitcher		
Milk, double vine [scarce]		450.00
Syrup, hexagonal		550.00
Syrup, round		170.00
Water, double vine		145.00
*Water, single vine		135.00
Plate, 6¼"		72.50
Salt		
Covered, footed [rare]		130.00
Open, footed		30.00
Sauce		17.50
Spooner		
Double vine		48.00
Single vine		40.00
Sugar bowl		
Double vine		80.00
Single vine		70.00
Tumbler		49.50
Whiskey glass		120.00
Wine		45.00

*Reproduced Item

BIGLER

Bowl		$	45.00
Celery			60.00
Champagne			75.00
Cordial			75.00
Goblet			28.00
Mug			45.00
Plate, toddy			35.00

Salt		11.00
Tumbler, water		45.00

BIRD AND STRAWBERRY
[Bluebird]

Bowl			
5"		$	12.00
7½", berry, footed			40.00
9½", oval, footed			42.50
10½", berry			50.00
Butter dish, covered			29.00
Cake stand, 9"			29.00
Compote, covered, 6"			40.00
Creamer			40.00
Cup, punch			10.50
Goblet			19.00
Pickle dish			17.50
Sauce, 5¼"			8.00
Spooner			14.00
Sugar bowl, covered			29.00
Tumbler			11.50
Wine			16.00

BLACKBERRY
[See Colored Glass Section]

BLAZE
[Stedman]

Bowl, 7", 8"		$	21.50
Butter dish			46.00
Celery			55.00
Champagne			45.00
Cheese plate			21.50
Compote			
Covered, 7", 8", low standard			55.00

Open, 8", 9", 10", high standard ..	40.00
Open, 8", 9", low standard	32.00
Cordial	40.00
Creamer	65.00
Custard cup	17.00
Decanter	40.00
Dish, oval	16.00
Egg cup	22.50
Goblet	32.50
Lemonade glass	25.00
Pickle	13.00
Plate	
6" . . . •	17.00
7"	21.50
Sauce	
4"	8.50
5"	9.50
Shakers, pair	23.00
Spooner	30.00
Sugar bowl	46.00
Tumbler	25.00
Wine	40.00

BLEEDING HEART

Bowl	
Berry, covered, 7¼", 8¼"	27.50
Waste	27.50
Butter dish	46.00
Cake stand, 9½"	50.00
Compote	
Covered, high standard	55.00
Covered, low standard	46.00
Covered, oval	45.00
Cordial	26.00
Creamer	40.00
Dish, oval	21.00
Egg cup	24.00
Goblet	
Plain stem	24.00
Knob stem	29.00
Mug	26.50
Pickle	
Oval	21.00
Relish dish, 4 sections	55.00
Pitcher	
Milk	63.00
Water	68.50
Plate	60.00
Platter, oval	60.00

Salt, oval	24.00
Sauce	11.50
Spooner	35.00
Sugar bowl	46.00
Tumbler	
Footed	28.00
Water	25.50
Wine	30.00

BLOCK AND FAN
[Romeo]

A pattern of the mid 1880's, made by Richards & Hartley Glass Co., located in Tarentum, Pa.

Bowl	
7½" . . . . $	15.00
9¾"	22.50
Butter dish	29.00
Cake stand	21.50
Celery	17.50
Compote	29.00
Cordial	14.50
Creamer	21.50
Cruet, handled, original stopper	
Large	30.00
Small	22.50
Goblet	18.50
Lamp	19.00
Marmalade jar	18.50
Pickle	11.50
Pitcher	26.00
Plate	17.50
Sauce	9.00
Shakers, pair	25.00
Spooner	15.00
Sugar bowl	29.00
Tumbler	14.50
Wine	21.00

BLOCK AND PLEAT
[Three Stories, Persian]

Bowl	
Oval, 8" . . . . $	10.50
Oval, 9"	11.50
Oval, 10"	13.00
Fruit, round, 6"	9.00
Fruit, round, 7"	10.50

Fruit, round, 8"	12.00
Butter dish, covered	25.00
Celery	16.00
Creamer	15.00
Goblet	14.50
Mug	12.00
Pickle, handled	13.50
Pitcher, water	25.00
Platter, bread, oval	16.50
Sauce	
Flat, 5"	6.00
Footed, 4"	7.50
Spooner	14.50
Sugar bowl, covered	25.00
Tumbler	9.50

BOW-TIE

Made by Thompson Glass Co., C. 1890, in Uniontown, Pa.

Bowl, open, 10"	$ 40.00
Butter dish	57.50
Cake stand	50.00
Compote, open, 10", on standard	78.50
Creamer	40.00
Goblet	35.00
Marmalade jar	39.50
Pitcher	60.00
Salt, individual, open	9.50
Sauce	12.50
Spooner	22.50
Sugar bowl, covered	57.00
Wine	25.00

BROKEN COLUMN
[Irish Column, Rattan and Notched Rib]

Made in Findlay, Ohio about 1891-92 by Columbia Glass Co.

Banana stand	$ 35.00
Bowl	
Berry, various sizes	17.50
Covered, various sizes	20.00
Butter dish	30.00
Cake stand	32.50
Celery	24.00
Compote	
Covered, high standard	40.00
Open, high standard	30.00
Cracker jar	25.00
Creamer	22.50
Cruet	17.50
Cup and saucer	24.00
Dish, oblong	16.00
Finger bowl	14.50
*Goblet	25.00
Pickle	12.00
Pitcher, ½ gallon	35.00
Plate	
6"	13.50
7" [scarce]	32.50
8"	22.50
Sauce	8.50
Shakers, pair	18.50
Spooner	14.50
Sugar bowl	32.50
Syrup	23.50
Tumbler	13.50
Water bottle	25.00
Wine	17.50

*Reproduced Item

BRYCE
[Ribbon Candy]

First made by Bryce Bros., Pittsburgh, Pa. in the late 1880's. Factory was acquired by U. S. Glass Co. in 1889. The pattern was again produced in 1898-99.

Bowl	
Berry, 8"	$ 12.50

Covered, 5", 6"	17.50
Covered, 7", 8"	22.50
Butter dish	25.00
Cake stand	19.50
Celery	16.00
Compote	
Covered, high standard	37.50
Covered, low standard	32.00
Open, high standard	24.00
Cordial	12.00
Creamer	23.50
Cruet	15.00
Goblet	14.50
Honey dish, covered	15.00
Pickle	9.50
Pitcher	
Milk, quart	25.00
Syrup	19.50
Water, ½ gallon	30.00
Plate	
6", 7", 8"	12.50
9", 10"	20.00
Spooner	15.00
Sugar bowl	24.50
Tumbler	14.50
Wine	14.00

BUCKLE

Made by Gillinder & Sons in Philadelphia, Pa., in 1870's. Possibly earlier by Sandwich Glass Co., In Massachusetts.

Butter dish	$ 65.00
Compote	
Covered, high standard	60.00
Covered, low standard	52.50

Cordial	50.00
Creamer	70.00
Dish, oval	30.00
Egg cup	32.50
Goblet	42.50
Pickle	30.00
Pitcher	92.50
Salt	
Footed	15.00
Oval	24.50
Sauce	12.50
Spooner	42.50
Sugar bowl	48.00
Tumbler	37.50
Wine	50.00

BUCKLE, BANDED

Butter dish	$ 45.00
Compote, covered	50.00
Cordial	30.00
Creamer	40.00
Egg cup	18.50
Goblet	25.00
Pickle, oval	22.50
Pitcher	
Syrup	27.50
Water	55.00
Salt, master, footd	16.50
Sauce	8.00
Spooner	25.00
Sugar bowl	42.50
Tumbler	20.00
Wine	15.00

BUCKLE, LATE
[Jasper]

Butter dish	$ 27.50
Cake stand	35.00
Celery	25.00
Compote	
Covered, 8", 9", high standard	39.50
Open, 10", 12", scalloped edge	42.50
Creamer	30.00
Dish, oval, deep	12.50
*Goblet	19.50
Lamp	28.50
Pickle	15.00

Pitcher	30.00
Salt, footed	10.50
Sauce	
Flat, 4½"	9.50
Large, 5½"	15.00
Shakers, pair	24.00
Spooner	30.00
Sugar bowl	32.50
Wine	18.50

*Reproduced Item

BUCKLE WITH STAR
[Orient]

Bowl, covered, 6"	$ 30.00
Butter dish	35.00
Cake stand	21.50
Celery	17.50
Compote	
Covered, large, high standard	47.50
Covered, small, high standard	34.00
Covered, low standard	36.50
Creamer	45.00
Dish	
Oval, 7", 8"	17.50
Oval, 9", 10"	30.00
Goblet	24.00
Marmalade jar	17.50
Pickle	20.00
Pitcher	
Syrup	40.00
Water	26.00
Salt, footed	13.50

Sauce	
Flat, 4"	12.00
Footed	8.50
Spooner	30.00
Sugar bowl	40.00
Tumbler	20.00
Wine	12.00

BUDDED IVY

Butter dish	$ 40.00
Compote	
Covered, high standard	50.00
Covered, low standard	45.00
Creamer	40.00
Goblet	37.50
Pickle	11.50
Pitcher	
Syrup	45.00
Water	29.00
Salt, footed	15.00
Sauce, 4"	7.50
Spooner	32.50
Sugar bowl	35.00

BULL'S EYE
[Lawrence]

Made by New England Glass Co. in early 1870's.

Butter dish	$ 75.00
Castor bottle	18.50
Celery	52.00
Champagne	63.50
Cologne bottle	50.00
Compote	
Open, large, high standard	75.00
Open, low standard	63.50

Cordial	35.00
Creamer	71.50
Cruet	40.50
Decanter	46.00
Egg cup	38.50
Goblet	37.50
Jar, covered	50.00
Lamp	60.00
Lemonade glass	27.50
Pickle	27.50
Salt	
Flat	17.50
Footed, oblong	29.00
Spooner	30.00
Sugar bowl	79.00
Tumbler	40.50
Water bottle	49.00
Wine	40.50

Mustard jar, Britannia, metal cover	49.00
Pitcher, tankard, 10¼"	115.00
Sauce	17.00
Spooner	46.00
Sugar bowl	83.50
Tumbler	
Water	46.00
Whiskey	72.50
Water bottle	106.50
Wine	34.50

BULL'S EYE WITH FLEUR-DE-LIS

Bowl, fruit, flat .... $	75.00
Butter dish	85.00
Celery	80.00
Compote	
Open, high standard	86.50
Open, low standard	72.00
Cordial	40.50
Creamer	100.50
Decanter	
Pint	55.00
Quart	79.00
Goblet	45.00
Lamp	
All glass	52.00
Marble base	100.00
Pitcher [scarce]	175.00
Plate, 10"	46.00
Salt, footed	29.00
Sugar bowl	85.00

BULL'S EYE WITH DIAMOND POINT
[Union]

Banana stand .... $	80.50
Bowl	
Flat, 6"	46.00
Flat, 7"	53.50
Flat, 8"	69.00
Butter dish	80.50
Candlesticks, pair	66.00
Celery	80.00
Champagne	63.50
Cologne bottle	67.00
Compote	
High standard, 6", 7"	106.50
High standard, 8", 9"	113.00
Low standard, 6", 7"	86.50
Low standard, 8", 9"	92.00
Cordial	57.50
Creamer	132.50
Decanter	
Bar lip, pint	75.00
Bar lip, quart	86.50
With stopper, pint	65.00
With stopper, quart	90.00
Egg cup	69.00
Goblet	55.00
Honey dish	20.00
Lemonade glass	46.00

BUTTON BAND

Bowl	$ 11.50
Butter dish	23.00
Cake stand	21.50
Compote, open, small	26.00
Creamer	19.00
Goblet	14.00
Pitcher, water	27.00
Sugar bowl	23.00
Tumbler	9.00
Wine	11.50

CABBAGE LEAF [CLEAR]

Bowl	$ 39.00
*Butter dish	49.00
*Celery	53.50
Cheese dish	45.50
*Compote, covered, high standard	66.00
*Creamer	40.50
Pickle dish, leaf-shape	22.50
*Pitcher, water	65.00
*Plate, rabbit head in center	41.50
*Sauce, 3½"	11.00
*Spooner	35.00
*Sugar bowl	60.00

*Reproduced Item

CABBAGE LEAF [FROSTED]

Bowl, covered	$ 56.00
*Butter dish	55.50
*Celery	57.00
Cheese dish	57.50
Compote, covered, high standard	86.50
*Creamer	52.00
Pickle dish, leaf-shape	40.00
Pitcher, water	75.00
*Plate, rabbit head center	46.00
Sauce, 3½"	14.50
Spooner	50.00
*Sugar bowl	75.00

NOTE: Goblet is of recent origin and is not listed.

*Reproduced Item

CABBAGE ROSE

Bowl, berry, oval	$ 24.00

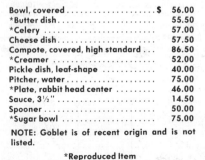

Butter dish	49.00
Cake stand, 11"	60.00
Celery	45.00
Compote	
Covered, 6", 7"	50.50
Covered, 8", 9"	56.00
Cordial	32.50
Creamer	55.00
Egg cup	23.00
*Goblet	42.50
Pickle	16.00
Pitcher	
Quart	57.50
3 pints [scarce]	100.50
Plate	
8½" [scarce]	57.50
10½" [rare]	144.00
Salt, footed	17.50
Sauce	11.50
Spooner	45.00
Sugar bowl	49.00
Tumbler	35.00
Wine [scarce]	36.00

*Reproduced Item

CABLE

Butter dish	$ 65.00
Celery	60.00
Champagne	65.00
Compote	
High standard	60.50
Low standard	49.00
Open, extra large	72.00
Cordial	55.00
Creamer	69.00

Decanter	
Pint	75.00
Quart	82.50
Egg cup	25.00
Goblet	47.50
Honey dish	11.00
Lamp	
All glass	52.00
Hand lamp	42.00
Marble base	65.00
Mug	60.00
Pitcher	167.00
Plate, 6"	49.00
Salt	
Celery dip	10.00
Footed	34.50
Sauce	11.00
Spooner	42.50
Sugar bowl	75.00
Tumbler, footed	65.00
Wine	55.00

CABLE WITH RING
[Cable with Ring and Star]

Early flint pattern, probably Sandwich, in the early 1860's.

Butter dish	$ 62.00
Compote, open, 8¼"	55.00
Creamer	80.00
Honey dish	16.00
Lamp	86.00
Sauce	14.00
Sugar bowl	63.50

CAMEO
[Classic Medallion, Ceres]

Butter dish	$ 33.00
Compote, open, low standard	34.50
Creamer	26.00
Mug	17.50
Sugar bowl	33.50

CANADIAN

Butter dish, covered	$ 37.50
Celery	30.00
Compote	
Covered, 6"	36.00
Covered, 7", 8"	41.50
Open, high standard	32.00
Open, low standard	26.00
Cordial	20.00
Creamer	35.00
Goblet	25.00
Marmalade jar	23.00
Pitcher	
Large	52.50
Small	38.50
Plate	
6"	21.00
8"	23.00
10"	27.50
Sauce	8.00
Footed, 4"	12.00
Spooner	30.00
Sugar bowl	34.50
Wine	14.50

CANDLEWICK
[Barred Raindrops]

Butter dish	$ 28.00
Compote, 7", covered	42.00
Creamer	21.00

Cup and saucer	18.50
Goblet	16.00
Pitcher, water	28.50
Plate, 7½ x 8¾"	18.00
Sauce	8.00
Spooner	16.50
Sugar bowl	27.50
Wine	16.00

CANE
[See Colored Glass Section]

CANE AND ROSETTE
[Flower Panelled Cane]

Bowl	$ 15.00
Butter dish	28.00
Cake stand	23.00
Compote	
Covered, 8", high standard	37.00
Open, 9", high standard	29.00
Cordial	10.50
Creamer	22.50
Egg cup	14.00
Goblet	11.50
Pitcher, water	30.50
Sauce	6.00
Spooner	14.50
Sugar bowl	28.00
Tumbler	10.50
Wine	10.00

NOTE: This pattern is occasionally found in cobalt blue.

CANNON BALL
[Atlas, Crystal Ball, Bullet]

Produced in Pittsburgh, Pa., C. 1890, by Bryce Bros.

Bowl	
Berry, large	$ 16.00

Berry, small	13.00
Butter dish	26.00
Cake stand	24.00
Celery	
Flat base	21.00
Footed	27.50
Cordial	14.00
Creamer	23.00
Goblet	24.50
Pitcher	27.50
Salt	
Large	8.00
Small	6.00
Sauce	9.00
Spooner	13.50
Sugar bowl	27.00
Toothpick holder	9.00
Tumbler	14.00
Wine	25.50

CAPE COD

Bowl, 6", small handle	$ 16.50
Butter dish	34.50
Celery	21.50
Compote	
Covered, 6"	34.50
Covered, 7", 8"	41.50
Open, high standard	34.00
Open, low standard	27.50
Cordial	17.50
Creamer	23.00
Cup and saucer	25.50
Goblet	26.50
Marmalade jar	26.00
Pitcher	
Large	40.00
Small	31.50
Plate	
Small, closed handles	21.00
6"	22.00
8"	23.00
10"	26.00
Sauce	
Flat, 4"	8.50
Footed, 4"	10.00
Spooner	21.00
Sugar bowl	34.50
Wine	16.50

CARAMEL SLAG
|See Colored Glass Section|

CARDINAL BIRD
|Blue Jay|

Butter dish	$	38.50
Cake stand		35.00
Compote, covered		40.00
Creamer		37.50
Goblet		32.00
Pitcher		52.50
Plate, 10", frosted, with girl and bird		
|scarce|		50.00
Sauce		
Flat, round		10.00
Footed, 4"		12.50
Footed, 5½"		15.00
Spooner		35.00
Sugar bowl		42.50

CATHEDRAL
|See Colored Glass Section|

CHAIN

Made by R. B. Curling and Sons at the Fort Pitt Glass Works in Pittsburgh, Pa. in the 1880's.

Butter dish	$	40.00
Cake stand		21.00
Compote, covered		34.50
Cordial		22.50
Creamer		35.00
Dish, oval		14.00
Goblet		19.00
Pickle		18.00
Pitcher, water		35.00
Plate		
7"		13.00

Bread		18.50
Platter		21.00
Sauce		
Flat		12.00
Footed		13.50
Shakers, pair		17.50
Spooner		27.50
Sugar bowl		37.50
Wine		22.50

CHAIN WITH STAR

Bowl, footed	$	14.00
Butter dish		35.00
Cake stand		21.50
Compote		
Covered, high standard		31.00
Covered, low standard		25.00
Cordial		20.00
Creamer		35.00
Dish, oval		15.50
Goblet		18.50
Pickle		12.50
Pitcher		35.00
Plate		
7½"		17.50
10"		25.00
Platter		21.00
Sauce		
Flat		12.00
Footed		13.50
Shakers, pair		17.50
Spooner		27.50
Sugar bowl		35.00
Wine		14.50

CHANDELIER
|Crown Jewels|

Made by O'Hara Glass Co., Pittsburgh, Pa. in early 1880's.

Bowl, finger	$	12.50
Butter dish		25.00
Compote		
Covered		34.50
Open		24.50
Creamer		19.00
Goblet		40.00
Pitcher, water		30.00
Sauce, flat		10.00

Spooner 19.00
Sugar 16.00

CHECKERBOARD

A late pattern, probably after the year 1900, in the Pittsburgh area.

Bowl
  Small .... $ 8.00
  Large 12.50
Butter dish, covered 21.00
Celery tray 10.50
Celery vase 14.50
Cheese dish 10.00
Creamer 14.50
Cruet 17.50
Goblet 11.50
*Honey dish, square, footed, covered 13.00
Pickle 9.00
Pitcher
  Milk 21.00
  Water 23.00
Plate, 10" 11.50
Sauce 6.50
Shakers, pair 14.50
Sherbet 8.00
Spooner 14.00
Sugar bowl, covered 21.00
Tumbler
  Iced tea 6.00
  Water 5.50
Wine 10.00
*Reproduced in clear and milk glass

CHERRY

^Butter dish .... $ 30.00
Compote
  Covered, high standard 41.50
  Open, high standard 32.00
  Open, low standard 30.00
^Creamer 31.00
^Goblet 25.00
Sauce 10.00
Spooner 12.50
^Sugar bowl 30.00
Wine 10.50
       ^Reproduced Item

CLASSIC

A pattern of the 1880 period, produced by Gillinder & Sons, Philadelphia, Pa.

Bowl, footed .... $ 34.50
Butter dish 78.50
Celery 55.50
Compote
  Covered 85.00
  On standard, 6" 55.50
Creamer 60.00
Goblet 75.00
Jar, sweetmeat 46.00
Pitcher
  Large 110.00
  Small 95.00
Plate
  Cleveland, President 60.50
  Jas. G. Blaine 60.00
  John A. Logan 62.00

Thos. H. Hendricks	60.00
Warrior	72.00
Sauce, footed	21.00
Spooner	52.50
Sugar bowl	72.50

CLEAR DIAGONAL BAND

Butter dish....................$	35.00
Celery	30.00
Compote	
Covered, high standard	37.00
Covered, low standard	29.00
Cordial	20.00
Creamer	35.00
Goblet	21.00
Marmalade jar	20.00
Pitcher, water..................	26.00
Plate..........................	15.50
Platter	40.00
Sauce	10.00
Shakers, pair....................	16.00
Spooner	27.00
Sugar bowl	37.50

CLEAR RIBBON

Butter dish.....................$	40.00
Cake stand	60.00
Celery	35.00
Compote, covered, large	62.50
Creamer	35.00
Dish, covered, oblong, 6", 7", 8"	35.00
Goblet	35.00
Pickle	25.00
Pitcher	60.00
Platter, oblong	32.00
Sauce	10.00

Spooner	35.00
Sugar bowl	42.00

CLEMATIS
[Rose Point Band]

Butter dish......................$	23.00
Creamer	35.00
Goblet	27.50
Lamp, 12", iron base	19.00
Pickle	9.00
Pitcher	40.00
Sauce	10.00
Spooner	32.50
Sugar bowl	40.00

COIN --- COLUMBIAN
[Spanish Coin]

Bowl	
Berry ....$	86.50
Finger	55.00
Butter dish.....................	109.00
Cake stand	83.50
Compote	
Covered, 6", 7", 8".............	161.00
Open, 7", 8", 9"	126.50
Creamer	86.50
Cruet	95.00
Goblet	75.00
Lamp	98.00
Pickle	40.50
Pitcher.........................	138.00
Sauce	27.50
Shakers, pair....................	92.00
Spooner	57.50

Sugar bowl	113.50
Syrup [scarce]	132.50
Toothpick	55.50
Tray, water	83.50
Tumbler	69.00

COIN [U. S.]

Produced by Hobbs, Brockhunier Co., Wheeling, W. Va. for three or four months. Stopped by U. S. Treasury as design imitated U. S. coins.

Bowl	
Berry, dollar	$ 258.50
Berry, half dollar	220.00
Berry, quarters	209.00
Waste, quarters	143.00
Bread tray	
Dollar	264.00
*Half dollar	230.00
Butter dish	
Dollar	495.00
Half dollar	451.00
Cake stand	
Dollar	412.50
Half dollar	379.50
Celery, half dollar	302.50
Champagne, half dime	181.50
Claret, half dime	148.50
Compote	
High standard, covered:	
Dollar	550.00
Half dollar	495.00
Quarters	434.50
Low standard, covered:	
Quarters	313.50
Twenty-cent pieces	385.00
Open:	
Dollar	291.50
Half dollar	264.00
Quarters	247.50
Creamer, quarters	302.50
Cruet, quarters. Stopper, dimes	286.00
Epergne	
Dollar	418.00
Quarters	385.00

Goblet	
Dollar	324.50
Dime	275.00
Lamp	
Square bowl, on standard:	
Dollar	291.50
Half dollar	247.50
Round bowl, panelled, on standard:	
Dollar	302.50
Half dollar	231.00
Quarter	209.00
Handled, round bowl, panelled, twenty-cent pieces	264.00
Flaring bowl, on standard, plain coins	253.00
Mug, dollar	192.50
Pickle dish	
Half dollar	181.50
Quarters	154.00
Pitcher	
Milk, half dollar	412.50
Water, dollar	495.00
Preserve dish	
Dollar	198.00
Half dollar	181.50
Salt and pepper shakers, pair, quarters	308.00
Sauce	
Flat, quarters	110.00
Footed, quarters	143.00
Spooner, quarters	192.50
Sugar bowl	
Covered, half dollar	495.00
Covered, quarters	440.00
Syrup jug, quarters	412.50
*Toothpick holder, dollar	126.50
Tray, water, dollar	258.50
Tumbler	
*Dollar on base [scarce]	209.00
Dimes	181.50
Wine, half dimes [scarce]	286.00
*Reproduced Item	

COLORADO
[See Colored Glass Section]

COLUMBIA

The pattern was made by U. S. Glass Co. in 1907.

Bowl, 7", 8"	$ 11.50
Butter dish, covered	17.50
Celery tray	11.00
Creamer	13.00
Cruet	11.50
Pickle jar, open	9.00
Pitcher, water	19.00

Plate

Bread	11.00
8"	9.50
Relish dish	8.00
Salts, round and square, pair	10.00
Sauce, 4½"	5.50
Spooner	11.50
Sugar bowl, covered	17.50
Syrup jug	11.50
Toothpick	6.00
Tumbler	7.00
Vase	8.00

COMET

An early flint glass made in Sandwich in the 1840-1850 period. Sometimes called Horn of Plenty, but is not related in design. Also two other unidentical patterns made in the late 1800's by McKee, Doyle & Co., and U. S. Glass Company.

Butter dish

Plain knob, covered	$ 85.00
Washington knob, covered	175.00
Creamer	100.00
Goblet	62.50
Mug	75.00
Pitcher	250.00
Spooner	65.00
Tumbler	
Water	100.00
Whiskey	90.00

CONNECTICUT

One of the U. S. Glass Co. States' patterns. C. 1895.

Bowl

Round, 8"	$ 10.00
Round, 4", 6"	9.50
Butter dish	15.50
Cake stand, 10"	16.00
Celery tray	8.50
Creamer	14.50
Pickle	8.50
Pitcher	
½ gallon, tankard	19.00
1 quart, tankard	17.50
1 pint, tankard	16.00
Shakers, pair	11.50
Tumbler	
Handled	8.00
Plain	6.00

CORD AND TASSEL

Produced by Central Glass Co., Wheeling, W. Va. in the early 1870's.

Butter dish	$ 27.50
Cake stand, 8½"	24.50
Celery	30.00
Compote	
Covered, high standard	34.00
Covered, low standard	30.00
Cordial	22.50
Creamer	35.00
Dish, oval	11.50
Egg cup	13.50
Goblet	22.50
Lamp	29.00
Pitcher	
Syrup	29.00
Water	45.00

Sauce	12.00
Spooner	27.50
Sugar bowl	35.00
Wine	15.50

CORDOVA

Made in the early 1890's by O'Hara Glass Co., Pittsburgh, Pa.

Bowl		
Covered	$	16.00
Finger		10.50
Open		11.50
Butter dish		18.50
Cake stand		17.50
Celery		15.00
Compote		
Covered, high standard		21.00
Open, high standard		17.50
Creamer		15.50
Cruet		14.00
Pitcher		
Syrup		17.50
Water		23.00
Sauce		5.50
Spooner		11.50
Sugar bowl		17.50
Toothpick		8.00
Tumbler		10.00

COSMOS
[See General Section]

COTTAGE
[Dinner Bell, Fine Cut Band]

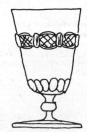

Bowl, berry	$	11.00
Butter dish		21.50
Cake stand		19.50
Celery		15.00
Compote		
Covered, low standard		29.00
Open, low standard		20.00
Open, high standard		19.50
Creamer		15.00
Cruet		12.00
Cup and saucer		15.00
Dish, oval, deep		9.00
Fruit bowl, high standard		21.50
Goblet		11.50
Pickle		8.50
Pitcher		
Pint		17.00
Quart		20.00
½ gallon		22.50
Syrup		15.50
Plate		
6", 7"		11.50
8", 9"		14.50
Shakers, pair		12.00
Spooner		13.50
Sugar bowl		22.50
Tray, water		17.00
Tumbler		8.00
Wine		9.00

[Also found in dark green]

CROESUS
[See Colored Glass Section]

CROW'S FOOT
[Yale, Fan Band]

Made C. 1895 by McKee Glass Co., Jeannette, Pa.

Butter dish	$	23.00
Cake stand		21.50
Celery		17.50
Compote		28.00
Cordial		12.50
Creamer		17.50
Goblet		16.50
Pitcher		
Syrup		17.50
Water		28.00

Plate	17.50
Sauce	8.50
Shakers, pair	17.50
Spooner	14.50
Sugar bowl	23.00
Tumbler	11.00

CRYSTAL

Ale glass ....$	19.00
Bowl	
8"	34.50
10"	39.50
Butter dish	34.00
Celery	26.00
Champagne	27.50
Compote	
Covered, 8", footed	37.50
Covered, 6", high standard	40.50
Open, high standard, 10"	45.00
Cordial	17.50
Creamer	45.00
Decanter, quart	35.00
Egg cup	17.50
Goblet	25.00
Pitcher	60.00
Sauce	10.00
Spooner	27.50
Sugar bowl	50.00
Tumbler	
Bar	25.00
½ pint	35.00
Gill	33.00
Footed	40.00
Wine	32.50

CRYSTAL WEDDING
[Crystal Anniversary]

A pattern of the late 1880's by Adams Glass Co., of Pittsburgh, Pa.

Banana dish ....$	40.50
Bowl, berry	21.50
Butter dish	32.50
Cake stand, 12"	40.50
Celery	23.00
*Compote	
Open, low standard	26.00

Covered, high standard	55.50
Covered, low standard	40.50
Creamer	27.50
*Goblet	26.00
Lamp	27.50
Pitcher	40.50
Sauce	8.00
Shakers, pair	21.00
Spooner	19.00
Sugar bowl	34.50
Tumbler	14.00

*Reproduced Item

CUBE WITH FAN

Bottle, water.....................$	21.50
Bowl	
Finger	11.50
Rose	14.00
Celery	16.50
Dish, jelly	11.00
Goblet	11.00
Jar, covered	11.50
Plate	
5"	10.50
7¾"	12.50
Salt dip	3.50
Sugar bowl, covered	21.50
Tumbler	8.00

CUPID AND VENUS
[Guardian Angel, Minerva]

Made in Tarentum, Pa. [Pittsburgh area] by the Hartley Glass Co.

Bowl, covered, 8¾", footed ....$	34.50
Butter dish	63.50
Cake plate, 11"	40.50

Celery	37.50
Champagne	34.50
Compote	
Covered, high standard	49.00
Covered, low standard	46.00
Open, high standard	37.50
Cordial	45.00
Creamer	40.00
Cruet, vinegar	34.50
Dish	
Oval, large	17.50
Oval, small	14.00
Goblet	45.00
Marmalade jar	37.00
Mug	
2"	17.50
2½"	24.00
3½"	26.00
Pickle	14.50
Pitcher	
Large	50.00
Small	40.00
Plate	
Bread	32.50
10½", round	32.50
Sauce	
Flat, round	12.00
Footed	11.50
Spooner	40.00
Sugar bowl	55.00
Wine [scarce]	65.00

CURRANT

Reputed to be of Sandwich origin. Later by Campbell, Jones & Co. of Pittsburgh in the late 1870's.

Butter dish	$	52.50
Cake stand, 9½"		55.00
Celery		40.00
Compote		
Covered, 8", high standard		45.00
Covered, 8", low standard		40.00
Covered, 9", low standard		45.00
Cordial		30.00
Creamer		45.00
Dish		
Oval, 5x7"		20.00
Oval, 6x9"		22.00
Egg cup		18.50
Goblet		26.00
Pickle		10.50
Pitcher		55.00
Sauce		
Flat		8.50
Footed		10.00
Spooner		35.00
Sugar bowl		45.00
Tumbler, footed		27.50
Wine		32.50

CURRIER AND IVES

Reportedly made by Bellaire Glass Co. at Findlay, Ohio in the late 1880's. Although named after the famous printmaker of its era, there was no connection between the companies.

Butter dish	$	34.00
Cordial		14.50
Creamer		21.50
Cup and saucer		25.50
Decanter		23.00
Dish, boat shaped, 5½x9½"		20.00
Goblet		21.50
Lamp		19.00
Pitcher		
Large		27.50
Small		20.00
Plate, 10", dog and rabbit		21.00
Sauce		8.00
Shakers, pair		19.00
Spooner		16.00
Sugar bowl		34.50

Tray, water	33.50
Wine	14.50

CURTAIN
[Sultan]

Produced by Bryce Bros., Pittsburgh, Pa., over a period of years in the 1870's into early 1880's.

Bowl, waste	$ 14.50
Butter dish	35.00
Cake stand	22.00
Celery	27.50
Compote	
Covered, high standard, small	37.00
Covered, high standard, large	45.00
Covered, collared base	34.50
Creamer	32.50
Dish, celery boat	18.50
Goblet	22.50
Mug, large	14.50
Pickle	17.50
Pitcher	
Quart	35.00
½ gallon	45.00
Plate	
Square, 7"	18.50
Square, bread, large	22.50
Sauce, 5", footed	12.00
Shakers, pair	18.50
Spooner	27.50
Sugar bowl	35.00
Tray, round	37.50
Tumbler	22.00

CUT LOG
[Cat's Eye and Block, Ethol]

Butter dish	$ 38.00
Cake stand, high standard	45.00

Celery	25.00
Compote	
Covered	33.50
*Covered, 6"	27.50
Open	30.00
Creamer	
3"	7.50
5"	18.50
Cruet	
5½"	14.50
6½"	16.50
Dish, covered, handled	13.50
Goblet	30.00
Honey dish	17.50
Mug	14.50
Mustard jar	11.50
Olive dish, round, handled	8.00
Pickle	10.50
Pitcher, water	31.50
Sauce	6.50
Shakers, pair	14.00
Spooner	12.50
Sugar bowl, covered	25.50
Tumbler	8.50
Wine	16.00

*Reproduced Item

DAHLIA
[See Colored Glass Section]

DAISY AND BUTTON
[See Colored Glass Section]

DAISY AND BUTTON WITH CROSS BARS
[See Colored Glass Section]

DAISY AND BUTTON WITH NARCISSUS
[Daisy and Button with Clear Lily]
[Often found "flashed" with gold]

*Bowl, round	$ 14.00
Butter dish	24.50
Celery	18.50
Compote, open	25.50
Creamer	16.50
Goblet	14.50
Pickle	10.00
Pitcher, water	25.00
Sauce, 4"	7.00
Shakers, pair	15.00

Spooner	14.50
Sugar bowl	25.50
Tumbler	9.50
*Wine	11.50

*Reproduced Item

DAISY AND BUTTON WITH V ORNAMENT
|See Colored Glass Section|

DAKOTA
|Baby Thumbprint, Thumbprint Band|

A popular collector's item produced in Pittsburgh, Pa. in the 1890's by Doyle Glass Company.

Bowl, berry	$	23.00
Butter dish, covered		40.00
Cake stand, 10½"		35.00
Celery		34.00
Compote		
Covered, 5", 6"		34.00
Covered, 7", 8"		40.50
Etched, high standard		62.50
Covered, 9", 10"		43.50
Covered, 12"		48.50
Open, 6"		34.00
Creamer		25.00
Dish, oblong		18.50
Goblet		26.00
Mug		14.50
Pitcher, water		65.00
Plate, round		19.00
Sauce		
Flat		10.00
Footed		17.50
Shakers, pair		23.00
Spooner		25.00
Sugar bowl		37.50
Tumbler		29.00
Wine		21.00

DEER AND DOG

Butter dish	$	62.50
Celery		52.50
Compote		
Covered		80.00

Open	60.00
Creamer	52.00
Goblet	49.00
Pitcher, water	75.00
Sauce	17.50
Spooner	37.50
Sugar bowl, covered	57.50

DEER AND PINE TREE
|Deer and Doe|

Originally attributed to Sandwich Co. in 1860's. Later made C. 1880's - probably by one of the Pittsburgh glass plants.

Bowl, waste	$	27.50
Butter dish		52.00
Cake stand		65.00
Celery		50.00
Compote		
Covered, oblong, large		75.00
Covered, various sizes		60.50
Open, large, high standard		48.50
Creamer		45.00
Dish		18.50
*Goblet		40.00
Marmalade jar		37.50
Mug		
Large		30.00
Small		27.50
Pickle		18.50
Pitcher		
Large		54.50

Small	44.00
Platter	
8x13", clear	42.50
9x15", clear [scarce]	60.00
Salt, oblong, footed	11.50
Sauce	
Flat	10.00
Footed, two sides	16.00
Spooner	40.00
Sugar bowl	53.50
Tray, water	65.00
*Reproduced Item	

DELAWARE
[See Colored Glass Section]

DEW AND RAINDROP

A late pattern made by the Kokomo Glass Co., Kokomo, Ind., in the early 1900's. Produced in clear, gilded and ruby flashed.

Bowl, berry	$ 37.50
Butter dish	50.00
Cordial	37.50
Creamer	45.00
Cup, sherbet	25.00
*Goblet	42.50
Pitcher	60.00
Sauce	12.00
Shakers, pair	40.00
Spooner	35.00
Sugar bowl	55.00
Tumbler	32.00
*Wine	37.50
*Reproduced Item	

DEWDROP

Bowl	$ 25.00
Butter dish	45.00
Compote, covered, 9¼", high standard	42.50
Creamer	40.00
Goblet	25.00
Pickle, double	45.00
Pitcher	45.00
Salt	9.50
Sauce	10.00
Sugar bowl	42.50

DEWDROP WITH STAR

Made by Campbell, Jones & Co., Pittsburgh, Pa. in the late 1870's.

Butter dish	$ 60.00
Cake stand	
Large	75.00
Small	65.00
Celery	50.00
Compote	
Covered, high standard	66.00
Covered, low standard	57.00
Covered, footed, 6", star base	47.00
Covered, footed, 7", star base	52.00
Cordial	40.00
Creamer	52.50
Goblet	37.50
Lamp	75.00
Pickle	15.00
Pitcher	65.00
Plate	
4½"	15.00
5¼", 5½"	16.00
6", 6½"	16.50
7", *7¼"	18.00
8¼"	20.00
9"	23.50
11"	30.00
11" honey plate, with large cover	69.00
10", with sheaf of wheat	22.50
11", with sheaf of wheat	27.50
*Salt, footed	18.50
Sauce	
Flat	10.00

*Footed	11.50
Spooner	42.50
Sugar bowl	57.50
Tumbler	25.00

*Reproduced Item

DEWEY
[See Colored Glass Section]

DIAGONAL BAND WITH FAN

Butter dish	$ 32.50
Celery	30.00
Champagne	14.50
Compote	
Covered, high standard	35.00
Covered, low standard	30.00
Cordial	11.50
Creamer	25.00
Goblet	22.50
Marmalade jar	14.50
Pickle	10.50
Pitcher	30.00
Plate	
6"	10.00
7"	15.00
8"	18.00
Sauce, footed	9.00
Shakers, pair	14.50
Spooner	20.00
Sugar bowl	32.00
Wine	11.00

DIAMOND CUT WITH LEAF

Butter dish	$ 34.00
Cordial	22.00
Creamer	30.00
Cup, small, 2½", handled	14.50
Goblet	22.00

Plate		
7¼"		18.00
9½"		24.00

DIAMOND MEDALLION

Butter dish	$ 22.50
Cake stand	15.00
Celery	15.50
Compote, covered	27.50
Creamer	9.00
Goblet	11.50
Pitcher, water	26.00
Plate, 10"	13.50
Sauce	6.00
Spooner	13.00
Sugar bowl	18.00
Wine	10.00

DIAMOND POINT
[Sharp Diamond, Grant Pineapple]

A product of McKee Glass Co. of Pittsburgh, Pa., C. 1887-90. Sandwich Glass Co. made a similar pattern in the 1830-40 period.

Ale glass	$ 32.50
Bowl	
Covered, 7", 8"	37.50
Open, 7", 8"	33.00
Butter dish	65.00
Castor bottle	14.50
Celery	55.00
Champagne	50.00
Compote	
Covered, 6", high standard	69.00
Covered, 7", 8", high standard	77.50
Covered, 6", 7", 8", low standard	63.50
Open, 6", 7", 8", low standard	39.00
Open, 9", 10", low standard	45.00
Cordial	55.00

Creamer	57.50
Cruet	65.00
Decanter	
Bar lip, pint	46.00
Bar lip, quart	57.50
With stopper, pint	49.00
With stopper, quart	63.50
Dish	
Oval, 7", 8"	21.00
Oval, 9", 10"	28.00
Egg cup	26.00
Goblet	40.00
Honey dish	10.50
Jug	
½ pint	35.00
Pint	42.50
Quart	52.50
3 pints	57.50
Lamp, whale oil	60.00
Lemonade glass	30.00
Mug	37.00
Pitcher	
½ pint	45.00
Pint	50.00
Quart	60.00
3 pints	65.00
Plate	
3"	11.50
6"	20.00
7"	22.00
8"	27.50
5½", star center	32.50
Large, deep, 8"	35.00
Small, deep, 6"	30.00
Salt, covered, footed	40.50
Sauce	11.50
Spooner	42.50
Sugar bowl	55.00
Syrup jug	40.00
Tumbler	
Jelly	25.00
Water	30.00
Whiskey	35.00
Wine	50.00

DIAMOND QUILTED
[See Colored Glass Section]

DIAMOND SUNBURST

Butter dish	$ 27.50
Cake stand	22.50
Celery	18.50
Compote, covered, high standard	34.50
Cordial	10.50
Creamer	23.00
Dish, oval	11.50
Goblet	18.50
Lamp	17.50
Pickle	10.00
Pitcher	22.00
Salt, footed	10.50
Sauce	6.50
Shakers, pair	14.00
Spooner	14.50
Sugar bowl	27.50
Tumbler	12.50
Wine	12.50

DIAMOND THUMBPRINT
[Diamond Concave]

Early pattern attributed to Sandwich Glass Co.
Later made by McKee & Bros. C. 1860 in Pittsburgh, Pa.

Bowl	$ 85.00
Butter dish	143.50
Celery	200.00
Champagne [scarce]	165.00
Compote	
Open, low standard	86.50
Open, high standard, medium	115.00
Open, high standard, large	144.00
Cordial	125.00
Creamer	126.50
Decanter	
Pint	110.00
Quart	85.00
Goblet [rare]	250.00
Honey dish	25.00
Lamp	
All glass	77.50
Marble base	70.00
Fluid lamp, 3 burners	253.00
Mug, handled	98.00
Pitcher, water [scarce]	275.00
Sauce	21.00
Spooner	50.00

Sugar bowl	150.00
Tumbler	
Water........................	75.00
Whiskey	75.00
Wine [scarce]	100.00

DOLPHIN [FROSTED]
[Codfish, Frog, Turtle]

Butter dish, covered............... $	86.50
Compote, high standard, open......	65.00
Creamer	75.00
Goblet	50.00
Pitcher, water, 10"...............	100.00
Spooner........................	30.00
Sugar bowl	85.00

DOUBLE LOOP AND DART

Butter dish...................... $	45.00
Celery	42.50
Compote	42.50
Cordial	25.00
Creamer	35.00
Egg cup	12.50
Goblet	22.50
Pitcher	50.00
Plate, 6" [scarce]	47.50
Salt, footed	16.50
Sauce	12.50
Spooner........................	32.50
Sugar bowl	45.00
Tumbler, footed	25.00
Wine...........................	18.00

DOUBLE RIBBON

Butter dish...................... $	35.00
Celery	20.50
Compote, open, high standard......	45.00

Creamer	35.00
Egg cup	18.50
Goblet	32.50
Pickle	12.00
Pitcher	45.00
Sauce, footed	8.50
Spooner........................	37.50
Sugar bowl	48.00

DOUBLE SPEAR

Butter dish...................... $	25.00
Celery	30.00
Compote, covered, high standard ...	38.00
Creamer	35.00
Dish, oval, deep	18.00
Goblet	27.50
Pickle	12.00
Pitcher, water...................	40.00
Sauce	12.50
Spooner........................	30.00
Sugar bowl	40.00

DRAPERY
[Lace]

Made by Doyle & Co. of Pittsburgh in the 1870's. Reported to have been made by Sandwich Glass Co. at an earlier period.

Butter dish	$	42.00
Compote, covered		38.50
Creamer		32.00
Dish, oval		14.50
Goblet		26.00
Pitcher		27.50
Plate, 6"		17.50
Sauce		8.50
Spooner		28.50
Sugar bowl		32.00

EGG IN SAND
[Bean]

Butter dish	$	32.50
Cake stand		25.50
Compote		40.50
Cordial		13.50
Creamer		20.00
Goblet		17.50
Pitcher		
Milk		23.00
Water		27.50
Sauce		6.50
Shakers, pair		23.00
Spooner		14.50
Sugar bowl		33.50
Tray, bread		19.00
Tumbler		14.00
Wine		14.50

EGYPTIAN
[Parthenon]

Butter dish, covered	$	52.50
Celery		30.00

Compote	
Covered, low standard	44.50
Open, high standard, sphinx on	
base, large	37.00
Same as above, small	30.00
Creamer	30.00
Goblet	27.50
Honey dish	11.00
Pickle, oval	25.00
Pitcher, water	42.50
Plate, cake, handled	30.00
Platter	
Cleopatra	30.00
Salt Lake Temple	45.00
Sauce	
Flat	12.00
Footed, 4½"	14.00
Spooner	28.50
Sugar bowl	34.50

EIGHTEEN-NINETY

Bowl, berry	$	10.00
Butter dish		17.50
Celery		12.50
Creamer		14.50
Pitcher, water		20.50
Shakers		
Salt and pepper, pair		12.50
Sugar		13.50
Spooner		11.00
Sugar bowl, covered		17.50

EMERALD GREEN HERRINGBONE
[See Colored Glass Section]

ESTHER
[See Colored Glass Section]

ETRUSCAN

Butter dish	$	50.00
Cake stand		72.50
Compote		
Covered, 8", high standard		75.00
Open, 8", low standard		65.00
Creamer		45.00
Dish, oval		24.00
Egg cup		24.00
Goblet		37.50

Salt, footed	18.50
Sauce	8.50
Spooner	35.00
Sugar bowl	50.00
Tumbler	22.50

EUGENIE

Butter dish	$ 55.50
Castor bottle	17.50
Celery	57.50
Champagne	50.00
Compote, covered, on standard	77.50
Cordial	47.50
Creamer [scarce]	120.00
Egg cup	24.00
Goblet	38.50
Sauce, flat	15.00
Spooner	50.00
Sugar bowl [scarce]	161.00
Tumbler, footed	42.50
Wine	45.00

EUREKA

| Butter dish | $ 45.00 |
| Champagne | 25.00 |

Compote		
Covered, 7", 8", high standard	80.00
Open, 7", 8", low standard	65.00
Cordial	28.50
Creamer	42.50
Dish, oval, shallow	20.00
Egg cup	25.00
Goblet	26.50
Salt, footed	16.50
Sauce	12.50
Spooner	24.50
Sugar	45.00
Tumbler, footed	20.00
Wine	25.00

EXCELSIOR

Made by a number of glass companies - Ihmsen and Co. C. 1850's; McKee Bros., Pittsburg, C. 1870; earlier at Sandwich.

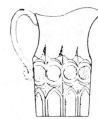

Ale glass	$ 50.00
Bitters bottle	37.50
Bowl	
Covered, flat	92.50
Open, 10"	82.50
Butter dish	55.00
Candlesticks, pair	86.50
Celery	66.00
Champagne	63.00
Claret	24.50
Compote	
Covered, low standard	92.00
Open, 10", high standard	63.50
Cordial	16.00
Creamer	75.00
Decanter	
Small, footed	48.00
Pint	48.50
Quart	55.50
Egg cup	
Double	39.00
Single	26.00
Goblet	
Plain	37.50
With Maltese Cross	42.00
Lamp, whale oil	75.00

Pitcher

Milk [scarce]	....	167.00
Syrup	....	75.00
Water [scarce]	....	172.50
Salt, footed	....	25.50
Spooner	....	29.00
Sugar bowl	....	110.00
Tumbler		
Footed	....	55.00
Jelly	....	30.00
Water	....	35.00
Vase	....	30.50
Wine	....	50.00

EYEWINKER
[Diamond Point Discs]

Banana dish	.... $	36.50
Bowl, berry	....	17.50
*Butter dish	....	34.50
Cake stand	....	46.00
Compote		
Covered	....	34.50
Open	....	27.50
*Creamer	....	24.50
Cruet	....	16.50
*Lamp	....	28.00
Pitcher		
Milk	....	27.50
Syrup	....	31.50
*Water	....	37.00
Plate, 7¾"	....	17.50
*Sauce	....	8.50
*Sugar bowl	....	36.50
*Toothpick holder	....	11.50
*Tumbler	....	11.50

*Reproduced Item

FAN WITH ACANTHUS LEAF
[Bijou]

Bowl, berry, 9"	.... $	11.50
Butter dish, covered	....	21.50
Celery	....	13.50
Creamer	....	13.50
Dish, jelly, covered	....	11.50
Mug	....	8.50
Pickle	....	8.00

Pitcher, water	....	18.50
Plate, cake, flat	....	14.00
Sauce	....	5.50
Sugar bowl, covered	....	21.00
Tumbler	....	5.50

FAN WITH DIAMOND

Butter dish	.... $	24.50
Compote		
Covered, high standard	....	40.00
Covered, low standard	....	30.00
Cordial	....	15.00
Creamer	....	25.00
Dish, oval, 6¾ x9"	....	22.50
Egg cup	....	14.50
Goblet	....	21.50
Pickle	....	10.00
Pitcher	....	30.00
Sauce, flat, 4"	....	10.00
Spooner	....	22.50
Sugar bowl	....	30.00

FEATHER
[Finecut & Feather, Indiana Swirl]

Reportedly made either by the Indiana Tumbler and Glass Co., Greentown, Ind., or Indiana Glass Co., Dunkirk, Ind., C. 1896.

Banana dish	.... $	34.50
Bowl, 7½", 8½"	....	14.50

Butter dish	22.50
Cake stand	
8½"	20.00
11" [scarce]	30.00
Celery	17.50
Compote	
Covered, low standard, 8¼"	45.00
High standard	32.50
Jelly, 4½" high	12.50
Cordial	11.50
Creamer	20.00
Cruet	22.50
Dish, oval	11.50
Goblet	25.00
Pitcher, water	25.00
Plate, 10"	22.50
Sauce, footed, 5¼"	15.00
Spooner	12.50
Sugar bowl, covered	22.50
Toothpick holder	30.00
Tumbler	27.50
Wine	20.00

FESTOON

Bowl	
Berry	$ 25.00
Finger	18.50
Butter dish	27.50
Cake stand, 9"	26.00
Celery	19.00
Compote, on standard	31.50
Creamer	23.00
Pickle dish	18.50
Pickle jar	28.50
Pitcher	45.00
Plate	
7¼" [scarce]	29.00
8½" [scarce]	32.50
9¼"	23.00
Sauce, 4½", flat	8.00
Spooner	26.50
Sugar bowl	27.50
Tray, round, 10"	25.00
Tumbler	20.00
Wine	14.50

FINE CUT
[See Colored Glass Section]

FINE CUT AND PANEL
[See Colored Glass Section]

FINE RIB

Ale glass	$ 37.00
Bitters bottle	40.50
Bowl	
Covered, 7"	63.50
Shallow	37.50
Butter dish	56.00
Castor bottle	14.50
Celery	37.00
Champagne	27.50
Compote	
Covered, 7", 8", high standard	83.00
Covered, 7", 8", low standard	75.00
Open, 7", 8", low standard	49.00
Open, 9", 10", low standard	52.00
Cordial	45.00
Creamer	80.50
Cup, custard	31.50
Decanter	
Bar lip, pint	37.50
Bar lip, quart	40.50
With stopper, pint	72.50
With stopper, quart	87.50
Dish	
Oval, 7", 8"	34.50
Oval, 9", 10"	41.50
Egg cup, double, covered	55.00
Goblet	37.50
Honey dish	11.50
Jug	
Pint	57.50
Quart	63.50
Three pints	75.00
Lamp	49.00
Lemonade glass	35.00
Mug	42.50
Pitcher	125.00
Plate	
6"	37.50
7"	40.00
Salt	
Celery dip	9.50
Covered, on stem	40.50
Large, open, footed	20.50
Oval	23.00
Sauce	12.00
Spooner	45.00

Sugar bowl	56.00
Tumbler	
Jelly	25.00
Water	30.00
Whiskey	35.00
Water bottle, with tumble-up	92.50
Whiskey taster	17.50
Wine	29.00

FISHSCALE
[Coral]

Produced by Bryce Bros., Pittsburgh, Pa., in the mid 1880's.

Bowl, covered, 7", 8", square with round base ....$	20.50
Butter dish	34.50
Cake stand	
9"	24.00
10½"	27.50
Celery	35.00
Compote	
Covered, various sizes------------40.00 to 60.00	
Open, 4½", high standard	25.00
Open, 6", high standard	29.00
Creamer	28.50
Goblet	27.50
Lamp, handled	19.00
Mug, large	20.00
Pickle	19.50
Pitcher	
Large	35.00
Small	27.50
Plate	
Round, 7"	17.50
Square, 8"	20.00
Square with rounded corners, 9"	22.50
Sauce	
Flat	10.00
Footed	14.00
Shakers	
Salt and pepper [scarce]	38.50
Sugar	18.50
Spooner	30.00
Sugar bowl	34.50
Tray, water, round	30.00
Tumbler	22.00

FLATTENED DIAMOND

Butter dish ....$	20.00
Celery	14.00
Creamer	17.00
Goblet	11.50
Sauce	5.50
Spooner	11.50
Sugar bowl	21.00

FLATTENED HOBNAIL

Bowl, berry ....$	16.50
Butter dish	27.50
Cake stand	35.00
Celery	30.00
Cordial	10.50
Creamer	27.50
Cruet	29.00
Goblet	18.00
Pickle	8.50
Pitcher	
Globular	27.50
Straight sides	21.50
Plate, 4½"	16.50
Sauce	9.50
Shakers, pair	22.50
Spooner	27.50
Sugar bowl	32.50
Tray	20.50
*Tumbler	20.00
Wine	24.00

*Reproduced Item

FLATTENED SAWTOOTH

Bowl	
Finger ....$	22.50
Flat, 10"	50.00
Celery	45.00
Celery tray	28.50
Compote, covered	42.50

Cordial	37.50
Creamer	27.50
Decanter	40.00
Egg cup	23.50
Goblet	28.00
Ice tub	35.00
Pitcher	60.00
Plate	
6"	20.00
7"	30.00
Salt	
Covered	35.00
Footed	20.00
Round, flat	15.00
Sauce	12.00
Spooner	40.00
Sugar bowl	32.50
Tumbler	35.00

FLOWER POT
|Flower Plant, Potted Plant|

Butter dish	$ 40.00
Cake stand, 10½"	42.50
Compote, open, 7"	37.50
Creamer	28.50
Pitcher	
Small	37.00
Large	44.50
Sauce	
Open, flat	12.00
On standard	14.00
Spooner	37.50
Sugar bowl	37.50
Tray, bread	35.00
Tumbler	14.50

FLUTE

Research has indicated there are no less than 15 different Flute patterns. The main difference is usually a variation in the design. The pattern is first attributed to the Sandwich factory in the 1850's and 60's, and made of

flint glass. Prices on these earlier items are 100% higher than those quoted below.

Ale glass	$ 17.50
Bitters bottle	23.00
Candlesticks, pair	41.50
Champagne	23.00
Creamer	29.00
Cup, footed	17.50
Decanter	34.50
Egg cup	14.00
Goblet	17.50
Lamp	23.00
Spooner	14.50
Tumbler	
Gill	10.00
½ pint	10.50
Jelly	10.50
Toy, ½ gill	9.00
Wine	14.50

FROSTED ARTICHOKE

Bowl, 8"	$ 42.00
Butter dish	57.50
Cake stand	44.50
Celery	34.50
Compote, footed	75.00
Creamer	37.00
*Goblet	25.00
Lamp	34.50
Pitcher	
Syrup	32.00
Water	72.00
Sauce	13.50
Spooner	25.00
Sugar bowl	57.50
Tray, water	34.50
Tumbler	17.50
*Reproduced Item	

FROSTED CIRCLE

Produced by Bryce Bros., Pittsburgh, Pa. in the late 1870's. Later by U. S. Glass Co. in the early 1890's.

Bowl
Covered, 7", 8", flat.............$	25.00
Open, 8", 9"	17.50
Butter dish, covered..............	45.00
Cake stand, 9", 10"	65.00
Celery	50.00
Champagne.....................	47.50
Claret..........................	38.50

Compote
Open, high standard	40.00
Covered, 7", 8", high standard ...	52.00
Creamer	42.50
Cruet	50.00
*Goblet	45.00
Lamp	50.00
Pickle jar	47.00

Pitcher
Syrup	55.00
Water........................	65.00

Plate
4"	16.00
7"	22.00
9"	24.00
Sauce, 3¼", 4"	10.00
Shakers, pair....................	45.00
Spooner	40.00
Sugar bowl	45.00
Tumbler.......................	30.00
Wine..........................	35.00

*Reproduced Item

FROSTED LEAF

Butter dish.......................$	90.00
Celery	75.00
Champagne.....................	145.00

Compote
Covered.......................	103.50
Open	60.50
Cordial	125.00
Creamer	95.00
Decanter, quart	92.00
Egg cup [scarce]	43.00
Goblet	50.00
Pitcher, water [very scarce]	316.50
Salt, footed	25.00
Sauce	18.00
Spooner	55.00
Sugar bowl	85.00
Tumbler.......................	44.50
Wine..........................	115.00

FROSTED LION, See LION

FROSTED RIBBON

Made by Bakewell, Pears & Co., Pittsburgh, Pa. in 1870's; later by Geo. Duncan & Sons in Pittsburgh.

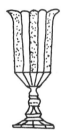

Ale glass ....$	21.50
Bitters bottle	19.50
Butter dish.....................	40.50
Celery	47.50
Champagne.....................	42.00

Compote
Covered, high standard	52.00
Covered, low standard	40.50
Open, dolphin standard	86.50
Cordial	32.50
Creamer	72.50
Dish, octagonal, 8", 9"............	23.00
Egg cup	22.50
*Goblet	35.00
Pitcher, water...................	45.00
Salt, footed	14.00
Sauce	12.00
Spooner	45.00
Sugar bowl	75.00
Tray	29.00

```
Tumbler .........................  32.50
Wine ............................  37.00
              *Reproduced Item
```

FROSTED STORK
[Flamingo]

Produced by Crystal Glass Co., Bridgeport, Ohio, C. 1880.

```
Bowl, waste......................$  35.00
Butter dish......................  52.00
Creamer .........................  57.50
Goblet ..........................  52.50
Marmalade .......................  40.50
Pickle castor ...................  109.00
Pitcher, water...................  78.50
Plate, 9"........................  35.00
Platter, 9"......................  42.00
Sauce ...........................  13.00
Spooner .........................  50.00
Sugar bowl, covered, with finial ....  69.50
Tray ............................  65.00
```

FUCHSIA

```
Butter dish......................$  40.50
Cake stand ......................  32.50
Celery ..........................  26.00
Compote, open ...................  49.00
Creamer .........................  31.00
Goblet ..........................  26.00
Plate, 10".......................  30.50
Spooner .........................  19.00
Sugar bowl ......................  45.50
Tumbler .........................  17.50
```

GARFIELD DRAPE

The pattern was issued in 1881, after the assassination of President Garfield, by Adams & Co., Pittsburgh, Pa.

```
Bowl ............................$  25.00
Butter dish......................  37.50
Cake stand ......................  55.00
Compote
    Covered, high standard .........  55.00
    Covered, low standard .........  42.50
Creamer .........................  50.00
Egg cup .........................  17.50
Goblet ..........................  30.00
Honey dish ......................  12.00
Pickle ..........................  18.50
Pitcher
    Milk .........................  35.00
    Water.........................  50.00
Plate
    Memorial, 11" ................  46.00
    Edge cut to line of drapery, 10"...  34.50
Sauce
    Flat..........................  8.00
    Footed .......................  10.00
Spooner .........................  32.50
Sugar bowl ......................  40.00
```

GIBSON GIRL
[Goddess of Liberty, Cameo]

```
Butter dish......................$  42.00
Creamer .........................  37.50
Pitcher, water...................  54.00
Plate, 10".......................  30.00
Spooner .........................  42.50
Sugar bowl ......................  45.00
Tumbler .........................  17.00
```

GOOD LUCK, See HORSESHOE

GOOSEBERRY

```
Butter dish......................$  33.00
Compote
    Covered, high standard, large....  49.00
```

Covered, high standard, 6"	40.00
Creamer	35.00
*Goblet	26.50
Honey dish	9.00

Lemonade glass	26.00
Pickle	11.50
Pitcher	
Syrup	32.50
Water	47.50
Sauce	10.00
Spooner	30.00
Sugar bowl	35.00
Tumbler	20.00

*Reproduced Item

GOTHIC

First made by McKee & Bros. in 1850's; possibly reissued in 1870's.

Bowl, flat, 8"	$ 37.50
Butter dish	60.00
Cake stand	40.50
Castor bottle	14.00
Champagne [scarce]	65.00
Compote	
Covered, on standard	120.00
Open, footed	65.00
Cordial	50.00
Creamer	75.00
Egg cup	21.00
Goblet	37.50
Plate [scarce]	37.00
Sauce	14.50
Spooner	45.00
Sugar bowl	75.00
Tumbler	45.00
Wine [scarce]	65.00

GRAPE AND FESTOON

Made by Doyle & Co., Pittsburgh, Pa. in early 1870's.

Butter dish	$ 60.00
Celery	52.50
Compote	
Covered, high standard	55.00
Covered, low standard	36.00
Cordial	35.00
Creamer	52.50
Dish, oval, large	15.00
Egg cup	14.50
Goblet	30.00
Pickle	17.50
Pitcher	60.00
Plate, 6"	25.00
Salt, footed	18.00
Sauce	10.00
Spooner	32.50
Sugar bowl	42.50
Wine	14.00

GRAPE BAND

Butter dish	$ 32.50
Compote	
Covered, high standard	60.00
Covered, low standard	48.00
Cordial	35.00
Goblet	18.00
Pickle	11.50
Pitcher	50.00
Plate, 6"	22.50
Salt, footed	12.50
Sauce	10.00
Spooner	30.00

Sugar bowl	35.00
Tumbler	20.00
Wine	16.00

GRAPE WITH THUMBPRINT

Bowl ....$	25.00
Butter dish	48.00
Celery	32.50
Creamer	45.00
Goblet	27.50
Pitcher, water	55.00
Sauce	10.00
Spooner	35.00
Sugar bowl	45.00
Syrup	35.00
Tumbler	20.00

GRASSHOPPER
|Locust, Long Spear|

Butter dish ....$	37.50
Celery	23.00
Compote, covered	45.50
Creamer	23.00
*Goblet	24.00
Pickle	14.50
Pitcher, water	40.50
Sauce	10.00
Spooner	16.00
Sugar bowl	24.00

*Reproduced Item

HAMILTON

Butter dish......................$	63.50
Castor set	109.50
Celery	52.00
Champagne	37.50

Compote	
Open, high standard	63.00
Covered, 6", high standard	103.50
Open, low standard, deep bowl	57.50
Open, low standard, shallow bowl	49.00
Cordial	37.50
Creamer	
Applied handle	75.00
Pressed handle	47.50
Decanter	60.00
Egg cup	28.50
Honey dish	11.50
Pitcher	
Syrup	52.00
Water	110.00
Plate, 6"	40.50
Salt, footed	23.00
Sauce	13.50
Spooner	29.00
Sugar bowl	63.50
Tumbler	
Water	50.00
Whiskey	50.00
Wine	52.00

HAMILTON WITH FROSTED LEAF

Butter dish.......................$	95.00
Celery	85.00
Compote	
Open, high standard	72.50
Open, low standard	60.00
Cordial	75.00
Creamer	65.00
Egg cup	28.00
Goblet	52.50
Lamp	75.00
Salt, footed	35.00
Sauce	11.50

Spooner	50.00
Sugar bowl	65.00
Tumbler	45.00

HAND

Made C. 1880 by O'Hara Glass Co., Pittsburgh, Pa.

Bowl
7", 8"	$ 21.00
9", 10"	25.50
Butter dish	41.50
Cake stand	34.50
Celery	30.00
Compote	
Covered, high standard	42.50
Open	27.50
Creamer	30.50
Goblet	29.00
Honey dish	13.00
Marmalade jar	26.00
Pickle	14.00
Pitcher	52.00
Platter, 8x10½"	26.00
Sauce	9.00
Spooner	28.50
Sugar bowl	43.00
Wine	20.50

HARP

Produced by Bryce Bros. of Pittsburgh, Pa. C. 1850. Made of flint glass.

Butter dish	$ 82.50
Compote, 6", covered, low standard	138.00

Goblet [rare]	264.50
Lamp	100.50
Salt, open	30.50
Sauce	26.00
Spill holder	45.00

HARTFORD

A product of Fostoria Glass Co., Moundsville, W. Va., after 1891.

Bowl
Berry, 5½", 6"	$ 11.50
Berry, 8"	14.50
Finger	10.00
Footed, 4½", 5½"	9.00
Footed, 6", 7"	11.50
Footed, 8"	13.50
Oblong, 7", 8"	14.00
Oblong, 9"	17.00
Butter dish, covered	23.00
Celery	14.50
Creamer	16.00
Dish, olive, 5½"	7.50
Nappy, 5½", handled	9.00
Salt dip	3.00
Sauce, 4½"	6.00
Shakers, pair	13.00
Spoon basket	15.50
Spooner	11.50
Sugar bowl	
Covered, footed base	23.00
Covered, plain base	19.00
Syrup jug	13.50
Tumbler	7.50

HEART WITH THUMBPRINT
[Bull's Eye in Heart, Columbia]

Produced by the Tarentum Glass Co., Tarentum, Pa., about 1899.

Bowl, berry, 9" .... $	20.00
Butter dish	37.50
Celery	20.00
Creamer	
Regular	27.50
Individual	19.00
Cruet	45.00
Goblet	19.00
Pitcher	34.50
Plate	30.50
Sauce	8.50
Spooner	16.00
Sugar bowl	
Covered.....................	39.00
Individual	21.00
Tumbler	10.50
Vases, pair, 10"	26.00
Wine, 4"........................	26.50

HERRINGBONE
[Florida]

One of the States' patterns produced by U. S. Glass Co. in the 1890's.

Butter dish .... $	36.00
Compote	37.50
Creamer	30.00
Goblet	18.00
Pickle	12.00
Pitcher	35.00
Sauce	8.50
Shakers, pair....................	20.00
Spooner	25.00
Sugar	32.50

HIDALGO
[Frosted Waffle]

Made by Adams & Co., in Pittsburgh, Pa., in the early 1880's.

Bowl	
Large .... $	14.00
Small	11.00
Butter dish......................	29.00
Celery	17.50
Compote	
Open, high standard	30.50

Covered, high standard	40.50
Cup and saucer..................	11.50
Goblet	14.50
Pickle	10.00
Pitcher	
Milk	26.50
Syrup	18.50
Plate, 10".......................	17.50
Sauce	
Flat.........................	6.00
Footed	9.00
Shakers, pair....................	13.50
Spooner	11.00
Sugar bowl	29.00
Sugar shaker....................	11.50
Tray, water	22.50
Tumbler	11.00

HOBNAIL, BALL FOOT

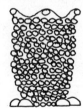

Bowl, berry .... $	32.50
Butter dish......................	40.00
Celery	32.50
Creamer	30.00
Sauce	11.50
Spooner	27.50
Sugar bowl	39.00

HOBNAIL BAND

Bowl	
9½" diam..................... $	17.00
8¼" diam.....................	14.50
Butter dish......................	27.50
Candleholders, 4" high, ball top	29.00
Celery dish, 10½" long	20.00
Centerpiece, half moons, each	
three-legged..................	34.50

Champagne	15.50
Coaster	7.00
Creamer	19.00
Cup and saucer	17.00
Custard	9.50
Dish	
Server, five sections	21.50
Square, four handles	17.50
Finger bowl, 5-1/8" diam.	11.00
Goblet	14.50
Juice tumbler	9.00
Pickle dish, divided, 5¾" diam.	10.50
Pitcher, water	39.00
Plate	
Dinner, 10-7/8" diam.	14.00
Divided, 8-3/8" diam.	12.00
Pie, handles, 7-13/16" diam.	10.00
Sandwich, 7-3/8" diam.	9.50
Sauce. 5-1/8" diam.	7.50
Shakers, in matching holder. Set	16.00
Spooner	15.50
Sugar bowl	30.00
Tumbler	11.50

HOBNAIL, FAN TOP
[See Colored Glass Section]

HOBNAIL, FLATTENED
[See Flattened Hobnail]

HOBNAIL, OPALESCENT
[See Colored Glass Section]

HOBNAIL, PANELLED
[See Colored Glass Section]

HOBNAIL, POINTED
[See Colored Glass Section]

HOBNAIL, PRINTED
[See Colored Glass Section]

HOBNAIL, THUMBPRINT BASE
[See Colored Glass Section]

HOLLY

Made by Sandwich Glass Co., late 1860's, early 1870's.

Butter dish	$	46.00

Compote	
Covered, high standard	63.50
Covered, low standard	57.50
Creamer	52.00
Egg cup	35.00
Goblet [scarce]	52.00
Pickle	11.50
Pitcher	63.50
Salt, footed	13.50
Sauce	12.00
Spooner	30.00
Sugar bowl	46.00
Tumbler, footed	29.50
Wine	37.50

HOLLY AMBER
[See Colored Glass Section]

HONEYCOMB

A popular pattern, made by numerous glass firms, C. 1860-1900.

Ale glass	$	14.50
Bitters bottle		13.50
Bowl		
Covered, 6", 7"		16.00
Footed, 8", 9"		25.00
Footed, 10"		33.00
Finger		11.50
Butter dish		26.00
Castor bottle		9.00
Celery		34.50
Champagne		42.00
Compote		
Covered, high standard		43.00
Covered, low standard		40.00
Open		34.00
Cordial		12.00

Creamer	25.50
Cup, custard, handled	15.50
Decanter	
Pint	17.50
Quart	29.00
Dish, oval	12.00
Egg cup	16.00
Goblet	21.50
Honey dish	20.00
Jug	
½ pint	20.00
Pint	26.00
Quart	29.00
Three pints	36.50
Lamp	
All glass	21.50
Marble base	26.00
Lemonade glass	15.50
Mug, ½ pint	11.00
Pitcher, 9"	32.50
Plate	
6"	11.50
7"	14.50
Pomade jar	13.00
Salt	
Covered, on standard	19.00
Open, on standard	10.50
Sauce	7.00
Shakers, pair	16.50
Spooner	11.50
Sugar bowl	27.00
Tumbler	
½ pint	13.00
⅓ pint	15.00
Footed	14.50
Water bottle	21.50
Wine	28.00

HONEYCOMB AND STAR

Butter dish	$ 42.00
Cake plate, on standard	42.00
Celery	40.00
Compote, covered	47.50
Creamer	42.00
Spooner	30.00
Sugar bowl	36.00
Tumbler	22.00

HORN OF PLENTY

Reputed to have first been made by Sandwich Glass Co., later by Bryce, McKee & Co., Pittsburgh, Pa., in the 1850's.

Bowl, flat, 8½" diam.	$ 57.50
Butter dish	
Conventional knob	100.00
Washington's head	450.00
Celery	98.00
Claret, flared top, 5" high	230.00
Compote	
Covered, 6", on standard	190.00
Covered, oblong	155.00
Open, extra large, high standard	115.00
Open, 7¼", low standard	91.50
Open, low standard	83.50
Oval, on standard	316.00
Cordial	69.00
Creamer	138.00
Decanter	
Pint	86.50
Quart	98.00
½ gallon	109.00
Egg cup	46.00
*Goblet	75.00
Honey dish	18.50
Lamp	
*All glass	103.50
Marble base	86.50
Mug	100.00
Pepper sauce bottle	40.50
Pickle	49.00
Pitcher	
Milk	258.50
Water	230.00
Plate, 6"	75.00
Salt, oval	21.50
Sauce, 4½", rayed base	29.00
Scent bottle	46.00
Spooner	43.00
Sugar bowl	109.00
*Tumbler	
Water	55.00
Whiskey	60.00
Wine	48.50

*Reproduced Item

HORSESHOE
[Good Luck, Prayer Rug]

A pattern of Adams & Co., Pittsburgh, Pa., in the early 1880's.

Bowl
Berry, oval .... $	21.50
Waste	14.50
Butter dish.......................	45.00

Cake stand
8"	30.00
9"	35.00
10"	45.00
Celery	35.00
Cheese dish, covered	83.50

Compote
Covered, 7½", low standard	43.50
Open, large, high standard	41.50
Covered, large, high standard....	49.00
Cordial	38.50
Creamer	35.00

Dish
Covered, oblong	37.50
Open, 6x9", oblong............	33.00

Goblet
Knob stem.....................	31.00
Plain round stem	25.50
Marmalade jar	31.50
Pickle..........................	17.50

Pitcher
Large	50.00
Small	45.00

Plate
7¼"	23.00
8¼"	29.00
10"	40.50

Platter
Oval..........................	45.00
*Double horseshoe handles, 10x14".......................	52.00

Salt
Celery dip, shape of horseshoe...	15.00
Master salt, shape of horseshoe .	24.00

Sauce
Flat, 4½"......................	9.00
Footed, 4"	11.50
Spooner.......................	37.50
Sugar bowl	47.50

*Reproduced Item

HUBER

A popular pattern made by a number of glass firms ranging from Sandwich Glass Co. to Bakewell & Pears Co. of Pittsburgh, Pa., through the 1860's, in flint glass.

Ale glass .... $	15.50
Bitters bottle	21.00
Bowl, covered, 6", 7"	28.50
Butter dish......................	34.50
Celery	22.50
Champagne......................	30.00

Compote
Covered, 8", 9", high standard ...	49.00
Covered, 10", high standard	60.00
Covered, 7", 8", low standard	43.00
Cordial..........................	25.00
Creamer	45.00
Cup, custard	13.50

Decanter
Bar lip, pint	30.00
Bar lip, quart..................	42.50
With stopper, pint	40.00
With stopper, quart	50.00
Dish	20.00
Egg cup, handled	35.00
Goblet	20.00
Honey dish	9.00

Jug
Quart.........................	35.00
Three pints	42.50
Lemonade glass	14.00
Mug	20.00
Pitcher.........................	34.50

Plate
6"	20.00
7"	25.00

Salt
Celery dip	15.00
Footed	17.50
Sauce	12.50
Spooner	18.00
Sugar bowl	34.50

Tumbler
Gill...........................	15.00
½ pint	20.00
Jelly	20.00
Wine...........................	25.00

HUMMING BIRD
[See Colored Glass Section]

ICICLE
[See Colored Glass Section]

ILLINOIS

Another of the States' patterns made by U. S. Glass Co., in the late 1890's.

Bowl
Finger ....$	9.00
Round, 8"	10.00
Round, 6"	9.50
Butter dish.....................	21.50
Candleholder	11.50
Celery, tall.....................	13.50
Celery tray, 11"	11.00
Cheese dish, covered	20.50

Creamer
Large	15.50
Medium.....................	12.50
Cruet	12.00
Olive dish	7.50
Pickle	9.50

Pitcher
½ gallon	25.50
Water........................	19.00

Plate
Round, 7"	9.50
Square, 7"....................	10.00
Salt, individual	3.50
Shakers, pair...................	14.00
Spooner........................	11.00
Spoon tray	8.00
Sugar bowl, covered	21.50
Sugar shaker...................	11.50
Toothpick holder	7.50
Tray, ice cream	8.50
Tumbler	7.00

INVERTED FERN

Butter dish.....................$	62.50
Champagne [scarce]	85.00
Compote, open	52.00
Cordial.........................	37.50
Creamer	75.00
Egg cup	25.00

Goblet
Plain base	25.00
Rayed base	30.00
Honey dish	10.50
Pitcher [rare]	201.00
Plate, 6" [scarce]	125.00
Salt, footed	17.50
Sauce	11.50
Spooner........................	37.50
Sugar bowl	72.00

Tumbler
Water.........................	52.00
Whiskey	57.50
Wine............................	54.50

IVY, RIBBED

Bitters bottle ....$	49.00
Bowl, flat, 8½" diam.	92.00
Butter dish.....................	63.00
Castor bottle	25.50
Celery [rare]	---------

Compote
Covered, small, on standard	126.50
Open, high standard, scalloped edge........................	83.50
Open, low standard, scalloped edge........................	69.00
Cordial	63.50
Creamer	106.50

Decanter
½ pint	62.00
Pint..........................	71.00
Quart	79.00
Egg cup	30.00
Goblet	42.50
Honey dish	11.50
Lamp	85.00
Mug	150.00

Pitcher [extremely rare] . . . .   ----------
Salt
   Covered, footed 125.00
   Open, beaded edge 34.50
   Open, scalloped edge 28.00
Sauce 12.00
Spooner 45.00
Sugar bowl 80.00
Tumbler
   Water 65.00
   Whiskey 50.00
Wine 34.50

IVY, ROYAL, See ROYAL IVY
[See Colored Glass Section]

IVY IN SNOW
[Forest Ware]

A product of the Cooperative Flint Glass Co. of Beaver Falls, Pa., in the late 1880 period.

Bowl, flat, 8" diam. . . . . $ 25.00
*Butter dish 45.00
*Cake stand 65.00
*Celery 45.00
Compote
   Covered, small, high standard 59.50
   Covered, medium, high standard .   57.50
   Covered, large, high standard 65.00
Cordial 32.50
*Creamer 28.00
Cup and saucer 24.00
*Goblet 27.50
Marmalade jar 40.00
*Pitcher 65.00
Plate, 10" 25.00
Sauce
   Flat, round, 4" 10.00
   Deep, 6" 15.00
Spooner 37.50
*Sugar bowl 47.50
Tumbler 28.00
Wine 30.00
*Reproduced Item

JACOB'S COAT
[See Colored Glass Section]

JACOB'S LADDER
[Maltese]

Produced by Bryce Bros., Pittsburgh, Pa. in the 1870's.

Bowl, flat, 6" . . . . $ 22.00
Butter dish 45.00
Cake stand 26.00
Celery 40.00
Compote
   Covered, large, high standard 48.50
   Open, large, on standard, scal-
   loped edge 37.50
   Open, Dolphin standard, [scarce] .   200.00
Cordial 35.00
Creamer 40.00
Dish, oval, 6", 7" 15.00
Goblet 34.50
Marmalade jar 50.00
Mug 23.00
Pickle 22.50
Pitcher
   Syrup, plain top 35.00
   Syrup, knight's head knob 45.00
   Water 60.00
Plate, 6½" 22.50
Salt
   Master, footed 18.50
   Flat, round 10.50
Sauce
   Flat, 3½", 4" 10.00
   Footed, 4½" 11.00
Spooner 37.50
Sugar bowl 40.00
Tumbler 30.00
Wine 15.50

JEWEL WITH DEWDROP
[Kansas]

Originally produced by Cooperative Flint Glass Co., Beaver Falls, Pa. Later produced by

U. S. Glass Co. under the name of "Kansas" in 1907.

Bowl
Berry, 6" ....$ 12.50
Berry, 7", 8" 17.50
Butter dish...................... 32.50
Cake stand
8" 25.00
9" 32.50
10" 37.50
Celery 30.00
Compote
Covered, high standard, deep bowl.......................... 42.00
Open, high standard 28.50
Cordial 24.50
Creamer 35.00
Cup............................. 12.00
Dish, oblong 12.50
Goblet 32.50
Mug 12.00
Pickle 11.00
Pitcher
Syrup 28.50
Water......................... 32.50
Platter, bread 17.50
Sauce 10.00
Shakers, pair.................... 30.00
Spooner 32.50
Sugar bowl 35.00
Toothpick holder 15.00
Tumbler 26.50

JUMBO

Made by Canton Glass Co., Canton, Ohio, C. 1883.

Butter dish
Round ....$ 115.00
Oblong 172.50
Castor set, 3 bottles.............. 144.00

Compote, covered, 7" 144.00
Creamer 100.00
Cup and saucer.................. 65.00
Dish, covered, frosted 72.50
Goblet [scarce] 145.00
Marmalade jar, covered 135.00
Spooner 60.00
Spoon rack [scarce] 167.00
Sugar bowl 125.00

KING'S CROWN

Also known as "Ruby Thumbprint" when flashed with red color. Practically every piece has been reproduced.

Banana dish ....$ 49.00
Bowl
Berry 17.50
Punch......................... 126.50
Sawtooth edge 21.50
Butter dish...................... 37.50
Cake stand, 10" 37.50
Castor bottle 11.00
Castor set, all glass 52.00
Compote
Open, high standard 37.00
Open, large 48.50
Cordial 12.00
Creamer
Large 25.00
Small 19.00
Cup and saucer.................. 26.00
Dish
Boat shaped, 8" 18.00
Cheese 40.50
Olive 12.00
Oval, 6"....................... 13.50
Oval, 10"..................... 15.50
Goblet 12.50
Mustard jar, covered 12.00
Pickle 12.00
Pitcher
Round, quart.................. 34.00
Round, 2 quarts 40.00
Tall, slender, large 42.00
Tall, slender, small 41.50
Sauce
Boat shaped 9.00

Round, belled, 4x4¼"..........	11.50
Round, 5", 6"	14.00
Shakers, pair	34.50
Spooner	12.00
Sugar bowl	37.50
Toothpick holder	11.00
Tumbler........................	12.00
Wine...........................	12.00

*Reproduced Item

LATTICE
[Diamond Bar]

Made by King, Son & Co., Pittsburgh, Pa., C. 1880.

Bowl, waste......................$	16.50
Butter dish......................	39.50
Cake stand	32.00
Celery	26.50
Compote, covered, high standard ...	35.00
Cordial.........................	17.50
Creamer	29.50
Egg cup	15.00
Goblet	20.00
Lamp	40.00
Marmalade jar	22.50
Pickle	12.50
Pitcher	
Syrup	30.00
Water........................	36.50
Plate	
6¼"	12.00
7¼"	16.00
10"	19.00
Platter, oblong, inscribed	35.00
Sauce	
Flat..........................	7.50
Footed	9.50
Shakers, pair....................	15.00
Spooner	32.50
Sugar bowl	32.50
Tray, water	35.00
Wine...........................	14.00

LEAF AND DART

Butter dish......................$	52.50
Celery	40.00
Compote, covered, low standard....	48.00
Cordial	32.50

Creamer	45.00
Egg cup	22.50
Goblet..........................	28.50
Lamp	30.00
Pitcher..........................	65.00
Salt	
Covered, on standard	52.50
Open, on standard.............	35.00
Sauce	12.00
Spooner.........................	40.00
Sugar bowl	40.00
Tumbler, footed	45.00
Wine...........................	30.00

LIBERTY BELL
[Centennial]

Made by Gillinder & Co., Philadelphia, Pa. Made for the year of the Centennial, 1876.

Bowl, footed	
6" ....$	85.00
7"	85.00
8"	72.50
Butter dish......................	100.00
Celery	75.00
Child's set. Butter dish, creamer,	
spooner, sugar bowl	125.00
Compote	
Open, 6"	62.50
Open, 8"	75.00
Creamer, applied handle	100.00
Goblet. knob stem	40.00

Mug, snail handle [rare]	275.00
Pickle	35.00
Pitcher, water. Reeded, applied handle [rare]	500.00
Plate	
6"	54.50
8"	57.50
10"	69.50
Platter	
7x11½"	95.00
9½x13". M.G., John Hancock	200.00
Salt	
Individual	25.00
Master salt	45.00
Shaker top, bell shaped	65.00
Sauce	
Flat, round [scarce]	30.00
Flat, closed handles, 4½"	20.00
Footed	25.00
Shakers, pan, original tops	180.00
Spooner	75.00
Sugar bowl, covered	85.00

LILY OF THE VALLEY

Butter dish .... $	42.00
Cake stand	32.00
Celery	40.00
Compote, covered, high standard ...	66.00
Cordial	35.00
Creamer, footed	45.00
Cruet	50.00
Dish, oval	22.00
Goblet	33.00
Pickle	18.00
Pitcher	
Water	67.00
Milk [scarce]	80.50
Salt, covered, footed	42.00
Sauce	10.00
Spooner	25.00
Sugar bowl, footed	45.00
Wine [scarce]	31.00

LINCOLN DRAPE

Butter dish .... $	75.00
Celery	80.00
Compote, open	48.50

Cordial	70.00
Creamer	95.00
Decanter	75.00
Egg cup	35.00
Goblet	60.00
Lamp	49.00
Pitcher	
Syrup	85.00
Water	185.00
Plate, 6"	45.00
Salt, footed	34.50
Sauce, flat, 4½"	14.50
Spooner	50.00
Sugar bowl	75.00
Tumbler	26.00
Wine	18.50

LINCOLN DRAPE WITH TASSEL

Butter dish .... $	85.00
Compote, open, low standard	60.00
Egg cup	40.00
Goblet	75.00
Spooner	55.00
Sugar bowl	110.00

LION

Made by Gillinder & Sons, Philadelphia, Pa., in the 1870's.

*Butter dish	
Knob, crouched lion .... $	83.00
Knob, lion head	94.50
*Celery	85.00
Compote	
Covered, extra large, high standard	150.00
Covered, low standard	120.00

Covered, 5", on standard	120.00
Covered, collared base	100.00
Oblong, 5½ x 9", collared base	100.00
*Cordial	100.00
Creamer	90.00
Dish, cheese [scarce]	180.00
*Egg cup	65.00
*Goblet	80.00
Lamp	130.00
Marmalade jar	
Knob, crouched lion	85.00
Knob, lion head	90.00
Paperweight	34.00
Pickle	42.50
Pitcher	
Milk	150.00
Syrup	100.00
*Water	90.00
*Plate, bread, 10½"	62.50
Platter, oval	60.00
Salt, master, oval	75.00
*Sauce	
Footed, small	15.00
Footed, medium	18.00
Footed, large	22.50
Spooner	67.50
*Sugar bowl	
Knob, crouched lion	100.00
Knob, lion head	120.00
Tumbler, lion heads in relief	75.00
Wine	110.00

*Reproduced Item

LOCKET ON CHAIN
[See Colored Glass Section]

LOG CABIN

Made by Central Glass Co., Wheeling, W. Va., C. 1875.

Butter dish	$ 75.00
Compote, covered, on standard	125.00

Creamer	60.00
Mustard	40.00
Pitcher	120.00
Sauce	16.50
Spooner	45.00
Sugar bowl [scarce]	95.00

LOOP AND DART

Made by Portland Glass Co., Portland, Maine in the 1860's.

Butter dish	$ 40.00
Celery	38.50
Compote, 8", low standard	34.50
Cordial	32.50
Creamer	60.00
Egg cup	17.50
Goblet	27.50
Pickle	10.50
Pitcher	57.50
Plate, 6"	50.00
Salt, footed	20.00
Sauce	8.50
Spooner	35.00
Sugar bowl	40.00
Tumbler	
Footed	32.00
Water	30.00

LOOP AND DART
WITH DIAMOND ORNAMENT

Butter dish	$ 52.50
Celery	50.00
Compote, 8", low standard	48.00

Cordial	25.00
Creamer	52.50
Egg cup	25.00
Goblet	30.00
Lamp, iron base	28.00
Pickle	9.50
Pitcher	60.00
Plate, 6"	48.00
Sauce	7.50
Spooner	40.00
Sugar bowl	50.00
Tumbler	35.00

LOOP AND DART
WITH ROUND ORNAMENT

Butter dish	$ 57.50
Celery	50.00
Compote, 8", low standard	60.00
Cordial	35.00
Creamer	52.50
Cup plate	21.50
Dish, 9¼"	13.00
Egg cup	26.50
Goblet	30.00
Pickle	18.00
Pitcher	72.00
Plate, 6"	50.00
Salt, footed	22.50
Sauce	12.00
Spooner	42.50
Sugar bowl	60.00
Tumbler	
Footed	35.00
Water	40.00

LOOP WITH DEWDROPS

Early maker unknown. Reproduced by U. S. Glass Company in 1892.

Bowl, berry, 7", 8"	$ 17.50
Butter dish	32.00
Cake stand	42.00
Celery	40.00
Compote	
Covered, 6", 7", high standard	35.00
Covered, 8", high standard	44.50
Open, 4½", footed	20.00
Cordial	13.00

Creamer	30.00
Cup and saucer	25.00
Dish, oval, 8", 9"	15.00
Goblet	22.50
Marmalade jar	19.00
Mug	12.00
Pickle	18.00
Pitcher	
Syrup	28.50
Water	30.00
Plate, bread	24.50
Sauce	
Flat, 4"	6.50
Footed, 4"	12.00
Shakers, pair	25.00
Spooner	30.00
Sugar bowl	31.00
Tumbler	25.00
Wine	25.00

LOTUS
[Garden of Eden]

Butter dish, covered	$ 47.50
Cake stand	35.50
Creamer, small	24.00
Goblet	
Plain	42.50
Serpent head	45.00
Mug, handled	21.50
Pickle, oval	14.00
Salt, master	19.50
Sugar bowl, covered	42.00
Tray, bread	22.50

MAGNET AND GRAPE
[Frosted Leaf]

Butter dish	$ 85.00
Celery	95.00
Champagne	85.00

Compote, open, large	85.00
Cordial	75.00
*Creamer	85.00
Decanter	
Pint.	57.50
Quart	80.50
Egg cup	36.50
*Goblet	
Knob stem.	55.00
Plain stem	45.00
Salt, footed	30.00
Sauce	12.50
Spooner	32.00
*Sugar bowl	75.00
Tumbler	
Water.	40.00
Whiskey	55.00
Wine.	48.50

*Reproduced Item

MAGNET AND GRAPE
[Stippled Leaf]

Butter dish.	$	65.00
Compote, open		42.50
Cordial		52.50
Creamer		65.00
Goblet		42.50
Pitcher		55.00
Salt, footed		18.00
Sauce		10.00
Spooner		42.50
Sugar bowl		65.00
Tumbler		35.00

MAIZE
[See Colored Glass Section]

MANHATTAN

Made by U. S. Glass Co., C. 1902.

Bowl		
7", 8"	$	11.50
8½", 9½"		13.50
Berry, 10", 11"		16.50
Berry, 12½"		18.00
Fruit, 9½"		12.00
Punch, large		108.00
Butter dish.		29.00
Cake stand		29.50
Celery, tall.		16.50
Compote		
9½"		27.00
10½"		30.50
*Creamer		
Individual		8.00
Large		15.00
Dish, jelly, 6".		8.00
Pickle		8.50
Pitcher		
½ gallon, tankard		23.00
½ gallon, water		19.00
Plate		
5"		11.50
9½"		14.00
*11", 12"		16.50
Sauce		
4½", flat		6.00
5", footed		6.00
Spooner		11.50
Sugar bowl		
Covered.		27.00
*Open, individual		11.50
Tumbler		
ᴸIced tea		7.50
Water.		6.00
Water bottle		14.00

*Reproduced Item

MAPLE LEAF
[See Colored Glass Section]

MARQUISETTE

Butter dish.	$	40.00
Celery		35.00

Compote
Covered, low standard 48.50
Open, high standard 47.50
Cordial 32.50
Creamer 45.00
Dish, oval 20.00
Goblet 30.00
Pickle 20.00
Pitcher 42.50
Sauce, flat, 4" 10.00
Spooner 30.00
Sugar bowl 45.00
Wine 25.00

MASCOTTE
|Ethol, Fern and Waffle|

Bowl, 8" . . . . $ 12.50
Butter dish, covered, etched 35.00
Creamer and sugar, covered 40.00
Jar, covered. Patd. May 20, 1873 . . .   38.00
Plate only to cheese dish 18.00
Sugar, covered 22.50
Tray, water leaf etched 35.00

MASONIC
|Inverted Prism|

Bowl
Berry . . . . $ 18.50
Small 16.00
Butter dish
Covered, flat 30.00
Covered, footed 32.00
Open 25.00
Cake stand 28.50

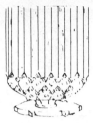

Creamer 32.50
Honey dish, covered, flat, square . . .   18.00
Pitcher, tankard 40.00
Sardine box 15.00
Sauce 8.00
Spooner 32.50
Sugar bowl 32.50
Tumbler 15.00

MEDALLION
|See Colored Glass Section|

MELROSE
|See Colored Glass Section|

MICHIGAN
|Panelled Jewel|

Bowl
Berry, 7½", 8½" . . . . $ 15.00
Berry, 10" 18.50
Butter dish
Covered, large 30.00
Covered, small 25.00
Champagne 22.50
Creamer
Individual 15.00
Large 25.00
Cruet 22.50
Cup 10.00
Goblet 25.00
Olive dish 10.00
Pitcher
½ gallon tankard 27.50
3 pints 32.50
Plate, round, 5½" 14.50
Shakers, pair 15.00
Spooner 18.50
Sugar bowl 27.50

Tumbler	20.00
Water bottle or carafe	20.00
Wine	18.50

MINERVA
|Guardian Angel|

Butter dish, covered	$ 65.00
Cake stand	
9"	65.00
13"	75.00
Celery	21.50
Champagne |rare|	63.50
Compote	
Covered, high standard	60.00
Covered, low standard	46.00
Cordial	16.00
Creamer	40.00
Dish, oblong, 2½" deep	25.00
Goblet	40.00
Marmalade jar	35.00
Pickle, inscribed	35.00
Pitcher	54.00
Plate	
Small	35.00
Closed handles, 9"	40.00
Platter	32.00
Sauce	
Flat, round	12.00
Footed, round	15.00
Spooner	40.00
Sugar bowl	40.00

MINNESOTA

Bowl	
Berry, round, 6", 7", 8"	$ 19.50
Round, flared edge, 4½"	17.50
Round, flared edge, 7½", 8½"	19.00
Round, flared edge, 9½"	21.00
Square, 6", 7", 8"	21.00

Butter dish	37.00
Celery tray	
10"	22.50
13"	25.00
Compote	
Round, 6", 7", 8"	50.00
Square, 6", 7", 8"	45.00
Creamer	25.00
Dish	
Candy, 9"	14.50
Jelly, 8"	13.00
Oval, low, 7", 8"	13.00
Preserve, 9"	14.00
Goblet	18.50
Pickle, 7½"	11.50
Pitcher	
½ gallon, tankard	33.00
¾ gallon, water	30.00
Sauce, flat, 4", 4½"	9.00
Spooner	19.00
Sugar bowl, covered	37.00
Tumbler	12.00
Wine	15.00

MONKEY
|See Colored Glass Section|

MOON AND STAR
|Palace, Star and Punty,
Bull's Eye and Star|

Made by several manufacturers from Sandwich, 1870's; Palace, Pioneer Glass, 1892; Wilson, 1890; and also Cooperative Flint Glass in the 1890's.

Bowl	
Berry, 6"	$ 22.50
Berry, 7"	24.00
Berry, 8"	26.00
Berry, 10"	30.00
Fruit, 12½"	60.00
*Waste	25.00
*Butter dish	56.00
Cake stand, 6" diam.	49.00
Celery	42.50
*Champagne, flared top	45.00
Claret	35.00

Compote

Covered, 7", collared base	45.00
*Covered, 8", high standard	60.50
Covered, 10", collared base	75.00
*Covered, 10", high standard	95.00
Open, high standard	46.00
Creamer	60.00
*Cruet	62.50

Dish

Cheese	52.00
Oblong, 8"	32.00
*Egg cup	33.00

*Goblet

Clear	32.50
Frosted	38.00
Lamp	52.00
Pickle	18.00

Pitcher

Syrup	65.00
*Water	109.00
Platter, oblong	37.50
*Salt, celery dip	13.00

Sauce

Flat	13.50
Footed	14.00
*Shakers, pair, 4"	38.50
*Spooner, 5¼"	40.00
*Sugar bowl	56.00
*Toothpick holder	16.50
Tray	52.50
*Tumbler, 4½"	40.00
*Wine, 4½"	28.50

*Reproduced Item

NAILHEAD
[Gem, Barrelled Block]

Butter dish	$	40.00
Cake stand		45.00
Celery		40.00

Compote

Covered, 8"	35.00
Open, high standard	30.00
Cordial	22.50
Creamer	30.00
Goblet	18.50
Pitcher	40.00

Plate

Round, 9"	27.50
Square, 7"	25.00

Sauce	10.00
Shakers, pair	18.50
Spooner	30.00
Sugar bowl	40.00
Tumbler	17.50
Wine	9.00

NEVADA

Bowl, 6", 7", 8"	$	11.50
Butter dish		20.00
Cake stand, 10"		17.50
Celery, tall		13.50

Compote

Covered, 6", 7", 8"	29.00
Open, 6", 7", 8"	22.50
Cracker jar	19.50
Creamer	14.00
Cruet	13.50

Dish

Oval, 7", 8", 9"	10.50
Oval, 10", 11"	12.00
Pickle	7.50

Pitcher

½ gallon, tankard	19.00
3 pints	17.50
Water	17.50

Salt

Individual	3.50
Master	7.00
Sauce	6.00
Shakers, pair	12.50
Spooner	9.50
Sugar bowl, covered	21.50
Syrup	13.50
Toothpick holder	6.00
Tumbler	7.00

NEW ENGLAND PINEAPPLE
[Pineapple, Loop and Jewel]

Bowl, fruit	$	69.00
Butter dish		95.00
Castor bottle		24.50
Castor set		115.00
Celery		62.50
Champagne		63.50

Compote

Covered, 6", high standard	132.50
Open, small, high standard	100.00
Open, large, high standard	125.00

Open, small, low standard	72.00
Open, large, low standard	75.00
Open, extra large, high standard	103.50
Cordial	46.00
Creamer [scarce]	175.00
Cruet	63.50
Decanter	
Pint	98.00
Quart	115.00
Egg cup	28.50
*Goblet	40.50
Honey dish	14.00
Jug, tall	98.00
Mug, small	66.00
Pitcher [small]	230.00
Plate, 6"	86.50
Salt, footed	30.00
Sauce	15.00
Spooner	60.00
Sugar bowl	92.00
Tumbler	
Footed [scarce]	80.00
Water	46.00
Whiskey	56.00
*Wine	65.00

*Reproduced Item

NEW HAMPSHIRE

Biscuit jar, covered	$ 22.50
Bowl	
Flared, 6½", 7½", 8½"	10.50
Round, 6½", 7½", 8½"	11.50
Square, 6½", 7½", 8½"	13.00
Butter dish	25.00
Celery	22.50
Champagne	15.00
Creamer	
Individual	12.00

Large	20.00
Goblet	14.50
Lemonade cup	10.00
Mug	
Large	14.50
Medium	12.50
Pitcher	
½ gallon, tankard	25.00
3 pints, water	30.00
¾ gallon, water	32.50
Sauce	
Round, deep	5.50
Round, flared	5.50
Round, shallow, 4"	5.00
Square	6.00
Sugar bowl	
Covered	25.00
Medium, open handles	18.50
Syrup	32.50
Tumbler	12.50
Wine	15.00

NEW JERSEY

Bowl	
Flared, 8", 9", 10"	$ 12.00
Oval, 6", 8", 10"	10.00
Round, high, 6", 7", 8"	11.00
Butter dish	25.00
Cake stand, 8"	22.50
Celery	16.50
Celery tray	10.00
Compote	
Open, 6", 7", 8"	24.50
Jelly, covered, 5"	28.00
Creamer	14.50
Cruet	13.50
Goblet	15.00
Molasses jar	13.50
Pickle	8.50
Pitcher	
1 gallon, applied handle	35.00
3 pints, applied handle	40.00
½ gallon, pressed handle	25.00
Plate, round, 8"	10.00
Sauce, 4"	6.00
Shakers, pair	40.00
Spooner	15.00
Sugar bowl, covered	19.50
Syrup	15.00

Toothpick holder	6.00
Tumbler	10.50
Wine	12.00

NIAGARA

Bowl, berry	$ 10.00
Butter dish, covered	20.00
Celery	14.00
Creamer	16.00
Cruet	13.50
Pitcher, tankard	19.00
Sauce	5.50
Shakers, pair	12.50
Spooner	12.50
Sugar bowl, covered	21.00
Syrup	14.00
Tumbler	9.00

OAK, ROYAL, See ROYAL OAK
[See Colored Glass Section]

ONE HUNDRED ONE

Made by Bellaire Goblet Co., Findlay, Ohio in the late 1870's.

Butter dish	$ 50.00
Cake stand	40.00
Celery	50.00
Compote, covered, low standard	45.00
Creamer	35.00
Dish, oval, deep	16.50
Goblet	25.00
Lamp, hand	40.00
Pickle	14.50
Pitcher, water [scarce]	75.00

Plate	
7"	16.00
8"	18.00
9"	19.50
11"	25.00
Bread, motto	50.00
Sauce	
Flat	10.00
Footed	12.00
Shakers, pair	22.50
Spooner	32.50
Sugar bowl	30.00

OPALESCENT HOBNAIL
[See Colored Glass Section]

OPEN ROSE

Butter dish	$ 35.00
Celery	24.00
Compote	
Covered, high standard	50.00
Covered, low standard	45.00
Creamer	35.00
Dish, oval, 6x9½"	18.00
Egg cup	18.00
Goblet	21.50
Pickle	12.00
Pitcher	40.00
Salt, footed	12.50
Sauce	7.50
Spooner	20.00
Sugar bowl	40.00
Tumbler	25.00

OVAL MITRE

Bowl, covered, 4x6"	$ 25.00
Butter dish	38.00
Creamer	45.00

Compote	
Covered, 6", high standard	54.00
Open, 6", 8"	40.00
Dish, oval........................	16.00
Goblet	30.00
Sauce	7.50
Spooner	22.50
Sugar bowl	45.00

OVAL STAR

Bowl		
Large ....$		14.00
Small		10.00
Butter dish.......................		20.00
Compote		
Covered.......................		28.00
Open		22.00
Creamer		16.00
Pickle		7.00
Pitcher, water...................		20.00
Sauce		5.50
Spooner		11.50
Tumbler		7.00
Wine.............................		7.50

PALMETTE
[Spades, Hearts and Spades]

Butter chip, 2"....................$	4.50
Butter, covered...................	27.50
Cake stand	25.00
Castor bottle.....................	12.00
Celery	27.50
Compote	
Covered, low standard	45.00
Open, footed, 8"	27.50
Cordial..........................	25.00
Creamer, applied handle	38.50

Egg cup	18.00
Goblet	20.00
Lamp	32.00
Pickle	15.00
Pitcher, water, bulbous	58.50
Plate, cake, handled	
Clear	16.00
Amber	23.50
Blue	30.50
Relish scoop	14.00
Salt shaker, flat base.............	20.00
Sauce	
4", flat	12.00
5-1/8", round	7.50
6¼", round	8.00
Spooner .`........................	20.00
Sugar bowl	30.00
Syrup	32.00
Tumbler	
Footed	22.00
Water........................	18.50
Vegetable dish	
8"	12.00
9¼"	15.00
Wine............................	16.00

PANELLED CHERRY

Bowl		
Berry, covered ....$		35.00
Berry, 6 sauces. Set		135.00
Butter dish......................		35.00
Compote, covered, low standard....		37.50
Creamer		32.50
Goblet		25.00
Pitcher		
Syrup		25.00
Water........................		35.00
Sauce		
Flat..........................		12.00
Footed		14.00
Spooner		16.50
Sugar bowl		35.00
Tumbler		18.00

PANELLED DAISY
[Brazil, Oval Medallion]

Bowl		
Covered, 8", flat................$		12.50
Waste		14.50

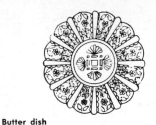

Butter dish			Goblet	
Flat	30.00		Dewdrops on base	32.50
Footed	37.50		Plain base	28.50
Cake stand			Lemonade glass	35.00
8", 9"	30.00		Liqueur glass	12.50
10", 11"	35.00		Marmalade jar	25.00
Celery	35.00		Pickle	20.00
Compote			Pitcher	34.50
Covered, 5", 6", high standard	45.00		Plate	
Covered, 7", 8", high standard	50.00		7"	22.00
Open, 10", 11", high standard	35.00		11"	25.00
Creamer [scarce]	39.00		Platter	
Dish			Oblong, handled	48.00
Oval, 7", 8"	20.00		Oval	40.00
Oval, 9", 10"	25.00		Sauce	
*Goblet	27.50		Flat	8.00
Lamp, hand	22.50		Footed	10.00
Mug	24.50		Spooner	35.00
Pickle	15.00		Sugar bowl	40.00
Pitcher			Tumbler	27.50
Syrup	32.50		Wine	18.50
Water	42.50			

Plate
| Round, 7¼" | 22.00 |
| Square, 9½" | 25.00 |

Sauce
| Flat | 10.00 |
| Footed, round | 12.00 |

Shaker
Salt and pepper, pair	30.00
Sugar	28.50
Spooner	35.00
Sugar bowl	45.00
Tray	36.00
*Tumbler	25.00

*Reproduced Item

PANELLED DIAMOND POINT
[Fluted Diamond Point]

Butter dish	$	40.00
Celery		37.50
Creamer		35.00
Goblet		30.00
Pitcher		35.00
Sauce		10.00
Spooner		30.00
Sugar bowl		35.00

PANELLED DEWDROP
[Stippled Dewdrop]

Butter dish	$	45.00
Celery		40.00
Compote		
Covered, 8", on standard		50.00
Open, high standard		40.00
Cordial		35.00
Creamer		37.50
Dish, oval, collared base		25.00

PANELLED FORGET-ME-NOT
[See Colored Glass Section]

PANELLED GRAPE
[Heavy Panelled Grape]

Ale glass ....$	18.00
*Bowl, crimped, 12"	24.00
*Butter dish.....................	45.00
*Celery	45.00
Compote	
Covered, 5"....................	32.50
*Covered, large	55.00
Open, 6½", low standard........	35.00
*Cordial.......................	30.00
*Creamer, vine handled	45.00
Cup	
Punch.......................	12.50
Sherbet	23.50
Dish, oval......................	24.50
*Goblet	40.00
*Lemonade glass	22.50
Liqueur glass....................	15.00
Mug	12.50
Pickle	12.50
Pitcher	
*Large	65.00
Small	42.50
Syrup	50.00
*Plate, 10"	22.50
Salt...........................	12.50
*Sauce	
Oval.........................	10.00
Round, 4¼"	12.00
*Spooner......................	37.50
*Sugar bowl	45.00
Toothpick holder	15.00
*Tumbler	
Jelly	25.00
Water.......................	35.00
*Wine........................	25.00

*Reproduced Item

PANELLED GRAPE, LATE

Bowl, berry ....$	26.50
Butter dish......................	40.00
Creamer	35.00
Dish, covered	34.50
*Goblet	23.50
Pitcher	
Milk	40.00

Syrup	35.00
Water.........................	35.00
Sauce	11.50
Spooner	17.50
Sugar bowl	35.00
Tumbler	12.50
Wine..........................	15.00

*Reproduced Item

PANELLED THISTLE

Made by J. B. Higbee Glass Co., Bridgeville, Pa., in the early 1900's.

Banana stand ....$	55.00
Bowl	
Berry, 7", 8", 9"	27.50
Rose.........................	22.50
Butter dish.....................	40.00
Cake stand	
Large	35.00
Small	28.50
Celery tray	16.50
Celery vase	35.00
Compote	
Jelly	25.00
Open, small	25.00
Open, medium	35.00
Open, large	45.00
Cordial........................	25.00
Creamer	30.00
Cruet	45.00
Cup, sherbet	30.00
Dish	
Honey, covered, square, footed ..	50.00
Oblong	25.00
Oval, curled edges	30.00
*Goblet	35.00

Pickle, 7½", 8¼"	18.50
Pitcher	
Large	50.00
Small	35.00
Plate	
*7¼"	25.00
8¼"	27.50
9¼"	30.00
10¼"	32.00
*Salt	
Celery dip	15.00
Footed	25.00
Sauce	10.00
Shakers, pair	40.00
Spooner	30.00
Sugar bowl	40.00
Toothpick holder	6.00
Tumbler	
Lemonade [scarce]	40.00
Water	30.00
Vase	
Large	45.00
Small	35.00
Wine	25.00

*Reproduced Item

PAVONIA
[Pineapple Stem]

Bowl	$ 16.00
Butter dish	36.00
Cake stand	
Large	32.00
Small	25.00
Celery	27.00
Compote	
Covered, high standard	54.00
Open, high standard	44.00
Creamer	27.00
Goblet	24.00
Pitcher	
Milk, etched	62.50
Water	34.00
Salt, individual	6.00
Sauce	
Flat	6.00

Footed	8.00
Spooner	21.00
Sugar bowl	37.00
Tumbler	14.00
Wine	29.00

PEACOCK FEATHER
[Georgia, Peacock Eye]

Originally an early Sandwich pattern. Later reissued by U. S. Glass Co. as part of their States' series.

Bowl, berry	$ 22.00
Butter dish	32.00
Cake stand	
9", 10"	30.00
11"	35.00
Celery boat	21.50
Compote	
Deep, covered, high standard	39.00
Shallow, high standard	23.00
Creamer	40.00
Cruet	25.00
Dish, oval	15.00
Lamp, hand	35.00
Pickle	12.00
Pitcher	
Syrup	30.00
Water	50.00
Sauce	11.00
Shakers, pair	28.00
Spooner	35.00
Sugar bowl	35.00
Tumbler	22.50

PENNSYLVANIA

Bowl	
Pointed, 6", 7", 8"	$ 14.00
Punch	48.50
Round, 8"	15.00
Square, 8"	16.00

Butter dish	
Covered, large	30.00
Covered, small	25.00
Celery	37.50
Celery tray	12.00
Cheese dish, covered	30.00
Creamer	
Large	20.00
Small	15.00
Cruet	14.00
Cup	7.50
Decanter	18.50
Dish	
Jelly	9.50
Olive	7.50
Pickle	7.50
Goblet	15.00
Pitcher	
½ gallon, tankard	27.50
1½ pints, tankard	22.50
Syrup	18.00
Water	25.00
Plate, round, 7"	11.00
Sauce	
Pointed	5.00
Round, 4"	6.50
Square	6.50
Shaker	
Large, pair	22.50
Medium, pair	20.00
Small, pair	15.00
Spooner	35.00
Sugar bowl	
Covered, large	22.50
Open, small, handles	15.00
Tumbler	
Champagne	9.50
Water	7.50
Whiskey	8.50
Water bottle	20.00

PICKET
[London]

Made by the King Glass Co., Pittsburgh, Pa. in the late 1800's.

Bowl, waste	$ 17.50
Butter dish	36.00

Celery	25.00
Compote	
Covered, 6", high standard	40.00
Covered, 8", high standard	47.50
Covered, oblong, low standard	45.00
Open, high standard	32.00
Open, low standard	25.00
Creamer	32.00
Goblet	25.00
Marmalade jar	22.50
Match holder	15.00
Pickle jar, covered	27.50
Pitcher	45.00
Salt	
Celery dip	6.50
Large	16.00
Sauce	11.00
Sugar bowl	35.00
Tray, water	39.50

PINEAPPLE AND FAN
[Shepherd's Plaid, Diamond Block and Fan
Pittsburgh Daisy]

Made by Adams & Co., Pittsburgh, Pa. and the
U. S. Glass Co. in 1891.

Bowl	
Berry, 8", 9"	$ 17.50
Fruit, with plate, 8"	21.00
Low, 10"	17.50
Punch, 12"	48.50
Salad, 13"	44.50
Butter dish	32.50
Celery	
Medium	25.50
Tall	27.50
Creamer	
Individual	18.00
Large	28.00
Cup	
Custard	13.00
Lemonade	11.00
Mug	12.00
Pitcher	
Pint, water	20.00
Quart, water	26.00
½ gallon, tankard	31.50
½ gallon, water	29.00
¾ gallon, tankard	34.50
Plate, 6½"	11.50
Sauce, 4", 4½"	7.50

Spooner	16.00
Sugar bowl	
Individual, covered	20.50
Large, covered	33.00
Sugar shaker	16.50
Sweetmeat dish, 5", 6"	21.00
Tumbler	
Water	9.00
Whiskey	12.00

PLEAT AND PANEL
[Derby]

Made by Bryce Bros., Pittsburgh, Pa., C. 1870-1880.

Bowl		
5x8"	$	28.00
Waste [scarce]		37.50
Butter dish		38.50
Cake stand		
9"		40.00
9¾"		42.50
Celery		35.00
Compote		
Covered, 8", square, high standard		53.50
Open, low standard		33.00
Creamer		35.00
Dish		
Covered, oblong		35.00
Covered, square		42.50
*Goblet		19.00
Lamp		25.00
Marmalade jar		28.50
Pickle		11.00
Pitcher		45.00
Plate		
3½" [scarce]		32.00
6"		16.50
*7½", square		25.00
8½" [scarce]		34.50
Platter		
Closed handles		22.50
Open handles		28.50
Sauce		
Flat, handled		15.00
On standard, open		17.50
On standard, covered		20.00
Shakers, pair		35.00

Spooner	40.00
Sugar bowl	40.00
Tray, water [scarce]	50.00
Wine [scarce]	30.00

*Reproduced Item

PLUME

Made by Adams Glass Co., C. 1874.

Bowl		
Berry	$	27.50
Finger		16.50
Oval		42.50
Butter dish		35.00
Cake stand		32.50
Celery		22.50
Compote		
Covered		50.00
Open		35.00
Creamer		27.50
Goblet		30.00
Pickle		12.50
Pitcher, water		35.00
Sauce		8.50
Spooner		20.00
Sugar bowl		30.00
Tumbler		12.50
Water tray		20.00

POLAR BEAR
[Iceberg, Artic, North Pole]

Made by Crystal Glass Co., Bridgeport, Ohio, C. 1880.

Bowl		
Ice, with seals	$	80.00
Waste		55.00
Butter dish		80.00

Creamer	60.00
Goblet	
Clear [rare]	85.00
Frosted	75.00
Pickle	27.50
Pitcher	125.00
Platter, oval, handled, 16½"	80.00
Sauce	22.50
Spooner	35.00
Sugar bowl	75.00
Tray	
Bread	77.50
Water	125.00

POPCORN

Made by Sandwich Glass Co., C. 1860.

Butter dish	$	51.00
Cordial		48.00
Creamer		60.00
Goblet		
With ear		40.00
Without ear		35.00
Pitcher		60.00
Sauce		13.50
Spooner		40.00
Sugar bowl		60.00
Wine		25.00

POWDER AND SHOT
[Powderhorn and Shot]

Butter dish	$	51.00
Castor bottle		17.50
Celery		43.00
Compote		
Covered, high standard		66.00

Covered, low standard	58.50
Creamer	50.00
Egg cup	21.50
Goblet	45.00
Pickle	12.50
Pitcher	60.00
Salt, footed	18.00
Sauce	10.00
Spooner	32.50
Sugar bowl	60.00

PRESSED LEAF

First made by Sandwich Glass Co., then by McKee Bros. in 1868; also made by Central Glass Co., Wheeling, W.Va., C. 1881.

Bowl		
Open, high	$	18.00
Covered, 7", 8"		28.00
Butter dish		40.00
Cake stand		60.00
Champagne		35.00
Compote		
Covered, 6", high standard		40.00
Covered, 7", 8", high standard		44.50
Covered, 7", 8", low standard		43.50
Cordial		16.50
Creamer		45.00
Dish		
Oval, 5", 6"		13.00
8", 9"		16.50
Egg cup		22.50
Goblet		27.50
Lamp, hand		35.00
Pickle		11.50
Pitcher		80.00
Salt, footed		18.00
Sauce		12.50
Spooner		25.00
Sugar bowl		40.00
Wine		35.00

PRIMROSE
[See Colored Glass Section]

PRINCESS FEATHER
[Rochelle, Lacy Medallion]

Made by Rochelle, Bakewell, Pears & Co; later made by U. S. Glass Co. in 1880.

Butter dish	$ 55.00
Celery	37.50
Compote	
Covered, 6", high standard	60.50
Covered, 7", high standard	69.00
Covered, low standard	55.00
Covered, grape vine design on flange	79.00
Open, 8", low standard	40.00
Creamer	55.00
Dish, oval, 8", 9"	34.00
Egg cup	26.00
Goblet	30.00
Honey dish	11.00
Lamp, kerosene	50.00
Pickle	20.00
Pitcher	
Quart	80.50
½ gallon	95.00
Plate	
6"	24.00
7"	26.00
8"	28.00
9", cake, closed handles	37.50
Salt, footed	22.50
Sauce	9.50
Spooner	35.00
Sugar bowl	55.00

PRINTED HOBNAIL
[See Colored Glass Section]

PRISCILLA
[Alexis, Sun and Star]

Made by Dalzell, Gillmore & Leighton Co., Findlay, Ohio in the late 1890's.

Banana stand	$ 45.50
Bowl	
Square, 8"	15.50
Flat, 10½"	17.50
*Rose	25.00
Butter dish	40.50
Cake stand, 10"	34.50
Celery	22.50
*Compote	
Covered, 7"	46.00
Jelly	15.50
Open, 7½"	34.50
Creamer	28.50
Cruet	18.00
Cup and saucer	32.50
*Goblet	19.00
Mug	12.00
Pickle	22.50
Plate, 10½", turned-up edge	25.00
*Sauce, 4½"	6.50
Spooner	20.00
Sugar bowl, covered	35.00
Syrup	50.00
*Toothpick holder	20.00
Tumbler	10.50
*Wine	25.00

*Reproduced Item

PRISM AND FLUTE

Bowl, covered	$ 23.00
Butter dish	25.00
Cake stand	
7½"	14.00
9"	16.00
10½"	18.00
12½"	22.00
Celery	22.50
Compote	
7", 8", high standard	28.00
8", 9", low standard	26.50
Cordial	15.00
Creamer	19.00
Egg cup	12.00
Goblet	12.00
Pickle	13.00
Pitcher, water	40.00

Plate

6"	13.00
8"	16.50
Sauce	6.00
Tumbler, footed	12.00
Wine	15.00

PRISM WITH DIAMOND POINTS

Bowl, deep	$ 25.00
Butter dish	55.00
Compote, 6", covered [rare]	85.00
Cordial	28.00
Creamer	65.00
Egg cup	25.00
Goblet	
Plain stem	25.00
Knob stem	42.50
Pickle	27.50
Pitcher	75.00
Salt	16.50
Sauce	12.50
Spooner	35.00
Sugar bowl	50.00
Tumbler	35.00
Wine	45.00

PSYCHE AND CUPID
[Cupid and Psyche]

Butter dish	$ 42.00
Celery	40.00
Compote, high standard	53.50
Creamer	40.00
Goblet	25.00
Marmalade jar	21.50
Pickle	12.00
Pitcher	52.50
Sauce	9.50

Spooner	40.00
Sugar bowl	42.50
Wine	23.50

PURPLE SLAG
[See Colored Glass Section]

RAIN DROP
[See Colored Glass Section]

RED BLOCK

Made by Doyle & Co.; later by U. S. Glass Co. in 1892.

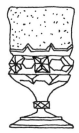

Bowl	
Berry	$ 43.50
Rose	50.00
Butter dish	64.50
Celery	51.00
Cordial	26.50
Creamer	
Large	60.00
Small	45.00
Cruet	42.50
Decanter	70.00
Dish	
Cheese	78.00
Oblong, 8", 9"	28.50
Oblong, 10"	38.00
*Goblet	41.50
Mug	23.50
Pitcher	74.50
Sauce	10.50
Shakers, pair	34.50
Spooner	27.00
Sugar bowl	59.50
Tumbler	23.50
Wine bottle	43.00
*Wine	25.50

*Reproduced Item

REVERSE TORPEDO

Banana dish	$ 100.00
Bowl	
5¾"	27.50

75

Nappy	39.50
Cake stand	85.00
Compote	
6"	40.00
8", pie crust top	48.50
Sauce	20.00

RIBBED GRAPE

Butter dish	$	68.50
Celery		41.50
Compote		
Cover, 6"		120.00
Open, low standard		55.00
Cordial		53.50
Creamer		115.00
Goblet		40.00
Pitcher		149.50
Plate, 6"		37.50
Sauce		18.00
Spooner		26.50
Sugar bowl		68.50

RIBBED IVY, See IVY, RIBBED

RIBBED PALM
[Acanthus, Sprig, Oak Leaf, Royal]

Made by McKee & Bros., Pittsburgh, Pa., C. 1868.

Bowl, flat	$	20.50
Butter dish		72.50
Castor set, pewter base		63.50
Celery		75.00
Compote		
Covered, 6" [scarce]		113.50

Open, 7", 8", high standard	48.50
Open, 10", high standard	59.00
Open, low standard	40.00
Cordial	32.00
Creamer	74.50
Dish, oval, 8", 9"	31.00
Egg cup	35.00
Goblet	40.00
Lamp, all glass	65.00
Pickle	30.00
Pitcher, water [scarce]	110.00
Plate, 6"	28.50
Salt, footed	21.00
Sauce	13.50
Spooner	50.00
Sugar bowl	52.50
Tumbler	40.00
Wine	50.00

RIBBED THUMBPRINT

Bowl, berry	$	15.00
Butter dish, covered		28.50
Compote, jelly		18.50
Creamer		20.00
Cruet		18.00
Pitcher, water		25.00
Sauce		8.00
Shakers, pair		25.00
Spooner		25.00
Sugar bowl, covered		22.50
Toothpick holder		10.00
Tumbler		12.00

RIBBON

Bowl, waste [scarce]	$	45.00
Butter dish		54.00
Cake stand		45.00
Celery		38.50

Cheese dish	72.00
Cologne bottle	23.50
Compote	
Open, high standard, classic figure of woman	106.50
Open, 7", low standard	36.00
Oblong, on standard, dolphin	141.50
Round, on standard, dolphin	138.00
Cordial	34.50
Creamer	55.00
*Goblet	35.00
Pickle castor, in metal frame	94.00
Pitcher	
Large	85.00
Small	65.00
Plate [rare]	100.00
Platter, oblong, cut corners, 9x13"	65.00
Sauce	
Footed	18.50
Handled	20.00
Round	17.50
Spooner	37.50
Sugar bowl	60.00
Tray, water, 15x16¼"	87.00
Wine [very scarce]	82.50

*Reproduced Item

ROMAN KEY

Bowl, berry	$ 43.00
Butter dish	56.00
Cake stand, 12"	40.00
Celery	55.50
Champagne	48.50
Compote, open, high standard	61.00
Cordial	16.00
Creamer	60.00
Egg cup	21.50
Goblet	26.00
Pickle [relish]	20.50

Pitcher, water [scarce]	98.00
Plate [scarce]	83.50
Salt, footed	21.00
Sauce	12.00
Spooner	18.00
Sugar bowl	55.00
Tumbler	
Footed	40.00
Water	35.00
Wine	35.00

ROMAN ROSETTE

Made by Bryce, Walker & Co. in 1875, and by U. S. Glass Co. in 1892 and 1898.

Bowl	
Berry, 7", 8"	$ 20.00
Berry, coverd, 9"	28.00
Butter dish	34.50
Cake stand, 9", 10", [scarce]	49.00
Castor set, glass	50.00
Celery	30.00
Compote	
Covered, 6", on standard	41.50
Covered, 8", on standard	52.00
Open, 4½", on standard	32.00
Cordial	18.00
Creamer	40.00
Dish	13.50
*Goblet	19.00
Mug	
Large	17.00
Small	15.00
Mustard jar	13.50
Pickle	16.00
Pitcher	
Quart	45.00
½ gallon, water	46.00
Syrup	31.00
Plate, 7¼" [scarce]	38.50
Platter, bread, 9x11"	32.50
Sauce	
Flat	7.50
Footed	9.50
Shakers, pair	22.00
Spooner	32.50
Sugar bowl	40.00
Tumbler	28.00
Wine	32.50

*Reproduced Item

ROSE IN SNOW
[See Colored Glass Section]

ROSE SPRIG
[See Colored Glass Section]

ROSETTE
[Magic]

Made by Bryce Bros., and U. S. Glass Co.

Bowl

Covered, 7¼" .... $	32.50
Waste	14.50
Butter dish......................	35.00
Cake stand, 8½"	28.50
Celery	20.00

Compote

Covered, 7", 8", high standard ...	41.00
Open, 4½", footed	27.50
Cordial	13.50
Creamer	30.00
Goblet	24.00
Pickle	21.00
Pitcher	40.00

Plate

7"	25.00
9", handled	32.00
Sauce	8.00
Shakers, pair....................	35.00
Spooner	35.00
Sugar bowl	35.00
Tray, water	30.00
Tumbler	15.00
Wine...........................	18.50

ROYAL IVY
[See Colored Glass Section]

ROYAL OAK
[See Colored Glass Section]

RUBY THUMBPRINT
[Excelsior; King's Crown when not colored]

Made by Adams & Co., C. 1890.

Bowl

Berry .... $	50.00

*Punch........................	172.50
Sawtooth edge, 7", 8½"	50.00
Butter dish......................	65.00
Castor bottle	16.50
Castor set	132.50
Celery	62.50

Compote

Covered, 6", 7", high standard ...	103.50
Covered, 8", 9", high standard ...	126.50
*Open, 5", high standard	75.00
Open, large	85.00
Cordial	23.00

Creamer

Large	66.50
Small	34.50
Cup and saucer..................	40.00
Decanter	125.00

Dish

Banana	75.00
Boat shaped, 8"	50.00
Cheese	86.50
Olive	35.00
Oval, 6".....................	30.50
Oval, 10"....................	40.50
*Goblet	37.50
Mustard jar, covered	32.00
Pickle	27.50

Pitcher

Milk, etched	95.00
Round, quart..................	75.00
Round, 2 quarts	95.00
Tall, slender, large	125.00
Tall, slender, small	90.00

Sauce

Boat shaped	29.00
Round, belled, 4x4½"...........	23.00
Round, 5", 6"	23.00
Shakers, pair....................	50.00
Spooner	55.00
Sugar bowl	65.00
Toothpick holder	25.00
Tumbler	35.00
*Wine..........................	37.50

*Reproduced Item

SAWTOOTH
[Diamond Point, Pineapple, Roanoke]

Made by New England Glass Co. and Sandwich
Glass Co.; later by Ripley and Company.

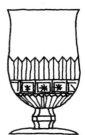

Bowl

Covered, 7"...................$	48.00
Open, 8", 9"	41.00
Open, 10"	55.00
Butter dish......................	63.50
Cake stand, 9", 10"	43.50
Celery	65.00
Champagne, knob stem	60.00

Compote

Covered, 6", 7"................	75.00
Covered, 8", 9"................	80.00
Covered, 10", 11"	90.00
Covered, 12"	100.00
Open, 6", 7"	37.50
Open, 8"	40.00
Open, 10"	50.00
Cordial........................	50.00
Creamer	70.00
Cruet	55.00
Decanter	52.50

Dish

Honey	12.00
Small, oval, covered, lion knob and handles	67.50
Large, oval, lion knob and handles	79.00
Egg cup	35.00
*Goblet.......................	40.00
Lamp	66.00
Pitcher, milk	65.00
Pomade jar	50.00

Salt

Covered, footed	37.50
Open, smooth edge	18.00

Sauce

4"	12.00
5"	13.50
Spooner.......................	50.00
Sugar bowl	63.50

Tray

10"	34.50
11"	44.50
12"	52.00
14"	69.00

Tumbler

Footed	55.00
Water........................	30.00
Water bottle, with tumble-up	75.00
*Wine........................	55.00

*Reproduced Item

SAWTOOTH AND STAR
[See Colored Glass Section]

SAXON

Bowl, 8" ....$	25.00
Butter dish......................	42.50
Celery	40.00

Compote

Covered, high standard	42.50
Covered, 6", sweetmeat jar	60.00
Open, low standard.............	40.00
Creamer	40.00
Dish, oval, 8", 9".................	32.00
Egg cup	21.50
Goblet	21.50
Pickle.........................	17.50

Pitcher

Quart.......................	40.00
½ gallon	45.00
Plate, 6".......................	20.00
Platter, bread, oval, 12"	32.50
Salt...........................	10.00
Sauce	12.00
Spooner.......................	32.50
Sugar bowl	35.00
Tumbler.......................	18.00
Wine..........................	22.00

SCROLL
[Taunton, Stippled Scroll]

Butter dish.......................$	32.50
Celery	25.00

Compote

Covered, high standard	45.00
Covered, low standard	35.00
Cordial	18.00
Creamer	30.00
Dish, oval	18.00
Egg cup	15.00
Goblet	20.00
Pickle	15.00
Pitcher	30.00
Salt	10.00
Sauce	10.00
Spooner	25.00
Sugar bowl	34.50
Tumbler	15.00

SCROLL WITH FLOWERS

Made by Central Glass Co. in the 1870's; then later by Northwood.

Butter dish	$	30.00
Cake plate, handled		35.00
Celery		30.00
Compote, covered, low standard		40.00
Cordial		25.00
Creamer		35.00
Egg cup		18.50
Goblet		24.50
Mustard jar, covered		30.00
Pickle		18.00
Pitcher		36.00
Salt, footed		14.50
Sauce		10.00
Shakers, pair		25.00
Spooner		30.00
Sugar bowl		35.00
Wine		15.00

SHELL AND JEWEL
[Victor]

Made by Westmoreland Glass Co., C. 1893.

Banana stand	$	36.50
Bowl, 8"		18.00
Butter dish		35.00
Cake stand		29.50
Compote, open, high standard		28.50
Creamer		22.00

Dish, honey, covered	16.00
Pitcher, water	28.50
Sauce	12.00
Spooner	18.50
Sugar bowl	25.00
Tray, water	26.50
Tumbler	12.50

SHELL AND TASSEL

Butter dish, round or square	$	60.00
Cake stand		
Large		55.00
Small [rare]		65.00
Celery vase		
Round		35.00
Square		50.00
Compote		
Covered, high standard		62.50
Open, 4½"		47.50
Open, high standard		40.00
Creamer		
Round		40.00
Square		45.00
Dish, oval		95.00
*Goblet		37.50
Marmalade jar		39.50
Pickle		25.00
Pitcher		
Round		50.00
Square		60.00
Platter		
Oblong, rounded corners		45.00
Oval, large		45.00
Oval, small		35.00
Salt		17.50
Sauce, 4½"		12.00
Shakers, pair [scarce]		60.00
Spooner		
Round		30.00

Square	45.00
Sugar bowl	
Round, dog finial	52.50
Square	60.00
Tray	
Oblong, large	69.50
Oblong, small	45.00
Vases, pair	100.00

*Reproduced Item

SHERATON
[See Colored Glass Section]

SINGLE ROSE

Butter dish	$	25.00
Creamer		19.00
Spooner		15.00
Sugar bowl		25.00

SMOCKING

Butter dish, covered	$	75.00
Compote, footed		85.00
Creamer, applied handle		87.50
Egg cup		45.00
Goblet		55.00
Lamp, 9"		82.00
Spill holder		35.00
Spooner		32.50
Sugar bowl		75.00
Wine		25.00

SNAIL

Bowl		
Berry	$	28.50
Finger		18.00
Butter dish		50.00

Cake stand	45.00
Celery	24.50
Compote, covered	40.00
Creamer	
Individual	15.00
Regular	30.00
Cruet	25.00
Dish	
Banana	100.00
Cheese, covered	48.00
Goblet	30.00
Pitcher, water	75.00
Plate, 7"	35.00
Shaker	
Salt, individual	12.00
Salt and pepper, pair	32.50
Sugar	22.50
Spooner	22.50
Sugar bowl	
Individual	15.00
Large, covered	35.00
Syrup	40.00
Tumbler	25.00
Wine	29.50

SOUTHERN IVY

Bowl, berry	$	25.00
Butter dish		30.00
Creamer		25.00
Cruet		35.00
Egg cup		18.00
Pitcher, water		40.00
Sauce		9.50
Spooner		22.00
Sugar bowl		35.00
Tumbler		20.00

SPIRALLED IVY

Butter dish	$	37.50

Creamer	30.00
Pitcher	
Large	45.00
Small	35.00
Sauce	9.50
Spooner	30.00
Sugar bowl	40.00
Tumbler	18.00

SPIREA BAND
|See Colored Glass Section|

SPRIG
|Barley, Indian Tree|

Made by Bryce, Higbee & Co., Pittsburgh, Pa., C. 1880.

Bowl, berry	$	15.00
Butter dish		32.50
Cake stand		40.00
Celery		32.00
Compote		
Covered, high standard		41.00
Open, high standard		29.00
Open, low standard		26.00
Creamer		31.00
Dish, oval		18.00
Goblet		25.00
Pickle		12.00
Pitcher, water		40.00
Platter		23.00
Sauce		
Flat		8.50
Footed		9.00
Spooner		24.00
Sugar bowl		34.50
Tumbler		20.00
Wine		22.00

STAR ROSETTED

Made by McKee & Bros., Pittsburgh, Pa., C. 1875.

Butter dish	$	39.00
Compote		
Open, high standard		42.50
Open, small, low standard		32.00
Creamer		30.00
Goblet		25.00
Pickle		15.00
Pitcher		45.00
Plate, 10", "A Good Mother"		42.50
Sauce		8.50
Spooner		26.50
Sugar bowl		39.00

STATES, THE

Made by U. S. Glass Co. in 1905.

Butter dish, covered	$	24.50
Celery		15.00
Compote, open, 7"		19.50
Creamer		16.00
Cup, punch		10.00
Dish		
Cupped		12.00
Relish, handled		11.50
Pitcher, water, gold trim		23.00
Plate, large		13.00
Sugar bowl, covered		24.50
Toothpick holder		6.50
Tumbler		10.00

STEDMAN
[Blaze]

Celery	$	29.00

Champagne	37.50
Cheese dish, covered	46.00
Compote	
Covered, 7", 8", high standard	60.00
Open, low standard	35.00
Creamer	55.00
Decanter	37.00
Egg cup	17.00
Goblet	21.50
Lamp	34.50
Plate, 6"	21.00
Salt	
Flat	9.50
Round	10.50
Sauce	8.00
Spooner	24.00
Sugar bowl	55.00
Syrup	45.00
Tumbler	23.00
Wine	35.00

STIPPLED BAND

Butter dish	$ 35.00
Celery	25.00
Compote	
Covered, high standard	35.00
Covered, low standard	32.50
Open, high standard	27.50
Open, low standard	22.50
Creamer	25.00
Goblet	15.00
Pitcher, water	30.00
Salt, footed	12.50
Spooner	25.00
Sugar bowl	28.00
Tumbler	20.00

STIPPLED CHAIN

Made by Gillinder & Sons, C. 1870's.

Butter dish, covered	$ 26.50

Creamer	28.50
Goblet	17.50
Pickle dish	15.00
Pitcher, water	35.00
Salt, footed	10.00
Sauce	7.50
Spooner	30.00
Sugar bowl, covered	35.00

STIPPLED CHERRY

Reportedly made by Lancaster Glass Co. in the 1880's.

Bowl, berry	$ 25.00
Butter dish	35.00
Celery	32.50
Creamer	34.50
Pitcher	38.00
Plate	
6"	20.00
9¼", bread	25.00
Sauce	8.00
Spooner	25.00
Sugar bowl	32.50
Tumbler	18.50

STIPPLED DAISY

Bowl, berry, large	$ 25.00
Compote, open, beaded edge, 8¼"	26.50

Creamer	25.00
Dish, oblong, 4-3/8x7"	22.50
Sauce, flat, 4¼"	10.00
Spooner	25.00
Sugar bowl, covered	30.00
Tumbler	20.00
Tray, oblong, small	18.00
Wine	18.00

Tumbler	
Bar	16.00
Footed	22.50
Gill	16.50
½ pint	18.00
Wine	24.50

STIPPLED GRAPE AND FESTOON

Made by Doyle & Co., Pittsburgh, Pa., C. 1870. Also made in clear but stippled is the rarest of this pattern.

Butter dish	$ 55.00
Celery	48.00
Compote, covered, low standard	49.00
Cordial	30.00
Creamer	45.00
Dish, oval	20.00
Egg cup	18.50
Goblet	24.50
Pickle	12.50
Pitcher	56.00
Plate	18.50
Sauce	12.00
Spooner	28.00
Sugar bowl	41.50
Wine	18.00

STIPPLED FORGET-ME-NOT
[Forget-Me-Not In Snow]

Made by Bryce Bros. in the 1880's; and after 1891, by the Model Flint Glass Co.

Bowl, waste	$ 15.50
Butter dish	25.00
Cake stand	
Large	32.00
Small	30.00
Celery	33.00
Compote	
Covered, 6"	42.50
Covered, 7", 8"	54.50
Cordial	19.50
Creamer	31.50
Cup and saucer	27.00
Goblet	28.00
Lamp, handled	30.00
Mug	14.00
Mustard jar	14.50
Pickle	17.50
Pitcher	
Large	42.50
Small	32.50
Syrup	36.00
Plate	
7", baby center	24.50
7", star center	23.50
9", kitten center, handled	32.50
Salt	17.50
Sauce	
Flat	8.50
Footed	12.50
Spooner	35.00
Sugar bowl	44.00
Toothpick holder	17.50
Tray, water	37.50

STIPPLED IVY

Bowl, berry	$ 25.00
Butter dish	45.00
Compote	
Covered, low standard	47.50
Open, high standard	36.00

Creamer	45.00
Egg cup	16.50
Goblet	30.00
Pickle	15.00
Salt, footed	11.00
Sauce	12.00
Spooner	32.00
Sugar bowl	50.00
Syrup	45.00
Tumbler	20.00
Wine	18.50

STIPPLED STAR

Made by Gillinder & Sons, Greensburg, Pa., in the 1870's.

Butter dish	$	39.50
Celery		28.50
Compote		
Open, large, high standard		49.00
Open, small, high standard		41.50
*Creamer		44.50
Dish, oval, 8"		21.00
Egg cup		25.50
*Goblet		29.50
Pickle		14.00
Pitcher		57.50
Sauce		
Flat, 4"		10.00
Flat, 6"		12.50
Spooner		30.00
*Sugar bowl, covered		39.50
Tumbler		15.00

*Reproduced Item

STRAWBERRY
[See Colored Glass Section]

STRAWBERRY AND CURRANT
[Currants and leaves on reverse]

Butter dish	$	34.50
Celery		37.50
Cheese dish		40.50
Compote		
Covered, on standard		45.00

Open	34.50
Creamer	40.00
*Goblet	27.50
Pitcher	
Large	45.00
Small	40.00
Sauce	11.00
Spooner	35.00
Sugar bowl	40.00
Tumbler	25.00

*Reproduced in clear, amber,
blue and green

SUMMIT

Manufactured by Thompson Glass Co., Union-town, Pa., in the early 1890's.

Bowl, pie crust edge, 7¼"	$	18.50
Butter dish		45.00
Celery		27.50
Compote, pie crust edge, open, high standard, 8"		50.00
Creamer		35.00
Pitcher, tankard, large		52.50
Relish dish, one handle		20.00

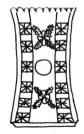

Spooner	22.50
Sugar	45.00
Tumbler	24.50

SUNBURST

Made by McKee & Bros. in the late 1890's.

Bowl, finger	$	13.50
Butter dish		28.00
Cake stand		24.50
Celery		21.50
Compote, low standard		30.00
Cordial		13.00
Creamer		22.50
Cruet		22.00
Dish, oblong, deep		13.00
Egg cup		13.50
Goblet		14.00
Marmalade jar		23.50
Pickle		
Double, 8", 10"		15.00
Single		12.00
Pitcher		
Large		32.50
Small		27.00
Plate		
6"		13.50
7"		16.00
11", bread, with motto		20.00
Sauce		7.00
Spooner		18.00
Sugar bowl		27.50
Wine		12.50

SWAN
[See Colored Glass Section]

SWIRL
[See Colored Glass Section]

TEARDROP AND TASSEL
[Sampson]

Made by the Indiana Tumbler & Goblet Co., C. 1890's.

Bowl, berry	$	22.50
Butter dish		37.50

Compote	
Covered, 6", 8", high standard	45.00
Open, 6", 8"	28.50
Creamer	32.50
Goblet	30.00
Pickle	15.00
Pitcher	40.00
Sauce	10.00
Shakers, pair	30.00
Spooner	27.50
Sugar bowl	40.00
Tumbler	18.00
Wine [scarce]	30.00

TEXAS
[Loop with Stippled Panels]

Bowl		
Berry, flat, 7½", 8½", 9½"	$	12.50
Berry, footed, 7½", 8½", 9½"		14.00
Scalloped, 6", 7", 8"		13.50
Butter dish		23.00
Cake stand		
Footed, 10", high standard		30.00
Footed, 10", low standard		25.00
Celery		15.00
Celery tray		10.00
Compote		
4", jelly, low standard		18.00
5", jelly, high standard		22.50
6", 7", 8", high standard, covered		35.00
*Creamer		16.00
Cruet		16.00
Dish		
Olive		8.50
Preserve, 8"		11.50
Goblet		16.50
Horseradish jar		9.50
Pickle		10.00
Pitcher, 3 pints		20.00
Plate, 9"		12.00

Sauce, 4"	6.00
Shaker	
Large, pair	17.00
Small, pair	15.00
Spooner	11.50
*Sugar bowl	23.00
Toothpick holder	7.00
Tumbler	10.00
Wine	15.00

*Reproduced Item

THE STATES, See STATES, THE

THISTLE

Made by Bakewell, Pears and Co., C. 1875.

*Bowl, berry, covered	$ 30.00
*Butter dish	35.00
Cake stand	45.00
Compote	
Covered, high standard	40.00
Covered, low standard	30.00
Cordial	25.00
Creamer	40.00
Decanter	60.00
Dish, oval, deep	22.50
Egg cup	20.00
*Goblet	32.50
Pickle	12.00
*Pitcher, large	45.00
Salt, footed	13.50
*Sauce	12.00
*Spooner	35.00
*Sugar bowl	45.00
Tumbler	
Footed	30.00
Water	25.00
Wine	28.50

*Reproduced Item

THOUSAND EYE
[See Colored Glass Section]

THOMPSON NO. 77

Made by the Thompson Glass Co., Uniontown, Pa. in 1892. Some items were ruby stained and/or etched.

Bowl	
5¼" diam., 3" deep	$ 32.50
Open, flat, 8½"	25.00
Butter dish	42.50
Cordial	18.00
Creamer	
Individual	19.50
Large	30.00
Spooner	22.50

Sugar	
Individual	19.50
Large	35.00
Syrup	32.00
Tumbler	22.50

THREE FACES
[Three Sisters]

Made by George A. Duncan & Sons, Pittsburgh, Pa. in 1878.

Butter dish	$ 110.00
*Cake stand	
8", 9"	75.00
10", 11"	110.00
Celery	75.00

*Champagne	175.00
*Claret	100.00
Compote	
Covered, large	165.00
*Covered, small, 6½"	110.00
Open, high standard	80.00
*Cracker jar [rare]	400.00
*Creamer	90.00
*Goblet	72.00
*Lamp	140.00
Marmalade jar	85.00
Pitcher	
Milk	185.00
Water, ½ gallon [rare]	240.00
*Salt dip	32.50
*Sauce	30.00
*Shakers, pair	60.00
*Spooner	60.00
*Sugar bowl	110.00
Syrup	85.00
Tumbler	50.00
*Wine	75.00

*Reproduced Item

THREE-IN-ONE

Bowl, berry, fluted	$	20.00
Butter dish		35.00
Celery		25.00
Compote		
6"		22.50
8", 9"		28.50
10", fluted		37.50
Cracker jar		38.00
Creamer		
Individual		15.00
Regular		20.00
Pickle jar		16.00
Pitcher, squatty		22.50
Spooner		20.00
Sugar bowl		
Individual		15.00
Regular		20.00
Toothpick holder		10.00

THREE PANEL
[See Colored Glass Section]

THUMBPRINT

Ale glass	$	35.00

Bowl	
Covered	48.00
Finger	35.00
Punch, 12x23½"	475.00
Butter dish	76.50
Cake stand	
Regular	90.00
13" [scarce]	175.00
Castor bottle	20.00
Celery	105.00
Champagne	55.00
Compote	
Covered, 6", med. high standard	80.00
Covered, 7", high standard	100.00
Covered, 8", high standard	125.00
Covered, 10", high standard	140.00
Open, 6", low standard	55.00
Open, 8", 9", low standard	60.00
Cordial	35.00
Creamer	65.00
Decanter, quart	100.00
Egg cup	35.00
Goblet	
Barrel shape	35.00
Knob stem	40.00
Honey dish	12.00
Mug, ½ pint	25.00
Pickle	20.00
Pitcher, water	175.00
Plate, 8" [There are only 6 plates known in the Thumbprint pattern .	-----------
Salt	
Footed	25.00
Individual	15.00
Sauce, 4", 4½"	12.50
Spooner	35.00
Sugar bowl	82.50
Tumbler	
Footed	40.00
Water	27.50
Whiskey [scarce]	55.00
Wine	50.00

TORPEDO
[Pygmy, Fisheye]

Made by Thompson Glass Co., Uniontown, Pa.,
in 1889.

Banana stand ....$	52.00
Bowl	
4", rose (scarce)	34.50
7", open, flared rim	24.50
7", 8", covered	32.00
8", 8¼", open, flared rim	28.50
9", 9½", flared rim	26.00
Waste, scalloped top	17.50
Butter dish, covered...............	55.50
Cake stand, 9", 10"	46.00
Celery, scalloped top	33.00
Compote	
4", covered, jelly	41.50
5", open, jelly, flared rim	33.00
6", covered, high standard	63.50
6", open, flared rim, high standard	44.50
7", 8", covered, high standard	72.00
8¼", 8¾", open, flared rim, high	
standard	46.00
Creamer	
Flat, collared base, medium	32.00
Footed, large	34.50
Footed, medium...............	29.00
Cruet	34.50
Cup and saucer...................	33.00
Decanter	40.50
Goblet	40.00
Honey dish, 6", covered	17.50
Lamp	
3-3/8", handled, flat base	26.00
5¼", handled, footed base	29.00
8", 8¼", plain base, pattern on	
base........................	24.50
Marmalade jar, covered (scarce) ...	52.00
Pitcher	
Milk, 8¾", tankard	50.00
Syrup, brass top	41.50
Water, 10-7/8", barrel type	50.00
Water, 11½", 12", tankard	60.00
Salt	
Individual, 1-5/8" diam.	10.00
Master, 3" diam.	18.50
Sauce	
3½", flat, honey...............	10.00
3½", footed, honey	12.00
4¼", footed	13.50
4¼", 4-5/8", flat	12.00
Shaker	
Salt and pepper, 2¼", pair.......	29.00
Salt and pepper, 3", pair.........	33.00
Spooner, scalloped top	25.00

Sugar bowl, covered	55.00
Tray	
Water, 10", round (scarce).......	55.00
Water, 11¾", clover-shaped	50.00
Tumbler	39.50
Wine...........................	22.00

TREE OF LIFE
(Tree of Life--Pittsburgh, Tree of Life with Hand)

Made by Duncan's and Sons, Pittsburgh in the mid 1880's.

Bowl	
Finger ....$	14.00
Flat, 8".......................	13.50
Flat, 10"......................	19.50
Waste	15.00
Butter dish, hand & ball on cover	49.50
Cake stand, 10"	85.00
Celery	27.50
Compote	
Covered, hand holding ball on	
pedestal	91.00
Open, 9", hand stem	63.50
Open, 10", hand stem	67.50
Open, child holding book stem ...	126.50
Creamer	40.00
Cup, punch	12.00
Goblet	31.50
Mug	35.00
Pitcher, water...................	55.00
Plate, 7".......................	17.00
Spooner	23.50
Sugar bowl, hand & ball on cover ...	65.00
Tray, bread	34.50
Tumbler, footed	25.00
Wine...........................	28.00

TULIP

Butter dish......................$	75.00
Celery	65.00
Compote, covered	
Large, high standard	90.00
Small, low standard.............	72.50
Creamer	85.00
Cruet	65.00
Decanter, stoppered	
Half pint	52.00

Pint	60.00
Quart, Tulip stopper	100.00
Egg cup	30.00
Goblet	
Faceted, knob stem	40.00
Late, band on knob	25.00
Honey dish	12.50
Mug, large, applied handle	50.00
Pitcher, large	125.00
Plate, 6"	50.00
Salt, footed	
Smooth top	21.50
Pointed top	30.00
Spooner	42.00
Sugar bowl	78.50
Tumbler	38.50

TULIP WITH SAWTOOTH

Made by Bryce Bros., Pittsburgh, Pa., in the early 1860's.

Butter dish	$ 65.00
Celery	45.50
Champagne	32.50
Compote	
Covered, large, high standard	100.00
Covered, small, high standard	75.00
Open, large	84.50
Cordial	25.00
Creamer	95.00
Cruet	55.00
Decanter	
Half pint	42.50
Pint	50.00
Quart	55.00
Egg cup [scarce]	35.00
Goblet	35.00

Honey dish	17.50
Jug	
Pint	82.50
Quart	110.00
Lamp	75.00
Lemonade glass	35.00
Pitcher	110.00
Plate, 6"	37.50
Pomade jar	30.00
Salt	
Footed, smooth top	14.00
Pointed edge	20.00
Sauce	12.00
Spooner	25.00
Sugar bowl	75.00
Tumbler	
Footed	25.00
Water	30.00
*Wine	34.50

*Reproduced Item

TWO PANEL
[See Colored Glass Section]

UTAH

Bowl	
Covered, 6", 7", 8"	$ 11.50
Open, 6", 7", 8"	9.00
Butter dish	
Large	20.00
Small	14.00
Cake plate	
9", 10"	14.50
11"	17.00
Cake stand	
7", 9"	16.00
10"	18.00
Celery	16.00
Compote	
5", jelly, open	12.50
6", jelly, covered	21.00
6", 7", 8", covered	30.00
6", 7", 8", open	17.50
Dish, oval, low standard, 7",8",9"	11.00
Goblet	12.00
Pickle	9.00
Pitcher, 3 pints	17.50
Sauce, 4"	5.50
Shaker	
Salt and pepper, pair	14.00

Salt and pepper, pair, in holder ...	16.50
Spooner	12.00
Sugar bowl, covered	20.00
Syrup	14.00
Tumbler	9.00

VICTORIA

Made by Bakewell, Pears & Co., early 1860's.

Butter dish, 8", low standard .... $	65.00
Cake stand	
9"	65.00
15"	90.00
Compote, covered	
6", high standard, sweetmeat	36.00
8", high standard	42.00
8", low standard	35.00
10", high standard	35.00
10", low standard	42.00
Creamer	85.00
Sugar bowl [rare]	125.00

VIKING
[Old Man of the Mountains, Bearded Head, Prophet]

Bowl	
Covered .... $	30.00
Open	20.00
Butter dish	30.00
Cake plate	47.50
Celery	30.00
Compote, covered	65.00
Creamer	30.00
Egg cup	25.00
Goblet	28.50
Pickle	16.00
Pitcher, water	50.00

Platter	25.00
Salt, large	20.00
Sauce	11.00
Spooner	20.00
Sugar bowl, covered	37.50
Tumbler, small	40.00

VIRGINIA
[Galloway, Late Block, Foster, Mirror]

Made by the U. S. Glass Co., C. 1901.

Bowl	
Flared, 7½", 8½" 9½" .... $	18.00
Straight, 6", 7", 8"	16.00
Butter dish, covered	28.00
Celery	23.50
Celery tray	
Pointed, oblong	18.00
Straight	18.00
Compote	
Covered, footed, 6", 7", 8"	35.00
Open, footed, 6", 7", 8"	25.00
Creamer	
Individual	16.00
Large	22.50
Cruet	18.50
Dish	
BonBon, 5½"	12.00
Olive	10.00
Goblet	22.50
Pitcher	
½ gallon, tankard	35.00
Water	28.50
Sardine box	12.00
Sauce	
Flared, 4"	8.00
Straight, 4", 4½"	9.00
Spooner	20.00
Sugar bowl	
Covered, large	30.00
Open, small	15.00
Toothpick holder	6.50
Tumbler	25.00
Water bottle	20.00
Wine	18.50

WAFFLE

Butter dish .... $	60.00
Celery	50.00

Champagne	48.00
Compote	
Covered, high standard	57.50
Open, 8", high standard	38.50
Cordial	40.00
Creamer [scarce]	89.00
Decanter, with stopper	65.00
Egg cup	25.00
Goblet	38.50
Lamp	
All glass	75.00
Marble base	70.00
Pitcher	80.00
Plate, 6"	30.00
Salt, footed	18.00
Sauce	9.50
Spooner	45.00
Sugar bowl	75.00
Tumbler	
Water	48.00
Whiskey	45.00
Wine	45.00

WAFFLE AND THUMBPRINT

Made by New England Glass Co.; later reproduced by Bryce, Walker & Co., Pittsburgh, Pa., in the late 1850's.

Bowl	
6"	$ 30.00
7¼"	35.00
Butter dish	100.50
Celery	75.00
Champagne	68.50
Claret	75.00
Compote	
Open, large, high standard	85.00
Open, small, high standard	50.00
Open, small, low standard	45.00
Creamer	95.00

Decanter	
Pint	62.50
Quart	75.00
Egg cup	30.00
Goblet	50.00
Lamp, hand	50.00
Pitcher [scarce]	190.00
Salt, master	25.00
Spooner	50.00
Sugar bowl, covered	100.00
Tumbler	
Water	45.00
Whiskey	50.00
Wine	65.00

WASHINGTON [EARLY]

Bowl, oval, 6¼ x 9¼"	$ 45.00
Bitters bottle	48.00
Butter dish, covered	125.00
Celery	65.00
Champagne	70.00
Compote, covered	
6", high standard	72.50
10", high standard	125.00
Creamer	100.00
Egg cup	42.50
Goblet	55.00
Pickle	30.00
Pitcher	
Syrup	100.00
Water	205.00
Salt, master	27.50
Sauce, 4½"	15.00
Spooner	48.00
Sugar bowl	87.50
Tumbler	45.00
Wine	65.00

WASHINGTON [LATE]

Bowl	
Covered, 5", 6"	$ 10.50
Covered, 7", 8"	12.00
Open, 5", 6", 7", 8"	10.00
Butter dish	20.50
Cake stand	
8", 9"	19.50

10", 11"	22.50
Celery tray	14.50
Champagne	12.50
Claret	13.00
Compote	
Covered, 5", 6"	27.50
Covered, 7", 8"	30.00
Fruit, open, 7½", 8½", 9½"	25.00
Open, 5", 6"	18.00
Open, 7", 8"	20.00
Cordial	11.00
Creamer	14.00
Cruet	13.50
Dish	
6", 8"	10.00
10"	12.50
Olive	7.00
Goblet	
8-ounce	12.50
10-ounce	15.00
Pickle	7.50
Pitcher	
½ pint, water	14.00
1 pint, water	16.00
1 quart, water	16.50
3 pints, tankard	22.50
3 pints, water	18.50
½ gallon, tankard	25.00
Sauce	
3", 3½"	6.00
4"	7.00
Spooner	12.00
Sugar bowl, covered	20.50
Toothpick holder	6.50
Tumbler	10.00
Wine	12.00

WESTWARD-HO
[Ploneer, Tippecanoe]

Made by Gillinder & Sons, Philadelphia, Pa., in the late 1870's.

*Butter dish	$ 125.00
Celery	95.00
Compote	
*5", covered, high standard [rare]	250.00
*6", covered, high standard	125.00
8", covered, high standard	175.00
*Cordial	95.00
*Creamer	95.00

*Goblet	
Clear	75.00
Frosted	65.00
Marmalade jar [scarce]	140.00
Mug [scarce]	60.00
Pickle	45.00
Pitcher	
Milk	185.00
*Water	155.00
Platter, oval	85.00
*Sauce	
3½"	17.50
4"	22.50
4½"	75.00
Spooner	75.00
*Sugar bowl, covered	125.00
*Wine	100.00

NOTE: Goblets were originally produced in clear and frosted only. Reproductions are on the market in amethyst, blue, green, clear and frosted.

*Reproduced Item

WHEAT AND BARLEY
[See Colored Glass Section]

WILDFLOWER
[See Colored Glass Section]

WILD ROSE WITH BOW KNOTS

Bowl	$ 19.00
Butter dish	25.00
Creamer	19.50
Sauce	7.50
Spooner	15.00
Sugar bowl, covered	25.00

WILLOW OAK
[See Colored Glass Section]

WINDFLOWER

Butter dish, covered..............$	50.00
Celery	32.50
Compote	
Covered, high standard	60.00
Covered, low standard	50.00
Cordial.........................	38.00
Creamer	35.00
Dish, oval, deep	20.00
Egg cup	22.00
Goblet	30.00
Pickle	18.00
Pitcher	55.00
Salt, footed	25.00
Sauce	15.00
Spooner.........................	28.50
Sugar bowl, covered	45.00
Tumbler	40.00
Wine...........................	45.00

WISCONSIN, See BEADED DEWDROP

ZIPPER
[Cobb, Late Sawtooth]

Butter dish.......................$	24.00
Celery	17.50
Compote, covered	35.00
Creamer	16.50
Cruet	20.00
Egg cup	18.50
Goblet	12.50
Lamp	27.50
Pitcher, water	26.50
Sauce	
Flat...........................	5.50
Footed	6.50
Spooner........................	16.50
Sugar bowl	24.00
Sugar shaker.....................	25.00
Toothpick holder	14.00
Wine...........................	25.00

COLORED GLASS PATTERNS

Quotations listed on Pattern Glass are retail prices in perfect condition. The Clear Glass Section precedes this group and is designated as "Section One." Items marked with an asterisk (*) have been, or are now being reproduced.

AMBERETTE

Amberette was first made in 1897-98, by the firm of Dalzell, Gilmore and Leighton Co., Findlay, Ohio. The glass is a combination of satin finish panels and figured bands of flashed or stained old gold [amber]. The deep mitres on either side are bright crystal.

Issued during the first period of the great Alaska Gold Rush, the pattern was first called "Klondike." The satin or frosted panels portray snow while the amber bands depict gold.

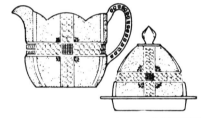

Butter dish	$ 110.00
Compote, covered, collared base, 8"	132.50
Creamer	78.50
Pickle dish, 6x9½"	45.50
Pitcher	
Water, square	115.00
Water, tankard	100.00
Sauce	
Footed	28.00
Flat, 4½"	23.00
Flat, scalloped top, 5"	21.00
Shakers, pair	57.00
Spooner	42.00
Sugar bowl	
Covered	110.00
Open	78.00
Syrup	92.00
Toothpick holder	40.50
Tray, 5½" square	45.50
Tumbler	48.50

BARRED FORGET-ME-NOT

Made by Canton Glass Co., Canton, Ohio, C. 1883.

	Clear	Amber	Blue	Apple Green
Bowl, berry	$ 14.00	19.00	$ 22.50	$ 27.50
Butter dish	25.00	35.00	42.00	50.00
Cake stand				
Large	25.00	37.50	42.00	62.50
Medium	26.00	32.50	35.00	50.00
Celery	27.00	33.50	37.00	49.00

Compote

Covered, low standard	30.00	50.00	60.00	65.00
Covered, high standard	35.00	52.00	60.00	72.50
Cordial	18.00	30.00	35.00	40.00
Creamer.........................	24.00	30.00	35.00	42.50
Goblet	18.00	22.50	30.00	40.00
Pickle	14.00	22.50	27.50	35.00
Pitcher	30.00	39.00	43.00	57.50
Plate, 9", handled................	18.00	35.00	40.00	50.00
Sauce	7.50	12.00	16.50	17.50
Spooner	25.00	35.00	45.00	60.00
Sugar bowl	30.00	35.00	40.00	50.00
Wine............................	15.00	28.00	34.00	40.00

BASKETWEAVE, OPEN
[Plaid]

	Clear	Amber	Yellow	Blue	Green
Bowl					
Berry ....$	24.00	$ 28.50	$ 28.50	$ 48.00	$ 55.00
Covered, flat	22.00	30.00	30.00	38.00	45.00
Waste	15.00	20.00	20.00	30.00	37.00
Butter dish	30.50	40.50	40.50	49.00	57.00
Compote, covered	35.00	50.00	50.00	60.00	78.00
Cordial	18.00	25.00	25.00	30.00	40.00
Creamer..........................	22.00	38.00	38.00	44.00	55.00
Cup and saucer	21.00	32.00	32.00	34.50	45.00
Egg cup	14.00	28.00	28.00	30.00	40.00
*Goblet	15.00	20.00	20.00	28.00	40.00
Lamp	21.00	32.00	32.00	34.50	45.00
Mug	14.00	21.00	21.00	26.00	40.00
Pickle	10.50	20.00	20.00	23.00	35.00
Pitcher					
Milk	32.00	41.00	41.00	46.00	56.00
Syrup	35.00	45.00	45.00	60.00	65.00
*Water......................	33.00	41.50	41.50	46.00	56.00
Plate, handled	20.00	27.50	27.50	40.00	50.00
Salt, celery dip	6.00	10.50	10.50	12.00	22.00
Sauce	7.50	12.00	12.00	16.00	26.00
Shakers, pair.....................	20.00	28.00	28.00	32.50	45.00
Spooner	15.00	22.00	22.00	28.00	35.00
Sugar bowl	30.50	40.00	40.00	50.00	60.00
Tray, 12"	21.00	30.50	30.50	40.00	45.00
Tumbler	13.00	20.00	20.00	22.50	35.00
Wine............................	10.50	18.00	18.00	21.00	32.00

*Reproduced Item

BEADED GRAPE
[California]

Made by U. S. Glass Co., Pittsburgh, Pa., C. 1880's.

	Clear	Apple Green
Butter dish..............................$	43.50	$ 66.00
Cake stand	41.50	60.00
Celery	37.50	55.00
Compote		
*On high standard....................	60.00	100.00
Open, 4" high........................	41.50	57.50
Shallow, on standard	40.00	62.50
Cordial	28.00	40.50
Creamer	45.00	75.00
Cruet	32.50	55.00
Dish		
Oblong, 6¼x8¼"	30.00	50.00
Square, 5¼", 6¼"..................	27.50	42.50
Square, 7¼", 8¼"..................	25.50	40.00
*Goblet	40.00	70.00
Pickle	14.50	27.00
Pitcher		
Round	45.00	86.50
Square............................	40.50	64.00
Platter	40.00	65.00
*Plate, 8¼" square	21.00	40.00
*Sauce, 4", 4½"....................	9.50	18.00
Shaker		
Salt and pepper, pair	34.50	56.00
Sugar	25.50	34.50
Spooner..............................	35.00	50.00
Sugar bowl	45.00	66.50
Toothpick holder	20.00	32.00
*Tumbler.............................	27.00	40.50
*Wine................................	20.50	40.00

*Reproduced Item

BLACKBERRY

Made by Wm. Leighton, Jr., Wheeling, W. Va., C. 1870.

	Clear	Milk Glass
Bowl, round, covered..................$	24.00	$ 50.00
*Butter dish......................	52.00	75.00
*Celery	57.50	126.50
Champagne...........................	40.00	60.50
Compote		
Covered, high standard	72.00	155.50
Covered, low standard	60.50	150.00
*Creamer	55.00	100.00
Dish, oval, 8¼x5½"	50.00	185.00
Egg cup		
Double............................	37.50	100.00
*Single...........................	---------	34.00
*Goblet	40.00	72.00
Honey dish	15.00	40.00

Lamp, clear bowl, milk glass base........	---------	75.00
*Pitcher, water [scarce]	150.00	500.00
Salt, footed	25.00	60.00
Sauce	13.50	25.00
Spooner	45.00	75.00
*Sugar bowl	65.00	75.00
Tumbler	20.00	34.50

*Reproduced Item

CANE

Made by Gillinder Glass Co., McKee Glass Co., C. 1875-85.

	Clear	Amber	Vaseline	Blue	*Apple Green
Bowl, waste...................... $	17.00	$ 25.50	$ 25.50	$ 27.00	$ 25.00
Butter dish	33.50	45.00	45.00	50.00	40.50
Compote, open, high standard......	26.50	41.50	41.50	50.00	38.50
Creamer	21.50	35.00	35.00	44.00	36.00
Goblet	22.50	30.00	30.00	35.00	32.50
Marmalade jar	18.00	30.50	30.50	37.50	30.00
Pickle, oval	13.50	24.50	24.50	26.00	22.50
Pitcher	25.00	41.00	41.00	48.50	40.00
Plate, toddy, 4½"...............	12.50	21.00	21.00	27.00	21.00
Sauce	9.00	17.00	17.00	16.50	17.00
Shakers, pair....................	21.50	34.50	34.50	37.00	29.00
Spooner	25.00	30.00	30.00	40.00	35.00
Sugar bowl	31.50	48.50	48.50	52.50	44.50
Tray, water	25.00	41.50	41.50	46.00	40.00
Tumbler	17.50	23.00	23.00	28.00	23.50

*Apple green is the most common color in this pattern

Cactus

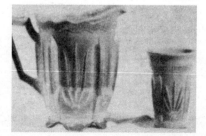

CARAMEL SLAG

Bowl	
6½" diam. Cactus .... $	66.00
7" diam. Cactus	77.50
8" diam. Cactus	100.50
Butter dish, covered. Cactus	162.00
Candlesticks, pair	120.00
Celery	108.00
Compote	
Covered, low foot	234.00
Open, high standard	180.00
Cracker jar, covered. Cactus	168.00
Creamer	
Cactus	106.50

Fine Cut. Medallion	90.00	
Cruet, vinegar		
Cactus, original stopper	162.00	
Palm Leaf, original stopper	132.00	
Cup, punch. Hearts of Loch Lavern . .	48.00	
*Dish, covered. Dolphin	170.00	
Goblet	180.00	
Mug		
4½", drinking scenes	66.00	
Beaded Rib, handled	72.00	
Cactus	75.00	
Hearts of Loch Lavern	60.00	
Nappy, handled, tri-cornered	72.00	
Pitcher		
6". Cactus	62.00	
Water. Cactus	240.00	
Water. Panelled [Belknap 275] . . .	205.00	
Plate		
10", open edge	150.00	
Serenade	145.00	
Sauce		
Cactus	60.00	
Shell	60.00	
*Shakers, pair. Cactus	110.00	

Spooner	78.00
Sugar bowl	
Covered. Cactus	162.00
Open. Cactus	102.00
Flower Flange	120.00
Kitten-in-Basket. Basketweave	
bottom, kitten's head on top	150.00
Syrup. Cord & Drapery	150.00
Toothpick holder	
Boot	60.00
*Cactus	72.00
Wild Rose	60.00
Tray	150.00
Tumbler	
*Cactus	72.00
Cord & Drapery	65.00
Geneva	65.00
Hearts of Loch Lavern	78.00
Leaf Bracket	45.00
Palm Leaf	70.00
Plain	50.00
Shell	70.00
Uneeda Biscuit. Tall	60.00
*Reproduced Item	

CATHEDRAL
[Orion]

Made by Bryce Bros., Pittsburgh, Pa., C. 1880's.

	Clear	Vaseline	Amber	Blue	Amethyst
Bowl, berry, 7", 8" . . . . $	21.00	$ 31.00	$ 31.00	$ 37.00	$ 57.50
Butter dish	38.50	50.00	50.00	57.50	82.50
Cake stand	30.00	46.00	46.00	48.50	80.00
Compote					
Covered, 8x11"	49.50	72.00	72.00	80.50	136.00
Open, on standard	32.00	52.00	52.00	63.50	80.00
Cordial	20.00	25.00	25.00	30.00	45.00
Creamer	35.00	41.50	41.50	53.50	77.50
Egg cup	18.00	32.00	32.00	37.50	45.00
Goblet	25.00	40.00	40.00	46.00	75.00
Pitcher, water	45.00	75.00	75.00	71.50	101.50
Sauce					
Flat, 4"	14.00	18.00	18.00	19.00	21.50
Footed, 4"	15.00	19.00	19.00	21.50	25.50
Footed, 4½"	15.00	21.00	21.00	23.00	27.50
Spooner	25.00	27.50	27.50	32.00	45.00
Sugar bowl	40.00	50.00	50.00	57.50	92.00
Tumbler	17.50	26.50	26.50	30.00	42.00
Wine	22.50	30.00	30.00	35.00	55.00

COLORADO
Made by U. S. Glass Co., C. 1897.

	Clear	Ruby Base	Blue	Green	*Amethyst
Banana dish ....$	46.50	$ 71.50	$ 66.00	$ 75.00	$ 132.00
Butter dish	42.00	74.00	80.00	88.00	124.00
Cheese dish, footed, low	33.00	66.00	71.00	79.00	93.50
Creamer					
Individual	20.00	40.00	45.00	48.00	55.00
Large	30.00	55.00	71.50	66.00	69.00
Dish					
Crimped edge, 4", 5"	15.50	31.00	33.00	37.00	44.00
Crimped edge, 6", 7"	17.00	33.00	36.00	48.00	48.00
Crimped edge, 8"	18.50	37.00	40.00	41.50	52.50
Flared edge, 4", 5"	16.00	30.00	30.50	40.00	48.50
Flared edge, 6", 7"	17.00	31.00	37.00	42.50	51.50
Flared edge, 8"	18.00	32.50	40.00	45.00	52.50
Footed, round, 5"	17.00	31.00	33.00	43.50	49.50
Shakers, pair	20.00	31.00	36.00	40.00	55.00
Spooner	20.00	30.00	33.00	37.50	60.00
Sugar bowl					
Individual	20.00	30.00	35.50	40.00	55.00
Large, covered	41.50	77.00	81.50	93.50	126.50
Toothpick holder	12.00	21.00	24.00	25.00	33.00
Tumbler	14.00	25.00	27.50	33.00	41.50

*Very Scarce

CROESUS

	Clear	Emerald Green	Amethyst
Bowl, berry ....$	45.00	$ 100.00	$ 140.00
Butter dish	70.00	145.00	175.00
Celery	50.00	95.00	165.00
Creamer	45.00	100.00	135.00
Cruet	50.00	110.00	165.00
Dish, berry, boat-shaped	47.50	95.00	135.00
Pickle	25.00	50.00	65.00

Pitcher, water	85.00	160.00	200.00
Sauce	17.00	30.00	55.00
Shakers, salt and pepper, pair	35.00	70.00	100.00
Spooner	35.00	70.00	85.00
Sugar bowl, covered	75.00	125.00	175.00
Syrup	50.00	95.00	75.00
Toothpick holder	25.00	50.00	75.00
Tumbler	25.00	50.00	75.00

DAHLIA
[Stippled Dahlia, Marsh Pink, Square Fuchsia]

	Clear	Amber	Blue	Green
Butter dish ....$	47.00	$ 52.00	$ 55.00	$ 62.00
Cake stand	28.50	33.50	36.50	43.00
Champagne	35.00	40.00	43.00	50.00
Compote, covered, high standard	55.00	60.00	65.00	70.00
Cordial	27.50	32.00	36.00	45.00
Creamer	42.00	45.00	48.00	55.00
Egg cup, double	45.00	50.00	53.00	60.00
Goblet [scarce]	35.00	40.00	45.00	50.00
Mug				
Large	37.50	45.00	47.50	55.00
Small	23.00	28.00	31.00	37.00
Pickle	18.00	24.00	27.50	34.50
Pitcher				
Milk	40.00	45.00	48.00	55.00
Water	47.50	55.00	60.00	65.00
Plate				
7"	22.50	27.00	32.00	35.00
9", cake, closed handles	27.50	32.00	35.00	42.00
Platter, oval, grape handles	38.00	43.00	46.50	53.00
Sauce	10.00	15.00	18.00	25.00
Spill	20.00	25.00	28.00	35.00
Spooner	30.00	35.00	38.00	45.00
Sugar bowl, covered	45.00	50.00	53.00	60.00
Wine	27.50	30.00	35.00	40.00

DAISY AND BUTTON
[Oval Medallion, Panelled Daisy]

Made by Gillinder and Sons, C. 1876; Hobbs, Brockunier and Co., Wheeling, W. Va. Also souvenir items for centennials, but practically every piece of Daisy and Button has been reproduced.

	Clear	Vaseline	Amber	Blue	Apple Green
Basket ....$	16.00	$ 25.00	$ 25.00	$ 34.50	$ 40.00
Boat. Canoe	16.50	30.00	30.00	35.00	36.50

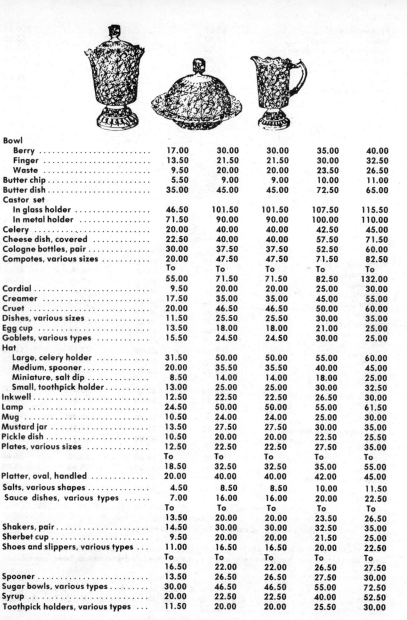

Bowl					
Berry	17.00	30.00	30.00	35.00	40.00
Finger	13.50	21.50	21.50	30.00	32.50
Waste	9.50	20.00	20.00	23.50	26.50
Butter chip	5.50	9.00	9.00	10.00	11.00
Butter dish	35.00	45.00	45.00	72.50	65.00
Castor set					
In glass holder	46.50	101.50	101.50	107.50	115.50
In metal holder	71.50	90.00	90.00	100.00	110.00
Celery	20.00	40.00	40.00	42.50	45.00
Cheese dish, covered	22.50	40.00	40.00	57.50	71.50
Cologne bottles, pair	30.00	37.50	37.50	52.50	60.00
Compotes, various sizes	20.00	47.50	47.50	71.50	82.50
	To	To	To	To	To
	55.00	71.50	71.50	82.50	132.00
Cordial	9.50	20.00	20.00	25.00	30.00
Creamer	17.50	35.00	35.00	45.00	55.00
Cruet	20.00	46.50	46.50	50.00	60.00
Dishes, various sizes	11.50	25.50	25.50	30.00	35.00
Egg cup	13.50	18.00	18.00	21.00	25.00
Goblets, various types	15.50	24.50	24.50	30.00	25.00
Hat					
Large, celery holder	31.50	50.00	50.00	55.00	60.00
Medium, spooner..............	20.00	35.50	35.50	40.00	45.00
Miniature, salt dip	8.50	14.00	14.00	18.00	25.00
Small, toothpick holder	13.00	25.00	25.00	30.00	32.50
Inkwell	12.50	22.50	22.50	26.50	30.00
Lamp	24.50	50.00	50.00	55.00	61.50
Mug	10.50	24.00	24.00	25.00	30.00
Mustard jar	13.50	27.50	27.50	30.00	35.00
Pickle dish	10.50	20.00	20.00	22.50	25.50
Plates, various sizes	12.50	22.50	22.50	27.50	35.00
	To	To	To	To	To
	18.50	32.50	32.50	35.00	55.00
Platter, oval, handled	20.00	40.00	40.00	42.00	45.00
Salts, various shapes	4.50	8.50	8.50	10.00	11.50
Sauce dishes, various types	7.00	16.00	16.00	20.00	22.50
	To	To	To	To	To
	13.50	20.00	20.00	23.50	26.50
Shakers, pair	14.50	30.00	30.00	32.50	35.00
Sherbet cup	9.50	20.00	20.00	21.50	25.00
Shoes and slippers, various types ...	11.00	16.50	16.50	20.00	22.50
	To	To	To	To	To
	16.50	22.00	22.00	26.50	27.50
Spooner	13.50	26.50	26.50	27.50	30.00
Sugar bowls, various types	30.00	46.50	46.50	55.00	72.50
Syrup	20.00	22.50	22.50	40.00	52.50
Toothpick holders, various types ...	11.50	20.00	20.00	25.50	30.00

Trays, various shapes & sizes	20.00	38.50	38.50	45.00	47.50
	To	To	To	To	To
	27.50	47.50	47.50	55.00	60.00
Tumblers, various sizes	11.00	25.00	25.00	25.50	30.00
	To	To	To	To	To
	16.50	27.50	27.50	30.00	35.00
Vase. Hand holding cornucopia	15.00	30.00	30.00	34.50	37.50
Water Pitcher					
Bulbous	35.00	50.00	50.00	55.00	60.00
Cylindrical	35.00	46.50	46.50	50.00	57.50
Panelled	24.50	43.50	43.50	45.50	50.00
Wine	8.50	20.00	20.00	22.50	25.00

DAISY AND BUTTON WITH CROSS BARS
[Mikado]

	Clear	Amber	Vaseline	Blue
Bowl				
Open, 6" ....$	17.00	$ 27.50	$ 27.50	$ 32.00
Open, 8"	19.00	31.50	31.50	41.00
Butter dish				
Flat...........................	24.50	41.50	41.50	46.50
Footed	32.50	44.50	44.50	52.00
Compote				
Covered, 8"...................	40.00	60.00	60.00	70.00
Open, 8"	26.50	40.00	40.00	45.50
Creamer				
Individual	18.50	29.50	29.50	36.50
Regular	24.50	38.50	38.50	46.00
Cruet	30.50	51.50	51.50	60.00
Goblet	21.00	35.00	35.00	42.00
Mug				
Small	13.50	21.50	21.50	26.50
Large	18.50	25.50	25.50	32.00
Pickle	13.00	21.00	21.00	26.00
Pitcher				
Quart	24.50	45.00	45.00	50.00
½ gallon	31.00	53.50	53.50	60.00
Sauce				
Flat...........................	8.00	16.50	16.50	18.50
Footed	10.00	18.50	18.50	20.00
Shakers, pair.....................	21.00	35.00	35.00	40.00
Spooner	24.00	40.00	40.00	45.00
Sugar bowl, covered	32.00	45.50	45.50	52.00
Syrup	24.50	37.50	37.50	42.00
Toothpick holder	11.00	21.50	21.50	28.50
Tray, water	27.00	34.50	34.50	44.50
Tumbler	13.50	25.00	25.00	26.00
Wine...........................	17.50	25.50	25.50	30.00

DAISY AND BUTTON WITH "V" ORNAMENT

Made by A. J. Beatty & Co., C. 1886-1887.

	Clear	Vaseline	Amber	Blue
Bowl				
Berry, 8" ....$	16.00	$ 34.50	$ 34.50	$ 42.50
Finger	14.00	28.00	28.00	32.00
Butter dish.....................	24.50	46.00	46.00	52.00
Celery	20.00	40.00	40.00	50.00
Creamer	19.50	36.50	36.50	42.00
Dish, oblong	14.50	23.50	23.50	30.00
Goblet	17.50	31.00	31.00	38.50
Mug	13.50	20.00	20.00	23.50
Pitcher, quart	32.00	53.00	53.00	60.00
Sauce	10.00	14.00	14.00	17.50
Spooner.......................	15.50	34.50	34.50	35.00
Sugar bowl	24.50	44.50	44.50	50.00
Toothpick holder	9.50	16.00	16.00	22.50
Tray, water	30.00	42.50	42.50	45.50
Tumbler	13.50	24.50	24.50	28.50

DELAWARE
[Four-Petal Flower]

Made by U. S. Glass Co., C. 1899.

	Clear	Rose W/Gilt	Green W/Gilt	*Amethyst
Bowl				
Fruit, boat-shaped ....$	25.00	$ 75.00	$ 85.00	$ 125.00
Round	20.00	60.00	75.00	100.00
Butter dish.....................	30.00	90.00	95.00	150.00
Celery..........................	20.00	60.00	65.00	100.00
Creamer........................	24.00	72.00	85.00	120.00
Cruet	22.50	67.50	75.00	112.50
Cup, punch	10.00	30.00	35.00	50.00
Pitcher, water	30.00	90.00	100.00	150.00
Powder box, covered.............	40.00	145.00	160.00	200.00
Puff box, covered	45.00	135.00	145.00	225.00
Sauce	12.00	36.00	46.00	60.00
Spooner	18.00	54.00	60.00	90.00
Sugar bowl	35.00	105.00	115.00	175.00
Toothpick holder	10.00	30.00	35.00	50.00
Tumbler	12.50	37.50	47.50	62.50

*Very Scarce

DEWEY
[Flower Flange]

Made by Indiana Tumbler & Goblet Co., C. 1894.

	Clear	Canary	Green	Amber	Caramel
Butter dish ....$	22.50	$ 45.00	$ 50.00	$ 45.00	$ 75.00
Creamer.........................	20.00	37.50	40.00	37.50	44.50
Cruet	25.00	45.00	47.50	45.00	65.00
Pitcher, water	35.00	65.00	70.00	65.00	75.00
Sauce	8.50	16.00	18.00	16.00	21.50
Shakers, salt and pepper, pair	25.00	45.00	54.50	45.00	70.00
Spooner	22.50	40.00	42.00	40.00	65.00
Sugar bowl	25.00	45.00	55.00	45.00	74.50
Tumbler	16.50	32.00	37.50	32.00	48.50

DIAMOND QUILTED

	Clear	Vaseline	Amber	Blue	Amethyst
Bowl					
7½" ....$	15.50	$ 34.50	$ 34.50	$ 45.00	$ 60.00
Waste	13.00	30.00	30.00	34.50	36.50
Butter dish	32.50	42.50	42.50	55.00	60.00
Celery	26.50	46.00	46.00	50.00	61.50
Champagne.....................	17.50	30.00	30.00	36.50	41.50
Compote					
Covered, high standard	42.00	55.00	55.00	72.50	115.00
Covered, low standard	36.00	52.50	52.50	67.00	90.00
Open, high standard	26.50	35.50	35.50	50.00	59.50
Cordial	12.00	31.00	31.00	34.50	70.00
Creamer	21.50	46.00	46.00	57.50	85.00
Dish, covered, footed, oblong	24.50	57.00	57.00	62.50	72.50
*Goblet	25.00	40.00	40.00	42.50	55.00
Pickle	15.00	25.00	25.00	28.50	35.00
Pitcher					
Large	37.50	57.00	57.00	70.00	115.00
Small	41.50	63.00	63.00	72.00	125.00

Sauce					
Flat, round	14.00	25.00	25.00	30.00	32.50
Footed	18.00	30.00	30.00	35.00	37.50
Spooner	25.00	30.00	30.00	35.00	45.00
Sugar bowl	32.50	42.50	42.50	55.00	60.00
Tray, water	26.50	41.50	41.50	44.50	57.50
Tumbler					
*Water........................	11.50	27.00	27.00	26.00	37.50
Whiskey, handled	17.50	34.50	34.50	40.00	52.00
Wine	10.00	18.00	18.00	25.00	30.00

*Reproduced Item

EMERALD GREEN HERRINGBONE
[Panelled Herringbone]

Made by U. S. Glass Co., C. 1880's.

	Clear	Green
Bowl, berry, large .... $	30.00	$ 55.00
Butter dish	30.00	60.00
Cake stand	30.00	65.00
Celery	30.00	55.00
Compote, open, high standard..........	35.00	75.00
Cordial.............................	20.00	35.00
Creamer	25.00	52.50
Cruet	24.00	45.00
*Goblet	22.50	40.00
Pickle..............................	18.00	30.00
Pitcher	40.00	75.00
Plate		
7¼"	18.00	38.50
9¼"	20.00	42.00
Sauce	10.00	18.50
Shakers, pair	25.00	42.00
Spooner.............................	25.00	40.00
Sugar bowl	25.00	45.00
Toothpick holder	12.00	20.00
Tumbler	15.00	25.00
Wine................................	12.00	25.00

*Reproduced in Clear, Green, Amber and Blue

ESTHER
[Prism with Block]

	Clear	Green
Bowl, berry, 8" .... $	20.00	$ 28.50
Butter dish, covered	41.50	72.50
Celery tray, 11"	15.00	30.00
Celery vase [rare]	---------	80.00
Compote		
Covered, 5"	27.50	45.00
Open, 6"	18.50	33.50
Creamer	19.50	50.00
Cruet	28.00	55.00
Goblet	20.00	37.50
Pickle..............................	12.50	25.00
Pitcher, water........................	38.50	75.00
Sauce, footed	7.00	18.50
Spooner.............................	18.50	30.00
Sugar bowl, covered	27.00	55.00

Toothpick holder	20.00	40.00	
Tumbler	12.00	24.00	
Wine	28.50	35.00	

FINE CUT

Made by Bryce Bros., Pittsburgh, Pa., C. 1870's.

	Clear	Vaseline	Amber	Blue
Bowl				
Finger ....$	14.50	$ 21.50	$ 21.50	$ 26.00
Waste	16.50	25.00	25.00	26.50
Butter dish	31.50	44.50	44.50	55.00
Compote, covered	40.00	70.00	70.00	75.00
Creamer	25.00	38.50	38.50	46.50
Cruet	16.50	36.00	36.00	44.00
Dish, oblong	21.00	32.00	32.00	40.00
Goblet	22.00	31.50	31.50	38.50
Mustard jar	15.00	27.50	27.50	32.50
Pitcher				
Syrup	19.00	32.00	32.00	36.00
Water	30.00	39.50	39.50	47.50
Plate				
6¼"	16.00	25.50	25.50	30.00
7¼"	19.00	28.50	28.50	33.00
10¼"	25.50	37.50	37.50	44.00
Sauce	8.50	16.50	16.50	17.50
Spooner	25.00	35.00	35.00	42.50
Sugar bowl	31.50	44.50	44.50	54.00
Tray				
Bread	18.50	32.50	32.50	35.00
Water	21.50	36.00	36.00	43.50

FINE CUT AND PANEL
[Nailhead and Panel]

Made by U. S. Glass Co. in the early 1890's, and by many firms in the Pittsburgh area.

	Clear	Amber	Yellow	Blue
Bowl, waste ....$	12.00	$ 25.50	$ 25.50	$ 30.00
Butter dish	30.00	43.50	43.50	48.00
Celery	28.00	35.00	35.00	45.00
Compote, open, high standard	27.00	47.50	47.50	60.00
Cordial	14.50	25.50	25.50	30.00
Creamer	22.50	41.50	41.50	50.50
Dish, oblong	20.00	28.00	28.00	37.50
Goblet	22.50	30.00	30.00	*40.00
Lamp, 10", handled	22.50	40.00	40.00	47.50
Pickle	15.00	22.00	22.00	25.00
Pitcher	30.50	54.00	54.00	48.00
Plate				
6¼"	14.50	25.50	25.50	30.00

7¼"	19.00	27.00	27.00	32.00
Platter	24.00	30.00	30.00	40.00
Sauce	7.50	14.50	14.50	17.50
Shakers, pair....................	21.00	38.50	38.50	43.50
Spooner	25.00	30.00	30.00	40.00
Sugar bowl	31.50	45.50	45.50	50.00
Toothpick holder	8.50	15.50	15.50	20.00
Tray	21.50	32.50	32.50	38.50
Tumbler	14.50	22.50	22.50	27.00
Wine..........................	15.00	18.00	18.00	22.50

*Scarce

FRANCESWARE

Made by Hobbs, Brockunier and Co., Wheeling, W.Va., in the 1880's.
A clear or frosted hobnail or swirl pattern glass with amber stained
top rims. It may either be pressed or mold blown.

	Clear	Frosted
Bowl		
4", Hobnail ....$	32.50	$ 50.00
7½", Hobnail	48.50	85.00
Box, 5½", round, covered, Hobnail	---------	65.00
Butter dish, Hobnail	65.00	85.00
Creamer, Hobnail	30.00	45.00
Dish, 4½" square, Hobnail	18.50	28.50
Pickle, Swirl	25.00	37.50
Pitcher		
8½", Hobnail	100.00	125.00
11", Hobnail	140.00	175.00
Shakers, pair		
Salt and pepper, Hobnail	22.50	40.00
Salt and pepper, Swirl................	25.00	45.00
Spooner, Hobnail	30.00	45.00
Sugar, covered, Hobnail	45.00	65.00
Sugar shaker, Swirl	67.50	92.50
Toothpick holder, Hobnail	22.00	32.50
Tumbler, Hobnail	28.50	40.00

HOBNAIL, FAN TOP

	Clear	Amber	Blue
*Bowl			
Large, deep ....$	27.00	$ 45.00	$ 55.00
6" diam...................	21.00	27.00	32.50
Shallow	21.50	32.00	34.50
Butter dish	36.00	54.00	63.00

Celery	27.50	42.50	48.00
Creamer	28.50	40.00	40.00
Dish, oblong	19.50	26.50	35.00
Goblet	21.50	36.50	46.50
Platter, 12"	35.00	47.50	55.00
Salt, individual, small	8.50	14.00	17.50
*Sauce	11.00	17.50	21.50
Sugar bowl	36.00	54.00	63.00
Tray, 8x12"	15.00	27.50	35.00

*Reproduced Item

HOBNAIL, OPALESCENT

	Opalescent	Blue Opalescent	Yellow Opalescent
*Bowl			
Flat, 9½" ....$	50.00	$ 65.00	$ 70.00
Footed, 8"	55.00	70.00	75.00
Finger	30.00	42.00	52.50
Butter dish	62.50	78.50	100.00
Celery	50.00	70.00	70.00
Creamer	54.50	60.00	65.00
Cup, handled	27.50	40.00	50.00
Pickle	25.50	39.50	47.50
Platter, 9½ x14"	65.00	80.00	87.50
Spooner	40.00	50.00	55.00
Sugar bowl	62.50	78.50	100.00
*Tumbler	30.00	42.00	50.00
Water bottle (rare)	80.00	---------	---------

*Reproduced Item

HOBNAIL, PANELLED

Made by Bryce Bros., Pittsburgh, Pa., C. 1875-1885.

	Clear	Vaseline	Amber	Blue
Bowl, 8" ....$	30.00	$ 25.50	$ 25.50	$ 27.50
Butter dish, covered	27.00	46.00	46.00	48.50
Celery	30.00	35.00	35.00	41.50
Compote, high standard	30.00	46.00	46.00	52.00
Creamer	21.00	34.50	34.50	40.00

	Clear	Amber	Blue	Apple Green
Goblet	17.50	28.50	28.50	35.00
Plate				
4½"	12.00	21.50	21.50	25.00
7"	18.00	25.00	25.00	31.00
Sauce, 4"	8.50	16.50	16.50	17.50
Spooner	15.00	25.00	25.00	30.00
Sugar bowl	30.00	46.00	46.00	50.00
Wine	10.00	21.00	21.00	22.50

HOBNAIL, POINTED

	Clear	Amber	Blue	Apple Green
*Barber bottle	$ 20.50	$ 40.00	$ 44.00	$ 47.00
*Bowl, berry	28.00	54.50	60.00	66.00
Butter dish	32.50	45.00	52.00	75.00
Cake stand, 10"	34.50	48.00	55.50	66.00
Celery	30.00	30.00	47.50	75.00
Child's set. Butter dish, creamer, spooner & sugar bowl	33.00	43.50	50.00	60.00
Compote, 8x8"	40.00	55.00	60.00	75.00
Cordial	18.00	25.00	30.00	37.00
Creamer	24.00	30.00	35.00	41.50
*Cup and saucer	20.00	33.00	36.50	45.00
Dish				
Bone	13.50	20.00	21.50	26.50
Oblong, 8x12"	21.50	40.00	41.50	46.50
Egg cup, double	20.00	28.00	30.00	35.00
Goblet	26.50	37.00	40.00	45.00
Inkwell	14.00	20.00	25.00	30.00
*Mug	15.00	22.00	25.00	27.00
Mustard jar	16.00	25.00	27.00	30.00
Pickle	14.00	20.00	22.00	25.50
*Pitcher				
Milk	31.50	52.50	57.00	71.50
Syrup	25.50	40.00	44.00	50.00
Water	36.00	71.50	74.50	80.00
Plate				
7½"	17.00	25.00	27.50	35.00
Toddy, 4½"	10.00	15.50	20.00	20.50

Platter, 4½ x7"	25.00	32.50	35.00	40.00
Salt				
Celery dip	8.00	13.00	14.00	16.00
Round	8.50	13.50	15.00	17.00
Square	8.50	13.50	16.00	20.00
*Sauce	10.00	14.00	16.00	20.00
*Shakers, pair	20.00	27.50	30.00	36.50
Spooner	25.00	25.00	45.00	60.00
*Sugar bowl	37.50	50.00	60.00	65.00
Toothpick holder	10.50	17.50	20.00	25.00
Tray				
Pen	14.00	20.00	25.00	25.50
Water........................	24.50	36.00	40.00	42.50
*Tumbler	14.00	20.50	25.50	27.50
*Vinegar cruet	20.00	42.50	47.00	50.00
*Wine.........................	10.00	18.00	20.00	27.50

*Reproduced Item

HOBNAIL, PRINTED

	Clear	Amber	Canary	Blue	Green
Butter dish ....$	24.50	$ 37.50	$ 37.50	$ 41.50	$ 46.00
Celery	21.50	34.00	34.00	36.50	40.00
Creamer	17.00	28.50	28.50	30.00	32.50
Goblet	16.50	23.50	23.50	38.50	30.50
Mug	13.50	21.00	21.00	21.50	25.00
Mustard jar	15.00	21.50	21.50	23.00	27.50
Pitcher	32.00	46.00	46.00	50.00	60.00
Sauce	8.50	13.00	13.00	15.00	16.50
Spooner	20.00	35.00	35.00	40.00	45.00
Sugar bowl	25.00	41.50	41.50	44.50	50.00
Tray	21.00	34.50	34.50	40.00	45.00
Tumbler	14.00	21.00	21.00	23.00	26.50
Wine	15.00	25.00	25.00	30.00	35.00

HOBNAIL, THUMBPRINT BASE

	Clear	Amber	Blue
Bowl			
Berry, 9", 10" ....$	26.00	$ 57.00	$ 70.00
Waste	16.50	28.00	30.50

Butter dish	28.00	42.00	65.00
Celery	27.00	41.50	46.00
Child's set. Butter dish, sugar bowl, creamer and spooner	40.00	52.50	70.00
Creamer	25.00	36.50	40.00
Mustard jar	16.50	26.50	30.00
Pitcher, water	41.50	65.00	85.00
Salt, celery dip	8.50	13.00	14.50
Shakers, pair	20.00	34.00	37.50
Spooner	24.00	30.00	40.00
Sugar bowl	28.50	42.00	63.00
Tray, water	21.50	36.50	42.00

HOLLY AMBER
[Golden Agate]

Made by Indiana Tumbler & Goblet Co., C. 1903.

Bowl, 7", 8"	$ 750.00
*Butter dish	1250.00
Cake stand	1500.00
Compote	
*Covered, large	1750.00
*Jelly	975.00
Creamer, 4½"	500.00
*Cruet	1000.00
Mustard	400.00
Nappy, handled	550.00
Parfait	500.00
Pickle dish	550.00
Pitcher, 10"	2000.00
*Plate, 7½"	800.00
Sauce	
Flat	300.00
Footed	350.00
Shakers, pair	800.00
Spooner	550.00
*Toothpick holder	350.00
Tray, water, 9¼"	950.00
*Tumbler	500.00

*Reproduced Item

HUMMING BIRD
[Flying Robin, Bird and Fern]

	Clear	Amber	Canary	Blue
Bowl, finger	$ 15.00	$ 22.50	$ 22.50	$ 25.00
Butter dish	30.00	42.00	42.00	48.50
Celery	22.50	37.50	37.50	45.00
Creamer	25.00	34.50	34.50	42.00
Goblet	22.50	30.00	30.00	35.00
Pickle	9.50	17.00	17.00	20.00
Pitcher				
Milk	27.50	37.50	37.50	42.00
Water	26.00	36.50	36.50	40.00

Sauce	7.00	13.00	13.00	14.50
Spooner	18.00	25.00	25.00	30.00
Sugar bowl	30.00	42.00	42.00	48.50
Tray, water	21.00	34.50	34.50	37.50
Wine	25.00	30.00	30.00	35.00

ICICLE

	Clear	Milk Glass
Butter dish.........................$	40.00	$ 80.00
Butter pat	10.00	18.50
Compote		
Covered, 6", high standard	40.00	70.00
Covered, 8", high standard	50.00	80.00
Open, low standard	27.50	60.00
Creamer	32.50	55.00
Dish, oval, 8"	25.00	40.00
Goblet	30.00	45.00
Pickle	15.00	27.50
Pitcher	45.00	75.00
Salt, large	12.00	17.50
Sauce	12.00	20.00
Spooner	35.00	45.00
Sugar bowl	40.00	65.00

JACOB'S COAT

Made in the 1880's by an unknown maker.

	Clear	Amber
Bowl, berry ....$	21.00	$ 34.50
Butter dish	28.00	43.50
Celery	30.00	40.00
Creamer	30.00	35.00
Goblet	22.50	30.00
Pickle	13.50	23.00
Sauce	9.00	14.00
Spooner	25.00	30.00
Sugar bowl	36.00	42.50

LOCKET ON CHAIN

	Clear	Green
Bowl, berry, 8" ....$	13.00	$ 21.50
Butter dish, covered	25.00	$ 35.00
Cake stand	22.00	32.00
Celery	18.00	25.00
Compote, open, 8"	24.00	30.00
Creamer	18.00	25.00
Cruet	17.00	37.50
Goblet	14.50	20.00
Pickle	8.00	16.50
Pitcher		
Milk	21.00	32.00
Water	23.00	40.50
Plate, 8"	14.00	26.00
Sauce, 4"	8.50	15.00
Shakers, pair	18.00	31.50
Spooner	15.00	22.50
Sugar bowl	25.00	40.00
Syrup	17.50	31.50
Toothpick holder	9.50	16.00
Tumbler	10.00	17.50

MAIZE

A novelty glass designed by Joseph Locke and
made by Libbey & Son, Toledo, Ohio, C. 1889.

Bowl	Milk White
Berry, 9"	$ 65.00
Finger, 5"	42.50
Butter dish	125.00
Celery	85.00
Castor set, 3 pieces	135.00
Creamer	85.00
Cruet	85.00
Decanter	
Pint	80.00
Quart	95.00
Pitcher	
Syrup	75.00
*Water	100.00
Sauce	30.00
Spooner	60.00
Sugar bowl	95.00
Sugar shaker	85.00
Toothpick holder	45.00
*Tumbler	50.00
Water bottle [carafe]	78.50

*Reproduced Item

MAPLE LEAF
Made by Gillinder & Sons, C. 1880's.

	Clear	Frosted	Vaseline	Amber	Blue	Green
Bowl, oval, footed	$ 20.00	$ 26.50	$ 30.50	$ 30.50	$ 36.00	$ 40.00
*Butter dish	31.00	40.00	46.50	46.50	55.00	65.00
Celery	27.50	40.00	44.00	44.00	46.50	60.00
Compote						
Covered, high standard	65.00	88.00	108.50	108.50	110.00	127.00
*Round, footed, open	40.00	58.00	66.00	66.00	90.00	95.00
*Creamer	32.50	56.00	65.00	65.00	74.50	80.00
Dish						
Covered, oval on stippled feet	30.00	45.00	50.00	50.00	64.50	60.00
Open, oval, not footed	20.00	37.50	42.50	42.50	45.00	50.00
*Goblet	65.00	95.00	110.00	110.00	160.00	175.00
Pitcher						
*Large	36.00	32.00	55.00	55.00	65.00	75.00
Small	35.00	40.00	60.00	60.00	66.00	70.00
Plate						
10"	24.00	33.00	45.00	45.00	48.50	55.00
10½". Grant Peace	20.00	28.50	35.00	35.00	40.00	45.00
Platter, oval	26.50	32.00	42.50	42.50	45.00	50.00
Sauce, 5", 6", footed	10.00	14.00	17.00	17.00	20.00	22.50
*Spooner	16.50	25.00	23.00	23.00	27.00	32.50
*Sugar bowl	31.00	40.00	46.00	46.00	55.00	65.00
*Tumbler	14.50	20.00	25.00	25.00	27.50	30.00

*Reproduced Item

114

MEDALLION

	Clear	Vaseline	Amber	Blue	Apple Green
Bowl, waste ....$	12.00	$ 27.00	$ 27.00	$ 28.50	$ 33.00
Butter dish........................	30.00	42.50	42.50	45.00	50.00
Cake stand	27.00	42.00	42.00	48.00	50.00
Celery	21.00	37.50	37.50	40.00	45.00
Compote, covered, high standard ...	36.00	55.00	55.00	60.00	70.00
Creamer	22.50	40.00	40.00	45.00	50.00
Goblet	17.00	27.00	27.00	31.50	34.50
Pickle	14.00	22.00	22.00	23.00	25.00
Pitcher, water....................	30.00	40.00	40.00	50.00	55.00
Sauce					
Footed	9.00	17.00	17.00	18.00	20.00
Flat.........................	7.50	13.50	13.50	16.00	17.50
Spooner	22.50	26.00	26.00	30.00	35.00
Sugar bowl	23.00	44.00	44.00	46.50	51.00
Tray, water	22.00	35.00	35.00	38.00	41.50
Tumbler.........................	14.00	23.50	23.50	25.00	27.50
Wine............................	20.00	27.00	27.00	32.00	34.50

MELROSE

	Clear	Etched
Bowl		
Berry ....$	18.00	$ 25.00
Footed, 6"	15.00	22.50
Waste	12.00	18.00
Butter dish...........................	25.00	35.00
Cake stand	29.50	40.00
Celery	18.00	25.00
Compote		
Covered,6", high standard	35.00	42.50
Covered, 8", high standard	40.00	55.00
Open, 6"	22.50	25.00
Open, 8"	25.00	27.50
Creamer	15.00	23.00

Goblet	12.00	18.00
Mug	8.50	12.00
Pickle	10.00	15.00
Pitcher		
Quart	20.00	25.00
½ gallon	25.50	30.00
Plate		
8"	10.00	13.50
9"	11.00	16.00
10"	12.00	18.00
Sauce	6.50	8.50
Spooner	14.00	18.00
Sugar bowl	22.50	26.50
Tray, water	20.00	25.00
Tumbler	7.50	10.00
Wine	9.50	12.50

MONKEY

Made by George A. Duncan & Sons, Washington, Pa., C. 1880's.

	Clear	Opalescent
Bowl		
Fruit, 8½"	$ 80.00	$ 125.00
Waste	65.00	90.00
Butter dish	100.00	175.00
Creamer	65.00	110.00
Mug	55.00	85.00
Pitcher	125.00	250.00
*Spooner	65.00	125.00
Sugar bowl	100.00	175.00
*Toothpick holder	45.00	110.00
Tumbler	45.00	110.00

*Reproduced Item

OPALESCENT HOBNAIL, See HOBNAIL, OPALESCENT

OPEN BASKETWEAVE, See BASKETWEAVE, OPEN

PANELLED FORGET-ME-NOT
[Regal]

Made by Bryce Bros., Pittsburgh, Pa., C. 1870's.

	Clear	Yellow	Amber	Blue
Bowl, covered	$ 21.00	$ 30.00	$ 30.00	$ 32.50
Butter dish	30.00	42.00	42.00	52.00
Cake stand	31.00	41.50	41.50	50.00
Celery	26.00	40.00	40.00	46.50

Compote				
Covered, high standard	42.00	62.50	62.50	71.00
Open, large, flaring sides	28.50	46.00	46.00	60.00
Cordial	21.00	26.00	26.00	30.50
Creamer...........................	25.00	32.50	32.50	42.50
Goblet	21.00	30.00	30.00	40.00
Marmalade jar	20.00	30.00	30.00	37.50
Pickle	13.50	21.00	21.00	23.00
Pitcher	30.00	45.00	45.00	50.00
Platter, oval......................	20.00	30.00	30.00	36.00
Sauce				
Flat...........................	8.25	12.50	12.50	15.50
Footed	11.50	15.50	15.50	18.00
Shakers, pair.....................	21.00	32.00	32.00	35.00
Spooner	18.00	24.00	24.00	30.00
Sugar bowl	27.00	37.50	37.50	45.00
Wine [scarce]	28.00	37.50	37.50	44.00

PRIMROSE

Made by Canton Glass Co., Canton, Ohio, C. 1880's.

	Clear	Vaseline	Amber	Blue
Bowl				
Berry ....$	21.50	$ 33.50	$ 33.50	$ 40.00
Waste	16.00	21.50	21.50	26.00
Butter dish.......................	34.00	47.50	47.50	57.50
Cake standard	30.00	41.50	41.50	50.00
Celery	25.50	35.00	35.00	41.50
Compote				
Covered, 6"....................	41.50	60.00	60.00	67.50
Covered, 8"....................	43.50	65.00	65.00	72.00
Cordial	19.00	30.00	30.00	32.00
Creamer	30.00	40.00	40.00	45.00
Egg cup	17.00	22.50	22.50	26.50
Goblet				
Knob stem	26.50	36.50	36.50	45.00
Plain stem	17.50	30.00	30.00	38.50
Marmalade jar	22.00	31.50	31.50	36.00
Pickle	11.50	20.00	20.00	25.00
Pitcher	41.50	65.00	65.00	80.00
Plate				
4½"	14.00	22.00	22.00	27.00
6"	22.00	30.00	30.00	34.50
7"	22.50	32.50	32.50	38.00
8¼", cake	22.50	32.00	32.00	36.00
Platter	25.00	42.50	42.50	47.50
Sauce	10.50	16.00	16.00	20.00
Spooner	28.00	32.50	32.50	40.00
Sugar bowl, covered	30.00	50.00	50.00	60.00
Tray	25.00	32.50	32.50	37.50

PRINTED HOBNAIL, See HOBNAIL, PRINTED

PURPLE SLAG

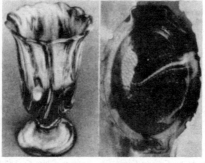

Basket. Handled, braided pattern.		Pitcher	
Sowerby marked. Novelty .... $	50.00	*Milk, 6½", 3 roses, stippled	
Bowl, footed	95.00	background	195.00
Butter dish.......................	165.00	Water........................	175.00
Cake stand, 11½"	150.00	Plate, 10", open edge	150.00
Candlesticks, pair	125.00	Salt. Kettle-shaped. Sowerby	
Celery, 8-1/8"....................	125.00	marked, dated Sept. 18, 1877	45.00
Compote		Sauce	59.50
Covered, low standard	225.00	Spooner	
Open, high standard	175.00	Acanthus Leaf	76.50
Creamer		Flower Panel	80.00
Fish-shaped, dated 11-24-1882 ...	135.00	Footed	75.00
Flower Panel	90.00	*Sugar bowl, Flower Panel.........	140.00
Scroll with Acanthus, 4½"	110.00	Toothpick holder. Boot	47.50
Sunflower	110.00	Tray	150.00
Dish		Tumbler	
Small, round	60.00	Water........................	65.00
Square.......................	65.00	Whiskey	75.00
*Goblet	175.00	Vase	
Lamp, slag base, clear font.........	150.00	Cylindrical, 3x6", ring & flower	
Match holder		motif, pair	120.00
3¾", 4 small feet [Millard 232]...	60.00	Disc-shaped. Sowerby marked,	
Ring handles [Millard 233].......	65.00	scene of mother and child picking	
Mug	68.50	apples. Embossed all over	150.00
*Reproduced Item		Urn-type with shell & flower decor .	100.00

RAINDROP

	Clear	Amber	Yellow	Blue	Green	Milk Glass
Bowl, finger ....$	10.50 $	18.50 $	18.50 $	21.50 $	23.00 $	25.00
Butter dish	26.00	41.50	41.50	48.50	51.00	57.50
Compote						
Open, high standard	26.00	34.50	34.50	38.50	41.50	45.00
Open, low standard	21.00	30.00	30.00	34.50	37.50	42.00
Creamer.....................	20.00	25.00	25.00	28.50	32.00	36.50
Cup and saucer	21.50	26.00	26.00	30.00	31.00	34.50
Egg cup	14.00	21.00	21.00	22.50	23.00	25.00
Pickle	13.50	18.00	18.00	21.00	21.50	23.00

Pitcher, syrup	25.00	35.00	35.00	45.00	50.00	55.00
Plate, handled	20.00	24.50	24.50	28.00	31.00	34.50
Sauce						
Flat	8.00	14.50	14.50	15.50	17.00	21.50
Footed	10.50	17.00	17.00	18.50	20.00	22.00
Tray, water	21.00	31.00	31.00	40.00	48.50	50.00

ROSE-IN-SNOW

Made by Bryce Bros., Pittsburgh, Pa., C. 1870's.

	Clear	Amber	Vaseline	Blue
Butter dish				
Round, flat ....$	55.00	$ 60.00	$ 60.00	$ 70.00
Square	55.00	60.00	60.00	70.00
Cake stand [scarce]	100.00	125.00	125.00	135.00
Compote				
Covered, high standard	70.00	103.50	103.50	115.00
Covered, low standard	63.50	87.00	87.00	96.00
Creamer				
Round	40.00	47.50	47.50	55.00
Square	50.00	55.00	55.00	65.00
Dish				
Oval, large	38.50	54.00	54.00	60.50
Oval, small	30.00	32.00	32.00	46.50
Square, covered	35.00	49.50	49.50	60.00
*Goblet	34.00	45.00	45.00	50.00
Lemonade glass	30.00	41.50	41.50	44.50
Marmalade jar	85.00	95.00	95.00	105.00
*Mug	35.00	42.50	42.50	50.00
Pickle				
Double, 8¼x7" [scarce]	65.00	80.00	80.00	100.00
Oval, handles at ends	21.00	32.00	32.00	40.00
Pitcher	60.00	87.50	87.50	105.00
Plate				
5" [scarce]	40.00	45.00	45.00	55.00

	Clear	Amber	Yellow	Blue
6"	25.00	30.00	30.00	40.00
7¼"	27.50	35.00	35.00	45.00
*9" [heavily reproduced]	35.00	40.00	40.00	50.00
Sauce				
Flat, round	9.00	16.50	16.50	18.00
Square	14.00	21.00	21.00	22.50
Spooner				
Round	35.00	45.00	45.00	55.00
Square	42.50	47.50	47.50	55.00
Sugar bowl				
Round	36.00	54.50	54.50	62.50
Square	42.00	60.00	60.00	68.50
Tumbler	36.50	47.00	47.00	50.00

*Reproduced Item

ROSE SPRIG

Made by Campbell, Jones & Co., Pittsburgh, Pa., C. 1886.

	Clear	Amber	Yellow	Blue
Butter dish	$ 32.50	$ 46.00	$ 46.00	$ 50.00
Cake stand	27.00	40.00	40.00	45.00
Celery	25.50	35.00	35.00	42.00
Compote				
Covered, high standard	37.50	52.50	52.50	63.50
Open, extra large	30.00	41.50	41.50	50.00
Cordial	14.50	30.00	30.00	35.00
Creamer	24.00	37.50	37.50	45.00
Dish				
Boat-shaped	20.00	26.00	26.00	34.50
Oblong, deep	17.00	23.00	23.00	30.00
Square, handled	18.00	22.00	22.00	28.00
Goblet	22.50	30.50	30.50	42.00
Lemonade glass	21.00	31.00	31.00	46.00
Mug	24.50	30.00	30.00	35.00
Pickle	14.50	21.00	21.00	24.00
Pitcher				
Large	35.00	40.00	40.00	55.00
Small	29.50	35.00	35.00	45.00
Plate				
6½"	17.50	25.00	25.00	28.50
10"	25.00	35.00	35.00	42.00
Platter	22.50	32.00	32.00	40.00
Salt, sleigh	32.50	46.50	46.50	50.00
Sauce, footed	10.50	16.50	16.50	21.00
Spooner	18.00	25.00	25.00	38.50
Sugar bowl	32.50	48.00	48.00	55.00
Tray, water	24.00	36.50	36.50	42.00
Tumbler	19.00	26.00	26.00	35.00
Wine	28.00	32.50	32.50	37.50

ROYAL IVY

Made by Northwood Glass Co., Martins Ferry, Ohio. C. 1889-90.

	Frosted to Cranberry
Bowl, 7", open .... $	92.00
Butter dish, covered...............	115.00
Creamer	80.50
Cruet	115.00
Pitcher	
Syrup	75.00
Water.........................	132.50
Shaker	
Salt and pepper, pair............	70.00
Sugar	57.50
Sugar bowl, covered	115.00
Toothpick holder	44.00
Tumbler	50.00

ROYAL OAK

Made by Northwood Glass Co., Martins Ferry, Ohio, C. 1899.

	Frosted to Cranberry
Bowl	
8" .... $	100.00
Finger	52.00
Butter dish......................	126.50
Creamer	86.50
Cruet	115.00
Pitcher, water, square mouth	132.00
Shakers, pair....................	70.00
Spooner	57.50
Sugar bowl	126.50
Syrup	78.00
Toothpick holder	46.00
Tumbler	52.00

SAWTOOTH AND STAR
[O'Hara Diamond, Ruby Star "Flashed"]

	Clear	Red Flashed
Bowl .... $	10.00	$ 22.00
Butter dish, covered....................	22.50	40.00

Compote, small, open	16.50	27.00
Creamer	17.00	26.50
Cruet	14.50	27.00
Cup and saucer	17.50	30.00
Goblet	15.00	27.50
Pickle	13.50	22.50
Plate	14.00	22.00
Sauce	7.50	11.00
Shaker		
Salt and pepper, pair	16.50	25.00
Sugar	15.00	24.50
Spooner	15.00	22.50
Sugar bowl, covered	22.50	40.50
Wine	10.50	17.50

SHERATON
[Ida]

Made by Bryce, Higbee & Co., Pittsburgh, Pa., C. 1880's.

	Clear	Amber	Blue
Bowl, berry	$ 16.00	$ 27.00	$ 30.00
Butter dish	26.50	41.50	45.00
Compote, covered	33.00	55.00	65.00
Creamer	16.50	30.00	35.00
Goblet	15.00	22.50	28.00
Pitcher			
Milk	15.00	25.00	34.50
Water	25.00	37.50	40.00
Plate			
Bread	15.00	30.00	40.00
P. F. Memorial, frosted center	50.00	---------	---------
Sauce, flat	7.50	13.50	14.50
Spooner	15.00	19.50	25.00
Sugar bowl, covered	26.50	41.50	46.50
Wine	10.00	15.00	17.50

SPIREA BAND
[Square and Dot, Square Dot, Earl]

Made by Bryce, Higbee & Co., Pittsburgh, Pa., C. 1885.

	Clear	Amber	Vaseline	Blue	Green
Bowl, berry	$ 17.00	$ 30.00	$ 30.00	$ 36.00	$ 40.00
Butter dish, covered	30.00	40.00	40.00	45.00	50.00
Cake stand	21.00	32.50	32.50	38.50	45.00
Celery	16.50	30.00	30.00	33.00	40.00
Compote					
Covered	38.50	60.00	60.00	75.00	85.00
Open	26.00	40.00	40.00	43.50	46.50

Cordial	15.00	30.00	30.00	33.00	37.00
Creamer	17.50	36.00	36.00	40.00	45.00
Goblet	13.50	30.00	30.00	31.50	33.00
Pitcher, water	26.00	41.50	41.50	48.00	56.00
Platter, oval	20.00	32.00	32.00	36.00	45.00
Relish	15.00	18.50	18.50	22.50	30.00
Sauce					
Flat	8.50	13.50	13.50	16.00	17.00
Footed	9.00	17.00	17.00	17.50	22.00
Shakers, pair	21.00	33.00	33.00	37.00	40.50
Spooner	17.00	22.50	22.50	27.00	32.00
Sugar bowl, covered	27.00	43.50	43.50	50.00	55.00
Wine	10.50	19.00	19.00	22.00	23.50

STRAWBERRY

	Clear		Milk Glass
Butter dish ....$	50.00	$	85.00
Compote			
Covered, 8", high standard	60.00		120.00
Covered, 8", low standard	50.00		100.00
Creamer	37.50		75.00
*Egg cup	17.00		35.00
*Goblet	25.00		55.00
Honey dish	12.00		24.50
Pickle	15.00		30.00
Pitcher			
Syrup	30.00		60.00
Water	60.00		120.00
Salt	12.00		25.00
Sauce	12.00		25.00
Spooner	25.00		50.00
Sugar bowl, covered	35.00		72.50

*Reproduced Item

SWAN

	Clear	Amber	Yellow	Blue
Butter dish ....$	65.00	$ 70.00	$ 70.00	$ 80.00
Creamer	45.00	50.00	50.00	55.00
Dish, oval, covered	40.00	65.00	65.00	75.00
Goblet	45.00	60.00	60.00	74.50
Pitcher, water	50.00	60.00	60.00	70.00
Sauce				
Footed	12.00	15.00	15.00	20.00
Round, flat	9.00	13.00	13.00	15.00
Spooner	35.00	40.00	40.00	50.00
Sugar bowl	45.00	55.00	55.00	65.00

SWIRL
[Jersey Swirl]

	Clear	Amber	Yellow	Blue
Bowl, berry ....$	18.00	$ 30.00	$ 30.00	$ 32.00
Butter dish	31.00	42.00	42.00	50.00
Cake stand	30.00	40.00	40.00	50.00
Candlesticks, pair	30.00	42.00	42.00	50.00
Celery	26.00	34.50	34.50	42.00
Compote				
Covered, high standard	34.50	46.00	46.00	51.50
Covered, collared base	30.00	41.50	41.50	48.50
Creamer	25.50	34.50	34.50	40.00
Cup, sherbet	11.50	21.50	21.50	26.00
Goblet				
*Large	21.50	---------	---------	---------
Regular	26.00	37.50	37.50	43.00
Pitcher, water	32.00	46.00	46.00	52.50
Plate				
6¼"	18.50	27.00	27.00	30.00
8"	22.50	30.00	30.00	33.50
10"	28.00	34.50	34.50	37.50
Salt				
Celery dip	7.50	10.50	10.50	12.00
Large	10.50	14.00	14.00	16.00
Sauce	9.00	12.00	12.00	15.00
Shakers, pair	21.00	30.00	30.00	32.00
Spooner	25.00	30.00	30.00	40.00
Sugar bowl	31.00	45.00	45.00	48.50
Tray	25.00	34.50	34.50	40.00
Tumbler	16.00	25.00	25.00	28.00
Wine	15.00	27.50	27.50	35.00

*Reproduced Item

THOUSAND EYE

Made by Richards & Hartley, C. 1888; New Brighton Glass Co., New Brighton, Pa., C. 1889.

	Clear	Amber	Vaseline	Blue	Apple Green
Bowl					
Berry ....$	25.50	$ 37.50	$ 37.50	$ 40.00	$ 46.50
Waste	20.00	28.00	28.00	34.00	38.00
Butter dish					
Knob stem....................	44.00	60.00	60.00	66.00	74.00
Plain stem	40.00	52.50	52.50	60.00	66.00
Cake stand					
Knob stem....................	36.00	58.00	58.00	65.00	80.00
Plain stem	33.00	55.00	55.00	68.50	71.50
Celery					
Knob stem....................	32.50	45.00	45.00	52.50	60.00
Plain stem	32.00	42.50	42.50	48.00	55.00
Cologne bottle	20.00	27.50	27.50	33.00	40.00
Compote					
Covered, 6" diam., knob stem, high standard	50.00	65.00	65.00	66.00	78.00
Open, plain stem	42.50	55.00	55.00	70.00	80.00
Cordial	21.00	33.00	33.00	40.00	46.00
Creamer					
Knob stem....................	42.50	50.00	50.00	60.00	65.00
Plain stem	40.00	47.00	47.00	55.00	60.00
Cruet					
Knob stem....................	33.00	46.50	46.50	50.00	57.00
*Plain stem	30.00	41.50	41.50	46.00	50.00
Egg cup [very scarce]	50.00	61.00	61.00	66.00	70.00
*Goblet	30.00	40.00	40.00	41.50	50.00
*Hat, match holder	14.00	20.00	20.00	24.00	26.50
Honey dish	16.00	23.00	23.00	26.50	30.00
Lamp					
Handled, small	51.00	71.50	71.50	77.00	82.50
High standard, large	60.50	87.50	87.50	100.00	110.00
*Mug	14.00	20.50	20.50	25.00	27.00
Pickle	20.00	22.00	22.00	26.50	26.50
Pitcher					
Large, plain or knob stem........	40.00	50.00	50.00	60.00	78.00
Small, knob stem	36.00	46.50	46.50	55.00	65.00
Small, plain stem	42.00	52.50	52.50	65.00	80.00
Plate					
Round, 6", alphabet border	30.00	38.00	38.00	40.00	43.00
Square, 6"	20.00	24.50	24.50	28.00	32.40
*Square, 8"	20.50	30.00	30.00	31.50	35.00

Square, 10"	24.00	33.00	33.00	40.00	45.00
Platter, oblong, 8x11"	30.00	40.00	40.00	45.00	55.00
Sauce					
Flat	10.00	14.00	14.00	16.00	19.50
Footed, plain stem	11.00	14.50	14.50	17.00	19.00
Footed, knob stem	13.50	15.00	15.00	18.00	20.00
Shakers, pair	25.00	36.00	36.00	40.00	45.00
Spooner					
Knob stem	20.00	26.50	26.50	30.00	35.50
Plain stem	16.50	24.00	24.00	26.50	30.00
Sugar bowl					
Knob base	46.50	60.00	60.00	66.00	76.50
Plain base	40.00	54.00	54.00	60.50	68.50
Syrup	41.50	60.00	60.00	66.00	80.00
Tray					
Water, oval	47.00	60.00	60.00	65.00	75.00
Water, round	40.00	50.00	50.00	55.00	60.00
*Tumbler					
Jelly	17.00	23.50	23.50	26.50	35.00
Water.........................	20.00	28.00	28.00	35.00	40.00
*Twine holder....................	20.00	35.50	35.50	40.00	47.00
*Wine..........................	19.00	26.00	26.00	30.00	40.00

*Reproduced Item

THREE PANEL

Made by Hartley & Co., Tarentum, Pa., C. 1888.

	Clear	Amber	Yellow	Blue
Bowl, 9", footed ....$	30.00	$ 37.50	$ 37.50	$ 45.00
Butter dish	31.00	45.00	45.00	48.50
Celery	30.00	42.00	42.00	45.50
Compote, open, low standard				
7"	21.50	32.00	32.00	36.00
8½", 9"	22.50	32.00	32.00	37.50
10"	24.50	34.50	34.50	42.00
Creamer..........................	23.00	31.00	31.00	34.50
Cruet	21.50	36.50	36.50	57.00
Goblet	22.50	30.00	30.00	35.00
Mug	13.00	20.00	20.00	23.00
Pitcher, water	34.50	48.50	48.50	57.00
Sauce	9.00	14.00	14.00	16.50
Spooner	18.00	25.00	25.00	32.50
Sugar bowl	31.00	44.50	44.50	48.50
Tumbler	17.00	18.50	18.50	28.50

TWO PANEL

Bowl	Clear	Amber	Yellow	Blue	Green
Fruit, 10½" ....$	15.00	$ 22.00	$ 22.00	$ 23.00	$ 27.00
Oval, 5½ x7"	13.50	21.00	21.00	22.50	27.00
Waste	13.00	20.00	20.00	22.00	25.00
Butter dish	28.00	41.50	41.50	46.00	52.50
Celery	20.00	27.50	27.50	35.00	40.00
Compote					
Covered, high standard	32.50	45.00	45.00	50.00	60.00
Open, high standard	20.00	30.00	30.00	35.00	40.00
Open, low standard............	18.00	25.50	25.50	30.00	37.50
Cordial	15.50	23.00	23.00	26.00	30.50
Creamer	24.00	29.50	29.50	30.00	35.00
Dish					
Flat..........................	17.00	26.00	26.00	30.00	35.00
Oval, deep	15.50	18.50	18.50	23.00	28.50
*Goblet	20.00	30.00	30.00	32.50	38.50
Lamp	28.00	41.50	41.50	51.00	56.00
Marmalade jar	21.00	32.00	32.00	37.50	46.00
Mug	14.50	21.00	21.00	24.00	25.00
Pickle	13.00	20.00	20.00	22.50	28.00
Pitcher	35.00	47.50	47.50	55.00	60.00
Platter	22.50	29.50	29.50	32.50	36.00
Salt					
Celery dip	8.00	13.00	13.00	16.50	18.00
Large, flat	10.50	17.50	17.50	21.00	22.50
Sauce					
Flat..........................	9.00	14.00	14.00	14.50	16.50
Footed	10.50	16.50	16.50	17.50	21.00
Shakers, pair....................	21.00	34.50	34.50	37.50	40.00
Spooner	25.00	30.00	30.00	33.00	40.00
Sugar bowl	28.50	35.50	35.50	40.00	45.00
Tray, water	30.00	40.00	40.00	45.00	50.00
Tumbler	13.00	20.00	20.00	23.00	28.50
*Wine.........................	16.50	23.00	23.00	26.00	31.00

*Reproduced Item

WHEAT AND BARLEY
[Oats and Barley, Hops and Barley, Duquesne]

Made by Bryce Bros. in the early 1870's; also by U. S. Glass Co., C. 1889.

	Clear	Amber	Yellow	Blue
Bowl, covered, 8" ....$	28.00	$ 38.00	$ 38.00	$ 42.00
Butter dish	32.00	40.00	40.00	50.00
Cake stand				
8", 9"	26.00	37.00	37.00	45.50
10"	30.00	42.00	42.00	50.00

Compote				
Covered, 7", 8", high standard ...	36.00	50.00	50.00	59.50
Open, high standard	27.00	40.00	40.00	41.50
Creamer	21.50	31.00	31.00	40.00
Goblet	21.00	36.00	36.00	40.00
Mug	17.00	27.00	27.00	30.00
Pitcher				
Large	34.50	48.50	48.50	60.00
Milk	28.00	40.00	40.00	50.00
Syrup	25.00	40.00	40.00	50.00
Water.......................	25.00	35.00	35.00	45.00
Plate				
7"	23.00	32.00	32.00	34.50
9", closed handles	22.50	30.00	30.00	35.00
Sauce				
Flat.........................	9.00	11.00	11.00	13.50
Footed, 4"	11.00	16.50	16.50	17.00
Shakers, pair....................	21.00	30.00	30.00	40.00
Spooner	18.00	22.50	22.50	30.00
Sugar bowl, covered	27.50	37.50	37.50	42.50
Tumbler				
Footed	17.50	24.50	24.50	28.00
Water	15.50	21.50	21.50	25.00
Wine..........................	12.00	18.00	18.00	25.00

WILDFLOWER

Made by Adams & Co., Pittsburgh, Pa., C. 1874; also by U. S. Glass Co., C. 1898.

	Clear	Amber	Yellow	Blue	Green
Bowl					
5¼" square, cut corners ....$	15.50	$ 23.00	$ 23.00	$ 26.00	$ 28.00
6½" square, cut corners, covered..	20.00	28.00	28.00	30.00	32.00
7¼" square, cut corners, covered.	21.00	32.00	32.00	37.50	40.50
Waste	22.50	34.50	34.50	40.50	41.50
Butter dish					
Collared base	30.50	45.00	45.00	48.50	55.00
Flat........................	26.50	37.50	37.50	45.00	48.50
Cake stand					
Large	31.00	41.50	41.50	45.00	50.00
Small	27.00	37.50	37.50	41.50	45.50

Celery	26.00	42.00	42.00	46.00	52.00
Champagne [scarce]	32.00	57.50	57.50	62.50	70.00
Compote					
Covered, 6", high standard	37.50	52.50	52.50	60.50	70.00
Covered, 8", high standard	41.50	60.00	60.00	63.50	75.00
Covered, 8", low standard	37.00	50.00	50.00	55.00	65.00
Open, high standard	26.00	40.00	40.00	41.50	46.00
Cordial	23.00	31.00	31.00	37.50	42.00
Creamer	24.00	32.50	32.50	40.00	46.50
Dish					
Covered, 7¼" square	22.50	32.00	32.00	34.50	40.50
Open, square	15.50	25.50	25.50	30.00	32.00
*Goblet	21.00	34.50	34.50	40.00	45.00
Pickle	14.00	22.50	22.50	24.50	30.00
Pitcher					
Syrup	37.50	60.00	60.00	65.00	70.00
Water........................	31.00	42.00	42.00	50.00	55.00
*Plate, 10"	21.50	30.00	30.00	37.00	41.50
Platter, 10", oblong	24.00	32.50	32.50	40.00	45.00
Salt, boat on turtle's back	27.50	36.50	36.50	40.00	42.50
Sauce					
Flat, round	8.00	11.50	11.50	13.00	14.00
Flat, square...................	9.00	13.00	13.00	14.00	15.00
Footed, round	10.00	14.50	14.50	17.00	18.50
Shakers, pair.....................	28.00	34.50	34.50	37.50	45.00
Spooner	35.00	40.00	40.00	45.00	50.00
Sugar bowl	31.00	46.00	46.00	50.00	57.00
Tray, water	32.00	41.50	41.50	50.00	57.50
*Tumbler	20.00	28.00	28.00	30.00	32.00
*Wine...........................	21.50	28.50	28.50	32.00	34.50

*Reproduced Item

WILLOW OAK
[Oak Leaf, Acorn, Thistle, Wreath]

Made by Bryce Bros., Pittsburgh, Pa., C. 1880's.

	Clear	Amber	Blue
Bowl			
Berry ....$	20.00	$ 28.00	$ 35.00
Waste	15.50	25.00	26.00
Butter dish	35.00	42.50	55.00
Cake stand	35.00	45.00	55.00
Celery...........................	32.50	40.00	50.00
Compote			
Covered, 7½", high standard	34.50	50.00	60.50
Covered, 9", high standard	37.00	62.50	75.00

Creamer........................	23.50	32.00	37.50
Goblet	21.00	37.50	44.50
Mug	22.00	32.00	40.00
Pitcher			
Large	37.50	50.00	60.00
Small	20.00	35.00	45.00
Plate			
7"	25.00	30.00	34.50
9", closed handles	26.00	32.00	37.50
Platter, oblong	22.50	30.00	35.00
Sauce			
Flat........................	8.50	14.00	15.50
Footed, round	10.50	17.00	20.00
Shakers, pair....................	24.00	30.00	35.00
Spooner	25.00	30.00	40.00
Sugar bowl	35.00	45.00	50.00
Tray, water, 10¾", round	23.00	33.00	36.50
Tumbler	17.00	23.00	26.00

PATTERN GLASS
PATTERNS WITH TWO OR MORE NAMES

A

Acanthus - Ribbed Palm, Sprig, Oak Leaf, Royal
Acme - Butterfly with Spray
Actress - Goddess of Liberty, Theatrical, Annie
Adonis - Washboard
Alabama - Beaded Bull's Eye and Drape
Alaska - Lion's Leg
Alexis - Priscilla, Sun and Star
Almond Thumbprint - Pointed Thumbprint, Finger Print
Amazon - Sawtooth Band
Amberette - Klondike
America -Swirl and Diamond
Andes - Beaded Tulip
Annie - Actress, Goddess of Liberty, Theatrical
Antimicassar - Tidy, Lambrequin
Arabian - Ionic
Art - Teardrop and Diamond Block, Job's Tears
Art Novo - Dogwood
Artic - Polar Bear, North Pole, Iceberg
Atlas - Bullet, Cannon Ball
Atlanta - Clear Lion Head
Aurora - Diamond Horseshoe
Austrian - Finecut Medallion

B

Baby Thumbprint - Dakota, Etched Band and Baby Thumbprint
Baltimore Pear - Twin Pear, Double Pear, Maryland Pear, Gypsy
Bamboo - Broken Column, Notched Rib, Irish Column, Rattan and Bamboo
Banded Raindrops - Candlewick
Bar and Diamond - Kokomo
Barley - Sprig, Indian Tree
Barred Hobnail - Winona
Barrelled Block - Gem, Nailhead
Basketweave, Open - Plaid
Bead Swag - Bead Yoke
Bead Yoke - Bead Swag
Beaded Bull's Eye and Drape - Alabama
Beaded Dewdrop - Wisconsin
Beaded Grape - California
Beaded Jewel - Lacy Dewdrop
Beaded Loop - Oregon
Beaded Oval and Scroll - Dot
Beaded Panel - Beaded Square
Beaded Square - Beaded Panel
Beaded Tulip - Andes
Bean - Egg in Sand

Bearded Man - Viking,Old Man of the Mountains, Bearded Head, Bearded Prophet, Queen Anne
Bearded Prophet - Bearded Head, Bearded Man, Viking, Old Man of the Mountains, Queen Anne
Beatty Rib - Ribbed Opal
Bellflower - Ribbed Leaf
Berkeley - Blocked Arches
Bevelled Star - Pride
Bijou - Fan with Acanthus Leaf
Bird and Fern - Humming Bird, Flying Robin
Bird and Strawberry - Bluebird
Bird in Ring - Grace, Japanese, Fan, Butterfly with Fan
Blaze - Stedman
Block and Fan - Romeo
Block and Pleat - Persian, Three Stories
Block and Star - Valencia Waffle
Block with Stars - Hanover
Blocked Arches - Berkeley
Bluebird - Bird and Strawberry
Blue Jay - Cardinal
Boston - Plain with Flat Ring
Brazil - Primrose, Panelled Daisy
Brilliant - Stars and Stripes
Broken Column - Irish Column, Rattan and Bamboo, Notched Rib, Bamboo
Bryce - Ribbon Candy, Figure Eight
Buckle and Star - Orient
Bullet - Atlas, Cannon Ball, Crystal Ball, Pinwheel
Bull's Eye - Lawrence
Bull's Eye and Star - Palace, Star and Punty, Moon and Star
Bull's Eye in Heart - Columbia, Heart with Thumbprint
Bull's Eye with Diamond Point - Union
Butterfly with Fan - Grace, Japanese, Fan, Bird in Ring
Butterfly with Spray - Acme
Buttressed Arch - Buttressed Loop
Buttressed Loop - Buttressed Arch

C

Cable with Ring - Cable with Ring and Star
Cable with Ring and Star - Cable with Ring
California - Beaded Grape
Cameo - Classical Medallion, Ceres, Goddess of Liberty
Candlewick - Banded Raindrops
Cane and Rosette - Flower Panelled Cane
Cannon Ball - Atlas, Bullet, Crystal Ball

Cardinal - Blue Jay
Cathedral - Orion
Cat's Eye and Block - Cut Log, Ethol
Centennial - Liberty Bell
Ceres - Cameo, Classical Medallion, Goddess of Liberty, Theatrical
Chandelier - Crown Jewels
Chastity - Melon
Chestnut Oak - Old Acorn
Chippendale - Quadruped
Chrysanthemum Leaf - Curled Leaf
Clear Lily - Daisy and Button with Narcissus
Classic Medallion - Cameo, Ceres
Clematis - Rose Point Band
Cobb - Late Sawtooth, Zipper
Cockle Burr - Stippled Star, Variant
Codfish - Dolphin, Fish, Frog, Turtle
Coin - Silver Age
Columbia - Heart with Thumbprint, Bull's Eye in Heart
Column Block - Panel and Star
Compact - Snail
Coral - Fishscale
Cordate Leaf - Homestead
Cord Drapery - Indiana
Cottage - Fine Cut Band, Dinner Bell
Cranesbill - Wild Geranium
Crossbar and Finecut - Etched Fern, Etched Fern and Waffle
Crowfoot - Fan Band, Yale
Crown Jewels - Chandelier
Crystal Anniversary - Crystal Wedding
Crystal Ball - Atlas, Bullet, Cannon Ball, Pinwheel
Crystal Wedding - Crystal Anniversary
Cupid and Psyche - Psyche and Cupid
Cupid and Venus - Minerva, Guardian Angel
Curled Leaf - Chrysanthemum Leaf
Curtain - Sultan
Cut Log - Cat's Eye and Block, Ethol
Czarina - Diamond Point and Fan

D

Dahlia - Marsh Pink, Square Fuchsia, Stippled Dahlia
Daisy - Lacy Daisy
Daisy and Bluebell - Mosaic
Daisy and Button - Oval Medallion, Panelled Daisy
Daisy and Button, Panelled - Ellrose
Daisy and Button with Crossbars - Mikado
Daisy and Button with Narcissus - Clear Lily
Daisy and Button with Oval Panels - Panelled Diamond Cut and Fan, Hartly
Daisy Medallion - Sunburst Medallion
Daisy Square - Panelled Thousand Eyes
Daisy Whorl - Daisy Whorl with Diamond Point
Daisy Whorl with Diamond Point - Daisy Whorl

Dakota - Baby Thumbprint, Etched Band and Baby Thumbprint, Thumbprint Band
Deer and Doe - Deer and Pinetree
Deer and Pinetree - Deer and Doe
Delaware - Four Petal Flower
Derby - Pleat and Panel
Dewdrops and Flowers - Stippled Violets
Dewey - Flower Flange
Diamond and Concave - Diamond Thumbprint
Diamond Horseshoe - Aurora
Diamond Bar - Lattice
Diamond Block and Fan - Shepherd's Plaid, Pineapple and Fan, Pittsburgh Daisy
Diamond Lace - Hob Star
Diamond Point - Sawtooth, Pineapple, Roanoke, Sharp Diamond and Grant, Grant Pineapple, Cobb
Diamond Point and Fan - Czarina
Diamond Point Discs - Eyewinker
Diamond Pointed - Raised Diamonds
Diamond Thumbprint - Diamond and Concave
Diamond with Diamond Point - English
Dinner Bell - Cottage, Fine Cut Band
Dogwood - Art Novo
Dolphin - Codfish, Fish, Frog, Turtle
Doric - Feather, Indiana, Swirl, Swirl and Feather, Feather and Quill
Dot - Beaded Oval and Scroll
Double Loop - Maypole, Silver Sheen
Double Pear - Baltimore Pear, Twin Pear, Maryland Pear, Gypsy
Double Prism - Heck
Draped Leaf - Butterfly
Draped Top - Victoria [Riverside]
Drapery - Lace
Duquesne - Wheat and Barley, Oats and Barley, Hops and Barley

E

Earl - Spirea Band, Square and Dot
Egg in Sand - Bean
Egyptian - Parthenon
Elite - Pillow and Sunburst
Ellrose - Daisy and Button, Panelled
Emerald Green Herringbone - Panelled Herringbone, Florida
English - Diamond with Diamond Point
Esther - Prism with Block
Etched Fan and Baby Thumbprint - Baby Thumbprint, Dakota
Etched Fern - Crossbar and Finecut, Etched Fern and Waffle
Etched Fern and Waffle - Mascotte, Etched Fern
Etched Pineapple Stem - Pavonia
Ethol - Cat's Eye and Block, Cut Log
Eva - Henrietta
Excelsior - Ruby Thumbprint, King's Crown

Exposition Set - Nail
Eyewinker - Diamond Point Discs

F

Fagot - Vera
Fan - Grace, Japanese, Butterfly with Fan, Bird in Ring
Fan Band - Crowfoot, Yale
Fan with Acanthus Leaf - Bijou
Feather - Doric, Indiana, Swirl, Swirl and Feather, Indiana Swirl, Feather and Quill
Feather and Quill - Feather, Doric, Indiana, Indiana Swirl, Swirl and Feather
Figure Eight - Ribbon Candy, Bryce
File - Ribbed Sawtooth
Fine Cut, Four Panel - Heavy Panelled Finecut
Finecut and Diamond - Grand
Finecut and Feather - Swirl, Prince's Feather, Feather
Finecut Band - Cottage, Dinner Bell
Finecut Bar - Panama
Finecut Medallion - Austrian
Finecut with Panels - Nailhead and Panel
Finger Print - Almond Thumbprint, Pointed Thumbprint
Fish - Codfish, Dolphin, Frog, Turtle
Fisheye - Treebark, Pygmy, Torpedo
Fishscale - Coral
Flamingo - Frosted Stork
Flat Panel - Pleating
Fleur-de-lis and Drapes - Fleur-de-lis and Tassel
Florence - Nelly
Florida - Sunken Primrose, Herringbone, Emerald Green Herringbone
Florida Palm - Perfection
Flower Flange - Dewey
Flower Panelled Cane - Cane and Rosette
Flower Plant - Potted Plant, Flower Pot
Flower Pot - Flower Plant, Potted Plant
Flower Spray with Scrolls - Intaglio
Fluted Diamond Point - Panelled Diamond Point
Flying Robin - Humming Bird, Bird and Fern
Forest Ware - Ivy in Snow
Forget-me-not in Snow   -   Stippled Forget-me-not
Foster - Late Block, Virginia, Galloway
Four-Petal Flower - Delaware
Frog - Codfish, Dolphin, Fish, Turtle
Frosted Eagle - Frosted Hawk
Frosted Hawk - Frosted Eagle
Frosted Stork - Flamingo
Frosted Waffle - Hidalgo
Fulton - Martha's Tears

G

Galloway - Virginia, Foster, Mirror

Garden of Eden - Tree of Life, Lotus
Gem - Barrelled Block, Nailhead
Georgia - Pattee Cross, Peacock Eye, Peacock Feather
Geneva - Shell and Scroll
Gibson Girl - Goddess of Liberty, Cameo
Goddess of Liberty - Annie, Actress, Theatrical, Ceres, Cameo, Gibson Girl
Golden Agate - Holly Amber
Good Luck - Horseshoe, Prayer Rug
Grace - Japanese, Fan, Butterfly with Fan, Bird in Ring
Grand - Finecut and Diamond
Grant Pineapple - Diamond Point, Sharp Diamond and Grant, Sawtooth, Pineapple
Grasshopper - Locust, Long Spear
Guardian Angel - Minerva, Cupid and Venus
Gypsy - Baltimore Pear, Twin Pear, Maryland Pear, Double Pear

H

Hand - Pennsylvania
Hanover - Block with Stars
Hartly - Daisy and Button with Oval Panels, Panelled Diamond Cut and Fan
Heart of Loch Laven - Shuttle
Heart with Thumbprint - Columbia, Bull's Eye Heart
Hearts and Spades - Palmette, Spades
Heavy Panelled Finecut - Finecut Four-Panel
Heavy Panelled Grape - Panelled Grape
Heck - Double Prism
Henrietta - Eva
Herringbone - Florida
Hidalgo - Frosted Waffle
High Hob - Teasel
Hobble Skirt - Radiant
Hobnail, Barred - Winona
Hob Star - Diamond Lace
Holly Amber - Golden Agate
Home - Square and Diamond Bands
Homestead - Cordate Leaf
Honeycomb - Pitt Diamond
Hops and Barley - Wheat and Barley, Oats and Barley, Duquesne
Hops Band - Pressed Leaf Band
Horseshoe - Good Luck, Prayer Rug
Humming Bird - Flying Robin, Bird and Fern

I

Iceberg - Polar Bear, Artic, North Pole
Icicle - Late Icicle
Ida - Sheraton
Indian Tree - Barley, Sprig
Indiana - Cord Drapery, Doric, Feather, Swirl, Swirl and Feather, Feather and Quill

Intaglio - Flower Spray with Scrolls
Inverted Prism - Masonic
Ionic - Arabian
Irish Column - Broken Column, Bamboo, Rattan
and Bamboo, Notched Rib
Ivorina Verde - Winged Scroll
Ivy in Snow - Forest Ware

J

Jacob's Ladder, Late - Maltese
Japanese - Grace, Fan, Butterfly with Fan
Jasper - Late Buckle
Jersey - Kitchen Stove
Jersey Swirl - Swirl
Jewel and Crescent - Tennessee
Jewel and Festoon - Queen's Necklace
Jewel with Dewdrop - Kansas
Job's Tears - Art, Teardrop and Diamond Block

K

Kaleidoscope - Puritan, Majestic
Kansas - Jewel with Dewdrop
King's Crown - Excelsior, Ruby Thumbprint
Kirkland - Sunk Daisy
Kitchen Stove - Jersey
Klondike - Amberette
Kokomo - Bar and Diamond

L

Lace - Drapery
Lacy Dewdrop - Beaded Jewel
Lacy Daisy - Daisy
Lacy Medallion - Rochelle, Princess Feather
Lacy Valance - Persian Shawl
Lady Hamilton - Peerless
Lambrequin - Tidy, Antimicassar
Late Block - Virginia, Galloway, Foster
Late Buckle - Jasper
Late Icicle - Icicle
Late Jacob's Ladder - Maltese
Late Rosette - Tweed
Late Sawtooth - Cobb, Sawtooth, Zipper
Lattice - Diamond Bar
Lawrence - Bull's Eye
Leaf - Maple Leaf, Petal and Loop, O'Hara
Liberty Bell - Centennial
Lion, Late - Atlanta
Lion's Leg - Alaska
Locust - Grasshopper, Long Spear
London - Picket
Long Spear - Grasshopper, Locust
Loop and Fan - Maryland
Loop and Jewel - New England Pineapple,
Pineapple
Loop with Stippled Panels - Texas
Lotus - Garden of Eden
Louisiana - Sharp Oval and Diamond
Lutz - Swirl and Ball, Ray

M

Magic - Rosette
Maine - Panelled Flower, Stippled Primrose
Majestic - Puritan, Kaleidoscope
Maltese - Late Jacob's Ladder
Maple Leaf - Leaf
Marsh Pink - Dahlia, Square Fuchsia, Stippled
Dahlia
Martha's Tears - Fulton
Maryland - Loop and Fan
Maryland Pear - Baltimore Pear, Twin Pear,
Double Pear, Gypsy
Mascotte - Ethol, Fern and Waffle
Masonic - Inverted Prism
Maypole - Silver Sheen, Double Loop
Melon - Chastity
Michigan - Panelled Jewel
Mikado - Daisy and Button with Crossbar
Minerva - Guardian Angel, Cupid and Venus
Mirror - Virginia, Galloway
Moon and Star - Star and Punty, Bull's Eye and
Star, Palace
Mosaic - Daisy and Bluebell

N

Nail - Exposition Set
Nailhead - Gem, Barrelled Block
Nailhead and Panel - Finecut and Panel
National - Reward
Nelly - Florence
Neptune - Old Man of the Woods, Old Man,
Santa Claus
New England Pineapple - Diamond Point,
Sawtooth, Pineapple, Loop and Jewel
North Pole - Polar Bear, Artic, Iceberg
Notched Rib - Bamboo, Broken Column, Irish
Column, Rattan and Bamboo

O

Oak Leaf - Acanthus, Sprig, Ribbed Palm,
Royal
Oats and Barley - Wheat and Barley, Hops and
Barley, Duquesne
O'Hara - Petal and Loop, Leaf
O'Hara Diamond - Ruby Star
Old Acorn - Chestnut Oak
Old Man - Neptune, Old Man of the Woods,
Santa Claus
Old Man of the Mountains - Bearded Man,
Bearded Prophet, Viking, Queen Anne
Old Man of the Woods - Neptune, Santa Claus,
Old Man
Open Basketweave - Plaid
Oregon - Beaded Loop
Orient - Buckle and Star
Orion - Cathedral
Oval Loop - Question Mark

Oval Medallion - Daisy and Button, Panelled
Daisy

P

Palace - Moon and Star, Bull's Eye and Star,
Star and Punty
Palmette - Spades, Hearts and Spades
Panama - Fine Cut Bar
Panel and Star - Column Block
Panelled Daisy - Oval Medallion, Brazil
Panelled Dewdrop - Stippled Dewdrop
Panelled Diamond Cut and Fan - Hartly, Daisy
and Button with Oval Panels
Panelled Diamond Point - Fluted Diamond
Point
Panelled Flower - Stippled Primrose, Maine
Panelled Forget-me-not - Regal
Panelled Grape - Heavy Panelled Grape
Panelled Herringbone - Emerald Green
Herringbone, Florida
Panelled Jewel - Michigan
Panelled Thousand Eyes - Daisy Square
Parthenon - Egyptian
Pattee Cross - Georgia
Pavonia - Etched Pineapple Stem
Peacock Eye - Peacock Feather, Georgia
Peacock Feather - Georgia, Peacock Eye
Peerless - Lady Hamilton
Pennsylvania - Hand
Perfection - Florida Palm
Persian - Block and Pleat, Three Stories
Persian Shawl - Lacy Valance
Petal and Loop - O'Hara, Leaf
Picket - London
Pillar and Bull's Eye - Thistle
Pillow and Sunburst - Elite
Pineapple - Diamond Point, Sawtooth, Sharp
Diamond and Grant, Grant Pineapple, New
England Pineapple, Loop and Jewel
Pineapple and Fan - Shepherd's Plaid,
Diamond Block and Fan, Pittsburgh Daisy
Pioneer - Westward-Ho, Tippecanoe
Pinwheel - Cannon Ball, Sterling
Pitt Diamond - Honeycomb
Pittsburgh Daisy - Pineapple and Fan
Plaid - Basketweave, Open
Plain with Flat Ring - Boston
Pleat and Panel - Derby
Pleating - Flat Panel
Pointed Thumbprint - Almond Thumbprint,
Finger Print
Polar Bear - Iceberg, Artic, North Pole
Portland - Tree of Life
Portland with Diamond Point Band - Virginia
Potted Plant - Flower Plant, Flower Pot
Powder and Shot - Powderhorn and Shot
Powderhorn and Shot - Powder and Shot

Pressed Leaf Band - Hops Band
Pride - Bevelled Star
Primrose - Panelled Daisy, Brazil
Princess Feather - Rochelle, Lacy Medallion
Priscilla - Alexis, Sun and Star
Prism with Block - Esther
Psyche and Cupid - Cupid and Psyche
Puritan - Majestic, Kaleidoscope
Pygmy - Torpedo, Fisheye

Q

Quadruped - Chippendale
Queen Anne - Viking, Old Man of the
Mountains, Bearded Prophet, Bearded Man
Queen's Necklace - Jewel and Festoon
Question Mark - Oval Loop

R

Radiant - Hobble Skirt
Raised Diamond - Diamond Pointed
Rattan and Bamboo - Bamboo, Broken Column,
Notched Rib, Irish Column
Ray - Swirl and Ball, Lutz
Regal - Panelled Forget-me-not
Reward - National
Ribbed Leaf - Bellflower
Ribbed Opal - Beatty Rib
Ribbed Palm - Acanthus, Sprig, OakLeaf, Royal
Ribbed Sawtooth - File
Ribbon Candy - Figure Eight, Bryce
Roanoke - Sawtooth
Rochelle - Princess Feather, Lacy Medallion
Romeo - Block and Fan
Rose Point Band - Clematis
Rosette - Magic
Royal - Sprig, Ribbed Palm, Acanthus, Oak
Leaf
Ruby Star - O'Hara Diamond
Ruby Thumbprint - Excelsior, King's Crown

S

Sampson - Teardrop and Tassel
Santa Claus - Old Man, Old Man of the Woods,
Neptune
Sawtooth - Diamond Point, Pineapple,
Roanoke, Cobb
Sawtooth and Star - O'Hara Diamond, Ruby
Star "Flashed"
Sawtooth Band - Amazon
Scroll - Taunton, Stippled Scroll
Sharp Diamond and Grant - Grant Pineapple,
Diamond Point, Sawtooth, Pineapple
Sharp Oval and Diamond - Louisiana
Shell and Jewel - Victor
Shell and Scroll - Geneva
Shepherd's Plaid - Pineapple and Fan,
Diamond Block and Fan, Pittsburgh Daisy

Sheraton - Ida
Shuttle - Heart of Loch Laven
Silver Age - Coin
Silver Sheen - Maypole, Double Loop
Snail - Compact
Soda - Tree of Life with Sprig
Spades - Palmette, Hearts and Spades
Spirea Band - Earl, Square and Dot
Sprig - Barley,Indian Tree
Square and Diamond Bands - Home
Square and Dot - Earl, Spirea
Square Fuchsia - Marsh Pink, Dahlia, Stippled
   Dahlia
Star and Punty - Moon and Star, Bull's Eye and
   Star, Palace
Stars and Stripes - Brilliant
Stedman - Blaze
Sterling - Pinwheel
Stippled Dahlia - Square Fuchsia, March Pink,
   Dahlia
Stippled Dewdrop - Panelled Dewdrop
Stippled Forget-me-not - Forget-me-not in
   Snow
Stippled Primrose - Maine, Panelled Flower
Stippled Scroll - Taunton, Scroll
Stippled Star, Variant - Cockle Burr
Stippled Violets - Dewdrops and Flowers
Sultan - Curtain
Sun and Star - Priscilla, Alexis
Sunburst Medallion - Daisy Medallion
Sunk Daisy - Kirkland
Sunken Primrose - Florida
Swirl - Finecut and Feather, Princess Feather,
   Feather, Doric, Indiana, Jersey Swirl
Swirl and Ball - Ray, Lutz
Swirl and Diamond - America
Swirl and Feather - Doric, Feather, Indiana
   Swirl, Feather and Quill

T

Taunton - Scroll, Stippled Scroll
Teardrop - Teardrop and Thumbprint
Teardrop and Diamond Block - Art, Job's Tears
Teardrop and Tassel - Sampson
Teardrop and Thumbprint - Teardrop
Teasel - High Hob
Teepee - Wigwam
Tennessee - Jewel and Crescent
Texas - Loop with Stippled Panels
Texas Bull's Eye - Texas Bull's Eye Variant

Theatrical - Goddess of Liberty, Annie, Actress
Three Sisters - Three Graces, Three Fates,
   Three Faces
Three Stories - Persian, Block and Pleat
Thumbprint Band - Baby Thumbprint, Dakota
Tidy - Antimicassar, Lambrequin
Tippecanoe - Westward-Ho, Pioneer
Torpedo, Pgymy, Fisheye
Treebark - Fisheve
Tree of Life - Tree of Life--Pittsburgh, Tree of
   Life with Hand
Tree of Life with Sprig - Soda
Tulip - Andes, Beaded Tulip
Turtle - Codfish, Dolphin, Frog, Fish
Tweed - Late Rosette
Twin Pear - Baltimore Pear, Double Pear,
   Gypsy, Maryland Pear

U

Union - Bull's Eye with Diamond Point

V

Valencia Waffle - Block and Star
Vera - Fagot
Victor - Shell and Jewel
Victoria |Riverside| - Draped Top
Viking - Bearded Man, Bearded Prophet, Old
   Man of the Mountains, Queen Anne
Virginia - Late Block, Foster, Mirror, Galloway

W

Waffle and Thumbprint - Palace
Washboard - Adonis
Water Lily - Wild Iris
Westward-Ho - Pioneer, Tippecanoe
Wheat and Barley - Oats and Barley, Hops
   and Barley, Duquesne
Wigwam - Teepee
Wild Geranium - Cranesbill
Wild Iris - Water Lily
Winged Scroll - Ivorina Verde
Winona - Barred Hobnail
Wisconsin - Beaded Dewdrop

XYZ

Yale - Fan Band, Crowfoot
Zipper - Cobb, Late Sawtooth

GENERAL SECTION

ABC PLATES

Plates made especially for children with the alphabet around the outer rim. Center decorations often consisted of animals, great men, maxims or Aesop's Fables. They were made of various materials including porcelains, pottery, glass, tin and pewter.

CHINA

"Swing Swong." 7½" diam. White with blue transfer $47.00

5"	David and Goliath in colored scene........................$	25.00
5"	General Grant...............	28.00
5¼"	New Pony. Staffordshire, raised alphabet, colorful transfer.....	22.50
5"	Robinson Crusoe	29.50
6"	Canary, bullfinch & goldfinch ..	35.00
6"	Little boys at marble play......	25.00
6"	Our Donkey and Foal, with boy and girl decoration	25.00
6"	Reuben interceding with brethren for life of Joseph	24.00
6"	"The Gleaners"	30.00
6"	Those Children, etc.	25.00
6¼"	Emma	23.50
6¼"	Owl center. Hands in sign language around border	28.50
6¼"	The Lord's Prayer. Transfer	22.00
7"	Allertons. Comic transfer......	25.00
7"	Benjamin Franklin............	30.00
7"	Boatman capturing seal. "England"	25.00

7"	Cow grazing in center. "Adams," embossed alphabet rim	25.00
7"	Crusoe finding footprints	35.00
7"	December. Old man, holly, goat, turkeys. Green	26.50
7"	Early Rugby scene	28.50
7"	Eye of God, harps, cherubs, 4-line verse. Ironstone	35.00
7"	Girl bathing. With puss-in-boots scene......................	26.50
7"	Horse racing scene	26.50
7".	Kitten and puppy peeking from pitcher......................	24.00
7"	Kitten in clothes..............	28.50
7"	Little Jockey. Black and white transfer of child on dog	27.50
7"	The Guardian. Staffordshire....	35.00
7"	Tired of play	22.50
7¼"	Cat and Four Kittens	27.50
7¼"	Crusoe Rescues Friday	35.00
7¼"	Hunters and Dogs	24.00
7¼"	Little Jack Horner	28.50
7¼"	Meakin. Football scene	30.00
7¼"	Red Riding Hood Meets the Wolf.	38.50
7¼"	The Dancing Master	22.50
7¼"	The New Pony	25.00
7½"	The Potter's Art	30.00
7½"	See Saw, Margy Daw. Blue	25.00
7¾"	Capitol at Washington	28.00
7¾"	Playing at Lovers	32.50
8"	Bible scene. Samuel before Eli	27.50
8"	Elves. 3-Crown. Germany	27.50

"The Little Bear." 7¼" diam. White with blue transfer $37.00

8"	Fishing Elephant. Staffordshire type	29.50
8"	Golden-crested wrens	25.00

8"	Little Bo Peep	26.50
8"	Mother and Daughter, Dear to Each. With a Love Surpassing Speech. Early Staffordshire, transfer in blue, brown, green and red	45.00
8"	Punctuality	24.50
8"	Rabbit center. Hands in sign language	27.50
8"	Whittington and His Cat	30.00
8"	Young Artist at Easel. H/P	36.50
8"	Young Sergeant	24.00
8"	Youth, woman, child, fowl. Black transfer	35.00
8½"	Red Riding Hood. Late Delft . . .	25.00
8½"	Red Riding Hood Meets the Wolf	28.00

* GLASS

6"	Clock center	28.50
6"	Deer center, frosted	55.00
6"	Elephant center	20.00
6"	Hen and Chicks	25.00
6"	Numbers 1 thru 10 in center . . .	25.00
6"	Rabbit center, frosted rim	35.00
6"	"Sancho Panza and Dapple." Frosted rim	35.00
6"	Star center	22.50
6"	Stork center, frosted rim	35.00
6½"	Dog head center	25.00
6½"	Little Bo Peep. This Little Pig Went to Market, The Hunting Bears, Hey Diddle, Diddle. Iridescent blue	28.50
7"	Centennial	85.00
8"	Child's head. Frosted alphabet around rim	32.50

TIN

5½"	Victoria-Albert	22.50
5½"	Washington center	45.00
6"	Alphabet, numbers	20.00
6"	Old Into Young	20.00
6¼"	Girl on swing	20.00
6¼"	Jumbo	23.50
8"	I Killed Cock Robin	32.00
8"	Robin and Sparrow Verse	24.50
9"	Hey Diddle Diddle	22.00

*Reproduced Item

ADAMS ROSE PATTERN

The Chinaware is decorated with brilliant red roses and green leaves on a white background. It was made by Adams & Son, Circa 1820-1840, in the Staffordshire district of England. A variant of the pattern was made later but the colors are not as brilliant and the background is a darker or 'dirty' white. This type is known as Late Adams Rose pattern and commands less than the price of the early product.

Plate. 10½" diam. Early $165.00

Bowls		
6½". Late	$	55.00
10½". Scalloped edge. Early		400.00
Creamers		
Early		135.00
Late		75.00
Cups and Saucers		
Scalloped edge. Early		120.00
Plain rim. Late		62.50
Pitchers		
7" high. Late		175.00
16" high. Large, about 5 gallons . .		700.00
Plates		
7½". Early		125.00
7½". Late		65.00
9½". Marked "Adams"		150.00
9½". Late		85.00
10". Soup. Early		160.00
10½". Early		165.00
10½". Late		80.00
Sugar Bowls		
6¼" high. Impressed "Wood"		165.00
Late		85.00
Teapots		
5". Late		100.00
8". Early		185.00

ADVERTISING CARDS

Advertising cards or trade cards were a popular means of advertising during the Victorian era. Manufacturers used these black and white and colored cards as a giveaway item with their products.

ADAMS AND WESTLAKE NON-EXPLOSIVE STOVES. The Seven

Wonders of the World

Colossus of Rhodes	$ 2.00
Egyptian Pyramids	2.00
Hanging Garden of Babylon	2.00
Olympus	2.00
Statue of Jupiter	2.00
The Mausoleum	2.00
The Pharos Watchtower	2.00
The Temple of Diana	2.00

"Use Oberne." Hosick & Co's. Linen Soap $2.50

AYERS
"Grandma, See What I Brought You"........................ 1.50
Hair Vigor, Mermaids and Sinking Ship 1.50
Sarsaparilla. Woman with child on shoulder. "Gives health and sunny hours" 1.50
"The Fight for the Standard" 2.25

R. W. BELL CO.
Soapona - Boy and girl leaving church 1.25
Soapona - Boy chasing girl 1.50

BON AMI
"Cats can, but Bon Ami cannot scratch for it lacks grit" 2.50

CLARKS THREAD
"Capitol at Washington" 2.50
"Sunrise in Desert" 2.50

CURTIS DAVIS & CO. Welcome Soap
Boy and girl shaking hands 1.50

Girl and dog	1.50
Girl on knees caressing mother	1.50

DIAMOND DYES
Child dyeing doll and cat 3.25
Girl in hammock. Hold in light for color change.................. 3.50

DOBBINS ELECTRIC SOAP
At first the infant, Mewling and Puking in the nurse's arms 1.85
Judge with hand behind reaching for bar of soap 1.85
"Mere oblivion. Sans teeth, sans eyes, sans taste, sans everything" . 1.85
"The lover sighs like a furnace" .. 1.85

FLEISCHMANN'S YEAST
Birds on fence 1.25

HIGGINS GERMAN LAUNDRY SOAP
Captain and sailor 1.50
Captain and two girls 1.50
Sailor boy and girl 1.50

KENDALL MFG. CO. Soapine Cards
Boy climbing rope held by star ... 1.50
Boy on telephone pole 1.50
Girl with mountain in distance ... 1.50
Sailor in rigging. Dream of home . 1.50
Sailor boy on ship mast.......... 1.50
Train, man and woman walking tracks........................ 2.00
Universal family................ 1.50
Woman hanging laundry 1.75
Woman with bow and arrow 1.75

"Ask For." Western School Shoes. Mfgd. by I. P. Farnum & Co., 240 Madison Ave., Chicago $3.00

DR. KILMER'S REMEDIES - Prompt Parilla

Liver pills - sick pig with owl, monkey and fox 2.50

JAS. S. KIRK & CO., Soapmaker's, Chicago

American Family 2.00
Blue India 1.50
Columbia 1.50
Coronet 1.50
Mottled German 1.50
Queen of the Laundry 1.50
Savon Imperial 1.50
White Celon 1.50
White Russian 1.50

LAZELL'S UNRIVALLED PERFUMES

Mustached cavalier mounted on horse 1.25
Two girls on white horse crossing stream 1.25

PINKERTON'S ORIENTAL COMBINATION COFFEE

John W. Pinkerton & Co. Oriental Coffee & Spice Mills, Zanesville, Ohio. Girl, bird and spider web . . . 2.00
"Potts, Mrs." Sad irons. "Jumbo always carries one in his trunk" . . 3.50

REYNOLDS BROS. SHOES

Frogs Fighting 1.75

THE ROYAL PHARMACEUTIC CO.
Royal Elixir

Miss Forster, Miss Ulmar, Miss St. Maur. "Three Little Maids from School" 4.00
Sallie Williams as "Peep Bo" 3.50
Sallie Williams as "Pitti-Sing" 3.50
Verona Jarbeau as "Yum-Yum" . . . 3.50

UNION CARD CO.

Side-wheeler boat in rough water "Going into Provincetown Harbor, Cape Cod" 3.00

WHITE SEWING MACHINES

"Best in the World" 2.00

ADVERTISING ITEMS

Many companies around the turn of the century used various items to advertise their products. Cards, trays and signs were the most popular. Some firms, such as the Coca Cola Company, have continued this means of advertising today. Other articles employed were special display containers, canisters, store fixtures and small premiums given to the customer.

COCA COLA

Bottles. See BOTTLES
Bottle Opener. Original box . . . . $ 7.50

Case, Carrying. Wood, 6-bottle, 1929 20.00
Case, Wooden. 48-bottle, with lid and latch 100.00
Route Pads 2.00
Ruler 3.50
Sign. Bottle-shape, ceramic, 1950 . . . 30.00
Sign. 3-section cardboard. 42" long. Autumn leaves 55.00
*Thermometer. Tin, bottle-shape, 1923 . . . . 35.00

Trays
1904. St. Louis World's Fair 95.00
1906. 10½ x 13", oval. Relieves fatigue 350.00
1914. Betty tray. Large, oval 125.00
1917. "Elaine." 8½ x 19" 75.00
1917. 4½ x 6" 64.00
1921 . . . . 50.00
1923. Flapper Girl, Rec. 62.50
1925 . . . . 45.00
1927 . . . . 35.00
1929 . . . . 35.00

Coca Cola Tray, 1917. "Elaine," 8½ x 9"
$75.00

1930. Girl in bathing suit	65.00
1932. Girl in yellow bathing suit	55.00
1934. Tarzan	40.00
1935	35.00
1936	30.00
1937. Girl in yellow bathing suit	35.00
1938. Girl, afternoon	25.00
1939. Girl on diving board	25.00
1940. Girl fishing	25.00
1941. Girl on ice skates	28.50
1942	22.50
1943	22.50
1950. Girl with coke in hand	15.00
1956. 13½ x 18½"	12.00
1960	12.00
1961. Flower garden	10.00

PLANTER PEANUTS

Doll, Rag. 20". "Mr. Peanut" . . . . $	24.00
Jar	
Barrel-shape. 12"	125.00
Square, peanut handle	75.00
Serving Set. Tin, one large dish, four	
individuals. Set	12.50
Spoon, Nut. Silverplated	6.00

POSTERS, CIRCUS

"Cody's Pioneer Circus." 14x42"	9.50
"Dale's Animal 3-Ring Circus," 21x28"	9.50
1896 Ringling Bros. Barnum & Bailey	
"Landing of Columbus" Theme . . .	100.00
1908 Barnum & Bailey	75.00
1927 Ringling Bros. Barnum & Bailey	40.00
Von Bros. "3 Ring Wild Animal	
Circus," 14x42"	9.50

SIGNS

American Navy. Canvas, 23x57".	
Dark blue and yellow	60.00
Armour. 3-section cardboard.	
40x75". Multicolors	60.00
Bull Durham. Cardboard, 14x22".	
People in 1900 attire & package . .	28.50
Bunte Candy. Cloth banner, 30x67",	
blue and gold	35.00
Butcher's. Cast iron. Saw, knife,	
cleaver. 32" long	85.00
DeLaval Cream Separator. Tin,	
25x36". Original frame	200.00
Devilish Good Cigars. 9¾ x 13¾".	
Original hanging chain. 3	
toddlers, box of cigars	100.00
Lydia Pinkham Portrait. Cardboard,	
22x31"	50.00
Moxie. Old house with 3 Palmer Cox	
Brownies. Case of Moxie. 14x22".	
C. 1900	125.00

Mr. Esquire. "You Saw it in Esquire"
$10.00

Tuxedo Tobacco. Cardboard,	
14x22". Picture of early auto,	
package & clothing. C. 1920	27.50

TRAYS

Beer

1900. Pabst. 12x17". Factory	
scene	45.00
1914. Eagle Breweries. Girl, oval .	40.00
ABC Lager	38.00
King's Bohemian	38.00
King's Pure Malt. N/P	29.50
Ruhstaller's early vintage auto	
with two girls in back seat	60.00

Change

DeLaval Cream Separators. Little	
boy, mother and cows	40.00
Fairy Soap	22.50

Moxie. 6". Lady with violets	35.00
Nugrape. 1920	28.50
Sears, Roebuck & Co., Chicago	25.00
Store in Penna. Girl in wheatfield carrying stocks	30.00
Whiterock. Nude on rock	55.00

MISCELLANEOUS

Alarm Clock. Red Goose Shoes. Ornate, metal case	35.00
Ash Tray. "Goodrich Tires." Glass tray, rubber tire rim	12.50
Bookmark. "Borden's Malted Milk." 1906	3.00
Cake Pan. "Swansdown Cake Flour," dated 1923	6.00
Calendar. "Budweiser." 1941	10.00
Canister, Store. Tiger Tobacco. Large, round	50.00
Clock. "Whitman's Chocolate." Wall-type, metal	125.00
Cradle, Tin. "Kleinert's Water Proof Baby Pants." 7½ x 8½ x 12½"	75.00
Display Rack. "Smith Brothers Cough Drops." Tin	50.00
Fan. "Bissell's Carpet Sweeper." Paper and wood	7.50
Knife, Pocket. "Falstaff" 1870-1970	4.50
Medicine Cabinet, Patent. "Mungon's Homeopathic Remedies." Tin and glass	185.00
Mirror, Pocket. "Bright Bird's Eye Tobacco"	15.00
Pin Back. 7/8" metal. "Ford"	3.00
Pitcher. "Burnett's White Satin Gin." Pottery	12.50
Plate. 8". "Union Pacific Tea Company." Tin	20.00

*Reproduced Item

AGATA GLASS

A glass with spots or blotches of a different shade or color. The mottled effect was produced by applying alcohol to clear or cranberry glass before it was tempered.

Bowls

3" high	$1500.00
4½" high. Handled	1800.00
5" high. Acid finish	1600.00
Finger. Mottled	1100.00
Celery	1350.00
Cruet. Mottled	1250.00
Dish, Tricorn. Folded sides, 1¼" high, 5" side diam.	1200.00

Pitchers

| 6¾" high. Square mouth | 3500.00 |
| Milk. Rich rose shading to pale | |

Bowl. 5" high. Acid finish....$1600.00

pink. Gold and blue mottling, applied, hollow, reeded Agata handle	3000.00
With 3 tumblers. Set	5250.00
Sugar Bowl. 4½" high	2000.00

Toothpick Holders

Crimped top	950.00
Square top	450.00
Trefoil top	550.00
Tumbler	750.00
Vase. 4½" high, 3½" diam. Pinched sides, frilly top, blue mottling	1200.00
Whiskey	875.00

AKRO AGATE GLASS

The Akro Agate Company was formed in 1911, first as jobbers selling marbles made by the Navarre Glass Marble Specialty Co. to chain stores and wholesalers.

In 1914 the owners moved from near Akron, Ohio to Clarksburg, W. Va. where cheap labor and a plentiful supply of natural gas were available. They opened a factory known as The Akro Agate Co. for production of marbles and continued in profitable operation until 1929.

In 1932 the company diversified and started making bowls, ash trays, flower pots, etc., in green, red and blue onyx. Operations continued successfully until 1948. Finally, because of the lack of profits, the firm was dissolved and the factory and equipment were sold in 1951.

| Ash Tray. Square, cobalt and white..$ | 5.00 |
| Bowl. 5" long, 3" wide. Green Slag. Raised flower decor | 18.50 |

142

Basket. 6" long, med. blue, in metal
frame. 4 scroll feet $25.00

Child's Set. 28 pieces - 6 each cups, saucers, octagonal bowls, plates, sugar and teapot, with lids. Set . . .	45.00
Cigarette Holder	12.50
Creamer. Jade green, small	15.00
Cup and Saucer. Orange and white . .	18.50
Dish. Leaf-shaped, orange, blue	7.50
Jar. Covered. "Mexicali," Sombre Ru lid, pumpkin and white. 4½" high, 3" diam.	30.00
Lamp. 14" high, brown and cream . . .	42.50
Match Holder. Horn of Plenty. Orange and white	17.50

Planters
5½" long, 3" wide. Red and white, leaf and blossom decor	15.00
3x3¼x6". Ivory metal stand, ribbed light orange, darker leaves, cream-colored flowers. Signed	18.00
Souvenir. Watkins Glen. Shell-shaped, white with orange	12.50
Sugar. Child's. Green	6.50
Toothpick Holder. Urn-shaped, blue and white	8.50

Tumblers
Green and white	18.50
Toy size	5.00

Vases
3¼" high. Green and white, floral design	15.00
4½" high. Pink, orange and white. Lily design	20.00

ALMANACS

The almanac was consulted religiously by
people of this country in the 18th and 19th
centuries as a guide to daily activities. Crops
were planted when the phase of the moon
was considered proper. Family activities and
outings were planned by using the almanac.
Almanacs after 1880 are fairly common and
sell for approximately $3.50 to $6.50 each.

1776--North American Almanac, Samuel Sterns . . . . $	35.00
1783--Bickerstaff's New England Almanac, Norwich	30.00
1791--N. Strong, Almanac, Hartford .	24.00
1794--The New England Almanack by Nathan Daboll, New London	20.00
1796--Nehemiah Strong's Almanac, Hartford	20.00
1797--Hagerstown Town & Country Almanack, First Edition	75.00
1805--New England Almanac by Nathan Daboll, New London . .	25.00
1808--New England Almanac by Nathan Daboll, New London . .	25.00
1808--The Virginia Farmer's Almanac by Benjamin Bates, Richmond	27.50
1810--New England Almanac by Nathan Daboll	20.00
1811--New England Almanac by Nathan Daboll	20.00
1812--Low's, Boston	10.00

National Comic Almanac, 1851 . $7.50

AMBERINA GLASS

Amberina, or "Rose-Amber" ware is a transparent combination of glass shading from ruby to an amber tint. It was first made by the New England Glass Company, Cambridge, Massachusetts in 1883. The trade name "Amberina" was devised by Edward J. Libbey, head official of the company.

The product was made by adding gold to the glass batch in the pot. The glass was amber colored upon being blown or molded to shape. The ruby color was developed when the item was reheated to the correct temperature. The practice of the day was to reheat one end of the article and then the other to produce the ruby-red color. The idea was eventually conceived to heat just one end of an item and to market it as a two-tone glass. A wide market developed and Amberina was in demand for approximately ten years. Today Amberina glass is scarce.

Pitcher. 7½" diam. Bulbous with 4" square top. Clear reeded, applied handle $250.00

Boat Dish. 14" long, Daisy and Button ....$ 240.00

Bottles

Cologne. 8" high, signed "Libbey," pedestaled with stopper......... 425.00

Water. ITP. 8" high.............. 165.00

Bowls

Daisy and Button. 9" square, 2¾" deep......................... 250.00

Diamond Optic. 4½" diam. 110.00

Diamond Quilted. 8" diam. 200.00

Finger. D.Q., with plate 150.00

Fluted, applied handles 175.00

Punch. 11¼" diam. 650.00

Punch. Covered, 13" high, ovid, large ITP, reeded finial 550.00

Ruffled. 7" diam., signed "Libbey" 250.00

Swirled. Ribbed body, 7" diam., 3" high. Applied gold 325.00

Butter Dish. Covered, glass insert . . . 250.00
Butter Pat. Daisy and Button design . 75.00

Candlesticks. 10" high, pair 175.00
Carafe. 6" high. Panelled, bulbous
  body, 4 dimples, applied amber
  rigaree at shoulder. Fuchsia, N. E.
  Glass Co. 325.00
Celery Vases
  4¼" high. Deep Fuchsia 150.00
  4½" high. Diamond Quilted.
  Brown scalloped, square top 225.00
  5" high. Octagon rim, Diamond
  Quilted 195.00
  6¼" high. Mt. Washington, square
  top, Diamond Quilted 275.00
  6½" high. Three amber feet form
  end of leaf sprays around bulbous
  base. Crimped top, side rigaree . . 250.00
  Plain 150.00
Creamers
  Inverted Thumbprint. Clear handle 175.00
  Miniature tankard 150.00
Cruets
  Baby   Thumbprint.   Original
  stopper 250.00
  Inverted Thumbprint. Original
  stopper, amberina handle 300.00
  4" high. Applied clear glass
  handle, amber stopper 275.00
  7" high. Amber handle, ground
  stopper. Wheeling 300.00
  Plain 200.00
Cups
  Punch. Inverted Thumbprint 125.00
  Punch. Baby Inverted Thumbprint,
  clear applied handle 100.00
  Punch. Set of six 650.00
Decanter
  Large 400.00
  Wine. Ruffled top, applied clear
  handle, cut stopper 245.00
Epergne. Bowl 7½" diam., center
  flower holder 7" high. 8¼"
  overall ht. Fuchsia color app.
  one-half way down. Signed
  "Libbey" in pontil 950.00
Ice Bucket. 6½" diam., 3½" high.
  Fuchsia color. N. E. Glass Co. 350.00
Lamp. Miniature, with shade 325.00
Mug. Handled 95.00
Mustard Pot. Pewter top 150.00
Pitchers
  7" high. Inverted Thumbprint,
  applied handle, bulbous 190.00
  Milk. 8" high, Inverted Thumbprint 245.00
  Syrup. Silver collar & handle, deep
  coloring 275.00
  Water. Blown, ruffled top, clear
  reeded handle 300.00

Water. Inverted Thumbprint 250.00
Water. Inverted Thumbprint, with
  six matching tumblers. Set 650.00
  Water. Swirl pattern 260.00
  Water. 11" high, enameled 250.00
Plates
  7" 80.00
  7", expanded diamond 150.00
  9½", floral decor 125.00
Salt and Pepper Shakers. Tall,
  slender, pewter tops. Pair 175.00
Salt, Master. 1¼" high, 3½" diam.,
  on pedestal, ruffled edge 95.00
Salt Shakers
  Enamel decor 95.00
  ITP, pewter top 85.00
Sauces
  4". Diamond Quilted. Early coloring with dark ruby shading to
  base. New England Glass Co. 82.50
  4¼" diam. 75.00
  5" square. Daisy and Button 65.00

Punch Bowl. 11¼" diam., 6½" deep.
  Red to yellow base $750.00

Shade. Flared, ruffled 175.00
Sherbet 100.00
Spooner. Diamond Quilted. Mt.
  Washington 175.00
Sugar Bowl 225.00
Sugar Bowls and Creamers
  Amber reeded handles, square
  tops 300.00
  Melon ribbed 225.00
Sugar Shaker. ITP. Pewter top 175.00
Toothpick Holders
  Daisy and Button 150.00
  Diamond Quilted 160.00
  Square top 150.00
  Trefoil 185.00
Tumblers
  Baby Inverted Thumbprint 75.00
  Diamond Quilted, ground pontil . . 95.00

Enameled flower decor..........	85.00
Expanded diamond	115.00
Inverted Thumbprint	85.00
Juice. Inverted Thumbprint	125.00
Lemonade	100.00
Swirl pattern..................	125.00

Vases

2¼" high. ITP, bulbous	100.00
4½" high. Signed Libbey	275.00
5" high. Lily shape. Plated holder by "Tufts, Boston." 7½" overall ht. Swirl pattern..................	175.00
6"high. Hobnail	165.00
6½" high. D.Q., bulbous	135.00
6½" high, 3¾" diam. Reverse ITP. New England Glass Co...........	165.00
7" high. Jack-in-the-Pulpit	125.00
9" high. Ribbed, 3-pour top	225.00
10¼" high. Jack-in-the-Pulpit. Swirl pattern, fuchsia to amber ...	300.00
12" high. Tulip top, bulbous bottom. ITP	225.00
15" high. Fluted top, pedestal base	285.00
16" high. Jack-in-the-Pulpit. Libbey	500.00
Whiskey Glass	135.00

AMBERINA GLASS [PLATED]

Plated Amberina has a fiery opalescent [white] lining in addition to the usual amberina characteristics of amber blending cranberry. Another characteristic is the vertical ribbing. It was a product of the New England Glass Company, East Cambridge, Massachusetts.

A cased Wheeling glass of similar nature has an opaque white lining but does not show opalescence when held to light. Neither does it have the vertical ribbing.

Bowl. 8" diam., 3½" high	$6000.00
Cup, Punch	2800.00
Dish. Oblong with 4 feet	5000.00

Pitchers

3¾" high, 3-scalloped top	3500.00
6" high. Milk	4000.00
9" high	6000.00

AMPHORA WARE

The dictionary defines amphora as a two-handled vessel with a narrow neck used by the ancient Greeks to hold wine, water, oil, etc. Amphora wares found in antique shops today were made in Austria in the late 1800's. They are usually marked "Amphora" with a crown.

Syrup jug with silverplated underplate
$4000.00

Vase. 9½" high, pink day lilies, green leaves on matte grey ground. Four handles $30.00

Baskets

6x7". Incised and flowers in relief. Predominately blue. Art Deco type .... $ 30.00

7x11". Floral and cupid decor. "Amphora" with crown 150.00

Urn. 12x14". Green glaze, purple highlights, high relief gold flowers. Signed "Amphora" with crown ... 225.00

Vases

8" high. Gold, green with pink leaves, gold pine cones. Signed ... 85.00

9" high. Gold, pink, cream tones. Signed 95.00

9½" high. Gold ground, yellow and green flowers. Artist signed and marked "Amphora" with crown........................ 165.00

10½" high. Tannish-green with lavender and purple seaweed decor. 4-handled, gold trim 175.00

11" high. Scenic, gold tones. Signed 175.00

11" high. Art Deco style. Maroon, white, green, blue floral decor. Signed 105.00

12" high. Bronze coloring with blue tones. Signed 125.00

ANIMAL DISHES [COVERED]

A variety of covered animal dishes have been made of clear, colored and opal [milk glass] glass. Others have been made of pottery - notably Staffordshire types. The bases usually have a slightly depressed, inner rim into which the cover fits.

Rooster. 5" long, blue milk glass, white head $75.00

Cat. 5½". Milk glass, ribbed base
$65.00

Camel. White milk glass .... $ 65.00

Cat. Atterbury. White milk glass 115.00

Cat. Blue milk glass, white head. 5" long 85.00

Chicken on sleigh. White milk glass . 4" long 87.50

Chicks and eggs on nest. White milk glass. 3" 65.00

Chicks with chicken. Round, basket base. Frosted 100.00

Cockatoo. Staffordshire. 3½" 125.00

Cow. Frosted, 6" 75.00

Dogs

Blue milk glass, white head. 5¼" . 95.00

White milk glass. 5" 75.00

Dolphin. Milk glass 42.50

Dove. 4x4¼". Basketweave base, McKee. White milk glass. Signed .. 225.00

Ducks

Clear glass. 6½" 50.00

Frosted. 6½" 60.00

Frosted. 7½" 65.00

*Milk glass, white. 5" 75.00

Sandwich milk glass. 6½". Pair ... 250.00

Eagle. White milk glass. "American Hen"........................ 75.00

Elephant. Clear.................. 25.00

Fish. White milk glass. Atterbury ... 150.00

Hens

Colored glass:

*5". Dark amber 75.00

6½". Honey amber 80.00

Frosted:

6½" 40.00

7" 45.00

Milk Glass:

*5". White.................... 50.00

5". White with blue head 55.00

6½". White	50.00
6½". Blue	62.50
6½". White with blue head, on lacy nest	125.00
6½". Blue with white head	75.00
7". White with lacy nest and caramel-flecked back	150.00
7½". White	100.00
7½". Blue	125.00
Parian:	
7"	165.00
Staffordshire:	
2½". Good coloring	95.00
3½". Vivid coloring	125.00
6½". Brilliant coloring on caramel nest	195.00
7". Yellow nest, green exterior	225.00
8". White, brown basket base	100.00
Lamb. White, hexagon base	55.00

Lions

Blue with white head, on blue picket base	65.00
White. Lacy base. Pat. date Aug. 6, 1889	135.00
Man O' War. White milk glass. 7"	57.50

Moses in Bullrushes. White base, grass design	100.00

Owls

White milk glass. Atterbury	135.00
7". Glass eyes	70.00
Owl and Pussycat. Cheese dish	210.00
Quail. White milk glass. 5"	55.00

Rabbits

*White milk glass. 5"	65.00
White milk glass. Mule-eared	50.00
*Rooster. Milk glass, ribbed base	35.00

Swans

5". Blue glass	95.00
5". White milk glass, closed neck	75.00
6". Staffordshire	225.00
6½". Sandwich clear glass with frosted head and neck	85.00
7". Clear glass. "Pat. applied For" under top	65.00
7". Sandwich milk glass. Pair	275.00
7". White milk glass, open neck, lacy nest	125.00

Turkeys

5", white. McKee	150.00
8". Hen, Staffordshire, white with brown nest	150.00
9". Hen. Leeds	250.00

*Reproduced Item

ART DECO

The Art Deco period was named for an exhibition held in Paris in 1927, "L'Exposition Internationale des Arts Decoratifs." It is a later period than Art Nouveau but sometimes crosses since they are relatively close in time and are often confused with the flowing and sensuous female forms of the earlier era.

The designs of Art Deco are angular and of simple lines. This was the period of skyscrapers, movie idols and the cubist work of Picasso and Legras. It was used for every conceivable object being produced in the 1920's-1930's, including ceramics, furniture, glass and metals, not only in Europe but in America as well.

This is a special market for the "new collector," and the best of these styles is now commanding prices comparable to those of the 18th century pieces.

Pitcher. 5½" high. White ground, blue and gold designs, black handle. "Margaret Clarke," B&C France $45.00

Andirons. Solid brass, square column tapering to step tops	$ 125.00
Arm Chair. 33" high. Maple [tiger eye], brown leather insert, chinese red lacquer in fret work	160.00
Ash Tray. 5½ x 5½". Bronze, footed base, kneeling Egyptian woman	65.00
Bedroom Suite. 3 pieces. Walnut	100.00
Biscuit Jar. 6" high. Spode "Valamour," off white	12.50
Bookends. 6x8". Bronzed metal, nude girl sitting on open book. Signed K&Co. Pair	35.00
Bottle, Perfume. 6" high, crystal	50.00
Bowl. Royal Worcester. Black enamel. H/P red flowers with gold stems, gold edging. 8" square, C 1918	65.00

Candelabra. 15" high. Bronze, three-lite, straight line. Signed E. Hurley 300.00
Cigarette Case and Holder 35.00
Compacts
4", round, sterling 25.00
Enameled. Yellow H/P flowers, black and white border, enameled handled 35.00
Demitasse Set. 4 each, cups and saucers, with creamer and sugar. Geometric pattern of leaves in green, black, platinum on white ground. Marked Empire Ivory Ware. Grosvenor pattern 50.00
Desk Calendar. 4" high 6-5/8x6-3/8" base, bronze finish, ornate initial in circle. C. 1930 .... 25.00
Dest Set. Bradley Hubbard. Heavy inkwell, paper clip, rocking blotter, triple stamp box 125.00
Lamps
8¾" high. Gold metal nude, afghan hound. Hobnail glass shade 47.00
9½" high. Metal, nude lady, pond, 4 swans 49.00
10½" high. Henitz, bronze, mushroom-shaped shade with silver decor 150.00
11" high. Bronze, dancing girl on marble plinth. Brass shade, crystal prisms. Signed Braver Austria 340.00
13" high. Table. Bronzed metal with 3 standing nudes. Arms raised, holding globe-shaped marigold shade with geometric sculptured design 100.00
Two nudes, standing, holding large pink satin ball shade. Dated 1927 .... 75.00
Shoe Buckles. 1½" steel backs and clips. Late 1930's. Assorted styles in navy, grey, brown or black silver enamels. Pair............. 5.00
Smoking Set. Double bronze. One side holds cigarettes; other, 3 ashtrays, match box. Sterling trim 35.00
Statues
Dancer. Nude female, 17" high, bronze by H. G. Danzmann....... 300.00
Dancer with Ivory. Bronze by P. Tereszcuk 550.00
Heads. Male and female. Bronze by D. H. Chiparus 1200.00
Skaters. Ivory faces. Bronze, 13x14". Signed Jaquemin 700.00
Sugar Shaker. 5½" high. Creamer 4½" high on pedestal. Hexagon shape. Marked "Made in Japan." Set 13.00

Tape Measure. One side "Century of Progress Chicago 1934." Other, "Hall of Science viewed from the Electrical Bldg." 16.50
Vases
5½" high. Footed, bulbous, bright yellow streaks of rose on deep colored font 35.00
6" high. French Art glass with flared rim. Pear-shaped, enamel blue and yellow stylized pussy willows on clear ground. Signed Goupy 140.00
8½" high. Black Satin 40.00
12" high. "Ruel" signed. Enamel decor 125.00
12" high. Parrot. Allover enamel. Marked "Keramis" and "Made in Belgium." Pair 190.00
Amethyst. Silver & diamond decor 135.00
Metal. Signed, numbered. DeLaven 150.00

ART NOUVEAU

The French term for the "new art" had its beginning in the 1890's and swept the

Lamp. Approx. 20" high, 9" square base. Bronze, signed "Fayral" $350.00

continent and America for almost 40 years. Some of its more recognized artists were Galle', Lalique and Tiffany. But there were other artists of the period, not as proficient or promoted; and knowledgeable collectors are now searching out their works. Art Nouveau can be identified easily by its flowing and sensuous lines, floral forms, insects, and the feminine form. These designs were incorporated on almost everything produced at that time, from art glass to furniture, to silver, to personal objects.

Bookends

Brass. Reclining female, nude, with arched back and flowing hair. Pair .... $ 55.00
Brass. Crazy looking frog in tail-coat, carrying top hat. Pair 45.00
Bronze. 6¼" high. Nude girl. Pair 37.50

Boxes

Covered. Unger Bros. Sterling 125.00
Round. 3x5", pewter design on top. Tomato red, acid finish. Signed M. Hess 85.00
Button Hook. 6½" long. Sterling 16.50
Candlestick. 10" high, flowers with intertwined stems. Ornate, silver-plated 16.50
Chamberstick. 6" high. Battery operated, bronze finish. "Candle" Pat. 1915 .... 25.00
Dish. Pewter. Nude. Signed Kazserzim 65.00

Figurines

Girl, Dancing. 9" high, bronze, ivory face and hands 225.00
Girl. White, blue drape, platinum trim. German 150.00
Siamese Dancer. 15" high, ivory hands, face, midriff. 2 colored stones in head piece. Electrified base, onyx pedestal 300.00
Fountain Pen, Lady's. Sterling, floral decor 10.00
Handbag. Black velvet, silver frame . 25.00
Hand Mirror. Sterling. Unger Bros. Sculptured woman's head with flowing tresses, irises, swans and rising sun 85.00

Jewelry

Pendant. Brittania metal. Lady with flowing hair 7.50
Pin. 1" diam. Sterling front, girl's face, flowing hair.............. 12.50

Jewelry Boxes

Hinged. 3½" long, four feet. Girl on lid, windmill, etc. Orig. lining 15.00
Ring. Goldplated, pink lining 15.00

Lamps

11" high. Gilded nymphet supporting pedestal with ball shade of cased spatter glass in red, yellow and white 45.00
13" high. Nude female lying on dolphin in waves, hand holds place for shade 35.00
15" high. Cobra-shaped, jeweled . 175.00
16" high. Red lustre glass in bronze holder shape of flowers, leaves and vines 185.00
18" high. Bronzed base with 3" medallion of woman's head. 10" diam. art glass shade, amber mottling on yellow ground 150.00
Cobra head. Jeweled, large figure of child holding onto head of cobra. Gold gilt, art glass shade. Signed 135.00
Letter Opener. Figural dog head 15.00
Letter Holder. 4½ x 5½". Large, two sections. 4 ladies, side profiles with long flowing hair, long stemmed, floral decor.......... 45.00
Stamp Case. Sterling 12.00
Tea Strainer. Pierced corner, fits over cup. 7" long 25.00

Trays

Bronze. 4x8". Girl watching sunrise. Signed Maxim 125.00
Crumb Set. Brass, embossed gargoyle, horn of plenty, sheaf of wheat 25.00
Pin. 6x7". Oval, sterling 16.50
Sterling. 3x5". Flowing-haired woman, flowers in relief 35.00

Vases

3½" high. Rozenberg, eggshell ... 650.00
8" high. Bulbous, stylized flowers on light/dark blue panels. Artist initialed. Royal Doulton. Pair 75.00
8½" high. Robin. Porcelain 85.00
9½" high. Metal girl with flowing hair, flowers, handled.......... 55.00
10½" high. Panelled blue opalescent to emerald green. Heavy French enameled poppies 85.00
10½" high. Lady with flowing hair. Signed Asch, Royal Bonn mark 165.00
22" high. Bronzed 35.00

Wax Letter Seal. Sterling $30.00

AURENE GLASS

A type of art glass invented by Frederick Carder, an Englishman. The name "Aurene" was bestowed upon the glass by the originator from the Latin "Aureus" - a Roman gold coin. Aurene glass has a smooth uniform iridescent goldlike surface, although some is either silvery or dark blue. It was manufactured by the Steuben Glass Works from about 1904 to 1930. Most items were permanently marked in ink under glaze with the word "Aurene", although some items were marked with paper labels only.

Sherbet. 4½" high. Signed ...$175.00

Atomizer. 2" high, 6" diam., low-footed ....$	125.00
Baskets	
8x8". Flared top, iridescent gold and blue, applied handle	350.00
Miniature, handled	225.00
Biscuit Jar. Straight sides, gold, blue and red colors. Signed	425.00
Bottles	
6" high. Ruffled and stretched orange, red, blue, green highlights	250.00
6½" high. Blue color, blossom stopper	325.00
Cologne. 6½" high, irid. peacock blue. 2½" diam. pedestal base. Original stopper	425.00
Cologne. Gold	250.00
Perfume. 4½" high, signed	375.00

Bowls	
2" high, 7" diam., blue, footed, folded-in rim. Signed, numbered..	240.00
2½" high, 7" diam., signed	250.00
4" high, 9½" diam. Peacock blue. Flared, collar base. Steuben	550.00
4½" high. Rose bowl. Pinched top	375.00
10" diam. Signed	425.00
12" diam., 3 feet. Signed	450.00
Finger, with tray. Signed	450.00
Candlesticks	
4" high, futuristic shape. Signed ..	150.00
7" high, gold, signed, Steuben....	250.00
8" high, blue twist. Signed. Pair ..	600.00
10" high, gold, signed	350.00
Blue, twisted stem. Signed	350.00
Centerpieces	
10¼" diam., 1½" high. Signed ...	175.00
12" diam., gold.................	325.00
13" diam., 3" high, deep blue, roll-over rim	400.00
Champagne......................	150.00
Compote. 8¼" high, 6" diam., blue..	275.00
Cordial, 5", stemmed, gold.........	140.00
Cordial Set. 10¼" decanter with six 2¼" cordials. Swirl pattern on bottle and neck, flaring lip. Gold. Set	575.00
Cup, Sherbet, with Plate. Signed	145.00
Cuspidor, Ladies'. Miniature, gold, signed	275.00
Dishes	
Bonbon. Iridescent peacock blue .	175.00
Bonbon. 1¾" diam., signed "Aurene 532" and "Fred Carder" .	200.00
Fruit. Clear to blue. Signed Steuben.....................	200.00
Nut, Master. 4¾" diam., 1½" deep	150.00
Goblet. Twisted stem, signed.......	155.00
Lamp Shades	
2x5". Signed Steuben. Pair.......	125.00
5". Bell-shaped, green and white leaf, clear outside	75.00
7", gold, signed	85.00
16" high, 10½" wide. Brown Steuben. Brass base. Original	795.00
Parfait. 4½" high. Signed "F.Carder"	260.00
Plate, Sherbet. Calcite, gold........	125.00
Salt. 1½" high, gold color, signed ...	150.00
Sugar and Creamer. Steuben gold. Both signed and numbered, 756 [Rare]	550.00
Tazza. Footed, double twisted stem, scalloped edge. Signed..........	500.00
Vases	
3" high. Irid. silver and gold with green tendrils and lily-pad leaves. Signed	225.00
3½" high. Flared top, 3 feet......	265.00
4¼" high. Irid. blue, scalloped top	300.00

5" high. Tri-cornered, iridescent ..	225.00
5" high. Signed and nod	275.00
5¼" high. Blue irid., panelled body, flaring rim. Signed	285.00
5½" high. Bell-shaped, signed ...	295.00
5½" high. Fluted, flared. Pencil-thin base. Signed	285.00
5½" high. Footed, ruffled top. Small white blossoms and green vines on irid. amber ground......	325.00
6" high. Jack-in-the-Pulpit. Rose overtones	375.00
6" high. 3 stems in blue	485.00
6¼" high, 5½" widest diam. Shell-shaped body of mottled rose, green and gold glass with iridescent sheen	350.00
6½" high. Paperweight vase, #2622, irid., signed	425.00
7" high. Opaque white glass with red, gold and irid. markings......	385.00
8" high. Deep blue, transparent top, lighter blue swirl. Signed	350.00
8¼" high. Gold, leaf design at top	425.00
9" high. Gold, lily-pad decor	375.00
10" high. Brilliant blue, scalloped top	400.00
10" high. Flared, ruffled top. Signed Steuben	475.00
13½" high. Peach color, green trumpet-shaped decoration, finely lined with red	500.00
Miniature. Jack-in-the-Pulpit. Signed	250.00
Wine. 4½" high. Gold, twisted stem. Signed	160.00

AUSTRIAN WARE

During the late 19th and early 20th centuries, much fine porcelain and pottery were produced in Austria. Although Carlsbad [known as Karlsbad after World War I when

Bowl. Open, 5¾" diam. Handpainted border of yellow roses. Artist signed
$16.50

Cup and Saucer. White with pink roses, green leaf trim. Imperial China. $12.50

Austria became a part of Czechoslovakia] was the center of the industry, other factories existed.

These factories were either held or supported by American monies; thus their wares were produced mainly for export to the United States. The U. S. firm of Lazarus and Rosenfeldt imported large amounts of porcelain from Czechoslovakia after World War I, marked "Victoria."

Cache Pot. China, 6½" diam., 3¼" high. Handled, fluted, small sprays in pink, lustre touches, inside clay liner ....$	25.00
Dresser Set. 4 pieces. Bluebird underglaze. Signed	35.00
Hair Receivers	
Gold scroll edging. Tiny rose decor. Victoria	13.50
Rust to yellow with roses. Victoria	17.50
Plates	
9½". H/P pink, yellow roses, tinted background. Signed	15.00
Sardine. Pink floral, sardine handles. Marked Victoria........	16.00
Salt and Pepper Shakers. Hand-painted florals. Pair............	12.00
Vases. 8¼" high. Floral decor on medallion. Green and white. Pair.	100.00

AUTOGRAPHS

Adams, John Quincy. Autograph letter signed January 4, 1822, as Sec. of State, to Langdon Cheves, Pres. of the Bank of the U.S. concerning the President's commissions to Cheves and four others as directors of the bank ...$	350.00
Alexandra. Consort of Edward VII. Autograph letter signed January	

15, 1885, on Sandringham letter-
head, re--personal matters. 4pp ..   35.00
Bunche, Ralph J. Autograph signed
first day cover honoring the U.N.
Secretariat 12.50
Carreno, Teresa. Autograph original
Elliot and Fry cabinet photo
1891, by the vibrant 19th century
pianist. Framed 75.00
Caruso, Enrico. Autograph original
profile, pen-and-ink, self-carica-
ture, signed London, 1904. Framed   365.00
Cowl, Jane. Autograph letter signed
December 10, 1930, on Maxine
Elliott Theatre letterhead giving
advice about going on the stage.
2pp.........................   15.00
Darwin, Charles. Autograph letter
signed to "my dear Hooker"
[his collaborator, Joseph Dalton
Hooker]......................   425.00
Debussy, Claude. Scarce autograph
bars of music from the first act
prelude of Pelleas et Melisande
signed January 1917. Framed 1750.00
Du Maurier, Gerald. Original Ellis
and Walery cabinet photograph
signed on the mount 15.00
Eisenhower, Dwight D. Autograph
White House letter signed Nov. 1,
1956, to an admirer. "A letter like
yours is a heart-warming experience for me." Framed 265.00
Eisenhower, Mamie Doud. Autograph thank you letter signed Oct.
28, 1951, with envelope post-
marked S.H.A.P.E. Paris. 2pp 35.00
George III. Autograph signature
framed with engraved portrait in
royal robes 100.00
Goldsborough, Admiral L.M. Autograph greeting signed, "Rear
Admiral, U.S. Navy, by the des-
troyer of the Confederate Fleet" ..   85.00
Harding, Warren G. Autograph
original Edmonston photograph,
probably as President, signed and
inscribed 137.50
Hughes, Langston. Autograph, 4½"
signature and greeting framed
with portrait 85.00
Huxley, Thomas H. Autograph third
person letter, July 25, accepting
an invitation 10.00
Ingersoll, Robert, G. Autograph
letter signed Feb. 10, 1899, 2pp
8vo..........................   17.50
Johnson, Andrew. Autograph large
signature and framed portrait 125.00

La Guardia, Fiorello. Autograph
unusual portrait framed, signature   75.00
MacArthur, Douglas. Autograph
typed thank you letter signed,
framed in green/gilt with characteristic photo in uniform 150.00
May, Charles H. autograph sympa-
thetic letter signed on Mayo Clinic
letterhead, October 7, 1931,
advising a prospective patient ...   125.00
Menchen, H. L. Autograph typed
letter signed Oct. 25, 1948, to a
journalist, "Quacks always flour-
ish amazingly in this great Chris-
tian Republic." 1p 50.00
Monet, Claude. Autograph, early
long 27-line note signed. The
dreary weather prevents his
finishing the floral today. Will
come Wednesday with as many
canvasses as he can carry.
Framed, with reproduction of his
portrait by Renoir 475.00
Nixon, Richard. Signed portrait cut
from a magazine, probably as
Vice President 25.00
Paderewski, Ignace Jan. Autograph
music bars signed Dec. 15, 1909,
framed with portrait 135.00

Pope Pius XII

Roosevelt, Eleanor. Typed letter
signed Nov. 4, 1947, framed with
Pach Bros. photo 75.00
Roosevelt, Franklin D. Original
Harris and Ewing Presidential
photograph inscribed and signed.
Framed 175.00
Roosevelt, Theodore. Clear signature, Nov. 4, 1907, as President ..   125.00
Shaw, George Bernard. Early letter
signed June 22, 1891, as music
critic, asking to be removed from
a press list. Framed 295.00
Sims, Admiral William S. Letter
signed on U.S. Naval Forces
letterhead Oct. 26, 1918, to the
Lord Mayor of London. 1p 12mo ..   22.50
Stanbury, Henry. Letter signed on
Attorney General's office letterhead, Nov. 21, 1867 by Pres.
Johnson's Atty. Gen. who re-
signed to be his chief counsel in
the impeachment...............   85.00

Stevenson, Adlai. Signature on
Bolshoi Ballet letterhead 85.00
Taft, William Howard. Cryptic White
House letter signed, Jan. 6, 1910,
to U. S. Circuit Judge J. W.
Warrington on court matters.
Framed in silver/blue tones with
engraving 200.00
Thibaud, Jacques. Royal Albert Hall
concert program boldly signed ... 12.50

Vanderbilt, William K. Autograph
letter with "On board Eagle"
letterhead signed Jan. 4, 1921, by
the yachtsman, financier 35.00
Wagner, Richard. Autograph letter
signed April 13, '77. Framed in
gilt/brown tones with profile
etching. Trans. 750.00
Warren, Earl. Typed greeting signed
on Supreme Court card. Framed .. 100.00
Wilkins, Sir Hubert. Autograph
greeting signed on large card 7.50

AUTO ITEMS AND LITERATURE

The motor carriage developed into the
automobile between 1900 and 1910. More
than 200 different makes were marketed
in the past. Most have been consigned to the
junk yard but a number of accessories, such as
horns, lights, name plates, license plates, etc.,
remain for the collector of automobiliana.

Advertisement. Goodrich & Palmer
Tires. 26x30" ad of "Babette."
1903..........................$ 27.50
Audel's Automobile Guide, 1915 ... 25.00
Auto and Truck Wiring Manual.
1912-20. Blueprints, 678 pages ... 40.00
Auto Blue Book. New England,
1917.......................... 18.50
Auto Green Book. A.L.A., Vol. 1,
1922.......................... 15.00
Auto Green Book. New York and
New England, 1922 .... 15.00

License Plate. Penna. 1915 ....$15.00

Front Cover, "Cole Sets World's Record"
$25.00

Auto Green Book, 1926 .... 15.00
Automobile Handbook. Putnam's
1918. Brokaw & Storr 17.50
"Automobile Joker." 1906, illus.
booklet of auto jokes 20.00
Carbide Tank. For running board.
Newly brass plated 125.00
Clock, Dash. Stevens Duryea. Brass,
bevelled case, 8-day, key wind.
Hoffecker Co., Boston. Running ... 50.00
Emblems
  Buick. Chipped 10.00
  Chevrolet. Chipped 10.00
  Dodge 12.50
  Dort. Chipped 10.00
  Essex 25.00
  Graham Bros. Chipped 12.00
  Hupmobile. Chipped 12.00
  Maxwell 28.50
  Nash 25.00
  Studebaker. Discolored 12.50
Gas Tank. For 1910 Buick Roadster .. 100.00
Gear Shift Handle. Banded agate.
1½" diam...................... 18.50
Gear Shift Knob. Marblized orange,
brown and white 10.00
Headlights, Cadillac. 1915, pair 165.00
Horns
  Brass English. "King of the Road."
  No. 34 .... 125.00

Brass, flexible tube, no bulb	85.00
Brass. 21" long. India [modern] . .	35.00
Old. Bulb type.	125.00
Old. Plunger type.	30.00
Jack. Ford Model "T"	22.50

Lamps

"Dietz Eureda." 7½" high, clear lens in front, red glass in rear	50.00
Driving. Brass	100.00
Everready Mazada Kit. Original bulbs. C. 1910.	10.00
Ford Model "T". Black. Pair	75.00
Hupmobile. "Adlake Balanced Draft." 8½" high, original brackets	48.50
Interior, electric car. Brass, 2¾x5". Pair	125.00

License Plates

1910, 1912, 1914, enameled. Each	10.00
Calif. World's Fair. 1939, pair	25.00
Maine, 1948	6.00

Magazines

"Automobile Engineering." 5 vols. [II thru VI], 1920	50.00
"Automotive Oddities." Amusing, true data of the industry since its beginning. 1932, 40 pages	15.00
Manual, Owner's. Studebaker. Big 6 and Special 6, 1923	14.50
Magneto. Ford, Model "N", for 4-cylinder engine	75.00

Motor Meters

1916 Boyce	35.00
1916 Dodge	40.00
Midget, Boyce. Working	22.50
Parasol. Touring car accessory. Silk, yellow with green trim	18.00
Poster. Kaufmann's. Early auto accessoiries. 1910, 22x28"	19.50
Pump, Tire. Marked Ford, new base .	20.00

Radiator Cap Ornaments

Bird. Large, winged	30.00
Buick. Blue glass	35.00
Whippet. Mounted on walnut base.	27.50
Radiator Emblem. Mack truck, chrome	25.00
Road Map of New York State in Soconyland. 1927	7.50
Robe, Car. Squirrel on branch in perfect condition	50.00

Sales Catalogues

Chevrolet Trucks. About 1922, 22 pages.	10.00
Franklin Car. 1918. Hard cover, 77 pages.	30.00
Keystone Car Equipment. Bus, streetcar. Interior lights, bells,	

signs. 166 pages	12.50
Oldsmobile folder. 1923	7.50
White Motor Cars. App. 1919. 18 pages, glossy, colored illustrations	25.00
Seat, Leather. 1922 Packard Opera Coupe. Set.	100.00
Spark Coil. For early car	60.00
Spark Plugs. 1906 Model T. Mounted on wood block. Set of four	16.00
Steering Wheel. 1925 Durant	55.00

Tail Lights

1928. Red, says "Dodge"	18.50
Model T. Brass top on 1915 model Pair	35.00
Vases. Used to hold flowers in electric car. Tiffin black satin glass. C. 1920. Pair	57.50

AUTOMOBILES

In 1947 the Antique Automobile Club of America [AACA] devised a system of car classification to assist in the restoration and preservation of old cars. They classify any land motor vehicle [including buses, motorcycles, fire trucks, etc] made prior to 1930 as an authentic antique vehicle.

The Classic Car Club of America [CCCA] recognizes all models from 1925 through 1948 as authentic classics.

Vehicles manufactured from 1948 to 1964 are classified by the Mile Stone Club [MSC] as classics.

Prices are for unrestored, good unrestored and restored. An unrestored vehicle is one that requires considerable rebuilding, but is not a basket case. A good, unrestored is a complete, drivable car, but is in need of cosmetic repairs [paint, upholstery, chrome, etc.] to bring it up to show quality. A point system is used in classifying restored cars for varying degrees of restoration.

The prices listed herein are for vehicles in good, unrestored condition.

Buick. 1908. Model E Runabout	$5000.00
Buick. 1928. Club Sedan	2000.00
Buick. 1942. Formal Sedan	1850.00
Cadillac. 1919	4500.00
Cadillac. 1939. Conv. Sedan V-16 . . .	9500.00
Cadillac. 1946. Model 62 Club Coupe .	750.00
Cadillac. 1961. Coupe DeVille.	450.00
Chevrolet. 1913. Touring Car	2250.00
Chevrolet. 1947. Convertible	850.00
Chevrolet. 1955. Belaire V-8 Hard Top, 2-Door.	800.00
Chevrolet. 1956. Corvette	3400.00
Chevrolet. 1961. Impala 4-Door Hard Top	500.00
Chrysler. 1928. 2-Door Sedan	2000.00

Chrysler. 1932. Imperial, 8-Cylinder,
7-Passenger Sedan 5000.00
Chrysler. 1958. New Yorker, 4-Door,
Hard Top 500.00
Dodge. 1962. 8-80, 4-Door Sedan . . . 450.00
Edsel. 1958. Citation Convertible . . . 1000.00
Edsel. 1960. 2-Door, Hard Top 850.00
Ford. 1920. Touring Car 1500.00
Ford. 1925. Roadster 1850.00
Ford. 1929. Roadster. Pick Up 2000.00
Ford. 1936. Convertible Sedan 5000.00
Ford. 1942. Station Wagon V-8 . . . . . 1850.00
Ford. 1957. Thunderbird Convertible 3000.00
Ford. 1959. Convertible Sunliner 750.00
Ford. 1962. Galaxie 500.00
Hudson. 1946. Super 6 Brougham . . . 800.00
Hudson. 1950. Pace Maker Coupe . . . 550.00
Hudson. 1955. Custom Hornet Sedan 750.00
Jaguar. 1948. Mark V Saloon 2500.00
Jaguar. 1953. SK 120 Coupe 2500.00
Jaguar. 1961. Mark II. 4-Door Sedan. 2500.00
Lincoln. 1928 7-Pass. Touring 12000.00
Lincoln. 1933. V-12 Club Sedan 3500.00
Lincoln. 1941. Coupe Continental . . . 4000.00
Lincoln. 1948. Coupe 4200.00
Lincoln. 1956. Continental Mark II . . . 3500.00
Lincoln. 1959. Mark IV Conv. 1200.00
Mercedes-Benz. 1952. 300 Coupe . . . 4500.00
Mercedes-Benz. 1956. 300 Conv. Sed. 6500.00
Mercedes-Benz. 1961. 190 SL Rdstr. . 2200.00

1905 Franklin. Light Tonneau. High
Point Restoration

Oldsmobile. 1956. 88 2-Door, Hard
Top 700.00
Oldsmobile. 1960. 98 Convertible . . . 700.00
Oldsmobile. 1962. Starfire Coupe . . . 600.00
Packard. 1933. V-12 CLB Sedan 5000.00
Packard. 1940. Custom Super 8 Limo. 2500.00
Packard. 1955. Clipper. 4-Door 700.00
Packard. 1958. 4-Door Sedan 600.00
Plymouth. 1948. Station Wagon 1000.00
Plymouth. 1950. Conv. Coupe 650.00

Plymouth. 1960. Fury, 2-Door, Hard
Top 400.00
Plymouth. 1963. Belvedere. 2-Door,
Hard Top 450.00
Rolls Royce. 1932. Brewster Limo. . . . 6000.00
Rolls Royce. 1940. Wraith. 5-Pass. . . . 4200.00
Rolls Royce. 1947. Silver Wraith
Deville 6500.00
Rolls Royce. 1950. Silver Cloud I.
4-Door 5500.00
Rolls Royce. 1960. Silver Cloud II
Sedan 5000.00
Studebaker. 1947. Starlight Com.
Coupe 750.00
Studebaker. 1953. Champion Regal
Coupe 800.00

MISCELLANEOUS

Fire Engines
1928. Chevrolet 1200.00
1931. Diamond T Pumper 1750.00
1935. Ford Hook and Ladder 1500.00
1944 Mack 1250.00
Trucks
1932. Chevrolet ½-Ton Pick-Up . . . 650.00
1934. Ford V-8 Pick-Up 1000.00
1939. Diamond T ¾-Ton Pick-Up . . 900.00
1940. International 1½-Ton Stake 750.00
1949. Dodge ½-Ton Pick-Up 700.00

BACCARAT GLASS

Baccarat glass was made at Baccarat in
Alsace-Lorraine, France. The factory is
primarily known for producing beautiful
paperweights in the last fifty years of the past
century. Many kinds of fine glassware are also
made.

Atomizer. Blue and clear glass with
original label . . . . $ 50.00

Bowl. "Swirl." Late $32.50

Rose Bowl. 3½" high. Cut enameled in gold, blue and white forget-me-nots
$125.00

Bobeches. Signed, heavy crystal. Pair	25.00
Bottles, Perfume	
3½" high. Pyramid, sphinx stopper. Signed	48.50
4" high, including stopper	32.50
2½ x 4¼". Clear, fancy, open top. Signed "Guerlain, Paris, France, Baccarat, France"	22.00
5½" high	45.00
6" high. Gold stripes, gold star on cut stopper. Signed	60.00
8" high. Original stopper	65.00
8" high. Houbigant, heavy cut, polished crystal. Gold stopper. Signed	72.00
Bowls	
5½". Scalloped edge, swirl design. Footed, signed	65.00
7". Lacy, with matching plate	50.00
7½ x 19". Centerpiece. Amberina swirl in ornate gold color holder. Signed	325.00
8". Cut, intricate pattern, cut edge	125.00
10". Cut from ruby to pale rose glass	300.00
Boxes	
1¾ x 2-1/8 x 3-5/8". Covered, rectangular, swirl glass 'Rose Tiente.' Signed	35.00
Dresser. Silverplated lid. Diagonal amber and diamond point pattern	42.00
Candlesticks	
8" high. Serpents coiling around	

Champagnes. 7" high, engraved. Set of ten	250.00
Compotes	
Etched oak leaves and grapes, gold trim	125.00
Open. 8" diam., amber block pattern. 1890. Signed	160.00
Cordials. Set of six	150.00
Cruet. Amberina swirl	65.00
Cup and Saucer	75.00
Decanters	
8½" high. Lacy, original stopper	65.00
10½" high. Applied fleur-de-lis and scroll work	75.00
Pair, with 12 wines. Set	450.00
Dishes	
Lacy, rectangular, footed	52.50
Relish. 9½", rubina color. Signed	55.00
Rose to light amber, scalloped edge. 3½ x 9½". "Rose Teinte"	47.50
Epergne. 13" high. Single lily	165.00
Goblet. Gold decor, simulated amethyst jewels on crystal glass. 12" high	145.00
Inkwell. Large, clear bowl with 4 deep green leaves, brass top	120.00
Jar	
Ginger. Brass cover and bail, cranberry on frosted. Signed	125.00
Jam. Covered, Amberina swirl. Signed	75.00
Lamps	
Oil. Amberina swirl	65.00
Pharmacy. Swirl. Signed "Pharmacie L. Miller"	95.00
Letter Opener. 9" long, crystal. Signed	30.00
Paperweights	
Concentric canes. 2" diam.	175.00
Kennedy, 1963. Ltd. edition	350.00
Lace background, animal silhouettes. Signed and dated "B 1848"	1000.00
Millefiori. C. 1840	325.00
Washington, George	350.00
Pitchers	
8¼". Diamond quilted pattern. Clear, applied handle	75.00
10¼". Oval, taupe and white mottled	100.00
Shade, Gas Light. Round, 5" high, 6" top opening, 5" opening vase. Vaseline, brilliant diamond point, signed "Baccarat Depose'	55.00
Sugar. Open, footed, clear daisy and leaf design	55.00
Sugar and Creamer. 3 x 3", with 5 x 9" handled tray. Set	65.00
Toothpick Holder	28.50

Tray, Pin	16.50

Tumblers

Blue swirl pattern	25.00
Clear swirl. Footed	25.00
Ruby swirl. With matching 6¼" plate. Signed	72.50
Tumble-Up with Plate. Set	125.00

Vases

5" high. Lacy Baccarat, C. 1870	125.00
6¼" high. Crackle cranberry, footed, signed with label	130.00
6½" high. Cameo cut, gold-washed metal base. Pair	165.00
11½" high. Cameo cut, cranberry flowers and leaves, gold trim. Pair	325.00

BANKS, GLASS

Bear. 8" long	$ 6.50
Beehive Coke Oven. Green	10.00
Charlie Chaplin. 3-¾"	35.00

Food Bottle Bank. "Lincoln Pure Fruit Flavored Orange Syrup." Pint . . $12.50

House. "Save with Pittsburgh Paints." 3 high	12.00
Independence Hall. 7½"	75.00
Liberty Bell. Carnival glass	20.00
Liberty Bell. Tin screw base marked "Robinson & Loeble, Phila., Pa." 5" high. Made in amber and milk glass	30.00

BANKS, MECHANICAL

Banks which display some type of action when a coin is inserted are known as mechanical banks. The majority of the approximately 300 different known banks were manufactured between 1850 and 1935. The retail prices listed herein are for unrepaired banks in good condition and will vary upwards or downwards, depending upon the individual condition of the bank. For further information and prices regarding old mechanical banks contact Stephen A. Steckbeck, Collector, 200 W. Superior St., Ft. Wayne, Indiana 46802.

*Acrobat	$ 650.00
Afghanistan	650.00
Always Did 'Spise' a Mule. Darky sitting on bench in front	150.00
*Always Did 'Spise' a Mule. Darky riding mule	150.00
*Artillery. 4-sided block house	150.00
Artillery. 8-sided block house	1200.00
Atlas	650.00
*Bad Accident	300.00
Bamboula Bank	300.00
Bank of Education & Economy	500.00
Bank Teller	3000.00
Bear. Slot in chest, no lettering	350.00
*Bear with paws around tree	200.00
*Bill E. Grin. Bust	350.00
*Bird on Roof of Church	500.00
Bowery	3000.00
Bowing Man in Cupola	1500.00
*Boy on Trapeze	300.00
*Boy robbing bird's nest	450.00
Boy Scout Camp	500.00
*Boys Stealing Watermelons	390.00
Breadwinner	2000.00
British Lion. Tin	500.00
*Buffalo butting	560.00
Building, small, 8-sided [Snap-It]	150.00
*Bull and Bear	2000.00
Bureau. Wood	200.00
Bureau. Wood, patent applied for	400.00
Butting Ram	700.00
*Cabin	80.00
Calamity or Football	1200.00
Called Out	3000.00
Calumet Bank. Tin	100.00
*Camera or Kodak	1500.00

*Cannon, U.S. & Spain	800.00
*Cat and Mouse	300.00
Cat jumps for mouse [Springing Cat]	2000.00
Chandlers Bank	300.00
Chief Big Moon	350.00
*Chimpanzee	700.00
Chinaman in Boat	3000.00
Chinaman reclining on log [Reclining Chinaman]	520.00
Chocolat Menier. Tin	100.00
Circus	1200.00
*Circus Ticket Collector W/Barrel	450.00
Clever Dick. Tin	850.00
Clock Registering, dime	200.00
Clowns, 3, w/elephant on tub	300.00
Clown & Dog. Tin	1000.00
Clown Bank. Tin	200.00
Clown on Bar. Iron and tin	2000.00
*Clown on Globe	350.00
Coin Registering Bank	200.00
Columbian Savings Bank	100.00
*Columbus World's Fair Bank	300.00
Confectionery Store	1500.00
*Cow. Milking or Kicking	650.00
*Creedmore	120.00
Crescent Cash Register	250.00
Cupola Bank	800.00
Dapper Dan	375.00
*Darktown Battery	350.00
Darky Bust. Tin	200.00
Darky Fisherman. Lead	5000.00
*Dentist	900.00
Dime Saving Bank. Pistol	200.00
Dinah with sleeve	125.00
Dinah with no sleeve. Aluminum	150.00
Ding Dong Bell	2500.00
Dog Barking. Safe	165.00
*Dog, Bull. Standing	200.00
Dog, Bull. Savings Bank	800.00
*Dog Charges Boy	350.00
*Dog on Oblong Base	260.00
Dog on Turntable	100.00
*Dog, Speaking	175.00
*Dog, Trick	190.00
*Dog, Trick. Modern w/solid base	95.00
Dog with tray	700.00
Droste's Spaar -*Automaat	300.00
*Eagles and Eaglets	175.00
Electric Safe	300.00
Elephant, Baby, open at X O'clock	3000.00
Elephant. Jumbo on wheels, small	500.00
Elephant. Light of Asia	900.00
*Elephant. Modern	60.00
Elephant. Man in Howdah	160.00
*Elephant with locked howdah	500.00
Elephant. 3 stars	160.00
Elephant. Small, on small wheels with tusks	800.00
Elephant. Made in Canada	300.00
Elephant Wiggles	50.00

Five-Cent Adding Bank	300.00
Football Bank	1000.00
Football. 1 black player with watermelon	5000.00
*Fortune Teller. Building [Automatic coin savings bank]	500.00
Fortune Teller. Drop a coin and I will tell your fortune	1000.00
Fortune Teller. Safe	420.00
Fowler	1600.00
Freedman's Bank	5000.00
"Freedman's Bureau," chest	500.00
*Frogs [2]	200.00
Frog on Arched Track. Tin	3000.00
Frog on Rock	150.00
Frog on round lattice base	120.00
Frog, or toad, on Stump	150.00
Frog and Serpent. Tin	5000.00
Fun Producing Savings Bank	600.00
*Gem	140.00
Germania Exchange	3000.00
Giant	2500.00
Giant in Tower. English	1500.00
*Girl in Victorian Chair with dog on lap	1750.00
Girl Skipping Rope	2500.00

Santa Claus at Chimney $250.00

"Give Me A Penny"	800.00
*Goat, Butting	330.00
*Goat, Frog and Old Man	825.00
*Goat. Little Billy	1000.00
Guessing Bank	800.00
Guessing Bank. Woman's figure	2500.00
Hall's Excelsior	60.00
Hall's Lilliput	150.00
*Harlequin, Clown & Columbine	5000.00
Harold Lloyd. Tin	1000.00
Hen. Setting	500.00
Hindu with Turban	575.00
Hold the Fort	850.00
Home Bank	220.00
Home Bank. Lithographed tin ejects receipt	100.00
Hoop-La	300.00
*Horse Race. Race Course	600.00
*Humpty Dumpty	150.00
Indian Chief. Aluminum	1500.00
*Indian Shooting Bear	220.00
Initiating Bank. First Degree	1500.00
Japanese Ball Tosser	3000.00
Jocko, Musical	1600.00
Joe Socko Novelty	300.00
John Bull's Money Box	2500.00
Jolly Joe Clown Bank	600.00
*Jolly N. Aluminum, English Bust	125.00
*Jolly N. Bust, fixed eyes	150.00
*Jolly N. Butterfly Tie	125.00
*Jolly N.	100.00
*Jolly N., moves ears, high hat. Aluminum	175.00
*Jolly N., Shepherd	100.00
*Jolly N., Stevens	100.00
*Jolly N., with high hat. Iron	150.00
*Jonah and the Whale	390.00
Jonah and the Whale. Jonah emerges from mouth	5000.00
*Katzenjammer Kids	1200.00
Kick Inn	390.00
Kiltie Bank	300.00
*Leap Frog	375.00
Liberty Bell	280.00
Lighthouse	350.00
*Lions & Monkeys	200.00
Lion Hunter	800.00
Little Hi Hat	500.00
*Little Joe	100.00
*Little Mo	600.00
Locomotive Savings Bank	500.00
Lucky Wheel Money Box	300.00
Magic	160.00
Magic Safe. Tin	200.00
Magic. Tin, foreign	500.00
*Magician	475.00
Mammy and Child	475.00
*Mason and Hod Carrier	475.00
Merry-Go-Round	4000.00
Mickey Mouse. Tin	1000.00
Mikado	2500.00
Minstrel	150.00
Minstrel. Cross-legged	335.00
*Monkey and Coconut	400.00
Monkey and Organ Grinder	100.00
Monkey and Parrot. Tin	300.00
Monkey with tray. Tin	300.00
Monkey and Tray, coin in stomach	750.00
Mosque	200.00
Motor Bank, Trolley	2500.00
*Mule Entering Barn	200.00
*Mule Bucking. Miniature	350.00
Music Bank. Tin	400.00
Musical Savings Bank	900.00
National Bank	420.00
New Bank	200.00
New Bank. Lever in front center	400.00
*North Pole, flag pops up	3000.00
Novelty	95.00
Old Woman That Lived in a Shoe	5000.00
*Organ Bank, Cat and Dog	170.00
*Organ Bank, Monkey, Boy & Girl	200.00
Organ Bank with monkey only	160.00
Organ Bank, tiny, with monkey on top	295.00
Organ Grinder & Dancing Bear	800.00
*Owl. Head turns	90.00
Owl with Book. Slot in Book	120.00
Owl with Book. Slot in Head	200.00
*Paddy and His Pig	350.00
Panorama Bank	900.00
Pascall Savings Bank. Tin	300.00
Patronize the Blind	1200.00
*Pegleg Beggar	500.00
Pelican. Feed the Goose	300.00
Pelican. Arab	400.00
Pelican. Mammy	400.00
Pelican. Man Thumbs Nose	300.00
Pelican. Rabbit in Mouth	500.00
*Perfection Registering	1500.00
Piano, plays music	1500.00
Picture Gallery	800.00
*Pig. Bismark	800.00
Pig in High Chair	240.00
*Pony, Trick	180.00
Popeye Knockout Bank	300.00
Preacher in Pulpit	5000.00
*Presto. Mouse on Roof	3000.00
Presto. Small building	110.00
Presto. Penny changes to quarter	3000.00
*Professor Pugfrog	1200.00
Pump and Bucket	520.00
Punch and Judy. Iron and tin	1000.00
*Punch and Judy. Small letters	200.00
*Punch and Judy. Large letters	200.00
Queen Victoria	3000.00
Rabbit. Small, standing	200.00
*Rabbit. Tall, standing	300.00
Rabbit in Cabbage	130.00

*Trapper's Cabin $180.00

Red Riding Hood	3000.00
Rival	5000.00
Robot. Aluminum	900.00
Roller Skating Rink	3500.00
Rooster	100.00
Royal Trick Elephant Bank. Tin	800.00
Safe Deposit Bank. Tin elephant	1000.00
Safe, top springs open. U.S. Bank . . .	500.00
Saluting Sailor	600.00
Sambo	450.00
*Santa Claus at Chimney	250.00
Savo Bank	100.00
Schley. "Admiral Schley Bottling Up	
Cevera"	3000.00
Scotchman. Tin	215.00
Seek Him Frisk	4000.00
Sentry Bank. Tin	600.00
*Sewing Machine	1500.00
*Shoot the Chute	3000.00
Shoot That Hat Bank	2500.00
Signal Cabin	400.00
*Squirrel and Tree Stump	450.00
"Stollwerck Bros.," vending, tin	150.00
"Stollwerck's Victoria Savings"	150.00
*Stump Speaker	300.00
Sweet Thrift Bank. Tin	100.00
Tabby Bank	195.00
*Tammany	75.00
Tank & Cannon	300.00
Target [Fort & Cannon]	3000.00
*Teddy and the Bear	225.00
10-Cent Adding Bank	600.00
Thrifty Animal Bank	200.00
Thrifty Tom. Tin Jigger Bank	300.00
Time is Money	1500.00
Time Lock Savings Bank	600.00

"Time" Registering, mechanical clock	200.00
Tommy	1500.00
Tower Bank	800.00
Treasure Chest Music Bank	300.00
Trick Savings Bank. Wood	150.00
Try Your Weight Scale Bank	800.00
Turtle	4000.00
20th Century Savings Bank	500.00
Two Ducks in a Pond	500.00
*Uncle Remus	975.00
*Uncle Sam	300.00
*Uncle Sam. Bust	500.00
Volunteer Bank	200.00
Watch Bank	300.00
Watch Bank, dime disappears	600.00
U. S. Bank	975.00
Weedens Plantation	350.00
*William Tell	175.00
Wimbleton	2000.00
Winner Savings Bank	1800.00
Wireless	175.00
Woodpecker	1200.00
*World's Fair Bank	300.00
World's Banker. Tin	800.00
X-Ray Bank, Smyth	700.00
Zoo	390.00

*Reproduced Item

BANKS, STILL
METAL

Banks, usually cast of metal [in the shape of animals, buildings, men or other figures], in which a slot is provided for inserting coins, are known as "still" banks.

"Burglar Proof House Safe. With key. Cl $85.00

Arabian Safe.....................$	32.50
Atlas............................	45.00
Bank Building	
3½"..........................	28.60
4½"..........................	35.00
5½"..........................	37.50
*Baseball Player	60.00
Battleship Maine	70.00
Bear, Sitting	40.00
Bear, Standing. 5½".............	45.00
Bear, Teddy. Small	36.50
*Billiken	38.00
Black Beauty [horse]	50.00
Black Mammy	75.00
Blackamoor......................	48.50
Boy Scout	55.00
*Buffalo, Standing	52.00
*Bull...........................	60.00
*Bull Dog, Sitting	47.50
*Bull Dog, Standing	45.00
*Buster Brown and Dog...........	75.00
Camel, Standing. Small	45.00
Casey Jones Train. Engine 572. 5"	
long	40.00
*Cash Register	65.00
*Cat, Sitting	45.00
*Cat with Ball	78.50
*"City Bank" Building. Large	45.00
Clock	57.00
*Clown, Standing	55.00
Cocker Spaniel	45.00
*"Coin Deposit Bank"	35.00
"Columbia" Building. [World's Fair] ..	46.50
Cow	45.00
Crown	27.50
Decker's Pig	42.50
Deer, with Antlers	50.00
Dog on Tub	55.00
*Dog, St. Bernard, with pack	48.50
Dog, Shepherd	47.50
Dog with fly on hip	47.50
Dog with Pack, 5¼x8"...........	45.00
Donkey, Standing	50.00
Donkey, with saddle	55.00
Duck, large	45.00
Dutch boy sitting on keg	25.00
E. River Savings Bank, Rochester	37.00
*Elephant on Tub	45.00
*Elephant, Standing.............	45.00
Flat Iron Building. 5½"	35.00
Frog	40.00
Gas Stove. "York, Abendroth Bros.	
N. Y."..........................	55.00
General Eisenhower	37.50
General Pershing	37.50
Gollywog.......................	45.00
"Good Luck" Billiken	50.00
Goose [Red Goose Shoes]	40.00
Hansel & Gretel Cigar Box Bank. Tin,	
5x6½x7½", deep	50.00

Heatrola	42.00
"Home Savings Bank." Dog head	
finial	45.00
Horse, Prancing	50.00
*Horse, Rearing	45.00
Horse, standing still	45.00
Horseshoe. Good Luck, encircling	
horse. Bust of Columbus at top	
and dog at base. Columbia Expo-	
sition item....................	75.00
Independence Hall. Enterprize Mfg.	
Co., Phila., 1875. Bronzed	65.00
*Indian Head	50.00
Indian Maiden. Head	50.00
*Indian, Standing	55.00
Junior Cash Register	35.00
Junior Safe	37.50
Kitten, 4¾".....................	40.00
Kitten, 5", with neck bow	42.00
Liberty Bell [iron]. 1776-1876	65.00
Lion, small	35.00
*Lion, standing	45.00

Bear with Staff. 6" high. Brass, CI
$75.00

Clown. Painted. Tin $25.00

Little Daisy	35.00
Lunch Pail, with handle	42.50
*Mail Box	35.00
Mickey Mouse. 5", marked "Walt Disney Prod."	50.00
Mule. 6½x7", saddled	45.00
Mutt & Jeff	65.00
Negro	55.00
Old South Church. 9"	60.00
Orphan Annie. Tin	28.50
Owl	47.50
"Pass Around the Hat"	47.50
Pig. "A Christmas Roast"	50.00
*Pig. Sitting	38.00
*Pig. "Thrifty"	40.00
Polar Bear	50.00
*Policeman, Irish	60.00
*Policeman, Standing	55.00
Possum	40.00
Postal Savings Bank. 4½", 1902	47.50
Puppy, Sitting	40.00
Puppy, white with black spots	45.00
*Rabbit. Large	45.00
Radio	49.50
Radio, Majestic	55.00
Refrigerator, G. E.	40.00
Rival Bank	37.50
Rooster, Standing	46.50
Roper, Gas Stove	60.00
Royal Safe Deposit. Safe	45.00
Safe. 4", dated 1897	42.50
Safe. 6", combination lock	50.00
Saratoga Trunk	40.00
Satchel. 3x6"	55.00

*Security Safe Deposit." Double combination, dated 1917	48.50
Sharecropper	45.00
*Sheep	45.00
Soldier, World War I	60.00
"Sport." Safe type, 3", dated 1-8-82 .	48.00
State Bank	45.00
Statue of Liberty	55.00
Steamboat "Arcade"	60.00
Tank Bank, USA 1918	57.00
Teddy Bear	45.00
Teddy Roosevelt	60.00
Telephone [wall type]	45.00
Top Hat. "Pass Around Hat"	47.50
Trader's Bank [Canada]. 1891	54.00
*Treasury Building	35.00
Treasury Safe, 5"	42.50
*Turkey, Standing	50.00
Union Bank [Safe]	45.00
"Washington Mansion, Mt. Vernon." 3" to top of chimney	39.50
Woolworth Building	
5¾"	40.00
7"	50.00

*Reproduced Item

BANKS, STILL
POTTERY

Acorn. "Acorn Stoves." 3", light brown glaze . . . . $	28.00
Apple. Red	22.50
Barrel. Gilt hoops	20.00
Bear, Sitting. 6"	32.00
Beehive. 4¼", brown mottled slipware	28.50
Bell. 5½", heavy unglazed red clay . . .	22.50
Bird	22.00

Pottery. Apple-shaped $22.50

Black face, with turban. 4½"	40.00
Boy's Head. With cap	22.50
Buffalo	25.00
Cash Register. White/yellow glaze ..	25.00
Cask. "Kentucky Wild Cat--I'm Thirsty." 3¼"	28.50
Cat. Staffordshire. White and yellow, on green/white cushion	40.00
Chicago World's Fair, 5" diam., shape of globe	22.50
Child's Head. With bonnet, brown glaze	25.00
Cottage	27.50
Dwarf Head. Brown enameled pottery........................	35.00
Elephant. Seated, 3", slipware	25.00
Frog. 4", coin goes in mouth	20.00
Jug. 4", slot for coin. No handle.....	18.50
Jug. 4½", made in Athens, N.Y.	17.50
Lion. 6".........................	20.00
Lion's Head	22.50
Monkey. Mottled yellow and brown .	25.00
Pig. Bennington	30.00
Pig in green pocketbook	28.50
Pig. Fat, mottled slipware	32.50
Pig. Gray, with splotches	20.00
Pig. Pennsylvania, red slipware, 10"	115.00
Poodle Head. Staffordshire. 3¾ x4½". Black collar/ears, gold lock	37.50
Ram. Rockingham type	32.00
Redware. 4" high	25.00
Rooster, Standing	22.00
Round. 4½", brown	22.50
Scarecrow. Man. Bennington	45.00
Shoe. High button. 5", tan glaze	75.00
Tree Stump. 3½ x4½"	15.00
Turnip. Marked "Charity"	25.00
Walrus. Rockingham glaze	75.00
Watermelon, Slice. 4x9½", hanging-type. Chalkware........	45.00

BARBED WIRE

Barbed wire collecting has recently become a fast-growing hobby, especially in the mid-western and southwestern parts of the United States.

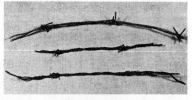

Common variety

It is estimated that there are more than 10,000 active collectors who seek examples of the more than 600 kinds of wire which were patented in the late 1800's. Eighteen-inch pieces bring from $1.00 for the common variety to as much as $100.00 for rare examples of the "devil's rope" as some people refer to it.

BAROMETERS

The barometer became popular in Victorian England. Essentially, it is an instrument for measuring the atmospheric pressure which, in turn, aids in the forecasting of weather. For example, low pressure indicates the coming of rain, snow or a storm, while high pressure means fair weather.

Anaroid. 26" long, with thermometer. Oak $95.00

Banjo	
Mahogany. John Berringer.......$	65.00
Rosewood. English..............	250.00
Desk. Brass. Germany.............	15.00
Stick. Rosewood. Ivory dial. English .	150.00
Wall. Oak. 27" high. Brass dial, 2 twisted columns. English	180.00

BASALT

A type of black vitreous pottery originally made in ancient times and rediscovered in the latter part of the 18th century by Josiah Wedgwood. It was later produced by other English potters.

Atomizers

4" high, including sterling silver top. Wedgwood, impressed with flowers in white and leaves around base, classical figures and trees around neck. England . . . . . . $	75.00
6" high, dancing figures	72.50

Bowls

9½". Acorn border	195.00
12". Acanthus decor. Marked Wedgwood	220.00
Bust. Mercury. 18" high, mark on plinth and bust. Incised Wedgwood. Black	500.00
Bust. Shakespeare. Half life-size. C. 1800, marked Wedgwood	365.00
Candlesticks. 12" high. Pair	195.00
Chalice. 3" deep, beaded pedestal base. Marked Wedgwood	175.00

Creamers

Plain.	75.00
4¼" high, 6½" from handle to spout. Black glaze inside thistle, wild rose and harp scrolls	95.00
Cup and Saucer. Plain. Impressed Wedgwood	100.00
Foo Dog. Carved, 3" high, on base . .	40.00
Inkwell. Impressed Wedgwood	82.50
Medallions. 2¼ x 2¾", marked Wedgwood and Bentley. George III, Queen Charlotte. Pair	500.00

Pitchers

5¼". Helmet shape. Unmarked. Eng. C. 1790, thin potting, engine turning	120.00
6½". Relief of Flaxman figures around base with border of leaves and bunches of grapes at top. Black Basalt Wedgwood	115.00
8". Ribbed top, scrolled bulbous center	185.00
Planter. 8" high, 7" top width. Wedgwood border. Made in England	85.00
Plaque. 8" oval. Hercules carrying wild boar and lion. Old framed Wedgwood	350.00
Spitoon, Ladies'. Wedgwood. 5" across top, indented vertical lines, center bands of basketweave pattern	115.00
Sugar and Creamer. Wedgwood. Squatty shape. Set	160.00

Sugar Bowls

2¼". Covered, impressed Wedgwood	150.00
7". Widow finial	165.00

Teapots

4½". Marked Wedgwood, Etruria, England	150.00
5". Marked Wedgwood	165.00
8½". Classic design	195.00

Vases

5". Spill. Floral base, relief	150.00
6". C. 1890, marked Wedgwood, England. Pair	235.00

BASKETS

Recently collectors have shown interest in old baskets, especially the splint type. The maker would weave thin, flexible wooden strips into various-size baskets which were used for a

Bowl. 8" diam., 3½" deep. EPNS rim. Impressed Wedgwood, England
$165.00

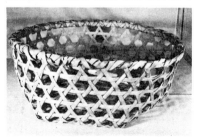

Cheese Basket. 25" diam., 9" deep
$135.00

variety of purposes. In the days before paper bags, each housewife who went shopping carried her purchases home in her basket. Smaller ones were used for gathering eggs or as lunch baskets for school children.

Picnic Basket. 21" long, 13" wide, 11½" high. Hinged lid, double handles. C. 1930 .... $25.00

Yarn Basket. 11" diam. Handled $26.00

Apple. Shaker .... $ 55.00
Egg. 10x13". 12" high, including handle. Central Penna. 32.50
Indian
  4½x7". Dark/light brown. "Hupa" 95.00
  7x11½x16". Splint. Red painted flowers 100.00

8x9½". Figural designs. Apache" . 85.00
Lunch. 5x8". Double handles 22.00
Nantucket. 14" diam. 110.00
  Wicker. Picnic. Large, 1930's 26.50
  4½" high, 7¼" top diam. Handleless . 30.00
  11" high, 13" top diam., 8" bottom diam., round body, 4" top rim. Early 40.00

BATTERSEA ENAMEL

A process of fusing enamel onto metal was first used in England at Battersea, C. 1750. However, much of the production was in the Staffordshire district. The name "Battersea" is now a generic or general name for enamel on such items as patch, pill and snuff boxes, candleholders, and door knobs. Battersea enamel boxes are being reproduced today in France.

Box. 1¼x2" long. Fishing scene
$350.00

*Boxes
  "And tighter the knot, the farther apart." Heart-shaped, yellow base $ 350.00
  Angel decor. 1¾x3" 350.00
  "Coaching." Shield-shaped. Pink base 375.00
  "Esteem the Giver." Yellow base with rust, colored bird on nest 250.00
  Heart-shaped. 1¼x3". Fresh gathered peas. Multicolored top, blue side 475.00
  Hexagonal-shaped. 1¼" wide. Verse in black on white top, yellow sides 375.00
  "Lay Hold on Time While in Your Prime." Blue base, round, 1x2" ... 400.00
  "Love is Eternal." Blue base 325.00
  Oval. ¾x1½". Colorful angel on swing. Flesh-colored sides 325.00

166

Box. Heart-shaped. Periwinkle blue, white ground. "Success to the Fleet"
$325.00

Oval. 1½x2". Lady seated on mound. Tree in background. Pink rose on front, blue forget-me-nots on inside of lid	375.00
"Racing and You See the Race." Cover in colors, robin-egg blue base, 1½x2½"	425.00
Bottle. 5½" high. Stoppered. Classical figures. Pastel colors	375.00
Knobs. Curtain tie backs or mirror supports. Pair	150.00

*Reproduced Item

BAVARIAN CHINA

Bavaria was an important pottery and china production center in Germany, similar to the Staffordshire district in England. However, very little of the production from this area was imported into this country before 1870. The term covers the products of several companies operating there.

Cup and Saucer. Creme with maroon. Baker's Chocolate Lady Portrait	$ 22.50
Dish, Celery. 5" wide, 12" long. Lavender blossoms on white ground, lustre edge	15.00
Hat Pin Holder. Marked	22.00

Plate. 9½" diam. Scalloped, pierced border. Multicolored floral design, gold trim. Schumann, Arzberg . $65.00

Plates

7½". Portrait of seated maiden, cupid and arrows. Rose sprays and gold embossed areas	18.50
8¼". Purple grapes, pink florals around entire plate. Small white area with most of surface covered with fruits or florals	35.00
8½". Heavy gold rim, pink rose decor. Dated, artist signed	18.50
8½". Portraits. George and Martha Washington. J&C. Louise Bavaria. Pair	55.00
9½". Game plate. Large quail, rich shading and scene. Quail stands on large rock, strewn with mosses and bits of branches. Head up, listening	55.00
Sugar Bowl. 4" high, white ground with pink roses, gold trim	12.50

Dish. 10" diam. Pierced sides, floral decor, gold trim $85.00

Sugar and Creamer. H/P, covered iris decor, deep gold trim. Set	25.00
Sugar Shaker. 4½" high. H/P pink and blue florals	15.00
Syrup with Underplate. Covered, pastel, gold trim. Set	25.00

Tea Sets

Handpainted, violets and marked Z. S. Mignon	40.00
Teapot, sugar and creamer. Panels divided by narrow, black, vertical panels. Pink roses in panels	55.00
Tray, Pin. Schumann. Blue forget-me-nots in center and on sides. Much gold, pierced border	10.00
Vase. 6½" high. Floral decor, gold trim	18.50

BELLEEK

A delicate iridescent type of porcelain first made at Fermanagh, Ireland in 1857. It has a pearly lustre and in keeping with its likeness to the sea, many items were made in the form of shells and similar shapes. It is seldom thicker than a sheet of writing paper, light in weight but extremely durable.

Marks of the Irish company include a harp with a crown above; a hound, harp and tower with the name "Belleek" printed below. Some items have the name "Belleek Co., Fermanagh" with no other identifying mark. China made after 1891 has the words "Ireland" or "Eire" added. The company continued until World War I. It discontinued operations for a period and then resumed production.

Belleek was made in America by a number of firms. The first producer was Ott & Brewer Co., at Trenton, N.J., in 1884. They used a crown and sword mark, a crescent mark, the mark O. & B., and the firm name in a circle. It was succeeded in 1894 by the Cook Pottery Co., whose mark was three feathers with the word "Etruria."

Another early American manufacturer was The Willets Mfg. Co. which made tea sets, vases, small picture frames and cabinet pieces. The company used two marks -- the letter "W" in the form of a serpent and the other with the word "Belleek" above the same mark.

The American Art China Works was established in 1891 and began making Belleek china in 1892. The majority of its output was made for amateurs to decorate. "R.E.Co/China/Trenton" within a circle was their mark.

The Ceramic Art Co. started business in 1889 and made a large variety of items--from clock cases and vanity sets to vases and tea and coffee services. Their mark was an artist's palette with the company's initials.

The Columbian Art Co. began operating in 1893 and produced novelties in Belleek, such as toby jugs and souvenir items. Their mark was a shield with the letters "M" and "W" inside, "Belleek" above with a ribbon scroll and the word "Trenton" below with the abbreviation "N.J."

Lenox, Inc. was organized in 1906 by Walter Scott Lenox and is still producing fine porcelain tableware. However, Belleek novelties were discontinued about the time of World War I. The company used two marks. Undecorated articles made for amateur painters show an artist's palette with the letter "L" below. Other pieces are marked with a script "L" in a laurel wreath, below is "Lenox" and "Made in U.S.A."

Animals

Bird. White, 2ndBM. #526 .... $	85.00
Pig, Sitting. 3", yellow feet and ears, creamy white	25.00
Swan. 4½". Plain. Fermanagh	55.00
Swan. 6". Irish. Fermanagh	125.00
Terrier, Sitting. 3", creamy white .	27.50

Baskets

3x10½". Ivory. Mkd. Belleek Co., Fermanagh, Ireland	60.00
6½", handpainted. Fermanagh ...	100.00

Bowls

Finger. Irish harp and hound mark	35.00
Rose. 4½" diam.	45.00
2¼" high. Club-shaped, lattice work sides, basketweave base. Large roses on sides. C. 1900	95.00
3½" high. Handpainted, applied flowers. Lease D 539, green mark F	40.00
3½" diam., Shellware, marked ...	45.00

Cauldrons

Shamrock decor, old mark	50.00
"Witches," 4x4¼", two handles ..	55.00

Coffee Pots

10½". Art Nouveau style. White, green,tan, gold handles. Lenox ...	75.00
Limpert pattern. Black	95.00

Creamers

4" high. Shamrock, 2nd BM	30.00
4½" high. Bacchus heads, grape..	50.00
Ivy. Twisted handle. 2nd BM	50.00
Shape of girl	65.00
Shell pattern. Green, Harp and Crown mark	52.50
Shell and coral pattern. Footed, 2nd BM	35.00

Shellware, pink handle 47.50
Cups and Saucers
  Alternating green/cream panels,
  black harp & hound mk. [1st mk] . . 50.00
  Second black mk. Erne. Irish.
  White, yellow lustre trim 29.50
  Third mark 30.00
  Chocolate. Ming pattern 25.00
  Neptune pattern. Lease #225 and
  2nd BM 45.00
  Shell pattern. 2nd BM 37.50
Dishes
  5" diam., floral decor. Palette mk.
  Lenox 27.50
  5½" diam. Cloverleaf, openwork
  sides with 3 cream roses and
  green leaves and shamrocks,
  applied around edge 72.50
  6¼" long, 2" high. Heart-shaped
  harp and hound mark 45.00
  Bon-Bon. 5" diam., 2½" high.
  roses on edge, openwork 55.00
  Lenox. Handled decor with
  stippled rays flanked by Key flutes
  and serrated edge 30.00
Frames, Picture. 1st BM. Pair 275.00
Goblet. 3½". Pink trim. 1st BM 55.00
Hat Pin Holder. 5", white lustre type . 32.50
Jam Jar Holder. Basketweave design
  with green clover leaves. Lid and
  underplate. Set 60.00
Juice Set. Transparent ivory porce-
  lain, raised enamel decor of fruit,
  grapes. Pitcher, four matching
  tumblers. Set 200.00

Mush Set. Bowl, 3½" diam., creamer,
4" high. Black mark. Fermanagh,
Ireland $110.00

Mugs
2½" high. Irish, rope handle, 2nd
  BM. Net pattern, yellow lustre 85.00
2¼" high. Shamrock decor,
  inscribed "Portrush" 45.00

5½" high. Salmon pink, pale
  H/P grapes. Leaf design handle,
  base. Willets, signed 65.00
5½" high. Portrait of cavalier.
  Artist signed 60.00
  Golfer decor 90.00
Mustard. Covered, basketweave
  design with shamrocks 42.50
Pitchers
  5" high. 1st BM. Ivy cream pattern.
  Rope handle 75.00
  6" high. Aberdeen. H/P, green mk. . 65.00
  Neptune. Pink and gold. 3 BM 55.00
Plates
  4¼". 3rd BM 20.00
  6x6". All white, 2nd BM 27.50
  6¼". 3 sprays of shamrocks,
  basketweave border 32.50
  8". 3rd mark 26.50
  9". Shell, pink trim 70.00
  10". Dinner. Coxon Belleek 50.00
  10½". Cake. Shamrock, 2nd BM . . 60.00
  Bread. Limpet Lease #83. BM 65.00
  Bread. Neptune, 3 BM 35.00
Platter. Twig handles, 9", 2nd black
  mark 48.50
Pot. 3", flowered, crinkled 2nd BM . . . 62.50
Salts
  Floral and gold, heart-shaped.
  H/P, American. Set of 4 . . . . 40.00
  Individual. Pink rose decor. BM . . . 22.00
  Individual. Star-shaped. 3rd BM . . 15.00
  Master. Neptune pattern, pink
  accents, black mark 45.00
  Master. Scalloped shell and green
  coral. 2nd BM 40.00
Sea Horse. 3½ x5", black mark 90.00
Sugar Bowls
  Bacchus. Open, black hound harp
  mark. Ireland 40.00
  Basketweave and green sham-
  rocks, covered 50.00
  Basketweave and green sham-
  rocks, 2½" high, open 40.00
  Neptune. Pink and gold. 2nd BM . . 55.00
Sugars and Creamers
  Bacchus. Yellow lustre lining.
  Black mark and numbered 120.00
  Neptune. 2nd BM 85.00
  Shamrock pattern. BM 85.00
  Shell pattern. Green hound, harp
  castle mark 60.00
  Souvenir of "Cork International
  Expo 1903." 2nd BM 80.00
Teakettle 87.50
Teapots
  Basketweave. Shamrocks 95.00
  Cone. 2nd BM 150.00
  Hexagonal. Green, 2nd BM 150.00
  Limpet Cob pattern 95.00

Shamrock. 2nd BM	78.50

Tea Sets
3 pieces. Teapot, covered sugar bowl, creamer. White shellware. Set 175.00
15 pieces. Coral pattern. 2nd BM. Teapot, covered sugar, creamer, 4 each cups and saucers, 4 plates. Set 295.00
30 pieces. Bacchus pattern. 10 plates embossed with Bacchus head and grapes, 10 each cups and saucers. Set 550.00
Tea Strainer and Stand 42.50

Trays
Bread. 10½" wide. Irish. 1st BM. Decorated in gold/deep brown . . . 110.00
Leaf-shaped. 4¼" long. Pink shading 32.50
14x17". 2nd BM. Deeply swirled pattern with pink turned-up, scalloped edge 195.00

Tubs
4½" high. Irish, basketweave and green shamrocks 55.00
Shamrock trim, 3rd mark 40.00
Tumbler. Black hound and harp mark, panelled and ribbed 47.50

Vases
3½" high [2nd period], 3-footed with applied flowers 65.00
6" high. Aberdeen, colored flowers, 3rd BM 80.00
6" high. Short, fluted neck, pink and yellow roses 85.00
6¾" high. Lily Spill. 2nd black mark 75.00
7¼" high. Painted country scene, 3 handles 90.00
7½" high. White with mixed floral bouquet decor 95.00
9" high. Pearly lustre on pearl white 135.00
12" high. Marked [American] 175.00
12" high, 3½" top opening, 5¾" base diam. 23" circum. Marked Lenox Belleek. Art Nouveau, 6-sided stylized gold peacock feathers with irid. purple, blue eyes on sage green ground. Signed A.D. 150.00
13" high. Hollyhocks on pale green to lavender background. Willets Mfg. Co. 150.00
15" high. Decorated with two parrots. Willets 175.00
16" high, 5" diam. Slender. Mother standing, cuddling baby. Initialed, green mark, artist's

palette	225.00
Writing Paper Rack	45.00

BELLS

Bells have played an important part in the life of man since ancient times. He has had many uses for them - they have called him to worship, tolled at his death, struck the time, summoned him to school, warned him of the approach of enemies, invited him to dinner, bade him to assemble - and the lowly alarm clock has urged him to arise and be about his daily work.

Brass Bell. 16th century $165.00

Bird. Bronze Ibis. Turkish-carved, tall one piece. Outside clapper & bird . . $	75.00
Call. Silverplated, dolphin handle . . .	22.50
China. H/P. Top is candlestick. Signed Polly on side	30.00
Chinaman with Que Que. Brass	25.00

Donkey brass bells. 22 on leather strap $175.00

Church. 22" high without frame. Iron, made by American Bell Foundry, Northville, Michigan, U.S.A......................... 250.00

Church Gong
   1-tier, brass 90.00
   3-tier, brass 125.00

Cow
   Brass 25.00
   *Iron 15.00

"Cutter." Nickel, with iron strap. Set of three 50.00

Elephant Bell. 7¾" high to top of handle. Brass $27.50

Desk Bell. Brass and iron. Pat. 1856 and 1863 .... 15.00
Donkey. Open brass. 10 bells on leather strap 125.00
Dutch Girl. Knitting sock. 3½" high, brass fig. Pealed, hot embossed design 29.50
Dutch Boy and Girl. Figural......... 18.50
El Camino Real. Small 18.00
Elephant 27.50
Farm. Iron, large, mounted in bracket 135.00
Goose. Small, double clapper, original strap 20.00
Hame. Swedish. Set of 5 .... 85.00
Hand. Brass. 12½" high 85.00
Hotel. Desk-type. Nickelplated, on marble base 22.50
Lady with Hoop Skirt. 4" high 24.50
Liberty. Bronze, 4¼" high, marked "Colonial 1832-1925" 30.00
Locomotive
   12". Activated by air, complete ... 295.00
   17". Brass. "Great Northern," complete 250.00
   17". "Union Pacific." Vertical mounting from front. Scarce, complete 425.00
School
   Brass. Wood handle, 5" high 48.00
   Brass. Wood handle, 10" high 80.00
Ship's
   Brass 45.00
   U.S.N. Solid brass with side mount dated 1898, eagle finial, from Brunswick, Ga. shipyard........ 150.00
Sleigh
   17 burnished brass, restrung on old strap 175.00
   String, 20 bells, graduated sizes, on leather strap. Swedish........ 225.00
   String, 25 bells, graduated sizes, cleaned, good leather strap...... 250.00
   String, 25 bells, brass, not cleaned 200.00
   27 bells, brass on strap, small 125.00
   String, 30 bells. Iron, 1¼" diam... 125.00
Soldier, Roman. 3½" high.......... 20.00
Sterling. 4½" high, 950 Amer....... 35.00
Temple. Japanese, lizard handles, engraved with dragons and flowers. 5¼" high 48.50
Town Crier. Large................. 78.50
Trolley Car
   6" diam. Iron................... 85.00
   12" diam. Brass, including mounting bracket. 5" high, pull cord 100.00
Turtle. Tortoise top, iron legs and head. Wind-up type, bell rings when head or tail is pressed. Germany...................... 45.00
                    *Reproduced Item

Although bells made of metal are more practical, glass bells were produced in England and in the United States in the early 1800's. They can be found in clear and colored glass, large or small. Some were made to be used on the tea tray or dining table, while others were purely decorative, an example of the glass blower's talent and the glass manufacturer's product.

Glass bells are still being manufactured. Be careful of the reproductions which are coming in from Europe.

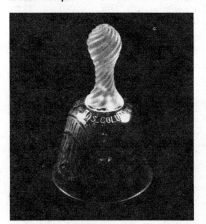

Columbian Exposition 1893. Swirled handle, metal clapper $40.00

Amber. Clear glass handle ....$	95.00
Bristol. 11½" high	85.00
Bristol. Wedding bell. Red barrel in swirl pattern, clear swirl handle, 4-ball finial. 13¼", with clapper ..	125.00
Cranberry. Swirl pattern. Clear glass handle	125.00
Custard souvenir. "Seaside Pavilion Corpus Christi".................	42.50
Cut Glass	57.50
Etched. 7½" high	30.00
Green. Dark	62.50
Milk Glass. 5½" high, chain links form handle, metal clapper	40.00
Nailsea. Clear glass handle	125.00
Tiffany. Iridescent, clear handle	200.00
Venetian. Latticino. Pink, blue, yellow, green with gold edges, alternating with white stripes. 4¼" high.....................	125.00

It was first made in Rockingham, England, and is sometimes designated as Bennington Rockingham pottery. The first pottery established in the United States was in 1783 at Bennington, Vermont.

The original ware was salt-glazed crocks and jugs which were unlike the later mottled brown-glazed ware now known as Bennington. A full line of kitchen utensils as well as cuspidors and copies of various English "Statuary Ware" were produced.

After 1850 Parian pottery of a dull opaque white was made into figurines, toby jugs, pitchers, brooches and pins.

The brown-type Bennington was also produced in St. Johnsbury, Middlebury and Dorset, Vermont, at Baltimore, Md., and at some potteries in the Ohio Valley.

Reproduction of the cow creamer and hound-handled pitchers have been on the market in recent years.

Bed Pan ....$	85.00
Bowls	
7½"	50.00
8½". Tulip pattern impressed on bottom.......................	55.00
10"	65.00
11"	65.00
13½", octagonal	90.00
Box. Sleeping child on top..........	85.00
Bucket. 9½" diam., wire handle	100.00
Cake Mold. 9"....................	52.50
Candleholder. 3½", with handle	75.00
Churn. Butter	125.00
Coffee Pot. 9½" high..............	140.00
Cracker Jar. Covered..............	110.00
Creamers	
*Cow. Covered..................	115.00
Oval, bulbous	75.00

Bowl. 16" diam., 7" high $95.00

Parian Hand Vase. 7½" high . . . $85.00

Dishes	
10" diam., deep	60.00
Pudding. 3x9½". Brown glaze with yellow mottling. Flared out sides	55.00
Vegetable. 10" diam., with raised hearts in bottom	95.00
Door Knobs. Set	50.00
Flasks	
Book. "Departed Spirits"	150.00
Coachman. 10½". Signed, 1849 mk	350.00
Pint. Tavern scene	100.00
Foot Warmer. Bennington	135.00
Hound. 10" high, sitting on a 4½x8" base	195.00
Inkwell. 3¼"	200.00
Jar. Covered, handled 8x9½", brown on yellow	95.00
Jug. 16" high	145.00
Lamp. 7½" high. Scarce	200.00
Mugs	
Frog, in bottom	130.00
Parrots in relief. 6" high	55.00
Pitchers	
Boar and stag scene. 2-quart, pewter lid	225.00
Castle scene	200.00
"Dear Game"	100.00
Frog in bottom, name on front. 11".	200.00
*Hound handle. American eagle under spout, birds and animals on sides	325.00
Hound handle. 11½" high, 6-qt. . .	600.00
Hunter, dogs and birds	250.00
Wild Rose	300.00
8½x8½". Deep brown, yellow. Peacock pattern	135.00
Plates	
8¼"	45.00
9¾"	55.00
10½"	75.00
Pudding Mold	75.00
Salt Box. Hanging type	100.00
Shoe. High top	50.00
Soap Dish. 4½" diam.	50.00
Syrup Jug. Signed, with U.S.P. ribbon mark. Rare	375.00
Teapots	
Tall. plain	90.00
2-quart, Mandarin	150.00
Tiebacks. Pair	75.00
Tobacco Jars	
10" high. Covered. Marked 129B Bennington	450.00
Man smoking, wearing skull cap . .	170.00
Toby Jugs	
Duke of Wellington. Made by U.S. Pottery Co., Bennington, Vermont. C. 1850	350.00

Cup. Custard. Mottled	25.00
Cuspidors	
6" high. Pineapple design. Brown glaze	50.00
7" diam.	50.00
8" diam.	65.00
9½" base, 7½" top, 4½" diam. Signed, marked Lyman Fenton & Company. Brown flint enamel	185.00
Plain, small	40.00
Shell pattern, brown glaze	70.00
Stars, lady in flowing robe	80.00

Pie Plate. 9½" diam., 3" deep . . $55.00

Man wearing tricorn hat covered in good streaky brown glaze	65.00
Pint. Jolly Good Fellow	275.00
Vases	
7" high. Raised water lily	100.00
7½" high. Belleek-type. Portrait base, petalled top. Iridescent white	125.00
Wash Board. In wooden frame	120.00
Wash Bowl and Pitcher. Brown china, panelled. Set	325.00
*Reproduced Item	

BISQUE

The term "bisque" or biscuit china, is used to designate ware which has been fired only once and is not glazed. The body is soft and porous but will no longer soften in water as air-dried china will. Some items are decorated while others are put on the market in the state in which they came from the kiln. In recent years new items and reproductions have entered the market.

*Angel. Posed above Holy Water Font. 8" high, 3½" wide . . . . $	100.00
Baby kitten with pacifier	60.00
Babies, Piano	
*Holding toy doll. 8"	130.00
*Large. On tummy	200.00
*Sitting. 13" high	245.00
Box. Egg-shaped, footed, covered. Cover has 3-dimensional scene of windmill, houses, sailboat in soft blue, brown. 4-footed	35.00
Bust of girl. 5½" high, blonde hair, blue hat and blouse, gold beads . .	57.50
Cherub on swan sleigh. Pink and white, gold trim	50.00
Figurines	
3" high. 3 children in tub	100.00
5" high. Black boy sitting on cut open watermelon, eating the slice. Colorful and detailed	50.00
7¼" high. Maid in Victorian dress	40.00
8". Boy with gun and dog	55.00

9½" high. Boy and girl in pastel colors. Pair	60.00
11" high, 10" long. Woman sitting side saddle on donkey, dog. Chantilly, France	125.00
11¼" high. Sailor and girl at ship's wheel. Pair	165.00
15" high. Boy and girl dressed as tennis players, colorful. Pair	95.00
Font, Holy Water. Cross, heart, roses, dove. Hanging-type, 5" high, 2½" wide	30.00
Girls	
Against stump, blowing horn	42.50
*With basket. 9" high	40.00
With swan, on horn-of-plenty. Pink and blue, small	25.00

Planters. 8¼" high. Man and woman on horseback. French. Pair . . . $125.00

Krazy Kat. 3½" high	30.00
Madonna. 9" high	40.00
Match Holders	
3½". Dutch girl holding pitcher . . .	27.50
5½". Girl holding doll	35.00
8". "Happy Hooligan"	39.50
Monkey Horn Player. Blue coat, black hat	40.00
Negro boy on camel	32.50
Pig. 3¼" high. "Nudder" wearing green and gold cutaway suit, holding bouquet of flowers on green pedestal	50.00
Pitcher. Strawberry	30.00
Sheep. 3¼" high	18.50
Shoes	
4½" long, blue flower with yellow center, lavender frill	42.50
6¼" long, 2 white love birds at top, 3 blue birds on side	50.00
Tobacco Jar. Dark girl with kerchief .	32.50
Vases	
5½" high, 5" wide	36.00
6" high. Boy seated under arbor, glazed	40.00
6" high. Girls in garden. Yellow and brown, glazed. Pair	55.00
*Reproduced Item	

BOHEMIAN GLASS

Bohemia was formerly an independent country but is now part of Czechoslovakia. It is famed for producing the "flashed" colored glass, overlay, cut and etched glass. The ruby colored "flashed" or "stained" glass is one of the better known products; however, it was also produced in black, blue, yellow and green colors.

Much of the so-called Bohemian glass was imitated in Switzerland, England and parts of Germany to sell at low prices. The glass was first imported into this country about 1825 and is still being brought in today. Most of the Bohemian glass desired by collectors today is of the 1875-1900 period.

Basket. Pale pink with applied thorn handle, twisted loop . . . . $	95.00
Beaker. Red with gold sprays and wide gilt rim. 8 facets	85.00
*Bell. 4½" high, deer, castle, clear glass handle, clear clapper on chain	80.00

Castor. 3 bottles, 14½" high, in Sheffield-type holder $150.00

Cruet. 5¾" high. Clear handle, with stopper $75.00

Bottles

5". Red designs. 18K gold trim. . . .	375.00
7". Alternating ruby and clear panels. Pair.	225.00
7¼". White overlay decoration. Pair	275.00
8". Cologne. Amber, panels of forget-me-nots and other engraved flowers	75.00
15". Red. Pair	165.00
Perfume. 5", enameled, vintage decor, original stopper	38.50
Box, Powder. Covered, bird and butterfly decor	82.50

Bowls

Finger. Vintage pattern	47.50
Red. 4½" diam., 3½" high. Vintage pattern	60.00
Butter Dish. Covered, ruby etched deer and castle	95.00
Celery Holder. Ruby red, etched building, scrolls, etc. C. 1875	75.00
Chalice. 10" high, amber, enameled overlay	135.00

Compotes

Covered. 15" high, ruby, etched deer and foliage decor 200.00

Open. 7" high, 8¼" diam. Red, deer and castle 155.00

Cordial. Vintage pattern 30.00

Cordial Set. Brown bottle, tray and 4 glasses in frosted lily-of-the-valley pattern 150.00

Cruet. Gold and colored jewels 125.00

Cuspidor. Open 49.50

Decanters

12" high. Vintage pattern........ 100.00

12½" high. Vintage pattern. Deep red to clear. Pair 185.00

14" high, 7½" diam., ruby. Deer and pine decor. With 6 wines. Set . 200.00

14¼" high, narrow, with original stopper 120.00

15¼" high. Stoppered. Ruby, deer and castle 125.00

Dish, Candy. Covered, 10" high, etched bird and deer decor 75.00

Door Knob Set 50.00

Glass, Juice. Etched bird and castle decor. Ruby coloring 27.50

Goblet. Knob stem. Vintage pattern . 75.00

Lamp. 12" high, cobalt overlay 150.00

Lustres. Small prisms. Pair 200.00

Mug. 4½" high, clear handle 47.50

Vases. 12" high. Frosted white panels, floral decor. Pair $200.00

Pitchers

Quart. Red. Vintage pattern 125.00

Water. Vintage, with 3 rows of clear rosebuds, applied handle ... 140.00

Powder Jar. Covered, red with frosted white decor............. 48.00

Salt and Pepper Shakers. Castor size, in fancy silverplated frame. Deer and castle 65.00

Salts. Clear with gold vintage decor, on 3 ribbed, scrolled feet. Set of four 60.00

Soap Dish. With attached drain 36.50

Sugar Bowl. Covered, amber, etched hunting scene.................. 125.00

Toilet Set. 3 pieces - pair of cologne bottles with original stoppers and squatty, covered powder jar. Blown........................ 125.00

Tumblers

Deer. Green 35.00

Flowers and Birds 37.50

Vintage 42.50

Vintage, footed 47.50

Vases

5" high. Ruby, castle, deer and decor 75.00

7½" high. Floral decor, pedestal base 75.00

10" high. Red. Pair............ 135.00

12¼" high. Flowers and bird 100.00

12½" high. Castle, leaf and deer decor on red ground, clear base .. 125.00

13" high. Amethyst to clear with heavy gold overlay 150.00

Water Set. With tumble-up. Vintage pattern, red 85.00

Wine Glass. Vintage pattern 30.00

Wine Set. Decanter and 6 glasses. Red deer and castle design 200.00

*Reproduced Item

BONE

Items carved from dried animal bones are listed in this section.

Back Scratcher. Chinese, hand carved ....$ 12.50

Spoons. 5¼" long. Each $4.00

Clothes Pin. Hand carved	9.00
Flour Scoop. Heavy, hand carved ...	30.00
Knives and Forks. In lined wooden case, 6 each. Set	45.00
Letter Opener. Carved figure at top .	10.00
Napkin Rings	
Plain.........................	6.50
Carved.......................	8.50
Sled. 6" long, leather lacing	13.50
Spoon. 8" long, plain	12.00
Tea Caddy Spoon	17.50

BOOK ENDS

Book ends have been made from practically every material imaginable -- from petrified wood to metals of all types.

Art Nouveau. Bronze over full, plaster figure. Pair ....$ 45.00

Sliding. 27" fully extended. Brass. Art Nouveau-type $65.00

Birds on stepped brass bases. Hand-carved, Rose Quartz. Pair ..	135.00
Dogs. Brass, marble base. Pair	25.00
Elephant. Iron. Pair	18.00
"Geisha Girl," 4½", bronze	22.00
Horseheads. Pair	10.00
"Lincoln Cabin," 4", cast iron	35.00
Napoleon Bust. Armor bronze. Artist signed	45.00
Owls. Brass, expandable. Pair	27.50
Pirate. 7" high, iron, painted light green. Pair	30.00
Ship design, 5" high. Roycroft	28.00
Ship. Pirate vessel. Brass, painted, two pieces....................	25.00

Metal figures on white and green marble bases. Pair $85.00	
Urn and Flowers. Carved. Soapstone. Pair	35.00
Wood, Petrified. 5½x8". Cut and polished bases. 12 lbs. Pair	55.00

BOOT JACKS

Various types of boot jacks were made to facilitate the removal of boots, the popular footwear of three or four generations ago. Some were constructed of wood, while others were made of metals such as brass or iron. Two of the popular designs were "Beetle" and "Naughty Nellie."

Beetle. Brass, 10"................$ 65.00	
*Beetle. Harp shape. Iron, 11½"....	40.00
Buggy Wrench. Pittsburgh Novelty Works	50.00
Cast Iron. On 8½" double barrel cap pistol. Legend. "American Bull Dog Boot Jack," unfolded into two sections lengthwise to make jack .	55.00
Cast Iron. "Use Musselman's Boot Jack Plug"....................	20.00

Walnut base, cast-iron frame, carpeted top $35.00

Wood. 17" long, square nails .. $10.00

Cast Iron and Maplewood. Pat. 1859.
Top wood piece in shape of shoe
   sole. 15" 30.00
Cow Horns. Wood................. 35.00
Double. Ornate, iron. Pat. 1869 ..... 35.00
Downs & Co. 13". Center design 25.00
Folding or Traveling. 8"........... 35.00
Lady Scroll 16.50
Mechanical. Iron, with carpet-
   covered, movable jaws to grip
   boot. Pat. 1850................. 30.00
Metal. Bowed-type, 7". Name "C.
   Hull, Birm." on back and "Regd.
   Boot Jack"..................... 18.50
*Naughty Nellie. Iron 30.00
Naughty Nellie. Brass 60.00
Try-It. Iron 15.00
Wood. 16" 12.50
Wood. Oval ends with square nails.
   25" 17.50
Wood. Pine, hand-hewn 10.00
*Reproduced Item

BOTTLES

APOTHECARY

Apothecary or drug store bottles were used as storage containers for the various compounds and drugs found in old-time drug establishments.

6 high. Clear, with stopper .... $ 7.50
7¼" high to top of stopper. Ribbed,
   emerald green 50.00
7½" high, 5½" diam., free blown,
   clear.......................... 25.00
7½" high. Rough pontil 15.00
8½" high, 3¼" diam., 1¼" stopper,
   wide mouth.................... 16.50
8½" high. White porcelain, floral
   decor. "Azahar" and "Menta." Pair 40.00

9½" high. Clear glass with gold
   label. "Kino" lettered in black 37.50
9½" high. Drug bottle with ground
   pontil 22.50
11" high, 4½" diam., 2¼" stopper,
   wide mouth.................... 25.00
12" high. "Capsicum" 35.00
12" high. Drug bottle with ground
   stopper 25.00
13" high. Fancy stopper with mouth,
   clear.......................... 25.00
14" high. Bulbous, fancy ITP pedestal
   and base 30.00
15" high. Glass, round, slender.
   Thumbprint base and cover 30.00

Apothecary Bottle. 8½" high. Tr. Opii
Camph $22.00

Apothecary Bottle. 12½" high. Aq. Rosae. Clear glass............$35.00

23½" high to top of ground stopper.
Pair 250.00
Jar. Quart. "Ext. Amygd. A" on side.
Clear glass 12.50

AVON

After Shave Sample, 1936	22.50
Alpine Flask	50.00
Attention Cologne, 1947...........	70.00
Bath Season, 1967	5.00
Bath Urn, 1967	9.00
Bath Urn, milk glass, 1963	7.50
Bay Rum Jug, 1964................	7.00
Bay Rum Keg, 1965	14.50
Blacksmith Anvil, 1972	4.00
Books. Amber....................	6.50
Boot, gold top	3.50
Boot, silver top	6.50
Bud Vase, 1962..................	10.00
Bud Vase, 1966..................	9.00

Bud Vase, 1968..................	8.00
Candleholder, frosted glass	9.00
Candleholder, red	10.00
Candleholder, milk glass, 1964	6.00
Candlestick	7.50
Captain's Choice..................	7.00
Car, Dune Buggy..................	4.50
Casey's Lantern, amber............	12.50
Casey's Lantern, red	12.50
Christmas Call	10.00
Christmas Ornaments	
Angel........................	8.00
Balls.........................	6.00
Candle.......................	12.00
Icicle	6.50
Sparkler	6.00
Tree	8.00
Clock, Grandfather	5.00
Cotillion, 1961	8.50
Crystal Chandelier	3.50
Crystal Glory, 1962	10.00
Decanter, Armoire................	4.50
Decanter, Inkwell................	5.50
Decisions, 1965	20.00
Defender	15.00
Demi Cup, 1968	12.50
Demonstrator Fragrances	
Set of 7	6.00
Set of 14	10.00
Dollars & Scents	20.00
Dolphin	7.50
Duck, Mallard	7.50
Elephant	8.00
First Edition, Book	4.00
First Mate	8.00
Fox Hunt Set	27.50
Fragrance Bell, 1965	5.00
Futura	15.00
Gavel...........................	12.00
General 4-4-0	3.50
Gentleman's Collection...........	15.00
Globe...........................	7.50
Golf Club	5.00
Greek Goddess	8.00

Straight Eight Car $4.50

Heart, Set of 3	18.00
Here's My Heart Cologne Mist	9.50
Ice Cream Sundae	12.50
Just Two. Boxed	50.00
Key Note	12.50
King for a Day, 1965	10.00
Ladies' Slipper. Frosted, boxed	5.00
Lamp	4.50
Man's World	5.00
Mickey Mouse. Boxed	5.00
Miss Lollipop Spray Mist	5.00
Motorcycle	4.50
Opening Play	10.00
Orchard Blossom Cologne, 1941	50.00
Pipe Dream	14.50
Pipe Full	2.00
Player Piano	5.00

Pretty Peach Spray Mist	12.50
Quaintance, Harmony Set. Boxed	30.00
Radio	2.75
Renaissance Trio	10.00
Riviera Decanter	12.00
Rose Fragrance. Frosted stopper	10.00
Royal Orb	17.50
Scimitar	12.50
Sheriff's Badge	9.50
Skin-So-Soft Decanter, 1964	13.50
Snail	7.00
Snoopy. Ace	3.50
Splash & Spray	18.50
Stamp Paid Test Bottle	45.00
Stein, 6 oz., 1965	7.00
Stein, Hunter's	10.00
Sterling Six Car	5.50
Straight Eight Car	4.50
To A Wild Rose Cologne, 1950	10.00
Topaze Gem Perfume	95.00
Town Pump	5.00
Twenty Paces. Blue box	85.00
Viking Horn	12.50
Weather or Not	4.50
Western Choice	16.00
Wild Country Saddle Kit	6.50
Windjammer	5.00

BARBER

These bottles were made of clear, colored and milk glass and were used for holding and dispensing hair tonic and shampoo preparations. Many of the colored bottles were imported from Bohemia.

Amber	55.00
Amethyst. Blown, enamel decor	65.00
Amethyst. 10". Flowers, leaves, white/gold. Pewter top, rough pontil	72.50
Bohemian Glass. 12-oz. capacity. Enamel floral decor	85.00
Bristol. Black enamel, 9½"	35.00
Bristol type, with original stopper. Elaborate decor of flower sprays allover	39.00
Carnival. Marigold	67.50
Chartreuse green. Raised enamel decor	72.50
Chartreuse green. Raised enamel decor, old bronze hunting dog with rabbit	140.00
Clamsbroth. 7" high. "Witch Hazel"	39.50
Clear ribbed, with blue bottom	55.00
Cobalt blue. Enamel decor. Pair	125.00
Cobalt Satin. Tapered, 4-sided, with two elongated ovals. C. 1880	75.00
Cranberry. ITP Pair	150.00

Swinger Golf Bag. 1969. Bravo After Shave. 5-oz. $5.00

Amethyst. 7" high, enameled floral decor......................$55.00

Opalescent. Late	25.00
Vaseline	90.00
Honey Amber. White stripes, quilted pattern, polished pontil, porcelain stopper	85.00
Mary Gregory. Cobalt, all white. Boy playing tennis. Stoppered	150.00
Milk Glass	
Bulbous base	50.00
Hexagon base	47.50
Octagon neck, opaque	37.50
Straight neck	45.00
Opalescent. Stripes	95.00
Red, brown & white splatter, 8"	58.50
Sapphire blue. Blown, thumbprint...	95.00
Satin Glass. Cranberry with white looping, pewter stopper. 10¼" high	165.00
Sea Foam. White milk glass, colorful painted flowers and leaves. 11" high	65.00
Sterling. Cone shape, 10" high, 2" base	125.00
Tiffany type	175.00

Cranberry. Overlay portrait of beautiful woman. Tall	115.00
Cranberry & Opaline. Overlay, blown & 3-mold pattern, swirled, 6½" high.....................	95.00
Cranberry & Opaline. Striped.......	95.00
Cut glass. Sterling top	70.00
End-of-Day Glass. Amber & white ...	52.50
Frosted glass. Pottery dispenser. "Water" & "Witch Hazel." Pair	40.00
Green. Embossed glass, bulbous, 5½" to top of metal shaker	45.00
Handpainted. Bluebirds, square	30.00
Hobnail	
Amber	82.00
Blue	87.50
Honey amber	85.00
Opalescent	87.50

BEER

Anheuser-Busch, Eagle-A monogram, amber..................	4.50
Ballantine's miniature	4.00
Bosch. Quart, amber	7.50
Budweiser. 24-oz. Conrad & Co......	13.50
Buffalo Brewing Co., San Francisco. Amber	7.50
Falstaff. 11½", embossed, green ...	10.00
Fort Pitt. Miniature...............	2.50
Free-blown. Quart; pontil. Early	25.00
Indianapolis Brewing Co. Embossed dancing girl. Green	6.50
Milk Glass	12.50
Pabst. Light purple	7.50
Red, dark. Quart.................	8.00
Schlitz. 12-oz., red	5.00
Terre Haute Brewing Co. Embossed, Amber	4.50

BITTERS

The bottles originally contained various concoctions of herbs which were mixed with alcohol and sold as tonics from about 1860 to 1900. "Old timers" have stated that many ardent W.C.T.U. members, in the early days of the Prohibition Movement, returned home exhausted after fighting "demon rum" at the local meeting house, regained their strength and stability by taking a liberal dose of a favorite bitters tonic which, unknown to them, had an alcohol content of 75% to 80%.

"Rex Bitters." Original contents $50.00

African Stomach Bitters. Amber, cylindrical, quart	42.50
Allen's, William. Congress Bitters, green Watson's 4	275.00
Angelica Bitter Tonic. Jos. Triner, Chicago. Amber	50.00
Atwood's Jaundice Bitters. Aqua, 12-sided. Moses Atwood, George-town, Mass. ½ pint	35.00
Augauer Bitters. Light green, orginal label. 8" high	65.00
Baker's Orange Grove Bitters. Amber, square, rope corners, qt. .	110.00
Barry's Tricophorous, o.p.	35.00
Berkshire. Pig. Olive amber	150.00
Bell's Cocktail Bitters. Amber, lady's legs	450.00
Bismarck. Bitters, W. H. Miller, N.Y., U.S.A.	60.00

Brown's Bitters. Amber	30.00
Brown's Celebrated Indian Herb Bitters. Amber, Watson's 57 Figural Indian Queen	300.00
Burdock's Blood Bitters	40.00
Cauldwell's Herb Bitters. Amber pontil	200.00
Clark's Vegetable Sherry Wine Bitters. Aqua, pontil, Watson's. Gallon	135.00
*Dr. Fisch's Bitters. Lt. amber	150.00
Dr. Flint's Quaker Bitters. Providence, R.I.	25.00
Doctor Henley's Wild Grape Root Bitters. Cylindrical, aqua, "IXL" in oval, quart	60.00
*Dr. J. Hostetter's Stomach Bitters . .	50.00
Dr. Jacob's Bitters. Thin whittle marked bottle	125.00
Dr. Langley's Bitters. Large, rare amber, labeled, 1864. Picture of Dr. Langley	150.00
Dr. Langley's Root & Herb Bitters, Aqua	40.00
Dr. Loew's. Celebrated Stomach, green	150.00
Dr. Pierce's Golden Medical Discovery, Buffalo, N.Y., aqua	45.00
Dr. C. W. Roback's Stomach Bitters. Light amber	100.00
Dr. Tompkins. Vegetable Bitters. Blue, green, rectangular	450.00
Dr. Vonhoph's Curacoa Bitters, dark reddish amber	75.00
Doyle's Hops Bitters. Amber, square, with bunch of hops and leaves. Qt.	48.50
Drake's S. T. 1860 Plantation Bitters. X on roof of log cabin-shaped bottle, amber, Patent 1862, ¾-quart	75.00
Durand's Stomach Bitters	32.50
E. Dexter Loveridge Wahoa Bitters. Pat. 1893. Roofed shoulders, amber	165.00
Electric Bitters. Amber, square with depressed panels. H. E. Bucklew & Co., Chicago, Ill.	38.50
Fish Bitters. Amber, Watson's 125	125.00
Gentiana Root & Herb. Light green . .	115.00
Goff's Herb, aqua	15.00
Greeley's Bourbon Whiskey Bitters. Barrel, olive green. Watson's 145	450.00
Hartshorn's Bitters	45.00
H. P. Herb Wild Cherry Bitters. Amber, log cabin shape, rope corners, Watson's 148, ¾ quart . .	200.00
Holtzermann's Stomach Bitters. Amber, Watson's 172	150.00
Kelly's Old Cabin Bitters. Amber, Watson's 199	550.00

Lash's Kidney & Liver Bitters, medium amber.................. 45.00
Malt Bitters Co. Boston, Mass. 20.00
Morning Star Bitters. Amber, Watson's 232 .... 225.00
Myer's American Stomach Bitters. Paper label only 100.00
National Bitters. Figural ear of corn, amber with base stain. Watson's 236........................... 275.00
Old Dr. Warren's Quaker Bitters 80.00
Old Sachem, barrel, amber, Watson's 244 .... 275.00
Paine's Celery Compound. 10" deep, amber.................. 50.00
*Perrine's Apple & Ginger Bitters. Amber, rope corners, log cabin shape, ¾-quart 45.00
Petzold's Genuine German Bitters. Amber. Watson's 256 .... 120.00
Pineapple Bitters. Dark honey amber. 275.00
Pinkerton's Wahoo Claisaya. Amber. 50.00
Plain. Amber, barrel shape, ¾-quart 35.00
Prickley Ash Bitters. Square, bevelled corners, ¾-quart 65.00
Richardson's. Green 50.00
Richardson's. S. O. Bitters 45.00
Romaine's Crimean Bitters. Amber, Watson's 282 .... 175.00
Saint Goddard Herb. Amber 65.00
Saint Jacobs 75.00
Sarsaparilla & Tomato Bitters. Aqua, F. Brown, Boston. Pint 50.00
Simon's Centennial. Aqua.......... 500.00
*Suffolk Bitters. Yellow Pig. Scarce, Watson's 322 .... 750.00
Tippecanoe Bitters. Deep amber 100.00
Travellers Bitters. Amber 65.00
*Warner's Safe Kidney & Liver Cure. Dark amber, picture of safe on front. "Rochester, N.Y." below, 9½" high...................... 30.00
Wheeler's Tonic Sherry Wine Bitters, with label, aqua, Watson's 518 ... 325.00
White's Stomach Bitters 50.00
Yerba Buena Bitters, Watson's 375. Amber....................... 90.00

*Reproduced Item

COUGH SYRUP

Dill's, White Pine & Tar 3.00
Dr. A. Boschee's German Syrup 4.50
Dr. Hess Distemper Fever & Cough Remedy 4.00
Dr. Hooker's Cough & Croup Syrup .. 4.00
Dr. Jayne's Expectorant. Aqua, 5½", quart 3.50
Dr. B. J. Kendall's Quick Relief 3.50

"Chamberlain's Cough Remedy." Pat. Medicine. Original package ...$15.00

Dr. King's New Discovery to Coughs and Colds 3.50
Indian Vegetable Cough Syrup & Blood Purifiers, S. B. Goffs 4.00

FIGURALS

Antelope. Horn-shaped. 15", twisted 30.00
Belt and mailed, gloved hand. 8½" high, 3" diam. at base. Clear. Pat. 1877. E. R. Durkee & Co., N.Y. 7.50
Black Man. 11½" high. Dressed in high hat and tails, playing banjo, ceramic 40.00
Crane. 14½" high, clear glass 22.50
Dog, brown 12.50
Dog, standing on hind legs. 13" high, clear glass..................... 15.00
*George Washington, 10", clear 9.50
Guitar. 16", amber glass, with cork . 12.50
Hessian Soldier. 7¼", clear glass ... 35.00

Japanese Gods. Seven, painted china	15.00
King's Gate. Caernarvon Castle	10.00
Leprechaun	12.00
Madonna. Cobalt, embossed head of infant at base	13.00
Monkey. Wrapped around green bottle......................	10.00
Mr. Pickwick. 9" high, clear	7.00
Nude. 13" high. Plump, draped. Partially frosted	45.00
Old Methuselah. Round, amber	10.00
Potato shape. 5" long, screw top. Embossed "World's Fair 1893" ...	20.00
Queen Elizabeth. Bust	22.50
Sailor Boy. 13" high. Clear glass	12.00
Santa Claus. Red Satin Glass. 1973 ..	60.00
Scotsman. 17" high	35.00
Skeleton in Shroud with 5 skull cups. "Poison." Mkd. Shofu	36.00
Taylor's Castle	12.00
Totem Pole. German Porcelain	35.00
Victorian Lady. Milk glass. 11" high .	22.50
Violin. 9" high, blue	30.00
*Violin. 10" high, clear	15.00

*Reproduced Item

FOOD

Capers. 6" high, green	4.00
Catsup. Heinz, large	20.00
Chase and Sanborn Coffee Importers. Rectangular, amber	3.50

Jumbo Peanut Butter. Frank Tea & Spice Co., Cincinnati, Ohio	4.00
Ketchup. No. 207	2.00
"Make Five Gallons of Delicious Drink. Hire's Improved Root Beer." 4½" high.....................	3.00
Mellines. Infants.................	7.50
My Wife's Salad Dressing. Sun square	4.00
New England Maple Syrup Co. Pint ..	12.50
S.S.P. Olive Oil. Ball base, long neck, aqua.......................	3.50
Peppersauce. 8" high, clear, tall and thin. 25 concentric lines	4.00
Peppersauce. Ridgy. Aqua, green, teal blue	7.50
Snow Crop Syrup. Shape of bear, bank slot in top	4.50
Worcestershire. Lea & Perrins. 11½" high, glass stopper	5.00
Yogurt. Quart	6.50

FRUIT JARS

ABC. Aqua, quart	150.00
American. Quart	50.00
Anchor Hocking Mason. Various sizes........................	1.00 to 2.00
Atlas Good Luck. Embossed clover front, amber. Gallon, ½ gallon, quart and pint. Each	6.00

Milk Bottle. "Dairylee Milk, Our New
Baby Top Bottle." Quart $6.00

"Mason's Patent. Nov. 30th 1858."
Maltese Cross. Quart $9.50

"Mason's Patent. Nov. 30th 1858." ½
gal. $4.00

Atlas. Mason's Pat. Quart	4.50
Ball Improved, band, blue, quart	5.50
Ball Perfect Mason. Amber, ½ gallon	30.00
Ball Perfect Mason. Purple tint, screw-on, porcelain liner	5.00
Ball Standard. Blue, wax seal, quart .	6.50
Beaver. Beaver chewing twig on front, glass lid, zinc ring. Made in Canada. Quart	27.50
Best. Quart	20.00
Boldt. Quart	7.50
Boyd's. Genuine Mason, green	4.00
Climax. Pat. 7/14/08 on base. Glass lid, wire closure, quart	7.50
Double Safety. Clear, lighting closure, quart	2.50
Economy. Pair	1.50

Electric. World in center, glass lid, wire clamp, quart	65.00
Electroglas Mason. Amber, quart ...	6.00
Empire. Stippled Cross. Quart	5.00
Eureka. Aqua, quart	45.00
Gem, The. Quart	8.00
Glenshaw Mason. Screw band, gallon lid, quart or pint	5.50
Globe. Amber, pint	30.00
Globe. Amber, quart	35.00
Green Mountain. Aqua, quart	10.00
Hero Cross. Mason Improved. ½ gallon	5.00
Jeannette Mason Home Packer. Pint	3.50
Kline. Aqua, quart	20.00
Kline. Jar with stopper. Oct. 27, 1863, ½ gallon................	100.00
Lamb Mason. Amber, quart	6.00
Lightning	
Amber, ½ gallon	25.00
Amber, gallon	35.00
Amber, quart	20.00
Aqua, glass lid, wire bail, quart ..	4.00
Mason. Pat. Nov. 30, 1858. Sunburst, moon and star above, ball on back. Orig. lid, aqua, ½ gallon ...	75.00
Mason. Improved, C.F.J. on back, aqua, quart...................	10.00
Mason's. Keystone, ½ gallon	15.00
Mason's Pat. Nov. 30, 1858. Aqua, various sizes. Each............2.00 to 4.00	
Millville. Atmospheric. Glass lid, metal clamp. Aqua, Pat. June 18, 1861, quart...................	40.00
Millville. Atmospheric, aqua, two-quart, complete	22.50
Queen. Aqua, quart..............	2.50
Queen, The. Aqua, ½ gallon	15.00
Quick Seal Dated, clear, quart/pint	4.00
Royal. Clear, quart	7.50
Safety Valve. Mkd. on bottom only. Clear, lid and clamp, ½ gallon ...	12.00
Whitall-Tatum. O.P. Pint	22.50
Woodbury. CWW on front. Lid with drain. ½ gallon	25.00

MALTS

Hoff's, whittled, O.G...............	6.50
Horlick's	
½ pint	2.00
Pint.........................	3.00
6-quart.......................	7.50
King, C. A. Pure Malt Dept. on bottom. Shape of Hoff, amber	5.00
Old Bushmill's Dist. Co., The Pure Malt Dept.....................	5.00

"Horlick's Malted Milk." Pint $3.00

MEDICINES

C. Berry & Co. 84 Leverett St., Boston, 1917. 9½" 5.00
"Black Gin for the Kidneys." Reverse, "Wm. F. Zoeller, Pittsburgh, Pa." Full of bubbles, amber, 9" square 10.00
Castoria. 5½" high 3.50
Coe's Dyspepsia Cure 5.00
Conners Blood Remedy 12.50
Cooper's New Discovery. Aqua 5.00
Creamer's Cure Sample 3.50
Dr. Carter Balsam 7.50
Dr. Crossman's Specific Mixture 3.50
Dr. Cumming's "Vecetine." Clear . . . 4.00
Dr. Harter's. Full 25.00

Dr. Hayne's Arabian Balsam 3.50
Dr. Jayne's Alterative. Aqua, flask shape, whittle marks, pontil 7.50
Dr. H. Kelsey, Lowell, Mass. 3.50
Dr. Kennedy's Medical Discovery . . . 4.00
Dr. Kilmer's Swamp Root 10.00
Dr. Sanford's Liver Invigorator 5.00
Dr. F. C. Wilkinson's Horse Liniment . 3.00
Elmer's Great French Remedy 3.50
Foley's Pain Relief 3.50
H. D. Fowler, Boston 4.00
Hibbard's Rheumatic Syrup. Amber, square 6.00
Household Panacea 7.50
Life Plant. Embossed bird. Milk glass, oval 12.50
Lindsey's Blood Plus Searcher 7.50
"L.Q.C. Wishart's Pine Tree Tar Cordial, Phila. Patent 1859." Embossed pine tree, emerald green, quart 40.00
Lydia Pinkham 5.00
Malydor Private Physician. ½ pint . . 7.50
Mustang Liniment 17.50
Paine's Celery Compound. Amber . . 7.50
Physician's Travelling Bottles. Clear blown glass, 2½" high 3.00
Shaker Digestive Cordial. Milk. Rectangular 10.00
Taylor's Cherokee Remedy 7.50

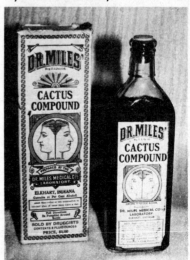

"Dr. Miles' Cactus Compound." Unopened bottle, original carton . . $16.50

Warner's Safe Kidney & Liver Cure
Amber, ½ pint 85.00
Amber, pint 60.00
Red. Melbourne. ½ pint 90.00
Red. Rochester. ½ pint 15.00
Wine of Life. C. W. Beggs, Sons & Co.
Original contents, sealed 15.00
Wm. Radam's Microbe Killer. With
label 35.00
World Famed Blood Mixture. Blue . . . 17.50
Wyeth Dose. Cobalt, complete 7.50

POISON

Bimal. Blue, 3½" high 22.50
Coffin-shape 12.50
Gift, Skull & Cross bones. Germany . 12.50
Not to be taken. Embossed 15.00
"Poison" Embossed
Quilted. Cobalt 15.00
Rectangular 7.50
Round 5.00
Vertical deep blue 25.00

SARSAPARILLA AND SODA

"Moxie" embossed $15.00

Sarsaparilla
Ayer's Compound Extract 7.50
Babcock's 45.00
DeWitt's 25.00
Dr. Townsend's. Green, quart 50.00
Hood's 4.00
Joy's 22.50
Soda
Canada Dry Ginger Ale 50
Coca Cola:
Amber. 1916 . . . . 30.00
Anniversary. Gold, 6½ oz. 35.00
Embossed on bottom 1.50
*Miniature 50
Script. Straight-sided 3.50
WWI, dated Nov. 16, 1915 . . . . . . 5.00
Dr. Pepper. Embossed 3.50
Gay-ola Cola 6.00
Moxie. Embossed 15.00
Moxie. Label 10.00
Nehi Lemon 2.50
Nu Grape 2.50
Orange Crush. Embossed 5.00
Pepsi Cola. Amber, 16-oz. 4.50
Royal Crown. 12-oz. 3.00
Soda & Mineral Co., Warren, Pa. . . 12.50
*Reproduced Item

SNUFF

These are small bottles made of porcelain
glass or cut from one piece of rock crystal,
agate, coral or jade. They are often intricately
engraved on the outer surface and sometimes
decorated with vegetable and mineral dyes on
the interior.

The habit of carrying snuff bottles originated in
the orient during the 18th century when snuff
was introduced as a medical cure-all. A large
number of bottles were exported to Europe
from China - especially the porcelain and glass
varieties. In Holland the bottles were used for
ungents or salves.

Agate. Moss. 1750-1850 . . . . 375.00
Beetlenut. Carved, bird and flower
motif 85.00
Chalcidony. Carved. Tapered 195.00
Chinese Export. Famile Rose. C. 1850 75.00
Chinese Export. Famile Rose. Chia
Ching 275.00
Chinese Export. Famile Rose. Tao
Kuang Period 300.00
Cinnabar. Red with carvings, white
jade top 235.00
Clambroth. 3" high, black koro
design. Ivory spoon 140.00
Cloisonne. Autumn foliage on blue
ground. Cloisonne stopper 200.00

3" high. Oriental figures seated.
Green, red stopper $55.00
Cloisonne. Floral 135.00
Cloisonne. 3" high, baby design 150.00
Glass. 2½" high. Carved
aquamarine, matching stopper.
1800-1900 . . . . 200.00
Glass. 2½" high. Inside painted.
Signed, Shin Mao Kit 225.00
Ivory. Man on camel 130.00
Ivory. 2½" high. Shape of man's
head 125.00
Jade. 3" high. Bridesmaid. Pebble-
shaped. Coral stopper, wooden
dipper 200.00
Jade. 3" high. Carved. Urn-shaped
with lion finial 235.00
Jade. 3" high. Muttonfat color 225.00
Jade. Brown, carved 225.00
Jade. White. 1¼x2x2½", on teak-
wood stand. Chinese 250.00
Lapis. Lazuli. Carved 130.00
Lapis. Lazuli. Oval, flattened 75.00
Mother of Pearl. Carved 65.00
Mother of Pearl. Ovate, flattened.
Scenic 50.00
Opal. Carved 375.00
Peking. Carved. Yellow 130.00
Peking. Carved, painted 200.00
Porcelain. 3½" high. White ground
with green and orange decor 150.00
Porcelain. Blue, gray and red under-
glaze. Two poems 185.00
Porcelain. Blue and white, vase-
shaped on teakwood stand. With
stopper and dipper 165.00
Porcelain. Dragons on yellow. C. 1850 95.00
Turquoise. Carved, 2½" high.
Chinese decor 275.00
Quart. 2½" high, on stand 160.00

Ardos

Clock 35.00
Duck, green 35.00
Rocker 25.00

Barsottini [Italy]

Elks Head 1869-1969 . . . . $12.00

Antique Carriage 7.50
Bacchus 9.00
Cannon 10.00
Colosseum 10.00
Donkey 6.50
Elephant 6.50
Elk's Head 12.00
Florentine Steeple 10.00
Fruit Basket 10.00
Lamp Lighter 15.00
Leaning Tower of Pisa 7.50

Love Birds	15.00
Monk with Wine Glass	12.50
Owl	12.50
Rabbit Gnawing on Carrot	12.50
Santa Claus with Bag of Toys	16.50
Wine Cask	22.00

Beam, Jim

The Beam Distillery was established in Kentucky by Jacob Beam in 1788. About 1880, Colonel James Beam [Jim Beam] began work at the family distillery making bourbon, which was to bear his name later.

The company began the novelty bottle-Bourbon business in 1953, when a cocktail shaker decanter was designated for the Christmas trade. It was an immediate success. In 1955, the 160th anniversary of the concern, the first bottle of the present executive series was issued, in the form of a decanter with a long pouring lip and a white stopper.

Trophy. 1970. Gray poodle $8.50

Centennial [First issue, 1960]

1960 - Santa Fe	235.00
1960 - Civil War. North or South. Each	37.50
1964 - St. Louis Arch	22.50
1966 - Alaska Purchase	16.00

1967 - Antioch	11.00
1967 - Cheyenne	8.00
1967 - St. Louis Arch	16.50
1968 - Laramie	8.50
1968 - Reno	10.00
1968 - San Diego	5.00
1969 - Baseball	10.00
1969 - Lombard Lilac	8.00
1969 - Portola Trek	6.50
1969 - Powell Expedition	7.50
1970 - Preakness	6.50
1970 - Riverside	12.00
1971 - Chicago Fire	10.00
1971 - Indianapolis Sesquicentennial	6.00
1972 - Colorado Springs	6.00
1972 - Dodge City	6.50
1972 - General Stark	9.50
1973 - Cherry Hill Country Club	10.00
1973 - Phi Sigma Kappa	7.50
1973 - Ralph's Meat Market	9.00
1973 - Reidsville, N. Carolina	12.00

Collector's

1966 - Collector's Edition. Set	25.00
1967 - Collector's Edition. Set	20.00
1968 - Collector's Edition. Set	18.50
1969 - Collector's Edition. Set	16.50
1972 - Collector's Edition. Set	15.00

Executive [First issue, 1955]

1955 - Royal Porcelain	250.00
1956 - Royal Gold	130.00
1957 - Royal DiMonte	85.00
1958 - Cherub, gray	100.00
1959 - Drinkers or Tavern	75.00
1960 - Cherub, blue	100.00
1961 - Chalice, gold	85.00
1962 - Flower Basket	62.50
1963 - Royal Rose	60.00
1964 - Royal Gold Diamond	60.00
1965 - Marbled Fantasy	80.00
1966 - Majestic	40.00
1967 - Prestige	25.00
1968 - Presidential	15.00
1969 - Sovereign	12.00
1970 - Charisma	12.00
1971 - Fantasia	13.00
1972 - Regency	18.00
1973 - Executive	13.50
1974 - Executive	15.00

Glass Specialties [First issue, 1953]

1953 - Cocktail Shaker	7.50
1954 - Pyrex Coffee Warmer	10.00
1955 - Ducks & Geese	8.00
1956 - Pyrex Coffee Warmer	8.00
1957 - Royal Opal	8.50
1958 - Royal Emperor	7.50
1960 - Olympia	7.50
1962 - Cleopatra Yellow	16.50
1963 - Delft Blue	6.50
1963 - Delft Rose	7.50

1963 - Dancing Scot, short	37.50
1963 - Dancing Scot, tall	12.50
1964 - Smoky Crystal Geni	9.00
1965 - Cameo Blue	6.00
1966 - Pressed Crystal Scotch	9.00
1967 - Pressed Crystal Ruby	10.00
1968 - Pressed Crystal Emerald	6.50
1969 - Pressed Crystal Opaline	7.50
1971 - Pressed Crystal Blue	6.00

Political [First issue, 1956]

1956 - Elephant Ash Tray	20.00
1956 - Donkey Ash Tray	20.00
1960 - Donkey	18.00
1960 - Elephant	18.00
1964 - Donkey Boxer	18.00
1964 - Elephant Boxer	18.00
1968 - Donkey, Clown	12.00
1968 - Elephant, Clown	12.00
1972 - Donkey, Football	10.00
1972 - Elephant, Football	10.00

Regal China [First Issue, 1955]

1955 - Ivory Ash Tray	26.50
1956 - Black Canasta	17.50
1958 - Alaska Star	75.00
1962 - Seattle World's Fair	25.00
1964 - N.Y. World's Fair	25.00
1965 - Green Fox	47.50
1966 - Turquoise Jug	7.50
1967 - Blue Fox	125.00
1967 - Hawaii	62.50
1967 - Redwood	11.50
1968 - Antique Trader	8.50
1968 - Cable Car	8.50
1968 - Cardinal	45.00
1968 - Slot Machine. Gray	9.00
1969 - Gold Fox	80.00
1969 - Grand Canyon, Arizona	16.50
1970 - Amvets	8.50
1970 - Bell Ringer. Plaid	10.00
1970 - Germany	8.00
1970 - Indianapolis 500	8.50
1970 - London Bridge	7.50
1970 - Mission Club	22.50
1970 - Paul Bunyan	8.50
1970 - P.G.A.	5.50
1970 - Shriner	8.50
1970 - Submarine	7.00
1971 - Mint 400	10.00
1971 - Olympia	5.00
1972 - Zimmerman's Brown Vase	8.00
1973 - Zimmerman Blue Beauty	15.00

Specialties [First issue, 1956]

1956 - Foremost, white and gold	135.00
1956 - Foremost, black and gold	145.00
1956 - Foremost, pink speckled	600.00
1957 - Harold's Club - Man in barrel. No. 1	465.00
1958 - Harold's Club - Man in barrel. No. 2	275.00

Political. Elephant, donkey clowns.
Each $12.00

1963 - Harold's Club Nevada Silver	180.00
1963 - Harrah's Club Grey	475.00
1963 - Harrah's Club Silver	900.00
1964 - First National Bank Chicago	2750.00
1965 - Harold's Club Pinwheel	72.50
1967 - Harold's Club VIP Exec.	55.00
1967 - Richard's New Mexico	6.50
1968 - Armanetti Vase	10.00
1968 - Black Katz	12.50
1968 - Harold's Club VIP	55.00
1969 - Harold's Club VIP	85.00
1970 - Harold's Club VIP	55.00
1971 - Armane TTI	12.50
1971 - Harold's Club VIP	50.00
1972 - Harold's Club VIP	40.00
1973 - Harold's Club VIP	35.00
1973 - ABC Liquor Stores	14.00

States [First issue, 1958]

1958 - Alaska	85.00
1959 - Hawaii	65.00
1959 - Colorado	47.50
1959 - Oregon	45.00
1960 - Kansas	68.50
1963 - Idaho	75.00
1963 - Montana	85.00
1963 - West Virginia	125.00
1963 - Nevada	60.00
1963 - New Jersey, blue	65.00
1964 - North Dakota	78.50
1965 - Wyoming	75.00
1966 - Ohio	14.50
1967 - Hawaii [re-issue]	50.00
1967 - Kentucky, brown	17.50
1967 - Nebraska	12.00

1967 - Pennsylvania	8.00
1968 - Arizona	6.50
1968 - Florida, white	7.50
1968 - Illinois	8.00
1969 - South Dakota	7.50
1970 - Maine	7.50
1972 - Delaware. Blue hen	8.50

Trophy [First issue, 1957]

1957 - Duck	42.50
1957 - Fish	38.50
1958 - Ram	190.00
1959 - Dog	67.50
1961 - Pheasant	18.50
1962 - Black Horse	22.00
1962 - Brown Horse	22.00
1962 - White Horse	22.00
1963 - Doe	37.50
1965 - Fox	40.00
1966 - Pheasant [Re-issue]	16.50
1966 - Eagle	16.00
1967 - Cats	11.50
1967 - Doe [Re-issue]	25.00
1967 - Fox [Re-issue]	30.00
1968 - Cardinal [Re-issue]	12.00
1969 - Blue Jay	8.50
1969 - Robin	8.50
1969 - Woodpecker	9.00
1970 - Poodle, grey	8.50
1971 - Wisconsin Muskie	10.00
1973 - Cardinal, female	18.00
1973 - Tiffiny	10.00
1974 - Blue Gill	10.00

Bischoff

Bell Tower	28.50
Chinese Man	35.00
Chinese Woman	35.00
Christmas Tree	55.00
Church with Bell	40.00
Clown	37.50
Coach	40.00
Egyptian Decanter, double	35.00
Fish. Dark red	18.50
Flower Decanter	35.00
Geese. Ruby	19.50
Mask. Grey	20.00
Matador	30.00
Rose	28.50
Senorita	35.00
Three-dimension Church	25.00
Venetian	22.50
Wild Geese	30.00

Bols

Ballerina	12.50
Blackberry Delft	15.00
Creme de Menthe Delft	12.00
Dutch Boy	20.00
Dutch Girl	20.00

Borghina [Italy]

African Bust Alborada	18.50

Cat, Black. Small	4.00
Cherubs with Mirror	9.50
Clowns with Mandolin	16.50
Dog	15.00
Egyptian Bust Sophia	15.00
European Bust	15.00
Horse Head	15.00
Leaning Tower	8.00
Mercedes Benz	6.50
Nubian Girl	7.00
Old Ford	7.50
Peasant Boy	7.50
Peasant Girl	7.50
Rooster	5.00
Santa Maria	7.50
Sedan Car	5.00

Brooks, Ezra

Alligator #1 and #2	15.00
American Legion. 1971	25.00
Antique Cannon	12.50
Antique Phonograph	15.00
Antique Slot Machine	22.50
Antique Telephone	13.50
Arizona	7.50
Balloon. Clown	13.50
Bare Knuckle Fighter	10.00
Beaver	12.50
Big Bertha	15.00
Big Daddy - Florida State	8.50
Big Red - Football #1	26.50
Big Red - Football #2	16.50
Big Red - Football #3	16.50
Bird Dog	10.00
Birthday Cake	14.00
Black Angus, 1973	17.50
Bordertown	12.00
Bowler	13.50
Brahma Bull	13.00

Cable Car. "Powell & Hyde Sts." $10.00

Overland Express [Stagecoach] $10.00

Bucket of Blood	17.50
Buffalo Hunt	12.50
Cable Cars	10.00
California Quail	7.50
Ceremonial Indian	22.50
Cheyenne Shootout	7.50
Chicago Water Tower	10.00
Christmas Decanters	10.00
Churchill	9.50
Clown on Drum, short	55.00
Clown on Drum, tall	70.00
Court Jester	12.50
Dead Wagon	10.00
Delta Belle	14.50
Dice	7.50
Distillery	20.00
Drum and Bugle Corps	15.00
Elk	12.50
Fire Engine	10.00
Fordson Tractor	16.00
Foremost Astronaut	10.00
Fresno Grape	11.50
Game Cock	14.00
Gold Miner	7.50
Gold Turkey	45.00
Golden Eagle	15.00
Golden Horseshoe	15.00
Golden Nugget	12.50
Golden Rooster #1	70.00
Grandfather Clock	9.50
Grizzly Bear	8.50
Gun Series, set of 4	20.00
Harold's Club Dice	12.50
Hereford	12.50
Historical Flasks, Set of 4	16.00
Hollywood Cops	15.00
Idaho Potato	22.50
Indian, Cigar Store	10.00
Indianapolis 500 Race Car	15.00
Iowa Statehouse	25.00
Jack of Diamonds	8.50

Japanese Pistol	65.00
Jayhawk #1 and #2	10.00
Kachina Doll	85.00
Katz Philharmonic	12.00
Kentucky Gentleman	17.50
Killer Whale	25.00
King of Clubs	10.00
Laurel and Hardy	27.50
Legionnaire	20.00
Liberty Bell	12.50
Lion on Rock	9.00
Liquor Square	16.50
Longhorn Steer	15.00
Maine Lighthouse	18.50
Maine Lobster	27.50
Man O'War	25.00
Military Tank	14.00
Mr. Foremost	15.00
Mr. Merchant	15.00
Missouri Mule	10.00
Motorcycle	12.00
Oil Gusher	10.00
Ontario 500	10.00
Panda Bear	15.00
Penguin	12.50

Pot Belly Stove $10.00

Penny Farthington	12.50
Phoenix Bird	50.00
Pirate	9.50
Pot Belly Stove	10.00
Queen of Hearts	8.00
Race Car	16.50
Ram	12.50
Razorback Hog	20.00
Reno Arch	8.50
Sailfish	10.00
Sea Captain	12.50
Senator	15.00
Silver Dollar	12.50
Silver Spur	12.50
Ski Boot	12.50
Snomobile	11.50
So. Carolina Game Cock	15.00
Sprint Racer	15.00
Stagecoach	10.00
Tecumseh	17.50
Tennis Player	15.00
Texas Longhorn	16.00
Ticker Tape	10.00
Tonopah	20.00
Trail Bike	14.50
Train	10.00
Trout and Fly	10.00
Virginia Cardinal	25.00
Washington Salmon	45.00
W. Va. Mountaineer	130.00
W. Va. Mountain Lady	20.00
Wheat Shocker	20.00
Wichita Centennial	18.00
Zimmerman Old Hat	12.50

Buton

Ceramic Book	25.00
Ceramic Cherry	20.00

Dant, J. W.

Alamo, black	7.50
American Legion	10.00
Bobwhite	13.50
Boston Tea Party	7.50
California Quail	10.00
Chukar Partridge	12.50
Crossing the Delaware	10.00
Eagles	10.00
Ft. Sill, Oklahoma	12.00
Indianapolis 500	12.50
Mountain Quail	12.50
Mt. Rushmore	12.00
Patrick Henry	12.00
Prairie Chicken	12.50
Ringnecked Pheasant	12.50
Ruffed Grouse	12.50
Woodcock	12.50
Wrong Way Charlie	25.00

Dickel, Geo.

Golf Club, large	12.50
Powder Horn	12.50

Double Springs

Bentley	14.50
Buick	18.00
Cadillac	15.00
Duffer	7.50
Ford. Model T	18.50
Georgia Bulldog	12.50
Golden Coyote	22.50
Hold That Tiger	16.50
Mercer	15.00
National Gun Owners Assn.	28.50
Peasant Boy, Girl	7.50
Pierce Arrow	18.50
Rolls Royce	20.00
Stanley Steamer	18.50
Stanley Steamer. 1911. 1971 issue	15.00
Stutz Bearcat	18.50
W. C. Fields	19.50
Wild Catter	6.50

Garnier [France]

Anses Vase	17.50
Apollo [Moon]	15.00
Baby Foot	10.00
Bacchus	12.50
Bellows	15.00
Black Cat	12.50
Bullfighters	15.00
Candlestick	10.00
Cardinal	16.50
Clown	17.50
Coffee Mill	18.00
Drunk on Lamp Post	12.50
Duck	16.50
Duo-Liqueur	8.50
Eiffel Tower	20.00
Elephant	15.00
Fiat 500, 1913	10.00
Flower Bouquet	10.00
Giraffe	17.50
Grey Cat	12.50
Indian	15.00
Jockey	15.00
Locomotive	14.50
Napoleon on Horse	12.50
Native Girl and Palm Tree	10.00
Old Watch	15.00
Painting with Easel	12.50
Paris Taxi	27.50
Parrot	25.00
Partridge	15.00
Rainbow	12.50
Rooster, black, maroon	15.00
Sheriff	17.50
Soldier, green, red	35.00
Violin	10.00

Gin

Bininger. Old London	47.50
Blankenheym and Nolet. Case shape, olive green. Pint	15.00

Geneva-style Gin. Product of Ohio ..	5.00
Gordon & Co.'s Dry Gin. Boar's head.	7.50
Ilier's Eagle. Miniature	25.00
Imperial Gin. H.H.S. & Co. I&W in base, case shape. Amber	20.00
H. Van Emden, Posthorn Gin. Sun purple	5.00
Vandenbergh & Co. 3-mold.........	40.00

Grenadier

Capt. U.S. Inf. Confederate	10.00
Capt. U.S. Inf. Union..............	10.00

Colonial Series

Baylors 3rd Continental [1778] ...	15.00
Continental Marines [1779]......	15.00
Eighteenth Continental [1778] ...	15.00
First Pennsylvania	25.00
Second Maryland [1777]	32.50

Fire Chief. Association of International Fire Chiefs. Centennial, 1873-1973 ....$28.50

Third New York [1775]	15.00
Corporal Grenadier	9.00
First Officer Guard...............	8.00
General George S. Custer	12.00
General Jeb Stuart...............	12.00
King's African Rifle Corp	12.00
King's African Rifle Corp. Quart.....	16.50

Napoleon Series

Eugene	12.00
Lanne........................	12.00
Lassel.......................	32.50
Murat........................	12.00
Napoleon	50.00
Officer Scots Fusileer	10.00
Sgt. Major Coldstream............	10.00

Harper, I. W.

Figurine, blue	25.00
Figurine, grey	25.00
Figurine, white	50.00
Nelson Co., ½ pint, metal cap	12.00
Nelson Co., quart, pottery jug	45.00
Wicker, covered, amber	50.00

House of Koshu

Geisha Cherry Blossom............	30.00
Geisha Chrysanthemum	30.00
Geisha Lily	30.00
Geisha Plum Blossom	30.00
Geisha Violet	30.00
Geisha Wisteria	30.00
Joan and Darby, set	16.00
Lion Man	12.50
Noh Mask	12.50
Okame........................	12.50
Pagoda, white..................	12.00
Red Lion Man	16.00
Sake God, painted	8.50
Sedan Chair....................	4.00
Seven Gods	7.00
Stone Lantern	27.50
Treasure Tower	8.50
Wine	1.50

Lionstone

Annie Christmas.................	22.50
Annie Oakley	22.50
Bar Scene. Set of 4	325.00
Bartender	38.50
Belly Robber	27.50
Bluebird......................	27.50
Boxers	30.00
Buffalo Hunter	40.00
Camp Cook	25.00
Camp Follower	28.50
Cardinal......................	30.00
Casual Indian	12.50
Circus. Set of 6	65.00
Country Doctor	18.50
Cowboy	12.50
Fireman #7	40.00
Football	32.50

"The Gambler" $14.50

Gambler	14.50
Golfer	32.50
Gold Panner	75.00
Jesse James	18.50
Meadowlark	23.50
Mountain Man	25.00
Proud Indian	12.50
Railroad Engineer	22.50
Riverboat Captain	18.50
Sheepherder	85.00
Squawman	37.50
Sod Buster	17.50
Stagecoach Driver	25.00
Telegraph Operator	20.00
Washington	35.00
Wood Hawk	50.00

Luxardo [Italy]

Apothecary Jar	15.00
Barrel, ceramic	15.00
Calypso Girl	17.50
Candlestick, alabaster	22.50

Cannon, Leather	45.00
Cellini Vase	30.00
Chess Horse	22.50
Coffee Carafe	17.50
Dolphin	50.00
Duck, green	35.00
Duck, leather	35.00
Eagle, onyx	50.00
Egyptian Vase	20.00
Fish, alabaster	38.50
Fish, gold and green	35.00
Fish, ruby	35.00
Giraffe, leather	30.00
Gold Pheasant	30.00
Gondola, large	18.00
Goose, alabaster	38.50
Jogan Buddha	30.00
Modern Pheasant	30.00
Nubian	20.00
Owl, onyx	35.00
Penguin, glass	40.00
Pheasant, glass, black	75.00
Puppy, sitting	32.50
Sphinx Head	20.00
Wobble	15.00
Zodiac, 1970	17.50

McCormick

Air Race, Pylon	18.00
Angelica Globe	20.00
Barrel	12.50
Billy the Kid	25.00
Coffee Mill	30.00
Jupiter 60 Locomotive	20.00

"Yellow Jackets" $18.50

Flagship Decanter 6.50
Fleur-De-Lis 10.00

"Doc Holliday" $24.00

Jupiter 60 Wood Tender 20.00
Pirates 10.00
Spirit of St. Louis 45.00
Wild Bill Hickock 22.50

O. B. R.
Hockey Series
    Boston Bruins 15.00
    Chicago Black Hawks 15.00
    Detroit Red Wings 15.00
    Minnesota North Stars 15.00
    New York Rangers 15.00
    St. Louis Blues 15.00

Transportation Series
    Balloon 8.50
    Fifth Avenue Bus 8.50
    Pierce Arrow 10.00
    River Queen 8.00
    Santa Maria 20.00
    Train Engine 18.50
    Wagon, Covered 12.00

Old Fitzgerald Prime. "Rip Van Winkle" $18.50

Memphis "Sesquicentennial." 1819-1969 .... $12.50

Gold Web	14.50
Hillbilly, 1969	8.50
Irish Patriots	12.50
Leprechaun	12.00
Monticello Decanter	7.50
Son of Erin Crock	12.00

Prohibition

Bottoms Up, 15 mo. old	24.50
Brookwood. 1 year old, Pa.	22.00
Denham's, 1 mo. old	33.00
"For Medicinal Use Only." Divided bottle to stock holders. Diagonal, ribbed, amber whiskey. Original labels, cap. 1916 stamp	22.00
Gay Party Gin. 1935	22.00
G.O.G. Boston	22.00
Hill Top, over one month old. Hartford	30.00
Indian Feathers, chief on bottle, over six months old	26.50
Kentucky Straight Whiskey. 1 year and 4 mo.	22.50
Knock Rummy, 6 mo. old	30.00
Oak Drum. "You Can't Beat It," drum-shaped	30.00
Oak Hill Hudson Valley. 3 mo. old	26.00
Oak Kay, less than one mo. old, diamond embossed glass	40.00
Old Barbee Rye. Spring 1917, for medicinal purposes only	38.00
Old Quaker Rye. 18 mo. old	27.00

"J. A. Dougherty's Sons Pure Rye Whiskey." Pa. Original contents and carton $35.00

Old Velvet. 17 years old. Prescription. Rare	140.00
Picardy. Apple Jack, Md.	36.00
Shipping Port. 100 proof, Ky.	33.50
Skipper's Favorite	22.00
Sky Scraper Whiskey, 4 mo. old, glass embossed with stars	45.00
Snug Harbor, green glass with coat of arms	36.00
Uncle Sam. Hat stopper. 9½"	46.50

Ski Country

Big Horn Ram	34.00
Blue Skier	20.00
Brown Bear	30.00
California Condor	32.50
Canadian Goose	37.50
Colorado School of Mines Burro	27.50
Gila Woodpecker	39.50
Golden Eagle	35.00
Golden Skier	55.00
Majestic Eagle, gallon	175.00
Peacock	30.00
Red Shouldered Hawk	28.50
Red Skier	15.00
Rocky Mountain Sheep	40.00
Snow Owl	50.00
Woodpecker	55.00

Wheaton Nuline

Apollo 11	15.00
Apollo 12	45.00
Apollo 13	6.50
Apollo 14	6.50
Apollo 15	6.50
Apollo 16	6.50
Bogart, Humphrey	6.00
Christmas, 1971	10.00
Edison, Thomas A.	7.00
Eisenhower, Dwight D.	8.00
Fields, W. C.	6.50
Franklin Benjamin	6.00
Harlow, Jean	5.00
Humphrey-Muskie	10.00
Jones, John Paul	6.50
Keller, Helen	6.50
Kennedy, John F.	25.00
Lincoln, Abraham	7.50
MacArthur, Douglas	7.00
Nixon - Agnew	12.50
Revere, Paul	7.50
Rogers, Will	6.50
Roosevelt, Theodore	8.50
Ross, Betsy	7.50
Sheriff's Assn.	15.00
Washington, George	8.00
Wilson, Woodrow	6.50

Whiskey Miniatures

| Beer | 1.00 to 3.00 |
| Beneagles | 5.00 to 8.00 |

Jacquin's. Creme de Cacao $1.00

Chivas Regal	1.25
Courvoisier	1.50
Dickel Powder Horn	5.00
Famous Firsts	10.00 to 15.00
Grenadier Soldiers	7.50
Haig and Haig pinch	1.50
Laurel and Hardy. Each	10.00
Lionstone	20.00 to 30.00
Ski Country	15.00 to 25.00
Tanqueray Martini	2.00
Vat 69 green	5.00

MISCELLANEOUS

Bar. Wine, round, amber, inset for ice.	10.00
Blown, hand. Globular, green, 8"	40.00
Blown, two mold, globular, green, 9"	22.50
Blown, three mold, 32-oz. Cylindrical, green	10.00
Household	
Clorox, amber, quart	1.00
Clorox, amber, gallon	1.50
Lestoil, blue, Franklin	7.50
Lestoil, purple. Embossed Eagle & Liberty	8.50
Ink	
Carter's, aqua, ½ pint	6.50
Carter's. Cathedral, cobalt, pint	30.00
Carter's. Cone, aqua, 2½" high	3.50
Stafford Ink. Cobalt, pint	7.00
Underwood's. Cobalt, 32-oz.	30.00
Jamaica Ginger	
F. Brown's, Philadelphia	4.00
Dana's Red Sea	4.00
Moody's Extract	4.00
Mineral Water	
Artesian Spring Co., Ballston Spa, Ballston, N.Y. Green	35.00
Cold Spring Water Co. Aqua, 5-pint	45.00
Hathorn Springs, Saratoga, N.Y. Green, 32-oz.	25.00

Medicine bottle. "Fayette Drug Co," Uniontown, Pa. Pint............$7.50

Wine. "Economy Wine." Pa. Currant   **$25.00**

Carter's "Ryto" Permanent Ink. Cobalt,
cathedral-shaped. Quart $45.00

Nursing
"Happy Baby" 6.00
"Kittens" 7.50
"Rabbit," Baby Bunting 5.00
Perfume
Daisy and Button. Screw cap 32.50
Figural. Shoe 35.00
Glass with sterling case, ground
stopper. Small 22.50
Pottery
Cucumber. Green and tan, 6" 27.50
"Ye   Olde   Fashioned   Ginger
Beer." 7½" 27.50
Wine
Handpainted.   Green   glass,
Mexican motif, wood screw cap . .   15.00
Hock. Amber 10.00
Hock. Teal blue 10.00
Vino Rosso. Cat, green 6.00

BRANDING IRONS

Branding irons were and still are used in the
western part of the United States to mark
animals. The "iron" is heated until hot and
then applied to the animal's hide. The print of
the iron remains and is used to identify
animals belonging to various owners. The
designs vary but are usually combinations of
letters, numbers or geometric markings.

Branding Iron. Initials "A.J." . . . $15.00

Wrought Iron
Letter "F", 20" long, wood handle . $ 20.00
Letter "O" 16.50
Letter "S". 16.50

Letter "U"	16.50
Letter "V"	16.50
Letters "CJ", 25" long	22.50
Letters "DR"	18.00
Letters "HA"	18.00
Letters "LC"	18.00
Letters "LS", wood handle	22.00

BRASS

A yellow alloy consisting mainly of copper and zinc, which is durable, malleable and ductile - or capable of being hammered out. The list below indicates that the metal was used in the past for a variety of utilitarian purposes.

Samovar. 28". Russian hallmark. "T.T."
$350.00

Andirons
7" high. Griffins. Pair	$ 85.00
9" high. Queen Anne. Pair	125.00
20" high. Twisted rope columns. Pair	85.00
25" high. Carved, decorated posts, curled feet, 3½" brass ball finials. Polished and lacquered. Pair	135.00
Anvil. 5" long, 2¼" high	15.00

Basket. Handled, French basket-weave ... 45.00

Bed Warmers
*Long pine handle	135.00
9½", including handle	40.00

Bells
Cow. Large	25.00
Dinner. Chinese, with seahorse on a turtle	22.50
School. 6" high, 3" diam., wood handle	50.00
Slave or Fireplace. 19" high, with striker. Polished and lacquered	100.00
Sleigh. 24" strap, 2¾" bells graduating to 1¼"	250.00

Bible Clips. With connecting brass chain ... 14.50
Bird Cage. Small ... 60.00
Boot Jack. "Naughty Nellie" ... 60.00

Bowls
6" diam., with collar, etched	25.00
7" diam., ball foot	30.00
8" diam., footed	42.50
12" diam., etched dragon design, teakwood base stand	60.00
14" diam. 18th century. Hammered by hand	90.00

Box. 2½ x7x7", hammered ... 25.00

Bucket. 9" high, 14" diam., with bail handle ... 155.00

Bullet Mold. Hinged end ... 45.00

Calling Card Holder. Ornate, woven wire, on easel ... 30.00

Candelabras
11", 3-branch type	125.00
18", 7 candles, arms turn separately	200.00
20", arm out straight. 7 candles, adjustable	235.00

Candleholders
Saucer-type	50.00
With snuffer, scissors and cone	85.00

*Candle Snuffer. With scissors, tray . 50.00
*Candlesticks
Beehive. 9", push up, burnished. Pair	100.00
Beehive. 9¾", push up, burnished. Pair	100.00
11½", push up. "The 1901"	150.00

Candelabras. 6-branch with additional florets and leaves. Pair $275.00

Beehive. 12", push up, burnished.
Pair 150.00
Saucer-type. Push up and snuffer . 60.00
Winged-dragon type 55.00
Cannons
Small, wood frame 35.00
Large, all brass................ 175.00
Chafing Dish and Tray 125.00
***Chestnut Roaster.** 18" long, brass
handles 60.00
Cigar Clipper. Desk size 25.00
Clamp, Paper. 3½" long, in form of
bird. Marked "China" 12.50
Coal Box. 12x16x17". Repousse'
decor on slanted front lift lid.
Ornate brass coal scoop with
holder on outside. Carrying
handle, brass ball feet 175.00
***Coal Hod** 135.00

Coffee Percolator. With alcohol
burner 65.00
Coffee Pot. Small 45.00
Cuspidors
12" high..................... 55.00
Mechanical turtle............. 85.00
***Dipper.** 6" diam., old 50.00
Door Knocker. 9" long, 18th century,
elongated urn design 50.00
Ferner. On 3 round legs 45.00
Fire Hose Nozzle 75.00
Fireplace Items
Fender. Brass posts and rail, iron
base. 23" long, C. 1880......... 150.00
Fork. 18" long, Shakespeare head
on handle 25.00

Fork. 20" long, owl handle 30.00
Lighter. Cape Cod 50.00
Foot Warmer. Oval-shaped 55.00
Frames
6", oval 30.00
8x14", Florentine, with easel 75.00
11x12", oval, for mirror. Victorian
cherub 65.00
13½x16", oval, for mirror. Victorian cherub 75.00
Ginger. Jar. 7½", Chinese engraved 60.00
Hand Warmer. 5x7". French, wood
handle 42.50
Heel Plates. Pennsylvania Dutch,
heart cutouts 20.00
Horn. Canal. 24" high, polished and
lacquered 100.00
Horse Bit 8.50
Horse Head. 3" high, surrounded by
horseshoe.................... 10.00
Ice Tongs 25.00
Jardinieres
5x5", hammered 50.00
8" high, 10" diam., 3 ball feet.
Polished 70.00

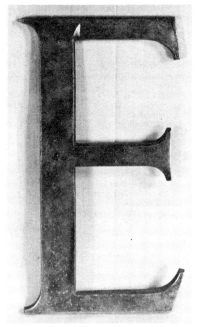

Letter "E." 12" high $27.50

10", stag head handle	130.00
Kettles	
6-quart	65.00
8-quart	75.00
10-quart	85.00
11-quart	90.00
6" high, 9½" diam. Bail handle. H. W. Hayden's Ansonia Brass Mfg. Co. Pat. Dec. 16, 1851	40.00
Jelly. 11½" diam. Hand-wrought iron handle	60.00
*Key	7.00
*Ladles	
3½" bowl, 15" handle	35.00
5½" bowl. 14" iron handle. Marked F. B. Co., Canton, Ohio. Patd. Jan. 20, '88	50.00
Lamp, Hanging. Store type with brass shade	150.00
Lock and Key. Old	50.00
Milk Pan. 16" diam.	75.00
Mortars and Pestles	
3½"	60.00
4"	65.00
5"	75.00
Mustache Curling Iron. With alcohol burner. Repousse' decor on handle and stand	48.50
Oil Can. 11" spout	30.00
Pails	
15" diam.	85.00
18½"diam., 12" high. Iron bail	100.00
Pan, Warming. Pierced top	145.00
Pancake Turner. Long, fancy iron handle	25.00
Paperweight. 5", dragon	35.00
Planter. Russian, 3-footed, lion's paw feet. 4" diam., 2" high	20.00
Plaques	
22x24". William Shakespeare bust in high relief. Inlaid and brass ornamented ebony frame. 29x32" outside frame	150.00
23" diam., Jeanne Seymour	65.00
24" diam., tavern scene in center, ornate border	75.00
Pot Hanger. With adjustable saw-tooth ratchet	135.00
Powder Horns, see Powder Flasks and Horns	
Powder Horns, see Powder Flasks and Horns	
Roasting Jack. Clockwork	100.00
Samovars	
Russian, old brass. With seal	250.00
Russian, complete with matching tray, waste bowl and teapot lid	400.00
Server. 8" high, hallmarked	195.00
Scale. Fairbanks #1602. 5½" high, brass scoop, original paint	85.00

Scale. 34" high, weighs 20 lbs. R. D. Simpson, maker, Edinburg. Weights contained	300.00
Scoops	
Candy, small	20.00
Scale, small	25.00
Scale, medium	27.50
Scale, large	35.00
Sugar	32.50
3x5½", with 3" handle	25.00
5¼x8¾", with 3¾" handle	30.00
7x11", with 4½" handle	40.00
Scuttle. Hammered, large bail and ornate handle	175.00
Sewing Bird	27.50
Skimmer. 7¾" diam.	65.00
Slide Bolt. Embossed decor, old	18.00
Stove, Hand. Warming, portable, charcoal burning	75.00
Sundial, 8½" diam., octagonal, old	100.00
Tea Caddy. 5½" high, 6-sided	50.00
Teakettles	
Acorns and raised leaves decor. Stand and burner	90.00
Amber handle, button feet	125.00
Tie Backs	
English Victorian, with white Bristol morning glories extending from top. Pair	60.00
French Victorian. Arm type. Pair	50.00
Trays	
8½" diam., for decanter	25.00
12" diam., heavy, round	85.00
14x21", open handles, light	85.00
15" diam., round. Center has stylized peacock. Late	35.00
Trivet. Fox and tree. Footed	60.00
Umbrella Holder	50.00
*Umbrella Stand. Lion ring handles	70.00
Urns. 16" high, ornate. Pair	175.00
Wall Sconces	
Single candle, dolphin top, mirror	95.00
Lyre shape, 3-branch candle holders with drip cups. Pair	225.00
With mirror. 8x23", 3 candle-holders. Pair	275.00
Watch Holder. Centered on embossed, round tray. Scrolls, shells, head	58.00
Weathervane Arrow. 23" long, filigree brass and cranberry glass, with owner's name in shank	250.00
Whistle. Steamboat. 10½" high, small size	100.00
*Reproduced Item	

BREAD PLATES

A special plate made for the serving of

biscuits, bread or rolls. Most of the earlier ones are of the pattern glass variety, while some are made of china and metal.

"Give Us This Day Our Daily Bread."
Clear pattern glass $30.00

Clear Glass Patterns

Actress
Lillian Neilson .... $ 52.50
Pinafore. 7x11½", oval 42.00
Beaded Band.................... 16.50
Beaded Loop Pleat Panel 27.50
Bible 45.00
"Bread is the Staff of Life." Jeweled
Band........................ 36.00
Bunker Hill Monument 48.00
Chain and Shield 32.00
Clear Ribbon 32.00
Cleveland 155.00
Coin
U.S. Dollar decor 264.00
*U.S. Half Dollar decor 230.00
Columbus Pilot. Wheel border 43.50
Constitution 65.00
Coronation. George IV. 1917. "God
Save the King." 10" 30.00
Coronation. George VI and Elizabeth 27.00
Crying Baby.................... 55.00
Cupid and Venus 32.50
Dancing Bears.................. 42.00
Dog Cart 43.50
Egg in Sand 19.00
Egyptian
Cleopatra 30.00
Salt Lake Temple 45.00
Eureka 30.00
Faith, Hope and Charity 55.00

Fitz Hugh Lee 20.00
Flower Pot...................... 35.00
Forget-Me-Not. Large, round, stip-
pled, handled. Kitten center 54.00
Frosted Stork 42.00
Garfield Drape 46.00
Garfield Memorial.11" 34.50
Garfield One Hundred One. Frosted . 35.00
"Give Us This Day, Etc." Wheat
center 35.00
Gladstone 22.50
G.O.P. Commemorative. 11-1/8 x
7-5/8" 85.00
Grant, General. Patriot & Soldier ... 35.00
Harrison, Morton 175.00
Hendricks 165.00
Heroes of Bunker Hill 47.50
Horseshoe
Single handle 45.00
*Double handle 52.00
Huckle 23.50
Independence Hall............... 82.50
Iowa City
"Be Industrious." Frosted center,
deer and doe border 65.00
Frosted Stork, 101 border, oval, 12" 36.00
Frosted Stork, 101 border, round,
10" 42.00
Girl with parrot. 101 border 60.00
Two cranes, frosted............. 45.50
"It Is Pleasant to Labor for Those We
Love" 41.50
Jewel With Dewdrop 17.50
Last Supper [common] 15.00
Lattice. Oblong 35.00
Liberty Bell
7x11½"...................... 95.00
9½x13¼", M. G. John Hancock .. 200.00
Lion
Frosted center, handled, back
plate 55.00
Frosted. "Give Us This Day," Rope
edge, 12" including handles 62.50
*Little Miss Muffet 39.00
Little Red Riding Hood 42.50
Loop With Dewdrops 24.50
Lotus. "Give Us This Day, Etc." 22.50
McCormick Reaper................ 70.00
McKinley. "It Is God's Way. His Will
Be Done" 38.50
Minerva........................ 32.00
Mitchell, John. Scarce 100.00
Moon and Star 37.50
Nellie Bly...................... 135.00
Niagara Falls. 11½x16". Frosted
and clear.................... 110.00
Old Statehouse.................. 60.00
One Hundred One. Bread Motto 50.00
Pacific Fleet. Rare 350.00

Panelled Daisy	36.00	Fine Cut and Panel		
Panelled Dewdrop		Clear	24.00
Oblong, handled	48.00	Amber	30.00
Oval	40.00	Blue	40.00
Pittsburgh Commandery. 8½", "The		Yellow	30.00
Milkmaid"	60.00	Hobnail, Fan Top	
Pleat and Panel	28.50	Clear	35.00
Polar Bear. Oval, handled, 16½"	80.00	Amber	47.50
President's Platter	57.50	Blue	55.00
Queen Victoria	38.50	Hobnail, Opalescent	
Railroad, Transcontinental	75.00	Opalescent	65.00
Ribbon, oblong, cut corners	65.50	Blue	80.00
Rock of Ages	47.50	Yellow	87.50
Rock of Ages. Atterbury. Clear		Hobnail, Pointed	
handles, center translucent, deep		Clear. 4½x7"	25.00
blue	175.00	Amber	32.50
Roman Rosette	32.50	Blue	35.00
Roosevelt, Theodore. Oval, frosted		Light Green	40.00
center. 7¾x10¼"	77.50	Knights of Labor	
Saxon. Oval, 12"	32.50	Blue	200.00
Sheaf of Wheat	35.00	Amber	200.00
Shell and Tassel. Oblong	45.00	Liberty Bell. Milk Glass	
Sprig	23.00	With John Hancock's signature	200.00
Star Rosetted. "A Good Mother, etc."	42.50	Without Signature. 7x11¼"	95.00
Sunburst	20.00	Maple Leaf	
Three Graces	55.00	Clear	26.50
Tree of Life	34.50	Amber	42.50
Viking	25.00	Blue	45.00
Virginia Dare	47.00	Frosted	32.00
Warrior. Frosted	95.00	Green	50.00
Washington		Vaseline	42.50
Frosted center. "First in War, etc."	100.00	Panelled Forget-Me-Not	
Frosted center. 1776-1876 Cen-		Clear	20.00
tennial	125.00	Amber	30.00
Waste Not, Want Not	37.50	Blue	36.00
Westward-Ho. Oval	85.00	Yellow	30.00
*Reproduced Item		Primrose	
		Clear	25.00
		Amber	42.50
Colored Glass Patterns		Blue	47.50
		Vaseline	42.50
Beaded Grape		Purple Slag	150.00
Clear	40.00		
Green	65.00	Rose Sprig	
Caramel Slag	150.00	Clear	22.50
Columbia. Amber	95.00	Amber	32.00
Daisy and Button, Oval, handled		Blue	40.00
Clear	20.00	Yellow	32.00
Amber	40.00	Sheraton	
Apple Green	45.00	Clear	15.00
Blue	45.00	Amber	30.00
Vaseline	40.00	Blue	40.00
Deer and Pine Tree		Shield	
Amber	40.00	Clear	75.00
Blue. 8x13"	75.00	Amethyst	150.00
Clear. 8x13"	42.50	Blue	125.00
Clear. 9x15". Scarce	60.00	Spirea Band	
Fine Cut		Blue	18.00
Clear	18.50	Thousand Eye	
Blue	35.00	Clear. Oblong, 8x11"	30.00
Vaseline	32.50		

Amber	40.00
Apple Green	55.00
Blue	45.00
Vaseline	40.00

Two Panel

Clear	22.50
Amber	29.50
Blue	32.50
Green	36.00
Yellow	29.50

Victoria Jubilee

Amber	20.00

Wildflower

Clear	24.00
Amber	32.50
Green	45.00
Blue	40.00
Yellow	32.50

Willow Oak

Clear. Oblong	27.00
Amber	30.00
Blue	35.00

BRIDE'S BASKETS

"Bride's Baskets" derive their name from the fact that in the period of 1895-1910, many were presented as wedding presents. The majority consisted of ruffled-edge dishes in blue or cranberry-colored glass held in a handled, silverplated frame. Occasionally a basket with a glass handle is seen on the market.

Bride's Basket. 6x8". Enameled, cased green bowl. S/P holder $160.00

Numerous reproductions are on the market which dim the enthusiasm of collectors and tend to keep prices of old items down.

Amethyst. IVP. 7" diam., enameled flowers. Ornate quad holder .....$	150.00
Apricot. Cased, fluted bowl, 9¼" diam. Ornate, footed frame, 10" diam., 11" high	175.00
Blue. Ruffled Satin Glass bowl in ornate plated holder	180.00
Cranberry. Meriden holder	125.00
Cranberry to pink at center. 10½" diam. Resilvered, ornate over-handle holder	150.00
Cranberry to white. Hobnail pattern, silverplated frame	235.00
Cranberry shading to white with enamel decor and red overlay	225.00
Cranberry. Spanish lace design. 13" to top of handle. Resilvered	150.00
Old Rose. 9½", acorn-type silver holder, marked Pairpoint	165.00
Pigeon Blood Satin. 9¼" diam., white enamel flowers. Frame re-silvered	200.00
Pink. Ruffled with white overlay on outside. In silverplated holder....	150.00
Pink. White lining and ruffled cranberry edge. In resilvered, footed holder consisting of 3 birds	175.00
Pink. 4½" diam., 7½" high. Tan, dark red and blue spatter with white lining and deep ruffled edge	165.00
Pink. 10¼" diam. Crimped and artistically-shaped overlay bowl. Amber applied rim. In original Rogers signed silverplate holder. Needs resilvering	125.00
Pink. 10½" diam., 5" high. Raspberry decor. Four-legged silver holder	185.00
Red. Iridescent, ribbed, enamel decor inside and out. Footed silver stand. Child as stem	250.00
Rose. Interior, rose with applied clear edge, white exterior. Ruffled in silverplated frame	145.00
Sandwich. Overshot, green ruffled edge. Old ornate footed silver-plated holder	180.00
Vasa Murrhina. Tan with gold flecks, oval. In plated holder	200.00
White. 5½" diam., with yellow lining and gold flecks, ruffled edge. Frame needs resilvering	115.00

BRISTOL GLASS

Bristol glass is the product of several glass houses in Bristol, England, which became a glass center in the middle 1700's. Much of the so-called early American glass ascribed to Amelung Glass Co., and other glass houses in this country was made in Bristol. The importation of this glass hastened the failure of the Amelung and Stiegel glass houses.

The majority of Bristol glass encountered in antique shops today is in the form of vases of the late Victorian period.

Bottle, Dresser. Original stopper. Pink satin, gold, rose, black enamel trim. 8½" high, 3¼" diam. ....$ 37.50
Bowl, Punch. Covered, enameled floral and gold decor 150.00
Boxes
   Patch. Hinged cover, enamel decor 58.00
   Powder. 3½" high. Heavy, dark blue glass. Lid decorated with playing children 65.00
Carafe with Tumbler 65.00
Cookie Jar. Light blue shading to white, painted cherries. Resilvered top.................... 95.00
Creamer. Overlay, pink rose-colored bulbous shape, applied crystal handle 42.50

Creamer, 5" high. Sugar, 4½" high. White. Pair $140.00

Decanter. 7¾" high. Bird decoration in gold with blue. Orange-flashed top. Pair...................... 95.00
Dish. Large, rectangular 50.00
Dresser Set. Pair of 10" bottles and covered powder jar 125.00
Ducks. 10". Standing with mouths open to form candleholders. Green and orange coloring. Pair . 100.00
Epergnes. Single tulip, cranberry, ruffled and fluted edges. Pair 250.00

Ewer. Green, floral and butterfly. Ruffled top, 8½" high. C. 1845 ... 65.00
Hand. Holding vase. Fluted top, soft green, gilt decor 60.00
Lamp, Fairy. Blue, swirled, enameled flowers 150.00
Mugs
   3¼", flower decor, applied handle. "Remember Me"........... 40.00
   Ale. Covered, 8¼" high, blue with gold decor, star cut bottom, applied handle 50.00
Pitchers
   4" high. Blue, white enamel decor, applied handle. "Remember Me" in gold 48.50
   5½" high. Smokey gray with blue handle and gold decoration 75.00
Plaque, Wall. 9½" diam. 35.00
Plate. 12" diam., handpainted 55.00
Potpourri. Cream, rose, gold decor ... 52.50
Ring Tree. 3" high, blue, decorated in bright gold 42.50
Shades. 14" diam., for hanging lamp:
   Red rose decor 65.00
   Spray of purple morning glories .. 65.00
Smoke Bell. 7" high, applied ruby ring. Self ring at top, original brass chain 18.00
Tumbler. White with black transfer. Peasant scene 12.50
Urn. 19" high, covered. Decorated in heavy enamel with cupids at play with lady. Cream ground 150.00

Vases
   5" high. Ruffled overlay pink edge. Handpainted bird on branch decor 35.00
   5¼" high. Cased pink fluted top, enameled butterfly and flowers .. 40.00
   6" high. Caramel, enamel decor. Pair 50.00
   6" high. Red band at top and bottom. Center section has floral decor on yellow ground. English .. 22.50
   6½" high. Frosted custard with flying ducks. Pair 75.00
   6¾" high, 2" diam., yellow bands, handpainted bird 25.00
   7" high. Stick, overlay. Rich pink rose coloring on tapered enamel body......................... 30.00
   8" high. Fireglow type with stick neck, 1" in diam. Handpainted flowers, leaves and stems 50.00
   8½" high. English. Opaque with fired enamel decor. Pair......... 85.00

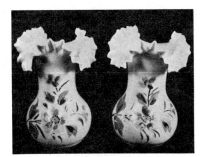

Vases. 7" high. Ruffled tops, yellow, brown blossoms, green leaves. Pair
$135.00

8¾" high. Clear, frosted handled, gilded enamel decor. Pair	85.00
10" high. Enameled branch and flowers on cream ground. English .	45.00
10½" high. "The Gleaners" transfer on side	60.00
10½" high. Soft green ground, autumn colors of flowers, leaves. Pair	55.00
12" high. Opaque white glass, satin finish, gold-colored enamel decor	75.00
12½" high. Green, "The Gleaners"	75.00
13" high. Pink with red, white and green strawberries and flowers in enamel. Pair	125.00
15" high. White, handpainted orange and blue floral decor, ruffled top	85.00
24" high. Blue glass with white casing. Multicolored flowers and gold leaf decor	100.00

BRONZE

Bronze is a combination of copper, tin and traces of other metals. Bronze has been used since Biblical times not only for art objects but also for utilitarian purposes.

After a slump in the Middle Ages, bronze was revived in the 17th, 18th and 19th centuries. Today bronzes have become a highly sophisticated collectible in the antique trade. Prices have reached new heights. A signed bronze commands a higher price than an unsigned object.

Do not confuse a "bronzed" object with a true bronze. A bronzed object is usually made of white metal and then coated with a reddish-brown material to give it a bronze appearance.

Animals

Bear. 6¾". Marble ball and base . . . . $	250.00
Bear and Bull Fighting. 4½x9½". A. Phimistor. Proctor, Gorham Co. . .	650.00
Bird. 5x7". Pautrot	400.00
Bird. Partridge, 6½x7". Moigniez . . .	350.00
Bird. Fish in mouth, 5x6½". De Labrierre	375.00
Bird, Battling. 9½x12". De Labrierre	750.00
Bisons, Battling. 25" long. Tiffland . .	850.00
Bull. 3½x5¼". Perrin	275.00
Bull. 5½x7½". Bayre	700.00
Bull. 13". Rose B [Rosa Bonheur]	1200.00
Bull Fighting Dog. 4½x7½". De Labrierre	375.00
Camel. 9x10"	250.00
Chickens, Seven. 6½x10" basket. Cain	550.00
Cow. 3½x5½". I. Bonheur	350.00
Dog. 1½x3½". Tail in mouth. Savage, Gorham Co.	275.00
Dog. 5x8½". Moigniez	500.00
Dog. Greyhound. 8x11". Mene	500.00
Dog. Manchester. Mene	375.00
Dog. Pointer. 8x11½". Mene	600.00
Dog. Retriever. 14" long. Moigniez . .	425.00
Dog. Scottie. 5x7". E. B. Parsons	400.00
Dog. Terrier. 4x8". Three rats and bucket. A. Leonard [Genezit]	325.00
Elephant. 5x7". Fratin	395.00
Elephant. 6½x8". Valton	500.00
Fox. 4¼x5". Peeking over rock at rabbit. Masson	450.00

Falconier on Arabian Horse, by P. J. Mene **$4500.00**

Goat. 6x10". Mene	475.00
Horse. 10x10¼". With saddle. Geschuetzt foundry	500.00
Jaguar. 7½x9½". A. L. Bayre	750.00
Lion. 12x22". Holding rabbit in jaws. De Labrierre	1500.00
Lizard. Bayre	300.00
Panther. 4½x7¾". Bayre	450.00
Pheasant. 7" long. Mene	395.00
Pheasant. 5½x9". Pautrot	475.00
Ram. 8x10". Lanceray	1350.00
Reindeer. 2x2-3/8"	100.00
Seal on Rocks. 5" high. E. Angela, Gorham and Co.	350.00
Stallion. 1¾x2½"	75.00
Tiger and Two Cubs. 8¼x14". Valton .	750.00

Busts

Dante. Near life size	275.00
Indian Head. 4x4¼". Head dress, mouth open. Renevez	600.00
Joan of Arc. 18" high. Chapu	1200.00
Lincoln. 7" high. G. O. Bissell	300.00
Lincoln. 11" high. L. Volk, Gorham . .	450.00
Man. 10" high. Marble column	250.00
Napoleon. Larger than life size	750.0C
Woman. 4" high. Russian dress. T. Teneszezok	750.00
Woman. 6¼" high. Victorian Barthoz	150.00

Figures

Arab. Boy riding donkey	150.00
Arab. Boy selling	150.00
Arab on Camel. 5x5"	225.00
Arab on Carpet. 5x6"	225.00
Arab Carrying Two Buckets. Debut, 13" high, C. 1880	450.00
Blacksmith. 20" high. Rere Gewso . .	1500.00
Boy Fishing. 17" high. Lavergue	700.00
Farmer. 9¼" high. Charles Levy	450.00
Farmer. 16½" high. Charles Levy	1200.00
Girl. Nude, 9" high. Paul Herz	125.00
Girl. Nude, on horse. 23" high. H. Haase	1000.00
Knight. 11" high	125.00
Lincoln, Abraham. 8¼" high. Bissell .	600.00
Milner. 9¼" high. Charles Levy	450.00
Napoleon. On rearing horse. 15x19"	950.00
Raphael. 13¼" high. Duchoieselle . .	500.00
Russian. On horse, 6x8", dated 1877	2000.00
Shepherd. Lanceray	1750.00
Race, The. 7x8". Boyer	2250.00
Woman Holding Hat. 9¾" high. Besierdido	650.00
Woman with Lyre. 12½" high. J. Bradier	850.00
Woman with Child. 18" high. Clodion	1150.00

Figures. Approx. 8" high. Gold-washed, ivory faces. Signed "Gory." Pair $2000.00

Miscellaneous

Ash Tray. Marble base. Gregoire	300.00
Bowl. 11¼" diam. Aqua marbled, grape handles. Soreneson	55.00
Door Knocker. Eagle	100.00
Planter. 6¼" diam. W. Henning	125.00
Plaques	
Garfield, President. 12x18". Hugh C. Robertson	550.00
Lincoln, Abraham. 6½" diam. Oak frame, signed Leo Nock 1914	150.00
Salver. 5x13". Footed. "John the Baptist." C. 1880. Emile Picault	750.00
Vases	
5¼" high. Cherubs, butterflies, dragonfly. Pair	150.00
8" high. Heads of women. Pair	175.00
11½" high. Foliage decor	100.00
15" high. Leaves form fountain, grotesque head pours water. Les Curieuses, Geschutz	700.00

BUFFALO POTTERY

Information regarding the beginning of Buffalo Pottery, Buffalo, N.Y. is rather sketchy.

It is believed that the establishment commenced business about 1903 or 1904. The company made a series of quart jugs in a variety of shapes...some were tall and graceful, others in quaint Dutch shapes. The decorations were underglaze in hand-tinted colors. The subjects were from history and literature and included John Paul Jones, Robin Hood, as well as the Dutch and Pilgrims.

In 1908 the company started marketing Deldare ware. It has a rich olive-green body. The underglaze decorations were in three styles...Old English, Indian camping scenes and hunting scenes. The firm also issued a series of commemorative plates depicting various scenes of historic interest.

Deldare Pitcher. 9" high. "With a Cane Superior Air." Reverse, "This Amazed Me" $275.00

Bowls

5½" diam. Floral, banded decor . . $	22.50
8" diam. Willow pattern. 1911....	27.50
9" diam. Open, Blue Willow, handled, dated 1909	38.50
Butter Pat. Blue Willow design	5.00
Butter Tub. Tab handles, Fern Rose pattern	20.00
Creamer. Roosevelt Bears. "Landing by Balloon in Chicago." 4" high ...	60.00
Cup, Master's. "Take Ye a Cuppe O' Kindness For Auld Lang Syne"	35.00

Dishes

Feeding. Campbell Kids. Signed Drayton	35.00

Sauce. 5" diam., Willow pattern ..	7.50
Vegetable. Covered, gold band decor	35.00
Fish Set. Six 9" plates, 15" platter, green edge. R. K. Beck. Set.......	150.00
Game Set. Four 9¼" plates, 15½" platter. R. K. Beck. Set...........	125.00
Gravy Boat. LaFrancerosa	27.50

Jugs

George Washington, 7½" high. Decorated with gold trim	250.00
Triumph......................	100.00
Wild Duck	100.00
Luncheon Set. Service for 6. Blue Bird pattern. Dated 1919. Set	150.00
Mug, Child's. Campbell Kids	35.00

Pitchers

4½" high. White ground, blue birds, blue rim	32.50
George Washington one side, Mt. Vernon on other side. Blue and white	150.00

Plates

Child's. Boy bringing candy to girl who has fallen	27.50
Soup. Willow pattern. 1911	15.00
Stag and Deer. With young at lake. "Beck"	30.00
7". Willow pattern	12.50
7½". Grant's Tomb	18.50
7½". Niagara Falls. Blue and green.......................	25.00
9". "The Gunner." Blue	55.00
9". Willow pattern. 1911	12.50
9". Wild Ducks. Turquoise ground .	40.00
9½". Tan, brown and red, dated 1912. Abino ware	45.00
9½". Blue Willow pattern. 1916 ..	18.00

Pitcher. Green and white. "Buffalo Hunting Scene" $150.00

10". Commemorative series with blue-green decor:

Faneuill Hall	35.00
Independence Hall	35.00
Mount Vernon	35.00
Niagara Falls	35.00
U. S. Capitol	35.00
White House, The	35.00
12". Blue Willow. 1916	20.00
Powder Jar. Covered	30.00
Sugar Bowl. Abino ware. 1912, signed Harris	75.00
Sugar Bowl and Creamer	60.00
Teapot. Blue and white argyle. Strainer hangs from cover. 1914, fully signed	65.00
Tobacco Jar. Large	65.00
Trivet. Blue and white, Willow design. 1911	15.00
Vase or Urn. 10½" high. Two-handled, scalloped top, bulbous. Handpainted	100.00

Deldare Ware

Bowls

Small. "The Start"	100.00
8". "Dr. Syntax--His Tour"	275.00
8". "Ye Lion Inn"	135.00
9". "Ye Village Street"	150.00
9". "Ye Village Tavern"	150.00
Candleholder. Shield back. Village Life	275.00

Candlesticks

Bayberry. Emerald. Pair	400.00
Colonial figures. 9" high. Pair	400.00
Creamer. Emerald. Syntax Dairymaid	200.00

Cups and Saucers

"Fallowfield Hunt." 1909	195.00
"Ye Olde Days." 1909	160.00

Mugs

"Beacon Bry," hunt. 1908	175.00
"Dr. Syntax Made Free of the Cellar." 4½" high	200.00
"Ye Lion Inn," 4½" high	175.00

Pitchers

5¾" high. "Which He Returned with a Curtsy." Gerhart	225.00
6¼". For milk. "To Demand My Annual Rent"	250.00
6½" high. "Ye Olden Days." Olive green. "Their manner of telling stories"	250.00
6½" high. "Fallowfield Hunt." Signed I. Gerhardt	300.00
9" high. Tankard. "Ye Village Streets"	275.00

Plates

6¼". "At Ye Lion Inn"	110.00

6½". Advertisement: "Hand Painted Deldare Ware Underglaze." Marked and dated 1908 on base	135.00
6½". "Dr. Syntax Presenting a Floral Offering." Emerald	200.00
7¼". "Dr. Syntax Soliloquizing" ...	225.00
7½". "The Fallowfield Hunt"	175.00
8½". "The Town Crier"	150.00
9½". "Ye Olden Times"	160.00
9½". "Dr. Syntax Loses His Wig" ..	250.00
10". "Dr. Syntax Making a Discovery"	300.00
10". "Village Gossips"	150.00
12". "Breakfast at the Three Pigeons." Hanging type	225.00
13½". "Ye Olde Lion Inn." Hanging type	250.00
14". "Fallowfield Hunt"	350.00
Sugar Bowl and Creamer. "Scenes of Village Life in Ye Olden Days"....	375.00
Tankard. 12½" high. "The Great Controversy," and "All you have to do to teach the Dutchmen English"	295.00

Tiles

"Fallowfield Hunt," 18½ x 25". Fullcry and Death." Pair	350.00
"Traveling Olde Days"	200.00
Tobacco Humidor. "The Inn." 7"	275.00

Trays

9¼ x 12½". "Dancing Ye Minuet" ..	265.00
10¼ x 12½". "Heirlooming"	275.00

BURMESE GLASS

Burmese glass is an art glass which originated and was manufactured by the Mt. Washington Glass Co., New Bedford, Mass., for a period of five or six years. It was discovered, by chance, when Fred Shirley, the new manager of the plant was making a small pot of ruby glass. He added gold which gives the coloring but the metal sank quickly to the bottom without mixing with the glass. He then added a quantity of Uranium Oxide which was used in making canary yellow glass. [Uranium Oxide is now the chief source of Uranium for bombs and atomic power]. The reaction of the gold, when the item was reheated, produced a soft canary yellow which shaded to flesh pink. The blending of the colors was so gradual that it was difficult to determine when one color ended and the other began.

Although some of the glass has a surface that is glazed or glossy, most of it has a smooth plush [satin] finish. The majority of items have no pattern, but some have either a ribbed, hobnail or diamond-quilted design. The pontil mark was often hidden by a "berry-shaped" piece of glass which was an added means of identification.

The glass was patented and the only other factory licensed to make it was Thos. Webb & Sons in England. It was first known by the name of "Bermise," but was later changed to "Burmese." The majority of items produced were tableware, plates, cups and saucers, pitchers of various sizes, including creamers and syrup jugs, berry bowls, salt and pepper shakers, sauces, cruets and a variety of different-sized vases.

Basket. 8¼" high. Mt. Washington.
    Footed with reeded Burmese
    handle attached. Delicate coloring $ 875.00

Bells
    3x3½". Ivy decor, scalloped
    bottom, pink interior only 275.00
    6" high, glossy type with pale
    amber-reeded loops. Crimped edge   450.00

Pitcher. 9½" high. Crimped top, irregular webbing in relief . . . $800.00

Biscuit Jar. Painted. Pairpoint decor, with H/P mums, number in lid and bottom. Blown scroll work. Signed   350.00

Bobeches
    2½" diam., crimped edge. Satin
    finish. Pair.   200.00
    3¼" diam., glossy finish. Pair 225.00

*Bowls
    2½ x5". Rectangular, bulging sides and opening. Rim edged in yellow and deep salmon pink color. 395.00
    4½" diam. Signed Webb. Scalloped edge 450.00
    10" diam., reeded feet, berry pontil 675.00
    Finger. 2¾" high. Salmon pink more than half way down. 325.00

Candlestick. Diamond Quilted, on four feet 575.00

Condiment Sets
    3 pieces. Salt, pepper and mustard in silver frame 750.00
    4 pieces. Covered mustard jar, salt, pepper and cruet in silver frame. 850.00

*Creamers
    4¼" high, reeded handle 500.00
    5½" high, crimped top 600.00

*Cruet. Acid finish 725.00

Cups
    Custard 300.00
    Punch. 350.00

*Cups and Saucers
    Demitasse. 400.00
    Regular 650.00

*Epergne. 26" high. Large ruffled bottom bowl, 15" diam., 10" diam. center bowl and 7" diam. third bowl. 2000.00

Ewer. 13" high. Salmon pink shading to bright yellow, applied yellow handle 1200.00

Lamp. With mushroom shade. 895.00

*Lamps, Fairy
    5" high. Salmon to yellow, signed and dated Clarke base 600.00
    5¼" high. Acid Queens. Signed Clarke cricklite holder. Webb seal in pontil 650.00
    5½ x6". Gunderson. Crimped edge on shade 650.00
    Complete with brass Clarke holder, 4 bud vases and large shade. Fine coloring 950.00

Mustard Pot. 3½" high. Ribbed satin finish 350.00

Nappie. 5" diam., handled. Mt. Washington 350.00

Perfume Bottle 365.00

*Pitcher, Water. Acid finish 1200.00

Plates
    5", slant rim 325.00
    6", glossy finish 375.00
    8", glossy finish 425.00
    12", blue harebells 750.00

Rose Bowls
  2¼" high. Body decorated with
  polychrome acorns and leaves.
  Salmon pink halfway down 450.00
  4" high. Egg-shaped. Crimped top,
  applied ruffled foot 500.00
  6½" high, 5" diam., acid finish.
  Footed, berry pontil............. 750.00
  Miniature 275.00
*Salt and Pepper Shakers. Ribbed
  yellow bottom shading to peach at
  top. Pair...................... 450.00
Sauce. 4" 200.00
Shades
  2" opening, 6" flare............ 400.00
  4½" opening, ruffled 650.00
Sherbet. Footed 350.00
Sugar Bowls
  3½" high, glossy finish 675.00
  5½" high, crimped top 795.00
Sugar Shaker. Pewter top 450.00
Syrup Jug....................... 650.00
*Toothpick Holders
  D.Q. body pattern, salmon pink
  halfway down. Mt. Washington... 350.00
  Satin finish. 2" tri-cornered.
  Handpainted floral 300.00
*Tumblers
  D.Q., salmon pink extending
  halfway down.................. 375.00
  Juice. 3" high, Webb acid decor,
  ivy vine, green shaded leaves 350.00
  Lemonade. D.Q., handled, glossy
  finish 395.00
  Lemonade. D.Q., small, acid finish . 395.00
  Mt. Washington 425.00
*Vases
  3¼" high, 3" diam. Salmon pink to
  base. Webb acid............... 465.00
  3½" high. Signed. Corset shape
  with 5-point rolled star top.
  Thomas Webb & Co., Queens
  Burmese incised on bottom 475.00
  4" high, 3" diam. Mt. Washington,
  ruffled top, footed 450.00
  6¼" high. Webb, stick neck,
  tapering to 4-sided dimpled base . 650.00
  6½" high. Floral decor. Round
  seal mark in pontil. Signed Webb . 750.00
  7½" high. Jack-in-the-Pulpit.
  Crimped edge, small matt finish .. 850.00
  8" high. Jack-in-the-Pulpit. Glossy,
  pink rim at top, yellow below 900.00
  9½" high. Scalloped top, bulbous
  base. Mt. Washington 750.00
  10" high. Lily, 3¼" base diam., 4"
  top diam. Acid finish 850.00
  10¼" high. Lily, 6" widest diam.,
  acid finish. Signed Webb. Pair 2000.00

  11¾" high. Acid finish. Pair...... 2250.00
  12" high. Lily, acid finish. Pair 2500.00
  12" high, 6½" widest diam.
  Gourd-shaped, with allover decor
  of gold leaves.................. 1200.00
  16" high. Mt. Washington, Lily top . 1500.00
  23" high. Trumpet shape, satin
  finish 2000.00
Whiskey Glass. Mt. Washington.
  Light salmon to canary 350.00
Wine............................ 395.00

*Reproduced Item

BUSTS

Items listed in this section have been
produced from various materials. A number of
England's prominent potteries made these
items between 1800-1900.

13" high. Parian. Robert Burns $195.00

Duke of Wellington. 6x6". Made of
  wax, framed. Green velvet background, round ....$ 75.00
Edward VII and Alexandra. 6½"

high. In Parian on marblized base. Impressed "Prince and Princess of Wales." Pair 100.00

Franklin, Ben. 9½" high. Parian 185.00

Goethe, Philosopher. Parian, 22½" high 275.00

King George V. 7½" high. Modeled in clay by L. Harradine. Doulton-Lambeth 125.00

Princess Louise. 4x15". Daughter of Queen Victoria. Parian. Incised on back, "Art Union of London-April 1, 1871, Mary Thornucroft, SC. Copeland." Front has embossed "Louise"....................... 185.00

Queen. Alexandra. 10½" high. Modeled in terra cotta. Impressed "Copeland 1884-Crystal Palace Art Union" 200.00

Roosevelt, Franklin D. 8" high 20.00

Sumner, Charles: 12¼" high. Polychrome. Emblem of Boston Sculpture Co. Probably Plaster of Paris .. 40.00

Washington, George. 8" high, modeled by Enoch Wood. C. 1800-10, impressed Washington on base 250.00

BUTTER MOLDS

These items are usually made of wood and are commonly known as butter printers. They are round, square or rectangular in shape and consist of two parts, the frame and a plunger with a hollow-cut pattern for impressing a design on the butter.

Their main purpose is to shape the butter into a form for packaging, as well as to produce a design which will be appealing to the buyer.

Eagle. 4¼" diam. $250.00

Clear glass. Wood handle ....$ 35.00

Cloverleaf design. Oblong 37.50

*Daisy design. Wood, 4" diam. 38.00

Fern design. Oblong 35.00

Fern leaf pattern. 4½" diam. 35.00

*Flower imprint. Wood. 4¾" diam... 35.00

Flowers, thistles, 8-print, 5x11"..... 40.00

Leaf design. Round, large 40.00

Letter "L". Oblong, wood frame..... 25.00

Letter "W". Round, wood frame..... 25.00

Maltese Cross. Hinged 50.00

*Pineapple design. Large, wood 50.00

Plunger. Rectangular, one pound, two maple imprints 58.00

*Sheaf of wheat 45.00

Sheaf of Wheat, two stars. Semicircle 175.00

Sheaves of Wheat. Rectangular 60.00

Strawberries, Two. Rectangular 65.00

Swan. One pound, plunger-type. Maple 60.00

Thistle. 1½" 25.00

*Reproduced Item

CALENDAR PLATES

Calendar plates and tiles were first issued in England shortly before the present century. In the United States they became popular after 1900. The majority were of the advertising type. The plates are made primarily of pottery and porcelain. Occasionally some are encountered which have been made of glass or tin.

1907. 9¼". Santa & Holly, calendar center ....$ 30.00

1907. Tin, girl's head 30.00

1908. 9½". Green border, green calendar leaves in center..... 18.50

1908. Large crossed U. S. flags 25.00

1908. Santa at chimney............ 30.00

1909. 7½". Calendar border, fruit center 20.00

1909. 8½". Calendar in border with small flowers and scenes, spread eagle holding scroll center 20.00

1909. 8½". Large flying green bird with ribbon................ 18.00

1909. 9". Pink rose center. Calendar around border 18.00

1909. 9¼". Santa on sleigh. Whip in hand, 4 reindeer 45.00

1909. 9½". Fruits and flowers 15.00

1909. Gibson girl bust. "Comp. of Carlson Tea and Butter Co., Naugatuck Conn.".......... 25.00

1909. Pretty girl and holly 22.00

1911. 9", transfer of flying duck. Compliments of Max D. Tobias, Pittsburgh, Pa. $25.00

1909. 9½". Transfer of lady. Advertisement $22.50

1909. Sailboat on scenic mountain lake. Florals and leaves	55.00
1910. 7". Yellow luster border with dog in center holding calendar	20.00
1910. 7½". Bright holly with gold trim	18.50
1910. 8". Dog carries pole with calendar suspended	16.50
1910. 8". Lighthouse center, Happy New Year on bottom.	20.00
1910. 8½". Betsy Ross making first flag	25.00
1910. 9½". Four cupids in bird nest with robin on tree	17.50
1910. Cherries	17.50
1911. New Year scene, "Should Auld Acquaintances".	26.00
1911. Sailboat Harbor Scene	16.00
1911. Wild ducks flying and adv. for Foxboro Coal Co., Foxboro, Mass.	18.50
1911-12. 1911 calendar with rising sun center. 1912 with red flowers in border.	20.00
1911-12. Double year rural scenic center	19.00
1912. 8". Calendar and airplane scene in center	30.00
1912. 8½". Owl on book-shaped calendar. Colorful winter scene in background. Will A. Ray. Rockefeller, Ill	22.50
1912. 8¾". Airplane decoration	30.00
1912. 9½". President Lincoln, Garfield and McKinley	30.00

1913. 7½". Girl on rock gazing into river.	17.50
1913. 7¾". Lady kneeling and peering into pool. Ohio	18.50
1913. 8¾". Calendar and pink decorations in border; house and rural scene in center	18.50
1913. 9¼". Aircraft over coastal town	25.00
1914. 8". Betsy Ross center	25.00
1914. 9¾". Washington's Tomb.	27.50
1915. 7¾". Map of Panama Canal crossed with flags	22.50
1915. 8½". Calendar with map of Panama Canal, U.S. flag, blue and gold trim	27.50
1916. 9½". Calendar and birds in center, floral border	17.50
1918. 9". Calendar and 4 birds in border, 2 deer, trees and stream in center	20.00
1919. 8¾". Calendar and pink flowers in border with flags of Belgium, France, England, U.S. in border. Large U.S. flag in center	30.00
1920. 7¼". War and Peace, flags . . .	27.50
1921. 8½". Calendar with bluebirds and pink flowers in borders. U.S. flag in center	18.50
1921. 9". Center has 5 flags of Allied Nations in WWI with dove of peace. Dated Nov. 11, 1918 . .	35.00
1923. 8½". Calendar with blue, yellow and red flowers at top, trees and stream in center. . . .	20.00

CALLING CARD CASES

In the Victorian era the habit of leaving a calling card became a popular social custom. The printed missive was taken from a card case and placed in a dish resting on a table in the hallway.

Card cases came in a variety of materials, from gold and silver to ivory and mother of pearl. The custom practically ended after World War I.

Sterling. Embossed with roses, with chain handle $35.00

Ivory. Carved flowers and vines.	
2½ x 4½" ....$	42.50
Mother of Pearl. Block design	35.00
Silver	
Coin. Hinged lid at end	35.00
Plated. 2½ x 4½"	20.00
Sterling. Embossed	60.00
Sterling. Green enameled	65.00
Tortoise Shell. Monogrammed......	25.00

CAMBRIDGE GLASS

The Cambridge Glass Company of Cambridge, Ohio started manufacturing colored glass items in the 1920's. Among the wares which are now popular with collectors are such colors as azurite, light blue, ivory, helio, primrose, violet, jade, carmen and ruby.

The factory, in its earlier years, produced pressed tablewares in crystal. In 1958 the plant closed and the molds were sold to Imperial Glass Co., Bellaire, Ohio.

Ash Tray. With standing pony, clear	
with stippled base ....$	20.00
Ball Jug with Stopper. 7" high, amber.	18.00
Basket. Small, novelty. Vaseline	16.50
Bell. Clear, nude lady, sapphire blue	
bell..........................	35.00

Bowls

6½". "Thistle" near-cut..........	14.50
7". Turquoise jade	35.00
7½". Rubina. Rounded sides	45.00
8¼". Pedestaled. GI's Heliotrope, Rams' Heads. 10" overall height ..	275.00
9". Amberina, tulip-shaped, unmarked	45.00
10". Seashell, three feet.........	100.00
13". Shallow, purple opaque	65.00
Flying lady. Crown Tuscan. Pink ..	125.00
Candelabrum. Dolphin, 10" high, original prisms and ring	50.00
Candleholder. Crown Tuscan, shell cup with dolphin base	60.00
Cigarette Box. Crown Tuscan. Dolphin feet, two trays and tiny three-footed shells	60.00
Compotes	
6" high. Stemmed. Crown Tuscan. Seashell pattern................	40.00
Cordial. Nude, clear, amethyst bowl.	30.00
Creamer. 3". Brown tones, with silver deposit Art Nouveau designs	125.00
Cruet. "Buzzsaw." Clear glass	22.50

Dishes

Bonbon. 7" wide, 2 handles. Brocaded acorns, carnival	35.00
Bone...........................	15.00
Covered, 7" diam. 3 feet, amber ..	21.50
Divided, 5½" diam., gold, etched rosepoint......................	25.00
Nut. Seashell. Crown Tuscan	12.00
Ivy Ball. 8½" high. Green crystal, footed, Ribbed Optic	37.50

Compote. Primrose $65.00

Luncheon Sets

Service for 4. 4 each cups and saucers, 4 dinner plates, 4 small breakfast or cake plates, 3 bread and butter plates. All marked with triangle mark. Set 85.00

Plates. 13", including handles . . $25.00

Service for 6. 20 pieces, with cream and sugar. Marked 50.00
Amber. 10 each cups and saucers, 10 8¼" plates, creamer, open sugar 125.00
Parfait. Pink 10.00
Pitcher, Water. "Martha Washington." Green................... 35.00
Plates
Bread and Butter. 6½", crystal. Etched rosepoint 45.00
Luncheon. Unsigned, green, set of six 30.00
Sandwich. Center handle, pink with gold band 10.00
5". Forest green. Block pattern ... 7.50
Platter. 16". Moonlight blue. Tulips .. 45.00
Salt Dip. Clear, unmarked.......... 12.00
Shot Glass. Amethyst, 2-oz. 6.00
Sugar and Creamer. Rosepoint 25.00
Sugar, Creamer and Tray. Caprice, moonlight blue. Set 30.00
Swans
3½", signed:
Apple Green 25.00
Black Amethyst 50.00
Crystal...................... 20.00
Dianthis Pink 22.50
Mandarin Gold............... 22.50
5", signed. Black 65.00
7" signed. Dianthis Pink 50.00
9" signed. Green 60.00
3½", unsigned:
Crystal...................... 12.50
Dianthis Pink 15.00
Emerald Green 15.00
Mandarin Gold............... 15.00
Milk White 25.00

Ruby Red 25.00
5" unsigned. Pink............... 30.00
9½" unsigned. Clear............ 35.00
Table Set. Covered butter, spooner, creamer, covered sugar, miniature. Clear..................... 60.00
Tumbler. Etched hunting scene, emerald green 12.00
Vases
3½" high. Crown Tuscan Cornucopian. 4-shell, pebble base 45.00
5". Sweet Pea. Amberina 75.00
10". high. Cornucopia. Crown Tuscan shell foot 125.00
10¼" high. Bud. Black amethyst with gold encrusted floral band .. 30.00
Wines
Nude stem, light amethyst 15.00
Pink 5.00

CAMEO GLASS

A type of art glass which originated in Alexandria, Egypt, C. 100-200 A.D. The oldest and most famous example of this glass is the original Barberini or Portland vase which was found near Rome in 1582. It contained the ashes of the late Emperor Alexander Serverus who was assassinated by his own soldiers in A.D. 235. It was made of dark blue glass with a layer of opaque glass fused onto the surface - the design then being cut through the opaque layer. The Wedgwood Portland vases are made of pottery instead of glass.

The majority of the Cameo glass found in antique shops and collections today was made in the 1884-1900 period. This later glass was made on the same principle as the ancient. A thin shell of glass was prepared and another color blown into it. A design was later cut through the outer layer leaving the inner layer exposed. Cameo glass is a form of "Cased glass."

Emile Galle', son of a French glassmaker, established a glass factory at Nancy, France, in 1884. Through experiments he developed and designed many fine articles of Cameo glass. Although much of the glass bears his signature, he merely made the original design and his many assistants and students did the actual work - even to the signing of his name to the various products of the factory. He died in 1904. Glass made after his death bears a star before the name Galle'.
Other makers of Cameo glass located in France include D'Argental, Daum [Bros.] Nancy, DeLatte [in 1920's]. The glass is being reproduced in limited quantities in France, but is very inferior and will not confuse anyone who collects Cameo.

Atomizers
  Double. 4-colored landscape . . . . . $ 450.00
  Scenic. Tan, brown and blue.
  Signed Galle' 450.00
Bottles
  Cologne. 7". Sterling Repousse'
  cap. Citron with white 875.00
  Perfume. 4". Lavender to pink.
  Daum Nancy 225.00
  Perfume. 4½". Cut flower atop
  stopper. Purple flowers, leaves,
  stems on camphor, lavender
  ground. Original paper label.
  Galle' 350.00

Vase. 10" high. Brown vines, leaves
with gold. Signed "Legras" . . . $395.00

Perfume. 6". Signed "Val St.
Lambert." Sharp hand cuttings of
cranberry-colored florals on
scrolly cut and frosted ground.
Silverplated stopper with cran-
berry jewels 125.00
5¾". Stoppered. Signed Galle' . . .   200.00
White with red, green and gold
palm leaves. Hallmark silver
mountings. Thomas Webb 200.00
Bowls
  3¼ x 6 x 13½". Cut and enameled
  scenes. Orange, green, brown on
  frosted white. LeGras 400.00
  5" diam., 2½" deep. Acid green
  ground, gold flowers, stems,
  berries. Daum Nancy 275.00
  8¼" diam. Tortoise shell, geo-
  metric pattern on yellow, frosted
  background. Charder 325.00
  Rose Bowl. Daum Nancy. Enam-
  eled yellow to orange with brown,
  sailboats. Signed Daum Nancy
  and artist RA 375.00
Boxes
  2¾ x 5". Scenic, carved and
  enameled band on lid. LeGras 300.00
  3 x 3¾". Covered, cylindrical shape   200.00
  Covered, tri-cornered, gray and
  rose. Galle' 350.00
  Compote. Footed, 6½" diam., 4"
  deep. Pastel and deep amethyst.
  Floral sprays decor 450.00
Dishes
  Candy. 1½ x 5". Triangular. Neu-
  tral tones 129.00
  Nut. Signed, 3-cornered, Cameo cut   150.00
Goblets
  3". Amethyst. Barberry pattern . . .   225.00
  Engraved, signed Joseph Locke . . .   250.00
Inkwells
  2¼ x 2¾". Blue, green frosted
  ground, lavender flowers, green
  leaves. Floral-trimmed decor on
  lid. Daum Nancy 300.00
  2¾" high. Gray background with
  colorful floral and French
  mottoes. Inkwell in center, 4
  openings for pens. Signed
  "Faience" 250.00
  4" high. Cranberry, white roses,
  silver bail and cover. Webb 350.00
  4" high. Green, yellow, brown and
  red. Daum Nancy 350.00
Jars
  6" high. Covered, light rose and
  blue. Galle' 400.00
  6½" high. Biscuit. Cut apricot
  florals on frosty ground. Signed
  "Muller" 395.00

Pitchers

8" high. Yellow with grapes and leaves in tan and red. Galle' 350.00

11" high. Blue, green, reds. Signed "La Verre Francias" with candy stripe 375.00

Plate. 7½". Blue morning glories and 4 butterflies on a frosted background, blue edge 300.00

Salts

1¼x2". Summer scene, signed Daum Nancy 125.00

Open. Blue and white, turtle-shape, 4 legs. Divided center, signed Faience. Pair 150.00

Shot Glass. 2x2½". Signed. Ferns on camphor and green glass background 100.00

Toothpick Holder. 2¼x2½". "St. Louis Nancy." Cameo cut dark flowers on satin-type light green background 165.00

Tumblers

4½" high. Mint green with frosted base. Mistletoe sprigs with white enamel berries 175.00

5" high. Signed Daum Nancy. Cut gold leaves and white berries on cranberry acid cut frosty glass background 200.00

Vases

1½". Green, blue, foliage, water. Daum Nancy 175.00

3". Galle' signed. Cameo cut purple berries and leaves on shaded lavender, satin-type background 175.00

4". Deep mauve on citrine. Butterfly, Galle' 225.00

4x5". Scalloped, brown sailboats, brown shoreline, pale green to yellow to green. S. LeGras 250.00

5x5". Low eared, with 4 dimpled sides. Flowers in relief 375.00

5". Oval top, red berries, leaves, mottled gray amber ground 375.00

5". Pink satin, puff coralene flowers. Webb 250.00

6½". Bulbous, pedestal base. Deep brown flowers, leaves on dark brown thru mottled blue to amber. Galle' 450.00

6½". Footed, green with purple flowers. Signed 575.00

8". Orange, brown flowers, green leaves on rust, yellow, orange ground. Daum Nancy 500.00

8". Carved flowers on orange, green frosted ground. Lovanka ... 300.00

Vase. 18" high. Burnt amber, trees on scenic background. signed D'Argental. 1977 Ed. $950.00

8". Signed St. Denis France. Deep cuttings of gold berries, leaves on acid cut green ground with red and brown tortoise shell color spatterings 300.00

8". Signed DeVez French. Scene is "Boy of Naples" engraved on base. Three layers and cuttings pink to blue to brown 485.00

9". Bulbous, pedestal base. Brown flowers, acorns, frosted blue ground. S. Galle' 550.00

12". Baluster vessel with flaring circular foot, splotched yellow and orange glass overlaid in cameo of multi-shaded colors 400.00

15". Signed L. Majorelle. Brown mold 550.00

15½". "Le Verre Francais." Deep cameo cut orange flowers, blue-berries on frosty vaseline ground. Cuttings leaning to Art Deco 300.00

25". Pink ground, red flowers. LeGras 650.00

31½". Leaf and Pod decor in shades of green/white on frosted ground. Shading to pink at top and base 1800.00

In the past few years a growing number of people have become interested in collecting cameras. A considerable amount of material is still available in this field.

Adlake Special Repeating Plate.
  C. 1898 .... $ 60.00
Baby Wizard. 4x5 folding plate
  camera mfgd. by Manhattan
  Optical Co. For bicyclists and
  tourists. Unidentified lens in
  Unicum shutter................ 55.00
Block Notes. 4.5x6 cm. cut film 225.00
Box Cameras. Plastic. 620 film.
  Herbert George Co., Chicago: Roy
  Rodgers, Official Girl Scout or
  Hero Imperial. Each............ 15.00
Box Camera. Vive V4. MPC Maga-
  zine, 4x5 plate 45.00
Capitol. "120" 6.50

Camera Tower. Box-type. Early 1900's
$9.50

Compact D. E. Montauk. Mfgd. by G.
  Gennert Co., N.Y. 4x5 folding
  plate camera, double extension
  bellows. Wollensak 4x5 rapid
  symetrical lens in Betax shutter .. 95.00
Cyclone Magazine No. 5. 1899...... 60.00

Daguerreotype. One-quarter plate.
  Chambered front and back. Back
  moves in and out like a drawer for
  rough focusing. Unmarked lens.
  Rosewood veneer box. Rare 2850.00
Empire State. No. 2, 8x10 view 100.00
Graflex, Auto. By Folmar & Schwing
  Div. of EKC. 7¼" Foss Epres f/4.5
  wide angle lens. With Graflex film
  pack adapter 160.00
Graflex Bag Magazine. For 3x4 glass
  plates........................ 50.00
Graflex Rollfilm. No. 3A, non-
  standard Kodak lens. C. 1910 .... 55.00
Hawkeye, Cartridge. No. 2A. Metal
  box........................... 10.00
Ica. 9x12 cm. folding plate 50.00
Iloca. 35mm Stereo. 1950's 50.00
Kewpie No. 2, rollfilm box-type 25.00
King Poco. Made by Rochester
  Camera & Supply Co. 5x7", double
  extension bellows which extend
  automatically when bed is
  opened. With case and 3 holders . 85.00
Kodak Box Cameras - Early
  1902 Brownie No. 2A, Model B ... 10.00
  1908 Brownie No. 2, Model D 10.00
  1916 Brownie No. 2C, Model A ... 7.50
  1925 Brownie No. 2A, Model C ... 7.50
Kodak Box Cameras - Late
  Brownie Junior, Six-20 .... 4.50
  Brownie Special, Six-20 .... 4.50
  Brownie Target, Six-16 .... 4.50
  Brownie Target, Six-20 .... 4.50
Kodak Folding
  No. 1, Model B. Serial 110239, last
  patent date 1898 .... 55.00
  No. 1, Model C. Serial 35077, 2nd
  No. 1 FPK made for one year,
  1905-06 .... 65.00
  No. 1A, Autographic Jr. 18.00
  No. 2A, Autographic. 1915 ...... 12.00
  No. 2C, Model A. Autographic
  Special, made by EKC. Anastigmat
  in Kodamatic shutter. Split image
  range finder. Last patent date,
  1922, original leather case 42.50
  No. 3, M-4, Eastman folding
  pocket, patent Sept. 8, 1902. Two
  cases 25.00
  No. 3, Series III 20.00
  No. 3, Model B-4................ 25.00
  No. 3A, Model A. Last patent date,

Portrait Camera and Tripod. Wooden
case.........................$225.00

1902. Early postcard size, rollfilm
camera 45.00
No. 3A, Model B-4, Pocket with
original leather carrying case 60.00
No. 3A, Model C. Autographic.... 20.00
No. 4, Serial #3598. Cartridge.
Bausch & Lomb RR lense in automatic shutter. 4x5 folding rollfilm.
Patent dated 1898.............. 75.00
No. 4, Model D. Panogram. Last
patent date, 1914. 3½x12"
pictures...................... 87.50
Petite. Light blue, one of the
all-color series of Petites with
matching case. Autographic back
and scribe.................... 30.00
Stereo. 35mm f/3.5 Kodak Anasto
lens. 1950's.................. 45.00
Leica 111f. Serial #525028 with
50mm f/3.5 Elmar lens. Over-
hauled and cleaned............ 150.00
Polaroid Land. Model 80 .... 15.00
Polaroid 95 .... 40.00
Premo No. 1, 1905............... 15.00
Premo Folding 5x7 with lens. 1900 .. 50.00
Premo Pocket C. 3¼x5" folding
plate camera 35.00
Ray. No. 1, 4x5 folding plate 45.00
Rolleiflex Orig. Serial #96693, f/3.8
Carl Zeiss Jena Lens No. 1262140
in Compur shutter 100.00
Seneca, Duo Special. 4x5 folding
plate camera. All black, inside
and out. Seneca 4x5 convertible
lens in Seneca Duo shutter....... 40.00
Seneca Folding Rollfilm............ 12.50
Seneca Pocket. No. 29, 4x5 folding
plate camera 40.00

Seneca Trio, Folding Scout No. 3A ... 35.00
Speed Graphic. 2¼x3¼". C. 1930 .. 75.00
Studio Camera. 5x12x15". Faormat
square bellow. C. 1885.......... 895.00
Telephoto Poco. A. 4x5 folding plate
camera 65.00
Tengor, Box. mfgd. by Zeiss Ikon.
Goerz Frontar Achromatic lens ... 40.00
Zeiss Ikon Cocarette 35.00

Movie and Projector
Cine-Kodak. 16mm, Serial #02226,
2nd model of the 1st crank movie
camera from Kodak. View finders
top and back. f3.5 lens. Motor
driven unit and battery-run attachment for camera. Original box ... 150.00
Keystone 35mm, Moviegraph.
Hand crank. illuminated by
electric light 55.00
Midas. 9½mm, combination cam-
era and projector with hand
crank. Illuminated by penlite
batteries inside. Taylor Hobson
Cam Anastigmat lens 50.00
Vitascope Movie Camera 58.50

CAMPAIGN ITEMS

Since the time of the campaign of Wm. Henry
Harrison for President of the United States in
1840, souvenirs such as buttons, badges,
banners, handkerchiefs, books, pamphlets
and medals have been distributed during the
campaigns to advertise or win favor for the
various candidates.

Ballot. Republican and Independent
ticket for President and Vice
President. Grover Cleveland and
Hendricks ....$ 18.00
Bandanas
20". Benjamin Harrison 60.00
23x24". Roosevelt and Fairbanks.
Flags, eagles and portraits.
Framed 95.00
Banner. Harrison and Morton.
22½x24".................... 50.00
Bookmark. Ike, Stevenson. 1956 .... 20.00
Buttons
Barker-Donnley 65.00
Browder-Ford................. 15.00
Bryan-Watson................. 65.00
Chafin-Watkins 12.50
Cleveland 9.50
Cleveland-Stevenson 28.50
Coolidge-Dawes................ 7.50
Corrigan 125.00
Davis-Bryan 225.00
David, John W. 1¼" 175.00
Debs and V.P. Candidate 70.00

Plate. Tin, 9½". "Grand Old Party," 1856-1908 ....$47.50

Dewey-Bricker	15.00
Dewey-Warren	5.00
FDR-Garner....................	25.00
FDR-Truman	15.00
FDR-Wallace	6.00
Foster-Ford	65.00
Foster-Gitlow	125.00
Grant-Colfax	50.00
Greeley.......................	85.00
Hancock	75.00
Hanley-Landrith	15.00
Harding-Coolidge	125.00
Hayes-Wheeler	30.00
Hoover-Curtis	28.50
Hughes, Chas. E.	16.50
Hughes-Fairbanks	25.00
"I Like Ike"	2.50
LaFollette-Wheeler	35.00
Landon-Knox	27.50
Lenke-O'Brien	12.50
McClellan	50.00
McKinley Portrait..............	16.00
Maloney-Remmel..............	125.00
Parker-Davis..................	8.50
Seymour-Blair.................	50.00
Smith, Al	7.50
Smith-Robinson	39.50
Stephenson-Kefauver	5.00
Stevenson-Sparkman	6.50
Taft-Sherman	6.00
Tilden-Hendricks	47.50
T. Roosevelt-Fairbanks	7.50
T. Roosevelt-Johnson	235.00
Truman-Barkley	18.50
Wilkie for President	5.00
Wilkie-McNary	3.50
Wilson-Marshall...............	10.00
Wooley-Metcalf	65.00

Cane. Bust of McKinley with words "Protection, 1896".............. 75.00

Crock. 10 gallon. Early, GOP. Elephant underglaze 150.00

Flags.Clay, Polk or Lincoln. Each 300.00

Handkerchiefs

Grover Cleveland and Thurman. Red portraits on silk	38.50
Benjamin Harrison, 1888. Blue cotton, red and white stars and flag..........................	35.00
Thurman. Red portrait on white silk	30.00
Hat. Blaine and Logan, Republican candidates, 1884	65.00
Jugate. Truman and Barkley	25.00

Mugs

Franklin Roosevelt.............	20.00
Harrison-Morton	85.00

Newspaper, 1956. Pass Dem. Convention 5.00

Pitcher, Pottery. Cleveland and Thurman [Sepia] 1888 Campaign . 42.50

Plates

Metal. 9½". Taft and Sherman in center. "Standard Bearers of G.O.P. 1856-1908" on rim	35.00
Milk Glass. Bust of Bryan in center, raised eagle, flags and stars form rim.................	35.00
"The Patriot and Soldier. Ulysses S. Grant"	35.00

Poster. "Deeds . . . Not Deficits". Landon and Knox.............$10.00

Portraits

Hoover, 13" long, diamond shape "McKinley Our Next President." Line etched ... 30.00 / 20.00

Poster. 1894 campaign on wood. Elephant and rooster in color. 9x19" ... 75.00

Ribbons

Andrew Johnson portrait, for re-election ... 40.00

Silk. 1892. Eagle and wording "REPUBLICANS." Reverse, ad for Whitehead & Hoag Co. Dated 22.50

Ring. Hoover. 1928 ... 15.00

Shield. Jefferson Campaign. C. 1802, on canvas. Rare ... 425.00

Snuff Boxes. Papier mache. Van Buren, Taylor, Clay. Each ... 200.00

Stickpins

Harrison portrait. Brass ... 15.00
McKinley head. Metal ... 30.00

Token. U.S. Grant for President on obverse. For Vice President, H. Wilson on reverse, hanging from eagle, dated 1872 ... 40.00

Tray, Pin. Taft and Sherman. 10" diam. 85.00

Watch Fobs

Lincoln. 1922-30 ... 26.00
T.R. Brass relief shell ... 25.00

CAMPHOR GLASS

Clear glass, after having been blown or pressed, is treated with Hydrofluoric Acid Vapor. The finished article has a cloudy white appearance similar to gum camphor in lump form.

Basket. Miniature, 4" high ... $ 12.50

Bottles

6½" high, including stopper. Drape pattern ... 20.00
Perfume. 4" high ... 14.50
Rabbit. Opening in tail ... 27.50
Scotch Whiskey ... 17.00

Bowls

4½" high. Covered, quilted pattern 17.50
6½" high, 7" diam. Embossed running horses encircling entire surface ... 40.00
Rose. 3½" high. Amber color, D&B pattern. Pleated top ... 27.50
Rose. 4" diam., H/P, blue flowers with gold trim ... 18.50

Boxes

3x5¼x5¾". Scroll design ... 25.00
4". Powder. Hinged cover ... 25.00
Round, hinged, enamel holly spray around bulbous center. 15". 50.00

Butter, Sugar and Creamer. Covered. Set ... 55.00

Candlesticks. 7" high. Made for Centennial Expo in Phila. 1876. pair 75.00

Chick and Egg. "Gillinder" ... 42.50

Compote and 2 Candleholders. Compote 8½" high, 8½" diam. at top. Candleholders 7¼" high. Stems are seated cherubs. Set ... 50.00

Creamer. Small, wild rose and bow-knot decoration ... 15.00

Cruet. Squatty base, enamel decor .. 25.00

Dishes

7". Open edge, fleur-de-lis joined by gold band. Water scene in center ... 15.00
Bird. Open ... 25.00
Duck. Covered ... 75.00
Fish. Covered ... 50.00
Hen. 7", covered ... 35.00
Hen. 8", covered ... 40.00
Salt. 5" long, swimming duck ... 20.00

Hands. Grapes and leaves at wrists . 26.50

Lamp. Dancers. C. 1920's ... 30.00
Owl. Standing, 3½" high, green eyes 18.50
Pitcher. 8½" high, reeded handle ... 30.00

Plates

6½". Chicks hatching. Easter Opening ... 15.00
7¼". Fleur-de-lis pattern ... 18.50
7¼". Owl ... 18.50

Playing Card Holder. 3¾" high, on four feet ... 12.50

Shoes

Lady's. 5" long ... 18.50
Marked, made by Libbey Glass

Boot. 2½" high ... $18.50

222

Co., Toledo, Ohio for 1893
World's Fair 22.50
Sweetmeat Jar. Pedestaled, em-
bossed flowers around square,
ribbed body. Enameling on cover . 28.50
Toothpick Holder 10.00
Trays
8x10½". Wild rose and bow-knot
pattern 12.50
Pin. Blue and silver trim 7.50
Vases
5". Painted with red tulips/daisies 26.50
8". Light green, sterling silver
overlay. Signed Rockwell and
number 92.50
8½". On 3 feet, bulbous, flower
motif 30.00
10". 4½" diam. at ruffled, turned-
down top. H/P decor of pink/blue
flowers, gold leaves/butterfly.
Pedestal base blown. Satin glass . 50.00

CANARY LUSTRE WARE

The ware dates back to the early 1800's and is
identified with the Staffordshire district of
England. It is extremely scarce today and
normally is offered at a high price compared
with some of the other wares of the period.
The body is yellow [canary] colored, the
transfer picture is usually in black and the
decoration is in lustre.

Jug. Transfer of Faith and Hope in
black, canary-colored body . . . . . . $ 750.00
Mugs
2¼" high. "A Present for a Good
Boy" 250.00

Pitcher. 5" high. "Sir Frances Burnett"
$500.00

7" high. Transfer of babies in black . 500.00
Child's. Red churchyard scene 210.00
Pitcher. 4½". "Faith and Hope" 425.00
Plate. 7". Rose in center, embossed
fruit around inner rim 575.00

CANDLEHOLDERS

Candleholders have been made in myriad
forms, sizes and shapes. Metal, glass, pottery,
porcelain and wood have been used in their
manufacture.

Brass. Ball shades. 22" high,
Pair . . . . $ 185.00
Brass. Beehive-type. See "BRASS"
Clambroth. Petal and L oop 135.00
Cloisonne. 11" high, multicolored.
Pair 135.00
Glass
Dolphin. Clear, single step 150.00
Dolphin. Vaseline, single step 275.00
Duck. 12" high. White glass with
shaded orange, gray, green 95.00

Brass. 19" high. Twisted stems,
hexagon-shaped bases. Pair . . $185.00

Cranberry. 7¼" high. Silverplated holders, enamel decoration, daisies, orange, white, blue. Pair $225.00

Heisey. Prisms hanging from bobeches.....................	65.00
Iron	
Hog-scraper type. Push-up	60.00
Hog-scraper. Hanging	70.00
Winged Dragon. 8" high. Pair	55.00
Porcelain. Saucer-type, handled. Germany.....................	19.50

CANDY CONTAINERS

After the turn of the present century candy makers resorted to the use of glass toys shaped like pistols, fire engines, cars, etc. as containers for their products. These items are now in demand by collectors. Many are presently being reproduced.

Airplane. "Spirit of Good Will." Small .... $	28.50
Autos	
Pierce Arrow	32.50
Stream Line...................	27.50
Zeppelin-type. Repainted tin bottom and wheels	32.50
Ball Player.....................	27.50
Battleship	22.50
Betty Boop.....................	24.00
Boat, Speed....................	18.50
Bus, Greyhound.................	25.00
Buster Brown with Tige	37.50
Carpet Sweeper	25.00
Charlie Chaplin by barrel	55.00
Clock, Alarm....................	40.00
Clock, Mantel	40.00
Dirigible. "Los Angles"	45.00
Dog, Scotty. Original candy. J. Crosetti Co.	25.00
Dog, Sitting. 3" high..............	10.00

Donkey pulling barrel	30.00
Duck, Sitting	22.50
Elephant, GOP	25.00
Fire Engine. Metal wheels	35.00
Fire Truck with driver	26.50
Gun with cap, 7½"...............	20.00
Horse and Cart. Paper top	20.00
House..........................	25.00
Kewpie, standing next to barrel	40.00
Lantern. Red glass globe...........	37.50
Liberty Bell. Amber glass, tin base ..	40.00
Liberty Bell. Blue	50.00
Locomotive #1026	18.00
Moon Mullins	40.00
Motorcycle	26.00
Nurser	7.00
Opera Glasses	35.00
Peter Rabbit	9.00
Pistol. Amber glass	32.50
Rabbit. Coming out of egg. Round tin closure.......................	60.00
Radio	30.00
Rolling Pin	25.00
Santa Claus. Climbing down chimney. Tin closure	60.00
Satchel with handle and tin slide....	22.00
Spark Plug	60.00

Telephone $28.50

Submarine	30.00
Telephone. Candlestick with pewter top and wooden receiver	32.00
Telephone Dial. Victory Glass Co.	30.00
Top, Spinning	25.00
Trolley, Toonerville	50.00
Trumpet. Milk glass	30.00
Turkey	20.00
Wheelbarrow	30.00
Windmill	37.50

CANES

Canes have been used by man since ancient times to assist him in getting about when injured or crippled. Later it became fashionable to "sport" gold and silver-headed walking sticks.

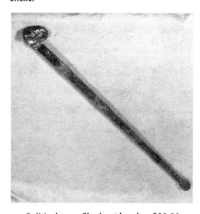

Political-type. Elephant head... $30.00

Golfer's. Wood $35.00

Bottle Cane. Glass inside liner for holding liquor. Removable head exposes cork. 36" long .... $ 140.00
Glass. 35" long. Clear glass with blue/red swirled ribbon inside ... 125.00

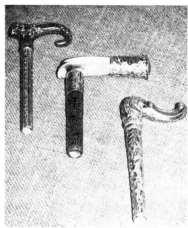

Gold. Each $50.00

Glass. Glassmaker's whimsy, green, 60" long	60.00
Gold Head Walking Stick. Fancy scrolls and initials. 36" long	65.00
Silver-Head Walking Stick. With initials	50.00
Sword Cane. Removing handle reveals sword blade concealed in cane body	155.00
Sword Cane. 35" long. Horn handle in shape of dog's head	135.00
Umbrella Cane. 34" long, black umbrella, wood case	85.00
Wood. Cherry, ordinary type	10.00

CANTON CHINA

This was originally a low cost porcelain chinaware which was brought to Europe and American from China by clipper ships. It was usually decorated in blue, but when done in brown, it was known as Canton Bistre. Most of this ware was not marked. It was exported from China for about 400 years until the Chinese Reds took over the country.

Basket. Handled, open lattice work. On matching tray with lattice border	$ 200.00
Bowls	
9½" diam. with square-cut corners	250.00
Rice. Cobalt blue, inside/outside decor	40.00
Butter Dish. Covered, 3 pieces, early, blue	175.00

225

Dish. Leaf-shaped, 5½ x 7½" . . $135.00

Butter Pat. Early, blue	15.00
Creamer. 4" high, handle extends 1"	
across top. Bent-down lip	85.00
Crocus Pot. 5½ x 8½"	75.00
Cups and Saucers	
Demitasse. Blue leaf pattern. Set	
of six	195.00
Rose	50.00
Dishes	
8 x 11". Leaf, open handles	125.00
8½" square, scalloped	100.00
Ginger Jar. Flat lid, blue	95.00

Plate. 10¼" square. Center design of cock $95.00

Jardiniere. 10" high, 7" top diam.	
Blue on white ground	185.00
Pitchers	
4" high, squat	87.50
8" high, water, blue and white . . .	165.00
Plates	
7½"	50.00
8½", early	89.50
8½", soup	50.00
8½". Bird in center, encircled by	
medallions of birds, flowers, fruit.	
Wide rim, heavy enameling	95.00
10". Scalloped edge, alternating	
swirls of gold on blue flowers on	
gold ground, gold design on red . .	165.00
10". 100-butterfly pattern	175.00
16". Scalloped edge, fish figures	
and tree decor	225.00
17½". Blue, red, green	250.00
Platters	
7 x 10"	95.00
8 x 10½"	110.00
12½ x 15½"	150.00
13 x 16". Blue and white "Nanking"	
pattern. Octagon sided	145.00
14½ x 17½"	175.00
16½ x 20½"	200.00
Sugar Bowl. Covered, large, blue	
and white. Two handles	125.00
Teapots	
4" high, 4" square base	120.00
8½" high. Wire handle. Chinese	
scene	175.00
9" high. Domed top	140.00
10½" high. Early, blue,	
on carved wood stand	250.00
Straight edges. Blue and white	255.00
Tile. 6" square, blue and white	55.00
Tray. Fish shape, blue, 10 x 11"	135.00
Umbrella Stand. 24½" high	250.00

CAPO-DI-MONTE CHINA

This ware was originally made in Italy from 1743 to 1760 in a soft paste, and again from 1770 to 1820 in hard paste. It is estimated that approximately 99% of the china on the market today bearing the "Crown" with "N" above is probably fake china. During the past century factories in France, Germany, Hungary and Italy have been using this mark. The original has a peculiar greyish color as compared with the fine colored porcelain paste items now on the market. To be accurate the porcelain should be designated "Capo-di-Monte-Type."

Bell. All crown mark . . . . $ 50.00

Box. Slipper-shaped, hinged. Signed
Crown "N" $350.00

Boxes
Glove. 3¼x4½x11". Padded
lining 450.00
Hinged. 2½x2½x3¾". Blue "N"
mark inside floral decor 100.00
Oval. 2¾" high. Hinged lid.
Figures in relief. Crown N Germany 175.00
Patch. 1½x3½". Raised relief
scene of four ladies in garden on
top. Sides decorated with 8
red/yellow flowers, two faces.
Mark underglaze 115.00
Round. 3½". Hinged King Neptune on cover with two horses
breaking through waves. Enameled floral decor 125.00
Trinket. Hinged, 3¼x4½". Children playing instruments in
allover relief design 175.00

Busts
3¾". Balzac 175.00
3¾" high. Schubert 175.00

Cups and Saucers
Demitasse.................... 115.00
Raised horse and chariot decor
with driver, angels on reverse,
Saucer decorated with raised floral
and wreath garlands. Signed
"Crown N" in blue underglaze 100.00
Ewer. 11" high, allover decor of
cherubs, people, animals 300.00

Figurines
4½" long. Tumbling. Pair 125.00
6½" high. Man holds hat for alms,
woman plays mandolin. Late. Pair 100.00
8¼" high. Boy playing bagpipes,
dressed as hobo, blue, rust, green
marked "Crown N" 155.00
8¾" high. 7 dwarfs playing
musical instruments. 3" figures
grouped around stump with one
atop 725.00
9¾" high. Child sitting on stump
holding tambourine. Pair 500.00
Inkwell. Double 185.00
Lamps. 28½" high. Custom made
silk shades. Pair............... 350.00

Pitcher. 7" high. Raised mask faces
with female torso handle, marked
N and Crown.................. 265.00
Plaques
3x4¼". Narrow hanging brass
frame. 5 children playing in
flower garden 85.00
5½x7¼". Lady in shell boat
drawn by dolphins, surrounded by
cherubs 220.00
11x15". Group of satyrs with
Bacchus on mule. N mark in blue
under crown 800.00
Plate, Armorial. Rim decorated with
figures, coat-of-arms in center ... 375.00
Stein. #1535/431 mark underglaze
in golden base. 10½" high, raised
figurines, multicolored finial in
form of sitting lions. Lion's head
handle 150.00
Tankard. 8½" high. Open, elephant
handle 400.00
Tea Sets
Teapot, sugar, creamer, 4 each
cups, saucers. Late 150.00

"Tony Weller." C. 1915. Germany
$65.00

Teapot, sugar, creamer, 6 demi-cups/saucers. Heavy gold inside cups, raised figures, animal heads on teapot, sugar and creamer handles. Marked Italy 250.00

Urns
Covered, 15" high. Marked N and Crown. Pair.................... 850.00
Footed, with cover and pistol-grip handle. Rare battle scenes. C. 1860........................ 95.00

Vases. 15" high, handled, square bases. Pair 800.00

Wall Pocket. Cherub in center, two birds either side, 1 held by cherub. All in relief, 18th century. Crown and N mark underglaze ... 275.00

CARLSBAD CHINA

This china was made at Carlsbad, Austria, by a number of factories. Most of the items found in shops and collections today were made after 1891.

Pitcher. 10½" high. Helmet-type, cream ground, white lilies, gold handle and trim. "Austria" $75.00

Bowls
3¼" diam. Cream ground with flowers in red, green and gold ...$ 24.00
6" diam. Classic figures 30.00

Cup and Saucer. Pink and yellow roses on white background. 1" gold scroll with blue top border .. 32.00

Dessert Set. Serving dish and 12 sauces with portrait centers. Pink with gold trim................. 100.00

Fish Sets
23" platter, sauce boat, 12 scalloped 8½" plates with fish centers and leaf border 240.00
12 9" plates with raised irregular border. Fish centers and gold trim . 250.00

Mayonnaise Set. Portrait, green with gold. Austria, signed........... 45.00

Pitcher. 11½" high. Pink ground with cobalt blue band at top and bottom. Gold floral decor, gold handle 65.00

Plates
8½". Oyster. Scalloped gold rim, violet decor.................... 35.00
8½''. Portrait center, green border with gold decor 40.00
11½". Hanging type. Dark green border with gold gilt, center scene of two ladies at tea, gentleman visitor 50.00

Platter. 15¼" long, blue floral decor 55.00

Tea Caddies
Pink to white background, woman with cupid decor 40.00
Covered, portrait of lady on side. Signed Victoria Carlsbad, Austria. 45.00

Tray, Perfume. 6½x9½". Pin compartments, crimped border with sepia, green florals on white. Some gold, signed 18.00

Tureen. Covered, 7½x12". Violets, daisies and leaves, gold trim 40.00

Vases
7" high. Cupids, gold 60.00
Pitcher. 9¼" high, lavish gold decoration 75.00
Pitcher. 11" high. Pink with blue and gold 90.00

CARNIVAL GLASS - AMERICAN

Carnival Glass, sometimes referred to as "Taffeta Glass" or "Poor Man's Tiffany," was made during the 1900-1925's. The majority was manufactured near Wheeling. W.Va. It was made to imitate fire iridescent art glass. Items made of Carnival glass have been reproduced profusely in various patterns and

228

colors. Imperial Glass Co. of Ohio, one of the largest producers of "new" Carnival glass, was recently purchased by the Lenox China Co. Lenox intends to discontinue some of Imperial's line and re-introduce others. These discontinued patterns and colors may become collectible.

For additional information on reproduced Carnival Glass, consult "Reproduction Alert List" by P. S. Warman.

ACORN

Berry Set. 7 pieces. Marigold	$ 125.00
Bowls	
6½" diam. Slag. Red	265.00
7½" diam. Blue	35.00
8½" diam. Marigold	20.00
Butter Dish. Green	220.00
Punch Base. Purple	125.00
Table Set. 4 pieces. Green	400.00

BEADED SHELL

Bowls, Rose	
Blue	75.00
Marigold	36.50
Dish, Candy	
Green	25.00
Purple	35.00
Tumbler. Purple	42.50

BLACKBERRY

Bowls	
6½" diam. Slag red	160.00
9" diam. Green	47.50
Compote, small. Blue.............	50.00

Candy Dish. 5" high. Purple, signed "Northwood" $45.00

Hat. Marigold	16.50

COIN DOT

Bowls	
7½" diam. Marigold	12.50
8½" diam. Aqua, opalescent.....	72.50
8½" diam. Purple	27.50
Pitcher, Water. Marigold...........	85.00
Water Set. 7 pieces. Marigold	250.00

CORN

Vases	
Blue	175.00
Ice Green	150.00
Marigold	135.00
Purple	200.00

FASHION

Bowls	
Punch. Marigold................	65.00
Rose. Marigold	35.00
Compote. 6" high. Marigold	10.00
Punch Set. 8 pieces. Marigold	120.00
Tumbler. Marigold	25.00
Water Set. 7 pieces. Marigold	225.00

GOOD LUCK

Bowls	
9" diam. Blue	92.50
9" diam. Green	40.00

GRAPE AND CABLE

Berry Set. With thumbprint, purple, 7 pieces	225.00
Bowls	
8" diam. Footed. Blue	65.00
8" diam. Footed. Purple	125.00
8" diam. Marigold with basket-weave	40.00
10" diam. Marigold	50.00
Butter Dish. Purple. "N"	175.00
Candle Lamp. Complete	500.00
Candlestick. Purple	85.00
Cologne. Stoppered. Complete. Marigold	300.00
Compote. Open. Purple...........	385.00
Cracker Jar. Purple "N"..........	265.00
Creamer. Purple. "N"	150.00
Dresser Trays	
Blue	155.00
Green	155.00
Marigold	125.00
Hair Receiver. Marigold	57.50
Hat. Fluted......................	57.50

Hat Pin Holders

Green	140.00
Marigold	125.00
Pitcher. Green	100.00
Powder Jar. Green	47.50
Punch Cup. Purple	35.00
Sauce. Purple. "N"	30.00
Shot Glass. Marigold	55.00
Spooner. Purple	135.00
Tumbler. Amethyst with thumbprint	32.00

Water Sets

Amethyst. 7 pieces	300.00
Marigold. 7 pieces	240.00

GRAPE AND GOTHIC ARCHES

Berry Set. 7 pieces. Blue	150.00
Butter Dish. Covered. Marigold	70.00
Pitcher. Blue	185.00
Sauce. Amethyst	25.00
Tumbler. Blue	27.50

HAMMERED

Bell. White	120.00

KITTEN

Banana Boat. Marigold	57.00

Bowls

Small. Marigold	42.50
Pinched. Marigold	60.00
Cup and Saucer	115.00
Dish. Miniature. Marigold	70.00
Sauce. Blue	50.00

Spooners

Blue	110.00
Marigold	65.00
Toothpick. Marigold	60.00

MAPLE LEAF

Berry Bowl. Master. Footed. Marigold	42.00
Butter Dish. Covered. Marigold	40.00
Creamer. Marigold	25.00
Spooner. Marigold	22.50
Sugar. Covered	35.00
Tumbler	22.50

ORANGE TREE

Bowls

9" diam. Fluted. Marigold	35.00
9" diam. Red	200.00
9¼" diam. White	110.00
10" diam. Footed. Marigold	55.00
11" diam. Marigold	95.00
Creamer. White	75.00
Hat Pin Holder. Blue	85.00

Mugs

Blue	47.50
Marigold	25.00

Punch Sets

Bowl, 6 cups. Blue	250.00
Bowl with base, 6 cups. Marigold	240.00
Sherbet. Marigold	20.00
Sugar. Open. Marigold	60.00
Wine. Green	45.00

ORIENTAL POPPY

Pitchers

Green	350.00
Marigold	325.00

Tumblers

Green	45.00
Ice Blue	75.00

Water Sets

Marigold. 7 pieces	500.00
Purple. 7 pieces	675.00

PEACOCK AT FOUNTAIN

Berry Sets

Blue. 7 pieces	250.00
Marigold	150.00
Bowl. 10" diam., footed. Marigold	125.00

Pitchers

Marigold	200.00
White	275.00
Punch Cup. Blue. "N"	37.00
Sauce. Purple	22.50
Spooner. Purple	68.00
Tumbler. Marigold	35.00
Table Set. 4 pieces. Purple	300.00

RASPBERRY

Pitcher. 7" high. Marigold	60.00
Tumbler. Purple	55.00

SINGING BIRD

Berry Set. 7 pieces. Purple	265.00
Creamer. Purple	65.00

Mugs

Blue	55.00
Green	50.00
Purple	50.00
Pitcher. Purple	235.00
Sugar. Covered. Purple	80.00
Tumbler. Green	35.00

STAG AND HOLLY

Bowls

3-3/8x7-7/8". 3-footed, fluted. Blue	60.00
9" diam. Footed. Marigold	65.00
11" diam. Footed. Marigold	75.00

STRAWBERRY

Berry Set. 7 pieces. Green	85.00
Bowls	
8½" diam. Ruffled. Purple	50.00
9" diam. Ruffled. Marigold	46.50
Dish. 8" diam. Marigold	52.00
Nappy. 2-handled. Marigold........	22.00
Plates	
8¾". Amethyst	135.00
9". With basketweave. Blue and	
purple satin	65.00
Tumbler. Scroll. Marigold	100.00

WINDMILL

Bowls	
6½" diam. Green	40.00

Vase. 9½" high. Green to amber.
"Thorn" pattern. Signed Northwood
$90.00

8" diam. White	60.00
Candy Dish. Handled, 7¼". Marigold	22.00
Pitcher. 4½ x 6½". Marigold	57.50
Sauce. Marigold	13.50
Tray,Dresser. Marigold	28.00

WREATHED CHERRY

Banana Boats	
Red...........................	285.00
White.........................	265.00
Water Set. 7 pieces. Marigold	350.00

CARNIVAL GLASS - AUSTRALIAN

BUTTERFLY

Lamp. Marigold	200.00

BUTTERFLY AND BELLS

Compotes	
4½ x 7". Marigold	55.00
4½ x 7". Purple	80.00

BUTTERFLY AND BUSH

Compotes	
4½ x 7". Purple	70.00
4½ x 7½". Marigold	55.00
6 x 8". Marigold	75.00

DRAGONFLY

Lamp. Marigold	200.00

KINGFISHER

Bowls	
5½" diam. Marigold	35.00
5½" diam. Purple	55.00

KOOKABURRA

Bowls	
5½" diam. Marigold	35.00
5½" diam. Purple	55.00

MAGPIE

Bowls	
5½" diam. Marigold	32.50
5½" diam. Purple	52.50

SWAN

Bowls	
5½" diam. Marigold	36.50
5½" diam. Purple	55.00
9½" diam. Purple	125.00

THUNDERBIRD

Bowls

5½" diam. Marigold	34.00
5½" diam. Purple	57.50
9½" diam. Purple	130.00

CASTOR SETS

A castor set is a container for condiments. It had its beginning in the early 1700's or possibly earlier. Castor sets found today probably date back to the late 1800's or early 1900's. They usually contain from three to seven pressed glass bottles in a silverplated frame. Some were made of cut glass with a sterling holder.

6 bottles, silverplated frame, ground stoppers $175.00

3-Bottle. Gothic . . . . $ 60.00
3-Bottle. 4½" high, 3-7/8" diam. Squared silverplated Sheffield holder. Square mustard pot, pepper shaker and rectangular shape salt dish. Allover cut pattern .	100.00
3-Bottle. Pressed, original stoppers, 6¼" high, pewter frame	80.00
4-Bottle. English type, square silverplated frame	135.00
4-Bottle. Miniature. Revolving tin base	60.00

4 bottles, 2 cruets, 1 salt, mustard with spoon. Slverplated. Simpson H. Miller Co. $145.00

4-Bottle. Cut glass in Rubina. Glass set in footed square silverplated holder with center handle 165.00
5-Bottle. Clear glass, blue glass base. 11" to top of handle 150.00
5-Bottle. Early flint glass with pewter holder 200.00
5-Bottle. Matching bottles, replated bottle tops and frame. 125.00
5-Bottle. With stand. Button band, pressed glass. All original 125.00
5-Bottle. Original Honeycomb resilvered, Meriden #39 . . . . 120.00
6-Bottle. 3 bottles with tulip stoppers, with salt, pepper and covered mustard. Resilvered frame 175.00
8-Bottle. Cut glass, sterling tops and tray. Ground stoppers. Hallmarked and documented. C. 1733 . . . . 2500.00

CATALOGUES AND MAGAZINES

Publications before 1915 are mainly in demand by collectors and libraries.

American Legion. Coronett, 1931 thru 1949, 30 copies . . . . $ 12.00
Automotive
    Auto Owners Supply Book. Western Auto, 1929, 128pp 15.00
    Chevrolet. 1923. Instructions on three 7x9" sheets 7.50
    Dort Motor Cars. 1916, 25pp 18.50
    Essex Instruction Book. March, 1926. 6x9", 45pp 5.50
    Ford. The Universal Car. 1916, 24pp. 15.00
    Ford Facts. 1920, 6x9", 72pp 14.50
    Ford. 1922, 18pp 12.50
    Ford.Sales folder, 1923. . . . . 10.00
    Pullman Automobile Book of Instructions, 1917. 6x9", 22pp 20.00
    White Motor Cars. 1916, 10x12", 18pp. 15.00
Bathing Suits. Millbury Co., Rahway, N.J., 1905. 3½x6", 65pp 6.50
Beadle's Dime Novel. Dialogues No. 7, 84pp, plus 12pp catalogue. Yellow paper wrapper, N.Y. 1882. 7.50
Belknap Hdwe., C 1910, 3784pp 60.00
Bicycles
    Cleveland Safety, H. A. Lozier, Cleveland, 1892. 6x9", 20pp 15.00
    Columbia. 1890, 6x9", 48pp 15.00
    Iver Johnson, 1897. 7x8", 32pp . . . 16.50
Cameras
    Camera, The. 1905, 7x10", 45pp. . 2.50
    Camera Craft, 1909. 7x10½", 90pp 4.50

Kodaks for Xmas. 1910, 5x6½", 32pp. 10.00
Country Gentleman. After 1910. Each 1.00
Debretts, Peerage, Baronetage & Knightage, London. 1899, 991pp . 24.50
DeLaval Cream Separators. 1916, 8½x11", 72pp 12.00
Diamonds & Precious Stones. S. C. Scott Mfg. Co. 1900, 4½x7", 72pp . 15.00
Ecclesiastical Statuary. Daprato Co. of Chicago. 11x14", 128pp. 12.50
Electric Light, Railway, Telephone & House Supplies, Electric Appliance Co., 1924. 7½x11", 472pp 27.50
Electric Street Cars. Bentley Knight Co., N.Y. 1887, 7x11", 25pp 20.00
Etude Music Magazines. 1910 thru 1930, each 2.00
Flags of the World. National Geographic Society, McCandless & Grosvenor, 1917. Hard cover, 420pp 28.50
Fordson Tractor. 1923, 8½x9", 4pp . . 5.50
Farm Wagons. Peter Schuttler Co., Chicago. Leather bound, 7x10", 113pp 20.00
Furniture & Floor Coverings. Peck & Hills Furniture, Chicago, 1923, 10½x14" hardbound, 480pp 47.50
Gas Engines
    Fairbanks Morse Gas Engine. 1915, 6x9", 12pp 4.00
    Sears, Roebuck. 1912, 8¼x10", 32pp. 20.00
Gears. Warner Co., Muncie, Ind., 1910, 72pp 12.50

"1911 Catalogue & Supplements of Military Goods." Francis Bannerman $35.00

Godey's Lady's Book. May 1884.....	25.00
Hamilton Watch. 1909............	5.00
Hardware. Wagner Mfg., Cedar Falls, Iowa. 1910, 83pp.........	17.50
Harness. Waterbury Co. 1893. 53pp..	15.00
Harper's Monthly	6.50
Harper's Weekly. Civil War period ..	8.50
Holekamp-Moore Instruments [Surgeons'], 986pp	20.00
House Supplies. Elec. Appliance Co., 1924. 7½x11". 472pp...........	27.50
Horse Cars of Mass. Highland Street Railway Trips to Oakland Gardens. 1880, 3½x5½", 4pp.......	9.50
Ice Boxes	
Herrick Refrigerators of Waterloo, Iowa. C. 1915, 6x9", 79pp....	13.50
Leonard Cleanables. 1916, Louisville, Ky., 6x9", 96pp	12.00
Indian Motorcycles. 1917, 8x10", 24pp..........................	17.50
Jewelry. Speigel, May Stern Co., Chicago, 1913, 7x9½", 47pp	7.00
Ladies' Home Journal. After 1908 ...	1.25
London Barn Equipment. 1923, 8x10½", 248pp	17.00
Lyon Bros., Chicago. General Wholesale, Summer 1907	22.50
McCalls. March 1903, August 1903. Each	6.00
McKesson & Robbins. 1881	11.50
Marlin Catalog For Repeating Rifles and Shotguns. 1918, 24pp	24.50
Montgomery Ward	
Fall and Winter, 1918	35.00
Fall and Winter, 1926	30.00
Fall and Winter, 1929	25.00
Morse Telegraphy. Philosophy and Practice. 1900	5.00
Movie Magazines. C. 1940's. Each ...	4.50
National Geographics. 1920's to to present. Each	.50
Overland. 1914, 9x11", 18pp.......	42.00
Parke-Davis. 1879, 41pp...........	7.00
Period Ornaments of Furniture. Woodwork & Interior Decoration. Decorator Supply Co., 1924. 9x12", 242pp	25.00
Petersons Magazine. 1882	8.50
Physician & Pharmacist Handbook. Squibb's, 1906. 6x9", 394pp	20.00
Pianos. Sterling, Fall River, Mass. 1893, 32pp, illustrated	17.50
Price Wrecker. Catalog #168. Chicago House Wrecking Co......	17.50
Reaping & Mowing Machines. Whitley, Fassler and Kelly, 1879. 56pp........................	15.00
St. Nicholas, 1884. 2 bound volumes	35.00

Saturday Evening Post. After 1908 ...	1.50
Sausage Making and Meat Curing. B. Heller Co., Chicago. 1913, 4x6½", 302pp	10.00
Scientific American, 1892. 52 weekly issues	40.00
Sears, Roebuck	
1902, 1162pp	55.00
1916, F&W, No. 133	45.00
Sharpe & Dohme, 1899, 183pp......	6.50
Singer Sewing Machines. 1897, 5x7½", 32pp	9.00
Sleighs. Sullivan Bros., Rochester, N.Y., 6½x7½", 24pp............	17.50
Sports Catalogues	
Reach Baseball Guide. 1908	17.50
Spalding Baseball Guide. 1915 ...	15.00
Telephone Switchboards & Signal Systems. 1910, 6½x9½", 56pp...	14.50
Typewriters. Oliver, 1902. 7x9¼", 24pp..........................	10.00
Victor Records. 1928, 200pp	7.00
Weston Electrical Instruments. 1920, 8x10", over 200pp	22.00
White Rotary Sewing Machines. 16pp........................	7.50
Winchester Firearms. 1908, 180pp ..	25.00
Youth Companion. Washington edition. 1912	2.00

CELADON CHINA

Celadon is an oriental porcelain which has been made for several centuries in China, Korea and Japan. The wares were usually made in colors of green, tones of blue/green

Plate. 9¾". Court scene. Mandarin
$225.00

and gray. Early pieces are scarce and command higher prices than later ones.

Vases. 9¼" high. Floral decor with bird on front. Squirrel handles with gold decor. C. 1800. Pair $375.00

Bowls
5" diam. Fern leaves in darker
Late .... $ 50.00
10¼" diam., 2½" high. Yellow-
brown, 18th century 150.00
Creamer and Sugar. Covered,
foliage design with gold 160.00
Cup and Saucer. Demitasse. Foliage
design 28.50
Inkwell. 2x3½x3¾". Openwork
sides, simulated bamboo cross
pieces 45.00
Plates
7". Bird, flowers, butterfly decor.
Early........................... 70.00
8x11". Leaf shape, pastel florals
and bug decor, ribbing 115.00
10". Peony and Shasta Daisies
with flying butterflies. Chin Lang
mark 85.00
Teapot. 5" high, 7½" diam. Bulbous,
covered. Raised pastel floral
decor. Late 52.50
Vases
7¾" high. Underglaze design
panels, ears, stds. Late. Pair 135.00
9¾" high. Raised pink and green
flowers. Early 110.00
17" high. 6-sided raised pink and
white flowers 275.00
12¾" high, 5¾" diam. base.
Green with splotches of dark
green around neck and body.
Dragon draped part way around
bulbous center. Chung Dynasty... 285.00
14" high, 15" diam. at widest.
Enamel work. Trees, white
flowers, bluebird on branch.
Allover decor 295.00

CELLULOID ITEMS

Celluloid was invented just before the 1870 decade, about midway in the Victorian era. The name was a trademark for a flammable material made of nitrocellulose and camphor. It was used in making toilet articles, photographic film and as a cheap substitute for materials made of amber and ivory. One of its chief uses was the making of men's so-called stiff collars.

Baby Rattle. 2½" diam. .... $ 6.50
Boxes
Collar. Lined 14.50
Hinged cover, satin lining.
plain........................... 10.00
Powder. Removable lid, round ... 7.00
Trinket. 3x4x12". Victorian.
Mottled in various tones of green
with decor of flowers. Lid has
center panel showing two children playing with lamb. Original
pink silk lining and scalloped
metal clasps 35.00
Bracelet. Bangle 7.50
Dresser Sets
8 pieces. Long box, round box
with glass insert. N/P nail buffer,
nail file, button hook, scissors,
shoe horn and mirror 28.50

Box. Covered, 2½" diam. Transfer on lid and front. Man and woman . $10.00

Ram. 3½x4½" $6.00

Tray, mirror, hair receiver, comb and brush	22.50
Elephant. 6" long, nodding. Child's natural color with beige blanket on back	12.00
Hair Receiver. Round	6.00
Hand Mirror. 10½" long, simulated tortoise shell. C. 1890	6.00
Manicure Set. 14 pieces. Leather roll case.....................	30.00
Napkin Ring	6.00
Shoe Horn. Ivory color	3.00
Tray, Dresser. 7x9", round corners ..	10.00
Vanity Case. Victorian. Decorated ..	45.00
Vase.Small, 6½" high	10.00

CHALKWARE

The term "Chalkware" is a misnomer. The various ornaments of this type were made of plaster of paris and decorated with water

Dog. 2¾x3¾" base. White, black trim, red dots $225.00

colors. Italian immigrants made and sold these items around the 1820-1865 period. In the past many collectors and dealers were under the impression that the ornaments were folk art of the Pennsylvania [Dutch] Germans. Investigations have revealed that the figurines and animals were copied from Staffordshire and other porcelain or pottery models.

Lamb on base. 8½" high. Grey body, tail and ears. Red inside ears . $250.00

Cat. 4½" high .... $	125.00
Compote. With fruit and bird	265.00
Dogs	
3¾" long, 2½" wide base. Original black and brown paint. Early. Pair	400.00
6¼" high. Red decor on gray background	175.00
11½" high.....................	220.00
Eagle, Spread. 9½"high, 12½"wide.	250.00
Hen. 6½" high	130.00
Pigeon	110.00
Rabbit. Sitting	127.50
Roosters	
6¼" high. Multicolored with gold .	150.00
11" high. Decorated	200.00
Sheep. Mother and baby sheep. 7" high	165.00
Squirrel	130.00
Stag. 15" high, 17" long	225.00

CHELSEA

A fine English china which was made to compete with Dresden in the home market. The plant began operating in the 1740's. The products can be divided into four periods: 1] Early period [1740's] with incised triangle and raised anchor mark. 2] The 1750's, red raised anchor mark. 3] The 1760's, the gold anchor period. 4] The Chinese-Derby period of the 1770's.

Bone ash was introduced to the body in 1758, the glaze was frequently "crazed" showing spots of green. In the Gold Anchor Period 1760, articles showed more sumptuous decorations as ground colors were in blue, pea green and red, along with elaborate gilding copied from Sevres Porcelain. Fancy rococo scroll work was also used on figures and vases. A new line of painting representing mythological scenes, birds in polychrome enamels and fruit was introduced. Wares decorated with the familiar grape or thistle pattern in relief and/or lustre are called Chelsea, but were made in the Staffordshire area and not in Chelsea. There is a movement to rename this decorated ware "Grandmother's Ware."

In 1924 a large number of molds and models of figurines were found at the Spode-Copeland Works and many items were again brought into production.

Bowl. 10" diam. Grape and leaf in gold lustre ....$	48.50
Butter Pat	5.50

Plate. 9½". Vintage pattern in gold
$55.00

Creamers	
Raised lustre flowers	50.00
Sprig pattern	37.50
Cups and Saucers	
Blue thistle	37.50
Handled, lustre grapes	35.00
Handleless, sprig pattern	42.50
Figurine. 8½" high. Woman with tray. White ground with rust, red and blue decor	200.00
Figurines. 9" high, hunter attired in red jacket; milkmaid wearing red skirt. Pair	395.00
Jardiniere. 11" high, covered. Hexagonal, iron rust anchor mark .	275.00
Plates	
7½". Late	25.00
9½"	60.00
10". Peafowl in brilliant colors. C. 1825........................	175.00
Cup..........................	12.50
Sauce. Lustre grapes	21.50
Sugar Bowl. Covered, lustre grapes .	125.00
Teapot. 9" high, squat-type. Blue lustre-type decor	150.00
Tea Set. Grape decor, 24 pieces	595.00

CHILDREN'S ITEMS

Nostalgia has taken hold and many people enjoy collecting children's and dolls' tableware and other items. Perhaps it is a reminder of their childhood, or they may be collecting an "heirloom-to-be" for a favorite child.

3 pieces. Teapot, creamer, covered sugar. White porcelain. Set $28.50

Bowls	
Berry. Lacy Lane. Set of five ......$	30.00
Punch. Whirling Star. Three stars, clear.....................	25.00
Butter Dishes	
Covered. Fennland	30.00
Covered. Flattened Diamond and Sunburst	15.00
Cake Stands	
Hawaiian Lei by Higbee. 3¼"	

Creamer and Sugar. "This is the dog that killed the cat" on creamer. "This is the cat" on sugar $35.00

6¾" diam. Pressed glass, bee marked	32.50
Panelled Palm	15.00
Candlesticks. Flute, clear. Pair	15.00

Condiment Sets

Hickman. Clear, complete	50.00
Hobnail. English. Cruet, open salt, pepper, clover leaf tray	40.00
Hobnail. Shaker, cruet, rectangular tray. Clear, English	27.50

Creamer with Mold. Azure blue, Sandwich Ivy 65.00

Creamers and Sugars

Arrowhead and oval	47.50
Cherry Blossom	45.00
Flattened D and Sun. Milk glass . . .	35.00
Sawtooth. Early flint, clear	55.00
Sweetheart	42.50

Dinner Sets

Akro Agate. Green, white. 16 pieces. Set	40.00
McKee Laurel. French ivory, green band trim. 14 pieces. Set	125.00
Nursery Tales. 10 pieces. Set	135.00
Doll's. English porcelain, white, violets and leaf trim. 18 pieces. Set	50.00
Doll's. Staffordshire blue and white. C. 1830. 54 pieces. Set	325.00
"Villeroy and Boch - Dresden." 16 pieces. Platter, chop dish, bowl, covered tureen, 5 soups, 6 plates, gravy boat. Mercury mark on each. Set	185.00

Dishes, Feeding

"Bunnykins." Santa bunny on Christmas cup. "A" mark	55.00
"Cinderella." 3 angels. KTK	14.00
"Peter Pan." Sterling	45.00
"See Saw Margery Daw." Divided . .	28.00
"Sunbonnet Babies." Cleveland China	155.00

Ice Cream Set. Platter with dip of ice cream, foliage border. 4 plates with alphabet border. Set 110.00

Feeding Dish. 7¼" diam. K.L.Austria. Strawberry decor $25.00

Lamp, Night. 2x3½". Signed "Little Harry's Night Lamp." Milk glass chimney	22.00
Pitcher, Water. Flute	12.50
Plate. Bo Peep. Pressed glass. C. 1900	12.50
Punch Bowl and 6 Cups. Flattened Diamond and Sunburst pattern. Set	65.00

Spooners

Pennsylvania	23.00
Snowflake. Clear	18.00

Table Sets

Cambridge. 3 pieces	50.00
Drum. 4 pieces	125.00

Bunnykins Creamer. 4" high, cream ground, green band, brown rabbits
$25.00

Oval Star. Covered butter,
creamer and sugar 60.00
Sunburst and Diamond. 3 pieces . . 48.50
Tulip and Honeycomb. 4 pieces . . . 65.00
Whirligig pattern. Covered sugar,
creamer, butter dish and spooner.
Set 62.00

Tea Sets
Doll's. Japan. Blue Willow 25.00
Lustre trim. 21 pieces 35.00
"Maiden Hair Fern." 1883 Registry
Staffordshire Ridgway. Blue/white 100.00
Majolica 165.00
Mother and Father Lions. High
teapot with lid, creamer, sugar, 5
plates, 4 cups, 3 saucers. Set 50.00
Victorian. White with gold trim.
Teapot, sugar, creamer, waste, 4
cups and saucers, 2-handled cake
plate. Set. 40.00
Tumbler. 2" oval star 5.00

CHINA MUGS

"A Brother's Gift." Green decora-
tions. "Josiah" on reverse.
Staffordshire type . . . . $ 50.00
"A Trifle for Fanny." Yellow with red
transfer name and border 68.50
Bryan and McKinley portraits in
sepia on white ground. 5" high, 2
handles. Marked "Compliments of
Raphael & Seugschmidt. Whole-
sale Liquor Dealers, Pittsburgh,
Pa." 75.00
"Chit Chat." 2½" high, pink decor . . . 36.00
"Eliza." Fruit and flowers 40.00
"For Eliza." Black transfer on blue
background 37.50

Farmer's Arms. "God Speed the Plow."
2½" high. B.&H. England $35.00

"History of the House that Jack
Built." Franklin Maxim 52.50
"Martha." 2½" high, children and
pink seesaw 45.00
"Mary." 2½" high, blue and white . . 42.50
"The Seasons." 2½" high. Franklin
Maxim 50.00
Staffordshire-type. 2¾" high, with
scene of blacksmith working.
Green, blue and brown, pink
lustre rim 48.50
"The Way to Wealth" or "Dr.
Franklin's Poor Richard." 2½" high 55.00
WX Transfer. 2¾" high. Staffordshire 55.00
Washington, George. Centennial,
eagles and flags. Copeland china . 75.00

CHINESE, See ORIENTAL ITEMS

CHRISTMAS ITEMS

The number, variety and shapes are so vast
that it would be difficult to classify them. Most
were used to hang on Christmas trees while
others were hung on lamp posts and
fireplaces to create a festive holiday
atmosphere.

Christmas tree light bulb. Figure of
Santa. Painted $12.00

Book. "The Life and Adventures of
Santa Claus" by Julie Lane. Santa
Claus Pub. Co. 1932 ....$22.50

Candleholders for tree.

Amber glass	Amethyst
$8.00	$10.00

Candleholders
   3½" high. Diamond Block and
   Honeycomb pattern. Glass cup.
   Amber 8.00
   3½" high. Glass cup, cobalt 10.00
Light Bulbs, Electric
   Clown 10.00
   Lantern. Occupied Japan 1.00
   Santa 12.00

Ornaments
   Ball. Amber, original wire 12.00
   Ball. 5" diam., gold, metal hanger 12.00
   Canary with brush-like tail. Blown 10.00
   Fruit shapes, glass, blown 8.00
   Peacock. Brush tail, blown glass .. 12.00

CIGAR CUTTERS, POCKET

Pocket-type cigar cutters were popular when
men wore vests to complete their suits of
clothing. The cutter was usually attached to a
watch chain. To a smoking man a cigar cutter
was not only utilitarian but it was often a fine
piece of jewelry as well. Many were made in
gold or silver, embossed and monogrammed.

Bottle-shaped. 2" long. Brass watch
   charm ....$ 9.00
Horseshoe-shaped. With buckle.
   Watch charm 35.00

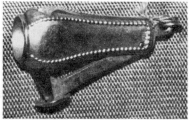

Combination cigar cutter and watch
fob. Open. 10K gold $45.00

Double Ring. 10K Nov. 9, 1916,
monogrammed "S" $45.00

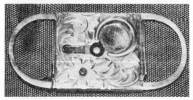

Sterling. Embossed $35.00

CIGAR STORE FIGURES, ETC.

Sixty to seventy-five years ago Cigar Store Indians, Squaws or Turks were familiar sights in front of cigar stores and tobacco shops. These figures are now scarce and command a good price when offered for sale. Today they are being reproduced in various sizes, styles and materials.

Cigar Store Indian. Over 7' high $7000.00
Cigar Store Indian Chief. Small 5500.00
Cigar Store Indian Chief. Tall 7200.00
Cigar Store Squaw. Small 4250.00
Cigar Store Squaw. Tall 5000.00
Cigar Store Turk 6000.00
Harnessmaker's   Horse.   No
    equipment 2500.00

Indian Chief "Strobel" $5000.00

Indian.   6' high, original paint.
    "Frank" 6000.00
Indian Maiden. Half life size. On
    base with wheels.   5'8" high,
    painted 5000.00
Indian Scout. 6'4½" overall height,
    including base 4250.00
Standing Figure. Cap, ruffled collar,
    red and blue costume. Holding
    box of cigars in left hand. On
    square base, 5'9" 5600.00

CINNABAR ITEMS

A red ware made of numerous layers of a heavy mercuric sulphide, often referred to as vermillion, and carved into bowls, buttons, snuff bottles and vases. The best of this ware was made in China.

Box. 3¾x5½". Red, black interior
$50.00

Boxes
    2x4x5¾". Deeply carved scene.
    Trees, man, bird cage. All edges
    brass bound . . . . $ 57.50
    2½x4½". Garden scene 45.00
    3½x5½". Two Chinese figures in
    garden with flowers and trees . . .   50.00
Plate. 9", red. Carved scene of
    people 195.00
Snuff Bottle 110.00
Tray. 8x12", carved, red color 175.00
Vases
    7" high, carved oriental figures
    and decor 100.00
    10½" high, Dragon design. Pair . .   235.00

CIVIL WAR AND RELATED ITEMS

Civil War items consist mainly of military items used in the war between the States [1861-65] in the United States.

Bayonets
    Socket. Tower Enfield, blockade
    mark . . . . $ 30.00

Socket. Tower Enfield, without
scabbards 25.00

Belt, Leather. Wide, brass buckle
and swordholder 30.00

Blinker Bridle. Marked with a faint
Richmond, Va. maker's name,
with bit 65.00

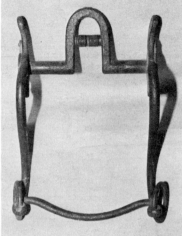

Horse Bit $40.00

Bowie Knives
Ivory handle, no make or
scabbard 85.00

"IXL." 1860's stage handle,
Wostenholme address. Fine
etchings of eagles, flags, leather
scabbard 375.00

Without scabbard. Wood handle,
brass guard, marked London.
Massive blade with classic lines . .   100.00

Buckles
Brass. 1851 pattern with wrong
Federal motto, with eagle and
wreath 22.50

Bronze, 1851 pattern with wrong
Federal motto, with eagle and
wreath 22.50

Oblong. Bannerman, copper
colored. Remake of the famous
Atlanta CSA. Hook back fitting . . .   10.00

Buttons
India Wars. On old cards, [6 to
set] unused 1870's enlisted type . .   7.50
Old Horstmann Navy type. Gilt
finish, 24 per card 25.00

Canteen. Wooden with iron supports
believed to be Confederate 60.00
Carbine. Starr with Yonkers, N.Y.
address. Replaced saddle ring and
fore-end 295.00
Cross Belt Plates. CW Battlefield 18.00
Cross Sabers. Brass, 7th Cavalry,
with letter "A" and "7" 14.50

Discharge Paper. Dated July 4, 1868,
framed 32.50
Dispatch Case. Leather 25.00
Drum. 15" high, 17" diam. Eagle
design on sides 350.00

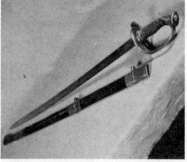

Sword. Cavalry $125.00

Enlistment Papers. Civil War from all
over the Union. All fully signed.
Each 20.00
Envelope. "The Innocent Cause of
the War" 7.00

Helmet Badge. New York. Shield and
eagle with company number in
center 15.00
Helmet Dress. 1870's. Cavalry. Brass
trim with eagle badge with spike .   90.00

Holster Cover. 1851 Navy Colt silver
flap over. Made of pure silver with
cannons and harp on face. On
reverse is South Carolina State
Crest and "From fellow officers of
the S.Carolina Reserve Force. To a
fine man Brigadier General James
Chestnut CSA January 3rd, 1875."
Mint 475.00

Mess Kit. Ivory handles, in original
   case 27.50

Muskets
   Enfield 2 band. Original with CW
     markings..................... 350.00
   Enfield 3 band. Original with CW
     markings..................... 350.00
   Tower Percussion. Converted
     from a Flintlock 250.00
Plume, Shako. Cavalry and Artillery.
   Genuine horse hair 13.50
Poster. Garnett's Brigade, in black
   and white 45.00

Pouches
   Ammo. McKeever. Marked with
   Custer's famous "7th Cavalry".... 22.50
   Hagnor. Marked "7th Cavalry,"
   with original contents 25.00
Prints, Battle. By Prang. Spottsyl-
   vania and Kenesaw Mountain. Full
   border, 21½ x15". Pair 125.00

Revolvers
   LeMat Brte. and Paxton ANV. All
   original except for replaced side
   ejector...................... 1000.00
   Relic Colt pattern. Copy of the
   1850's 85.00

Saddle. Cavalry. Civil War relic.
   McCullems and Militia types. Each 100.00
Saddle Bags
   Leather, marked with a small Va.
   address 115.00
   Maker's name inscribed in the
   leather. Set of 2 .... 200.00
Spurs
   Teardrop. 1" rowels with chins ... 30.00
   U.S. Cavalry. Buckles, no straps .. 17.50
Swords
   Cavalry 125.00
   Confederate. 34½" long 225.00
   Union Officer's. Brass trim,
   leather scabbard 175.00
Sword Belt Plates. Union NCO's 1851. 25.00
Tarpot, Cavalry. CW, old and original . 65.00

CLAMBROTH GLASS

Clambroth glass derives its name from the
color of the glass. The semi-opaque,
greyish-white color resembles the broth from
clams. This type of glassware was popular in
the Victorian period.

Bottle, Barber ....$ 20.00
Candlesticks. Dolphin. Pair......... 495.00

Mug. 3½" high. Embossed. Swans on
sides $25.00

Goblet. 7" high, souvenir-type 18.50
Mug. Birds and wheat pattern, fence
   post handle................... 20.00
Tumbler. Souvenir 9.50
Vases.9" high. Crimped top, pontil,
   H/P flowers. Matching pair 55.00

CLOCKS

The clock is one of man's most sophisticated
mechanical inventions. There were many
arrangements, cases and makers.
For more detailed information on early
American clocks, see Early American Clocks,
Volumes I, II and III by Warman.

ALARM CLOCKS

German. Fancy oak and brass
   spandrels, strikes once on half
   hour and hour.................$ 135.00
Ingraham. Advertising "Red Ball" ... 28.00
King. 6" iron case, no glass......... 25.00
Roy Rogers. Original animated 40.00
Seth Thomas. Automatic alarm,
   8-day, oak case 65.00

BANJO CLOCKS

Goodwin, W., Attleboro, N. Early,
   weighted, all original 1500.00
Howard. #4. Signed on dial........ 1750.00
Howard . #5..................... 485.00
Ingraham. Treasure Island case..... 375.00

Seward, Joshua. Rope front pre-
   sentation case, original glasses .. 2200.00
Seth Thomas. 42" 425.00
Stennes. Curtiss-type Girandole,
   case #15. Marriage scene 2000.00
Stennes. Gold front 1250.00
Tifft, H. Weighted 1100.00
Tifft-type, early, weighted, wooden
   bezel and wood throat 795.00
Unsigned, weighted 790.00
Waltham. Weight-driven, all original 1350.00
Waterbury. Weighted, heavy porce-
   lain dial, black, gold glasses, dark
   mission oak case 1050.00
Williard, A. Jr. Banjo as found 2200.00

BEEHIVE SHELF CLOCKS

Brown, J.C., Ripple front, original ... 425.00
Pratt, Daniel. Mahogany, frosted
   tablet, 8-day T&S 195.00
Terry and Andrews. 8-day T&S 195.00

BRACKET CLOCKS

English. 29" Baroque oak case.
   Double fuzee, strikes hours 950.00

Carriage-type. Music box attachment,
musical striking hour. 6½" high.
Pepoday. C. 1880 ....$150.00

Romeo and Juliet. French. C. 1820.
Made by Jacob Petit $750.00

English. Anchor escapement, not
   original, mint case, including
   silvering and gilding. C. 1760 .... 1150.00
English. Double fuzee. 8-day T&S.... 500.00
German. 2 train ¼ chime inlaid
   rosewood, full column 350.00
Vienna basket-top bracket verge.
   Ebony case, single strike all hours 850.00

CALENDAR SHELF AND WALL CLOCKS

Ithaca. Cottage model, day, date dial 650.00
Maranville, Galusha. Wall case 485.00
Prentiss. 38" wall, 60-day, heavy
   movement, calendar unit missing . 265.00
Seth Thomas. Parlor #4. Double dial . 650.00
Waterbury. George model. Calendar 135.00
Welch, E. N. 18" drop octagon, rose-
   wood and gold trim. Top glass
   cracked. T&S and calendar dial ... 190.00
Welch. Spring [B.B.Lewis] day & date
   dial 625.00

CARRIAGE CLOCKS

British United Clock Co. Cast
  carriage, not running 115.00
French. 5½" high. All bevel case.
  Porcelain dial, 8-day T&S 165.00
French. Signed D. & B. France 155.00
French. Unusual. Time only. 8-day... 145.00
Repeater. Rare 5-minute 1000.00

CHINA CASED CLOCKS

Ansonia. Blue, gold and multifloral
  design, 8-day T&S 225.00
Ansonia. Royal Bonn exposed
  escapement, 8-day T&S 200.00
Ansonia. Royal Bonn flowered case.
  8-day T&S 185.00
Ansonia. Royal Bonn open escape-
  ment, 8-day T&S 225.00
China clock with matching urns.
  Large, ornate 500.00

Shelf Clock. "Doric," made by
Ingraham & Co. Bristol, Conn. Pat. date
1871 .... $125.00

New Haven. Urn-shaped, embossed
  case, 8-day T&S 155.00

COTTAGE STYLE CLOCKS

Ithaca. #9 Shelf, walnut 8-day 600.00
Jerome. 9" miniature. Painted tablet 65.00
Jerome. 12" walnut. Label and good
  tablet, 30-hour 68.00
Welch, E.N. 9" miniature. Rosewood
  case 70.00

ELECTRIC DRIVEN CLOCKS

Bulle'. 10" shelf. Green marble,
  beveled glass, battery, early 265.00
Self Winding Clock Co. Wall, oak
  case, dry cell battery movement,
  1898. Perfect time piece......... 150.00
Sohm Electric Co. on dial, two large
  batteries on top, wall case, no top
  glass or second hand, heavy
  pendulum 145.00

GALLERY CLOCKS

Atkins. 2 fuzee, 30-day, octagon
  shape, 26" 400.00
Brewster and Ingraham, east-west
  movement.................... 185.00
E. and A. Ingraham.Round wood
  case, east-west movement....... 225.00
English. 15" walnut fuzee movement, no pendulum 125.00
Seth Thomas. 12" rosewood, no
  second hand 95.00
Seth Thomas. 17" rosewood veneer
  case, no glass, dial replaced 75.00
Seth Thomas. 18" gallery time only,
  30-day 325.00

GLASS ENCASED SHELF CLOCKS

Ansonia. 15½" brass, beveled glass
  case, cathedral gong, open
  escapement 345.00
French. Crystal regulator 190.00
French. Crystal regulators, mercury
  pendulum, mint. Marti et Cic 180.00
French. Curved glass gilt mantle
  mercury pendulum. T&S 30-day
  movement 325.00
Tiffany. Crystal regulator, mercury
  pendulum 275.00

KITCHEN SHELF CLOCKS

Ingraham. 22" oak 8-day T&S,
  calendar dial 155.00

Clock. Mantel-type $125.00

Ingraham. "Dewey." Oak 8-day T&S restored	185.00
New Haven. Oak 8-day T&S alarm . . .	120.00
Sessions. "Hiawatha" oak, 8-day T&S .	125.00
Seth Thomas. Oak, 8-day T&S	145.00
Waterbury. Oak barometer, thermometer, 8-day T&S	140.00
Waterbury. Pressed oak case, 8-day T&S	125.00
Waterbury. Walnut, 8-day T&S, alarm, ornate case	170.00
Welch. Oak, 8-day T&S, alarm	145.00
Welch. Robert E. Lee, pressed oak, 8-day T&S	210.00

MIRROR SIDE SHELF CLOCKS

Ansonia. Windsor model 8-day T&S . .	325.00
New Haven. 8-day T&S	350.00
New Haven. 8-day T&S, needs restoration	250.00
Waterbury. 8-day T&S	325.00

NEW ENGLAND MIRROR WALL & SHELF CLOCKS

Ives, Joseph. Conn. Rare mirror clock	2700.00
Morill, B. New Hampshire. Mirror, wheelbarrow movement	1700.00
Stennes. Massachusetts. Shelf	775.00

O. G. SHELF CLOCKS

Ansonia Brass Co. Weight-driven, T&S, good tablet rosewood	85.00

Brown, J. C. 8-day, all original, iron dial	175.00
Burch, Thomas. Pittsburgh, 30-hr T&S	125.00
Davis Clock Co. 30-hour, all original .	165.00
Jerome, Chauncey. 30-hour T&S. Bristol, Conn. label	125.00
Jerome, Chauncey. T&S with rare weight alarm, original tablet	115.00
Lang and Jones. Looking glass	165.00
New Haven. 30-hour	90.00
Rosewood. 30", 8-day, T&S movement. Partial label, good tablet . . .	95.00

PILLAR AND SCROLL SHELF CLOCKS

Downes	975.00
Eli Terry and Sons. Wood finials, wooden works, weight-driven, 30-hour, painted, bottom glass missing	1000.00
Seth Thomas. Off-center, wood movement, 30-hour	2500.00

O.G. "Thomas." Thomaston, Conn. Stylized floral, tablet in gold. Late $125.00

POT METAL OR IRON CASE MANTLE CLOCKS

Fancy. 16" iron front, 30-hour, newly
decorated case................. 135.00
F.D.R., Lincoln, Washington. "The
Steersmen." Animated drummer
on dial. Pot metal............... 75.00
F.D.R. Ship's wheel statue, animated
bartender. Circa, repeal of prohibition. Pot metal............. 75.00
"Farm, The." Animated drummer,
thermometer. Pot metal......... 85.00
Flash Light. Deposit box, alarm
clock, pressed steel............. 70.00
Kroeber, F. 12" iron case. Gothic
8-day T&S 170.00
Kroeber, F. Iron case, 1859
patented, 8-day, T&S............ 85.00
Mueller. Fancy iron case, 8-day T&S . 90.00
River Boat. Side-wheeler. No ani-
mation, pot metal 65.00

Wall Clock. Regulator, 2 weights.
Victorian-type, walnut case...$250.00

U.S. Miniature. Early, iron, MOP
decor, some missing. 8-day, time
only 45.00
Welch, E. N. Iron front case, label,
T&S, no top dial, bezel or
pendulum 70.00
Will Rogers. 12". Animated
drummers. Pot metal 75.00

RECTANGULAR SHELF CLOCKS [EARLY 1900]

Gilbert. "Anniversary." Bell on top,
black, 8-day T&S................ 155.00
Ingraham. Black mantle, 8-day, T&S . 85.00
Seth Thomas. Black paint, 8-day T&S 135.00

REGULATOR CLOCKS

Brille. Master regulator, sweep
second, battery-driven 375.00
Gilbert. 33" rectangular oak, time
and calendar dial. "Regulator" on
lower glass, pendulum missing ... 145.00
Meyer, Rudolph. Austrian, C. 1780.
Regulator 7½ feet high, 30-day
deadbeat, sweep second hand.
Porcelain dial. Signed 2250.00
Seth Thomas. #2. Light oak......... 625.00
Seth Thomas. Regulator #20, oak
case, 8-day, time only, seconds
beat, 14" dial. Graham deadbeat
movement, 62" case 1075.00
Seth Thomas Regulator #30, original
cherry finish 850.00
Seth Thomas. "Umbria" 15-day
spring-driven T&S, original oak
finish, 40" high................ 475.00
Vienna. 50" long. 3-weight. Serpentine, shaped like elongated figure
eight. Porcelain face 950.00
Vienna. Pinwheel wall regulator,
weight-driven. Lyre pendulum,
porcelain face, sweep second hand 1200.00
Vienna. Regulator. 60-beat, 30-day
movement. Open, wall mounted . 550.00
Waterbury. #18. Weight-driven 645.00
Waterbury. #18 two-weight regulator 500.00
Waterbury. 30-day spring-driven.... 275.00
Waterbury. Long drop regulator,
round wooden bezel, 8-day T&S,
spring-driven 325.00

SCHOOL HOUSE CLOCKS

Ansonia. N.Y. T&S, oak case........ 245.00
Ansonia. Rosewood, T&S calendar
dial. Small 195.00
Gilbert. Walnut case, calendar mvt. . 475.00

Gilbert. Advertising, with calendar .	250.00
Miniature. Round top, cherry case, mint	165.00
Pratt, Daniel. #70-type, in cherry, long drop	600.00
Waterbury. Oak. Mint	235.00
Waterbury. Oak. Short drop, calendar movement, new bezel and dial	200.00
Welch. Miniature, original label	225.00

STEEPLE SHELF CLOCKS

| Birge and Fuller. Steeple on steeple, 8-day wagon spring movement, all original except lower tablet ... | 2500.00 |

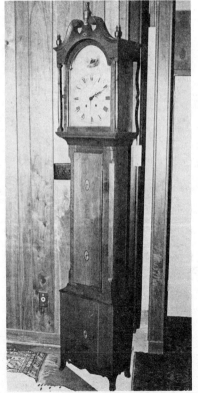

Tall Case. Hepplewhite, broken arch and pediment. Cherry, Pa....$1800.00

Brewster and Ingraham. Curved gothic steeple, original brass springs	650.00
Brewster and Ingraham. Sharp gothic, double brass spring	600.00
Elisha Manross. Small 23" steeple on steeple, 8-day double fuzee movement	1500.00
Terry and Andrews. 30-hour, steeple lyre movement, original glass tablet, strawberries	225.00
Terry and Andrews. Double steeple, walnut case, 8-day T&S lyre movement, cracked dial, worn tablets	825.00

"SWINGER" CLOCKS

Ansonia. Tin-can movement	975.00
Krober, F. Label, swinging doll in 17" walnut case	435.00
Jughans, Elephant	350.00

TALL CASE CLOCKS

Aitken. Scottish. Glasgow, 8-day mahogany case, painted dial	750.00
Benbow. American. Northport, three train bells movement. Mahogany case, moon dial	1850.00
Elliot. English. London. Three train bells, mahogany case, engraved brass dial	2250.00
Federal. Unsigned. 7'10". Mahogany, broken arch, 1820, 8-day brass movement, moon phase....	1800.00
Garrett. Phila. 8-day, cherry case, rocking ship	2100.00
Hoadley, S. Tall case, pine grained movement	1400.00
Hopkins, Asa. 30-hour, wood works .	1000.00
Ithaca. Oak painted white, not orig. .	400.00
Morbier. Old pegged case, simple pendulum, T&S	850.00
Speedman, 8-day oak case, painted dial	600.00
Wilder, Joshua. Grandmother	6000.00
Willard, Simon. Dial, signed, double arch top, fret work finials, walnut, 98" case, iron dial, 8-day T&S, calendar	10000.00
Willard, Simon. Iron dial, signed, Roxbury-style, mahogany fine inlays, single arch top, 3 plinths and finials, 8-day T&S, calendar ..	13500.00
Windmills, Joseph. London C. 1690. Rare, 8-day seconds and calendar. 7½ feet, walnut case, inlay needs minor repair	1500.00

Seth Thomas. 8-day, Westminster
chime....................... 95.00
Seth Thomas. Giant. Senora chime,
plays tune on 5 bells, carved
mahogany case, glass and
pendulum missing 185.00

TWO AND THREE TIER
EMPIRE SHELF CLOCKS

Birge and Peck. Empire case, 8-day
T&S......................... 450.00
Birge and Peck. Empire case, 8-day
T&S. Reverse painted tablets 350.00
C. & C. L. Ives. 3-tier. 8-day T&S.
Reverse painted tablets 450.00
Hoadley, Silas. 36" mantle, 30-hour,
wood movement 500.00
Hoadley, Silas. Upside-down,
30-hour, wood movement, con-
dition good, needs work 400.00

Black Forest Wall Clock. 3'8". Highly
carved with weights and chimes. Deer
finial. C. 1840-50 ....$2000.00

American, Hill, Ohio, center sweep
second hand, cherry case, moon
dial......................... 2150.00
Scottish. Mahogany veneer and
inlay, moon dial, calendar and
second hand, mint dial. C. 1800 .. 1300.00
Scottish. Oak case, 8-day T&S brass
dial with spandrels and chapter
ring. C. 1785 .... 750.00

TAMBOR SHELF CLOCKS

New Haven. 8-day, Westminster
chime....................... 95.00
Sessions. 8-day, Westminster chime . 95.00

Wag-on-Wall. Handpainted face with
red cabbage rose. 2 weights, strikes
on the hour. Black forest. C. 1825
$350.00

Jerome, Chauncey. Label. 18" mini-
  column, 2-tier. Loose veneer, no
  hands, T&S movement 100.00
Munger. "Black face," sore finger
  model 875.00
Seth Thomas. 8-day. T&S movement,
  rosewood case, yellow columns . .   290.00
Seth Thomas. Thomaston, Empire
  case, 8-day T&S 225.00
Wadsworth, Dyer. Triple-decker, all
  original, mint 475.00
Whiting, Riley. Carved half column
  and splat, wood movement 550.00

MISCELLANEOUS CLOCKS

Advertising
  Adner, Paris. Falling Ball, 8-day . .   950.00
  Baird. Papier-mache case 255.00
  Gilbert. Wood case, shape of
  whiskey flask. Mr. Boston, poor
  condition, not running. Old 33.00
"Ben Franklin." Thwaits and Reed . . .   450.00
Bracket Clock. Boulle. Bronze inlaid
  tortoise shell case, 40-day move-
  ment, silk thread suspension
  excellent condition 2000.00
Chronometer
  Hamilton 21. Brass case 110.00
  Marine. Ulysee Nardin. Original
  wooden box 1150.00
Deck Watches
  Complete. Longines 200.00
  Hamilton. Outer protective box . .   265.00
  Up, down indicator, large lum-
  inous dial 775.00
  Waltham. In gimbaled box 150.00
Gas Light. Waltham 125.00
Gravity. Good clock but incomplete
  rack. Ansonia 55.00
Keyhole. E. Howard 1500.00
Lantern. Joseph Knibb, London. C.
  1650 . . . . 3000.00
Minute Man. Chicago. 8-day watch-
  man's clock, leather carrying case   30.00
R.R. Clock. French. Brass, hanging.
  Face on opposite sides 450.00
Rotary
  Early model. Briggs 340.00
  Late model. Briggs 320.00
Ship's Bell
  Banjo. Chelsea 550.00
  Chelsea. Heavy brass 385.00
  Seth Thomas. 7" 200.00
  Seth Thomas. Heavy brass case.
  Early 200.00
Table Clock with alarm. Japanese . . 2800.00

Mark I Deck Clock. U. S. Navy . $175.00

Tavern Clock. English. C. 1790. 13"
  painted dial, 8-day, time only 550.00
Time Recorders
  Cincinnati. 42" oak case 300.00
  International 195.00
Tower Clock. Movement only, Seth
  Thomas, weights and pendulum
  not original 500.00
U.S. Army
  Message center. M-2. Original
  black case. Chelsea Mfg. 125.00
  Message Center. Original oak
  carrying case, fine 210.00
U.S. Navy
  Chelsea Mark I, 3 part Naval
  Bronze swing out case, 6" black
  dials, 1941 . . . .   225.00
  Seth Thomas. Lever, 6", silvered
  dial, side winder, nickeled case . .   135.00

CLOISONNE

This name applies to enamel work on a
metallic background. It originated in the
Orient in ancient times. The bulk of the items
found today was made in Europe and was
exported to this country in the latter part of
the Victorian era [1870-1900].

Bowls
  1¼ x 2¼". Small flower, gold
  decor. Bird on lid . . . . $ 50.00
  3½ x 4". Floral decor 57.50
  5" long. Duck-shaped, blue, cobalt
  and red 650.00

5x6". Covered, on legs 62.50
7". Footed, covered. Black/white
turquoise flowers, goldstone 125.00
7½". Round, covered, colorful
floral decor. Foo dog finial 145.00
12½" diam. Rare colors. Early 600.00
Nut. 3x3½" 47.50
Rice. 2½ x4½". Red, yellow
flowers over green. Green lining . 35.00
Rose. 4" diam. Lidded, black with
geometric design 85.00
Rose. Red ground 75.00
Box. 2" diam. Round jade insert
carved into vase and flower.
Pigeon blood with multicolored
flowers 225.00
Chargers
12" diam. Chinese. Bats flying
against pale blue ground, stylized
border in enamel 350.00
12" diam. Japanese. Scalloped
edge, dragon in center, pearl and
floral motif around borders 300.00
Crane. Standing, 14½" high. Blue
enamel ground, yellow, royal
blue and red, brass enameling on
wings 600.00
Cup and Saucer 75.00
Dish. Rectangular, on wood base . . . 85.00
Humidors
8" high. Color orange. Foo dog on
cover 175.00
Filigree enamel 140.00
Incense Burner. 9½" high, ball
shaped 65.00

Inkwell. Covered, white ground 85.00
Jars
3" high. With lid, footed 55.00
7" high. Blue, yellow dragons. Pair 275.00
9½" high. Black ground, multicolored flower motif. Impressed
"China" 135.00
12" high. Bulbous lid. Green,
butterflies, flowers. Marked 175.00
14" high, Covered, green ground,
chrysanthemums. Royal blue,
white, turquoise, etc. Oriental 150.00

Ginger Jar. 13" high. Teak base $195.00

Napkin Ring. Floral, butterfly decor . 25.00
Pipe, Opium 100.00
Pitcher. Small, 4" ewer, floral, geo-
metrical pattern 75.00
Plates
6". Colorful flowers, brass rim
base and edging 75.00
7¼". Landscape 67.50
11". Pair of colorful fans, blue
ground. Late 120.00
11¼". Hanging type. Flowers and
birds on light blue ground 225.00
12". Skyblue ground, two white
storks. Late 130.00
14". Butterfly, flowers 375.00
Plaque. 7x7½". Framed, narrow,
gold, beaded. Flowers, butterfly . . 115.00

Bowl. Covered. 7" high, tan ground,
blues, reds, greens, floral decor $125.00

Rabbit. 5½" long, colorful design ... 215.00
Tea Caddy 85.00
Teapots
  2½" high 125.00
  5x6". White ground, floral decor .. 225.00
Tea Set. Teapot, two gold-lined cups,
  sugar and creamer. Dragons,
  black ground, gold cloisonnes. Set 300.00
Toothpick Holder. Multicolored 30.00
Trays
  7x9". Chinese. Black ground with
  flowering plants, 5 butterflies in
  red, blue, white, green. C. 1850 .. 290.00
  10½" square. Opium-handled. 2
  saucers and lamp compartments.
  Bronze finials 275.00
Vases
  3½" high. 2" diam. Emerald
  green, purple serpents, multicolored birds 65.00

3½" high. 2" diam. Speckled
white ground, blue, maroon
shields, multicolored decor 85.00
4" high. Chinese design 110.00
5½" high. Dark blue ground,
white dragon, decorated in red
and green. Late 75.00
6" high. Enamel bird, cherry
blossoms on blue ground 125.00
7" high. Black ground, mountains,
home, waterfall, gold trim.
Oriental character. Signed 175.00
7" high. Stick. Black, DQ stems,
pink, grey flowers. Pair 175.00
7" high. Tan and turquoise
ground. Butterflies, birds, flowers
in panels 195.00
7½" high. Multicolor ground,
narrow medallions of emerald,
lavender, turquoise and cobalt ... 100.00
8" high. U.S. and Chinese flags on
blue floral background 275.00
9" high. Royal blue, butterflies,
gold decor..................... 145.00
9½" high. Blue ground, florals of
pinks, blue 100.00
9½" high. On teakwood stand.
Cutout design in top part. Pair.... 220.00
11" high. Moss green ground decor
of flowers, butterflies, birds. C.
1850. Pair 350.00
12" high, 4½" diam. Background
in shades of aqua, flowers. Three
larger panels with dragons
against goldstone black and rust
background 275.00
14" high. Tan ground with white,
purple flowers 325.00

CLOTHING

Styles of the past sometime amuse and
fascinate members of the present generation.
Old clothing is often used for advertising and
exhibition purposes. It is worn to balls and
parties and occasionally a woman's club will
have members who act as hostesses dress in
old costumes.

Bags
  Beaded. Multicolored, classical
  scene. Jeweled .... $ 50.00
  Mesh. Arrowhead design inlaid
  blue, black 18.00
  Mesh. Gold pouch, expanding top 22.50
  Mesh. Sterling 75.00
Cap. Black, white, fur ears, neck
  flaps........................ 10.00

Vase. Large, floral decor. Early $225.00

Lady's Evening Top. Black velvet, silver bugle beads form peacock across bodice $25.00

Cape, Fur. Hudson Seal	25.00
Coats	
1920's. Coonskin	77.50
1940. Black Sealskin with muff . . .	85.00
Dresses	
Black. 2-pc., lace trim. C. 1880	35.00
Black Sateen. Quarter moon design in white, full skirt, leg of mutton sleeves. C. 1880	40.00
Brown Chiffon Velvet. Dolman Sleeve, bias-cut skirt, matching hat. Jean Harlowe-style	45.00
Child's. White cotton, ribbon, lace trim, matching panties	20.00
White. Lace trim, "Godey"	50.00
Wine Velvet. C. 1940	12.50
Gown. Black silk, antique lace. Puffed sleeves, separate skirt over gray taffeta, basque blouse. Size 14	35.00
Hats	
Mourning. Black with feather	15.00
Opera, folding silk in original box	35.00
Plug-type. Black. C. 1825	35.00
Jabot, Lace. Small embroidered flowers	15.00
Jackets, Fur	
Leopard	65.00

Handbag. Beaded. 8x10" $25.00

Lady's shoes. High, black leather
$37.50

Mink. Collar and bracelet-length sleeves. Matching pillbox hat	85.00
Muskrat	45.00
Sable-dyed fur	50.00
Sheared Raccoon	60.00
Mantilla. Black lace, 2⅓x3⅓ yards. Triangular shape, scalloped edges. Floral design on net	55.00
Neck Piece. Fox, reddish gray	25.00
Night Gown. Woman's, long, white . .	10.00
Parasols	
Black ruffled taffeta	25.00
Linen, lady's	25.00
Robe. Buffalo fur, felt-lined, 54x64" . .	75.00
Shawl. Spanish silk, melon color, 44" long, fringed	55.00
Skirt Hoop	17.50
Suit, Man's. Size 40. Swallowtail-type with vest, stiff-bosomed shirt	65.00
Umbrella. Rolled gold, MOP handle, embossed design, no cloth	45.00

COALPORT

Coalport porcelain has been made by the Coalport Porcelain Works in England since the late 1700's. It is now being produced at Stoke-on-Trent and they are still making fine bone china. One of their more popular patterns is "Indian Tree."

Chocolate Set. 13 pieces. Pot, cups, saucers. Indian Tree. Set . . . . $	115.00
Cups and Saucers	
Demitasse. Jeweled	75.00
Forget-Me-Nots, Roses	35.00
Indian Tree	25.00
Pitcher. 5" high. Indian Tree	52.50

Mug. 2½" high. Can-shaped. "Japan"
$45.00

Plate. 8½". Green border, castle
  scene in center, gold trim 28.50
Vases
  4" high. Shell-shaped, oyster
  color. Pair 85.00
  6" high. Blue, gold handles, H/P
  scenic reverse designs on each
  side, gold trim. Pair 175.00

COFFEE MILLS

The coffee mill or grinder was first made in
the home size in the 1890's. It was made of
glass, metal or wood. Some grinders could be
attached to a wall, while others were used on
the countertop or lap.

IRON
  1-wheel and crank . . . . $ 125.00
  2-wheel, 17" high, repainted 325.00
  2-wheel, with crank. Eagle finial
  on dome. Original paint in good
  condition 325.00
  Squat, urn-shaped cup and cap
  dome, iron lift-lid side door 60.00
  7½" wheels, 9" high. Dated 1873 . .   175.00
  Wall type, with glass jar 37.50
  Wall type. Original red scroll with
  gold decor, made by National
  Specialty Co., Phila., Pa. 75.00
  Wall type. Universal. Metal con-
  tainer above 40.00
  White iron, white china jar, blue
  Delft-type scene. German 150.00
WOOD

  Dovetailed, iron cup with lid.
  Hinged door on base. Refinished .   60.00

Wood, one drawer, iron handle.
  "Pride" $40.00

Dovetailed. 6" square, embossed
iron top 65.00
Dovetailed. 6" square, early
pewter cup, iron crank, drawer.
Refinished 75.00

Single wheel, one drawer. 7½" high
$50.00

Pine. 5x5½x5-7/8". Brass fittings.
Refinished....................... 50.00
Wall type. 4½x7x10" high, glass
dome, round top 40.00
2½x2½x3". Iron cup and crank.
Drawer 50.00
7x7x8". Urn-shaped iron cup,
sliding doors, dovetailed drawer.
Good original finish 75.00
17" high. Iron wheel and cup, one
drawer. Peugeot, Brevetes,
S.G.D.G. 150.00

COIN OPERATED ITEMS

A wide variety of coin-operated machines
have been made in the past. Games of skill
and chance have always held a certain
fascination to mankind. Inflation and the
decreasing value of the dollar has made the
one-cent and nickel-type vending machines
obsolete. People are collecting this earlier
coin-operated item for entertainment in their
own homes and for nostalgic purposes.

Slot Machine. "Imp." 5-cent. Small
$100.00

Games
"Bailey." Poker, 1½x6x11".
Bailey Company ....$ 325.00
"Big Game Hunter." Counter-top . 150.00
"Booster." 5-cent, 3 dice in a cup.. 125.00
Dice. 2x11x11". Counter-top 45.00

"Electric Shock." 9x15x16".
Arcade-type. Battery operated ... 125.00
"Electric Spinner." 4x9x13".
Counter-top type dice game...... 100.00
"Grip and Arm Tester." Counter-
top 135.00
"Hit Me." 1, 5, 10, 25-cents. A
blackjack machine. Rare 250.00
"Kicker and Ketcher." 8x14x-
17½". Arcade-type. C. 1930 .... 145.00
"Lite a Pak." 10x10x12". Counter-
top type. C. 1930's 145.00
"Love Meter." 9x7x5x19". Arcade
wood type 150.00
"Magic Clock." 1, 5-cents.
Fortune-telling slot type 150.00
"Mercury." Counter-top type.
Cigarette..................... 150.00
"Mills Target Practice." 7x7x3x-
17½". Penny flip. C. 1920's 300.00
"Pak-O-Cigs." 1-cent, 3 dice in a
cup 130.00
"Poker," 5-cent, 5-reel slot machine
Wood case, electrically operated . 250.00
"Punch-A-Ball.' 5-cents, 2 locks,
keys 130.00
"Puritan Baby Bell." 1-cent,
7x11x11". Liberty Bell, 1776
decor, key operated jack pot 375.00
"Smiley, the Clown." 8x15½x25",
wood, arcade-type.............. 100.00
"The Gem." Counter-top type.
8x8x12½" 165.00
"Whirl-O-Ball." 5 balls for 1-cent,
keeps score 135.00
"Win-A-Pack." 1-cent, 3-reel
cigarette slot, no key 125.00
Vendors
Arcade Shooting Gallery. 1-cent.
Shoot the penny and get a gum
everytime 65.00
"Beaver Hat." 5-cent. Hot nuts, red
light on top of teardrop globe 50.00
Candy and Nuts. 1-cent, 4½x10x-
11", two-chain pull handles. C.
1920......................... 50.00
Cub. 1-cent play, small, vest-
pocket size 55.00
"Ford." 1-cent gum, chrome base,
round glass globe 50.00
Hershey Bar. 5-cent, 7x8x17",
porcelain..................... 30.00
"Kenny Magic Clock Gum." Wood,
8" wheel, lemon, cherries, bars .. 225.00

"Old Blue Regal." Teardrop globe,
not round 35.00
"Peanut." 10x19", 8-sided globe.
Vends 4 different items. Art Deco
decor 185.00

"Postage Stamp." 5x8x19½". Red, white, blue, porcelain front. C. 1940 .... 42.50

"Postage Stamp." Reel-type, glass, metal, hand crank 50.00

"Select-O-Vend." 1-cent, 7x8x18". Gum and candy. Dispenses 8 different items. C. 1940 .... 45.00

"Sun." 6½x6½x14". Peanut and candy 35.00

"The Fil A Lighter." 1-cent, lighter fluid 150.00

"The Free Play Bell." Gaming Peanut. 15" high, 10" globe. 1-cent 150.00

"The Silver Comet." 6x6x8". Cigarette, 1-cent 85.00

"Vender." 5-cent coin changer ... 125.00

"Victor." 1-cent, 8½x8½x14". Gum and candy. Baseball amusement game in front 55.00

Miscellaneous

Hurdy-Gurdy.................... 950.00

"Lady Fatima." Cigarette box, round, dispenses cigarette. C. 1929........................... 42.50

Money Fare Box. 7½x7½x19". Street-car type 75.00

National Cash Register. Brass, Model 129 .... 285.00

Parking Meter. 1-cent, all original, key 20.00

Punch Boards. Unused 5.00

National Cash Register. Brass, marble top above drawer. A. S. McLuckie
$295.00

"Rockola." 5-cent, slot machine with chewing gum dispenser on side, 1928 model 375.00

Slot, mini "Cub" 95.00

COIN SPOT GLASS

The glass derives its name from the opalescent spots appearing like coins in the glass. The usual glass colors are clear, light blue and cranberry in which the "spots" appear.

Water Set. Pitcher with 6 tumblers. White over pink. Bulbous, 8" high, crimped top, clear handle. Tumblers 4¼" high $165.00

Creamer. 4" high, red, clear handle
$55.00

Bride's Basket. Cranberry with
opalescent spots, in plated silver
frame.........................$ 200.00
Cruet. Cranberry, opalescent spots..   115.00
Cup. Opalescent reeded thorn handle   28.50
Dish. Ruffled, opalescent spots 35.00
Pitchers
    Large, light blue with spots 125.00
    Opal. Clear with ruffled top 85.00
    Opal. Tri-corn top. Applied handle   140.00
    Tankard size. Cranberry with
    opalescent spots 160.00
Sugar Shakers
    Cranberry with opalescent spots .   80.00
    Light blue with opalescent spots ...   70.00
Syrups
    Clear glass, opalescent spots 65.00
    Light blue, tin lid, opalescent
    spots 75.00
    Rubina. Cranberry to clear.
    Opalescent, original lid 95.00
Tumblers
    Blue, opalescent spots 30.00
    Clear glass, opalescent spots 25.00
    Cranberry, opalescent spots 32.00
Water Sets
    Cranberry. Pitcher, six tumblers ..   225.00
    White. Pitcher, five tumblers 175.00

COLLECTIBLE CHARACTER AND
PERSONALITY ITEMS

Nostalgia - a longing for the past - is the
fastest growing area in the collecting field. It
has resulted in a new market for items which
were offered, either free or for a few cents, by
candy, cereal and other companies as
premiums to children. Most of them have been
issued within the last thirty years. Many of the
articles are presently selling for one hundred to
one thousand times their original value.

Mickey Mouse with Donald Duck in
canoe. Pottery $30.00

Mug. "Little Orphan Annie" and
"Sandy." 3" high, pottery. Ovaltine
$25.00

Brownies
  Book. Palmer Cox, 320pp, 1st Ed. . $ 22.00
  Handkerchief, 1893 patent. 4 full
  Brownie figures in center, 6
  Brownie heads, corners, sides 16.00
  Pin. Palmer Cox. Sterling, 3 cops..   18.50
  Plates. Different designs and
  colors, 7", each 12.00
  Salt Shaker. Palmer Cox 16.00
  Spoon. Demitasse. Palmer Cox.
  Sterling with gold-washed bowl,
  enameled Brownie 22.00
Buck Rogers. U235 Atomic Pistol.
  Daisy Mfg. Co. 55.00
Buster Brown
  Button 15.00
  Cards, Playing. Complete deck ...   21.50
  Creamer. 3½ x5½", bulbous,
  ornate handle, scalloped base, rim   15.00
  Dictionary. 1927 ....   35.00
  Doll, Boy. 27". Adv. on base 95.00
  Knife, fork, spoon. Silver 35.00
  Plate. 7½". White, scalloped.
  Buster pouring tea for Tige 25.00
  Tin Shoe. 2¼" long. Toy snapped
  in open heel. Working..........   12.50
  Wrapping Paper. 18x30" 15.00
Campbell Kids
  Doll. 11½", compo head, molded
  hair, huge round brown eyes
  looking to side. Original clothes ..   85.00
  Plate. Child's..................   25.00
Captain Midnight
  Decoder. 1949 ....   16.00
  Glass. Ovaltine 10.00
Captain Video. Space Helmet, early
  1950's. Original box 11.50

Charley McCarthy
Doll. With monocle, all compo 27.00
Lapel Pin 6.00
Spoon. Detailed 7.00
Davey Crockett Badges. 1950's 3.00
Dick Tracy. Dart board............ 18.50
Donald Duck. Soda bottle 5.00
Fields, W. C. Pottery jug 18.00
Flash Gordon
Compass, Wrist. C. 1940's 10.00
Puzzle. Copyright 1951. K.F.S. 8.00
Fluberdub. Hand puppet 5.00
Gene Autry
Lunch Box. Tin, litho 10.00
Song Book. 1936 .... 6.00
Grumpy. Disney figure. Bisque, 2½" 6.50
Hopalong Cassidy
Gun and Holster Set. C. 1940's ... 17.50
Pencil Case. 4x8". Leather, with
signed photo of Hopy 7.50
Picture Gun and Theatre. Original
box, 7 films 26.50
Tumbler...................... 10.00
Howdy Doody
Beanie Kit, leather............. 6.00
Cards, Playing. Original box 3.50
Doll. 24", compo. Effanbee....... 75.00
Handkerchief 5.00
Howdy & Friends. 4" dolls, plastic .. 15.00
Water Float................... 8.00
Lone Ranger
Official Outfit. 5 pcs. Copyright
1942. Original illustrated box 20.00
Pistol. Tin cork. 10½" long 13.50
Mickey Mouse
Airplane. Hard rubber 18.00
Bank. Sides have Mik-Min,
Horace, Pluto. Pie-eyed MM on lid 26.50
Bell, Bicycle. Enamel painting on
cover. Signed Germany 12.50
Belt Buckle. Silverplate.......... 12.00
Books:
"The Adventures of Mickey
Mouse." David McKay Book #1,
1931 .... 13.50
"The Detective." Big Little Book,
Whitman 1934 .... 8.50
"Mickey Mouse Will Not Quit."
Mini book 6.00
Cups:
Baby. Mickey playing mandolin.
Silverplated 25.00
Custard. With spoon, silverplated 12.40
Doll. 11", compo. Black shirt,
orange pants, hands on hips,
mouth open, white gloves, shoes . 75.00
Figurines - Japanese Bisque:
Mickey holding cane. 4¼"...... 22.50
Mickey playing saxophone. 3½" 17.50
Mickey riding Pluto. 3x3½".... 15.00

Planter Peanut. Glass dish, 5½" diam.
S/P spoon with Mr. Peanut handle.
Carlton S/P. Set $12.50

Minnie. 4½" 26.50
Minnie. Standing, playing
accordion. 3½", original label .. 15.00
Minnie playing mandolin. 3½" .. 15.00
Figurines. Mickey, Minnie and
Pluto. Pot metal, 2½". Set of 3 ... 23.50
Hair Brush. 2x4"............... 8.00
Movie Projector. 2 rolls 16MM film 85.00
Ring. Die-cast metal signet. C. 1940 18.50
Tea Set. Teapot, creamer, sugar, 4
each cups, saucers, plates. Japan,
original box. Set 45.00
*Wrist Watch. Ingersol, round dial . 175.00
Mr. Peanut
Drinking mug 25.00
Vender bank.................. 25.00
Orphan Annie
Decoder, Manual. 1936 .... 25.00
Dress Up Kit. 8x12". Dated 1968 .. 12.50
Game. M. Bradley. Original box .. 12.50
Ring 23.00
Salt and Pepper Shakers. Pair 8.50
Pinochio. Salt and pepper shakers.
Mkd. "Handpainted Japan." Pair .. 8.50
Popeye. Crayon box, tin 8.00
Roy Rogers
Book. "Bullet and Trigger." Whit-
man, 1953 .... 5.00
Cap Pistol 8.00
Derringer. Miniature cap gun 5.00
Mug 12.00

Shirley Temple Cream Pitcher. Blue, white transfer $12.00

Shirley Temple
Books:
Capt. January and the Little Colonel. 1934 .... 10.00
Shirley Temple, the Real Little Girl 12.50
Shirley Temple in the Poor Little Rich Girl 12.50
Favorite Poems 7.00
Heidi. 1937 .... 15.00
Breakfast Set. Mug, cereal bowl, creamer. Blue glass, each item has picture at different age. Set .. 35.00
Creamer. Blue, 4½" high 12.00
Doll. 13", compo. All original..... 75.00
Doll. 22", all original 140.00
Dress. Large, red, white polka dots 30.00
Mirror. 1937 .... 21.00
Mug 15.00
Pitcher and Bowl. Set 28.00
Sugar. 6¼'" high. Bisque figure .. 15.00
Tea Set. 1961 .... 55.00
Superman. 1965 Movie Viewer. 2 films......................... 5.00
Will Rogers. Clock, electric 60.00
*Reproduced Item

COLLECTORS' PLATES, ETC.

The first collectors' plates were made by Bing and Grondahl in 1895. Royal Copenhagen issued their first Christmas plate in 1908. In recent years, it seems that everyone with a glass/pottery factory or a mint has been producing plates, bells, eggs, etc., commemorating practically every event imaginable. Vast numbers of 'new' collectibles have flooded the market and supply has exceeded demand; thus, prices on these collectibles have been affected accordingly.

Anri
1971 - Christmas ....$ 37.50
1972 - Christmas 42.50
1973 - Mother's Day 35.00
1974 - Birthday 27.00
1974 - Father's Day 50.00
1975 - Mother's Day 45.00
Bareuther
1967 - Christmas 75.00
1968 - Christmas 20.00
1969 - Christmas 15.00
1970 - Mother's Day 10.00
1971 - Father's Day 12.00
1971 - Mother's Day 15.00
1972 - Christmas 47.50
1972 - Thanksgiving 15.00
1973 - Christmas Bell 20.00
1973 - Father's Day 25.00
1974 - Christmas Bell 18.00
1974 - Thanksgiving 20.00
1975 - Thanksgiving 15.00

Berlin. Christmas 1971 ....$12.00
Berlin
1970 - Christmas 75.00
1971 - Mother's Day 22.50
1973 - Christmas 30.00
1974 - Bell 22.50
1975 - Christmas 22.50
Bing and Grondahl - Christmas
1895............2700.00 1897............ 900.00
1896............1650.00 1898............ 500.00

1899	750.00	1937	65.00
1900	575.00	1938	85.00
1901	300.00	1939	135.00
1902	275.00	1940	140.00
1903	175.00	1941	275.00
1904	120.00	1942	150.00
1905	100.00	1943	125.00
1906	85.00	1944	95.00
1907	110.00	1945	135.00
1908	67.50	1946	70.00
1909	90.00	1947	70.00
1910	75.00	1948	100.00
1911	75.00	1949	67.50
1912	72.00	1950	67.50
1913	72.00	1951	100.00
1914	65.00	1952	80.00
1915	100.00	1953	60.00
1916	65.00	1954	80.00
1917	75.00	1955	75.00
1918	67.50	1956	80.00
1919	85.00	1957	120.00
1920	60.00	1958	130.00
1921	60.00	1959	100.00
1922	60.00	1960	125.00
1923	60.00	1961	200.00
1924	60.00	1962	75.00
1925	60.00	1963	75.00
1926	60.00	1964	45.00
1927	65.00	1965	42.00
1928	60.00	1966	42.00
1929	75.00	1967	42.00
1930	84.00	1968	35.00
1931	75.00	1969	35.00
1932	75.00	1970	22.00
1933	60.00	1971	20.00
1934	75.00	1972	20.00
1935	60.00	1973	25.00
1936	60.00	1974	22.00

Royal Copenhagen Christmas Plate, 1967. The Royal Oak **$21.50**

Bing and Grondahl - Miscellaneous

1970 - Mother's Day	30.00
1971 - Mother's Day	7.50
1972 - Mother's Day	12.00
1973 - Mother's Day	13.00
1974 - Bell	100.00
1975 - Bell	40.00

Church - Christmas

1968	18.00
1969	12.00
1970	15.00
1971	15.00
1972	12.50
1973	15.00
1974	15.00

Dresden

1971 - Christmas	37.50
1972 - Christmas	15.00
1973 - Mother's Day	17.50
1974 - Mother's Day	20.00

Franklin Mint - Sterling

1970 - Bringing Home the Tree. First edition	500.00
1971 - Under the Mistletoe	165.00
1972 - Caroler's	160.00
1972 - Mother's Day. First edition .	145.00
1973 - Trimming the Tree	160.00
1974 - Hanging the Wreath	160.00
1975 - Christmas	165.00
1975 - Mother's Day	200.00

Furstenberg

1971 - Rabbits. Standard. First Ed. .	17.50
1971 - Three Wise Men. Deluxe First Edition	36.00
1972 - Easter	12.50
1972 - Mother's Day. First edition .	12.50
1973 - Christmas Eve. Deluxe	47.50
1973 - Easter Egg. First edition . . .	20.00

Berta Hummel. Mother's Day. 1974
$20.00

Bing and Grondahl Christmas Plate.
1967 ....$42.00

1974 - Christmas. Standard	27.50
1975 - Easter...................	25.00
1975 - Easter Egg	20.00
1975 - Mother's Day	26.50

Gorham - Christmas Plates

1973 - First Edition.............	27.50
1974 -........................	12.50
1975 -........................	12.50

Gorham - Christmas Snowflakes and Spoons

1970 - Snowflake...............	75.00
1971 - Snowflake...............	40.00
1971 - Spoon...................	30.00
1972 - Snowflake...............	40.00
1973 - Spoon...................	18.00
1974 - Snowflake...............	20.00
1974 - Spoon...................	15.00

Gorham - Remington

1973 - Old West. 1st Edition. Set of 4	100.00
1974 - "Spencer." Dear Child. First Edition	38.50
1975 - Set of 2.................	40.00

Gorham - Rockwell
Bells:

1975 - First Edition.............	22.00
1975 - Christmas	20.00
1976 - Bicentennial	25.00

Figurines - Four Seasons:

1972 - Set of 4. First Edition	275.00
1973 - Set of 4	235.00
1974 - Set of 4	250.00
1975 - Set of 4	250.00

Plates:

1973 - Butter Girl. First Edition ..	110.00
1974 - Scotty Gets His Tree	40.00
1974 - Streaker	30.00
1975 - Home from Fields	24.00
1975 - Mother's Day Doctor and and Doll. First Edition....	32.00
1975 - Christmas - Down Hill Daring. First Edition	25.00
1976 - Bicentennial. A President's Wife	75.00
1976 - Bicentennial. Ben Franklin	18.50

Plates - Four Seasons:

1971 - Boy and His Dog. First Edition. Set of 4.........	225.00
1972 - Young Love. Set of 4	60.00
1973 - Ages of Love. Set of 4 ...	72.50
1974 - Grandpa and Me. Set of 4.	60.00
1975 - Me and My Pal. Set of 4...	55.00

Haviland

1970 - Christmas. First Edition	175.00
1972 - Christmas	48.50
1973 - Christmas	25.00
1973 - Mother's Day. First Edition .	25.00
1974 - Bicentennial	45.00
1974 - Mother's Day	30.00
1975 - Christmas	28.50
1975 - Mother's Day	26.50

Haviland - Parlon

1971 - Unicorn in Captivity. First Edition	135.00
1972 - Christmas. First Edition	175.00
1973 - Tapestry	115.00
1974 - Christmas	50.00

Christmas Ornament. Hummel. "The Guardian Angel." 1974 ....$5.00

Wedgwood. Christmas 1974 ...$30.00		Peanuts. Christmas 1975 ......$13.00	
1975 - Unicorn	50.00	1973 - Mom ?	15.00
1975 - Mother's Day. First Edition	95.00	1974 - Christmas at Fireplace	45.00
		1975 - A Kiss for Lucy	13.00
Hummel - Berta		1975 - Woodstock, Santa Claus	13.00
1971 - Angel. First Edition	36.00	1976 - Bicentennial	15.00
1972 - Playing Hooky. First Edition	17.50	**Porsgrund**	
1973 - Christmas Creche	85.00	1968 - Christmas. First Edition	150.00
1974 - Christmas Bell	18.50	1969 - Christmas	12.50
1975 - Christmas Bell	20.00	1970 - Christmas Mug. 1st Ed.	20.00
1975 - Christmas Ornament	4.00	1970 - Mother's Day. 1st Edition	10.00
1975 - Mother's Day	22.50	1971 - Christmas	15.00
Hummel - Goebel		1971 - Mother's Day	9.00
1971 - Heavenly Angel. 1st Ed.	325.00	1972 - Christmas	16.00
1972 - Hear Ye, Hear Ye	30.00	1973 - Christmas Mug	23.00
1973 - Globe Trotter	35.00	1973 - Father's Day	10.00
1974 - Goose Girl	35.00	1974 - Christmas	22.50
1975 - Ride into Christmas. Figure	175.00	1974 - Easter	16.00
1975 - Ride into Christmas. Plate	42.50	1974 - Father's Day	11.00
1975 - Anniversary Plate. 1st Ed.	110.00	1975 - Christmas Mug	29.50
Jensen, Georg		1975 - Easter	18.00
1972 - Christmas. First Edition	28.50		
1973 - Mother's Day. First Edition	37.50		
1974 - Christmas	20.00	**Royal Copenhagen-Christmas Plates**	
1975 - Christmas	21.50	1908 - Madonna and Child. 1st Ed.	1350.00
1975 - Mother's Day	25.00	1909 - Danish Landscape	115.00
Noritake		1910 - The Magi	110.00
1971 - Easter Egg. First Edition	85.00	1911 - Danish Landscape	125.00
1972 - Christmas Bell. First Edition	16.50	1912 - Christmas Tree	112.50
1973 - Easter Egg	25.00	1913 - Frederik Church Spire	120.00
1973 - Valentine Heart. 1st Ed.	22.50	1914 - Holy Spirit Church	112.50
1974 - Christmas Bell	24.00	1915 - Danish Landscape	100.00
1974 - Doe and Fawn. First Edition	45.00	1916 - Shepherd at Christmas	80.00
1974 - Easter Egg	20.00	1917 - Our Saviour Church	75.00
1974 - Valentine Heart	17.50	1918 - Sheep and Shepherds	75.00
1975 - Christmas Bell	18.50	1919 - In the Park	72.50
Peanuts		1920 - Mary and Child Jesus	67.50
1972 - Charley Brown. First Edition	12.50	1921 - Aabenraa Marketplace	65.00
1972 - Snoopy guides sleigh. 1st Ed.	23.50	1922 - Three Singing Angels	60.00
1973 - Christmas Eve at Dog House	75.00	1923 - Danish Landscape	65.00

1924 - Sailing Ship	70.00
1925 - Christianshavn	65.00
1926 - Christianshavn Canal	65.00
1927 - Ship's Boy at Tiller	105.00
1928 - Vicar Family	70.00
1929 - Grundtvig Church	70.00
1930 - Fishing Boats	70.00
1931 - Mother and Child	75.00
1932 - Frederiksberg Gardens	75.00
1933 - Great Belt Ferry	80.00
1934 - The Hermitage Castle	100.00
1935 - Kronborg Castle	115.00
1936 - Roskilde Cathedral	110.00
1937 - Main Street Copenhagen	125.00
1938 - Round Church Ostelars	225.00
1939 - Greenland Pack Ice	225.00
1940 - The Good Shepherd	360.00
1941 - Danish Village Church	275.00
1942 - Bell Tower	350.00
1943 - Flight to Egypt	425.00
1944 - Danish Winter Scene	140.00
1945 - A Peaceful Motif	340.00
1946 - Zealand Village Church	130.00
1947 - The Good Shepherd	210.00
1948 - Noddebo Church	112.00
1949 - Our Lady's Cathedral	122.50
1950 - Boeslunde Church	135.00
1951 - Christmas Angel	260.00
1952 - Christmas in Forest	85.00

Noritake. 1974 Easter Egg $20.00

1953 - Frederiksborg Castle	80.00
1954 - Amalienbord Palace	110.00
1955 - Fano Girl	220.00
1956 - Rosenborg Castle	130.00
1957 - The Good Shepherd	84.50
1958 - Sunshine Over Greenland	100.00
1959 - Christmas Night	120.00
1960 - The Stag	125.00
1961 - Training Ship Danmark	115.00
1962 - The Little Mermaid	160.00
1963 - Hojsager Mill	52.50
1964 - Fetching the Tree	47.50
1965 - Little Skaters	48.50
1966 - Blackbird	40.00
1967 - The Royal Oak	21.50
1968 - The Last Umiak	21.50
1969 - The Old Farmyard	22.50
1970 - Christmas Rose and Cat	20.00
1971 - Hare in Winter	20.00
1972 - In the Desert	18.50
1973 - Train Homeward Bound	22.00
1974 - Winter Twilight	22.00
1975 - Queen's Palace	20.00

Royal Copenhagen - Mother's Day Plates

1971 - First Edition	40.00
1972 -	13.50
1973 -	17.50
1974 -	18.50
1975 -	19.00

Royale - (Germany)

1969 - Astronaut. First Edition	30.00
1969 - Christmas. First Edition	37.50
1970 - Annual (Crystal)	575.00
1971 - Christmas	16.50
1972 - Mother's Day	18.50
1973 - Father's Day	25.00
1973 - Mother's Day	45.00
1974 - Christmas	25.00
1974 - Mother's Day	25.00
1975 - Christmas	27.50

Veneto Flair

1970 - Madonna. First Edition	675.00
1971 - Christmas	200.00
1972 - Mother's Day	75.00
1973 - Christmas	50.00
1973 - Easter	100.00
1974 - Easter	50.00
1974 - Playmates. Set of 4	115.00
1975 - Candleholder. First Edition	17.50
1975 - Christmas	45.00
1975 - Christmas Bell	30.00
1975 - Easter Egg. First Edition	20.00

Wedgwood

1969 - Christmas. First Edition	265.00
1970 - Christmas	17.50
1971 - Calendar. First Edition	16.50
1971 - Children's Story. 1st Ed.	16.50
1972 - Bicentennial. First Edition	32.50
1973 - Calendar	22.50

"Royale" Christmas Plate. 1974. $25.00

1973 - Children's Story	24.00
1973 - Christmas	40.00
1973 - Mother's Day	24.00
1974 - Bicentennial	50.00
1974 - Christmas Mug	42.50
1974 - Mother's Day	30.00
1975 - Bicentennial	75.00
1975 - Children's Story	12.50
1975 - Christmas	32.50
1975 - Christmas Mug	47.50
1975 - "The Hunter Plate." Andrew Wyeth	35.00
1976 - Bicentennial	50.00

COMIC BOOKS

Through the centuries pictures have been used for visual storytelling - both serious and comic. In America, the first comic which became a Sunday feature was published in the New York World in February 1896. Since that time newspapers have carried comics as a daily and Sunday feature.

In the 1915-30 period, pulp magazines filled the need for adventure reading, however, before World War II, it appeared they had reached the saturation point and publishers secured rights and printed many back adventures of comic strip characters, such as Captain Easy, Orphan Annie, Maggie and Jiggs, Andy Gump, etc.

The comic book idea caught on and publishers had artists create special adventure plots and situations for such new characters as Superman, Capt. Marvel, Spy Smasher, Bulletman, Don Winslow, Military Comics, Air Fighters, Wings, Plastic Man, Smash Comics, Hit Comics, Police Comics, Western Comics and numerous other titles.

Comic books are still in good demand today, however, television is making in-roads on the industry.

A number of first issues of comic books are bringing fantastic prices - one, about $1800.00 by an alleged, rigged auction to create interest in the subject. The average comic book of the 1940-60 era will bring $1.00 to $2.00 when in fine condition. First and early issues bring more.

The prices listed below are for mint condition. The numbers represent issue numbers, i.e. #1 is first edition; #5, fifth issue, #10, tenth issue, etc. Check publishers and numbers. Different publishers published the same title in different years.

Comic. Ripley's "Believe It or Not! True Ghost Stories" $1.00

Bugs Bunny. Dell Publ. Co. #31-#50. Each .... $	1.00
Captain America. Timely. #101 - #130. Each	.50
Casper, The Friendly Ghost. Harvey Publ. #64-#100. Each	.50
Classic Comics, Gilberton Pub.	
#3. Count of Monte Cristo	12.00
#8 - Arabian Nights	10.00
#23 - Oliver Twist	7.50
#47. Twenty Thousand Leagues Under the Sea	2.50

#64. Treasure Island	2.50
#78. Joan of Arc	3.25
#125. Ox-Bow Incident	1.50
#163. Master of the World	1.50
Dagwood. Harvey Pub. #2-#12. Each	3.00
Donald Duck. Dell Publ. Co. #4-#6.Ea.	2.50
Flash Gordon. King/Charlton #15 . . .	.50
Green Hornet. Harvey Pub. #19 -	
#39. Each	7.50
Howdy Doody. Dell Publ. #1	5.00
Howdy Doody. Dell Publ. #7-#37. Each	2.00
Mickey Mouse. Dell Pub. after 1941,	
#25-#75. Each	2.00
Phantom, The. McKay Pub. 1949. #56 .	10.00
Roy Rogers. Dell Pub. #5-#50. Each . .	3.00
Strange Tales. Marvel Comics, Inc. #2	2.50
Superman. DC/National. #35	17.00
Superman. DC/National. #250	1.00
Tarzan. National Periodical. #215 -	
#230. Each	1.00

COMMEMORATIVE AND HISTORICAL GLASS

Commemorative, historical and souvenir items have always been popular in the collector's field. With the bicentennial celebration of 1976, people are more aware of such items. Some of the old patterns will be reproduced in goblets and bread plates and should be dated 1976.

Apothecary Jar. Statue of Liberty . . . $	135.00
Bread Plates, See "Bread Plates."	
Cannon on Drum. Milk glass	125.00
Compote. Jenny Lind	125.00
Goblets	
Phila. Centennial 1876	75.00
Shield and Keystone. Clear	47.50
Match Holder. "Goddess of Liberty."	
Wall-type, clear glass	47.50
Mugs	
"E Pluribus Unum." 13 stars and	
shield. Clear	57.50
"Liberty and the Republic." Amber	75.00
Paperweights	
Budda. Gillender. 1876. Amber . .	50.00
Memorial Hall. Gillender, 1876.	
Frosted	185.00
Pitchers	
Gridley	85.00
King George, 1937	28.50
Plates	
Automobile Roadster. Lindsey 141	35.00
50th Anniversay of McKee Glass,	
Jeannette, Pa. Opalescent blue.	
5½" diam.	28.50
Railroad Engine. Clear, covered.	
Lindsey #138	57.50
Santa Maria	40.00

Goblets. Engraved and etched. "Bull's Eye Mirror." Crystal. Set of 6 . . $300.00

Washington Hatchet. Libbey.	
Lindsey #253	75.00
Platters	
Blaine	120.00
Logan	100.00
Nelly Bly, "Around the World"	165.00
John Mitchel, "Labor Leader"	125.00
Salt. Liberty Bell	30.00
Slippers. Gillender, 1876. Pair	65.00
Statuette. M. J. Owens, inventor of	
automatic bottle machine	32.50
Tray, Designer's. Liberty Bell	72.50
Tumbler. McKinley, Our President	
Assassinated	16.50
Vase. Hand and Torch. Gillender,	
1876	47.50

COMMEMORATIVE PLATES, See
SOUVENIR PLATES

COMMEMORATIVE SPOONS, See
SPOONS, SOUVENIR

COPELAND SPODE CHINA

The firm was founded by Josiah Spode in 1770 in the Staffordshire section of England. Later, W. T. Copeland & Sons succeeded him, using the designation "Late Spode" on their wares. The firm made various types of ware including Salt Glaze, Jasperware, Delft, Porcelain figurines and fine dinner services. Still later the firm became known as Copeland and Garrett.

Cake Stand. 3" high, 9½" diam. Blue on white. "Spode's Tower." Late $25.00

Bowl. 9" diam., footed, scalloped rim, blue and white. Marked Copeland Spode's Tower, England $ ... 15.00
Compote. 8½" diam., 4-3/8" high. Blue border with Greek Key design. Signed Husten 35.00
Cracker Jar. White classical figures on blue ground 65.00
Creamers
   Helmet....................... 22.50
   Wildflower. 3¼" high 14.00
Cups and Saucers
   Mr. size. Pink tower mark. "England" 11.50
   Orange and gold. C. 1880 .... 75.00
Jug. Large, blue Jasper ground, applied grape vine, drinking scenes in cream. Applied cream band around rim, vine handle 100.00
Pitchers
   4½" high. Bulbous. Dark green, tan borders, ivory figures in relief . 25.00
   8¼" high. White with orange peel decor. Signed 85.00
   10" overall width from handle to spout. Hunt scene 95.00

Dish, Footed. 2½ x 9½" diam. Turquoise rim, trimmed in gold, violet bouquet in center $45.00

Blue and white, men on horses on fox chase...................... 120.00
Plaque. 10" diam., underglaze sepia painting. W. Yale. C 1857 .... 135.00
Plates
   8¼". Cream with green and brown leaf decor 27.50
   8½". Fighting warriors. Deep orange, black fluted rim 25.00

Pitcher. 5" high. Peach with cobalt and orange, gold trim. C. 1851-1885 $45.00

10". Peacocks in bold blues,
reds 15.00
Platters
9x15". Leaf and Acorn border 120.00
12½ x 16½". Blue and white
pasture scene. Copeland-Spode's
Italian. England 130.00
Soup Plate. Brown border, English
scene in center. 22.50
Soup Tureen. Matching ladle and
platter. Brown and white 195.00
Sugar and Creamer. Blue ground,
raised white hunting scene. Set . .   85.00
Tea Kettle. All china. Rare 300.00
Teapots
Dark blue and rust-colored floral
decor 150.00
9½" high, clear blue, gilded
handles. Fu dog finial on lid. Imported from England by Tiffany
Co. in late 19th century. 195.00
Tea Set. Miniature. Sugar bowl,
creamer and teapot. Decor of pink
roses and green leaves. Set 80.00
Vase. Jeweled urn-shape with gold
and pastel pink enameling.
Jeweled turquoise beading 115.00

COPENHAGEN, See ROYAL COPENHAGEN

COPPER

Copper has been an important material used
throughout the centuries. Milk buckets, pots
and pans do not tell the complete story. It was
also used for jewelry, plaques, lighting
fixtures, weathervanes and decorative items.

Apothecary's Still. Bulbous body,
pointed snout . . . .$ 100.00
*Bed Warmer. Pierced, wood handle   115.00
Boiler, Wash 48.00

Chafing Dish. Copper pan, brass
holder, wood handle. 2-qt. $75.00

Tea Kettle. American. C. 1825 $150.00

Chafing Dish. Covered. 9¼" dish,
fancy handles, wood grips and
knob. Wood handle on burner. 14"
coppy tray, perforated rim. Perfection. Manning-Bowman Co.,
1901. . . . .   100.00
*Coal Hod. Large, helmet-type. 16"
to top of handle. Polished and
lacquered 160.00
Coaching Horn. C. 1845. . . . .   95.00
Coffee Pots
10", burnished and lacquered 60.00
Pewter trim, burnished, lacquered   50.00
Rough condition 30.00
Compote. Openwork 43.50
Dipper. One gallon capacity. Burn-
ished and lacquered 50.00
Dow Pot. Dutch, large 175.00
Eagle. American. Large with copper
ball from old weathervane. 350.00
Funnel. Handled 29.50
Hot Dish. Porcelain liner. 9" diam. . .   50.00
Hot Water Bottle, Oval, screw top . . .   60.00
*Kettles
22" diam. 135.00
23" diam., 18" deep. Hammered
bail with extra heavy mountings .   145.00
24" diam. Apple butter 150.00
Water. English, burnished and
lacquered 75.00
Milk Bucket. With spout, lid and
handle. Bound with brass bands.
15" high, cleaned and buffed. 110.00
Milk Tank. 10-gallon., with spigot . . .   85.00
Mold. 2¼ x 2½". 25.00
Mug, Brewery. Solid, large 25.00
*Pails
9" diam. Bail handle 55.00
11½" diam. Bailed, two handles,
two pouring lips 65.00
16" diam. 80.00
24" diam. 100.00
*Pans
7" diam., 5" deep. 50.00

```
9½" diam., 5¼" deep, 2 handles .          60.00
10" diam., 7½" deep, iron handle          72.50
13" diam., 9" deep.............          85.00
```

Pitcher. Small, 1½" high 12.00
Planter. 6" diam. at bottom, flaring
    to 10" opening at top. 6" high, 3
    slits in bottom for draining.
    Hammered, dovetailed 40.00
Saucepan. Covered, 10" diam., 5"
    deep. 11" iron handles, pierced for
    hanging. Burnished, lacquered ...   60.00
Tea Kettles
    13" high. Strap handle, porcelain
    knob.........................   75.00
    American made Blada. Dove-
    tailed, fold down gooseneck spout .   200.00
    American, signed "Hunneman"
    Boston. Dovetailed side and
    bottom. 11½" to top of heavy
    handle 150.00
    Early. Iron handle, 3-legged iron
    trivet. Hinged cover on spout.....   100.00
    With gooseneck spouts:
        Footed......................   120.00
        Norwegian 72.50
        Swedish.....................   72.50
Tea Set. Medium size.Teapot, sugar,
    creamer and tray 130.00
Toast Rack 22.50
Tray. 15x18" 55.00
*Umbrella Stand. Brass lion handles   50.00
Vases
    8" high. Silver floral inlay........   45.00
    15½" high. Sterling silver inlay of
    ivy foliage 85.00
Water Can. 13" high to top of brass
    handle 60.00
Weather Vane. Cow, 15x25" 650.00
                *Reproduced Item

COPPER LUSTRE

Copper Lustre was first made in England by
the Staffordshire district potters between
1800 and 1805. The use of a copper compound
in the glaze resulted in a metallic copper-like
surface. The bulk of the ware imported into
the United States was between 1840 and
1890. A number of reproductions have come
onto the market recently, small creamers and
a so-called "Polka Jug" or pitcher. The new
ware is usually thicker and heavier than the
old.

Bowls
    4" diam., 2½" high. Dark blue
    band with raised red roses.......$ 45.00

Creamer. 6½" high. Sunderland pink
lustre lining. English. C. 1840 .$125.00

```
5" diam., 1½" high. Pedestaled.
Blue band with raised enameled
    design .......................          68.00
    5½" diam., covered ...........          85.00
Cups and Saucers
    Handpainted design ............          67.50
    Scalloped edge on saucer........          60.00
Dog. 8" high ....................          78.00
Flower Pots. Tub shaped, with
    stands. 4" high, mock shell
    handles. Pair .................          175.00
Goblets
    Blue band. Colored flowers ......          77.50
    Blue band. Girl and dog decor ....          75.00
    Cream band. Green and pink
    lustre vines ...................          45.00
Jug. Cream. 6½" high. Brown, blue .          125.00
Mugs
    3½" high. Plain ...............          47.50
    3¾" high. Orange band, floral
    decor .......................          55.00
    4" high, 4" diam. Pink lustre on
    rim, tan band .................          62.50
    Shaving. Floral sprays on blue
    bank, decorated handle .........          65.00
Pitchers
    2½" high. Plain ...............          30.00
    3" high. Sanded band ..........          45.00
    3½" high. Blue band with figure
    of girl and cat on either side .....          50.00
    4" high. Lustre schoolhouse
    on tan band..................          100.00
    4½" high. White band, red decor .          72.50
    5" high. Leaf decor at top.
    Masonic symbol on bottom ......          110.00
```

Teapot. 10" overall length $200.00

5½" high. Rough sand finish around middle	72.50
6" high. Man-of-the-Woods spout, dolphin handle	95.00
7" high. White band, floral decor .	120.00
7½" high. Decorated bands on yellow ground	200.00
Salts	
Footed, open	45.00
Lustre blue band, pedestaled	32.50
Master. Pedestaled, sanded band .	30.00
Sugar Bowl. Open, raised floral and leaf design on 2" blue border	85.00
Teapots	
6" high. Floral and leaf design on 2" blue band around middle. Same on lid	95.00
6½" high. Pink, green, white copper. 4 feet	200.00
Multicolored band	150.00
Toby Jug	175.00
Toothpick Holder. Sanded band	40.00
Urn. 8½" high, 8" across handles. 3½" green band, lustre decor	150.00

CORALENE

A type of "so-called" Art Glass made by the New England Glass Co., in the late 1880's and early 1890's. It is Satin glass with applied glass beading in a design similar to natural coral. A wheat and fleur-de-lis design was also used for decorating this glass.

Bowls, various types . . . . $	375.00
Cup, Punch. Scarce	380.00
Ewer. Blue, squatty type	500.00
Lamp, Finger. Pale blue diamond MOP satin glass	900.00
Perfume Bottle. 6", geometric design	140.00
Toilet Bottle. Blue, beaded decor	395.00
Tumblers	
4" high. Butterscotch satin glass.	

D.Q. seaweed pattern in blue coralene	200.00
4" high. Powder blue satin glass, D.Q., orange seaweed pattern. Signed	235.00
4¼" high. Pink MOP. Seaweed pattern in yellow	225.00
Vases	
4½" high. Rose-colored spherical body covered with coral branch beading. Smooth 2¼" opening at top, off-white casing	395.00
5" high. Satin glass ribbed [cased] D.Q. pattern from an opaque white at bottom to lemon yellow at top. Signed	325.00
5¾" high. Fan-shaped. Yellow on blue satin glass	375.00
6" high. Ruffled rim, white to pink satin	285.00
6¼" high. 6 panels, beaded fleur-de-lis decor	450.00

Perfume bottle with stopper. 6" high, blue glass with multicolored coral
$195.00

8" high. Coral branch beading on camphor satin ground. Blown	160.00
8½" high. Bulbous. White with pastel green satin and allover gold wheat design	500.00
11" high. Chartreuse, gold beading	600.00
11" high. Pink, D.Q., straw flowers and daisies	300.00
MOP. Peach, decorated with puffed butterflies and bees. Signed. "Patent"	450.00
MOP. Teardrops in light to dark orange shading, blue seaweed. Webb	450.00

CORONATION ITEMS

Interest in coronation items has been shown by a small group of collectors. The ruling heads of England, from the time of Queen Victoria to the present, are among the most desirable. They are usually made of chinaware or glass.

Mug. King Edward VIII $30.00

Ash Trays. Edward VIII in coronation robe. Royal Doulton dated 1937. Set of 4 in holder ....$	62.00
Beakers	
3" high. 1902. Coronation Dinner, Edward VII	27.00
King George V. 1902...........	32.00
Bottle. 9" high. King George V and Queen Mary. Royal Coat of Arms. Stoneware	25.00
Bowls	
7" diam. Elizabeth. Alfred Meakin	6.00
Queen Victoria. 1897. Stoneware.	25.00

Bust. 6" high. Queen Victoria. Terra Cotta. Signed, dated 1897	60.00
Cup. King George & Queen Elizabeth. Dated 1937. Registered and designed by Dame Laura Knight ..	35.00
Cup and Saucer. Victoria & Albert. Portrait. Purple transfer, pink lustre trim	68.00
Dishes	
4¼" square. Queen Elizabeth II ..	10.00
4x6". King Edward VIII. 1937	12.00
Handerchief. Elizabeth	3.75
Jug. King Edward VII, May 12, 1937. Lion handle, music box in base. "God Save the King." Limited Ed...	350.00
Medallion. Blue Jasper. Elizabeth and Phillip. 1953. 3¼x4¼". Pair .	95.00
Mugs	
King Edward VIII. 3¼" high	30.00
King George VI, Queen Elizabeth, 1937..........................	14.50
Queen Elizabeth II, June 2, 1953. 3¼" high, official design	15.00
Paperweight. St. Louis type. Elizabeth II. Modern.................	195.00
Pitcher. Queen Elizabeth II. Worcester bone china. Mash spout. 5½" high	40.00
Pitcher, Milk. Edward VIII. Adams Pottery.......................	26.50
Plaque. George and Elizabeth. Ivory color..........................	28.50
Plates	
George VI. Pressed glass	15.00
King Edward. 1937, 10"	13.50
King Edward VII. 1902, scalloped edges, 8".......................	18.50
King George V, Queen Mary. 9" ..	18.50
Queen Elizabeth. White, red. 9" ..	18.50
Queen Victoria. 60th Anniversary. Small	20.00
Queen Victoria Jubilee, 1887. 9½", Reg. #63164	48.00
Saucer. Deep. Queen Victoria. 1887 .	20.00
Sterling Spoons	
King George VI, small	12.00
Queen Victoria. 4¼" long. Cut out handle end. "1837-97" pressed in gold-washed bowl	17.50
Tea Caddy. George VI. Rington's	26.50
Tea Set. 21 pieces, china. Edward VII	225.00
Tumbler. Edward VII, Alexandra. 4" high, porcelain, 1902	25.00

COSMOS GLASS

A type of milk glass with a design of cosmos flowers in various color combinations of blue, red and yellow. The decorations are the "stained" or "flashed" type and colors are usually worn or faded on pieces which received considerable use.

Butter Dish. Covered, 8" diam., 5¾" high ....$	175.00
Castor Set. Salt, pepper, mustard ...	195.00
Creamer	120.00
Lamps	
Base, no shade. 8"	100.00
Miniature	125.00
Table.Complete, original	250.00

Butter Dish $175.00

Lemonade Set. Bulbous pitcher with lid. 6 mugs with cobalt blue handles	395.00
Pickle Castor. With tongs	185.00
Pitchers	
Water. 8¼" high	185.00
With 6 tumblers. Set	450.00
Salt Shakers	
From castor set	65.00
Matching pair	95.00
Spooner	78.50
Sugar Bowl. Covered	175.00
Syrup	145.00
Tumbler	65.00

CRACKER JARS

The cracker jar was, more or less, a companion to the old cookie jar. The types vary from crude pottery to fine satin glass with silverplated lids and bails. Many of the finer types were produced by silverplating companies from 1880 to 1900.

Adams. White on blue. Tunstall, England ....$	72.50
Beaded Drape pattern. Apple green .	175.00
Bristol. Turquoise, enamel cranes, floral decor. Strawberry finial on cover	135.00
China	
10" high, bulbous, transfer flower design	67.50
Blue and gold, floral decor, straight sides. Metal cover, bail ...	62.50
Silverplated lid and handle. Golfing scene decor	87.50
Cobalt Glass. Enameling, silver lid and bail	125.00
Limoges. 4¼" high. Yellow, with handles, edges and finial in gold .	65.00
Meissen-type. Blue floral decor on white ground. Silverplated top and handle	120.00

Glass. Pink frosted, floral decor. Silverplated handle and top ...$95.00

Mt. Washington. Typical Burmese coloring. Crown Milano enameled flowers. Signed M.W. 4044A in lid ... 325.00
Royal Worcester. Allover floral sprays, butterflies. Gold 140.00
Satin Glass
Pink, blue and gold decor, shell design around base. Top and handle resilvered 260.00
White to green with pink wild roses. Top, handle resilvered 145.00
White, pansy decor on front, back. Signed A.J.Hall, Meriden, Conn. . . 135.00
Staffordshire-type. White salt glaze. Allover design of leaves and poppies. Silver band, lid 135.00
Three-Face 395.00
Wedgwood. Dark blue, white figures. EPNS silver lid, 3 ball feet . . 130.00

CRANBERRY GLASS

Cranberry, or Ruby glass, was made by adding a small quantity of gold to a pot of glass. Objects were blown or molded and were amber in color. When reheated at a low temperature the ruby or cranberry shade, having a blue-violet tint, was developed. Cranberry glass is currently being reproduced but the new is not of the same quality as the original glass.

Barber Bottle. See Bottles, Barber."
Basket. 7½" diam., applied lily-of-the-valley and forget-me-not decor. Gilded metal frame and handle ....$ 125.00
Bells
5½" diam., 10" high. White porcelain handle, clapper 110.00
10¼" diam. English Bristol, clear handle. Late 95.00
12" high. Clear, applied handle... 150.00
13" high. Wedding. 3-color handle. Original clapper 175.00
Bobeches. Opalescent, ruffled edges. Pair 50.00
Bottle. 8" high. Thumbprint design, crystal stopper 72.50
Bowls
5½". Fluted rim, gold threading .. 45.00
5½"x6¼". Footed, applied flowers, ribbed sides 75.00
Milk. English. 5½"x9½".......... 130.00
Rose. Satin, 5" diam. 65.00
Boxes
3" high, 3¼" diam. Covered 85.00
Covered, on metal feet. Goldleaf-type decor................... 110.00

Jewel. Satin finish, 4½" diam. Florentine cameo portrait of lady on lid 165.00
Patch. Covered, gold filigree design 60.00
Pill. Gold mesh overlay.......... 65.00
White enamel portrait on hinged cover 75.00
Bucket, Ice. Enameled lily-of-the-valley decor. 5¼" high 125.00

Basket. English. Silverplated holder. C.1890.....................$75.00

Butter Dish. 6" high to top of crystal ball finial, underplate 6½" diam., 1½" deep 120.00
Castor. See "Pickle Castors."
Celery. ITP, scalloped top, enamel decor 85.00
Compotes
5" diam. Clear, blown stem 100.00
8" diam., 5½" clear standard 125.00
Cordial Set. Tray, decanter, 8 cordials 165.00
Creamers
3" high. Fluted, cloverleaf top 68.50

4½" high. Panelled, bulbous,
clear handle 65.00
Cruets. See "Cruets."
Cup, Loving. 3½" high. Clear
handles, silver rim 55.00
Decanters. See "Decanters, Glass."
Dish, Candy. 5½" diam. Clear,
melon-shaped lid. 9 sections 35.00
Epergnes
10" high. Single trumpet. Ruffled
top, satin intaglio flowers, leaves,
stems. Set in ornate silver base... 110.00
19" high. Single lily, clear ribbon
decor. Opal top to deep cranberry . 150.00
21" high. Center vase, 3 others,
13" high. Ruffled base bowl, 10"
diam., 2¾" deep. 4 trumpet-
shaped vases with ruffled tops,
with crystal petals winding
around bodies 285.00
Miniature. "Tree of Life." Cased .. 75.00
Ewers
7" high. Slender neck, swirled
pattern, ovid body, applied crystal
handle. Blown 65.00
8" high. White threaded neck,
clear handle 85.00
Finger Bowl 48.00
Gas Shades
7½" diam. Swirled, fluted rim 35.00
Hobnail 45.00
Goblet. Footed 42.50
Jars
Biscuit. 6" high, 5" diam.
Silverplate cover and bail handle.
Blown........................ 95.00
Bonbon. Covered, 6½" high to top
of crystal ball finial with cranberry
teardrop inside. Crystal stem,
enameled pedestal, gold flowers . 75.00
Lamps. See "Lamps, Glass."
Lustres. 14½" high. Top edged in
gold. Enameled gold flowers, 2
rows cut prisms, 7" long. Pair 335.00
Muffineer. 6" high, high dome
shape. S/P cover, silver rim 45.00
Mustard Jar. S/P top and spoon 42.50
Pickle Castors. See "Pickle Castors."
Pitchers
5½" high..................... 72.50
7½" high. ITP, 5 neck rings 95.00
7½" high. ITP, square top, clear,
applied, reeded handle, ground
pontil 100.00
7½" high. English. Flared, ribbed
top, clear, applied handle 100.00
8½" high. 22" circum. Clear glass,
applied handle encircles neck
rope. IVT design 245.00

10" high. IVT, pontil, clear handle. 130.00
Lemonade. White enamel trim ... 125.00

Salt, Master. Sterling holder with
spoon. 2 pieces 85.00
Sauce Boat. 4½" high, early, free
blown........................ 145.00
Salt and Pepper Shakers. 3½" high,
pear-shaped, silver tops. Pair 35.00
Sugar Bowl. Sterling frame, 9½" high 95.00
Sugar Bowl and Creamer. Applied,
clear handles. Set 130.00
Sugar Shakers
4¼" high. Lattice overlay 60.00
Panelled, enamel decor, gold top . 90.00
Plain......................... 50.00

Syrup 125.00
Toothpick Holders
Delaware. Gold 85.00
English. Applied, ruffled, clear
glass band around middle,
applied, clear feet 62.50
Tray. Round, 13", 2" deep 95.00
Tumblers
Diamond Quilted 30.00
ITP 42.50
Lemonade. Handled 50.00
Opalescent Coin Spot 37.50
Ribbed Swirl 37.50
Vases
4" high. Applied handles 50.00
6½" high. English. Crimped top,
applied white decor 65.00
8" high. Footed................. 75.00
8¼" high. Jack-in-the-Pulpit 75.00
8¼" high. Shell pattern, flared
neck. Pair 125.00
11" high. Opalescent, fluted 115.00
13¼" high. Clear bases, fluted
tops. Pair..................... 175.00
16½" high..................... 150.00
Vinaigrette. 2¼" high, 1" diam.
Clear stopper, decorated 50.00

Wash Set. Pitcher 7" high, with
applied crystal handle. Bowl 7"
diam., 1½" deep. Blown, rough
pontil. Set 145.00
Water Set. Deep cranberry. 9"
pitcher with 6 tumblers.......... 250.00
Wine Glass. Clear foot, stem 28.50

CROCKS, See POTTERY, EARLY

CROWN DERBY
See ROYAL CROWN DERBY

CROWN MILANO

A fine type of glass made at the Mt. Washington Glass Co., New Bedford, Mass., in the latter part of the 19th century. It is often decorated with flowers and leaves encrusted with gold and silver. Many pieces are signed with the letters "C.M." in the pontil.

Sweetmeat Jar. 4¾" high. Swirl pattern, floral decor. Silverplated lid, turtle finial $875.00

Bowls
Petal top, melon-ribbed, 4½" . . . . $	375.00
Rose. Deep colored roses on white background	475.00
Bride's Basket. Plated holder, wild rose decor	1350.00

Cracker Jars
Floral on white	500.00
Jeweled. Original paper label	600.00
Plated ball, cover. Fluted plated rim. Signed N.W. in cover	625.00
Swirl pattern. Small. Trimmed in gold colors, green, rust, apricot, raised swirls, gold bail and cover. Signed MW. in lid	395.00
Creamer. Signed	500.00
Cruet. Signed	650.00
Cup and Saucer. Demitasse	500.00
Ewer. 12¼" high. Yellow to beige ground, bronze gold decor of dragon, phoenix handle	1250.00
Humidor, Cigar. 5" high, cream ground with multicolored pansies	485.00

Jars
Covered. Albertine coloring, floral decor. 12" high, 20" diam. at lower bulbous part	750.00
Mustard. S/P lid. Crown mk. MW. .	375.00
Sweet Meat. Covered. 4¼" diam. Jeweled, metal lid, turtle finial	575.00
Jardiniere. 13x16". Pastel tans, pinks, green, yellow. Enamel leaf decor, gold and silver. "C.M." in pontil	750.00
Pitcher, Water. Signed	950.00
Sugar Bowl. Covered. Signed	625.00
Sugar Bowl and Creamer. Ivory ground, blue, pink and green H/P flowers. Orig. tops, handles. Set . .	1000.00
Syrup. Metal spout and top	750.00
Toothpick Holder. 2" high, 2¼" wide. Yellow ground, salmon pansies	375.00

Vases
5¼" high. Covered, white with sprays of red, yellow roses, blue, yellow daisies. 2 handles, gold trim	575.00
6" high. Blue forget-me-nots, raised enamel centers, gold rim rolled under	275.00
8½" high. Gold embossed in oakleaf and acorn design. Signed "C.M." and numbered	850.00
8¼" square. Oakleaf and acorn decor, 2 handles at neck. Unsigned	750.00
9¾" high. Coin gold on white satin. Signed	800.00

CRUETS

A small glass container used to hold and serve condiments, such as vinegar and oil, were an important item in the home. Almost every glass factory produced a cruet. Some were pressed, others were blown and/or cut. They came in many patterns and colors. Many are being or have been reproduced.

Amber
Blown, with applied blue handle and stopper . . . . $	67.50
Inverted Thumbprint, original matching stopper	75.00
Amberina. Plain	225.00

Amethyst
Deep, with brown oval panels and clear stopper	85.00
Light, with amber handle and stopper, melon shape	85.00

Baccarat. 10", original amber-swirl
    stopper 65.00
Blue
    Cobalt, clear stopper and handle . 70.00
    Inverted Thumbprint, blown with
    clear reeded handle and stopper . 75.00
    Milk Glass, with floral panels 67.50
    Clambroth. Applied blue rope
    body to form applied handle.
    Clear faceted stopper 72.50
Clear
    Bull's Eye 42.50
    Cut Glass. Small 80.00
    Cut Glass. 9¾" high 100.00
    Hobnail. Miniature 35.00
    Interlocking Hearts 32.50
    Threaded...................... 45.00
Cranberry
    8", original stopper 120.00
    11½". Wine, melon shape 150.00
    Hobnail 130.00
    IVT. Custard stopper,handle 125.00
    Opalescent Coin Spot. Clear
    handles and stopper 115.00
Crown Milano. Signed 650.00

8" high. Cranberry with white hobnails, clear handle and stopper $135.00

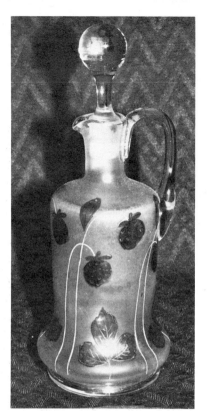

Pomona-type. 8" high. Red strawberries, green leaves, gold trim $165.00

Custard Glass
    Plain.......................... 85.00
    Chrysanthemum Sprig 150.00
    Inverted Fan & Feather 600.00
    Winged Scroll 210.00
Delaware. Green 65.00
Flowing Blue Centennial. 1815-1915.
    Lord Kitchner portrait on side,
    another lord on reverse. English
    Rd. #625614 .... 100.00
    Mary Gregory Glass. 7". Blue with
    white enamel decor of girl.
    Matching blue stopper 95.00
Nailsea. 6", blue with white satin
    glass looping, frosted base and
    handles 145.00
Overlay. Pink. Original stopper..... 85.00

Rubina. Hobnail pattern. Clear top and handle	125.00
Ruby top, block design. Flint	75.00
Sandwich. Overshot applied ribbed handle, cut stopper	160.00
Satin Glass. Pink MOP quilted, frosted stopper	195.00
Vaseline opalescent threaded glass. Lion leg trim, enamel flowers	87.50
Wheeling Peachblow	895.00
White Milk Glass. Royal Oak pattern. 4¾". Made by Northwood Co., Wheeling, W.Va., about 1900	82.50

CUP PLATES

Early cups and saucers which appeared on the American market were of the handleless variety with deep saucers. The custom of the period was to pour tea from the cup into the saucer and drink from it. This cooled the liquid, as people in those days were not used to drinking near-boiling liquids as we do today. The cup was placed on a small plate made for that purpose.

The first cup plates were made of pottery and came mainly from the Staffordshire section of England. Late in the 1830's and 1840's, Boston and Sandwich Glass Companies made the lacy glass type. The Fort Pitt Glass Works in Pittsburgh made the same type. Many other factories made the small glass items as well.

CHINA

3½" diam. Soft paste. Four, 3-lobed red flowers in center, green canary yellow. Embossed rosettes around edge in green, yellow and red .... $ 55.00

3¾" diam. Cream ground, 3 orange swags around shoulder. 5-pointed purple-pink flowers in center, green leaves, blue birds	30.00
3¾" diam. Creamware. "Woods Rose" pattern. Deep rust-red poppylike flowers, green leaves, blue bud. Rust red band around shoulder	50.00
3¾" diam. Creamware. "Woods Rose" pattern. Large purple-pink flower, green leaves. Purple-pink band around shoulder	50.00
3¾" diam. Soft paste, Leeds-type. 4 red tulips on stem in center, green leaves and black veining. Same decor in running vine around shoulder	55.00
3¾" diam. Pink Lustre	30.00
3¾" diam. Soft paste. Orange-red transfer of little girl with bird perched in hand	42.50
3¾" diam. Two 2½" green leaves with black veining, flanked by 1½" dark red flowers, green leaves and red buds	50.00
3¾" diam. Staffordshire. Brown transfer classic buildings, garden scene	28.00

GLASS

Benjamin Franklin, ship	23.00
Bunker Hill. Clear	13.50

China. 4" diam., white, brown. "Fishers" CE & M $12.00

Sandwich glass. 3½" diam., double heart with arrow in center $30.00

276

Bunker Hill. Open. Rare	47.50
Constitution. Small	15.00
Cadmus	18.50
Conventional	8.00
Diamond Quilted	12.50
Eagle. Lacy	25.00
Eagle, Midwestern. Early and rare	55.00
Heart. 14 hearts	15.00
Henry Clay	25.00
Log Cabin	19.50
"Torch"	30.00
Victoria and Albert	92.50

CUPS AND SAUCERS

A number of miscellaneous types of cups and saucers are listed under this heading.

Adams
Columbus. Blue ....$	27.50
"Cries of London." 6½" high	35.00
Gazelle. Pink	27.00
Pink	27.50
Seasons. Sepia	30.00
Arabian Pattern. Purple, handleless.	28.00

Buster Brown. Pouring tea for dog
Tige. Marked Germany	45.00

Farmer's
5½" cup, 8¾" diam. saucer. England. Ducks, sea foliage	32.50
Large. German inscription	32.50
Staffordshire. Large, motto "Take Ye a Cuppe O' Kindness, Etc."	37.50
French China. Large, violets	18.00
Handpainted. Currant spray	18.50
Handpainted. Holly, berries	18.50
Maastricht. Lavender	24.00

Mustache
Haviland china. Painted violets	36.50

Gift-type, with word "Daddy." Germany
$15.00

Ivory ground, wide cerise edge	34.50
Turquoise, burgundy, gold colors. Angelica Kaufmann, classic signed litho scene	55.00
Newhall. Oriental flower pot design, handleless	52.00

Staffordshire
"Bride of Lammermoor"	45.00
"Lily." Handleless	42.00

Note: Also see Canton, Chelsea, Haviland, Pink Lustre, Rose Medallion, Spatterware and Staffordshire China for additional listings.

CUSTARD GLASS

Custard glass is a cream or custard-colored, opaque glass. Most custard glass was produced at the Northwood Glass Company, Wheeling, W.Va. about 1898. Several other firms also manufactured this glassware. There are over 20 major patterns and some minor ones. Argonaut Shell and Chrysanthemum are two popular patterns.

Banana Boats
Chrysanthemum Sprig ....$	260.00
Louis XV. Signed Northwood	235.00

Berry Sets
Grape and Gothic Arch. Bowl, 4 small berry dishes. Signed Northwood	340.00
Louis XV. 7 pieces	365.00

Bowls
Argonaut Shell. 3x5¼"	110.00
Argonaut Shell. 8½x11½". Northwood	300.00
Beaded Circle. Large, enamel decor	175.00
Chrysanthemum Sprig. Berry	130.00
Gem. Fruit bowl. 3½x10"	85.00
Intaglio. Large, 9" diam., footed. Green and gold	250.00
Ivorina. Fruit bowl, 3½x8½"	90.00
Sunburst Cane. Punch bowl. 14½" diam., panelled	425.00

Butter Dishes
Argonaut Shell. Covered	250.00
Chrysanthemum Sprig	250.00
Inverted Fern. Covered	250.00
Ivorina. Covered	130.00
Louis XV	145.00
Panelled Flower. Covered	140.00
Winged Scroll. Covered	225.00

Celerys
Chrysanthemum Sprig	175.00
Georgia Gem. Lavender flowers	200.00
Winged Scroll	185.00

Compotes
Chrysanthemum Sprig. Signed Northwood	90.00
Jelly. Argonaut Shell	95.00

Creamers
Chrysanthemum Sprig	95.00
Inverted Fan and Feather	145.00
Nautilus. Signed Northwood	125.00
Winged Scroll	145.00

Cruets
Chrysanthemum Sprig	150.00
Louis XV	175.00
Plain	85.00
Ribbed Grape. Rose decor, original custard stopper	195.00
Winged Scroll	210.00

Goblets
Grape	75.00
Heisey. Beaded Swag. Rose decor	40.00
Mug. Miniature. Diamond and Peg	28.50

Pitchers
Argonaut Shell. Water	350.00
Chrysanthemum Sprig. High, gold feet	275.00
Plain	130.00

Plates
7". Three Fruits. Northwood	80.00
8". Grape. Signed Northwood	80.00
9". Lion. Fenton	80.00
Powder Jar. Covered. Winged Scroll. "Court House," Mantako, Kansas. Heisey	50.00
Rose Bowl. Persian Medallions. Square top, signed Northwood	95.00

Candleholders. 9¾" high. French. Pair
$85.00

Bowl. 11" long, footed. "Geneva"
$150.00

Salt and Pepper Shakers
Argonaut. Pair	450.00
Chrysanthemum Sprig. No tops. Pr.	175.00
Intaglio. Green and gold decor, original pewter tops. Pair	125.00
Louis XV. No tops. Pair	150.00
Winged Scroll. Pair	250.00

Sauce Dishes
Argonaut Shell	60.00
Chrysanthemum Sprig. Signed Northwood	70.00
Geneva. Footed	50.00
Inverted Fan and Feather	55.00
Louis XV	50.00

Spooners
Argonaut Shell. Signed Northwood	140.00
Chrysanthemum Sprig	150.00
Geneva	75.00
Honeycomb	60.00
Louis XV. Signed Northwood	85.00
Nautilus. Signed Northwood	80.00
Winged Scroll	85.00

Sugar Bowls
Beaded Circle. Covered	115.00
Chrysanthemum Sprig. Covered	250.00
Grape and Gothic Arch	100.00
Louis XV. Covered. Signed Northwood	125.00
Panelled Flower. Covered	100.00

Sugars and Creamers
Argonaut Shell. Northwood	250.00
Individual. Pictorial souvenir of Watertown, N.Y.	145.00
Syrup Jug. Spider Web. C. 1890	135.00

Table Sets
Argonaut Shell. 3 pcs. Northwood	475.00
Chrysanthemum Sprig, Butter, covered sugar, creamer, spooner. Signed Northwood	450.00
Intaglio. Covered butter, sugar and creamer. Green, gold decor	410.00
Louis XV. Covered butter, sugar, creamer and spooner	395.00

Maple Leaf. 5 pieces	650.00
Winged Cross. Ivorina Verde. 4 pcs.	365.00

Toothpick Holders

Argonaut Shell. Northwood	225.00
Chrysanthemum Sprig. Northwood	150.00

Tumblers

Argonaut Shell	125.00
Chrysanthemum Sprig	80.00
Intaglio	55.00
Inverted Fan and Feather	75.00
Louis XV	75.00
Winged Scroll	80.00

Water Sets

Chrysanthemum Sprig. Pitcher and 6 tumblers. Signed Northwood	650.00
Geneva. Pitcher, 6 tumblers	375.00
Inverted Fan and Feather. Pitcher, 6 tumblers	650.00
Louis XV. Pitcher, 3 tumblers.....	400.00

Punch Bowl. 9" diam. Separate pedestal. Libbey's "Ribbon and Star"
$750.00

CUT GLASS

Any incisory form of ornamenting glass with diamond or hard metal point by a lapidary's wheel is known as "cutting" glass. Cut Glass is reputed to have first been made by the ancient Romans. In the 1700's the art spread to Europe, England and Ireland. The popularity of the glass reached its peak in the early 1900's in the United States.

Atomizer. 5½" high .... $	45.00
Banana Boat. 9" long. Pinwheel, Star and Fan. Signed Fry	160.00

Baskets

7½" high to top of handle. Notched handle, cut wheat, step-cut sides	165.00
14½" high, 9" wide. Hobstar, Fan and Cane crosshatching	265.00

Bells

5½" high	85.00
6½" high. Full cut, silver handle ..	95.00
Bobeches. Pair	55.00

Bottles

Dresser. With stopper. Hobstar and Fan. 8½" high, 2½" diam. ...	80.00
Perfume. Purse size, sterling top ..	40.00
Perfume. 4" long, dresser-type. Signed Hawkes	68.50
Perfume. 4x6", flute cut with 24-point hobstar bases and sterling stoppers with pink enamel tops. Pair..............	175.00
9½" high. Full-length stopper. Hawkes	115.00
9-5/8x1½". Russian Cut Whiskey Limousine, Mono. Sterling top	75.00

Bowls

3½" high. 9" wide. Heavily cut, triangle shape	225.00
7¼" diam., 4¼" high. Footed, signed "Fry"	192.00
8". Iris pattern. Hawkes Gravic ...	195.00
8" diam. Hobstar	135.00
8" diam. Pinwheel pattern	135.00
8" diam. Sterling pattern	135.00
8" diam. Strawberry pattern, star bottom. Signed "Gravic Glass Hawkes"	200.00
8" diam., 4" high. Signed "Libbey"	195.00
8½x2¼". "Triple-square" shallow. Plate 74 Pearson I. Signed Clarke	220.00
9" diam. Ordinary cut pattern	100.00
9" diam. Straus Davies pattern. Unsigned. Sides pinched into square	145.00
9x3½". Brazilian pattern by Hawkes	175.00
9¼x3¾". Sheridan pattern. Signed "Fry"	225.00
10½" diam. Hobstar, Fan and Bull's Eye pattern	195.00
Finger. Diamond and Fan pattern .	72.50

Punch Bowls:

10¼" diam. 2 pcs. Hobstars, curved vesicas	725.00
11" diam., 12" high. Separate pedestal. Set	1000.00
14" diam. Separate base. Set.....	1000.00

14½" high, 12" top diam.
Pinwheel pattern. Signed Fry ... 1250.00

Boxes
Glove. 10½" long. Intaglio basket
on top 275.00
Puff. 4" high, 8" long 195.00
Round. 8" diam., 4" high. Beveled
mirror inside. Sterling rim and
hinges. Completely cut 295.00

Butter Dishes
5½" high. Domed cover. Plate 7"
diam. Harvard 275.00
6" high, 8" diam. Hobstars and
Canes........................ 300.00
Covered. Cane border........... 225.00
Butter Pat 22.50
Cake Stand. 12" diam. with gallery.
Hobstars and Fan............... 285.00
Candleholders
8" fluted stem with large tear-
drop. Star base. Pair 225.00
Rosebowl shape. Pair 150.00

Candlesticks. Curtain Drape. Five-
panel, hollow stems. 4" base, 8"
high. Pair...................... 210.00
Candy Jar. 5" high, 3½" diam.
Covered, miniature 175.00

Pitcher. 9½" high. Cosmos Spray.
Signed Fry $195.00

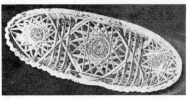

Celery. 11½" long $115.00

Carafes
Hobstar, Fan and Bull's Eye 150.00
Hobstar, Straw, Diamond and Fan.
Mushroom.................... 155.00
Celery
4½x11". Hobs and cross hatching 110.00
4½x11½". Hunt's Royal 135.00
4½x12". Notched prisms. White
House pattern 125.00
Champagnes
"Arcadia." 3¾" diam., 4½" high.
Notched stem, hobstar base. Set
of four 135.00
Russian pattern. Honeycomb
stems, rayed base. Set of six 385.00
Cheese and Cracker Dishes
Covered. Diamond, Fan pattern ... 200.00
10" underplate, 5" top dish. Cross
cut diamond pattern 180.00
11" underplate. 7½" high dome,
6-7/8" diam. Covered 2000.00
Clock Case. 5x8x10" long. Signed
Fry 250.00
Compotes
7½" high, 7" diam. 160.00
9½" high. Teardrop stem, curved
in top 235.00
10½" high, 7" diam. Hobstars,
strawberry diam. and cross
hatching prism, cut stem, hobstar
base 250.00
Cracker Jar. Miniature. 5¾x9¾" ... 175.00
Creamer. Pineapple and Fan. Small . 90.00
Cruets
9¾" 135.00
Small 100.00
Decanters
15" high to top of steeple stopper.
6" diam., mushroom-shaped, with
double gourd neck cut in hobstar
and fan with star base 185.00
Engraved thistle pattern, quilted
bottom. Signed Hawkes 160.00
Dishes
3x5¼x9". Ring-handled, leaf-
shaped....................... 110.00
15½", panel cut sides 175.00

Mayonnaise, with underplate.
Signed Clarke. Buzz & Prism. Set ... 115.00
Relish 52.50
Ferner. 4x7¼". Three feet 130.00
Goblets
   Diamond Cut.................. 55.00
   Pinwheel..................... 55.00
   Russian pattern. 6" high, 3½"
   diam., stemmed. Set of 8 .... 1800.00
   Strawberry and Fan............. 60.00
Hair Receiver. 2½x3". Cane, silver
   top 45.00
Ice Bucket. Harvard cut. 4¾x5¼"... 130.00
Ice Cream Tray. 8x12". Signed J.
   Hoare Co., Corning 200.00

Knife Rests
   3¾" long..................... 42.50
   4" long. Prism cut.............. 38.00
   5¼" long..................... 48.00
   5½" long..................... 50.00
Lamps
   14½" high, 8" diam. Signed
   Hawkes. Variations of Sheridan
   pattern. 1" band of sharp cross cut
   diamond. Large hobstar top 675.00
   18" high, 10" diam. shade.
   Intaglio cut leaves, flowers. Prisms 575.00
   29" high, with prisms. Harvard
   and floral 1200.00
   Boudoir. Small, domed shade cut
   daises, leaves. Prisms 300.00
Lamp Base. Florence pattern 200.00
Muffineer. Fine cut and panel,
   swirled sterling top 75.00
Mug. Tom and Jerry 275.00
Mustard. Covered, serrated prisms.. 65.00
Napkin Ring. Harvard cut 55.00
Nappies
   6" diam., handled 55.00
   7½", high, including handle. 6"
   diam. Shell-shaped handle, cut in
   panel of Russian............... 110.00
Paperweight, Inkwell. Zipper sterling hinged lid. 1902 .... 52.50
Pitchers
   7½" high. Bull's Eye pattern.
   32-pt. Hobstar base. Double notch
   handle 200.00
   7½" high. Deep intaglio flowers
   unpolished and leaves. Signed
   Hawkes 175.00
   8" high. Barrel, Libbey 200.00
   9" high. Intaglio flower pattern,
   deep and heavy. Signed Hoare ... 225.00
   "Meteor" pattern. 3-pint capacity . 185.00
   Water. Bulbous type 185.00
   Water. "Rambler" pattern 175.00
   Water. Tankard type 200.00

Plates
   6½". Large stars in medallions
   separated by drapes of small,
   heavy stars. Signed Hawkes 40.00
   10". Deep cutting, scalloped edge 200.00
   12". Harvard cut................ 225.00
   Ice Cream. 5¼". Sunburst pattern 55.00

Platter. 8½x21½". Boat-shaped,
   hobstar with small diamonds..... 260.00
Rose Bowl. Heavy cut, notched rim.
   Hobstar base, strawberry, fan and
   diamond point 150.00

Salt and Pepper Shakers
   2¾" high. Sterling tops. Light
   intaglio flowers. Signed Libbey.
   2¾" high. Sterling tops. Light
   intaglio flowers. Signed Libbey.
   Pair 57.50
   6" high. Glass cups. Pair......... 65.00

Salts
   Individual 16.00
   Master....................... 42.00

Decanter. 12½" high, squat bottom,
matching stopper $175.00

Spooner. In Hobstar cross cut diamond and fan, star base	75.00

Sugar Bowls and Creamers

Hobstar. Hawkes	130.00
Hobbs. 3x3½"	225.00
Marked "Libbey"	175.00
Pinwheel	165.00
Sugar Shaker. 5" high	95.00
Toothpick	50.50

Trays

Bread	150.00
11¾" diam. Engraved, silver rim. Signed Hawkes	135.00
13x9". Chain of hobstar and floral engraving. Signed Hawkes	175.00
Heart shape	85.00
Oval. 5½x8½". Harvard. Small button, scalloped edge	95.00

Tumblers

Marked "Fry"	60.00
Meriden. Greek Key	75.00
Ordinary	45.00
Whiskey. Pinwheel and fan. 16-rayed star at bottom	40.00

Bowl with attached underplate. 5" diam., sterling lid. "Strawberry." By Clarke	$175.00

Vases

3" high. Strawberry and Fan	60.00
3½" high. Miniature. Pair	80.00
5¾x5¾". Graves glass, fluted top. Unpolished flower, leaves, etc. Signed Hawkes	165.00
6½" high. Brilliant Period	65.00
9¼x4½". Pedestaled, engraved, fluted top. Signed Sinclaire	185.00
9½" high, 5" top diam. Roses, leaves. Signed Libbey	235.00
10" high. Brunswick pattern. Tubular, 3" wide. Signed Hawkes	225.00
10" high. Hobstars, engraving at top. Notched, fluted bottom, signed Hawkes	250.00
10" high. Tubular with narrowing	

top, 4½" widest diam. Engraved, signed Hawkes	235.00
12" high. Bulbous, flared top. Fine cut. Pair	500.00
12" high. Irving Cut Glass Co., Honesdale, Pa.	185.00
12" high, 5¼" diam. Meriden's Beverly pattern	285.00
13½" high, 5½" top diam. Pedestaled, engraved, fluted top. Signed Libbey	320.00
14" high. Queens pattern. Signed Hawkes	300.00
14" high. Trumpet. Signed Hoare	300.00

Water Sets

Pitcher, 6 tumblers. Hobs and fans. Signed Hawkes	475.00
Pitcher, 6 tumblers. Hobs, pinwheels and fans	375.00
Whiskey Set. Decanter, 6 doubleshot glasses. Honeycomb pattern. Set	325.00
Wine. 4" high. Flaring top, hobstar with diamond and fan	50.00
Wine Pourer. 7" high, two lips, pedestaled	100.00

CUT VELVET GLASS

Cut Velvet is Satin glass which shows the design in a high relief with the white lining showing where the pattern has been cut. It is usually ribbed, but is sometimes found with diamond quilting, the diamond shapes in high relief with the centers of the diamonds showing the white lining of the item.

Bowl. 5" diam. Rose color, D.Q. pattern, crimped, flared top	$ 185.00
Ewer. 10¼" high, 3-pour top with ruffled rim, bulbous body. 5½" diam. Green quilting over white, applied white handle	250.00
Pitcher. 5½" high. Pink cased	115.00
Rose Bowl. 4" high. Blue	200.00

Tumblers

D.W. Pink	75.00
D.Q. Pink	110.00

Vases

6" high. Bulbous bottom, blue stick neck	180.00
7" high. Pink	210.00
7½" high. Apple green, D.Q.	220.00
8" high. Deep pink	225.00
8½x5". Blue, fluted edge	325.00
9" high, 3¼" base. Blue on white, fluted top	185.00
10" high. Lavender over white ground	250.00

Vase. 9" high. Bulbous base, crimped
top. Blue $225.00

11¾" high. Raspberry color. D.Q.,
gourd-shaped 265.00
12" high. Deep rose on white
ground 275.00
14" high. Pink shading to deep,
red ruffled 5" top. On 3 rigaree
frosted feet. Enamel floral decor.
Raspberry pontil 295.00
Water Set. 8" pitcher with 6
tumblers. Butterscotch color. Set .   695.00

DAGUERREOTYPES

Daguerreotypes were the first photographic
pictures ever made. The process consists of a
bright copper plate being covered with silver
salts and placed between glass to protect the
surface. The action of light in the silver
compound produces the picture. The method
was discovered by Daguerre, a Frenchman, in
1839.

Apple Picker. Gutta Percha . . . . $ 30.00
Beehive. Gutta Percha 45.00
Boy. 3x3½" 18.00
Case. American eagle design 27.50
Case. Black, embossed locomotive
on cover 30.00
Cluster of Cherries. Gutta Percha . . .   25.00
Faithful Hound. Gutta Percha 32.50

Single case, 3¼x3¾". Gutta Percha
$35.00

Octagonal. About 2½x3" 30.00
Portraits. 3x3¾". In half cases. Set
of five 30.00
Round. 2½" diam. 25.00
2½x3". Gutta Percha, black. Case,
scrolls with floral center. Lady on
one side, velvet on other 27.50
2½x3". Gutta Percha, brown. Case
geometric design. Man on one
side, velvet other side 27.50
2½x3". Gutta Percha. Monitor & Fort   55.00
3x3½". Two children 18.50
3¼x3¼". Leather case, red velvet
lining, closed 34.50
3¼x3¾". Gutta Percha, black,
inside on velvet. "Bradley's
Gallery, Market St., Phila." Other
side, baby 40.00
3¼x3¾". Gutta Percha. Three Civil
War soldiers 42.50
3½x4". Case, eagle on shield, flags.
"The Union and Constitution."
Confederate soldier 45.00
4x6". Statue of war hero impressed
on cover 37.50
5x6". Picture of man with surly
expression 26.50

**DANISH CHRISTMAS PLATES, See
COLLECTORS' PLATES, ETC.**

DAVENPORT CHINA

The ware was made by John Davenport who opened a pottery at Longport in the Staffordshire district of England in 1793. Items made at the pottery are lightweight, cream colored and have a soft velvety texture. The mark consisted of an impressed anchor with the name Davenport above. Ironstone chinaware was produced at a later date. One pattern, "Cypress," was produced with mulberry-colored decorations. Davenport died in 1848, but his heirs continued the factory until 1886, at which time it closed.

Plate. 9", handpainted, pink background, butterflies, gold trim .. $35.00

Bowl. 10" diam., shallow. Orange floral decor. Gold trim, scalloped edge
$65.00

Bowl. 13" diam., 4½" high. Impressed Davenport and anchor mark. Man, woman, child, English scenic view. Floral border inside and out .... $ 130.00

Compotes
  9½" diam., 3" high. Grape and Leaf design 82.50
  10" diam. Longport scenic. C. 1850. Ornate gold handles, embossed green leaves against pink border, scene of lake, cattle, etc.............................. 60.00

Creamer. Bulbous, white with deep blue decor..................... 60.00

Cups and Saucers
  Coffee can shape. Imari decor impressed mark. C. 1806 .... 35.00
  Dark blue with floral border 50.00

Dishes
  6½ x 8 x 12½". Covered. In Corn pattern, corn-shaped handles 85.00

Cypress pattern. Impressed anchor, covered 85.00
Ewer. White with blue marbling. C. 1820........................ 85.00
Jug. Brilliant blue decor. C. 1800.... 150.00

Plates
  7". Dark blue willow. Blue anchor mark. Gilt trim. Late 25.00
  8½". Milkmaid and cow, floral border. Impressed Davenport and anchor 85.00
  8½". Naturalistic center, floral panel. 4-shaped compartments in pale apricot. C. 1825............ 135.00
  9½". C. 1820. Blue transfer of figures in romantic scene. Deep blue handles................... 100.00

Platters
  9½ x 12¼". Cypress pattern...... 65.00
  11 x 14". Imari pattern. Anchor mk . 75.00
  14 x 18". Dark blue border. Impressed anchor mark. C. 1835.... 85.00

Teapot. Tall, pink lustre decor 185.00
Tea Set. Spring pattern in red, green. Teapot, covered sugar, creamer, cup and saucer. Set 175.00
Tureen. Early. 12" long, castle scene in blue, shell handles 185.00

DECANTERS, GLASS

The primary use of the decanter was to hold wine or liquor. Many old-time taprooms used the bottles to store and dispense these beverages. The first decanters were simple in form and style but later became more globular and were decorated with scrolls and festoons.

The use of emblems, initials and names followed. Occasionally the container was decorated to represent the owner's occupation. Later they were adapted to home use.

"Sandwich Star." 11½" high. Ground stoppers. C. 1850. Pair $135.00

Amethyst. Deep, panelled, early flint	$ 140.00
Bohemian	
Frosted vintage design, clear panels	72.00
Red, plume stopper. Bold cut and etched Roman Key design. Clear cut panels	87.50
Red, pointed stopper. Vintage pattern and clear panels on both. Pair	135.00
Red, with traces of gold decor. Matched pair	165.00
Cut Glass	
Early. Cut and etched	100.00
Early. Hollow steeple stopper	75.00
Late	65.00
Late. Cut on bulbous bases. Pair . .	125.00
Flint Glass	
13½" high. Bronze stopper in shape of maiden carrying basket, goose at her side	58.00
Heavy, tall, with plume stopper . .	80.00
Heavy, wheel-cut panels	85.00

Ribbed Petticoat, heavy, or "River Boat" bottle	52.50
Sawtooth. Heavy, early, with original hollow Sawtooth stopper .	75.00
Vaseline Glass. 10" high to top of steeple shaped, crystal stopper. Applied crystal handle, blown, rough pontil	75.00
Vertically ribbed, cut stopper, iridescent hue	60.00
Waffle and Thumbprint	45.00
Waterford. Late. Pair	150.00

DECOYS

These are wood-turned models of water fowl, painted to the likeness and used in groups to lure live ducks into gun or net range.

14" long. Gray back, black body . . . . $	24.00
14½" long. Hand carved, solid. Glass eyes	42.00
16" long. Black, red, white decor. Early	28.50
16" long. Hand carved, brown paint, glass eyes	24.50
Black Breasted Plover. Pair	65.00
Canadian Goose. L. Parker	85.00
Cork. Red-headed duck	26.50
Golden Plover	29.50
Goshawk. 9½" high, 20½" long. Carved wood. By M. Wavercak . . .	475.00
Mallard. 16½" long	25.00
Ruffled Goose. 7" high, 14" long. Carved wood	125.00
Snipe	22.50
Yellow Legs	
Shallow	26.50
Winter	29.50

"Golden Eye." 13" long $40.00

DEDHAM POTTERY

The business was originally established as Chelsea Pottery in Chelsea, Mass., in 1860, by Alexander W. Robertson. In 1872, it was known as the Chelsea Keramic Art Works. In 1895, the pottery moved to Dedham, Mass., and the name was changed to Dedham Pottery. The famous Crackleware, or Dedham pottery, has an unusual spiderweb effect of blue in the glaze. The rabbit pattern was their most popular design. Other patterns include apple, azalea, bird-orange tree, butterfly, chicken, clover, crab, dolphin, duck, elephant, grape, horse chestnut, iris, lion, lobster, magnolia, owl, polar bear, snow tree, swan, turtle and water lily.

The following marks can be used to determine the approximate age of items made by the company. 1] Chelsea Keramic Art Works, name Robertson impressed--1876-1889. 2] C.P. US impressed in a cloverleaf--1891--1895. 3] Fore-shortened rabbit--1895-1896. 4] Conventional rabbit with Dedham Pottery stamped in blue--1897. 5] Word "Registered" added to rabbit mark--1929-1943.

Duck pattern. 8½" diam. Signed $85.00

Bowls

Rabbits	$ 95.00
Turtles. 7½" diam., 2½" deep	125.00
Rabbits on circle rim. Fruit on cover. 9¼" diam., 2-5/8" high	150.00
Butter Dish. Rabbit	125.00

Candlesticks

Azalea. Pair	135.00
Rabbit. Pair	150.00

Celery Dishes

Elephant	128.00
Rabbit	128.00
Chocolate Pot. Rabbit	140.00
Creamer. Rabbit, 4" high	95.00

Cups and Saucers

Duck	85.00
Elephant	85.00
Polar Bear	100.00
Pond Lily	85.00
Rabbit	85.00
Egg Cup, Double. Rabbit, 4" high	65.00
Mayonnaise Bowl. Rabbit. 6¼" diam.	80.00

Mugs

4¼" high, 4" diam. base, fruit band on top, rabbits below	125.00
Handled, large	67.50

Pitchers

5". Rabbit, bulbous	145.00
5". Night and Morning	350.00

Plates

Chop. Crab	125.00
Cup. Rabbit	100.00
Cup. Swan	100.00
5½". Rabbit	65.00
6". Dove	85.00
6". Horse Chestnut	85.00
6". Mushroom	80.00
6". Pond Lily	80.00
6". Puppy in center	200.00
6". Magnolia	80.00
6". Rabbit	75.00
6". Snowtree	75.00
7½". Azalea pattern	55.00
8". Magnolia	95.00
8". Rabbit	85.00
8½". Butterfly	85.00
8½". Duck	85.00
8½". Horse Chestnut	95.00
8½". Pond Lily	85.00
8½' Snowtree	100.00
8½". Turkey	95.00
10". Azalea	100.00
10". Butterfly	100.00
10". Dove	100.00
10". Duck border	100.00
10". Grape	100.00
10". Iris border	100.00
10". Rabbit	100.00
10". Waterlily	100.00
10¼". Mushroom	100.00
10¼". Rabbit	100.00
10¼". Rabbit. Raised "C.P.U.S." mark. Original paper label. "Special Plate No. II. Cream of Chelsea, 1893"	150.00
12½". Rabbit	165.00
Platter. Rabbit border. 6x10"	165.00
Salt and Pepper Shakers. Rabbit. Pair	125.00
Saucer. Rabbit	50.00
Sugar Bowl. Covered. Rabbit	125.00

Tiles

5½" square. Leaf and flower. C.
1897....................... 65.00
6" square. Horse Chestnut 65.00
Tray. Rabbit. Small, oblong 90.00

DELFT

Delft is usually referred to today as earthenware with a blue decoration on a white background. The glaze is produced with the use of a tin compound. A number of potteries produced the ware at Delft, Holland, near the beginning of the 17th century. It was made in England at Lambeth, Bristol and Liverpool. The majority of Delft found in the antique market today is from the late Victorian period to the World War I period.

Cow Creamer. Standing. Late .. $42.50

Bottles

3¾" high, 5½" wide. Liquor/wine.
Square shape, ships, windmill, lighthouse. Plaid pattern 40.00
8½" high. Dutch boy astride beer keg, holding two bottles. Farm and windmill scene, hat stopper .. 50.00
Perfume. German, with original stopper 35.00
Box. 7x2x1", covered 45.00
Cat. Sitting. 6" high, black and white.. 50.00
Clock, Boudoir. Windmill scene, running 140.00
Condiment Set. Delft-type. 15-piece set with windmill decor. Hanging salt box, 6 large covered jars, 6 small covered jars, 2 tall vinegar cruets........................ 87.50
Cracker Jar. Covered.............. 72.50
Creamers
Cow. Reclining 60.00
Cow. Standing 50.00
3" high....................... 30.00

4½" high..................... 35.00
5½" high, man standing 40.00
Cup and Saucer. Flared top......... 32.50
Decanter, Wine. 11" high 65.00
Dish. Covered. Boats 35.00
Ewer. 6½" high. Blue and white applied flowers 30.00
Inkwells
Small, with insert 30.00
Large lion and shield with thistle .. 80.00
Kitchen Utensil Holder. 14" long, 8" high 75.00
Lamps
12" high, applied flowers, high stem, ornate bowl and base...... 150.00
22" high. Parchment shade. Electrified 150.00
Lemon Squeezer. On pitcher base ... 35.00

Plate. 12½". Orange, blue floral decor. Bristol. Early $250.00

Liqueur Set. 9½" bottle, 8½" tray, four 2" handled mugs. Set 165.00
Mold. Melon. 5x7" 38.50
Plaques
8" diam., hanging type, crossed swords mark................... 40.00
8x15". Artist signed. With Delft 1840 mark. Sheepherder and dog scene 80.00
8½ x10¾". Typical windmill scene in blue on white ground 45.00
15½" diam., fancy scrolled border, colorful ship decor.......... 85.00
16" diam. Scenic, windmills, cows in pasture, blue and white flowers. Signed, impressed signature 95.00

Plates

8" diam. Boats	40.00
8" diam. Windmill scene	40.00
9" diam. Blue floral on white tin glaze. 18th century	75.00
Puzzle Mug	78.50

Shoes

4½" long	32.00
6½" long	35.00
Stein. German. ½ L. Blue and white windmills, sailboats. Inlaid lid, litho bottom. Two women reading letter	175.00
Tea Caddy	50.00

Tiles

Children playing	20.00
Soldiers and civilians in ancient costumes, birds, animals and flowers	20.00
Tulip design. Mulberry on white . .	20.00
Tobacco Jar. 5", fisherman's head . . .	65.00
Toothpick Holder	25.00

Trays

6x9", dresser	47.50
9½ x10¼", windmill scene, scalloped edge	50.00
14x18", oval, 2 handles, windmill scene and ships, 4 round feet, nickelplated edge	80.00
Urn. 17" high, with cover. Blue windmill decoration	95.00

Vases

4½" high. Sailboat scene in blue and white	42.00
5½" high, marked. Pair	75.00
8½" high. Olive green and yellow. Dutch scenes, figures	65.00
10" high, canal scenes	60.00
11" high. Bud. Square, floral	35.00
Vinegar Jugs. Blue decor, 8¾" high. Pair	80.00

DEPRESSION GLASS

Depression glass is a general term used to cover glassware manufactured during the so-called "Depression" years, 1929-1940. It is relatively inexpensive machine glass made in a variety of colors. To date more than 100 patterns have been found and several hundred occasional prices have been discovered.

Hocking, Jeannette, Federal, Imperial, Fostoria, Hazel-Atlas and Macbeth-Evans are known to have issued patterns in this glass.

Depression glass was not expensive in its day and was sold by five and ten-cent stores and used as premiums at carnivals and county fairs. It was also given as premiums in boxed cereals.

Colors range from amber, green, pink, yellow and crystal, with a number of special colors, including ruby red, cobalt blue, light blue, ultra marine [dark blue-green], amethyst and burgundy. It is also found in opaque blues, greens and whites. However, this last group of colors is relatively scarce.

ADAM

Green.

Berry Set . . . . $	35.00

Bowls

Oval	8.50
Three-legged, 10½", 8 matching sherbets. Set . . . . , . . .	50.00
Vegetable. Covered, 9"	8.50
Creamer	6.50
Cup and Saucer	7.00

Plates

Dinner. 9"	5.00
Sherbet. 6"	3.00
Platter	7.50
Sugar and Creamer. Open	12.00
Water Set	35.00

Pink.

Bowls

5¾"	5.50
7¾"	7.50
Butter Dish	37.50
Cake Plate	12.00
Candy Jar, covered	25.00
Creamer	6.50
Cup and Saucer	7.50
Pitcher. Quart	12.50

Plates

Cake	8.50
Dinner. 9"	5.00
Platter. 13"	9.50
Relish Dish	7.00
Sherbet	3.00

Sugars

Covered	12.00
Open	5.00

AMERICAN SWEETHEART

Clear. Sherbet, in metal holder	4.00

Monax.

Bowls

6"	6.00
8"	15.00
Cream Soup	7.50
Cup and Saucer	10.00

Plates

8"	4.50
9"	5.00
10"	7.50
11"	8.00
Platter	10.00

Salver. 12"	12.00
Set. 4 cups, 4 saucers, 4 - 6" plates, 1 - 12" salver, creamer and sugar. Set	85.00
Sherbet. Footed	4.50

Pink.
Bowls	
6"	4.50
9"	10.00
Creamer	3.50
Cup...........................	5.00
Plates	
Bread and Butter. 6"	3.00
Dinner. 10"	4.50
11"	6.00
Platter	6.50
Salver. 12"	7.00
Server. Tidbit. 2 plates	12.50
Sugar. Open	5.00

BLOCK OPTIC

Clear. Pitcher	5.00

Green.
Butter Dish. Rectangular.........	17.50
Creamer. Straight	4.50
Creamer and Sugar.Cone shape ..	8.50
Cup...........................	2.50
Plates	
6". Sherbet	2.00
8"	3.00
9"	3.50
Salt and Pepper	8.00
Sherbet	2.50
Tumblers	
5-oz. Juice...................	2.00
10-oz. Footed	4.50

Pink.
Creamer and Sugar	8.50
Cup and Saucer	4.50
Plate. 8"	2.50
Sherbet	2.50
Tumbler. 10-oz., footed..........	4.50

BUBBLE

Blue.
Bowl. 8¼".....................	6.50
Cup and Saucer	3.50
Plates	
Grill	4.00
6¾"	1.50
9½"	3.50
Platter	4.00

Crystal.
Bowls	
Soup..........................	2.50
4¼"	1.50
5¾". Deep	3.00
Candleholders. Pair.............	12.00

Cup...........................	2.50
Plates	
6¾"	1.50
9½"	3.00
Platter	4.00
Saucer	1.00
Sugar	3.50

Green.
Bowl. 5¼"....................	3.00
Creamer	6.00
Sugar, covered	7.50

CAMEO

Green.
Bottle, Ice Box	6.50
Candlesticks. Pair	22.50
Cookie Jar.....................	12.50
Cup...........................	3.50
Pitcher. 8"	16.00
Plates	
Cake	7.00
8"	5.00
9½"	6.00
Platter. 10½"	6.00
Sherbet. 5", stemmed	5.00
Sugar and Creamer	10.00
Tumbler. 6", footed	15.00
Vase. 8", bulbous...............	20.00

CHERRY BLOSSOM

Delfite.
Pitcher........................	40.00
Plate. 6"	10.00
Sherbet	15.00
Tray. Two handles, 10½"	16.50
Tumbler. 3½", footed	17.50

Green.
Bowl. 4¾".....................	5.00
Butter Dish	35.00
Creamer	10.00
Plates	
7"	5.50
Cake	12.50
Sherbet	5.00

Pink.
Bowls	
8½".........................	4.50
9". Handled	7.50
10½". Three-legged	15.00
Butter Dish	40.00
Creamer	5.00
Cup and Saucer	7.00
Pitcher........................	20.00
Pitcher, 6 tumblers. Set..........	55.00
Plate. Dinner, 9"	4.50
Platters	
11"	7.50

13", divided	55.00
Saucer	3.00
Sherbet	4.00
Sugar. Open	5.00
Tray. 10½"	10.00
Tumbler. 4"	7.00

CHERRY BLOSSOM, CHILD'S

Pink.

Creamer	10.00
Cup and Saucer	15.00
Plate	7.00
Saucer	6.50
Sugar	12.00

CLOVERLEAF

Black.

Salt and Pepper	12.50
Sherbet	8.50
Sugar and Creamer	15.00

COLONIAL [KNIFE & FORK]

Clear.

Butter Dish	32.50
Creamer	5.00

Green.

Bowl. 9"	7.50
Butter Dish	35.00
Plate. Dinner, 10"	6.00
Sugar and Creamer. Open	10.00

Pink.

Cup and Saucer	6.50
Pitcher. With 5 tumblers	4.00
Plate. Luncheon	3.50
Sherbet	4.00

CUBIST

Clear.

Creamer and Sugar	8.50
Tray. 7½", handled	4.00

Green.

Candy Jar. Covered	6.50
Plate. Sherbet, 6"	2.50

Pink.

Bowl. Deep, 4½" diam.	2.50
Creamer. 3"	4.00
Salt and Pepper	8.50
Sugar and Creamer. Open	8.00

DAISY

Amber.

Creamer and Sugar	10.00
Cup and Saucer	4.50
Plate. 8"	2.50
Clear. Cake plate, 11½"	5.50

DIAMOND QUILTED

Green.

Candle	4.00
Plates	
Luncheon	2.50
9"	4.00
Sherbet	2.50
Sugar and Creamer	7.00

DOGWOOD

Green.

Creamer	6.00
Cup and Saucer	8.50
Plates	
Dinner	6.00
Luncheon	4.50

Pink.

Cup and Saucer	4.50
Plates	
6"	2.50
8"	3.50
Sugar and Creamer	10.00
Tumblers	
4". Plain	3.00
5". Plain	4.00
5". Hand decorated	10.00

DORIC

Delfite. Sherbet	7.50

Green.

Creamer	4.50
Plate. Sherbet	2.50

Pink.

Bowls	
4½"	2.50
8"	7.00
Vegetable	8.50
Candy Jar	15.00
Creamer	4.00
Cup and Saucer	4.50
Pitcher	13.00
Plates	
Dessert. 6"	3.00
Dinner. 9"	5.00
Platter	9.50
Relish Dishes	
4x4"	3.50
4x8"	5.00
8x8"	8.50
Salt and Pepper	15.00
Sugar. Open	6.00

FLORAGOLD [LOUISE]

Bowls	
Berry	1.50

Fruit	2.00
Nut	4.50
10", scalloped	6.00
12"	7.50
Butter Dish. ¼ lb.	12.00
Creamer	2.00
Cup	2.50
Pitcher, Water	15.00
Sugar and Creamer	8.00
Tray. 13"	5.00
Tumbler	2.50

FLORAL

Green.
Bowls
4"	3.00
Vegetable. Oval, 9"	8.00
Butter Dish	37.50
Candy Jar. Covered	12.00
Cup	4.00
Jug. 32-oz.	12.00
Plate. Dinner, 9"	60.00
Sugar	6.00

Pink.
Bowls
7½"	5.50
Vegetable. Oval, 9"	7.50
Butter Dish	35.00
Candy. Covered	12.00
Creamer	5.00
Creamer and Sugar. Covered	10.00
Cup and Saucer	6.50
Pitcher	10.00

Plates
8"	4.50
9". Dinner	5.00

Salt and Peppers
4" high	14.00
6" high	18.00
Tumbler. 7-oz.	5.00

FLORENTINE NO. 2

Crystal.
Pitcher. 7½" high	22.50
Tumbler. 4"	4.50

Green.
Bowl. 5"	2.00
Cream Soup	2.00
Cup and Saucer	6.00
Pitcher. Cone shape	12.00
Plate. 10"	2.50
Salt and Pepper	18.00
Sugar. Open	3.00

Yellow.
Bowl, Berry	3.50
Creamer	6.00
Cup and Saucer	5.00

Parfait	15.00
Salt and Pepper	20.00
Soup, Cream. Handled	7.50
Tumbler. 5", flat	8.50

FRUITS

Green.
Cup and Saucer	5.00
Plate. Luncheon, 8"	4.00
Saucer	2.00

GEORGIAN [LOVEBIRDS]

Green.
Bowl. 5¾"	4.50
Butter Dish	37.00
Creamer	5.50
Plate. 8"	4.00

HOLIDAY

Pink.
Bowls
Berry	9.50
Soup	5.00
Vegetable. Oval	5.50
Butter Dish	17.50
Creamer and Sugar	6.50
Cup	2.50
Pitcher	8.00

Plates
Chop	7.50
Dinner. 9"	3.00
Sherbet. 6"	1.50
Platter	4.50

IRIS

Amber.
Bowls, Fruit
4½"	2.00
9"	4.50
11"	7.00
Butter Dish	18.50
Creamer	5.00
Pitcher. 9½"	17.50
Tumbler. 6", footed	8.00

Clear.
Berry Dish	1.50
Butter Dish	12.50
Candlesticks, double, Pair	10.00
Cup and Saucer	3.50
Pitcher. 9"	15.00

Plates
Cake	7.00
Dessert	3.00
Dinner	4.00
Sugar. Open	3.00
Tumbler	4.00

LACE EDGE

Pink.

Compote. Footed 5.00
Cup and Saucer 8.00
Nappies
  6½". Frosted 2.50
  7¾" 5.00
  9½". Ribbed 7.00
Plates
  8½". Salad 2.50
  10½". Dinner 4.00
  12¼". Platter 5.00
Saucer 4.50

MADRID

Amber.
Bowls
  Berry 3.50
  Cereal 4.50
  Vegetable. Oval, 10" 5.00
Candlesticks. Pair 10.00
Creamer and Sugar 6.50
Cup and Saucer 4.00
Dish, Jam 2.50
Jello Mold 2.50
Pitcher. 8" 15.00
Plates
  Bread and Butter. 6" 2.00
  Cake. 11½" 7.50
  Grille. 10¼" square 5.00
  9" 4.00
  Platter. 8¼ x 11¼" 7.00
Salt and Pepper 18.00
Sherbet 3.50
Tumblers
  4¼" 6.50
  5½" 7.50
Green.
Bowl. 5" 2.00
Cup 3.50
Saucer 2.00
Sherbet. V-shaped 4.00
Sugar Bowl 4.00
Pink.
Bowls
  Berry 3.00
  Console 10.00
  9" 5.50
Butter Dish 35.00
Candlesticks. Pair 15.00
Cup and Saucer 5.50
Plate, Cake 9.00

MAYFAIR

Green.
Bowl. 11", hat-shaped 15.00
Server, Sandwich 12.50

Pink.
Bowls
  5½" 3.50
  12". Flared rim 15.00
Butter Dish 34.00
Candy Jar. Footed 13.50
Cookie Jar. Covered 10.00
Cream Soup 6.00
Cup 3.50
Decanter. With stopper 40.00
Dish. 10", 3 sections 17.50
Goblet, Cocktail 22.50
Plates
  Cake. Footed 12.00
  Cake. Handled, 12" 8.50
  Luncheon, 8½" 3.50
Salt and Pepper 15.00
Shaker, Condiment 8.00
Tumblers
  4" 7.00
  6½". Footed 8.00

MISS AMERICA

Crystal.
Bowls
  Cereal/Fruit 3.00
  Vegetable. Oval 8.50
Celery 8.00
Cup 7.00
Plates
  Dinner. 10" 5.50
  Grill 6.00
  Salad 5.50
Salt and Pepper 16.00
Saucer 2.50
Sherbet 3.50
Water Set. Pitcher, 4 glasses. Set . 50.00
Pink.
Bowls
  Console. With candlesticks. Set . . 30.00
  Vegetable. Oval, 10" 10.00
  8¾". Curved at top 25.00
Butter Dish 50.00
Celery Tray 12.50
Creamer 8.50
Goblet. Juice, 4½", footed 9.50
Pitcher. Ice Tea 10.00
Plate. Dinner, 10" 6.50
Relish 8.50
Salt and Pepper 22.50
Sherbet 6.50
Sugar 12.00
Tumbler 7.50

MODERNTONE

Dark Blue.
Candlesticks. Pair 7.50
Creamer 3.00

Cup and Saucer	4.50
Plates	
6"	1.50
7"	2.00
8"	2.50
9"	3.00
10½". Cake	7.00
Salt and Pepper	7.00
Sherbet	2.50
Sugar and Creamer	5.50

NORMANDIE

Pink.
Bowls	
5" diam.	1.00
6½". Cereal	2.00
8½" diam.	3.50
Creamer	3.50
Cup	2.50
Plates	
Grill	2.00
Sherbet	1.00
8"	2.50
Sauce	1.00
Sugar	3.00
Tumbler. 4"	3.50
Platter	4.50

NUMBER 612 [HORSESHOE]

Green.
Bowl. 9"	6.00
Cup and Saucer	5.00
Plates	
Dinner	4.00
Luncheon	3.00
11½"	4.50
Saucer	1.50
Sherbet	2.50
Tumblers	
9-oz., footed	4.50
12-oz., footed	5.00

PATRICIAN

Amber.
Butter Dish	20.00
Cookie Jar. Covered	25.00
Cup and Saucer	4.50
Pitcher	32.00
Plate. Dinner, 10½"	3.50
Sugar and Creamer. Covered	8.50
Tumblers	
4½"	5.50
Ice Tea	7.50
Green.	
Bowl. 5"	2.50
Cup	2.50

Plate. 7½"	2.50
Sugar and Creamer	7.50
Tumbler. 4½"	5.00

PETALWARE

Cremax.
Bowl. 8¼" diam.	4.00
Creamer	2.00
Cup	2.00
Plates	
6"	1.00
9"	2.00
Saucer	1.00

PRINCESS

Green.
Bowl. 4½"	2.50
Butter Dish	30.00
Cookie Jar. Covered	12.00
Creamer	6.00
Cup and Saucer	4.50
Pitcher. 8"	18.50
Plates	
6". Sherbet	2.00
11½". Sandwich, handled	6.50
Relish. 4 sections	12.00
Sherbet	3.50
Shaker. Condiment, 5½"	6.50
Sugar and Creamer. Covered	12.00
Tumbler. 4", flat	8.00
Vase. 8" high	8.00
Pink.	
Bowls	
9" diam., octagon shape	5.00

"Green Princess" Cookie Jar. Covered,
7½" high $12.00

9½" diam., hat	5.00
Dish, Vegetable. 10" high	3.50
Plates	
8"	1.50
9½"	2.00
Sherbet. Footed	2.00
Vase. 8" high	7.00

Yellow.

Cup	2.50
Plates	
Dinner. 9½"	3.00
Grill. 11½"	4.00
Platter. 12"	7.50
Sherbet. 6"	2.00
Sugar and Creamer	8.00
Tumbler	6.50

ROYAL LACE

Crystal.

Candlestick. 3-legged. ruffled	5.00
Cookie Jar. Covered	16.50
Creamer and Sugar	8.00
Cream Soup	5.00
Jug. 8"	22.00
Plate. Dinner. 10"	4.00
Tumbler. 4"	5.00

Deep Blue [Cobalt].

Cookie Jar, covered	45.00
Cup and Saucer	15.00
Pitcher. 54-oz.	45.00
Plate. Dinner. 10"	10.00
Platter	18.50
Salt and Pepper	22.00
Soup. Two handles	12.50
Sugar and Creamer	30.00

Green.

Bowl. 10"	4.50
Plate. 8½"	3.00
Saucer	1.00
Sugar. Open	2.50
Vegetable. Oval. 10"	3.00

Pink.

Creamer and Sugar	8.00
Bowl. 10"	7.50
Platter. 13"	10.00
Salt and Pepper	10.00
Tumbler. 4¾"	4.50

SHARON

Amber.

Bowls	
8½"	2.50
10½"	5.00
Butter Dish	30.00
Creamer and Sugar	6.50
Pitcher. With 6 tumblers. Set	30.00
Salt and Pepper	20.00

Saucer	1.50
Sherbet. Footed	3.50
Tumbler. 6½", footed	8.50

Green.

Bowl. Vegetable	8.50
Butter Dish	30.00
Custard	2.00
Juice	2.00
Plate. Sandwich Cup	2.50
Sherbet	3.50
Tumbler. Footed	7.50

Pink.

Bowls	
8½"	3.00
10½"	7.00
Soup	4.00
Butter Dish	35.00
Creamer and Sugar	7.50
Cup and Saucer	5.50
Pitcher. With ice lip	35.00
Plates	
Bread and Butter. 6"	2.00
Cake	3.00
Dinner. 9½"	4.50
Platter	4.50
Salt and Pepper	22.00
Tumbler. 4"	6.50

SIERRA

Pink.

Bowl. Vegetable, oval	7.50
Butter Dish	25.00
Creamer	4.50
Cup and Saucer	5.50
Salt and Pepper	12.00
Tray. Serving, 10"	5.00

SPOKE

Amber.

Butter Dish. Covered	20.00
Cracker Jar. Covered	12.00
Creamer	2.00

Pink.

Bowl. Vegetable, oval, 10"	3.50
Cream Soup	7.00
Cup	2.00
Plate. 10½"	2.00
Platter	3.00
Saucer	1.50
Sherbet	1.50

SWIRL

Ultramarine.

Bowls	
5¼"	3.00
10". Footed	10.00
Nappy	6.00

Plate. 12½"	7.50
Salt and Pepper	17.50
Vase. 8½"	7.50

WINDSOR

Crystal.

Candlesticks. Pair	10.00
Coaster	1.50
Salt and Pepper	8.00
Trays	
4x4"	3.00
4x8"	5.00
8x10"	7.50

Pink.

Bowls	
Boat-shaped	12.50
4¾"	2.00
8½"	5.00
Butter Dish	20.00
Creamer and Sugar	12.50
Pitcher	10.00
Plate. Chop, 13½"	8.00
Saucer	1.50
Salt and Pepper	14.50
Tumbler. 4"	4.50

DOLL FURNITURE

Doll furniture not only served as play toys for children but sometimes it served as miniature examples of a cabinetmaker's skill.

Fine doll furniture and accessories were also enjoyed by many adults who decorated a "baby" house as a form of entertainment and amusement.

Beds

Brass. 4x21", with springs, pad, bolster, crocheted spread	$ 185.00
Brass. 21x24x30"	225.00
Brass. 19x29½". Original mattress and springs	150.00
Mahogany. Four poster. 22" high, bed, 7½x31"	75.00
Maple. 5¼x7½x11". High board top, low foot. With small afghan	60.00
Maple. 16x26". Turned posts, hickory side rails, rope bed, C. 1840	40.00
Bedroom Set. 6-pcs., 1" scale. 2 metal beds, tin wash stand with mirror, table, 2 chairs. Set	75.00
Bed, Tester. With canopy. Small	40.00
Bureaus	
Victorian. 5¼x8¾x8¾". 2 small drawers at top, 3 below. Maple	50.00
Victorian. 16" high, old mirror	90.00

Chairs

Ice Cream Parlor. Wire back, legs, tin seats. 5" high	7.50
Ladderback. Pair	22.50
Oval back	15.00
Rocking. 16" high, seat 6x7". Old pine	22.00
Wicker Rocker. 17" high, silk seat	25.00
Chest, Cedar. 3½x6½". 4 feet, with metal lock and key. Hinges and straps	6.50
Chest of Drawers	
Oak, 4 drawers, brass pulls	25.00
Period style, 5 drawers	37.50
Cradles	
Pine. 15" high, hooded. C. 1860	20.00
Walnut. Cutout hearts each end	45.00
Crib. Wicker. 10x16"	30.00
Highchair. 15" high. Pine with lifting foot tray. C. 1880	20.00
Parlor Set. 7-pcs., 1" scale. Sofa, 4 side chairs, table with drawer, roll-arm chair. Velvet upholstery	75.00
Piano. Upright	25.00
Stroller. Victorian. Restored and refinished	60.00
Trunk. For doll clothes	30.00
Wardrobe. Plywood, colored maple. Clothes bar, 2 doors above, 2 small doors below. 5¼x8½x10¼"	18.00
Wicker Set. 2 chairs, settee and table	65.00

Chest. Victorian-type. 4x7x9½". Oak
$35.00

DOLLS

Collecting antique dolls is an exciting, educational and rewarding experience. Dolls were made of many materials such as china, cloth, leather, papier mache, wood, etc. Today some contemporary dolls, such as Chatty Kathy and Poor Pitiful Pearl, are being added to collections as representatives of the period.

26". Staffordshire head, cloth body, black hair, old dress $240.00

Bahr-Proeschild Baby. No. 585. 16"
   high, blond hair, blue eyes .... $ 250.00
Beltons
   Fully jointed, dressed, blue eyes,
   closed mouth. 9" high, perfect
   condition 250.00
   26" high. Closed mouth, p.w. blue 650.00
Betty Boop. 7¼". Celluloid head
   swings side to side. Original box,
   labels 80.00
Bisques
   2½" high. Negro. Swivel head,
   original outfit 125.00
   3¼" high. Negro boy. Glass eyes,
   closed mouth 150.00
   5¼" high. Signed. O'Neill Kewpie
   tummy sticker 50.00
   Open mouth, sleeping eyes,
   leather body, cloth legs, marked
   "Made in Germany." 22" 100.00
   Baby Boy. 19". Tongue shows 125.00

Bru. Mechanical limbs, human hair 975.00
Bye-los
   Grace Storey Putman doll. Com-
   position head, not dressed 175.00
   Baby. Molded, copr. 1923 by
   Grace Storey Putnam. Geo.
   Borgfelt Corp. Label on dress,
   head marked. Cry box works. Blue
   sleep eyes. Head circum. 11½"... 325.00
Celluloid Boy. Old, 19" 85.00
China
   22" high, 11 vertical sausage curls,
   covered wagon style 300.00
   All original, black hair, blue eyes,
   deep shoulders, dressed in yellow
   calico. 23" 250.00
   Black molded hair, china hands
   and feet, cloth body. 24" high 300.00
Countess Angel. Blond Parian. In
   cocoa taffeta and pale cocoa lace.
   Ivory velvet bow, blue eyes, blue
   heart-shaped earrings in pierced
   ears 425.00

Bye-Lo Baby. Signed G. S. Putnam. Wicker-type cradle. Original label. Pat. 1922 ....$350.00

Creche. Wooden body, hands and legs. Gesso head, painted eyes, closed mouth, old dress. 18" high . 325.00

Dionne Quints. Made by Alexander. Composition heads, arms and legs. Cloth bodies, dressed. 16" high. Set of five dolls 250.00

Dolly Madison. Parian. Blond hair, blue eyes, dressed in pink velvet. 21" high 375.00

Eden Bebe. Paris. Open mouth, brown wig, pierced ears, blue jeweled eyes, jointed body. 14" high. Marked 165.00

Effanbee Honey Walker. 18½" high. Hard plastic, long dress, original clothes except shoes 35.00

French Character. Boy. 14" high, SFBJ, p.w. blue 725.00

French Child. 17" high. Incised Paris. C.M. blue, p.w. eyes. Voice box . . . 535.00

French Girl. 27" high. SFBJ. Sleep blue eyes 395.00

Fannie Brice. 11" high, compo., original clothes 150.00

French Fashion Dolls
Bisque head, brown hair wig, blown blue-gray eyes, kid body, arms and legs. Not dressed. 14" high 475.00
16" high. Closed mouth, paper-weight eyes 650.00

Frozen Charlie. Pink lustre face, black hair, brown eyes, closed mouth. 15" high 400.00

German Character. Boy. 9x14". Closed mouth, molded hair, incised 163, intaglio blue eyes . . . 850.00

Heubach. Brown eyes, open mouth, kid body, bisque hands, wig, dressed. 21" high 235.00

French. Blonde, blue-set eyes. Original dress and bonnet $195.00

French. Reddish-brown hair, set eyes. Open mouth, all fingers, nicely dressed $350.00

Gibson Girl. 21" high, closed mouth, lashed sleep blue eyes, incised 172, bisque arms 1495.00

Poor Pitiful Pearl. 12" high. Complete
$45.00

Googley, A.M. 13" high, blue glass eyes, closed mouth, br. wig on compo. jtd. body, dressed, marked "Germany 323. A 3/OM" 625.00

Jenny Linds
13½" high. Black dress, Staffordshire head, legs, hands 600.00
China head, black hair, 17" high .. 650.00

Jumeaus
18" high, C.M. Auburn hair, blue p.w. eyes 785.00
20" high. Closed mouth, p.w. br. eyes, signed. Voice box torso 950.00
36" high. Closed mouth, p.w. br. eyes, applied ears 1795.00

Kestners
"Alice", 12" high. Brown eyes, bisque hands 150.00
Baby. 15" high. Composition body, blue slant eyes, blonde wig, bisque head. Dressed in long white dress with lace trim 250.00
Boy. 18" high 185.00
#111. 24" high. Called "Daisy", all original 300.00

Kewpies
2". Seated bisque, holds roses.... 120.00
4". Celluloid. C. 1930 .... 6.00
9½". Bisque. Signed 225.00

Parian Quality. French. Pink kid arms and legs. Fully dressed. 14" . 450.00

Parian. Curly blonde hair, pierced ears, painted blue eyes, cloth body, legs, leather arms. 23" 375.00

Piano Baby. 7" high. Signed Heubach with G.H. mark. Sitting with hands in front, dimple, molded teeth, inta. eyes, bald head with brush marks, light blue, square neck, gown, large ears 175.00

Pin Cushion Doll. 1920s era. Molded hairdo, painted eyes and other features. 4" high. Mkd. Germany . 30.00

Rockabye #351. Black A.M. 14" high. Rub on nose and hair........... 275.00

Schoenhuts
Baby. Curved legs, original wig, dressed. 11" high.............. 200.00
Walking, original wig, 14" high, not dressed 200.00
Character. Dressed, 14" high..... 275.00
15". Girl. Spring joint 325.00
Baby. Painted eyes, hair wig, jointed, 16" high. Dtd. 1913 ...... 300.00
Spring-jointed, made of wood. 16" high, fully clothed 350.00
Girl. Original wig, dressed 16½" high 300.00

Shirley Temples
18" high. Original clothes, wig, etc 125.00
25" high. All original. Dress yellow voile 175.00
Vinyl body, small 50.00

Simon & Halbig. Brown eyes, pierced ears, body marked "Heinrich-Handwarch." Not dressed, 24" high 225.00

Snow Baby. See "Snow Babies"

Snow White. 15". Marked "Walt Disney 1937," compo. body,

Kestner. Signed Helbig. All original. Sleep eyes, moves head when she walks. Strawberry blond, with 4-pc. wardrobe $250.00

brown painted eyes to side. Red
molded hair ribbon. Dwarf trim
down skirt....................... 65.00
Sonja Henie. 17" high, all original,
skates on........................ 125.00
Steiners
21" high, bl. p.w. eyes, open
mouth, pierced ears, br. h.h. wig,
dressed, incised mark "A-3 Paris
La Parisien" 525.00
24" high. Closed mouth, pierced
ears, signed 525.00
29" high. Double row of teeth,
unbelievable face 1500.00
Wax
12" high. Glass eyes, blonde curly
wig. All original 275.00
28½" high. Lady doll, pierced
ears, painted high button shoes,
original dress 350.00
Wood. Queen Anne miniature.
Jointed arms and legs, original
clothes. 4½" high 400.00
World War II. 15½". In original
service uniforms. Molded on caps.
G.I. Joe, G.O.B. have labels
"Praise the Lord and Pass the
Ammunition." "W.A.V.E.S." on
girl. Each 50.00

Julia	10.00
Mammy Yokum	28.00
Pollyanna, 30"	25.00
Poor Pitiful Pearl, complete	45.00
Tippy Toes.....................	10.00
Tumbelina.....................	20.00
Twiggy........................	10.00

DOOR KNOCKERS

Centuries or more before the advent of the
electric doorbell, metal door knockers
announced the arrival of visitors at the front
door of a home. The majority was made of
brass; however, occasionally one was of iron.
One popular style of the period was a lion's
head.

Brass
Hand holding ball .... $ 55.00
Hand with apple and strike 45.00
Lion's head. 4½x7" 40.00
Wolf/Fox head. 4½x7" 40.00
Bronze
5". Hand with ruffled sleeve,
detailed...................... 60.00
8" long. Shape of ship, anchor
knocker 75.00

Pin Cushion Doll. 5" high. Porcelain.
Red molded hair with hair band $32.50

Miscellaneous, Modern
Alex. Big Huggums 12.50
Buffy 15.00
Chatty Kathy.................. 7.00
Giggles, Baby 12.50
Hoss Cartwright 20.00

"Trusty Servant." 3¼" high. Iron $22.50

Charles Dickens	60.00
Elephant and Castle	50.00
Grecian Head and Bust	50.00
Iron	
Glove in hand	30.00
Hand, Lady's. Clutching a ball, original black painted finish and brass striker button. 2½ x 5½"	30.00
Horseshoe and hammer	20.00
Parrot. 2½ x 3¼"	20.00
Spur with metal block below. Mounted on small wood plaque	28.50

DOOR STOPS

As the name indicates, door stops were used to hold doors at a desire place. Almost every home has a door or two which will not stay open. They were made of brass or iron, the latter predominating. Production of those ordinarily encountered in antique shops today was from the Mid-Victorian period to about 1920.

Aunt Jemima. Black dress, brownish-gray apron and scarf, red and white polka dot kerchief. Iron	$ 30.00
Black Sambo. With tiger. Iron	35.00
Bull. Iron	28.50
Cats	
4½" high. Black, iron	25.00
8½" high. Iron	30.00
9½" high. Fluffy gray tiger. Iron	35.00
Cockatoo. 7" high, iron	18.00
Cornucopia. 11" high. With flowers	25.00
Cottage. Cast iron	25.00
Court Jester and Dog. 12" high	38.00
Cricket. Iron	28.00
Dogs	
Airedale. Iron	27.50
Boxer. 7½". Clipped ears and tail. Brown	17.50
Bulldogs	
9½ x 9½". Boston	45.00
9 x 10½". Iron	28.50
Cockers	
6½" long	20.00
10½" long, reddish brown	25.00
Fox Terrier. 8 x 9½"	27.50
German Shepherd. Cast iron, marked Davison Co. 13 x 14"	34.50
Pointer. 9". Iron	27.50
Scottie. Iron	27.50
Setter. 15" high, ears to tail	30.00
Dolly Dimple with Doll. Iron	35.00
Elephant. 8" tail to tusk. Painted red	19.00
Fiddler tuning his violin. Cast iron	25.00
Flower in Basket. 8" high. Iron	25.00
Flowers in Basket. Brass	50.00

Fox, Sleeping. Brass	50.00
Frogs	
4" bronze	60.00
Iron	25.00
Horses	
7¾ x 8½". Black pot metal with red saddle	45.00
9 x 10". Bronze over iron. Saddled with stirrups, head down, munching grass	25.00
Indian with spear on galloping horse. 5½ x 6¼". Weighs 4 lbs.	60.00
Kitten. 7¼" high, painted yellow with blue ribbon. Iron	30.00
Kittens. 7½" high. Standing. Female has dappled gold-colored face and floral yellow dress. Male has black face, blue overalls. Pair	35.00
Lamb. Cast iron, painted black	30.00
Lighthouse of Gloucester, Mass. Dated 1920. 11½"	25.00
Lion. Large, iron	35.00
Little Red Riding Hood and Wolf. Iron. Pair	50.00
Parrot. 8¼". Blue, red and yellow. Iron	27.50
Ship. Mayflower. Iron	30.00
Snooper. 13½" high. Iron	45.00

Flower Basket. 10½" high $25.00

Union Civil War Officer. 7½" high.
Cast iron 25.00
Wagon. Conestoga. 7" high, iron 30.00
Windmill. 7" high, iron 28.50
Wolf. With chain leash, iron 35.00

DRESDEN

The first fine porcelain in Europe was discovered or invented by Johann Frederick Bottger at the Royal Saxon Porcelain Works at Meissen, Germany, about 1710. The ware is finely molded and decorated, often having applied raised flowers. The famous marks of the company are a variety of crossed swords in blue color under glaze.

The factory is still in existence although it is now behind the "Iron curtain." It has been reported that a new mark has been instituted since the Russian occupation that of a hammer and sickle. Department stores have recently been selling pieces showing the Meissen mark with a crown over it. Much of the ware in America today was brought in by importers in the latter part of the 19th century [1875-1900].

Basket. Handled, round, latticed,
painted robin in center, raised
flowers, painted sprigs ....$ 175.00
Bed. 6" long, 3" high. Colored
flowers, leaves in sprays, high-
lighted in gold 350.00
Bowls
10½"diam. Gold floral decor on
white. Cross swords 275.00
Solid bottom, open "spaghetti"
sides, colorful roses. Marked
"Germany." Late 80.00
Box. 3½x3½x5½". Painted floral
decor 300.00
Butter Dish. Covered, floral pattern.
Late 47.50
Candelabras
2-branch, boy & girl on each base,
applied flowers. Pair........... 950.00
5-candle. 19½" high. Figures of
boy and girl. Pair 800.00
Cat. Calico. 12" high 175.00
Chocolate Pot. 10½" high. Schuman
mark. Multicolored ground. Floral
decor 85.00
Compotes
9" diam. 4¼" high. 6 matching
plates. Red, gold decor with green
leaves. Marked Dresden, impressed F&M. Set 165.00
14" top diam., 17" high. Sword
marks on bottom 600.00

Cups and Saucers
Demitasse. Fluted, colored flowers, gold trim 75.00
From chocolate set. Flower band
and scattered flowers 55.00
Green Dragon 65.00
Handleless. German. C. 1820. 2
dark red roses, paper thin
porcelain. Fine "X" mark in blue
underglaze 80.00
Dishes. Boat-shape
6x8". Pale blue, pink, center
panel of man, woman in garden
scene, swan heads as handles.... 85.00
2½x9½x14½". Irregular edge,
lavender trim. Blue, orchid, white
flowers in center. 4 pierced
openings each end 95.00
Figurines
Boy & girl. 5¾" high. Porcelain.
Standing beside baskets, embossed work, flowers. Mkd 225.00

Cat. 12½" high. White, green eyes.
Signed....................$175.00

Frog Musicians. Blue crossed
swords............................ 300.00
Macaw. On tree stump. Red, 18"
high 155.00
Napoleonic Marshalls on Horse-
back. Le Prince Eugene or
Marshall Polly. Each 115.00
Swans. Mute. 9'11". Pair......... 175.00
"Violinist, The." Kandler period .. 1500.00

Frames

3½x5". Double portrait frames.
Gold border, surface covered with
small pink roses................. 125.00
6½x9". Scalloped, floral decor,
gilt scrolls 145.00
Beveled mirror. Cupids on top
holding flower wreath. Mkd 265.00

Lamps

5½" high, 5" base diam. Shell-
shaped bowl, raised flowers,
cupid at sides 275.00
10" high. Cherub on stem, raised
flowers on base, bowl. Cream
green, yellow 450.00
Lamp Base 14" high. Angel figurines 400.00

Mirrors

5½" diam. Hand. Porcelain ladies.
Unmarked, lavender, white violets. C. 1900 .... 35.00
10x12". Oval, cupids, applied
flowers 325.00
Place Cards. 3¾" high. Full figure of
girls holding 2-tiered lace skirt.
Marked. Pair................... 60.00

Plates

6". Dessert. Handpainted figure,
filigree edge, gold 45.00
9½". Portrait of woman 85.00
11". Landscape center, gilt scrolls 95.00
11". Floral, cherub center. Cross
swords........................ 250.00
Shoe. On chariot, being pulled by
cupid. 5¼" high. Garland of
roses, blue shoe. Mkd. KPM 135.00
Tea Caddy. Painted floral decor, gilt
trim 60.00

Teapots

5" high, 8" long. Footed, floral
decor......................... 100.00
17" high. Relief-molded hot water
kettle on stand, burner. Gold and
white. Late 135.00
Tea Set. Teapot, sugar bowl &
creamer. Floral and gold decor.
Set 250.00
Toast Rack. Divided compartments,
small handles 75.00
Tray. 15" diam. Floral, gold decor ... 75.00

Vases

7" high. White ground, multicolored floral decor............ 135.00
9¾" high. Covered. Porcelain
Oriental Mannu decor with
dragons as handles, Foo-dog finial
on lid. Multicolored, birds, flowers 250.00

DUNCAN AND MILLER GLASS

The firm was first started in Pittsburgh, Pa., in
the late 1860's, under the name of George
Duncan's Sons and Co. In 1893-94, the glass
works moved to Washington, Pa., where they
manufactured some of the finest handmade
glassware in America for sixty-three years. In
1957 the United States Glass Co., purchased
the firm, including the molds, and has
continued to produce Duncan-Miller products.
It was George Duncan, the founder, who
discovered the great talents of his designer,
John Ernest Miller, and recognized him to be
the greatest asset to the company. He later
became one of the owners, thus the name,
Duncan and Miller Glass.

The last catalogue issued by the company was
in 1953. It showed 480 different pieces of
many designs. A specialty were the
reproductions of the early American Sandwich
Glass. But probably the most famous Miller
design was his "Three-face" glassware, and
probably the most beautiful is the Duncan and
Miller "Swan."

Ash Trays. Ducks. 1-6", 4-3". Set ....$ 65.00

Baskets

7" high. Vaseline opal........... 45.00
7¾x9¾". Canterbury, clear 25.00

Bowls

8½"base, 8½" high. Greenish-
yellow, deep jagged edge, ground
bottom, heavy glass 26.50
8½", round. Greenish-yellow,
water lily shape, rounded points.. 18.00
10½" diam., 3" high. Canterbury,
clear.......................... 12.00
Punch Bowl. #42................ 65.00
Rose. 3½" high. Canterbury pink,
opalescent 25.00
Candlesticks. Teardrop, 5" high,
6½" wide. Clear, double. Pair 19.00
Celery. #42. Curled sides, 10" long .. 12.50
Console Set. Hobnail opalescent
pink. 12" bowl, pair of 4½"
candlesticks. Set 35.00
Dish. Swan. Opalescent, vaseline ... 35.00
Goblet. 6" high, 1" light amber band
at top 15.00

Glass Basket. 9¼" high. Clear . $25.00

Hats. 3½". Hobnail, blue or opal.
Each 20.00
Plates
   Bread & Butter, 6" 10.00
   Cake. 13½" diam. Canterbury,
   handled 12.00
Pitcher. Narrow Swirl 12.50
Punch Cups
   Hobnail, pink opal 7.00
   #42 .... 5.00
Salt. #14. Individual 3.50
Swans
   3½". Solid crystal 8.50
   6". Chartreuse Viking 12.00
   7½". Blue opal. Sylvan 65.00
   7½". Clear Sylvan 25.00
   7½". Vaseline 35.00
   10". Peach opalescent. 14" wing
   spread to top of neck 32.00
   10½". Clear 16.00
   10½". Green 35.00
   10½". Red.................... 50.00
   10½". Vaseline 45.00
Tumbler, 2½" high............... 10.00
Vases
   5" high, 7" diam. Canterbury, blue
   opalescent 25.00
   5¼" high, 6" diam. Blue opal..... 28.00

   7½" high, 4½" diam. Carribean
   sapphire blue pedestal 15.00
   8½" high, 7" diam. Clear 15.00
Whiskey. #42 .... 10.00
Wine. #42 .... 15.00

DURAND ART GLASS

Victor Durand, reputed to be a descendant of the French family which made Baccarat glass, started a factory in Vineland, New Jersey in 1924 or 1925, and sold the product under the name of "Durand Art Glass."
The glass resembled Tiffany in some respects, especially the golden sheen of some designs. Many of the pieces were made in red and sapphire blue, and occasionally stars were cut into the pattern. A Cameo type of glass was also produced. The glass was labeled with a sticker "Durand Art Glass," while some items were marked with the letter "V" in the pontil. The factory closed in 1931 due to the accidental death of Durand.

Bowls
   4¾" diam., 2½" high. Signed.
   Gold irid., flared ....$ 125.00
   11"diam., 2" deep. Flower. Deep
   blue, usual decor, vaseline-
   colored foot ....'. 350.00
   Rose. 4" high. Signed. Green
   lustre, King Tut decor over
   orange-yellow ground, 4" diam. .. 425.00
   Rose. Blue color 375.00
Candleholder. 3" high. Amber base,
   stem green bobeche. "Rose of
   Brixton" cut into bobeche........ 75.00

Rose Bowl. "King Tut" pattern. Signed
"V. & Durand" $650.00

Candlestick. 10" high. Silvery blue.
Signed 265.00
Compotes
5¾" high. Cranberry feather
pattern. Baluster stem 425.00
Covered. King Tut pattern. Green,
gold swirls 875.00
Goblet. Red, gold iridescent loopings 300.00
Lamps. 16" high. Buffet, green-gold
crackle. Pair 500.00
Lamp Shade. Bell-shaped, 10" high,
2" opening, 2" flaring to 9½" at
bottom. Deep green, outer layer
of heavy crackle over gold lining . 425.00
Liquor. 4½" high. Canary stem, 2"
round base, circular cut band. 5
blue & white feathers 200.00
Plate. Medium size, feathery pattern
with 4 stars placed to form square
outside the central design 325.00
Vases
4½" high. Gold lustre, green opal.
King Tut pattern 375.00
6¼" high. Pulled feather design,
threaded peach color. Sgnd 500.00
7" high. Blue iridescent. Signed.
Beehive 675.00
8" high. Signed. Yellow amber
threading. Multicolored, glossy
background 750.00

Vase. 10" high. Calcite, bulbous,
signed $425.00

8½" high. Jack-in-the-Pulpit. Gold
iridescent 425.00
8½" high. Fully signed, numbered. Orange cases, blue leaves,
vines, blue highlights on base 550.00
9" high. King Tut. Gold over white 650.00
13" high. Deep cranberry, milk
white Nailsea-type loopings at
base. Signed V. Durand 750.00
13" high. Moorish crackle. Banjo
shape, iridescent beige over
ambergris. Unsigned........... 400.00

END-OF-DAY GLASS

A multicolored or spotted glass, sometimes
called "spatter glass" made about 1885 to
1905. The name "End-of-Day" is derived from
the custom of glassblowers using the
remains of the day's glass from their various
pots (usually a variety of colors) and blowing
or molding objects of their own fancy. Some of
the glass was made commercially but was
never very popular as it was considered
distasteful by persons of distinction.

Pitcher. 5" high. Tortoise shell pattern
$75.00

Barber Bottle. See "Bottles, Barber."
Baskets
4½x6". Blue and yellow, clear
thorn handle.................... $ 85.00
5½x6". Thorn handle 95.00
Boot. 3¾" high. Multicolored,
applied, clear glass decor 85.00

Bowls

Finger. Swirl pattern in pink
opaque, yellow-white lining 37.50
Rose. Green 48.00
Candlesticks. Pair 100.00
Carafe with Tumbler. Pair 75.00
Cracker Jar. 9" high, cased in white,
yellow, red, green colors. Thorn
handle 100.00
Jam Pot. Silverplated cover, holder . 50.00
Lamp. Hand. Pink, clear, applied
handle 100.00

Mugs

3¾" high 40.00
4¼" high. Red, yellow, green,
blue. Clear glass handle 50.00
Perfume Bottle. Rose top, jewel,
finger chain and ring 47.50

Pitchers

9½" high. Spattered, blue, red,
white. Acid finish 150.00
Large, light pastel swirls 140.00
Rooster. On 3x6" base 35.00
Sugar Shaker. Pink 47.50
Syrup Jug. Pink 82.50

Tumblers

Pink, red, white 37.50
Pink, yellow, blue, deep red 37.50

Vases

2¾" high, 4½" 28.50
5¼" high. Ruffled top 50.00
7½" high. Clear glass, splashed
with blue, red, rose, green,
yellow, white. Ruffled top. 3 feet.
Pair 100.00
7½" high. Yellow, red, pink, black 50.00
8" high. Jack-in-the-Pulpit 50.00
8½" high. Bulbous bottom, slim
neck, flared to fluted top, pink,
white, clear 55.00
10" high. Cased in white. Yellow,
pink, orange color. Square top,
clear glass, crimped edge 65.00
12½" high. Cased glass, rainbow
coloring 75.00

EPERGNES

Epergnes are ornamental centerpieces for
tables, consisting of several tiers of
receptacles or dishes of elaborate design for
holding fruits and sweetmeats; or with vases
for holding flowers.

Blue. Crimped top and bowl, with
trimming . . . . $ 195.00
Blue. Satin glass, 1 lily 140.00
Canary. 14" high. 4 lilies, clear
bottoms, 7" beveled mirror
platform 150.00

15" diam. base, ruffled, 16" long. One
trumpet. Ruby glass $275.00

Clear to opalescent. 2 pieces, 12"
high 225.00
Clear-white glass with opalescent
effects, applied threads of green
glass. C. 1895-1900 . . . . 300.00
Cranberry. 3 arms in round metal
base with mirror. 16¾" high 275.00
Cranberry. Milk white bowl with
cranberry edge, clear rosettes
wound around holders. Venetian
glass 320.00
Cranberry. Light lower bowl with
darker pleated top and hobnails
around darker pleated ends. One
tube scattered white flowers 235.00
Cranberry. Crimped top and lower
bowl. 3 lilies 285.00
Cranberry opalescent. 4 lilies, 19½"
high 295.00
Emerald green filigree lilies [3]. 22"
to top of center lily, 10" deeply
scalloped base bowl 225.00
English ruby glass. Crimped bowl
with center trumpet only. 21½"
high 120.00
Pink. 10¾" ruffled bowl, 11" ruffled
lily. Silver frame 200.00
Red to opalescent, blue-white to
pale green. 9½" diam. Hollow
with rough pontil mark 125.00
Rose and pink. 16" high, upper
ruffled edge 5" diam. Lower edge,
9" diam. 235.00

Ruby, vaseline, opalescent. 6-way brass fitting, frilled trumpets and bowl 850.00
White Milk Glass. Green to white opalescent. 19" high, tall lily baskets with two hanging baskets and two stationary baskets 240.00
White Satin Glass. 12½" high, in silverplated standard. 3 arms support ruffled bowls, with enamel flowers and leaves 400.00

FAIENCE

The ware is red in color and has a tin glaze. Delft and Majolica are made by the same process of tin glazing.

Bird in cage. Gilded gold wire, white body with flower and leaf decor. Museum quality 500.00
Compote. 10" high. Signed Rouen ... 150.00
Hen with chicks, on back and under wings. French. Dark orange with black and yellow decor 235.00
Ink and Quill Holder. Glass well, 4 openings for quills, orange, yellow, blue decor. Unknown mark 65.00
Plates
  7½". Dull blue ground with raised fruit in center. Late. Set of 6 ...... 150.00

Pitcher. 7" high. Ivory, beige, rust, floral decor. "Avalon Faience" . $95.00

9½". Blue decor on white ground . 110.00
16½". Rooster decor in yellow and dark red. Early type 150.00
Platter. 14½ x 19½". Delft-type blue decor 145.00

FAIRY LAMPS

These are small glass candle-burning night lamps, usually consisting of a base and a shade. They were first made in 1857 in England by the Samuel Clarke Co. A variety was manufactured until 1910 when electricity made the flame lamps obsolete, except in rural areas.
The Phoenix Glass Co., Pittsburgh, Pa., was granted the exclusive right to manufacture the lamps in the United States. A wide variety was produced, from cheap colored glass to expensive art glass, such as Amberina, Burmese, Nailsea, Peachblow, Satin, etc.

7" high. Pink to apricot. MOP, ruffled saucer with petal-trimmed collar
$1200.00

Amber. 5½". Frosted, clear base ... $ 85.00
Amethysts
  11¼" high. Resembles Fine Cut, on tall, clear Cane standard 150.00
  Diamond Point Shade. Clear base, sulphide profiles of Napoleon and Josephine 185.00
Bisques
  Owl. White, brown nose, glass eye 115.00
  Three-Face. Pussy cat, pug & owl . 135.00
Blues
  Bristol glass, swirled, enameled flowers 150.00

Overshot, silver, swirl ribbed, pyramid shape 85.00
Royal. Overlay, faceted panels. Ormolu frame 225.00
Brasses
Blue, amber glass windows. 8½" . 125.00
Jeweled. 4½" high, 4½" diam. Ornate brass filigree shade. Multicolored jewels 100.00
Bull Dog Face. Bisque. 4¼" high 125.00
Burmeses
3¾" high. Clarke's Fairy Pyramid. Clear base, signed base and top .. 250.00
5" high. Clarke base. C. 1885 .... 300.00
Webb acid, reversible base. 3-pc. . 750.00
Camphor Glass Shade. Pattern molded to resemble pine cone. Plain camphor glass base. Aquamarine 195.00
Carmine. 6" high, milk glass base. Webb 600.00
Cranberry Frosted. 3¾" high, 2-7/8" diam. Marked Clarke. Clear pressed glass base, dome shade has opaque white looping 125.00
Cut Velvet. Rose color, herringbone design; white lining, clear Clarke holder 150.00

Diamond Points
Amber Top, clear base, 4" high ... 65.00
Blue top, clear base, 4" high 65.00
Diamond Quilted. Clear with clear base. Signed Clarke 50.00
End-of-Day. Cased in white. Soft colors of pink, rose, beige, green . 150.00
Lithophane. 7¼" high. Ormolu holder, blue enamel saucer 275.00
Millefiori Shade. Glass base, 4" high 150.00
Nailseas
Cranberry and white Satin glass. Clear base, 6" high 165.00
Rose. Matching crimped edge base 235.00
Ribbon Stripe. 4¾" high, yellow and opaque white, matching base. Signed Clarke 225.00
Royal Doulton. Ceramic and enameled base, decorated satin shade 345.00
Ruby Red Glass Top with white milk glass base 75.00
Satin Glass
Apricot shading 225.00
Blue to white. Ruffled, 6½" high .. 300.00
Deep yellow, rib mold. Standard shade and holder 225.00
Mother-of-Pearl. D.Q., ruffled shade and base. Large 275.00
White with pink stripes. Matching base. 5" high 85.00

Verre Moire. Blue. Powder blue frosted shade with white looping. Candle-cup base in clear, pressed glass. Signed Clarke 120.00

FAMILLE ROSE

Famille Rose is a Chinese export porcelain made C. 1790-1800. The opaque colors of the rose family in different shades of pink and carmine are in evidence. The ware is relatively scarce, in demand by collectors, and brings high prices in comparison with other chinaware which appeared on the American scene during the same period.

Bowl. 10½" diam. Low, footed, decorated on exterior, frieze of costumed actors over a petal-incised ground .... $ 485.00
Jardiniere. 13" diam., 7" high. C. 1800 .... 600.00

Charger. White ground with pink floral decor in center and on rim.... $650.00

Mug. 6" high, butterflies, blossoms.. 450.00
Pitcher. Small, covered 225.00
Plaque. 21" diam. Decorated on interior and exterior with flowering trees, insects 500.00
Plate. 9", lavender ground, sprays of rose blossoms 450.00
Vase. 12" high, figured panel, pink ground 575.00

FANS

In the days before electricity, the hand fan was the air conditioner of the period. Various styles and types were available, depending on the owner's economic standing in the community. Some were handpainted silk set with jewels while others were made of cheap printed "fan paper."

Ivory and silk. Pastel embroidered flowers and birds $32.00

Advertisement. Cardboard .... $	4.50
Celluloid. 7" long, pierced design ...	12.00
Centennial. 11" long, 1876 Philadelphia Horticultural Hall one side, eagle on reverse	80.00
Chiffon. Black lace. Embossing of Geraldine Farrar	25.00
Ivory. Carved fan, painted silk insert	50.00
Ivory. Carved fan, rose satin center .	50.00
Louis XVI. 19" across, 10" high, carved ivory center	150.00
Ostrich Feather. Black	22.50
Paper. Heavy, French handpainted. Ivory sticks, 10½" long, 20" opened	110.00
Paper. Wood sticks	9.50
Pastoral scene, man and woman. Marked R.N. 1198. 18 fretted metal sticks, gold finish. 8" high, 16" wide	100.00
Satin. 23" wide. Spread with thick marabou feathers. Ivory sticks ...	50.00
Wedding. Carved, pierced ivory sticks. 10½" long, handpainted pink flowers, forget-me-nots on silk	45.00
Wedding. White lace, pierced ivory sticks	50.00

FINDLAY GLASS, See ONYX GLASS

FIESTA WARE

The older and collectible Fiesta tableware was produced by the Homer Laughlin Company, East Liverpool, Ohio between 1936 and 1972.

It can be identified as 'true' Fiesta ware by the graduated rings that encircle the rims of plates and perimeters of bowls and cups. The more recent and new Fiesta dinnerware being produced today has straight sides.

Ash Tray. Gray .... $	15.00
Bowls, Dessert	
6". Red	5.50
6". Yellow	4.50
Bowls, Vegetable	
Dark green	12.50
Red	20.00
Rose	20.00
Yellow	12.50
Candleholders, Tripod	
Green	30.00
Ivory........................	30.00
Turquoise	30.00
Carafe. Cobalt	25.00
Cream Soups	
Gray........................	6.50
Rose........................	7.50
Turquoise	6.50
Yellow	6.50
Egg Cups	
Cobalt	12.50
Turquoise	12.50
Yellow	12.50
MarmaladeJar. Cobalt	49.50
Pitcher	8.50
Plates	
7". Salad. Green, ivory, yellow ...	3.00
9". Luncheon. Blue, turquoise, yellow	3.00
9½"	6.00
10". Dinner. Turquoise, green, ivory........................	3.50

Dish. Deep, 11" diam. Green $7.50

12". Chop	6.00
13". Chop	5.00
15". Chop. Ivory	5.00
Platter	7.00
Salt and Pepper Shakers. Pair	7.50
Sauce. Ivory, yellow, turquoise	2.00
Sugar and Creamer	8.50
Teapot. Large, ivory	17.50
Tray	7.00
Tumbler. Large	6.50
Vase, Bud. Yellow	15.00

FINGER BOWLS

Small bowls made of glass or metal for the purpose of cleansing fingers at the end of a meal. The practice of using finger bowls has been discontinued in most homes and restaurants, but a revival of this custom would add to the charm of gracious living.

Amber. Thumbprint. 4½" diam. ....$	28.50
Apple Green. Old, blown	35.00
Blue, cobalt	25.00
Blue, light. Old, blown	35.00
Bohemian Glass.Enamel floral decor	42.00
Brass. Chinese	15.00
Canary yellow. Old, blown	35.00
Cranberry. English, blown	45.00
Cranberry. Irid., 5" diam., 2½" deep. Tiffany color, in purple and gold. Raised moire pattern. Blown	35.00
Cut Glass. With matching plate. Diamond and Fan pattern. Set	60.00
Emerald green. Light band through center. 5½" diam.	35.00
Green. Old, blown	35.00
Pink [Maiden Blush]	22.50
Silverplated	17.00
Threaded Glass. Green, 5" diam.	40.00
Vaseline. Old, blown	35.00

Amberina. 5" diam. ITP $110.00

FIRE EQUIPMENT

In the days before mechanized fire equipment, firefighters utilized manpower for the job of extinguishing fires. Most of the first companies were of the volunteer nature. Each member owned his own leather bucket and helmet.

Property owners who carried insurance displayed a firemark made of iron or brass. In the last few years reproduction firemarks, cast of aliminum, have been placed on the market.

Bell. Brass. Operated by hand crank.
   Made by "New Departure Bell
   Co." Polished ....$ 150.00
Buckets
   Early, leather, owner's name and
   date 1807 .... 150.00

Leather bucket. Decorated with fireman's hat and hatchet $175.00

Leather Parmdee No. 1 New
England. C. 1800. Leather handle . 150.00
Fire Horn. Braided tassels.......... 200.00
Fire Marks
Cut logs center, "L.I. Co." in color,
hand forged 125.00
Hands, Clasped. Germantown
National Fire, 1843 .... 100.00
Hydrant, F.A. 1817 .... 75.00
Tree. 1784.................... 100.00
United Fireman's Ins. Co. 75.00
Helmets, Leather
"1878." Eagle finial 85.00
Eagle head on front. Brass 95.00
Fireman, trumpet finial.......... 75.00
Hose Nozzle. Brass, 12". Pat. 1897 .. 50.00
Sheet Music. "The Midnight Fire
Alarm." Colored litho front cover
showing engines pulled by horses
racing to fire 8.50

FIREPLACE EQUIPMENT

Until a half century ago the fireplace was the
main source of heat for each room in a home.
Various types of equipment have been
salvaged and offered for sale by antique
dealers.

Andirons, brass. Right and left. Queen
Anne foot. New England ball finial. C.
1810 .... $350.00

Andirons
Brass. 23½" high .... $ 165.00
Iron, ball on top 60.00
Bellows
Brass. 18" overall length, raised
ivy leaves, brass nozzle 55.00
Leather. 15" long, floral panels on
sides 50.00
Leather. Small 35.00
Wood. 20" long. Metal tip,
refinished 45.00
Wood. Brass tip 52.50

Coal Boxes
11½x14x14½". Brass covered,
hinged, slant lid with paper
picture. Brass feet 85.00
Brass. English 160.00
Coal Hod. Helmet-type with scoop.
Brass, burnished, lacquered 145.00
Crane. Iron. 17½" extended 47.50
Fenders
31" long. Iron base with screen,
brass top and finials 125.00
48" long. Brass, 3 claw feet 165.00
Grate. Iron, on legs. 9x17½" 48.40
Lighter. Cape Cod. Brass 35.00
Screens
37½" high. Screen, 18x24" panel.
Black lacquer, gold floral decor... 155.00
Hinged, 3-part. Roman Arch in
center of middle section 120.00
Spider. Early 95.00
Tools
Holder, shovel, poker and tongs.
Brass. Set 150.00

Fire Screen. Black and gold, lacquered,
oriental design $350.00

Set. English. 28" high, brass 150.00

Trammel. Hook. 39" long, hand-forged iron, extends to 59" for holding cooking pots over fireplace 130.00

FISCHER CHINA

In 1893 Morit Fischer founded the factory that produced Fischer wares in Herend, Hungary. This china's most outstanding characteristic is its elaborate, allover design in multicolors. The designs and colors are very much like those found in native Hungarian costumes.

Ewers

15" high. Brown, green, ivory majolica coloring. Signed and numbered. Late . . . . $ 80.00

16" high. High looping handle. Glossy brown finish with lighter flecks 185.00

17" high. Snake handle, floral decor on collar. 19th century 195.00

Vase. 9" high. Triangle top and base. Polychromed, gold trim. Signed. Made in Hungary. Late $35.00

20" high. Allover cutout, pink, and green lustre. Budapest. 300.00

Pitchers

9½" high. Ewer with ivorine ground. Pastel floral design. Budapest 125.00

15" high. Blue glaze, floral decor . 275.00

Urn. 12½" high, handled, open work, floral decor, gold trim 265.00

Vases

3" high. Gold top, cream bottom. Floral design. Signed. Late 35.00

8¼" high. 3" diam. near base. Multicolored enameling. open punch work, gold trim. Signed. Fischer-Budapest 245.00

10" high. Colorful enamel decor, open work, gold trim. Marked Fischer-Budapest 260.00

15" high. White ground, red, blue, gold trim. Open punch work top and bottom. Signed Fischer Budapest 375.00

FISH SETS

Fish sets were popular in the 1885-1905 period. The plates and platter were used when fish was served and generally were decorated with fish. Many of the sets now in existence are of Limoges or Austrian china.

12-piece set. Platter 22" long. White with various species of fish in brown, light gold trim. Impressed "Frieda"
$125.00

7-pc. set. Limoges, seashells, fish. 8¼" plates, 9½ x 16" platter . . . . . $ 175.00

7-pc. set. "Sie Back." 6 plates, platter . 110.00

8-pc. set. Bavarian. Platter, sauce boat, 6 plates 225.00

10-pc. set. "Selb Bavaria." H/P, covered casserole, gravy boat, 24" platter, six 9" plates 285.00

14-pc. set. "Elite" Limoges Chinaware. Seaweed in dark green, fish
in natural colors, edges of
burnished gold. In leatherette,
satin-lined case 300.00

14-pc. set. "Perle." 12 plates, platter,
sauce tureen. Limoges China..... 275.00

15-pc set. Haviland. Large platter,
sauce with tray, 12 plates 295.00

FLASHED [SOUVENIR] GLASS

In the late 1800's souvenir or commemorative
glass items were sold at expositions. The item
was usually made of an inexpensive pressed
glass and then partially "flashed" with ruby
red. Many bore the name of a place and a
date.

Mug. Handled, souvenir of Cincinnati,
Ohio $20.00

Tumbler. Souvenir of Irwin, Pa.. $18.50

Creamer. 2½" high. "Revere Beach
1905"........................ $ 20.00

Creamer and Sugar wth Double-
Handled Celery. Ruby corset
panels outlined in gold. Set 47.50

Mugs
Red Block. 3" high. World's Fair
1893..........................   20.00
Souvenir. Butter Arches. Red with
frosted band. "Winona July 1907"   20.00

Pitchers
2¼". World's Fair 1893, "Sister."
King's Crown pattern 25.00
4¼". "Riley" 1907. Indented panel
with Zipper pattern on bottom ...   42.50

Tumblers
King's Crown. Initialed 25.00
Red, clear Button Arches. "Alton
Bay, N.H." 22.50
"Triple Triangle." Red flashed 24.00

FLASKS

A flask is a container with a narrow neck,
used mainly for liquids. The whiskey flask is
shaped to fit a person's pocket. The historical
flasks of the late 18th century are very
desirable collectors' items and therefore
demand a good price.

Anchor and New London Glass
Works. Amber, pint .... $ 200.00
Byron & Scott. OP, amber, ½ pint ...   125.00
Chestnut. Blown, olive amber, 7½" .   50.00
Chestnut. Zanesville, 24 vertical
ribs. Dark amber, 6¾" 250.00
Corn For The World & Baltimore.
Green, quart...................   150.00
Cornucopia & Urn. Light olive, ½ pt. .   50.00
Cornucopia & Urn. OP, olive amber,
pint..........................   75.00
Double Eagle & Dot in Ovals. Amber,
½ pint 55.00
Double Eagle & Pittsburgh, Pa. in
oval. Amber, pint..............   75.00
Double Masonic Arch. Blue green, ½
pint..........................   200.00
Eagle & Cornucopia. Olive green, pt.   85.00
Eagle & For Pike's Peak. Aqua, ½
pint..........................   40.00
Eagle & Willington Glass Co. Green,
½ pint 120.00

South Jersey. 6" high, red color, pontil
mark $260.00

Eagle & Willington Glass Co. Olive
green, pint 100.00
For Pike's Peak, Eagle & Prospector.
Aqua, quart 45.00
Granite Glass Co. & Stoddard, N.H.
Amber, pint 60.00
Hunter, Fisherman, House. Aqua, 9"
high 125.00
Jenny Lind & Fisherville Glass
Works. Aqua, 9"................ 95.00
Masonic & Eagle. Olive amber, pint . 165.00
Midwestern, 32 Broken Swirled Ribs.
Light green, pint............... 150.00
Pumpkinseed. Amber, pint......... 22.50
Ravenna Glass Works. Aqua, pint,
7¾" high..................... 120.00
Regimental 85.00
Scroll. Clambroth, quart 100.00
Scroll. IP, blue aqua, quart 75.00
Scroll. OP, aqua, pint 35.00
Sheaf of Wheat. "Traveler's Com-
panion." Amber, quart 95.00
Sheaf of Wheat & Westford Glass Co.
Amber, pint 85.00
Stoddard & Double Eagle. Amber, ½
pint.......................... 55.00
Stoddard & Double Eagle. Olive
green, pint 65.00
Success To The Railroad. Olive
green, pint 150.00
Sunburst. Olive amber, ½ pint...... 250.00
Union & Clasped Hands. Aqua, ½ pt. 42.00
Union, Clasped Hands, Eagle. Aqua,
7½" high...................... 75.00
Washington, Eagle, Beaded Oval.
Green, pint 225.00
Washington & Taylor. Aqua, pint 95.00
Whiskeys
Flat oval. Sterling.............. 65.00
Sterling base, leather above.
Sterling top, pint 45.00
Webb Cameo. Ovid, pocket flask.
Hallmarked Sterling, goldwashed,
hinged lock top, 5¼" 725.00

FLOW BLUE

This term is used to denote Staffordshire and
other china on which the color "ran" during
the firing process and, upon being taken from
the kiln, had a smudged blue appearance.
Some of the better known patterns include
"Manilla," "Fairy Villas," "Scrinde" and
"Kyber."

Bone Dishes
Countess ....$ 12.50
Devon 15.00
Florida - Johnson 16.00

Deep Dish. 9" diam. "Sidney" ..$25.00
Lorne 12.50
Mikado 16.00
Bowls
Abbey pattern. 9" 45.00
Alaska. Serving, 9" 37.50
Amoy. Shallow, 7¼" 45.00
Argyle. 10" oval or round 42.50
Delph........................ 22.00
Regout's Flower 29.50
Ridgway. Osborne, soup........ 15.00
11". Fruit. Handled, rippled
scalloped border 60.00
Butter Dishes
Alaska. Covered 72.50
Fairy Villas. Covered........... 85.00
Labelle. Covered 75.00
Marie. Oval, covered 42.00

Plate. 10". "Melbourne." Gold trim
$27.50

Butter Pats

Argyle	10.00
Marie	5.00
Creamer and Sugar. Alaska	125.00
Creamer. Fairy Villas	62.00

Cups and Saucers

Amoy	50.00
Argyle. Grindley	35.00
Beaufort	35.00
Celtic	30.00
Florida	32.50
Haddon	30.00
Lorne. Demitasse	27.50
Lotus	35.00
Manilla	37.50
Stanley. Johnson Bros.	28.50
Temple	50.00
Watteau. Marked Staffordshire	30.00

Dinner Sets

Oregon. 32 pieces	600.00
Verona. Service for 12	1250.00

Dishes

Amoy. Covered vegetable. 12", octagonal	85.00
Fairy Villas. Vegetable, covered	95.00
Kesnick. Oval	48.50
Madras. Vegetable	60.00
Marguerite. Cov. veg. Grindley	28.50
Scinde. 6¾x8½", open	58.50
Warwick - Johnson. Covered vegetable, handled	55.00

Gravy Boats

Alaska	60.00
Pekin. Thos. Dimmock	45.00

Pitchers

7¾". Clarence. C. 1900. W. H. Grindley	95.00
10½". Morca. Goodwin. C. 1846	135.00

Plates

Alcock Scinde. 7-3/8"	32.50
Alcock Scinde. 10½"	40.00
Amoy. 6¼"	29.50
Amoy. 10"	35.00
Argyle. 8"	27.50
Chusan. 8¾"	30.00
Colley, Paris. Set of six	75.00
Devon. 11"	35.00
Eton. 9"	9.00
Fairy Villas. 9"	29.50
Fairy Villas. 10½"	35.00
Florida, Johnson. 8"	20.00
Florida, Johnson. 10"	27.00
Formosa. 9½"	32.00
Gotha. 9½"	30.00
Hong Kong. 9½"	35.00
Indian Jar. 9½"	35.00
Ironstone. 7-Petal Daisy. Brush strokes. Imp. "J.Keath." 9½"	38.00
Jeddo. 10½"	37.50
Kyber. 8½"	30.00

Platter. 12½" long. "Normandy" $40.00

Manilla. 7"	30.00
Manilla. 10½"	38.00
Marie. Grindley. 10"	22.50
Ming Po. 8½"	25.00
Mongul. 9"	20.00
Monarch [Myott]. 10"	24.00
Nankin. 7"	32.50
Non Pareil. 6"	12.50
Normandy. 8¾"	30.00
Oregon. 10½"	38.50
Oriental. 8"	35.00
Regent. 9"	18.00
Scinde. 7"	28.50
Shanghai. 8"	28.00
Shell. 7½"	18.50
Sobraon. 7"	22.50
Temple. 7"	27.50
Temple. 8½"	30.00
Temple. 9½"	32.50
Tonquin. 9"	38.50
Watteau. 8½"	27.00
Watteau. 9"	30.00

Platters

Amoy. 10x14"	75.00
Argyle. 8½x12½". Grindley	35.00
Argyle. 9x13"	58.50
Argyle. 10½x15¼"	65.00
Blantyre by Alcock	60.00
Chusan. Clemson. 14x18"	100.00
Coburg. 9½x12½"	75.00
Conway. 7¾x10½". New Wharf	35.00
Hong Kong. 14x18"	125.00
Kyber. 10"	38.00
Manilla. By Podmore, Walker & Co. 12x15½"	82.50
Mentone. 13x17". C. 1900	75.00
Non-Pariel. 16"	85.00
Ormonde. 12x16"	30.00
Pekin	90.00
Persian Bird. 14x18"	90.00
Scinde. Large	100.00
Sobraon. 10x14"	80.00

Tonquin. 10x14"	60.00

Sauce Dishes

Amoy.........................	17.00
Arabesque. 5"	15.00
Catherine Mermit	12.00
Fairy Villas	13.50
Non-Pariel	10.00
Scinde	18.00

Saucers

Amoy. 6".....................	18.00
Manilla	14.00

Soup Dishes

Amoy. 11". Davenport	38.50
Non-Pariel. Burgess & Leigh	28.50
Olympia	10.00
Scinde. 10½"	30.00
Sugar and Creamer. Alaska	125.00

Sugar Bowls

Arabesque	68.50
Hong Kong. Open	62.00
Manilla	75.00
Syrup Jug. La Belle. Original lid	55.00
Teapot with Tray. Hexagonal	95.00

Tureens

Hong Kong. 4½x5½x8". Ladle. Ironstone.....................	135.00
Madras. 12"	65.00
Melbourne. Small, with tray, ladle	125.00
Scinde. Large, with platter and rose knob	350.00
Wash Bowl. Sobraon. 13¼"	185.00
Wash Bowl and Pitcher. 12-sides. Floral decor, embossed leaves. Pitcher 13x17½". Set	250.00

FRAMES, See FURNITURE

FOSTORIA GLASS

Fostoria Glass Company began operations at Fostoria, Ohio in 1887. A few years later they moved to Moundsville, W. Va. where they

Finger Bowl with Underplate. Orange
$30.00

Goblet. "Holly" $20.00

continue to manufacture quality glassware. Many of their discontinued patterns and items are being collected today.

Bell. Glass .... $	9.50
Bowl. 10" diam. "Royal," amber footed flower	28.00
Bookends. Rearing horse, clear. Pair .	19.00
Candlesticks. 2-light, U-shaped. "American." Pair	28.00
Compote. 6" high, green. "Vintage" .	15.00
Cup and Saucer. "Fairfax"	4.00
Goblet. 10-oz., "June," crystal	8.50
Plate. Ruby glass	35.00
Rose Bowl. Pink, frosted, 5" high "Vintage"	35.00
Sherbet. "June," crystal	8.50
Vase. 9½" high. Footed, flared rim ..	10.00

FRANKOMA POTTERY

The factory was founded in 1936 at Sapulpa, Oklahoma by John N. Frank, a teacher of ceramics at the University of Oklahoma. In 1938 the factory burned, however, the business was re-established at another location in 1943. The firm continues in business today and employs more than 100 workmen. The founder died in November 1973 and his daughter, Joniece, is currently managing the business.

Bowl. 12" diam. Deep, mottled brown and yellow .... $	12.50
Cup and Saucer. Demitasse. Impressed mark	12.50
Honey Pot. Hive and embossed bee .	10.00
Jug. 8" high, aqua green to brown ..	18.00
Vases	
4½" high. Ball-shaped	10.00
6" high. Brown, impressed	12.50
6" high. Blue lustered. C. 1923 ...	22.50
Water Set. Lidded pitcher, 6 tumblers, in powder blue glaze decor. Set	38.00

FRY GLASS

The H. C. Fry Glass Company began operations in 1900 at Rochester, Pa. Their main product for the first 15 years or more was fine cut glass. As the demand waned, other types were produced.

A fine type of colored glass known as "Foval" is of interest to collectors now even though production did not begin until after 1925.

The glass is best described as being in pastel shades of smoky blues, pinks, greens and creams. Usually a combination of two colors was used together. For example, a compote bowl would be pink and the standard blue; whereas, another would have a blue bowl, a knobbed stem of clear glass and a blue base. A worker in the factory reported that not all pieces were stamped with the name "Fry," as just an occasional piece bore the mark. It was further reported that gold was used in the batches of glass in making "Foval" items.

The glass was expensive when retailed in its period and collectors are beginning to recognize its beauty and quality. The concern went bankrupt in 1929.

Bowls

8" diam., 4" high. Cut, 18-pt. Hobstar base, serrated edge. Sgnd. $	135.00
10" diam. Covered, marked "Fry" and dated	185.00

Bread Pan. Oven glass, marked, opalescent, dated, patented. Late	15.00
Butter Dish. Blue opalescent, deep blue knob on dome. Late	26.50
Candlesticks	
10½" high. Opalescent. Blue discs and threading. Pair	195.00
11" high. Pearlware. Blue spiral. Pair	285.00
Casserole. Oven glass, oval, signed .	18.50
Celery. 6¼" high, green	165.00
Cologne Bottle with Stopper. No trim, 6" high	85.00
Compotes	
3½" high, 12" diam. Signed. Green, white rims and wafer stem	125.00
7" high. Blue stem, bowl 5¾ wide .	155.00
10" high. Pink bowl, blue foot	178.50
12" high. Blue bowl and base, clear ball connector.............	180.00
14" high. Blue flared dome base under Foval bowl	225.00
Creamer	145.00
Cup and Saucer...................	85.00
Custard Cup. Dated 1919	35.00
Ewer. Bluish-opalescent in classic urn shape, applied orchid handles, 7¼ x 8" at top	185.00

Candleholders. 12" high. Deep blue, twisted stems. Pair $285.00

Goblet. Pedestaled stem. Rosaline pink, pearlware base and stem . . .	72.00
Juicer. Signed. Late	16.50
Luncheon Set. Blue rims, 4 plates, 4 soups, each 7½" diam., 4 cups and saucers. Set	495.00

Pitchers

Crystal with emerald green handle, knob on cover. 4 matching tumblers. Set	265.00
White. Applied blue handle. Lid with blue knob	165.00
Lemonade. 9½" high, jade green with cobalt blue handles, with 3 glasses. Set	100.00
11½" high. Covered, gold irid. with cobalt blue trim. Late	60.00

Plates

8½". Milky	40.00
9½". Blue trim on rim	55.00

Sherbets

Blue base	65.00
Clear green stem	47.50
Pink shaded, with plate. Set	85.00
Sugar Bowl. Covered	185.00

Teapots

On 8-footed hotplate. Smoky opalescent body, green handle and spout. Marked "Fry." Heat resisting glass	195.00
6½" high. Opalescent. Green handle, spout and finial	175.00
Tea Set. Miniature	125.00
Toothpick Holder. 3". Attached footed silver stand, silver rigaree halfway from top	45.00
Trivet. 9" diam. Opal color, 3 feet . . .	45.00

Vases

5" high. Grey blue with black applied band around top	87.50
7" high. Clear crackle glass with applied blue glass leaves	95.00
7½" high. Green base, cream body, blue bank around top edge .	145.00
12" high. Pink with green base . . .	195.00
Wine. Smoky crystal bowl with controlled bubble paperweight ball foot. 3¾" high. Unsigned	47.50

FULPER POTTERY

The American Pottery Company of Flemington, NJ. made pottery jugs and housewares from the early 1800's. They made Fulper Art Pottery from approximately 1910 to 1930.

Bowls

3-7/8x6¾". Art Deco with self base. Aqua green with flambe. Crackle glaze. Marked	60.00

4x10". Self-footed pedestal. Blue with yellow flambe, cobalt exterior. Bl. stamp mark	58.50
6". Lily, blue	48.50
13" diam., 2½" high. Pie crust edge, shaded moss rose with turquoise and blue running into it. Vertical ink mark	38.50
Candlesticks. Vivid blue matte and glossy glaze, tiny stars effect. 8" high, twisted stems, 4" diam. base. Pair	60.00
Compote. Marked. 3 gargoyles around base holding compote	150.00
Fairy Lamp. Electrified. 6¼" high, 4" base. Figure of girl in full skirt. Artist signed	58.00
Flower Holder. 7¾" high. Mushroom-shaped. Matte moss rose with light and dark blue crown ink mark and old label	42.00
Jardiniere. 6½" high, 8½" diam. Square handles with cutouts. Incised vertical mark and partial paper label	75.00

Bowl. 9½" diam. Flared. Blue predominating, shading to tan, red and black exterior. Signed $48.50

Jug. Brown tones. Original label	45.00
Lamp, Perfume. Pink, white lady	25.00
Pitcher. Signed	65.00
Pot. 10" widest diam. 7" high, blue . .	48.50

Vases

2½" high, 5" diam. Round, pushed down top, small neck opening. Green with grey and blue. Bl. stamp mark	42.50
4" high, 10" wide. Footed, flambe blue to cream	35.00
6" high. Waisted shape, speckled matte rose glaze, high gloss cobalt over glaze at top. Marked .	30.00
7" high, 4½" wide. Crackle, 3-handled. Blue top with pea green flambe. Bl. stamp mark	60.00

10½" high. Handles, aqua, flecked
and decorated with golden tan ...   75.00
12" high. High glaze mottled
green, browns, silver flecks 78.50

FURNITURE

Prices vary considerably on furniture. The
quality of workmanship, kind of wood, the
maker's name, if known, style and condition,
are all determining factors in influencing the
prices.

An attempt has been made to arrive at an
average price on each item listed. It is hoped
that this list will serve as a guide. However,
the above enumerated factors must be taken
into consideration in arriving at a representative price.

FURNITURE STYLES
APPROXIMATE DATES

William and Mary 1688-1710
Queen Anne 1710-1750
Chippendale 1754-1780
Hepplewhite 1786-1800
Sheraton 1790-1810
Empire 1810-1830
Duncan Phyfe 1800-1840
Early Victorian 1830-1868
Late Victorian 1870-1900

Bed. Oak $250.00

BEDS

Brass. C. 1890 ....$ 750.00
Brass, heavy. Single size, polished .. 345.00
Brass. With springs 500.00
Brass and Iron. Full size. Lacy
ornamentation 425.00
Cannon Ball Rope. Soft wood.
Refinished 250.00
Highback. Iron 60.00
Jenny Lind-Type
Day. Opens into double bed, with
pad and pillows 250.00
Half Size. Soft wood 200.00
¾ size. Walnut 250.00
Full size, spindle foot, solid
headboard. Original finish in
rough condition 375.00
Maple. Full size. Pineapple-carved
posts. 4' high 300.00
Maple. Full size. Turned posts. 40"
high 2000.00
Maple Canopy. Turned posts. 6' high.
Refinished 2000.00
Oak, heavy. Carved 100.00
Post Jester, Country. Dark stained .. 795.00
Rope Spool. Identical headboard and
footboard. Heavy posts 275.00
Sheraton Canopy. Maple. Twin size.
Flame finial, posts 74" high. C.
1810 .... 2500.00
Sheraton Canopy. Pine headboard,
square headposts. Fully reeded
with turned footposts 1500.00
Victorian Walnut. 82½" high head-
board, double size. Refinished ... 500.00

BENCHES

Church Bench. 36" high, 48" long.
Pine 135.00
Cobbler's Benches
Pine. 44" long, 17" wide, 2" solid
plank. Refinished 365.00

Cobbler's Bench. 20x41" long . $265.00

Kneeling Bench. 7½x8x20". Penna.
$22.50

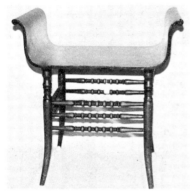

Sleigh Bench. 15x22x24". Bent Oak
$55.00

Solid plank. 18" wide, 1" thick,
17" high with drawers. Leather
seat and porcelain casters on legs ... 250.00
Kneeling Bench. Square nails.
6¼x7¼x14" long. New England . 65.00
Mammy Bench. Made in Western
Pennsylvania. Original green
paint. 6' long.................... 800.00
Water Bench. Pie trough lined with
zinc. 35" high 225.00
Water Bench. Bucket. Pine, poplar.
68" high back. 18x43" bench
space, 3 - 4" high side by side
drawers above, cupboards above
and below, 1 shelf, 2 panelled
doors 1200.00

BENTWOOD

Arm Chair 65.00
Chair. 16" diam. seat. 34½" high.
Market Thonet, One Park
Avenue, New York 45.00

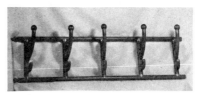

Bentwood Hat Rack. 9x36½". 5 swivel
hooks. Brass fittings $55.00

Child's High Chair................ 85.00
Cradle. Scarce................... 250.00
Easel........................... 37.50
Hat Rack. Muffler and glove holder.
7 pegs, 28" wide, 32" high 85.00
Rocker 250.00

BOOK CASES

Mahogany. English. C. 1815 .... 800.00
Oak. 5 slats, 6 shelves on large,
round pedestal base that re-
volves. 17½" square, 42½" high . 175.00
Travelling Bookshelf. English Col-
lapsible. George II. 6x24x28" 725.00

BOXES

Candle Box. Dovetailed Pine. Sliding
cover. 12" long. 5x5" ends 50.00
Candle Box. English, oak. C. 1850.
4x7x18" 75.00
Deed Box. 8½x14". Black leather,
6½" deep. Red leather trim, gold

Mahogany. 3¼x6¾x10-1/8". Paper
lined.Reverse painting on glass inside
of lid $42.50

Penna. Ballot. 6x7x11½". Brass
hardware $45.00

tacks, old brass escutcheon and
ring handle, on bottom a page
from Morning Courier & New York
Inquirer, 1834 .... 150.00
Wood. 5¾x8". Convex lid. Painted
yellow, green stripes. Floral
bouquet on top. Paper lined...... 50.00

CABINETS

Crescent. Adams. 18th century.
Angelica Kaufmann-type panels.
34x53"........................ 4500.00

New York. 16½x26½". Cherry.
Hepplewhite. C. 1800 .... $450.00

Curio. Rosewood, red lacquer. Lined
with tea paper. 13x24x45" 450.00
Miniature. English. Rosewood, early
19th century. 8½x12x22" 575.00
Tea Poy. English. Regency. Mahogany. 12x17½x32". C. 1810 ... 650.00

CANDLE SHIELDS

Floral needlepoint, brass stands. Pair   425.00
French. Needlepoint and beads.
Angel with cherubs. 21½" high ..   265.00

CANDLE STANDS

Cherry. Spade feet, small 275.00
Cherry. Tilt top, oval, with top in
place. 14¼x22¾x26½" 385.00
Curly Maple. Cutout, tilt top 400.00
Hepplewhite. Pine. 16½" square
top, 28¾" high. Natural finish....   165.00

New England. 18" high. C. 1710
$850.00

Mahogany. Tilt top, bird-claw feet...	200.00
Mahogany. Wishbone feet. C. 1860 .	265.00
Maple. Tripod base	200.00
Pine. 27" high, 27" square top, tapered Hepplewhite legs	175.00
Windsor. Turned, dish tray. Early 18th century. All original	1500.00

CHAIR AND ROCKERS

CHAIRS

Adams-style. 32" high. Cane seat, original black & gold decor	425.00
Arm. Maple, cane seat and rounded back	95.00
Arrowback. Plank seat	125.00
Bamboo. Maple. Rush seats, painted light tan with black in joints	275.00
Belter Side. Rosewood. Back scrolls, bunches of grapes and roses. Needlepoint seat	2000.00
Bent Half-Arrow. Original stencil decor	165.00
Captain's. Pine. Unfinished........	100.00
Captain's. Rollback type. Refinished .	225.00
Captain's High Chair. Foot rest, 28" high, original red paint	145.00

Child's Corner Chair. Basketry seat.
Shaker. Mt. Lebanon, N.Y.....$200.00

Chippendale. Ribbon back. C. 1840-50
$675.00

Carpet, Folding. E. W. Vaill, Worcester, Mass. C. 1863. 19" high	135.00
Child's Arm Chair. English. C. 1847. 17x20x28"	495.00
Child's Arrowback. Plank seat	135.00
Child's Captain. Hickory plank seat. Original condition	100.00
Child's High Chair. Variety of American woods. 36" high	60.00
Child's Highchair. Windsor-type arms	120.00
Chippendale Centennial. Dining. Cherry, 40½" high C. 1876	350.00
Chippendale Corner Marquetry	400.00
Chippendale Country. Slat back, 18th century. Split rush seat	375.00
Chippendale. English. Leather back, mahogany. C. 1760	850.00
Chippendale. English. George II. Mahogany. C. 1750. Pair	1250.00
Chippendale. Irish. Centennial. Ribbon-carved back. Reupholstered in dark red velvet. 40" high	600.00

Chippendale. Mahogany frame, rush
   seat 650.00
Curly Maple. Refinished 175.00
Edwardian. English. Rosewood. C.
   1910........................... 80.00
Empire. Mahogany, carved. Set of 4 . 350.00
Empire. Mahogany. Fiddle back, slip
   seat. Original condition 100.00
Empire. Side. Walnut 100.00

Hepplewhite Arm. English. Satinwood inlay at backsplat. Oval
   pattern at cross stretcher. Mahogany. C. 1795. Pair.............. 2500.00
Hepplewhite Side. Mahogany, rosettes in back of splats 400.00
Hitchcock. Set of six 1000.00
Hitchcock Pillowback. Windsor. Unrestored 200.00
Hitchcock type. Fancy turnings, rush
   seat. Refinished 135.00
Ladderback. Rush seat, ball-turned
   stretcher. C. 1740 .... 250.00
Ladderback. Splint seat. Original ... 50.00

Louis XV. Beechwood. Occasional
   armchair. Serpentine frame, covered with textured gold fabric.... 850.00
Maple. Plank seat, spindle back 60.00
Morris. Oak. Ball and claw feet,
   finials on brass rod. Back
   adjustment 50.00
Morris. Walnut. Carved lion's paw
   foot and arms, with ram's horn
   and acanthus leaf. Back adjustment 75.00
New England Pillowback Side. Eagle
   on splat. Original stencil. Rush
   seat 260.00
Oriental. Teak. Carved figures,
   flowers, foliage, dragon front
   feet. 46½" overall height. Made
   in Japan. C. 1900 .... 350.00
Plank Bottom. Painted black, gold
   stencil 60.00
Queen Anne. Corner. American.
   Pine and tiger maplewood. Duck
   feet, slanted, pierced slats. Deep
   scalloped skirt. Restored 450.00
Queen Anne. Corner. English,
   walnut, drop-in seat 2200.00

Folding Carpet Chair. Refinished
$125.00

Potty Chair. 41" high. Penna. Possibly
hand altered $70.00

Victorian Lady's. Re-upholstered, red velvet $500.00

Queen Anne. English. Cabriole legs. Walnut. Well-shaped knee and pad feet of golden color. Pair 2500.00
Queen Anne. Maple. Booted foot, scalloped apron. C. 1770 .... 1000.00
Queen Anne. Pilgrim armchair. Bulbous turnings. Spanish feet ... 1200.00
Queen Anne. Rhode Island country style, duck feet 800.00
Queen Anne. Scotland. Mahogany. Fan decoration, slip seat 550.00
Queen Anne Side. Country. Bulbous turnings, original ball feet, rope seat replaced 300.00
Queen Anne Side. English. Walnut. Drop-in seat, tapestry. C. 1710 ... 1000.00
Regency Dining. English. Reproduction. Sabre legs, mahogany. C. 1810. Set of four 750.00
Regency. English. Trafalgar. Mahogany. Black line. Set of four 1000.00
Tub Wing. English reproduction 500.00
Victorian Eastlake. Lady's chair. Re-upholstered 125.00

Victorian Gentleman's. Grape and nut carvings, shield back. Refinished 500.00
Victorian Lady's. Walnut. Finger carved, oval back 450.00
Victorian Side. Walnut frame. Needlepoint seat covering 200.00
Victorian Side. Walnut frame. Refinished 250.00
Victorian Side. Walnut. Rose back, needlepoint seat 250.00
Victorian Sleepy Hollow. Curved, serpentine front. Cabriole legs ... 500.00
William Penn-style. Dining. C. 1790, horsehair seats. Set of six 1500.00
Windsor Chairs
    Arm. Bow Back 500.00
    Arm. Maple legs, hickory bent-back. Made by Joseph Hensey, Phila. 1000.00
    Arm, Writing. Half-arrow back, with pillow-back rest. Stencil decor 1500.00
    Arm. 9 spindles, invalid chair hole closed, 4 legs come thru seat..... 440.00
    Bow Back. 7 spindles, black 75.00
    Bow Back. Early, refinished 100.00

Windsor. Comb back. Black, gold trim
$700.00

Bow Back. Signed. C. 1760. Set of
5 . . . . 2500.00
Brace Back. 9 spindles 450.00
Butterfly. Bamboo turning. Ori-
ginal condition 150.00
Child's Bow Back. Shaped arms,
original black paint 450.00
Fanback. 18th century. Set of 2 . . .   750.00
Fiddleback. Original stencil. Set of
4 . . . .   300.00
Rabbit Ears. Set of 4. . . . .   425.00
Rodback. Set of 2 . . . .   250.00
Seven Spindles. Refinished 300.00
Side. Step-down type. 150.00
Wing. English. Deep buttoned-in
hide. Mahogany, reproduction . . .   850.00

ROCKERS

Arrowback. Writing Arm. Western
Pennsylvania origin. Signed S. C.
Tebner. C. 1825. Original black
paint, red & yellow decor. Scarce .   950.00
Boston. Painted black 175.00
Boston. Refinished 240.00
Boston. Roll back 240.00

Rocking Chair. Pressed decoration on back. C. 1915 . . . . **$45.00**

Child's Victorian. Ring turnings,
on top & arms. Diagonal slot in
back covered with corduroy. Cane
seat 75.00
Comb Back. Painted 235.00
Ladderback. Double, bearing arms, 4
slats, finial at top of posts.
Original splint seat painted black .   145.00
Ladderback. Splint seat 65.00
Lincoln. Life-size grape carving 175.00
Mahogany. Swan-head arms. Orig-
inal 175.00
Platform. Carpet upholstery 165.00
Victorian, Lady's. Reupholstered,
green velvet 235.00
Victorian Sleepy Hollow-type. Up-
holstered 260.00
Windsor Arms. Bird cage. Refinished   375.00
Windsor. Bamboo turned. 7 spindles.
Shaped saddle seat. Rough cond-
ition 200.00

CHESTS

Apothecary. Pine. 15 drawers, 57"
long, 16" deep, 43½" high. Strip-
paneled ends 750.00
Blanket Chests
Pennsylvania Dutch. 2 drawers.
Chippendale brasses and feet.
Stippled light green with dull red
trim 1500.00
Pennsylvania Dutch. Painted
panels. C. 1820-1830. Original . . . 1650.00
Pine:
Miniature. Bracket foot, 19x10x-
11" high. Original 135.00
20x24x42". Refinished 200.00
Sheraton. Crotch curly maple 1400.00

19½x29x32½". Golden Oak. Original hardware, dovetail drawers. Serpentine top drawer **$135.00**

3 drawers over 2 over 5. 22½ x 40½ - x 66½". Original finish, replaced brasses, side columns $3800.00

Walnut. Somerset County, Pa. Lift top, 3 drawers, 51½" long, 22" wide, 27½" high. Original Dutch decoration under paint. Rough condition 650.00

Bow Front. Mahogany. Late 19th century. 36½" high, 39½" wide . . .   750.00
Bride's. Pine. Montgomery County, Pa. Name of "John Adam Scohr 1784" on front. Original 750.00

Chippendale. American walnut. 18th century. 63½" high, 41" long 4500.00
Chippendale. Bow front. Cherry, 23¾ x 34½ x 41½". Refinished 3500.00
Chippendale. Curly maple. Six drawers with original brasses. New England. C. 1800. 19x40x56" high 4000.00
Chippendale, Double. English. Dressing slide. Mahogany. C. 1800 . . . . 3500.00

Blanket Chest. 22x28x49". Chippendale style, pine strap hinges. Eastern Lancaster Co., Pa. C. 1780 . . . . $850.00

Cherry. Inlaid. 20¼ x 36¾ x 38¾". Pine and chestnut secondary woods. Original eagle brasses $1900.00

Original eagle brasses from chest [close up]

Chippendale. Scotland. Original brasses. Mahogany. 37x35½" high 1250.00

Chippendale. Three drawers over 2 drawers over four. Dovetailed, bracket feet, reeded quarter columns. 39x22½x64" high 3500.00

Chippendale. Walnut, four drawers, inset columns, 3'5" high. Refinished 3000.00

Chippendale Highboy. 6'3" high, 3'6" long. Walnut. Broken arch top. Refinished 5500.00

Chippendale Highboy. Mahogany. New England. C. 1770-80, all original 6000.00

Commode. Bedside. English. Georgian. Mahogany. C. 1800 .... 400.00

Commode. Bedside. English. Mahogany. C. 1820 .... 400.00

Commode. Bedside. English. Chippendale. Mahogany. Bottom section converted to a pull-out drawer. 18½x19x30" 750.00

Commode. English. Regency. Mahogany. C. 1805 .... 1000.00

Commode. Pine. Small size, lift top. Off-center drawer. Refinished 250.00

Curly "Tiger-Stripe" Maple. Chippendale style. 4 full and 2 half drawers. 18x38x45" 1250.00

Davenport. English. Rosewood. 19¼x25x34". C. 1810........... 850.00

Davenport. English. Victoria. Walnut. C. 1860 .... 450.00

Demi-Lune. Brown marble laid on top, inlaid, brass pulls, decor. 19¼x39x33" high 500.00

Hepplewhite. Cherry. Four drawers with inlay, plank ends 750.00

Hepplewhite. Mahogany inlay. Bow front. New England. Late 18th century 950.00

Hepplewhite. 24x39½x42. Mahogany and curly maple 1200.00

Hepplewhite. Pine. Four drawers with veneered mahogany fronts. Small size 650.00

Highboy. Cherry. New England origin. 9 drawers with brass pulls. 6' high 6500.00

Highboy. Walnut. Lancaster County, Pa. origin. 6'6" high, 22" wide, 9 drawers with brass pulls 5500.00

Louis XV. Bombe, inlaid. 2 drawers, 46x20x35½" high 4500.00

Lowboy. English. Pad feet with knees and tresses. Mahogany, original brasses. 18½x28x29" 3500.00

Lowboy. New England. Walnut. 31" high, 36" wide 7500.00

Ice Chest. Oak. Refinished ...$250.00

Miniature. 12x24x26½". Plank ends, inlaid escutcheons, replaced hardware. Sheraton. Pa. $625.00

Lowboy. Original brasses. Mahogany. George II.   30x18½x27" high. C. 1740 .... 3500.00

Mahogany. Chest and cabinet. Painted panels, 7'10" high, 49" wide. Chippendale style. C. 1795. English origin 2400.00

Maple Tiger Stripe. Refinished 1000.00

Maple. 4 drawers, 40" wide, 36" high. Turned legs 475.00

Maple. Turnip feet, 40" high. C. 1720. Original 1500.00

Victorian. 19½x40x73". Walnut, 3 drawers on bottom, 2 drawers on top, wooden knobs. Marble top, swivel mirror $350.00

Miniature Chests

Country style, pine, paneled and original 150.00

Sheraton style. Cherry, 14½x9" deep. Refinished 350.00

Sheraton style. Tiger maple. Paneled end, turned cherry feet. Refinished 450.00

Walnut. Ceramic drawer pulls, 4 drawers. 13¾" high, 13" wide ... 450.00

Walnut. 16x30x40". Marble top, carved pulls. Refinished 350.00

Oak Chests

Ice. 15x23x35". Refinished 240.00

2 drawers over 4 large drawers .. 100.00

Pennsylvania. Early. Cherry. French bracket feet. Bellflower inlay on posts. Divided top drawers. 13¾x41¾x39" high 1000.00

Pine Chests

Cottage type 225.00

3 long drawers. 34" wide, 29" high, cutout base. Refinished..... 175.00

4 long drawers, solid ends, cutout base. 40" wide, 42" high 350.00

4 long drawers, paneled ends, cutout base 175.00

4 long drawers, 38" wide, solid ends 350.00

4 long drawers, mirror on top 265.00

4 long drawers, solid ends, 46" high, 42½" long. Original curly maple knobs, turned feet 400.00

Queen Anne. Birch. 6 drawers on frame. C. 1750. Original 4000.00

Queen Anne. English. Walnut, original handles. 20x32½x33". C. 1710 .... 4000.00

Queen Anne. Massachusetts original. 62" high, 36" wide. Walnut with herringbone inlay. C. 1730. Original condition 18500.00

Queen Anne Highboy. Early American. C. 1790. Rough condition 5500.00

Sea Captain's Map Chest. Refinished   265.00

Sea Chest. Painted. 12½" deep, 14½" wide, 25½" long. Early hardware, strap hinges and handles. Initialed cover. Interior frame holds 15 bottles 250.00

Sea Chest. Pine, dovetailed construction, medium size 175.00

Sheraton. Walnut. Country type, split top drawers, turned legs. Refinished 850.00

Walnut. Chippendale period. O.G. bracket feet. Original except for brasses. Refinished 1750.00

Walnut. Victorian. 4 drawers, fruit carved handles. Refinished 450.00

Walnut. Victorian dresser. Carved pulls, marble insert on top. Swinging mirror. Original 475.00

COBBLER'S BENCHES, See BENCHES

CRADLES

Early. Primitive. 4 turned posts, solid
headboard with roll top. Solid
splayed sides, solid footboard,
rockers. Original red paint 175.00
Pine. 13x34" open sides. Original . . . 140.00
Pine. Hooded, dovetailed, 14x37".
Refinished 195.00
Pine. 43" rockers. Refinished 150.00
Victorian. Folding spool 120.00
Walnut. Hooded 250.00
Walnut. Open spindle-type con-
struction. Arms extend from high
back 175.00
Walnut. 45". Original condition 150.00

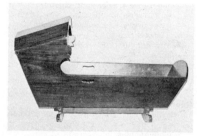

Bonnet-top. 44" long. Mahogany
$275.00

CUPBOARDS

Barber's. Hanging.23x37" striped
maple, glass door 65.00

Corner Cupboards.
Cherry:
Blown glass panels. 2 paneled
doors on bottom. 54" wide, 7'9"
high 1600.00

Cathedral door with blown glass
panes. French feet. 2 doors and 3
drawers on base of tiger maple.
8' high to top of center pediment.
Two pieces 3000.00
One drawer, 2 glass doors at
top, 2 solid drawers below. 42"
wide, 6'10" high. Original
condition 850.00
Chippendale influence, bow-
front, all original 3000.00
Queen Anne period. Two pieces,
7'8" high. Arched doors with
glass panels, butterfly shelves.

Original brass "H" hinges on
doors 4200.00

Mixed wood cupboard. 16½x37x78".
Pierced sides $195.00
Mahogany. Chippendale. Phila-
delphia. 7½' high. Ball and claw
feet, gadroon molding. Broken
arch top with flame finials 5000.00
Pennsylvania Dutch. Pine and
maple. Flat-back type, carved
pillars. Refinished 1200.00
Pine:
Bow-front doors, with glass.
2-piece, 7'10" high. Dental
molding, solid door, "H" hinges.
Refinished 1000.00
Flat-back, double glass doors,
6'10" high, 4' wide. Refinished . . 850.00
Walnut:
Chippendale-style. Pennsylvania.
Scrolled broken-arch top, 3 brass
finials and scrolled bracket feet.
Solid door. Refinished 3500.00
Solid door, 6½' high, good,
rough condition 650.00

Chippendale. 40½ x 44". Slant front.
Ox-bow. Block and fan interior.
Original brasses. C. 1765. Mahogany
$6800.00

Corner. 44x82". Pine. All original
$575.00

Two paneled doors, 40x82". Re-
finished 850.00
Hanging Cupboards
   Poplar, painted and stippled to
   resemble tiger maple. One shelf,
   20" wide, 29" high 350.00
   Three-shelf. Stripped, ready to
   finish. 2x3' 100.00
Jelly Cupboard.   Pennsylvania
   Dutch 850.00
Pewter Cupboard. 18th century pine.
   With plate rack 1000.00

DESKS

Chippendale style. Cherry. Slant
   front. 3'6" high, 32" wide at feet .. 2300.00
Chippendale. Maple. Slant front.
   Late 18th century. 40½" high, 45"
   wide. Scroll bracket feet 1750.00

Curly Maple. New England. Chippendale. Slant front. Writing
   height 31½", 43½" to top, 35¾"
   wide. Refinished 2500.00
Hepplewhite. Early Pennsylvania.
   Eagle inlay. Original condition ... 6000.00
Hepplewhite. Inlaid. 6 drawers, 6
   cubbies. Original hardware 995.00
Hepplewhite. Slant top. Solid mahogany case. Pine veneered
   drawer fronts, original brass bail
   pulls. Inlaid interior around
   drawer edges. C. 1790-1800 ..... 1500.00
Lady's Desk. Victorian, walnut, 4
   drawers below writing lid. 28" wide   450.00
Lady's Slant Top. Maple. 36" wide.
   Good writing interior 1000.00
Lap Desk. Mahogany, brass filigree,
   applied decor. 12" wide, 10" long .   125.00
Lap Desk. Mother-of-Pearl inlay
   decor, 16" long, 9¼" wide 140.00
Lap Desk. Walnut. Brass bound
   corners and strap work. Brass
   shield in top. 6x9½x15½" 140.00
Pine. Slant front, Sheraton legs. One
   deep drawer, well for chair. 32"
   wide, gallery at back. Refinished . 1000.00
Plantation Desk. Pine, rough 300.00
Postmaster's. Walnut, two pieces. C.
   1850 .... 1325.00
Roll Tops
   Oak. S-curve. American 495.00
   Oak. 36", S-curve 295.00
Schoolmaster's. Oak, cubbie-hole,
   slant top, two drawers. Refinished   285.00
Schoolmaster's. Walnut. Rough 275.00

Schoolmaster's Desk. 26x31x36". 1 drawer. Golden Oak $95.00

Schoolmaster's. Kneehole type. 4 drawers on each side, compartments on top. Mahogany veneer drawer fronts. Top 25x59" 450.00
Slant-Front. Mahogany. 4 drawers, drawer slides. English. 10¼x-39x44½" high 1250.00
Slant-Front. Scotland. Mahogany. 36" long, 40" high 1250.00
Victorian
7" high. Cylinder's 600.00
Lawyer's. Walnut. Signed Bethel, Maine 350.00
Store. Walnut, 6' wide, 21 teardrop handles, pigeon holes, refinished 395.00

DOUGH TROUGHS

Chestnut. Lid, 4 slender pine legs. 18x28x28" high Refinished 250.00

Dough Riser $375.00

Pine
Covered. 2 handles each end, 28" long 135.00
Pennsylvania Shaker type. 30¾" high, 32" long. Lid, splayed legs with stretchers. Rare 350.00
Square, tapered legs 135.00
Poplar. Covered, refinished 165.00
Tulip Wood [Poplar]. Cover, turned legs, dovetailed, 21x28x36". Pine-colored finish.............. 195.00
Walnut. Splayed legs, dovetailed corners, 20x27x39". Refinished .. 285.00

DRY SINKS

Butternut. Light walnut. 18x28½x-32". 2 doors, refinished 225.00
35" high, 20" wide, 42" long. 2 doors, 1 shelf inside. Original stippling and finish. Wood oak leaf, pull drawer. Plank ends..... 175.00
Pine
One door at base. 16½x30x32" high. Original condition 240.00
One drawer, 2 doors. Refinished . 325.00
Poplar and Pine. Highback. 4'2" 2 drawers, 2 doors below. Refinished 385.00

Miniature Dry Sink. 15x25½x37". 1 door below, two shelves $150.00

Poplar

Low back, doors below	175.00
Splash board, no drawers. 19½ x-49". Refinished	300.00
Walnut. 1 drawer, 2 doors below. 44" long, 33" high, unfinished	265.00

FLAX WHEELS

11½" deep, 16½" wide, 54" high . . .	150.00
American turnings, treadle missing .	125.00
American. Small, complete with distaff	185.00

FOOT STOOLS

Mahogany. England. Fluted leg, slip seat, 17" high, 16" wide	100.00
Mahogany Veneer. Beading around edge, slender cabriole legs. 14x10½x10" high	95.00
Mahogany Veneer. Empire style. Short, round legs. 8x8x12"	75.00
Octagon shape. 5x10½x12" long. Carpet-top lid opens to reveal Rockingham spitoon inside	135.00
Queen Anne-type feet. Blue needle-point ground, rose pattern. Late . .	100.00

FRAMES

Curly Maple. 1½ x15x17"	85.00
Gold Gilt	
7½ x20½" opening	35.00
10½ x12¾". Raised berries and leaves on top, bottom and sides . .	40.00
Mahogany. Gold liner. 35" square . .	65.00
Pine. Stripped to natural wood. 14x16"	35.00
Walnut Frames [Measurements given are for size of opening]	
8¼ x8½". Pair	50.00
8¾ x11", deep	30.00

Daguerrotype. 13x15". Mahogany with copper-type insert. Gold trim $45.00

8x12". Cross bar corners	25.00
11x15½". Carved, crisscross corners	32.00
16¼ x21", deep	55.00
17¼"x22". Gold gilt	65.00
18¼ x27½". Deep leaf carving around edge, gold liner. Pair	75.00
Shadow Box. 28x32". Double liner of gold and ebony. 7" deep	90.00
Walnut Frames, Oval.	
12x14"	32.50
12x14". Gold liner	45.00
13¼ x15¼". Gold liner. Pair	85.00
16x19"	100.00

HAT RACKS

Oval. 13" long. Gilded. Fruit and flowers. Pair $65.00

Mid-Victorian Hall Hat Rack. Expandable, 14 holders. Walnut 50.00

Accordion-type. 9 pegs 40.00
Walnut. Accordion-type. Porcelain
  tips on 7 pegs. Refinished 40.00
Walnut. Accordion-style, 9 porcelain
  tips 45.00
Walnut. Accordion-type. 12 pegs
  with porcelain tips. All original . . . 60.00

ICE CREAM PARLOR FURNITURE

Child's table with two chairs . . $100.00

Chairs
  Straight, heart back 55.00
  Straight, spectacle 55.00
  With arms 85.00
Stool, Counter. 30" high, 12" diam.
  seat 55.00
Table. 27" square, oak top 135.00
Table and 4 chairs. Table, 30"
  round wood top. Chairs, 14" diam.
  replaced seats. Refinished. Set . . . 300.00

LOVE SEATS

Victorian. 54" long. Porcelain casters,
original upholstery, button back
$550.00

Victorian. Mirror back. Upholstered
$700.00

Hepplewhite. Walnut, spade feet,
  bellflower inlay. Refinished and
  re-upholstered 850.00
Sheraton . Late. Refinished, reuphol-
  stered in velvet, nailhead trim.
  52x32x35" high 550.00
Victorian. Late. Walnut 300.00
Victorian. Walnut. Large size, rose
  carving on 3 crests. Refinished
  recovered 850.00
Victorian. Walnut. Mirror back,
  Original condition 550.00
Walnut. Finger carved. Refinished . . 500.00

MAGAZINE RACKS

Canterbury. English. Mahogany.
  15½x19½x25". Early 750.00
Oak. 13½x18". Turned spindles,
  pressed carving, brass studs 40.00

Canterbury. American. 14½x18x-
19½". Veneered $385.00

Wall-type. Victorian. 13½x23". $85.00

Wall Rack. Victorian. Walnut.
13½x26". Eastlake style. Carved,
turned posts each side, scrolled
and cutout design. Original 75.00

MANTELS

Adams-style. Carrara marble. Shelf,
70" long, 42x51". Eagle, acorn
and wheat motif............... 1000.00
Pine. C. 1810-1820. 52½" high, 68"
wide. Curved top section 250.00
Pine. Painted white 200.00
Walnut, Solid. Fireplace. Carved, C.
1860......................... 300.00

MIRRORS

Brass. Standing. Oval for dressing
table. Cupids and floral decor. 15"
high, 16" wide 125.00
Chippendale. Brass eagle finial,
14x27½", old glass, with 10x17"
liner 500.00
Chippendale. English. Mahogany.
18x26"........................ 600.00

Shaving Mirror. 15" high. Wooden
frame and pedestal $35.00

Chippendale. Inlaid mahogany, gilt
and banding. 21x40"............ 500.00
Convex Regency Wall Mirror. Carved
and gilded eagle. 34" high, 27"
wide......................... 1000.00
Courting Mirror. 12x16½".C. 1780 .. 600.00
Dresser Mirrors
Bird's Eye Maple. One drawer,
with glass 375.00
English. Applewood. Oval, one
drawer........................ 275.00
3 small drawers over 1 large
drawer. 8½x13x22¼" 650.00
Federal-type. Gilded frame, reverse
painting on glass tablet, 9½x11".
Overall dimensions 18½x32" 350.00
Mahogany. Two sections. Original
glass, painting in top. 18½x34" ... 235.00
O.G. 28x42" 125.00
O.G. Pine. 22½x32½". Thin old
glass. Refinished 150.00

Dresser Mirror. 13½x33x34½". Set jewelry drawer with lift-top lid. Cherry
$275.00

Serpentine Front. English. Hepplewhite. Mahogany. 7x14½x21" ...	650.00
Sheraton. Carved maple frame, 21x29", reeded pilaster, cornice. Unfinished	275.00
Toilet. English. Hepplewhite. Oval, mahogany. 8¼x17½x19½"	450.00
Victorian. Oval, gold leaf, 38x42", Ornate......................	500.00
Walnut. C. 1870. Reverse painting on glass above. Old glass. 12x19" ...	165.00

SECRETARIES

Empire. Mahogany veneer. Scroll front, bookcase top, 39½" wide, 67" high.....................	600.00
Federal. Mahogany. Two pieces. Top 11¾x42". Bottom 24½" deep. Overall height 84½". Labeled Pittsburgh, Pa.	1650.00
Hepplewhite. Cherry. Broken pediment top. French bracket feet. 7'8" high	3800.00
Hepplewhite. Mahogany. Tambour type, sliding doors	1650.00
Regency. Mahogany	1200.00
Sheraton. Mahogany, brass hardware and finials. 74" high, 40" wide........................	1800.00
Sheraton. Mahogany. Four drawers, arched door panels. C. 1815	1500.00

Secretary. Glass-panelled, 2 doors above. Roll-top desk opening. Victorian
$1250.00

Sheraton. Mahogany. Inlaid, small reeded legs, 40" wide, 54" high. Original panes	1200.00

SETTLES

Arrowback	600.00
Chippendale. Walnut. 3-seated, ribbon-back, ball and claw feet. 62½" long, 41" high, falcon arms. Made in Germany. Red brocade upholstered slip seat............	1750.00
Mammy Bench. 54" long. Original ..	650.00
Pennsylvania Dutch. Hitchcock-type. 6'4" long, 17" high, 20" deep. Hitchcock turnings, half spindles, deeply curved arms. Original paint	950.00

Mammy Bench. 72" long, with keeper. Restenciled with original design. 4-chair back $750.00

Close up of above bench showing details

Windsor-type. Bamboo style turnings. 6'7" long, 37½" overall height. Refinished 1000.00
Windsor-type. Duck bill arms, 8 legs, 6½" long, 36½" high, seat 17" wide. C. 1815. Original decor 1200.00
Windsor-type. Duckbill top. 47" long, 37" high. Hickory and pine. Small size. Refinished 850.00

SEWING MACHINES

Busy Bee. Hand-type. 3¼x6" base. New England 30.00

White Sewing Machine Co., Cleveland, Ohio. Last patent date June 3, 1913 . . . . 40.00

SEWING STANDS

Drop Leaf. Cherry and walnut. Two drawers 300.00
Empire Drop Leaf. One drawer 250.00
Mahogany. Tiered. England. 22" wide, 26" high 275.00
Mahogany. Two drawers, turned legs 225.00

Oriental. Dragonhead feet. Bone and ivory fittings. Top 19x26", 29½" high. Black finish with gold decor 350.00

Victorian. Walnut. 17½" top diam., 28" high, 3 legs 220.00

SIDEBOARDS

Chippendale. Walnut. Cabriole legs, handcarved trimmings. 38" high, 81" long, 23" wide. Original brass pulls. Made in Virginia 8500.00

Empire. Mahogany, with cherry top and ends. 45" long, 21" wide, 48" high. Large drawer at bottom, pie crust molding trim. Refinished. . . . 1000.00

Hepplewhite. Mahogany. 25" wide, 72" long, 40" high. Inlaid with bellflower design 3850.00

Hepplewhite. Mahogany. American, late 18th century. 41" high, 6'1" long 3500.00

Regency style. 5'6" long, 37" high. Tapered legs, acorn toes 1200.00

Sheraton. Mahogany, 6 legs 2000.00

Hepplewhite. 27¼x29½x67". Ivory. Tear drop. Escutcheon. Original brasses $3500.00

SOFAS

Belter. Carved Rosewood. C. 1845. Back enclosed by scrolls and crested with busts of famous persons, incuding George Washington. 6'2" long with castors 6000.00

Belter Love Seat. Tufted, upholstered 4000.00

Victorian. Finger carved, 59" long. Upholstered 750.00

Victorian. Mirror back, refinished, good upholstery............... 750.00

Victorian. Walnut, reupholstered in avocado velvet. 68" long, 32" high. 2 matching side chairs. Set .. 1250.00

Victorian. Walnut. Nut carving, 39" high, 6' long. Re-upholstered in ivory brocade 850.00

Victorian Love Seat. Walnut. Four side chairs and platform rocker. Paper label "pat" March 4, 1879. Original condition. Set 1250.00

SPICE BOXES

Oak. 4 drawers.................. 75.00
Oak. 8 drawers.................. 135.00
Pine. 8-drawer. 19th century. Original paint, brass pulls. 6x12x12" .. 95.00
Pine. 8 solid porcelain drawers 75.00

German. 8¾" high. Wooden, painted black. White porcelain knobs and plates $35.00

Rosewood. 12" high. Wooden pulls $125.00

Tin. Rectangular. Hinged lid. 6 containers. Original paint 40.00
Walnut. 6 drawers 75.00
Walnut. 8 drawers. Refinished. Porcelain..................... 100.00
Walnut. 8 small drawers, 1 large drawer. 19½" long, 10½" wide .. 125.00
Wood. 8 drawers. Wood knobs 85.00
Wood. Round. 7 individual containers. Table top.............. 40.00

SPINNING WHEELS

Continental-type. Complete 145.00
Early American-type. Complete..... 185.00
Standard-type. Complete and refinished 185.00
Standard-type. Small. Complete, original 170.00

SPOOL CABINETS

19¼x19¼x36". 10 glass fronts, 2 wood front drawers. Beveled

Scottish. Small $195.00

4x9¼x14½". Richardson's Spool Silk.
2 drawers $65.00

Cherry. 11x15x22". Sixcord Merrick's.
Refinished. 4 drawers $175.00

mirror on 3 sides. The Leonard Silk Co.	385.00
Cherry. Maple drawer fronts. 16¼x-24½x14½" high. Willimantic	200.00
Maple. 15x21x9" high. 2 drawers . . .	95.00
Oak. Two drawers	75.00

Oak. 5 drawers, plate glass display fronts. Corticelli, 15x21"	160.00
Oak. 22x30x15" high. Lift top, four drawers	100.00
Oak. J. P. Coats. Rotating type	395.00
Walnut. Two drawers, O.N.T.	100.00
Walnut. 17½ x 17½ x 11½" high. "Goffs Best Braid," 3 drawers, 6 original melon-shaped brasses . . .	150.00

STANDS

Pedestal. 36" high. Empire-type.
Mahogany $150.00

Cherry Stands

Dropleaf. One drawer, refinished.	250.00
Dropleaf. Two drawers	285.00
Dropleaf. 2 curly maple drawers . .	300.00
Hepplewhite. One drawer. Refinished	295.00
One drawer. Refinished	175.00
Two drawers. 29" high, 21" square top, turned legs. Refinished	250.00
Two drawers. Small turned legs, painted light green, stencilled. 17x18" top, 29" high	125.00
Mahogany Dropleaf. Two drawers, pedestal	375.00

Maple Stands

Dropleaf, two drawers	250.00
One drawer	175.00

Pine Stands

Bedside. One drawer, square tapered legs	125.00
Corner. American. Two shelves, one drawer, 36" high	300.00
Rosewood. Marble top, bamboo design, 32" high. Pair	600.00
Sheraton Night Stand. Cherry. Two drawers, 18x22" top, 28" high . . .	260.00

Wash Stands

English. Mahogany. Enclosed, early 19th century	750.00

Night Stand. 20x22½ x28½". Two drawers, turned legs. Wooden knobs. All original $125.00

Wash Stand. New England. 16½ x20x-37½". All original, with eagle decor, porcelain knob on bottom drawer
$395.00

Hepplewhite. English. Mahogany. Small with lift-up top. 13¼ x-14½ x33"	550.00
Mahogany-veneer Corner Stand. English, 34" high	300.00
Pine. 15x15x30". One drawer	85.00
Sheraton. English. C. 1785	1000.00
Victorian. Walnut, 31" high, 15½" wide, 28" long. One drawer, refinished	220.00

STEPS

Bed. Walnut, dovetailed. 2 drawers. Steps in red leather, gold tooled
$350.00

Bed. Sheraton. Walnut, two steps, lift
top lid. Needs refinishing 175.00
Bed. Sheraton. Three steps, original
carpet inlay, lift-top lids, bed
chamber under lower step 350.00
Bed. English. Mahogany. C. 1825. . . . 350.00
Library. English. C. 1890 . . . . 250.00

STOOLS

Foot Stool. 12" diam. Carpet upholstered top. Hinged. 3 porcelain feet
$40.00

Pine. 10x11x16" $35.00

Gout. English. Late Georgian. Ma-
hogany. C. 1820 . . . . 450.00
Gout. English. Late Victorian.
12x13x19" 275.00
Music. English Sheraton. C. 1810 . . . . 500.00
Piano. High back 75.00
Piano. 14" diam. seat. Glass ball
feet 50.00

Sheraton. English. Late 18th century.
Satinwood. 18½x20x25" 1000.00

TABLES

Banquet. Cherry dropleaf, rosewood
veneer apron, 42" wide, 92" long . 2250.00
Banquet. Duncan Phyfe. Three-
pedestal, reeded legs, brass claw
feet 2500.00
Banquet. Hepplewhite. England.
Mahogany, three sections, 9¼'
long, 29" high 3000.00
Birch Dropleaf. Two drawers, veneer
fronts. Turned legs, 8½" leaves,
18" square top, 29½" high 300.00
Bird Cage Tilt-Top. American Cherry.
39" diam., 27" high 950.00
Bird Cage Tilt-Top. Tea table.
Mahogany, 28½" high, 32" wide . 1200.00

Card Tables

Adam. English. Semi-circular.
Satinwood. 17¾x29x36". C. 1770 . 2500.00
Chippendale. Walnut. Ball and
claw feet. 33" wide, 27½" high . . . 1350.00
Duncan Phyfe-style. Mahogany,
lyre base, acanthus leaf decor on
legs, brass claw feet. Closed
35½" long, 18" deep 475.00
Duncan Phyfe. Turned, reeded
legs, with stretchers 750.00
Hepplewhite. New England.
Whitewood and Birdseye Maple.
With inlay, original top 600.00

Gate Leg. 24½" diam. Cherry, inlaid
and apron. Hepplewhite $1200.00

Queen Anne with Gaming Top.
England. Mahogany. 35½" long,
30" high...................... 2000.00

Regency. English. Satinwood.
Inlaid rosewood. C. 1815 .... 1200.00

Sheraton American. Cherry. 29"
high, 36" wide 500.00

Sheraton. Mahogany. Carved pedestal. 31" high, 38" wide with
leaves opened. C. 1820 .... 1650.00

Sheraton Mahogany. 4 reeded
¾ circle cutaway corners, one leg
swings out. 30" high, 17½x35½"
top closed 600.00

Sheraton Mahogany. Reeded legs,
serpentine front, maple inlay.
30½" high, 36" long, 19" wide.... 500.00

Cherry Dropleaf. Six legs, slender
turnings, 45" wide, 60" long.
Drawer in end. Refinished 500.00

Cherry Dropleaf. Six turned legs,
drawer in both ends. 46" long 650.00

Chippendale. American Maple.
Swing leg. Center of top 13x43".
Leaves are 15" wide 700.00

Chippendale Dropleaf. Mahogany.
Ball and claw feet with castors.
42" wide, 30" high 1000.00

Chippendale Pembroke. Cherry.
19½x35½" with leaves closed.
35½x37x28" high with leaves
opened 1250.00

Coffee. English. Mahogany. Brass
bound, oval. Modern 350.00

Coffee. English. Sheraton. Mahogany. 12x20x29½" 1750.00

Corner. English. George II. Mahogany. Very fine, slender pad feet.
28x29x30" 2250.00

Desk Table. Oak. 7' long. Fluted legs
on castors. C. 1915 .... 125.00

Pembroke. 17x42", 12" leaves.
Stretcher base. Maple. New Hampshire
$1250.00

Shoe-Foot Tavern. Eastern Pa. Chippendale..................... $1650.00

Drum. English. Mahogany. Fine
quality 950.00

Duncan Phyfe-type. Mahogany dining. Two end drawers. 28½" high,
58" wide with leaves open 650.00

French Marquetry. Mahogany. Late . 400.00

French Vetrine. 35½" wide, gold
finish, with beveled plate glass .. 750.00

Harvest. Pine, 5' long. Leaves
replaced 400.00

Harvest. Pine. 6' long, 21" wide 450.00

Harvest. Pine, 7' single board top,
21" wide, 9" leaves, turned legs.
Refinished and restored 750.00

Hutch. Pine. Round, 39" diam., 29"
high, maple legs. Refinished 500.00

Hutch. Pine. B/B top, 34" wide, 60"
long. Maple chair base is 28½"
high 600.00

Hutch. Old Red. Odd size chair and
½ with drawer 1400.00

Lazy Susan. Pine, 57" top, 39" susan. 485.00

Library Oak, with shelf 29" high.
23x23" top 75.00

Library. Walnut. Pennsylvania 850.00

Occasional. English. Sheraton. Two
top mahogany. 19x26½x33½"... 1850.00

Pembroke Tables
Cherry. Original condition 425.00
Cherry. Hepplewhite legs........ 425.00
English. Mahogany. 28x35". C.
1770......................... 1750.00
English. George II. Mahogany,
oval. 27x30x38" 950.00
English. Hepplewhite. Mahogany.
C. 1790 .... 850.00

Poker. Oak, round 36" diam. Swivels
on round, iron pedestal base.
Compartment for chips underneath 350.00

Table. 27x27½x38". One drawer with
porcelain knob. Tapered legs. Pine,
refinished $200.00

Queen Anne Dressing. Scotland.
Mahogany. 28" high, 30" long,
original brasses 2000.00
Queen Anne Dropleaf. Maple. New
England origin. Minor restorations
on the rounded leaves. Pad foot,
cutout ends. 48" long, 15" at
widest point 2250.00
Queen Anne. Maple. New England
type. 50" across top. 26½" high,
46" long, mule or biscuit feet.
Early 2700.00
Queen Anne. Walnut. Drake feet,
4'2" long, 28½" high. Early 3600.00
Round. Oak. 48" diam. Late 250.00
Serving. Walnut. Virginia, 18th
century. 28½" high, 48" wide 1000.00
Sheraton. Mahogany. Four reeded
legs, butterfly drop leaves. 30½"
high, 42½" long. Refinished 850.00
Sutherland. English. Victorian. Ma-
hogany 150.00
Tavern. Queen Anne. Pennsylvania.
Duck feet, large drawer 750.00
Tavern. Pine. Tapered legs, long
drawer in front. Wide, one-board
top. Original condition 400.00
Tavern. Pine. 20x31x37" high.
Refinished 450.00
Tavern. Walnut. Turned legs, doved
braces, splined top boards. Two
drawers, 28½x30x64" high. Early
Pennsylvania. C. 1740. Refinished 1700.00
Tea. English. Georgian. Mahogany . . 265.00
Tilt-Top. Maple, serpentine edge top,
36" square, slipper-foot base 650.00
Tilt-Top. Papier-mache top and base,
wood pedestal. Black lacquer,
gold trim, colorful floral center. V.
A. Richardson 285.00

Work Tables
English. Green leather top, fine
oak lining. Top drawer filled with
an extra writing slide and
numerous compartments. Original covering lids and original
lettering 3500.00
English. Regency. 16x29x32".
Mahogany 1000.00
Victorian. Walnut. English 350.00
Shaker. Mt. Lebanon 600.00

TABLES, MARBLE TOP

Victorian. Oval top, 18x22". 30" high
$265.00

Medium. Oval, carved base 375.00
Medium. Square 300.00
Regency. English 1200.00
Small. Walnut base. Oval, 29" high.
Top is 18" across and 14" wide.
Refinished 295.00
Turtle Top. Walnut base. Refinished.
34x22½x30" 425.00
Victorian. Late. 30½x23x18½".
Black marble insert 195.00

TEA CADDIES

6x6x12". 4 button feet $115.00

Lacquered, black. Metal containers.
  C. 1820 .... 275.00
Mahogany. 6x6½x10" 110.00
Mahogany. Brass trim, 2 compart-
  ments. 6¾x8-7/8x4-7/8". Blue
  moire lining 265.00
Rosewood. Brass hinges 100.00

TEA WAGONS

Wicker. Glass lift-off tray. Large front
  wheels $175.00

Walnut. Dropleaf. Two large and two
  small wheels. Silver drawer on
  one end with pull-out ashtray on
  other end. Large tray for top 175.00

TRUNKS

Leather. American. Large 150.00
Pine. Domed, with lock. Original
  condition 50.00

WAGON SEATS

14½x30x35". Black paint, rush seats.
Conn. Early 19th century $500.00

37½" long. Mounted on original
  springs $125.00

Leather. Upholstered. 37" wide, 21"
  high, low spindle arms with iron
  braces 250.00
Original scallops, old paint 200.00
Windsor-type. 32 turned spindles,
  heart design cut on either side.
  Refinished 300.00
Wood. Primitive 175.00

WHATNOTS

Corner. Soft wood, 5 shelves 200.00
Walnut
  Corner. Cupboard bottom with 4
  shelves above. 6' high 350.00
  5-shelf. 5' high, 3' wide at bottom
  shelf 375.00

342

What-Not Shelf. 58" high, 5 graduated
shelves $65.00

5 molded edge, graduated, serpentine shelves. Scroll back.
Original finish 225.00
Hanging. Leaf carved, 13x19",
folding type 95.00

WICKER ITEMS

Arm Chair. Painted white 65.00
Bassinet. White. 23" high including
  hood, 18" wide. Lace, frills 85.00
Bed, Baby. 18½ x30x34½". Metal
  spoke wheels, wire bottom, white   110.00
Chair. Gentleman's Edwardian 100.00
Chair. Lady's Rocker. Edwardian.
  Refinished, green velvet seat 175.00
Doll Carriage. 24" long, 31½" high
  to top shade. Wire wheels, brake,
  rubber tires. About 80 years old ..   85.00
Doll Cradle. 24" long. C. 1850 ......   45.00

Arm Chair. 31" high $75.00

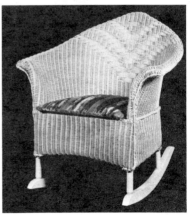

Child's Rocker. Upholstered slip seat
$50.00

Ferner 55.00
Parlor Set. 3-cushion couch, rocker,
  straight chair. Set 500.00
Rocker. Platform 185.00
Settee. 50" long, 23" deep, 31" high.
  "S" shape 175.00

Table. Oval, medium size 100.00
Tea Wagon. Removable glass tray
  top 200.00
Tray. Oval. Butterfly, fern under
  glass. 12" long, 8" wide 35.00

YARN HOLDER

Maple. Polished 6 tree branches.
  Wooden clamps. Primitive 45.00

YARN WINDERS

38" high. Wooden gears $85.00

Double Spool Winder. Scarce 150.00
Walnut. Complete 60.00
Walnut. Refinished. Complete 80.00

GAMES

Games are once again becoming a popular diversion from staid and uninteresting television programming.

"Stratego" by Milton Bradley. C. 1960
$5.00

Authors
  Milton Bradley .... $ 6.00
  Parker Bros., 1897 .... 6.50
Auto Game. Metal plate shaped like
  an old touring car. Object is to
  slide letters around and form
  word "automobile" 15.00
Batman Board. 13 Batman gum cards
  and 9 Bat Laff cards. All 1966
  National Periodical Pub. Lot 5.00
Chess Set. Ivory, carved, each pawn
  different. 6" high 300.00
Coast to Coast. The Master Toy Co.,
  New York 6.00
Cribbage Board. Ivory, carved
  Chinese border 45.00
Disneyland Card Game, dated 1964 . 4.00
Dominoes. Ivory and ebony, in wood
  box 22.00
Dr. Busby. Cards, dated 1843 .... 18.50
Game of Boy Scouts, Parker, 1912.
  Scout on cover 18.00
Game of India, MB. C. 1910, 11x11".
  Cover of tiger and elephant 18.00
Game of Tri-Bang, McLaughlin, 1898,
  8x16". Cover of birds in wicker
  carriage...................... 18.00
Halma. Dated 1885 .... 5.00
Jack Straws. Wooden in round case . 7.50
Little Red Riding Hood, MB. C. 1900,
  10'20", cover of girl and wolf..... 22.00
Mah Jongg Set. In brass bound
  Rosewood box 55.00
Napoleon. "The Little Colonel,"
  Parker, 1895, 18x18". Cover and
  boards of Napoleon............. 75.00
Old Maid. Milton Bradley 6.00

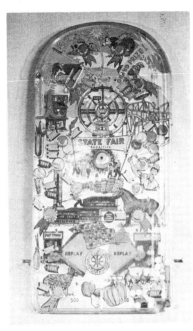

"State Fair" by Bagatelle $7.50

Panama Canal, Parker. C. 1900, 15x25". Steamship litho cover....	45.00
Peg. Baseball, Parker. C. 1910. Baseball player on cover	18.00
Pit Card game, Parker Bros., 1903 ..	5.00
Postman. Milton Bradley	7.50
Puzzle Peg. 6½" square. C. 1920. Lubbers & Bell Mfg. Co	5.00
Ten Pins. Bradley, wood dovetailed box, litho label children	15.00
Tiddly Winks. Milton Bradley	12.00
Touring Game. Parker Bros., 1926 ..	9.50
Uncle Sam's Mail, 1893. McLaughlin litho cover, all complete	65.00

GAUDY DUTCH

Gaudy Dutch is a highly decorated, light weight, soft-paste china. The ware is unmarked but is reputed to have been made in the Staffordshire section of England around the 1825 period for the Pennsylvania Dutch trade in the Philadelphia, York and Lancaster area. The patterns include Butterfly, Carnation, Dahlia, Double Rose, Dove, Grape, Oyster, Single Rose, Sunflower, Urn [also known as Vase or Flower Pot] and War Bonnet.

Gaudy Dutch should not be confused with Gaudy Ironstone which is a later product, much heavier, usually thicker and generally marked with the maker's name.

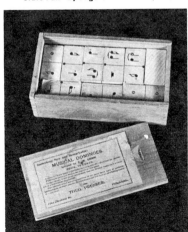

Musical Dominoes. Inv. by C. W. Grim. Theo. Presser. Phila. Wood box . $20.00

Plate. 9¾". "Grape" $750.00

Butterfly Pattern
Bowl. Small	$ 550.00
Creamer	475.00
Cup and Saucer	550.00

Plates

8¼"	600.00
9¾"	750.00

Carnation Pattern

Cup	275.00
Cup and Saucer	560.00

Plates

6½"	295.00
8¼"	625.00
9¾"	750.00
Toddy	400.00

Dahlia Pattern

Creamer	550.00
Sugar. Covered	800.00
Teapot	1000.00

Double Rose Pattern

Cup and Saucer	500.00
Plate. 7½"	600.00

Dove Pattern

Coffee Pot. 11"	2500.00
Cup and Saucer	575.00
Plate. 9¾"	760.00
Sugar Bowl. Covered	850.00

Grape Pattern

Sugar Bowl	875.00

Oyster Pattern

Cup and Saucer	550.00
Plate. 6½", sectional border	650.00

Single Rose Pattern

Cup and Saucer	525.00
Plate. 8¼"	675.00

Urn Pattern

Plate. 7½"	600.00

War Bonnet Pattern

Creamer. 4" high	875.00
Plate. 8¼"	700.00
Teapot	1250.00

GAUDY IRONSTONE

Gaudy Ironstone was introduced in the early 1850's to create more interest in ironstone ware. Staffordshire ware was being issued in various colors and color combinations during this period.

Gaudy Ironstone was decorated in the Imari style and some of the designs have a resemblance to Gaudy Welsh. The ware did not prove to be popular and after a few years production was discontinued.

Bowl. 7¾"	$ 65.00

Cups and Saucers

Blackberry decor in orange, red and blue. Small	75.00
Cobalt blue with orange and green flowers	137.50

Dishes

Mason's leaf shape. 7¼ x 11"	95.00

Milk Pitcher. C. 1860 . . . . $145.00

Sauce. 6¼" diam. Red, green, cobalt. Dated Wm. Adams & Co., Tunstall, England	40.00
Mug. 4"d. Carnation pattern	60.00

Pitchers

5" high. Blue, orange, green	115.00
7¼" high. Slender shape, scalloped rim. Decorated orange and yellow poppies. Marked "DANE" TR & CO." Late	60.00
Red, blue, green and yellow floral decor. Dolphin handle. Marked "Mason's" with crown mark	120.00

Plates

Dinner. Seeing Eye	62.50
Soup. Grape design in multicolors	48.50
8". Urn. Impressed "Mason's Patent Ironstone China." C. 1825	95.00

Platters

13x18". Mkd. "Mason's." Polychrome colors of pink, orange, green on ivory ground, some leaves in dark blue	145.00
20" long. In purple, yellow, orange, black, green, blue	165.00

GAUDY WELSH

A type of chinaware made after 1850. Although the designs are along those of Gaudy Dutch, the workmanship is not as fine. The body texture and weight also differ from Gaudy Dutch. One of the characteristics of the ware is its bluish-purple coloring. Among the existing patterns are Flower Basket, Morning Glory, Grape, Oyster, Shanghai, Strawberry, Tulip, Urn and Wagon Wheel.

Creamer. 5" high. Oyster pattern $47.50

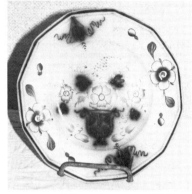

Plate. 7½". Urn pattern $50.00

Daisy and Chain Pattern
Creamer .... $	75.00
Plate	65.00
Sugar Bowl. Covered............	95.00
Teapot	135.00

Flower Basket [also known as "Urn or "Vase"] Pattern
Bowl. 10½" diam	132.50
Creamer	75.00
Mug. Handled	67.50
Plates	
8½" square	72.50
9"	82.50
9½"	85.00

Grape Pattern
Cups and Saucers	
Handled	65.00
Handleless	80.00

Morning Glory Pattern
Cup and Saucer	65.00
Dish. Cheese..................	65.00
Plate. 10"	87.50
Teapot. 5½" to top of finial	125.00

Oyster Pattern
Bowl. 8" diam. C. 1850	65.00
Creamer	75.00
Cup and Saucer	65.00
Mug. 3" high	65.00
Pitcher. Milk	120.00
Plates	
5½"	48.50
8¾"	55.00
9½"	85.00

Shanghai Pattern
Creamer	75.00

Strawberry Pattern
Creamer	85.00
Plate. 8¼"	75.00
Teapot	150.00

Tulip Pattern
Cup and Saucer	65.00
Cup Plate.....................	28.00
Pitcher, Milk	120.00
Plate. 7¾"	55.00
Teapot	125.00

Wagon Wheel Pattern
Pitcher and Bowl. Miniature. 3½" high	65.00
Plates	
5½"	48.50
8"	57.50

GIBSON GIRL PLATES

Charles Dana Gibson, eminent American artist, produced a series of 24 drawings entitled "The Widow and Her Friends," and the Royal Doulton Works at Lambeth, England reproduced the drawings on plates around the beginning of the present century.

Prices for the following range from $55.00 to $65.00 each:

Widow Series. "And Here, Winning New Friends And Not Losing The Old Ones We Leave Her" $55.00

A Message from the Outside World
A Quiet Dinner with Dr. Bottles
And Here Winning New Friends
Failing to Find Rest and Quiet in the
  Country She Decided to Return Home
Miss Babbles Brings a Copy of Morning Paper
Miss Babbles, the Authoress, Calls
  and Reads Aloud
Mr. Waddles Arrives Late and Finds
  Her Card Filled
Mrs. Diggs is Alarmed at Discovering
She Becomes a Trained Nurse
She Finds Some Consolation in Her Mirror
She Contemplates the Cloister
She Decides to Die in Spite of Dr.
  Bottles
She Finds Exercise Does Not Improve
  Her Spirits
She Goes into Colors
She Goes into Retreat
She Goes to the Fancy Dress Ball as
  "Juliet"
She is Disturbed By a Vision
She Looks for Relief Among the Old Ones
They All Go Skating
They Go Fishing
They Take a Morning Run

GIRANDOLES

Collectors and dealers generally refer to girandoles as mantel garnitures. A set consists of a centerpiece with a 3-branch candelabra and two side pieces for holding a single candle. The bases are usually made of marble or alabaster and the main body is cast of brass. Long cut prisms hang from the top.

3-piece set. Figural with marble bases. Cut glass prisms $350.00

3-piece Set. Bronze figures of Indians [scarce type]. 3-candle centerpiece, 18½" high; 16" side pieces. Marble bases, original finish .....$ 450.00
3-piece Set. French, 3-candle centerpiece, single candle side pieces. 2-piece marble bases. "Paul and Virginia" figures at base. Long prisms 325.00
3-piece Set. Two-step marble and brass bases. 20" centerpiece has 3 figures; 18" side pieces have 2 figures. Starcut prisms. Original finish 275.00
3-piece Set. 3-candle centerpiece, single candle side pieces. Single marble bases. Scene of bear robbing beehive. 40 colonial prisms suspended from grape-cluster bobeches 325.00
3-piece Set. 3-candle centerpiece. 19½" high. Side pieces, 15½" high. Marble bases, metal figural supports, long prisms 350.00

GLASS DECANTERS,
See DECANTERS, GLASS

GOOFUS GLASS

Goofus glass was first made after 1900 and was the original glass given away at carnivals. From about 1910 to 1920 this glass, first known as Mexican, competed with Carnival glass as we know it today, with Carnival glass winning out in the later years.

The glass had an embossed design which was painted in red, pink or purple. Next, bronze or gold metallic paint was applied to stems and leaves, making the pieces very flashy. Over the years the paint has oxidized, making the pieces look dull and drab. The colors, in some cases, can be brought back by gently using silver polish on areas which have not peeled. Several factories in the Ohio Valley and surrounding areas produced the glass - LaBelle Glass Co., Bridgeport, Ohio; Crescent Glass Co., Wellsburg, W. Va.; Imperial Glass Co., Bellaire, Ohio and the Northwood Glass Co., at Indiana, Pa.

Dish. 6" diam. Red flowers $22.00

Bowls
Berry. Large. Flat, bird and straw-berry . . . . $	18.50
Heart-shape. Large	16.50
Roses. Large	18.00
Strawberry. Large	18.00
9½" diam. Red carnation	15.00
10¼ x 3½". Low pedestal, red grapes with gold	15.00
Bread Tray. "Last Supper"	22.50
Decanter. With Stopper. Rose pat-tern	25.00

Tray. "The Last Supper" $30.00

Dish. Covered, oval. 8" long, 4" wide, 2¼" deep. Green with amethyst flowers. Gold dragon-flies on lid	27.50
Jars	
Painted peacocks	16.50
Pickle	16.00
Lamps	
Miniature. Rose with painted decor	35.00
Pedestal, complete with chimney .	30.00
Plates	
7". 1904 St. Louis World's Fair	12.00
7½". Carnations	7.50
8¾". Red on gold. Lady's Portrait .	25.00
Vase	12.00

GOUDA POTTERY

The town of Gouda, Holland has been known as a pottery-making center since the early 1700's. One of the first products of the potteries was the making of pipes as tobacco was being introduced into Europe from America.

Through the years various types of utilitarian pottery items were made at various factories. About 1900 the Art Nouveau period came into existence and continued through the middle 1920's. It was during this period in time that the colorful Gouda pottery, as we know it today, was manufactured. Again, it is being reproduced.

Vase. 5" high. 2-handled $65.00

As a passing note, Gouda is also a dairy center and is well known for its famous "Gouda" cheese.

Bean Pot. 3¾" diam., 2" high. Two handles, Kelat ....$	25.00
Bowls	
3½ x 7½". Matt green with blue, yellow, rust, cream, gold. Marked "Canada."	33.00
8" long, 5¼" wide, 1¾" deep. Massa, blues, greens, yellow. Artist signed	35.00
Small, shallow-type. Floral design	42.50
Candlesticks. 4" high., floral design, after 1900. Pair	75.00
Charger. 12" diam., 2" deep. Signed Housemark, "Plazeul" pattern. Pierced for hanging	145.00
Compotes	
3" high, 10" wide. Double handled. Signed Sluis, multicolor design on green background	35.00
7½" high. Multicolored leaf design	65.00
Coaster. Grape design	20.00
Decanter. 9" high. Handled, glazed. Regina orchid, magenta & green floral decor with black background	95.00
Ewer. 6 x 8½". Art Deco # 2505	155.00
Inkwell. 3" high. Hexagon shape. C. 1920.........................	50.00
Jar. 6" high. Covered. Glossy glaze, plump shape. Dutch Art Nouveau design. "Regina"	125.00
Jardinieres	
5" high. Multicolor Art Nouveau design on black bkgd...........	35.00
Large, floral & leaf design	85.00
Jug. 7½" high. Handled matt finish. "Candia." Initial "K". Art Nouveau design	85.00
Pitchers	
7" high. Usual coloring	75.00
Water. Black and white leaf and vine design	75.00
Plates	
6¾". Orange and yellow apples in center striped border, white background	15.00
7". Pansies, high glaze	55.00
12". Deep, multicolored, pierced for hanging. Mkd. Gouda, Holland, Pizo	60.00
Tobacco Jar. 6½" high. Scroll and leaf decor. C. 1900	75.00
Tray. 12½ x 17". Holland House Flambe pattern. Black ground	145.00

Trivet. 4" high. Damascus pattern. C. 1890.........................	75.00
Vases	
3" high. "Regina", matt finish. Commemorate Olympice of 1928. 1 paper label. Pair	75.00
4" high. Glazed, 2 handles, squat shape. Multicolored	65.00
5" high. High glaze with stylized floral design on black and green background	65.00
7½" high. High glass glaze. Orange background with stylized decor in white, black yellow enamel. Fully marked	120.00
10" high. Signed. Mkd. Arnheim, Holland. Isolde pattern. Art Deco, multicolored	100.00
10½" high. Design in reds, blues, yellow & black. C. 1925.........	155.00
12" high. Large Art Nouveau style with medallions depicting tulips. Pair	275.00

Vase. 9½" high $95.00

GRANITEWARE

Graniteware derives its name from iron utensils which were enameled with a speckled glaze resembling granite. For example, blue is mottled blue and white, while gray is mottled gray and white.

The ware became popular after 1900 and is now collected for decorative uses. It is also being reproduced.

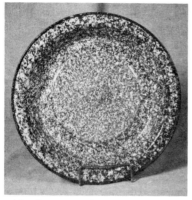

Pie Plate. 10¾". Gray and white $6.50

Bowls
Blue. 5½"	$	7.50
Blue. 8½"		15.00
Gray. 5½".		7.50
Green. 5½"		7.50

Coffee Pots
Blue	18.50
Gray	18.50
Green	20.00
Colander. Blue, handled, with base .	12.50
Dish Pan. Blue, 17" diam.	18.50

Mugs
Blue	6.00

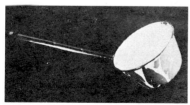

Water Dipper. 13¾" from handle to edge of bowl. Blue and white ..$10.00

Gray	6.00
Green	7.50
Pan. Blue, shallow	12.50
Pap Feeder. White with black trim, side handle	10.00

Pitchers
Blue	16.50
Gray	16.50
Green	20.00

Plates, Dinner
Blue	8.00
Gray	8.00
Green	10.00

Plates, Pie
Blue	6.50
Gray	6.50
Green	7.50
Salt Box. White, Word "Salt" in blue. Wooden cover	10.00
Soap Dish. Blue	6.00
Spoon, Mixing. White with black handle	3.00

Teapots
Blue	15.00
Gray	15.00
Green	18.50
Utensil Rack. Hanging. Gray, 21" high, 12" wide. Ladle, spoon, strainer, holder. Set	52.00
Water Dipper. Gray	8.50

GREENTOWN GLASS

Greentown glass, because of its beautiful colors, varied patterns and novelty shapes, is now becoming very desirable to art glass and pattern glass collectors.

The factory was started in 1894 in Greentown, Indiana under the name of Indiana Tumbler and Goblet Company. Later the factory consolidated with National Glass to become one of the two largest glass manufacturers in the country, the other being the United States Glass Company.

For chocolate and purple colors, see Colored Pattern Glass Section.

Bowls
Berry. Amber	$	35.00
1¾" high, 4" diam. Cord Drapery .		15.00

Butter Dishes
Amber. Small. Dewey	45.00
White. Daisy	65.00
#11. Gold flashed, covered	45.00

Compotes
Austrian	27.50
Large. Austrian	65.00

Creamers
Clear. 4½" high. Austrian	27.50

Mug. 5" high. Blue. "Serenade" $48.50

Masonic	37.50
Overall Lattice. Clear	22.50
Dishes	
Rabbit. Covered. Amber	55.00
Rabbit. Covered. White milk glass	75.00
Goblet. Austrian. Gold-flashed	20.00
Mugs	
Amber	24.00
Blue. Dwarf scene	28.50
Blue, opaque. Serenade scene	48.50
Green. Transparent. Serenade	60.00
Milk Glass. 5"	25.00
Shuttle. Clear	22.50
Parfait. 6" high. Scalloped, Flange pattern	45.00
Pitchers	
Squirrel, clear	115.00
Water. Overall Lattice. Clear	45.00
Plates	
6½". Serenade. White milk glass	50.00
6½". Serenade. Light blue milk glass	60.00
Sauce. Amber	20.00
Smoking Set. White	75.00
Spooner. #11. Ruby-flashed	35.00
Stein. Troubador. Dark blue	40.00
Sugars	
Clear, open. Austrian	25.00
Dewey. Covered	35.00
Cord and Drapery. Covered	25.00
Herringbone Buttress. Clear, covered	65.00
Sugar and Creamer. Covered sugar. Dewey pattern. Amber	58.50
Toothpicks	
Dog's head. Clear, frosted	65.00
Dog's head. Nile green	115.00
Witch's head. Nile green	95.00
Tumblers	
Amber. Cord and Drapery	75.00
Amber. Dewey	30.00
Blue. Teardrop and Tassel	40.00
Wheelbarrow. Nile Green	175.00
Wines	
Overall Lattice. Clear	10.00
Shuttle pattern. Clear	10.00

GUNS

For almost six centuries man has known the value of a gun. He has used it and misused it for survival and pleasure.

Guns had their beginning with the discovery of gun powder. Legend says that the first propulsive force of gunpowder was developed by a monk in the early 1300's. The invention of the pistol dates back to the 15th century when the Matchlock was devised. The pistol was designed for one-hand use. Most authorities agree that the name "pistol" was derived from the town of Pistola, Italy, where many of these first firearms were manufactured. Another explanation of the name is from the word "pistallo' or "pommell," a weapon used by mounted troops in the 15th century.

Guns have progressed from the early Matchlock to Wheellocks, Flintlocks, Breechloaders, repeaters and magazine arms. They continue with more modern manufacturers such as Colt, Remington, Winchester, etc.

COLT PISTOLS AND REVOLVERS

Army	
1860. Converted to 44CF	450.00
1860. Converted to 44CF (Thuer Conversion)	5000.00
1894. 41 cal.	275.00
Double Action. 45 cal.	450.00
Automatics	
1900 Model. 38 cal.	$ 375.00
1902 Model. 38 cal. Navy	325.00
1903 Model. 38 cal. Pocket	325.00
1905 Model. 45 cal.	295.00
1911-A Model. 45 cal. Commercial	275.00
Ace. 22 cal.	395.00
National Match. 45 cal.	425.00
Bisley	
5½" barrel. 38-40 cal.	395.00
7½" barrel. 38 cal. Flat top. Special	650.00

Over-and-Under-Type. Rifle on top, shot gun on bottom. Made by P. Cockler, Lewisburg, Pa. Nickel accessory box in stock $850.00

Derringer
No. 1. 41 cal. 500.00
No. 2. 41 cal. 310.00
No. 3. 41 cal. 300.00

Dragoon
No. 1 Model 6000.00
No. 2 Model 4500.00
No. 3 Model 3000.00
Baby. 1848 .... 1650.00
Shoulder stock for No. 3 Model .. 1500.00

Frontier
32-20 cal. Flat top 1400.00
38 cal. Flat top, handle marked 14
Pall Mall, London 2000.00
45 cal. 7½" barrel with bullet mold and loading tool cartridge slots in case 1000.00
45 cal. Factory engraving 850.00
Storekeeper's. Without eject 750.00
House. 41 cal. Cloverleaf or round cylinder 325.00
Marine, U.S. Model 1905. 38 cal. 325.00

Navy
1851. Brevette 1500.00
1851. Converted to 38 cal. 600.00
1851. Cut for shoulder stock 2400.00
1851. Ships engraved on cylinder . 850.00
1851. 36 cal. 700.00
1851. 36 cal. Square back trigger guard 1250.00
1851. (Thuer conversion) 6000.00
1853. Pocket. 600.00
1861. 36 cal. Round barrel 750.00
New Double Action. Lightning 175.00
New Line. 32 cal. 225.00
New Line. 38 cal. Police-thug 425.00
New Service Target. 45 cal. 295.00
Officer's Target. 38 cal. 7½" barrel, adjustable trigger 395.00

Paterson. 1836 Model. 9" hex barrel marked "Patent Arms Mfg. Co." .. 10000.00
Pocket. 1849, 31 cal. 650.00
Pocket. 1849 (Thuer conversion) 6500.00
Police. 1862 .... 450.00
Walker. 1847 .... 12000.00

FLINTLOCK PISTOLS

Belgium. Army 195.00
British. Baldwin 225.00
British. Blunderbuss Pistol. Funnel barrel, flintlock actions, 12" long. Pair 1500.00
British Cavalry. Marked G.R. Tower . 500.00
British. Double barrel center hammer marked D. Egg 225.00
British Navy. Marked G.R. Tower ... 300.00
British. Wheeler, marked London ... 250.00
Evans, O.E. Model 1808 .... 825.00
Evans, W.L. Navy. Model 1826 ...... 725.00
French. Army. Model 1763 .... 225.00
French. Army. Model 1777 .... 225.00
French. Brass trim 200.00
French. Double barrel 375.00
French. Side by side double. Travelers (silver trim) 350.00
Harper's Ferry. Model 1808, full stock 1000.00
Henry J. Model 1807, marked J. Henry, Phila. 825.00
Italian. F/L High Art Silver Inlay 245.00
Italian. Miquelet. Highly ornamented 225.00
Johnson, R. Model 1836 .... 265.00
Kentucky. With brass ornaments ... 1650.00
Miles. Model 1803 marked Miles and C. P. 850.00
North. Model 1808 .... 850.00
North. Model 1810 .... 900.00
North. Model 1811 .... 750.00
North. Model 1813 .... 750.00
North. Model 1813. Navy 695.00
North. Model 1816 .... 450.00
North. Model 1819 .... 500.00
North. Model 1836. Navy 750.00
Perkins. Model 1807 marked I. Perkins 900.00
Persian Rattail. All silver stock 500.00
Richmond. 1812 .... 1500.00
Spanish. Miquelet lock 245.00
Springfield. 1815 .... 2500.00
Springfield. Model 1818 .... 1750.00
Waters, A.H. Model 1836 .... 450.00

PERCUSSION PISTOLS AND REVOLVERS

Allen & Thurber. 6-shot Pepper-box . 175.00
Allen & Wheellock. 31 cal., 5-shot Pepperbox 275.00
Allen & Wheellock. 36 cal. Navy revolver...................... 295.00

Springfield Carbine Pistol. Maynard
lock, detachable stock. C. 1855
$1000.00

Allen & Wheellock. 44 cal. Army revolver	345.00
Allen's Patent. 31 cal. Gambler's pistol	150.00
Alsop. 36 cal. Navy revolver	295.00
Ames. Army, marked U.S.R., box lock	300.00
Ames. Navy, marked U.S.N., box lock	350.00
Ashton, H. Pistol	350.00
Bacon & Co. 36 cal. under hammer	225.00
Bacon Mfg. Co., 31 cal. revolver	225.00
Butterfield Army Revolver. 41 cal.	1200.00
Cooper. 36 cal. Navy	225.00
Derringer. Pocket pistol	450.00
Derringer. Model 1843, marked U.S.R. box lock	450.00
Derringer. 1847, marked U.S.N. box lock	475.00
Eagle Arms Co., N.Y. 25 cal., rim fire. 1859	125.00
Elgin Cutlass. Pistol	1850.00
Freeman's Patent. 44 cal.	650.00
Johnson, I.N. Model 1842	375.00
Joslin. Revolver	500.00
Lemat. 9-shot, 85-90% perfect	1200.00
Manhattan. 36 cal. Navy	135.00
Massachusetts Arms Co. 31 cal. revolver	425.00
Massachusetts Arms Co. Wesson & Leavitts Patent. 40 cal.	1350.00
Metropolitan Arms Co. 31 cal. revolver	400.00
Metropolitan Arms Co. 36 cal. Pocket Navy revolver	425.00
Palmetto. Armory. Model 1842	550.00
Pettingill's Patent. 36 cal. Navy	550.00
Pettingill's Patent. 44 cal.	525.00
Robbins & Lawrence. Pepperbox	350.00
Rogers & Spencer. Army revolver	425.00
Savage North. 36 cal.	225.00
Savage North. Navy. Figure eight iron frame	1850.00

Springfield Arms Co. Warner patent. 36 cal. revolver	500.00
Starr. Double action. Army	300.00
Starr. Double action. 36 cal. Navy	450.00
Starr. Single action. Army	400.00
Stevens. 32 cal., Lord Model. Silver engraving on barrel, mother-of-pearl handles. W.F. Cody (Buffalo Bill) on back of grip	7500.00
Tryon Derringer. 41 cal.	325.00
Union Arms Co. 31 cal. revolver	175.00
Walch. 31 cal., 10-shot. Pocket revolver	500.00
Walch. 36 cal. Navy	2000.00
Warner's Patent. 31 cal.	325.00
Waters. F/L Pistol converted to percussion	600.00
Waters, A.H. Model 1836. Original	500.00
Whitney. 31 cal., two trigger. 1st Model	410.00
Whitney. 36 cal. Navy	395.00

REMINGTON HAND GUNS

Army	
44 cal. New	375.00
44 cal. Old	425.00
50 cal. 3rd. Model. 1871	375.00
Beals	
1st Model	430.00
2nd Model	450.00
3rd Model	500.00
Belt Model. 36 cal.	375.00
Derringer. 22 cal., ring trigger. Elliot. Pat. October 1867	165.00
Derringer. 32 cal., ring trigger. Elliot	225.00
Derringer. 41 cal.	375.00
Frontier	
1875	600.00
1890	600.00
Navy	
36 cal. New	475.00
36 cal. Old	450.00
50 cal. 1865 1st Model	1200.00
50 cal. 1867. 2nd Model	400.00
Pocket. New Model	450.00
Pocket, Conversion. New Model	200.00
Police. New Model. 36 cal.	325.00
Police, Conversion. New Model	225.00
Rider	
31 cal.	225.00
32 cal.	375.00
36 cal.	500.00
Target. 22 cal. Model 1891. Single shot	275.00

SEMI-AUTOMATIC HAND GUNS

Belgium. High power, 9 mm	225.00
Belgium Bergman. 30 cal.	200.00

Borchardt Patent. Cased set. Complete	1500.00
Czechoslovakia. 25 cal.	125.00
Fiala. Repeating target with set of 3 barrels	275.00
German Luger. 9 mm	350.00
Italian Beretta. 38 cal.	130.00
Japanese. Nambu	195.00
Japanese. Baby Nambu	195.00
Luger. Artillery. 1916 to 1918. Adjustable rear sight	550.00
Luger. Carbine	575.00
Luger. Eagle, 30 cal.	1350.00
Luger. 6" barrel. Navy	425.00
Luger. 8" barrel	250.00
Mauser. Military	250.00
Radom, F.B. Polish, 9 mm	150.00
Russian Tokarev	130.00
Savage. 1907 Model, 32 cal.	135.00
Savage. #45 to 54. Cal. 32-40. H. Pope barreled; Schuetzen triggers and hooked butt	1750.00
Savage. Military, 45 cal.	375.00
Stevens. Walnut Hill #417-0. 22 cal.	175.00
Swedish Lahti. 9 mm	165.00
Walther. P.P. 22 cal.	225.00
Walther. 25 cal.	145.00
Walther. P.P. 32 cal.	150.00

SHOULDER GUNS

Czech. 24 cal. 8mm	235.00
Double Barrel Shotgun. F/L, unmarked	750.00
German K43. Semi-automatic with scope	400.00
Hungarian. 8mm. M35. Model 98-40	225.00
Ithaca. 4-E single trap 12 gauge	825.00
Jap. Carbine. 7.7 cal.	150.00
Jap. Rifle. 25 cal.	175.00
Jap. Take down rifle, 6.5 cal.	175.00
Jennings. Breech load rifle. 34 cal. 1850	850.00
Jennings. Repeating rifle. 54 cal. 1852	1500.00
Kentucky. Marked Fisher. Full stock brass patch box	400.00
Kentucky. Marked McCann. Full stock, brass trim	575.00
Kentucky. F/L marked Bedford County	775.00
Kentucky. F/L marked W. Barnhart, with silver trim	975.00
Kentucky. Percussion marked Bedford County	700.00
Kentucky Scheutzen. Signed J. Lenhart, Louisville, Ky.	625.00
Lee Navy. Straight pull. 6 mm. Model 1895	375.00

Flintlock. Lombard. St. London. "W. Bond." C. early 1800's. Matched pair
$475.00

Mauser. Model 98 cal. 8 mm. milled guard	450.00
Parker D.H.E. Grade 12 gauge	750.00
Sharps. 45-70 Old Reliable Model, target sights, Borchard action	350.00
Springfield. Model 1863, converted to 50-70, dated 1870	250.00
Springfield. Model 1863 percussion	300.00
Springfield. Model 1873, cal. 45-70	225.00
Springfield. Model 1873, carbine	225.00
Springfield. Model 1903. 30 cal.	225.00
Springfield. Model 1903. Nat. match type C stock	375.00
U.S. Burnside carbine, 4th model	275.00
U.S. Carbine Simeon North Model 1833	350.00
U.S. Eli Whitney Musket Model 1798, 69 cal.	450.00
U.S. F/L Model 1808, 69 cal.	600.00
U.S. Harpers Ferry. Model 1803	650.00
U.S. Joslyn carbine	275.00
U.S. Krag. Made at Springfield. Model 1896	295.00
U.S. Model 1861-63, made by Savage R.F.A. Co.	275.00
U.S. Musket Model 1795, Charleville pattern	550.00
U.S. Musket model 1809 contract arm	325.00
U.S. Musket 1812, marked B. Evans	400.00
U.S. Musket model 1821 contract arm	245.00
U.S. Musket 1835, often called Model 1840	510.00
U.S. Musketoon Model 1840, marked V.P. & U.S.	600.00
U.S. Musket model 1861	325.00
U.S. Poultney & Trimble carbine	275.00
U.S. Rifle. Model 1817, marked J.D. Johnson	325.00
U.S. Rifle model 1819. Hall patent	500.00

"The American Double Action." .32
cal. $75.00

U.S. Rifle model 1842. Percussion ...   295.00
U.S. Rifle carbine model 1855. 58
cal., Springfield 295.00
U.S. Rifle Rem. model 1858.
Maynard, 58 cal. 350.00
U.S. Rifle, model 1863. Remington
Arms Co. 210.00
U.S. Rifle model 1866. Breech
loading, 50 cal. 235.00
U.S. Rifle model 1870, rolling block,
50 cal. 225.00
U.S. Rifle model 1873, officer's
model, cal. 45-70 ....   525.00
U.S. Rifle model 1878. Hotchkiss
patent. Navy marks. Manufac-
tured by Winchester 365.00
U.S. Rifle model 1884, with ramrod
bayonet 350.00
U.S. Model 1917. Cal. 30-06, Eddy-
stone 225.00
U.S. Rifle Model 1917, made by
Remington 225.00
U.S. Rifle model 1922 M-2, 22 cal. ...   395.00
U.S. Sharps carbine 315.00
U.S. Sharps Borchard. 45 cal. 325.00
U.S. Sharps, 45-70 ....   400.00
U.S. Spencer. Butt loading repeating
carbine 300.00
U.S. Springfield. Model 1812 ....   340.00
U.S. Star carbine, 50 cal. 350.00
Wheellock. Austria. C. 1550 .... 1200.00
Winchester. High wall musket. 32-20
cal. 395.00
Winchester. High wall Scheutzen.
30-06 cal. 350.00
Winchester. Model 95 marked U.C.
Full stock 500.00
Winchester. Model 95 U.S. carbine ..   500.00
Winchester. Model 1866, 44 cal. 375.00
Winchester. Model 1866, military
musket with bayonet 500.00
Winchester. Model 1873 ....   325.00
Winchester. Model 1873, full mili-
tary stock 725.00
Winchester. 1873. RARE 10000.00
Winchester. Model 1876, plain
sporting rifle. 475.00

Winchester, S.S. Scheutzen rifle.
22-50 cal. 325.00

SMITH & WESSON HAND GUNS

American Model 1 SA, 44 cal. 395.00
Hand Ejector, 1st Model 395.00
Hand Ejector, 32-20 cal. Target 300.00
K22 Pre-World War II masterpiece ..   350.00
Ladysmiths 1st Model 575.00
Ladysmiths 2nd Model. 525.00
Ladysmiths 3rd Model with 6" barrel   700.00
Ladysmiths 3rd Model with 6" barrel
target sights 1000.00
Military and police 4" barrel. 38 cal .   150.00
Model No. 1, first issue 22 cal. 695.00
Model No. 1, 2nd Model 245.00
Model 2, 38 cal. Often called "Little
Russian" 275.00
Model No. 3, American, 44 cal. 440.00
Model 3. Russian, 44 cal. 350.00
Model No. 3, Russian markings 475.00
Model 3 SA, Russian target, 38-44
cal. 350.00
Model 320, repeating rifle 575.00
Model 320, repeating rifle with stock   575.00
Model 1917, 45 cal., automatic 275.00
New Century. 44 cal. Triple lock 525.00
New Century, target, 44 cal. 525.00
New Century or triple lock. Cal. 455 .   350.00
New Departure, 38 cal. 1st Model ..   300.00
New Departure, 38 cal. 2nd Model .   175.00
Perfected Model, 38 cal. 375.00
Regulation police, 38 cal. 285.00
Safety first issue, 32 cal. 250.00
Scofield Patent, 45 cal. 375.00
Target, 22 cal. 23-22 ....   300.00
Volcanic arms 41 cal., 8" barrel 600.00

MISCELLANEOUS
PISTOLS AND RIFLES

Allen. Cartridge Derringer. 41 cal. ..   175.00
Aston, H. & Co., Middletown, Conn.
Percussion pistol. C. 1851 ......   395.00
Bacon Arms Co. 32 cal. revolver 125.00
Boot Pistol. Ball and cap. C. 1850 ...   110.00
Chicago Fire Arms. Palm pistol 235.00
Conneticut Arms. Hammond Bull
Dog. 44 cal 165.00
Derringer (Philadelphia). 22 cal.
revolver. 225.00
Forehand & Wadsworth. Army, 44 cal.   215.00
Forehand & Wadsworth. Improved
model or 44 cal. Frontier 460.00
Hopkins & Allen. Army XL-8, 44 cal ..   320.00
Iver Johnson. 38 cal., 5 shot 75.00
Marlin. 32 cal. standard revolver ...   115.00

Merwin-Hulbert. Model 1876, Army
44 cal. 275.00
Merwin & Hulbert. Pocket Army 44
cal. 220.00
Moore's. Revolver, 7 shot, 32 cal. RF 115.00
National No. 1. 41 cal. Derringer. . . . 245.00
National No. 2. 41 cal. Derringer. . . . 270.00
Plant Cup Primer. Army. 42 cal 220.00
Prescott. Revolver, iron frame. Army 360.00
Reid. Knuckle duster, 22 cal. 200.00
Sharps. Pepperbox. No. 1, 4 shot. 22
cal. 350.00
Sharps & Hankins. Pepperbox, 32
cal. 225.00
Springfield. Carbine, detachable
stock, Maynard lock. C. 1855 . . . . 1000.00
J. Stevens, A. & J. Co., Chicopee
Falls, Mass., U.S.A. 32 cal. single
shot, wood grips, nickelplated.
Overall length 9" 80.00
Stevens. Hand target. 8" barrel, 22
cal. 165.00
Whitneyville. Armory revolver, 32
cal. 170.00

HAMPSHIRE POTTERY

Although Hampshire made a line of
color-glazed pottery as early as the 1880's, the
art pottery most commonly found in today's
antique shops was made by the Hampshire
Pottery in Keene, New Hampshire between
1871 and 1923.

Bowls
2¼" high, 8-7/8" wide. Raised
floral pattern, dark blue glaze.
Marked . . . . $ 45.00

Pitcher Vase. 6½" high. Gray, green
$65.00

3" high, 6" diam. Green with leaf
design 55.00
Pitcher. Tankard. 12" high, marked
JST & Co., Keene, N.H. Browns,
greens at top, bottom and handle.
Cream colors and pink asters 85.00
Vases
7" high. Matte green. MK. & MO
cipher 65.00
7½" high. Matte green with
acanthus leaves 65.00
9½" high. Green leaf decor 75.00

HANDPAINTED CHINA

Handpainted china became a fad during the
period 1890-1915. Women from towns of
considerable size would organize clubs to
seek instruction from available private
teachers.
The craze could be considered the "grand-
daddy" of do-it-yourself projects. The era
passed with the end of World War I, but not
before millions of pieces were painted. Most
of the blanks were imported from France and
Germany.
The average price on plates ranges from
$25.00 to $30.00, depending on the size,
color and quality of work. Large hanging
plaques bring from $40.00 to $75.00 with the
same conditions taken into consideration. [See
the "Haviland China" section].

Bowl. 13" diam. Burnt orange with
gold sketch of trees, mountain
foliage. Hutschenreuther, Selb,
Bavaria, Germany . . . . $ 65.00

Plate. 9¼". Yellow roses, shaded pink
edges. Dresden. Signed "C. H. Millier"
$42.50

Plate. 9½". Yellow and red roses, heavy gold edge $35.00

Jug, Cider. Painted with apples and
   leaves 45.00
Pitcher, Wine. 15" high, roses on
   pink to deep rich red ground.
   Gold-colored handle 67.50
Plates
   8". Red currants with green and
   rust-colored leaves, gold rim 27.50
   8½" diam. Wine background,
   handpainted showing old man tri-
   cornered hat................... 30.00
   10¼". Black, red raspberries,
   pink and white blossoms, gold
   trim 27.50
   11½" long, 10" wide. Red and
   yellow roses with green leaves.
   Gold decor around edge......... 55.00
   13". White ground, strawberries
   and foliage. Limoges........... 45.00

HARDWARE

Most of the hardware made before 1830 was hand wrought. Many of the items are being used today in the restoration of old homes.

Door Handle. Hand forged, 9" long.
   C. 1820 ....$ 28.50
Door handle and latch. Victorian type.
   1875.......................... 15.00
Door Knob and Bell. Iron 25.00
Door Knobs. Brass. C. 1815. Pair 30.00
Door Latch. Butterfly 35.00
Door Locks
   Early. Pennsylvania. Iron 45.00
   Large, one brass 35.00

Tramble or Pot Hanger. 48" long, iron
$150.00

Hinges, Strap
   12", slender, decorative ends. Pair   20.00
   18", same as above 25.00
   36", same as above 30.00
Hooks, Rafter. Crude 7.50
Key. Large, brass 12.50
Lift Latch. Complete, heart or spade . 30.00
Nail, Picture. M.G. head, brass bound 3.50
Pintle. Rattail, heart twist 12.00
Shutter Fastener. Iron 7.50

HAT PINS AND HAT PIN HOLDERS

Hat pins became popular in the late Victorian era, 1870-1900. Their principal use was to hold the large hats in place worn by ladies of the period. Women also used them as a protective device when annoyed or threatened by a man or dog. Many an ardent "swain" lost interest after being painfully stabbed with a pin.

HAT PINS

Amethyst stone ....$ 12.50
Art Nouveau. Large copper setting
   holds 1" long, ½" high eggshaped
   piece of mother-of-pearl. Change
   of colors. Artist signed 20.00

Beaded "Diamond" and "Huckleberry."
Each........................$12.00

Black glass top 10.00
Butterfly. Enameled in blue, laven-
der and white on gilt brass. Set on
spring so it flutters 25.00
Four-cornered brass top flowers 8.50
Gold-filled, filigree head, 9" long,
monogrammed 15.00
Mother-of-Pearl. Floral impressed,
9¼" long..................... 9.50
Porcelain. Handpainted 15.00
Rhinestone. 1¼" 8.50
Scotch Thistle. Large topaz blossom,
sterling setting, steel pin 14.50
Semi-precious stone 9.50
Sterling Silver. Plain top, steel pin... 14.50

HAT PIN HOLDERS

Nippon. Pink flowers, green leaves,
beading 18.00

Hat Pin Holder, with assorted hat pins

Royal Austrian. Green fern on white,
gold trim 20.00

HAVILAND CHINA

The history of Haviland China is complicated
and confusing because of the various
combinations of partnerships of the Haviland
brothers and their sons.

David Haviland, a New York china importer,
established a china factory at Limoges, France
in 1842, under the name of Haviland & Co. The
products were sold through the American firm
of D. G. & D. Haviland Co., of which David
Haviland was a partner.

In 1852 two other brothers were admitted to
the firm of D. G. & D. Haviland Co., and the
name Haviland Bros. & Co. was established.
The firm was discontinued in 1865.

Chronology of the various Haviland firms and
partnerships:

1835-36. Edmund and David Haviland, New
York china importers.

1837. David Haviland established his own
importing business.

1838. David's brother, Daniel, joined him to
establish the American firm of D. G. & D.
Haviland.

1842. David Haviland established a factory at
Limoges, France under the name of Haviland &
Co. His brother Daniel was a silent partner
and continued to manage the New York
importing firm.

1852. Daniel and David admitted two
brothers, Robert and Richard, to the D. G. & D.
Haviland firm. The name was then changed to
Haviland Bros. & Co.

1863. David withdrew from Haviland Bros. &
Co. to devote full time to the Limoges factory.

1865. Haviland Bros. & Co. suspended
business as importers and distributors.

1866. Daniel G. Haviland withdrew as a
partner from the French Limoges factory.

1874. David Haviland's sons, Charles Edward
Miller and Theodore, entered into partnership
with their father as Haviland & Co.

1879. David died and his sons, Charles Edward
and Theodore, continued business through
1891.

1892. The brothers, Charles Edward Miller and
Theodore, dissolved partnership. Charles
continued business under the name of
Haviland & Co., while Theodore began
operations as LaPorcelaine Theodore Haviland
at Limoges, France where he acquired a
factory. The white ware was marked
"Theodore Haviland" in a horseshoe with
"France" within, all in green. The decoration
marks varied. In 1892 the T. H. monogram
with "Limoges France" printed in red, and

"Porcelaine Mousseline" above was used. In 1914 the mark was "Theodore Haviland" [in italics] with "Limoges" below and "France" under that. The mark was usually in red with an occasional green coloring. In 1920 the italicizing of the name Theodore was discontinued after his death. The business was then conducted by his son, Wm. David Haviland.

1936. The company decided to make chinaware in America because of tariff regulations and rising costs in France.

1941. The assets of Haviland & Co. were obtained from the French heirs of Charles Edward Miller Haviland by Wm. David Haviland for the Theodore Haviland Co. The mark after 1941 was "Theodore Haviland, New York" in a vignette with "Made in America" below.

Chronology of the Charles Field Haviland firms:

1858. Chas. Field Haviland, a son of David's brother Robert, married the granddaughter of Francois Alluaud, owner of the Alluaud factory.

1859. Chas. Field Haviland established a decorating shop with blanks furnished by the Alluaud Works.

1870. Chas. Field Haviland & Co. was formed in New York between Chas. Field Haviland and Oliver A. Gager.

1876. Chas. Field Haviland became manager of Casseau Pottery Works, successor to the Alluaud Pottery. He used the mark "Ch. Field Haviland."

1881. Chas. Field Haviland retired from manufacturing and sold his interest in Chas. Field Haviland & Co. in New York to Oliver A. Gager who continued in the business until 1889 when he died. The firm name was changed to Haviland & Abbott. It ended operations about the time of World War I.

Sauce Boat with attached underplate. "Silver Anniversary." Red, green mark
$35.00

Coffee Set. 3 pieces. 10" covered coffee pot, 7" covered sugar bowl and creamer. Allover morning glory decor, gold knobs, cross bar	135.00
Creamer. Marked "C.F.H." Cupids in design, gold handles and gold edge..........................	35.00

Cups and Saucers

C. H. Field, Haviland Limoges, G.D.M., decorated with flowers and gold	25.00
Princess, Ranson	20.00
Demitasse. Pink roses in swags, tied with blue bows, gold trim	18.50
Decanter. 9" with stopper and floral decor. Marked Haviland Limoges .	37.50

Dinner Sets

Autumn Leaf pattern, service for 8	750.00
Marie pattern. Service for 12	1000.00
Ranson pattern. All white, 94 pieces, service for 12	950.00
Wedding Ring pattern, service for 12............................	1000.00

Dishes

Bone.........................	14.00
Covered. Haviland & Co., 8" diam. Silver Wedding pattern..........	60.00
Pickle. Small, oval, fluted edge. "Princess"	16.50
Relish. 4½x8". Rectangular. Schl. #342A	12.00
Sauce	6.50
Vegetable. Open. Ranson blank, oval. "Norma"	38.00
Vegetable. Open, oval. "Princess"	35.00

Dresser Trays

7¾x9½". Brown flowers and berries pattern................	27.50

Bouillon Cup and Saucer. Gold trim . $		20.00

Bowls

19" diam. Serving, fluted edge. "Princess"	45.00
Mayonnaise, on plate. Trailing Arbutus decor. Set.............	35.00
Butter Dish. Covered, with insert....	55.00

Butter Pats

"Princess Feather"..............	6.00
"Ranson"....................	6.00
Candlesticks. 4" high, gold lustre. Pr.	40.00
Cat. 10" high, yellow with white face, black eyes, nose and whiskers	100.00
Chocolate Pot. Blue-green flowers, fern-like leaves, gold trim	65.00

Vase. Redware. 10x11½" high. Signed Haviland & Co. Limoges. Peacock on brown and black glaze $285.00

8½ x 12½". Kidney-shape. Classic figure in wreath of green leaves. Gold trim on edge 35.00

Fish Platter. 8¼x21¾". Scene of trout caught in net, gold corners . . 50.00

Fish Set. 24" platter, 12 - 8¾" plates, handpainted fish in high relief, gold edges and scrolls. Set 235.00

Game Set. 16½" platter, 6 - 8½" plates, handpainted game. Signed. Set 175.00

Gravy Boats

   Attached to tray, blue forget-me-not decor 40.00

   Princess pattern, on standard 35.00

Ice Cream Set. Large oblong platter, 6 plates. Blue and white with folded corners. Set 85.00

Pitcher, Water. 7½" high. Yellow rose clusters on white ground. Scallloped rim, gold-trimmed handle 50.00

Plaque. 12½" diam., soft yellow and blue ground. Robin and butterfly, white dogwood branch. Signed and dated 55.00

Plates

6½". Pink rose sprays, scalloped edge 12.50

8½". Morning glory decor. Set of six 90.00

9½". Princess pattern. Made by Haviland & Co., Limoges 18.50

9½". Dinner. "Princess." No. 29A . 25.00

12½". Chop. Pink roses around edge plus larger ones forming inner circle 45.00

13". Chop. Pink rose decor, wide scalloped edge 50.00

13¼". Pink roses, gold brushed edge. Green with gold design border 45.00

13½". Chop. Lavender flowers. Marks, H.&Co. France, Haviland & Co. for Burley & Co., Chicago 45.00

Bread and Butter. Plain 8.00

Oyster. Blue cornflowers 30.00

Platters

8x9½" 27.50

10x14½" 35.00

11". Schl. No. 699 . . . . 28.50

14". French Mignonette 42.00

15". Schl. No. 245 on blank 45.00

Powder Box. Marked Haviland. H/P violets. Large hinged lid, heavy gold trim 48.00

Ramekin. Separate saucer. Blue bead festoons, foliage. 2-pc. set . . 16.50

Sugar Bowls

Covered. Plain 32.50

Covered, cupids in design, gold top and finial [C.F.H.] 40.00

Sugar Bowls and Creamers

Marked "Haviland & Co." Set 65.00

White background, floral decor, gold trim, 3½" high. Set 65.00

Teapot. 5" high, cupid design, gold trim [C.F.H.] 65.00

Tea Sets

Teapot, sugar bowl, creamer, 4 cups, saucers. Pink floral decor . . . 150.00

Wedding Ring pattern. Service for 8. Large teapot, covered sugar, creamer, open-handled cake plate, sauce dishes, cups and saucers. Set 400.00

Miniature, with tray 40.00

Soup. Blue flowers with brown vine decor, with ladle 95.00

Soup. Gold trim, rope design handles. 3x7½ x10", marked H&C 95.00

HEISEY GLASS

The A. H. Heisey Company started operations in April 1896 at Newark, Ohio. In addition to producing crystal pattern glass, a wide variety of colored glass, including milk and custard, was also made. The factory operated for a period of 60 years, closing in 1957. The trademark is the letter "H" inside a diamond.

Advertising Plaque. In glass with trademark . . . . $ 25.00

Ash Trays. 3" diam. Individual. Leaf-shaped. C. 1955. Set of 4 .. $30.00

Ash Tray. Heavy, star shaped, 5½"
diam., signed 15.00
Baskets
  Bride's. 9" frame, 8" diam. Signed   65.00
  Glass:
    5x9". Rayed bottom, ribbed with
    etched band. Applied handle.
    Signed 40.00
    6x8¾x10¼". Panelled. Clear,
    oblong, signed 45.00
    9¾" high. Apple green. Rayed
    pattern near base and on bottom.
    6-sided shape. 4½x7¼" 30.00
    14" high to top of handle. Etched 60.00
    15" high, 8 scalloped top panels,
    each crosshatched, petaled flow-
    ers and leaves. Octagon-shaped
    base. Signed 72.50
Berry Sets
  Ring Band Custard Glass. Bowl
  and six sauces 265.00
  Scalloped edge. 8½" bowl and six
  sauces 75.00
Bowls
  4½" diam. Panelled, rayed base . . 12.50
  4¾" diam. Crystolite. Matching
  tray, 8" diam, with ladle. Signed.
  Set 27.50
  6" diam., 1½" high. Pink.
  Diamond Quilted. Impressed star
  base. Signed 20.00
  8" diam. Fruit. Clear, panelled,
  scalloped edge 20.00
  9¼" diam., 2½" high. Signed 65.00
  9½" diam. Colonial pattern 22.50
  10" diam. Fruit. Fluted, signed . . . 30.00
  11" diam. Green, footed,
  scalloped edge 30.00
  Berry Bowl. Opal, beaded swag,
  gold trim 60.00
  Punch Bowl with 12 cups.
  "Victorian," signed 175.00
  Punch Bowl on Pedestal, with 14
  cups 250.00
  Rose Bowl. Quilted design, 7"
  high, 22½" diam. Marked 28.50

Butter Dish. Covered, Colonial
  pattern 40.00
Butter Pats
  Clear, signed 4.00
  "Old Williamsburg" pattern. Set of
  six 25.00
  Square, yellow, signed 6.50
Cake Stand. 9½". Locket on Chain . . 68.00
Candelabras. 10½", signed. Pair . . . 200.00
Candlesticks
  Crystal. 8". Marked 25.00
  Glass chamber-type, ring handle 12.00
  Peg, with flower bowl. Optic bowl
  with waved top. 2 pieces 45.00
Celerys
  Greek Key. 12" 22.50
  Green. 12". Rayed type base and
  8-sided shape 25.00
  Sahara. 13" 25.00
Champagnes
  Clear. Melody pattern 10.00
  Green stems, clear diamond
  quilted bowls. Signed 15.00
  Wedding Band 10.00
Coaster. Green. 5¼" 7.00
Compotes
  Clear. Diamond Quilted bowl with
  green stem and foot. 6¾" diam.,
  4½" high. Signed 30.00
  Green. Optic pattern, 4" high, 8"
  diam. Low pedestal foot 35.00
Cracker Jar. Base. Diamond Swag . . . 38.00
Creamers
  Clear. Miniature. Marked 12.50
  With 8" handled tray. Allover
  enameled flowers. Set 25.00
Cruets
  5¾" high. Pair 40.00
  Kalonyal pattern. Marked and
  blown. 8", original stopper 37.50
  Blown with embossed pineapples.
  Pineapple-shaped stopper. Signed 35.00

Bowl. 8½" diam. top. Flared. Signed
$30.00

Greek Key. Original stopper 30.00

Dishes

Bonbon. Pink, 10 swirled panels.
5½ x 7". Signed 17.50
Candy. Yellow with frosty crackle-
like finish. 6" diam., two handles .   17.50
Console. Large Greek Key. Signed   28.50
Covered. 5" diam. H/P, embossed
design border in green, blue and
gold trim. Rayed base with cut
outside panels. Cut knobbed dome   22.50
Lemon. Sahara 15.00
Pickle. Colonial pattern, divided . .   17.50
12" long, 4" wide. ray design in
bottom, panelled sides 15.00
Sauce/Finger Bowl. With under-
plate. Set 15.00
Sauce. Thumbprint and plain
panels. 2¼" diam. 6.00
Sauce. Octagon shape with open
handles on either side. Green,
4¼" across, 2" panelled sides.
9½" long, 3¼" wide, 4" curved
ends. Signed 27.50
Sundae. Clear, stemmed, 6½" . . .   6.50

Figurals, Signed

Mallard Duck. Wings half up 110.00
Mallard Duck. Wings down 110.00
Glass, Shot. Panelled, 2-oz 5.00

Goblets

Block pattern 12.50
Colonial pattern. Signed. Set of
six 50.00
Drape pattern 10.00
Hair Receiver. Covered. Star base.
Signed 15.00
Lamp Base. Crystal, 9½" high, single
socket, pull chain. Marked 40.00
Lemonade Set. Kalonyal pattern with
wide gold trim. Marked. Pitcher, 6
glasses 85.00
Mayonnaise. Rose. 3 pieces. Signed.
Set 45.00

Mustard Pots

Covered. Green with swirl
pattern. Marked 10.00
4". Covered. "Colonial" pattern . .   13.00
Perfume Bottle. 6½" high. Signed.
Decorated with wide blue band,
trimmed in gold 18.00

Pitchers

6¼" high. Greek Key. Signed 55.00
7½" high. Colonial pattern 45.00
Water. Diamond Quilted pattern
with set in cover. Round pontil and
applied handle. Signed 65.00

Plates

Cup. Clear, signed 4.00
Dessert. Pink. 6", signed 7.50

Fruit Bowl. 12½" diam. Flared top.
Signed $40.00
7¼". Shawl Dancer pattern.
Etched and cut. Signed. Set of 8 . . .   125.00
8". Fancy Loop 20.00
Luncheon 12.00
12". Etched flowers and leaves,
star bottom 30.00

Platters

Bread. Large 26.50
10 x 13". Clear, Colonial pattern,
rayed base 30.00
Powder Jar. Covered, brass lid.
Colonial pattern 25.00
Punch Cup. Greek Key 15.00
Salt and Pepper. Etched. Original tops   17.50
Salts. Open, swan shape, paper
label. Matched pair 15.00
Salver. "Punty and Diamond Point."
9½" 45.00
Sherbet. Lariat pattern. Signed 6.50

Spooners

Clear, Colonial pattern 15.00
Signed, Prince of Wales, Plumes.
Gold decor 38.00

Sugar and Creamers

Comet pattern. Pair 26.50
Daisy design. Etched 45.00
Covered, with silver filigree in
fancy design. 6" plate with cut
star base. 3 pieces 50.00
Victorian. Signed 35.00
Sugar Bowl. Sterling overlay. Sgd. . . .   28.50
Syrup. Etched, signed 29.00

Tobacco Jars

Dome top, metal insert. Signed . . .   65.00
6½" high. Moongleam 125.00

Toothpicks

Colonial 20.00
Ring Band. Red roses 65.00

Ring Band. Signed. Sheboygan ...	55.00
Tumbler. Custard glass. Beaded and roses	35.00
Vases	
7½" high. Colonial pattern. Bulbous shape	35.00
7½" high. Fan. Engraved and etched, green base. Signed	40.00
8-3/5" high, 5" diam. Silver Overlay. Round notched base. Sgd.	65.00
Wines	
5" high. Clear, signed. Set of 9 ...	95.00
Park Avenue	12.00
Platinum band. Signed	12.00

HITCHING POSTS

A post for temporarily tying up a horse was known as the hitching post. With the horse outmoded as a means of transportation with the invention of the horseless carriage, most all items adjunct with "Dobbin" are now being collected today, including the hitching post.

Jockey-type. CI. Painted	$250.00
Bear. European	$ 80.00
*Black Boy. Jockey-type with ring in hand. Painted	85.00
Horse's Head	
Cast Iron	65.00
Cast Iron on post. C. 1875	160.00
*Cast Iron. 8" high, painted black .	18.50

*Reproduced Item

HORN

Animal horns have been utilized in making various items such as drinking cups, small dishes, powder horns and snuff boxes, by the hornsmiths of past generations.

Bird. Made with several pieces of horn	$ 30.00

Horse's Head. CI, on pedestal . $160.00

Bottle Opener. Horn handle, 5½".
Sterling tip $28.00

Letter Opener. Crocodile head	15.00
Napkin Ring	6.00
Snuff Box. 2¾" long, 1¾" high. Removable lid with small brass ring	30.00
Snuff Container. In shape of powder horn. 3" long, screw top	25.00
Spoon. 9¾" long, bowl 3¼" wide ...	22.50
Tea Caddy Spoon. 5" long	15.00
Texas Longhorn Steer Horn. 40" long with historical engraving of Washington, Jefferson, Monroe, General Green, General Gates and General Schuyler	1000.00

Tumblers

2½" high, inset horn bottom	20.00
4½" high. Rare, with silver rim ...	65.00

HULL POTTERY

A type of Hull pottery was made as early as 1903 by the Acme Pottery Co., Crooksville, Ohio. They specialized in household items. In 1917, when Hull Pottery acquired the firm, they made an art pottery. It is this art pottery that was continued until 1950 and is considered collectible today.

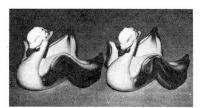

Planters. 4½" high. Ducks, spread wings, 6½" long. Green and yellow. Pair $20.00

Basket. 7". Flowers & bow at top .... $	16.00

Planters

6¼ x 10". Heart-shaped. Pink with roses	7.50
16½" long. Basketweave, dark pink with multicolored flowers. Signed	22.00
Tea Set. 3-pcs. Light green to pink. Branch handles	38.00

Vases

7" high. Pink to blue, embossed flowers, handled, pedestal	12.50
9" high. Pastel colors, floral decor both sides. Double handles	14.50

HUMMEL ITEMS

Hummel figurines are the creation of a German artist and nun, Sister Marie Innocentia Hummle. In 1934 her sketches of charming 'people' were transformed into three dimensionsl, bisque figurines by W. Goeble Porzellanfabrik, a German ceramic and porcelain manufacturer.

All authentic Hummels bear both the signature of M. T. Hummel and the Goebel trademark. The Goebel trademark has been modified over the productive years of Hummels. The various trademarks identify the years the particular Hummel was manufactured.

Hummel figurines, even those made between 1934 and 1945, are not true antiques, but because of their fine workmanship, they are considered good collectibles.

ASHTRAYS

Boy with Bird. 3¼ x 6¼" .... $	38.50
Happy Pastime. 3½ x 6¼"	35.00
Joyful. 3½ x 6". OM	30.00
Let's Sing. 3½ x 6¼"	37.50
Singing Lesson. 3½ x 6¾"	38.50

BOOKENDS

Apple Tree Boy and Girl. 5¼"	60.00
Bookworms. 5½"	100.00
Friends, She Loves Me...She Loves Me Not. 5¼"	95.00
Goose Girl and Farm Boy. 4¾"	100.00
Little Goat Herder and Feeding Time. 5½"	85.00
Playmates and Chick Girl. 4"	100.00

CANDLEHOLDERS

Angel Duet. 5"	37.50
Angel Trio. 3 Ass't. Sitting with candle. 2"	32.00
Christmas Angels. 3½"	36.50
Herald Angels. 2¼ x 4"	40.00
Lullaby. 3¼ x 5"	35.00
Silent Night. 9 x 12"	50.00

Retreat to Safety. 4" $30.00

CANDY BOXES

Chick Girl. 6¼"	45.00
Happy Pastime. 6"	45.00
Joyful. 6¼"	45.00
Playmates. 6¼"	45.00
Let's Sing. 6"	45.00
Singing Lesson. 6"	45.00

FIGURINES

A Fair Measure. 5½"	50.00
Accordion Boy. 5¼"	30.00
Adoration. 6¼"	60.00
Adventure Bound. 7¼x8"	850.00
Angel Duet. 5"	35.00
Angel Serenade. 3"	15.00
Angel Trio. 2½"	37.50
Angelic Care. 6½"	55.00
Angelic Sleep. 3½x5"	35.00
Angelic Song. 4¼"	30.00
Apple Tree Boy. 4" NM	25.00
Apple Tree Boy. 6". NM............	47.50
Apple Tree Boy. 10½". OM	275.00
Apple Tree Girl. 4". NM	22.50
Apple Tree Girl. 6". NM	47.50
Apple Tree Girl. 10½". OM	250.00
Artist. 5¼"	37.50
Auf Wiedersehen. 5¼". NM........	40.00
Autumn Harvest. 4¾". NM.........	42.00
Baker. 4¾"	32.50
Band Leader. 5¼"	35.00
Barnyard Hero. 4"	30.00
Barnyard Hero. 5½"	50.00
Bashful. 4¾"	35.00
Be Patient. 4¼"	30.00
Be Patient. 6¼"	45.00
Begging His Share. 5½"	35.00
Big Housecleaning. 3-15/16"	55.00
Bird Duet. 4". OM	30.00
Birthday Serenade . 4¼"	34.50
Blessed Event. 5½". NM	80.00
Bookworm. 4"	35.00
Bookworm. 5½"	75.00
Bookworm. 8".....................	330.00
Boots. 5½". NM	30.00
Boy with Toothache. 5½"	32.00
Brother. 5½".....................	29.50
Builder. 5½"	43.50
Busy Student. 4¼"	30.00
Candlelight. OM	85.00
Carnival. 6". OM..................	32.50
Celestial Musician. 7"	47.50
Chick Girl. 3½". OM	30.00
Chick Girl. 4¼"	40.00
Chicken-Licken. 4¾"	52.00
Children. Trio. 2½"	50.00
Children. Trio. 3½"	37.50
Chimney Sweep. 4"	17.50
Chimney Sweep. 5½"	30.00
Christ Child. 2x6"	24.00
Cinderella. 4-9/16"	50.00
Close Harmony. 5½"	50.00
Confidentially. 5½"	45.00
Congratulations. 6"	30.00
Coquettes. 5¼"	47.50
Crossroads. 6-11/16"	85.00
Culprits. 6¼"	40.00
Doctor. 4¾"	30.00
Doll Bath. 5¼"	37.50
Doll Mother. 4¾"..................	45.00
Drummer. 4¼". OM................	30.00
Duet. 5¼". OM...................	48.00
Easter Greetings. 5½"	45.00
Easter Playmates. 3-15/16"	50.00
Eventide. 4¾".....................	50.00
Farewell. 4¾". OM	45.00
Farm Boy. 5¼"	36.00
Favorite Pet. 4¼"..................	44.50
Feathered Friends. 4¾"	50.00
Feeding Time. Small, 4¼"	35.00
Feeding Time. Large, 5½"	45.00
Festival Harmony with Banjo. 8"	55.00
Festival Harmony with Banjo. 10¼" .	92.50
Festival Harmony with Horn. 8"......	50.00
Festival Harmony with Horn. 10¼"..	92.50
Flower Vendor. 5½"	45.00
Follow the Leader. 6-15/16"........	225.00
For Father. 5½"	35.00
For Mother. 5¼"	30.00
Friends. Small, 5". NM.............	34.50
Friends. Large, 11½". OM	265.00
Gay Adventure. 4-15/16"	42.50
Globe Trotter. 5¼"	32.50
Going to Grandma's. 4¾"	45.00
Good Friends. 4". OM	35.00
Good Hunting. 5¼". OM...........	45.00
Good Night. 3¼"	24.00

Good Shepherd. 6"	27.50
Goose Girl. 4"	30.00
Goose Girl. 4¾"	38.00
Goose Girl. 7½"	100.00
Guiding Angel. 2¾"	20.00
Happiness. 4¾"	25.00
Happy Birthday. 5½"	45.00
Happy Days . 4¼"	38.50
Happy Pastime. 3⅓¼"	30.00
Happy Traveller. 5"	24.50
Happy Traveller. 7¼". OM	92.50
Hear Ye! Hear Ye!. 5¼". NM	35.00
Hear Ye! Hear Ye!. 6". NM	50.00
Hear Ye! Hear Ye!. 7". OM	95.00
Heavenly Angel. 4¼". NM	22.50
Heavenly Angel. 6"	35.00
Heavenly Angel. 6¾"	40.00
Heavenly Angel. 8¾"	85.00
Heavenly Protection. 6¾"	60.00
Heavenly Protection. 9"	110.00
Hello. 6¼"	32.00
Holy Child. 6¾"	32.00
Holy Family. White. 3 pieces	82.50
Holy Family. Color. 3 pieces	82.50
Home From Market. 4¼"	27.50
Home From Market. 5½"	32.50
Homeward Bound. 5"	80.00
Infant Jesus. Color, 3¾"	13.50
Infant of Krumbad. 2½"	10.00
Infant of Krumbad. 3½"	14.50
Infant of Krumbad. 4¼"	18.50
Joyful. 3½". OM	20.00
Just Resting. 4"	25.00
Just Resting. 5½"	45.00
Kiss Me. 6"	44.00
Knitting Lesson. 7½". OM	100.00
Latest News. 5¼"	47.50
Let's Sing. 3¼"	27.50
Letter to Santa Claus. 7"	65.00
Little Bookkeeper. 4¾"	55.00
Little Cellist. 6". NM	35.00
Little Cellist. 8"	85.00
Little Fiddler. 4¾"	30.00
Little Fiddler. 6"	38.50
Little Fiddler. 7½". OM	92.00
Little Fiddler. 11½"	325.00
Little Gabriel. 5"	23.50
Little Gardener. 4¼"	22.50
Little Goat Herder. 5½"	45.00
Little Guardian. 3¾"	28.50
Little Helper. 4¼"	22.50
Little Hiker. 4¼"	20.00
Little Hiker. 6"	30.00
Little Pharmacist. 6"	40.00
Little Scholar. 5½". OM	30.00
Little Shopper. 4¾". NM	22.50
Little Sweeper. 4¼"	23.50
Little Tailor. 5½"	50.00
Little Thrifty. 5". NM	40.00
Little Tooter. 3¾"	23.50

Lost Sheep. 4¼"	23.50
Lost Sheep. 4½"	30.00
Lost Stocking. 4-3/8"	35.00
Lullaby. 3¼x5"	35.00
Mail Coach. 4¼x6¼"	125.00
March Winds. 5". OM	25.00
Max and Moritz. 5¼". NM	34.50
Meditation. 4¼". OM	24.50
Meditation. 5¼"	35.00
Merry Wanderer. 4½"	24.00
Merry Wanderer. 4¾"	32.00
Merry Wanderer. 6¼"	50.00
Merry Wanderer. 7"	85.00
Merry Wanderer. 9½"	325.00
Mischief Maker. 4-15/16"	45.00
Mother's Darling. 5½"	36.50
Mother's Helper. 5"	34.50
Mountaineer. 5¼". OM	45.00
Not For You. 6"	44.00
On Secret Path. 5-3/8"	47.00

Little Hiker. 4¼" $20.00

Orchestra. 5 pieces	145.00
Orchestra. 8 pieces	235.00
Out of Danger. 6¼"	50.00
Photographer. 4¾"	45.00
Playmates. 4"	25.00
Playmates. 5¼"	40.00
Postman. 5¼"	30.00
Prayer Before Battle. 4½"	35.00
Puppy Love. 4½"	35.00
Retreat to Safety. 4"	30.00
Retreat to Safety. 5½"	50.00
Ride into Christmas. 5¾"	90.00
Ring Around the Rosie. 6¾"	675.00
St. George. 6¾". OM	85.00
St. Joseph. Color. 7¾"	25.00
St. Joseph. Color. 7¾"	35.00
School Boy. 4"	30.00
School Boy. 5¼"	35.00
School Boys. 7½"	250.00
School Boys. 10"	500.00
School Girl. 4¼"	22.50
School Girl. 5¼"	30.00
School Girls. 7½"	260.00
School Girls. 9½"	500.00
Sensitive Hunter. 4¾". OM	32.00
Sensitive Hunter. 5½". OM	39.00
Sensitive Hunter. 7½". OM	82.00
Serenade. 4¾"	25.00
Serenade. 7½"	90.00
Shepherd's Boy. 4½"	35.00
She Loves Me, She Loves Me Not. 4¼"	35.00
Shining Light. 2¾"	20.00
Signs of Spring. 4"	30.00
Signs of Spring. 5"	45.00
Singing Lesson. 2¾"	24.50
Sister. 4¾"	24.50
Sister. 5½"	28.50
Skier. 5¼"	35.00
Smart Little Sister. 4¾"	45.00
Soldier Boy. 6"	27.50
Soloist. 4¾"	25.00
Spring Cheer. 5"	24.00
Spring Dance. 6¾"	125.00
Star Gazer. 4¾"	35.00
Stitch in Time. 6¾"	39.50
Stormy Weather. 6¼"	100.00
Street Singer. 5"	26.00
Strolling Along. 4¾"	30.00
Surprise. 4"	27.00
Surprise. 5½"	43.00
Sweet Music. 5¼"	34.00
Telling Her Secret. 5¼"	50.00
The Run-a-Way. 5-3/8"	50.00
To Market. 4½"	30.00
To Market. 5½"	45.00
Trumpet Boy. 4¾"	22.50
Tuneful Angel. 2¾"	18.00
Umbrella Boy. 4¾"	125.00
Umbrella Boy. 8"	400.00
Umbrella Girl. 4¾"	120.00

Umbrella Girl. 8"	400.00
Village Boy. 4"	18.50
Village Boy. 5¼". OM	25.00
Village Boy. 6"	35.00
Visiting an Invalid. 4-15/16"	45.00
Volunteers. 5¼"	45.00
Waiter. 6"	35.00
Wash Day. 6"	40.00
Wayside Devotion. 7½"	65.00
Wayside Devotion. 8¾". NM	98.50
Wayside Harmony. 4". NM	25.00
Wayside Harmony. 5". NM	35.00
Weary Wanderer. 6"	30.00
We Congratulate. 4"	40.00
Which Hand?. 5¼". NM	26.50
Worship. 5"	28.50

FONTS

Angel Duet. 2x4¾"	12.50
Angelic Prayer. 3x4"	8.50
Angels at Prayer. 2x4¾"	16.50
Angel with Birds. 2¾x3½"	8.50
Angel with Flowers. 2¾x4"	8.50
Child Jesus. 1½x5"	8.50
Devotion. 3x5"	12.00
Good Shepherd. 2¼x4¾"	10.00
Heavenly Angel. 2x4¾"	12.00
Holy Family. 3x4"	15.00

Sister. 4¾" high $24.50

Kneeling Angel. 5½"		12.00
Worship. 2¾ x 4¾"		14.00

LAMP BASES [WIRED]

Apple Tree Boy. 7½"		75.00
Apple Tree Girl. 7½"		75.00
Culprits. 9½"		95.00
Good Friends. 7½"		75.00
Just Resting. 7½"		75.00
Out of Danger. 9½"		95.00
She Loves Me, She Loves Me Not. 7½"		75.00
To Market. 9½"		95.00
Wayside Harmony. 7½"		75.00

MADONNAS

Flower Madonna. Color. 8¼"		60.00
Flower Madonna, White. 8¼"		30.00
Flower Madonna. Color. 11½"		150.00
Flower Madonna. White. 11½"		75.00
Madonna. 6½"		35.00
Madonna, Child. 2-pc. Color. 6½"		50.00
Madonna, Child. 2-pc. White. 6½"		25.00
Madonna with Halo. Color. 10½"		20.00
Madonna with Halo. White. 10½"		12.50
Madonna, Praying. Color. 10½"		20.00
Madonna, Praying. White. 10½"		12.50

MUSIC BOXES

Little Band. With candle		100.00
Little Band. Without candle		85.00

NATIVITY SETS

Holy Family. 3-pc. Color		75.00
Holy Family. 3-pc. White		60.00
12-piece Set. Figures only. Color		300.00
16-piece Set. Figures only. Color		375.00
16-piece Set. Figures only. Color. Lg.		1250.00
Stable Only. Fits 12 or 16-pc. small		30.00
Stable Only. Fits 3-pc. set		15.00

NATIVITY SETS COMPONENTS

Madonna and Child. White. 6½". 2-pc.		30.00
Madonna and Child. Color. 6½". 2-pc.		50.00
Madonna. 6½"		35.00
Infant Jesus. 3¾"		12.00
St. Joseph. White. 7¾"		20.00
St. Joseph. Color. 7¾"		30.00
Angel Serenade. 3"		15.00
Shepherd with Sheep. l-pc. 7½"		35.00
Shepherd Boy. 3¾"		20.00
Donkey. 5¼"		12.00
Cow. 6½"		12.00
King, Standing. 8½"		40.00
King, Kneeling, on One Knee. 5¾"		35.00
King, Kneeling on Both Knees. 5½"		25.00
Lamb. 2¼"		6.00
Camel. 8¼"		40.00
Flying Angel. Color. 3½"		20.00
Flying Angel. White. 3½"		10.00

PLATES [See Collectors' Plates]

WALL PLAQUES

Ba Bee Ring. 4¾ x 5¼". Set		40.00
Child in Bed. 2¾ x 2¾". Set		25.00
Madonna. 3½ x 4¼". Set		25.00

Mail Coach. 6¼". Set		65.00
Quartet. 6x6". NM. Set		65.00
Vacation Time. 4x4¼". NM. Set		50.00

NOTE: OM indicates old mark.
NM indicates new mark.

IMARI

An oriental type of gaudy decorated chinaware which was mainly imported into this country from Japan during the 1875-1895 period. The ware dates back to about 1650 in Japan. Some was brought to Colonial America by Dutch traders. Imitations of this ware were made at Worcester and other potteries in England during the 19th century.

Candleholder and/or Vase. Removable top $145.00

Imari-patterned wares are again being reproduced. To the Imari collector, the reproductions are evident. Check the "new" marks with the old for further identification.

Bowls

Punch. Large, typical colors	$ 650.00
6¾" diam. Blue and white	50.00
8½" diam., 6" high. Early	200.00
10" diam. Typical colors and decor on teakwood stand	250.00
10" diam. Octagon shape, decorated inside and out with typical colors and designs. 5½" high, on teakwood base	300.00
11" diam. Footed, royal blue, turquoise, tangerine and gold in allover enamel decor	300.00

Chargers

15¾" diam. Cobalt blue, orange and gold decor on white ground	225.00
16". Late	150.00
18". C. 1870	375.00
22". C. 1820	450.00
Cup and Saucer. Five colors with blue and rust predominating	45.00
Cups. Multicolor panels with gold. Blue and gold interiors. Pedestal bases. Set of four	160.00
Dish. Square with rounded corners, blue Japanese. C. 1860	90.00

Ginger Jars

8½" high. Covered, red and black colors	100.00
14". Covered	175.00
Match Box with Lid. 2x3½". 19th century	42.50

Plates

6 panels, red and blue floral decor, green foliage	75.00
6¾". Spode Copeland. Gold C. 1870	48.00
8". Bright coloring. Impressed Wedgwood	72.50
10". Alternating floral decorated panels, terra cotta, green and deep blue colors	85.00
11½". Dark blue, red basket of flowers in center	115.00
12"	135.00
Platter. 11½ x 14½". Blue, orange, red, gold. Cranes in center, blue background	135.00
Seats, Garden. 19½" high. Octagonal shape with blue and white decor. Pair	750.00

Vases

6½". Bottle shape, 2 medallions. Iron red and cobalt with gold traces. Pair	145.00

8". Typical colors and design. Early	175.00
10½" high, 8" diam.	265.00
16½". Blue figural decor, red scalloped petal-like tops, 6 characters under base. Pair	450.00

IMPERIAL GLASS

The Imperial Glass Company was organized in 1901 by a group of business men in Bellaire, Ohio. At first they mainly produced clear, pressed glass. In 1910 they began making the popular, inexpensive glass known as Carnival. Other products were known as NUCUT, Imperial Jewels [a type of iridescent glass], Free Hand Ware and NUART.

Recently Imperial acquired the molds and equipment of several other glass companies, namely Heisey, Cambridge and Central. Many of these molds are now being used and have become acceptable because they are marked to distinguish the reproductions from the originals.

Advertising Plaque	$ 12.50
Basket. 14¾" high, blue leaf and vine decor, lustred finish	160.00

Bowls

Fruit bowl with pedestal. 9½" high. "Nucut"	50.00
Rose bowl. 8½" high. Footed, "Nucut"	27.50
5½" high, 3½" base, 9" top diam. Stretch glass, flared top. Signed in relief on base	120.00

Creamer. 5" high. "Open Rose." White
$20.00

Vase. 8½" high. Amberina. Allover
dewdrop pattern $65.00

9½". Amethyst color with pearl-silver lustre....................	85.00

Candlesticks

8-3/8" high. Purple, green, gold, irid. gold rims. Pair	95.00
12" high. Cut, rosemarie color....	120.00

Candy Jar. Covered, 10" high, floral
design in rosemarie color........ 120.00

Compotes

Jelly. 4" high, footed. Beaded Band and Panel pattern	15.00
Nut. 4" diam. Iridescent	35.00
Console Set. Bowl, 8¾" diam., applied white rim and stem, body in blue with white leaves. Matching candlesticks, 10¾" high. Set	350.00
Cruet. 7½" high. Beaded Band and Panel	35.00
Gas Shade. 2½" high, 2¼" top rim. Irid. orange gold. Nuart. Signed ..	25.00
Goblet. 7¼" high. Clear, panelled. Signed	12.00
Lamp. 15½" high. Body clear with ruby lustre over body	100.00
Pitcher, Milk. 9" high, cut daisy design	35.00

Plates

10". Turn Amphoes. Incised and raised Christmas scene. Man with horse and sleigh	50.00
12½". Amethyst with pearlsilver lustre	60.00
Salt and Pepper. Beaded Band and Panel pattern. Pair	18.00
Sugar Bowl. Optic pattern, amethyst lustre	15.00
Sugar and Creamer. Rose Marie, pink. Pair.....................	55.00
Tumbler. Cut Daisy design	20.00

Vases

4½" high, 5½" top opening. Deep purple. Signed	65.00
6¼" high. Opaque white body, adventurine drag loops, gold lining	200.00
7¼" high. Crimped top, clear body with pearl-ruby lustre decor. In metal holder................	85.00
8½" high. Clear glass body with leaf and vine decor, applied blue rim	150.00
8¾" high. Opaque white leaf and vine decor over green body	150.00
9" high. Pitcher-type. Opaque white body, blue and white decor, applied handle	165.00
9½" high. White body, lustred with blue drag loops, blue foot. Handled......................	175.00
10" high. Clear, "Nucut".........	30.00
10½" high. Orange lustred, white body with blue leaf and vine decor	175.00
11" high. Jack-in-the-Pulpit shape with lustred metallic interior, opal lustred exterior with blue loopings	185.00
13½" high. Cut Daisy	48.50
Wine. 2½" high. Beaded Band and Panel	12.00

INDIAN ARTIFACTS AND CRAFTS

People have long been fascinated by the arts
and crafts of the primitive people who were
here to meet the white man. Columbus and
the early explorers called them Indians
because they were under the impression that
a new route to India had been found.

Items vary in age from 200 years to more than
2000 years. The majority of relics in which
collectors show interest today are made of
stone and, for the most part, are plentiful.

ARTIFACTS

Arrowheads

American .... $	1.50

Stone Tomahawk............$65.00

Bird point	1.50
Mexican	.50
Ax. 7" long. Large stone	65.00
Drill. 3½" long. Large stone	14.00
Flint. 3¾" long	10.00
Pipe. Clay	17.50
Powder Horn.....................	45.00
Spearheads	
Pink flint. 3¼"	8.50
Black flint. 3"	8.50

CRAFTS

Bag. American Leather. 12", leather fringe, red and black	30.00
Baskets	
Large urn shape. 19" high, 8½" opening. Green with red, yellow, black designs. Braided leather handles and decor	55.00
Makka. Covered	25.00
Tobacco. 6x6¾". Round, covered .	75.00
Beads	
Millefiori, matched elbow style. Red, blue, white, yellow. 32" long, 20 matched beads	100.00
Pompadours. Elbow style, 15 to strand. 28" long, blue, white	85.00
Shoshoni	30.00
Trade. Green Cantonese. 3' strand	20.00
Trade. Hudson Bay. Large, 30" long, rare hen eggs or yellow crow beads, 49 to strand	85.00

Trade. Old Chevron Paternosters [Our Father]. 30" long	85.00
Bowls	
4½" diam. Southwest, redware with black design..............	30.00
Canteen. Pottery, hand decorated. Hopi	165.00
Cradle. Shoshoni	100.00
Doll. Hopi Katchina. Ceremonial figure. 9½" high	50.00
Gloves	
Shoshoni. Beaded gauntlet	35.00
Sioux.Beaded.Multicoloredbeads. Geometric designs on borders of gloves, horse and horseshow in middle. C. 1910	125.00
Headdress. Feather	50.00
Moccasins	
4¼". Beaded baby. White and black beads. 80 years old	65.00
10" long. Men's. Multicolored beads. Chippewa	125.00
Pail, Trade. Brass	30.00
Pouches	
Drawstring. Tuskarora, beaded ..	125.00
Tobacco. Beaded	75.00
Purse. 6x9¾". Handloomed, chimayo, red, white, black. Indian motifs on turquoise ground. Silver eagle clasp	15.00
Robe. Tannu buffalo. Large.........	90.00

Rug. 27x57". Diamond design, outlined in alternating red and black with tan ground $100.00

Bowl. Pottery. Zuni $140.00

Rugs. C. 1920

Chimayo. 17x58", red, white, grey, blue, black	75.00
Mavajo. 17x35". Orange, black, brown, tan, red and white	50.00
Mavajo. 18x19". Brown, light brown and white	25.00
Mavajo. 18x35". Red, white, black gray	60.00
Navajo. 20x41". White, red, grey and black	75.00
Navajo. 26x33". Grey, black, white and red	65.00
Navajo. 6'x8'. Red, pink, green, yellow and black. 37 large roses. .	400.00
Sash, Beaded. Plains Indians. ½" wide, 60" long	30.00
Serape. 4x7 feet. Colorful.	35.00
Shield, War. Shawnee, buffalo face .	135.00
Stirrups. 9x10¼". Handmade rawhide. Comanche. Pair	150.00

INDIAN TREE PATTERN

The Indian Tree pattern came into popularity during the last half of the 19th century. The name is derived from an oriental shrub or tree. The ware, with its soft greens, blues and pinks, is most attractive and is still collectible in sets.

The pattern was made by numerous English potters including Burgess and Leigh, Minton, Coalport, Cauldon, Maddox and others.

Bowls. 9" diam. Cream Soup. Set of six . . . . $	45.00
Butter Dish. Covered. Burgess & Leigh	50.00
Compote. 2¾x7½". Footed	25.00

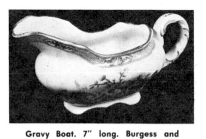

Gravy Boat. 7" long. Burgess and Leigh, England $35.00
Creamer	27.50
Cup and Saucer. Fluted-type.	22.00
Demitasse Cup and Saucer. Maddox	17.50
Coalport	17.50
Pitchers	
5" high. Burgess & Leigh	40.00
6" high. Royal Vitriol, John Maddox & Sons.	48.50
Plates	
8½". Soup Coalport.	16.50
9". Fluted, gilt trim	18.00
9½". Royal Vitriol. John Maddox & Sons	18.00
10". Johnson Bros.	20.00
10½". Cauldon.	20.00
Cake. Ear-like handles	37.50
Platter. 15½". Impressed Burleigh & Leigh	55.00
Salt and Pepper Shakers. Shape of beehive. Coalport. Pair	35.00
Sauce Dish	9.00
Sugar Bowl. Covered	45.00
Teapot. Covered	65.00
Tureen	75.00
Waste Bowl. Spade	15.00

INKWELLS

Inkwells have been in use since man first used fluids for writing. Recently a small village, buried for more than 2000 years, was discovered to have been occupied by a group of holy men known as the "Essenes." The group is believed to be responsible for writing some of the "Dead Sea Scrolls." Upon excavating a building, an inkwell showing evidence of dried ink, was found among the ruins.

Bennington. Brown glaze. Early. Figural head of man with nightcap $	50.00
Bottle. Crystal, 3¾" high. French, gray cover. Homan Mfg. Co.	25.00

5½" high. "Dorflinger." Ground stopper. Pastel colors in crystal $125.00

Brass

Crab, 8" wide, 6½" high, hinged cover with glass well, heavy cast brass 50.00

Elk head. Clear glass insert 40.00

Ornate. English. C. 1880 .... 75.00

Solid brass stand 15" long, 3¾" wide with 2 ornate hinged lids at either end, milk glass inserts. 2¼"x2¼" 50.00

Shell-shaped hinged cover at-

Double. Metal base, 5½"x9½". Horse separates milk glass bottles ...$85.00

tached to 9" pen tube with hinged cover 50.00

Swirl glass insert. Pat. 97 on inside hinge 40.00

Bronze

Art Nouveau type. 4-leaf clover shape with woman's head and flowing hair as lid 75.00

Bear chained to tree trunk. 3" high, hinged head opens to inkwell 100.00

Dogs. Two large. Gornik, Austrian sculptor 325.00

Dore. Glass insert 125.00

Mephistopheles. Crouching figure with ears as pen holders. Glass insert for ink. 2¾"x3" 135.00

Vienna. Cat, 6" lifelike pose and coloring 95.00

Negro. 6" long. Lid has negro boy with hat 185.00

China

2"diam., 2½" high. Small melon mold, purple flowers and pink roses on buff background, hinged lid, brass connections 50.00

3" square, 2" high. Handpainted on white, gold trim. T. & V. Limoges...................... 65.00

4¼" square, 2½" well. Pink handpainted roses, green leaves. Domed swirled lid, wide brass connection 70.00

4¼" long, 4" wide, 2" at top where well rests. Black imp with cap forms lid. Red, blue and yellow decor. German 35.00

Cloisonne. 6" square. Irregularly shaped tray resting on a stone wall 65.00

Delft. 2¾" square, 3½" high. Crossed mallets and windmill decor, domed lid, wide brass connector 60.00

Glass, Clear

Admiral Dewey, clear glass cover 65.00

Advertising. Large round top with legend. "N.Y. Ledger, The Great Home Advertising Medium" 30.00

Crystal. 2½" square. Sterling top, embossed and monogrammed ... 65.00

Crystal. 2 bottles on 6" gold plated stand. Pen included 60.00

1½" square, 2" high with hinged glass top and brass connector 20.00

2" square, 3" high with rounded high brass hinged lid 20.00

2¼" square, 3½" high, early swirled glass with matching lid. Sterling connector 35.00

3¹₁" high. Imperial German
helmet. Marked with embossed
eagle/Gesetzlich 45.00
4" long, 1¾" wide, 1¾" high. Star
on bottom, blown well in glass,
domed sterling lid 45.00
5" diam. base. Clamsbroth.
Turquoise blue asp encircling well .   85.00
Iridescent. Green glass, hinged
brass mask lid, 3¹₂" high 45.00

Iron
Cast. Camel. 9¹₂" long, 6" high . .   40.00
Crab. 5". Black enamel 25.00
Racing Car. Old style, 2 occupants
wearing goggles, 2 wells under
hood of car 95.00
Jacobus. Eclipse trade mark, green
base, clear dome 16.50
Milk Glass. 4" high. Hound dogs
made of milk glass. Iron base and
stand 100.00
Owl. 5" high. Pewter 85.00
Pairpoint. Hinged, ormolu lid 58.00
Porcelain. Raised floral and leaf
decor. Brass top with 2 large and
3 small wells, 1¼" diam. Small
removable glass insert in center
well, acorn finial, hinged lid 72.50
Pottery
Frog. Brown 20.00
Lion. Light tan 35.00
Rockingham. Sanded surface, bird
and snake, eggs in nest, pastel
color. Large 100.00
Rookwood. 6¼x9". Green bird
shaped tray, glass insert, 1921 . . .   65.00
Satin Glass. Blue swirl 125.00
School Desk. Black bakelite top 3.50
Staffordshire
Greyhound 65.00
3½" high. Square, hinged top,
pink and white with alternating
floral stripes 45.00
Tiffany
3¼" square, 3" high. Iridescent
green with filigree trim of roses
and leaves in floral effect in silver
over copper, hinged lid 250.00
4-1/8x4¼". Hinged cover 135.00

INSULATORS

The collecting of insulators, which were used
on telephone and electric lines, is one of the
latest hobbies. In the past few years price
guides have been published and interest in
collecting has increased.

Beehive. Aqua . . . .$ 4.75

Pottery. Brown glaze. Unmarked $2.50

Brookfield. 1865 date only 10.00
Brookfield X2. Aqua 3.25
Brookfield. Aqua, no number 2.00
Carnival #63. Pyrex 18.00
Corning Pyrex #441. Dark Carnival.
Mint CD 327 . . . .   60.00
Dwight pattern. Aqua 10.00
Diamond. Olive green 10.00
Gaynor #48-400. Aqua 8.50
Hemingray
#1. High voltage, triple petticoat,
green 15.00
#2. Provo 24.00

Hemingray #40. Glass $4.50

#9. Clear	2.50
#9. Purple, May 2, 1893	15.00
#12. Aqua, 1893	7.50
#13. Clear	5.00
#14. Vaseline	42.50
#16	1.75
#19. Cobalt blue	35.00
#23. Turquoise	17.50
#45. Clear	5.50
#62. Blue-green	15.00
Porcelain. Gray. 16" high	12.00
P.R.R. Signals. Green	5.00
Rubber, Marked Continental Rubber Works, W.V. Telegraph Co. 4"	9.50
Whitall-Tatum #1	2.00
Whitall-Tatum. Amethyst	12.50

IRON

Iron has been known for centuries and its beginning was about 3500 BC. In the Middle Ages it was used for decorative purposes, tools and weapons. In America it was used for utilitarian items such as grates, door hardware, stoves, kettles, candlesticks and other lighting devices, figurines, tools and a variety of other uses including rims for wheels on wagons and chains for pulling stumps. In the military line, guns, cannons, cannon balls and rifles were made of iron.

Eel Spear. Hand-forged 37.50

Andirons

14" long, snake feet. Pair	$ 42.50
14" long, knob top. Pair	50.00
19" long, large ball finials, horseshoe feet. Pair	65.00

Foot Scraper. "Mudder's Little Helper." 13x16" base................$65.00

Anvil. Miniature	8.00
Apple Peeler. Marked 1882	18.00
Belaying Pin. 17" long	12.50
Boot Scraper. 6¼" high, 4" wide, Scroll center and ends	16.50
Buggy Step	10.00
Candlesticks. Winged dragon shape. 6¾" high, 6¼" wide. Pair	20.00
Cannon, Miniature. Navy model, 7½" long, 4 iron wheels	69.50
Ceiling Hook for Lamp	4.58
*Cherry Seeder	15.00
Corn Dryer	6.50
Cuspidor. Shape and size of stove pipe hat	32.00
Dog. Pointer. 7½ x 16½"	65.00
Door Stops, see "Door Stops"	
Eagle. Wings out, head down, 31" long, 10" high. Weighs 40 pounds	175.00
Fence. Victorian iron, 100 feet with gate, 38" high. Good condition	500.00
Fence. 150 feet with gate and posts	650.00

Fireplace Items

Crane. 38" arm	100.00
Kettle. Urn-shaped, spike legs, iron lid and bail	40.00
Milk Warmer. Quart, spike legs, long iron handle	20.00
"S" Pot Hooks. To use on crane	5.00
Shovel, tongs and poker in stand. Set	50.00
Swinging Skillet. 13" diam., short feet	35.00
Tongs. Plain	15.00
Tongs and Brush. Set	25.00
Trammel. Hook, 24" long, hand forged, eye bolt, hinged hook for kettle	95.00
Waffle Iron. Trumpets and lyre design on lid	35.00
Flower Pot holders, 30" long. Scroll wall-type. Pair	25.00

Grinder. 2 grinding plates $12.00

Foot Scrapers
    Attached to oval fluted pan 25.00
    Scroll ends 25.00
Hand Cuffs. Chain joint, screw
    release 30.00
Harpoon. Early 6'3", cane shaft,
    barbed iron head 50.00
Hat, Gentleman's. High. C. 1880 . . . .   50.00
Hat Rack. 6 curved swinging arms . .   22.50
Hay Fork. 34" long. Bayonet-type . . .   18.00
*Hitching Post. Horse's head. C.
    1880 . . . .   160.00
Ice Creepers. Pair 15.00
Irons. See "Branding Irons" and
    "Irons, Smoothing, Etc."
Kettles. Footed, with bails
    Small 22.50
    Medium 35.00
    Large 50.00
Key. 6" long 7.50
Ladles
    Small 12.00
    5¼x6" bowl with pouring lip on
    either side. 22" handle 18.50
*Lamp. Bracket. Lacy frame, com-
    plete 25.00
Lantern. English bird cage, frosted
    glass 50.00
Mailbox. Cast iron 20.00
Match Holder, See "Match Holders"
Mortar and Pestle 35.00
Muffin Mold 12.50
Mustache Curler. Scissor type 9.00
Pans, Muffin. Space for 12 muffins . .   12.00
Paper Clip. Hound head 45.00
Pea Sheller. Dated 1866 . . . .   12.50
Plaque. 18½" round. U.S. Grant bust
    with dates 1822-1885 . . . .   100.00
Plate. 8½" 15.00

Poker 6.00
Porringer 18.50
Pump. Cast iron 45.00
Sausage Stuffer. 13" long, marked
    Brighton No. 2 . . . .   30.00
Sconces, Wall. 11" overall height.
    Flower-shaped cups extend out
    14". Pair 85.00
Shelf Brackets. Lacy type. 7x9". Pair .   12.50
Shoemaker's Nail Holder 30.00
Shoes. Cast iron. High button type.
    10" high. Pair 75.00
Skillet. Rattail type. Wrought iron,
    high feet, 9" diam. 45.00
Soap Dish. Wall type. Lacy design . . .   10.00
Spurs. Civil War. Pair 30.00
Steelyards. 50 lbs. 18.50
Stoves
    Kerosene. Portable. One burner,
    two 5" leaves. 19½x9½x11½".
    Crown #8, Troy, N.Y. Patd. 1881 . .   200.00
    Pot Belly. Cast iron, small size.
    One lid on top 31½" high 175.00
    Wood burning parlor stove. Dated
    1869. Whiteman & Cox, Phila., Pa.
    Water urn on top, 12" diam. at
    center. 51" high 235.00
Strap Hinges. 22" to 27" long. Heart
    finial. Pair 17.50
String Holder. See "String Holders"
Tea Kettles
    6½" high. Star on lid, No. 8 inside
    star 25.00
    8" high, 8" diam. Flat cover dated
    1863, recessed base 35.00
Toaster. 11½" long 35.00
Tobacco Cutter. See "Tobacco
    Cutters"
Tongs. Blacksmith's. 19", 22" long . . .   10.00
Traps
    Bear trap. 11¾" jaws, drag hooks,
    chains, etc.   90.00
    Beaver. 22½" double spring 45.00
    Fox trap. Early, hand forged 45.00
    Wolf. 26" double spring 45.00
Trivets
    Early Pennsylvania Dutch, han-
    dled. Hex sign 100.00
Washboard. Galvanized 12.50
Weather Vane. See "Weather
    Vanes"
Wheel. For measuring land 35.00
        *Reproduced Item

IRONS [SMOOTHING, ETC.]

Irons of past days were the humblest and
probably the most despised domestic object.

Today they are eagerly sought by collectors. Flat irons, or "sad" irons, are the easiest to find. The word "sad" is the obsolete term for solid. If you have ever handled one of these irons, you know they are quite heavy, and many a housewife was "sad" at the end of an ironing day. The flat iron can be found in many sizes and were shaped for various purposes evolving around the current fashions of the times - the ruffler, fluter, the egg, etc.

There were four methods of heating these irons: 1] the slug was heated and inserted on the iron; 2] the iron was heated directly by the fire; 3] charcoal was contained within the iron; 4]the self-heating gas iron.

Today, we have the electric iron which will probably be added to the collector's list because of the new permanent press fabrics.

Charcoal Iron wth Trivet. App. 10"
$50.00

Miniature. Swan iron on trivet. 5¼"
long $30.00

Box Irons
Cast iron with wood handle, has
slug or heater . . . . $ 22.50
No heater. Fancy plate or heat
shield under handle 15.00
Charcoal Irons
British Coat of Arms in brass, one
chimney. 56.00
Kaiser Bill's head for opener 46.00
Flat Iron. Child's. Black wood handle
and knob to lift off top on metal
clamp. "Dover No. 12 Sad Iron" in
relief on top of base 20.00
Fluting. 3pcs. Marked. Geneva Hand
Fluter on top piece. Mkd. on
bottom of stand "Stump, St. Joe,
Mo. Pat. April 30, 1878 . . . . 28.50
Gas Iron. Coleman. Good Value
Model 4A 7.50
Sad Irons
Child's. With wooden handle 25.00
Deeply etched design showing
rosettes surrounded by scrolls . . . 12.00
Hollow handle. Embossed "Sil-
vester's Patent Salter #5" 10.00
5¾" handle embossed "Geneva" . 10.00
Tailor's Iron. Embossed #12 . . . . 16.50

IRONSTONE

The first china of this type was patented in 1813 by C. J. Mason in England. It was a thin durable type of ware made from the slag of iron furnaces ground and mixed with clay. The thick heavy type now commonly referred to as ironstone is, in reality, graniteware and unlike the original ironstone. This later product was mass-produced after 1850 and was popular until the 1880-1890 period when the vogue shifted to French porcelains, especially Haviland China.

Bone Dish. Wheat pattern . . . . $ 12.50
Bowls
5½" soup. Meakin, birds and
morning glories 15.00
8" square, Meakin, birds and
morning glories 17.50
With pitcher. Small, Johnson
Bros., England. Set 32.50

Butter Dishes
Covered. Corn pattern 42.50
Covered. Meakin, birds and
morning glories 45.00
Butter Pat. Meakin, birds and
morning glories 4.00
Cake Plate. Square, Meakin, birds
and morning glories 35.00

Plate. 7½". Oriental scene in multi-colors ......'..............$35.00

Chamber Pot with Lid. Lily-of-the-Valley pattern. Large bud finial on lid. Marked Royal Stone China, Wedgwood & Co. 40.00

Coffee Pot. Large, tan and blue decoration 70.00

Compotes
8½" high...................... 65.00
10" high. Footed, ribbed......... 75.00

Corn Pudding Mold 25.00

Creamers
5½" high. Lively, Powell & Co.... 25.00
Meakin. Birds and morning glories 27.50

Cups and Saucers
Meakin. Birds and morning glories 22.50
Wedgwood. Handleless, laurel pattern 28.50

Door Knobs. Pair 15.00

Egg Cup 8.00

Gravy Boats
Cable pattern 20.00
Meakin. Birds and morning glories 25.00

Jug. Octagonal. 7" high, serpent handle. Blue Willow decor 65.00

Ladles
Gravy....................... 20.00
Soup........................ 35.00

Pickle Dish. Meakin, birds and morning glories 15.00

Pitchers
5½" high. Meakin 28.50
8" high. Milk. Lily-of-the-Valley. Burgess, Burslem............... 40.00
9" high. Corn pattern 50.00
9" high. Sheaf of wheat 50.00
Wash. Fuchsia, large 45.00

Plates
6". Meakin. Birds and morning glories 15.00
8½". Wheat pattern 18.50
9". Meakin. Birds and morning glories 20.00
10¼". Mason's. Imari pattern 25.00

Platters
8" long. Wheat pattern 35.00
13" long. Meakin. Birds and morning glories 45.00
14" long. Wedgwood & Co........ 25.00
14½". Lily-of-the-Valley 50.00
15x11½". Meakin 55.00
16" diam. Octagonal, J. Wedgwood, 1852................... 45.00
18¾". Wheat pattern, Elsmore & Foster 60.00
16x12". Corean pattern 50.00
Large, blue and white. Early Mason's 110.00

Pudding Mold. 6¾" long, 4¼" high. Oval-shaped, geometric pattern .. 25.00

Sauce Dish. Meakin, birds and morning glories 8.00

Shaving Mug 20.00

Soap Dishes
Covered. Oval, 4¼x6". Gold band decor 15.00
Covered. Wheat pattern 20.00

Sugar Bowls
Covered. Corn pattern 35.00
Covered. Lily-of-the-Valley, bud finial. "T. Hughes, Burslem"...... 50.00
Covered. Pear finial 45.00

Syrup. Pewter lid 40.00

Teapots
Copper lustre decor............. 72.00
9" square. Meakin.............. 65.00

Plate. 8¾". John Alcock. Flora . $25.00

10" high. Leaf pattern 75.00

Tureens

Covered. Lily-of-the-Valley. Small . 45.00

Covered, rectangular. Meakin, birds and morning glories 50.00

12". Edwards, nut finial 60.00

14x10". Fancy handles and finial, with ladle 120.00

Sauce with liner. Berlin shape 55.00

Soup with liner. Prairie shape 155.00

Soup. Sydenham, large 275.00

Soup. Large, wheat pattern, pedestal base. With tray and ladle. Set 125.00

Urn. 21" high. Flow Blue. Heavy white enamel flowers, gold trim . . 220.00

Vase. 5½" high, 8-sided, rust red with green and black. Marked Mason's Patent Ironstone 28.50

Vegetable Dishes

7x10". Covered, handled. Lily-of-the-Valley. "Anthony Shaw" 48.00

9½". Open 25.00

Covered. Wheat and Clover 42.00

Wash Sets

Pitcher and Bowl. Lily-of-theValley pattern 100.00

Rose decor, gold trim 95.00

IVORY

True Ivory is the yellowish-white dentine forming the main part of the teeth of tusks of animals, especially the elephant. It has been used for centuries for both practical and ornamental items. The material lends itself very well for carving.

Abacus. 1½x2". Carved . . . . $ 65.00

Bottle. 1½" high 48.50

Boxes

Jewelry. Carved lacy design, blue velvet lining, tray, mirrored lid . . . 125.00

Snuff. Painted garden scene with man and dog. Signed. Mavet, Paris 185.00

Trinket. 1¾x2½" diam. Miniature portrait framed in lid. Signed 85.00

Button Hook. Ivory handle 12.00

Cane Handle. Dog's head 37.50

Card Case. Carving of stag, foliage. Red silk lining 50.00

Chess Set. Red and white. 2¾" highest. Complete 150.00

Cigarette Holders

3½". Lioness 8.50

4½". Elephants, 5 graduated sizes 38.50

7". Dragon 15.00

Bird. 3¼" long. Tinted in red, yellow
$75.00

"Fisherman with Net." 5¾" high
$175.00

Figurines

Bear. 3" long, 2" high. Base is in form of wax sealer. C. 1880 . . . . . . 275.00

Boy with wheelbarrow. Driving goose. Lattice fence in rear 200.00

Dogs. 6", carved, Chinese Temple. Pair 395.00

Elephant. 2¾" high, 4½" long. Applied tusks 165.00

Elephant. Standing. 5" high, 2" long. Inlaid with stones and pearls 275.00

Farmer. 9" high. Basket and goose. Signed 275.00

Fishermen. One with net, one with net and fish. Pair 400.00

Horses. 5" high. Prancing with trappings. Wood base 395.00

Lion. 7½" long. Ruby eyes 200.00

Madonna. 12". Germany 75.00

Man with axe. 5½" high 175.00

Man with oar. 5½" high 175.00

Man with staff. 7" high 195.00

Man carrying wheat and raised hue. 11" high. Chinese. 19th century 325.00

Seven Immortals, on stand 650.00

Woman. with flowing robe, bowl in one hand, other arm raised. 9" high. C. 1880 . . . . 250.00

Horn, Hunting. 30" long. Carved with coat of arms, animals 500.00

Match Holder. Brass elephant, bead trim, brass spear and rim 75.00

Napkin Rings	
Carved scenes in 3 rings. Pair	35.00
Miniature. Plain	14.50
Portraits	
Miniature. In silver frame	200.00
Miniature. Round brass easel-type frame. H/P, artist signed. French .	250.00
Scabbard. 16¾" long, covered, with carved oriental warriors	65.00
Scrimschaw. See "Scrimshaws"	
Sewing Bird	28.50
Shoe Horns	
Plain, small	7.50
6¾" long. With carved birds and snake on handle	35.00
Teething Ring	17.50
Toothbrush. Carved ivory handle . . .	7.00
Toothpick Holder. Elephant handle . .	22.50
Vase. 10½" high. Steuben. Shape #2683	475.00

JACKFIELD POTTERY

Jackfield is a type of pottery made for table use. It has a red body and is sometimes decorated with scrolls and flowers in relief. It is covered with a thick black glaze but differs from basalt [made by Wedgwood] which is black throughout.

Cats. 12½" high, black with glass eyes, gold neck ribbon. Pair	$ 150.00
Coffee Pot. 9½" to top of finial	100.00
Cow Creamer	75.00
Cup and Saucer	50.00
Dogs. 10" high. Pair	65.00
Pot. Cache. 7½ x 7½". Enameled classical scenes front and back, two lions with ring handles trimmed in gold	125.00

Cow Creamer. App. 7" long $75.00

Teapots	
4½" high. All black glaze, small . .	75.00
7" high. Checkered design in relief. All black glaze	100.00
Vase. 4" high, design in relief, beaded top	55.00

JACK-IN-THE-PULPIT VASES

Near the turn of the present century, vases of various colors of glass, blown in the shape of a "jack-in-the-pulpit" flower, were in vogue.

5" high, ruffled top. Transparent green glass with enameled flowers, gold
$85.00

4¼". Victorian, milky opalescent, green exterior with deeper green lining	$ 35.00
5" high, 4" wide across top. Opalescent. Pair	125.00
5¼". Satin glass, orange to gold to yellow. Butterfly and leaves decor	125.00
6". Satin glass, blue lining, camphor glass feet	135.00
6" high. Vaseline with purple ruffled top	55.00
6½". Opalescent, green	45.00
7". Millefiori	175.00
7". Ruffled top, clear glass with shadings of green, purple and yellow	80.00
7". Vaseline to opalescent	65.00
7½". Signed "Quezal"	295.00
8". Green ribbed diamond puff body, with applied leaves	65.00

8". Pink shading to maroon, white
edge........................... 65.00
9" high, 5½" across flair. Cranberry.
Ornate, curled, clear ½" round
stem. Clear veined star shaped
leaves as base. Pair............. 65.00
9". Green base blending into spatter
of yellow, gold and pink 75.00
9". Light green shading to vaseline,
clear feet...................... 75.00
9½". Cranberry glass, white trim ... 75.00
10". Cranberry glass 75.00
10". L.C.Tiffany. Fully signed 600.00
11" high, 8¼" top diam. Green with
opalescent 75.00
12". Cranberry, ribbed top, scalloped edge, ribbed body with
clear pedestal base, rough pontil . 87.50
Rubina Glass. Green base shading to
cranberry, ruffled top, applied
green leaves around body, 2"
pedestal base, blown 65.00
Threaded blue opalescent lily in
Victorian silverplated holder..... 45.00

JADE

Jade is a semi-precious mineral used in Burma
and China for carving statues, idols, boxes,
incense burners, etc. The most common color
is green, however, it is found in rare colors of
mutton fat, grey, purple, rose, yellow, black,
green and in mottled colors.

Ash Tray. 1x3x3" ....$ 100.00
Beads
10mm, hand-knotted, 14K clasp,
16" long...................... 145.00
Jade and cultured pearls. 10mm
hand-knotted, 14K clasp. 16" long . 165.00
Birds
4½" long 150.00
5½" long 175.00
Boxes
3½" high...................... 300.00
Round, covered. 2¼" diam., apple
green shading to white 200.00
Bracelet. Green 65.00
Buckle. White dragon, 4¾" long 200.00
Buddhas
2" high....................... 145.00
6" high....................... 350.00
Bull. 5" long.................... 400.00
Elephant. 4" long 300.00
Figurines, Female
8" high, holding flowers. On
carved teakwood stand 650.00
Mutton fat on teak bases. Large,
pair 950.00

Carnelian, carved pendant. 14K gold
mounting and chain $95.00

Fish
2" long....................... 95.00
3½" long. Fantail goldfish. Plum.
On stand 175.00
3½" long. Fantail goldfish. Green.
On stand 145.00
5¼" long..................... 300.00
Foo Dogs. 3x3". Green coloring,
wooden stands. Pair 135.00
Frogs
1½" long..................... 95.00
3" long. Deep green on wood
stand 200.00
God of Longevity. 6½" high 550.00

Horses
4¼" high. Being groomed by boy.
Grey-white jade................ 500.00
5½" high. Tang 750.00
Hoti
2½" 250.00
8" high....................... 750.00
Ibex. 6" high 500.00
Incense Burner. Carved, mutton fat
jade with Fu-lion masks and lotus
vines. 6" high 350.00
Inkwells
Gray with black top, brass base .. 500.00
5" high, brass base, Foo dog finial 550.00

Kuan-Yin

5¼" high	300.00
8" high, deep green	500.00
Letter Opener. 6" long	75.00

Lions

2½ x 3". Mouths roaring. Green coloring, wooden stands	115.00
3½ x 5½". Sitting green winged Archaic lion. Temple. Fine carving	200.00
Ming Dog. 5" high	500.00

Paperweights

2¾" diam., round	175.00
3" long, oval	200.00

Quartz Chops

2½". Mottled grey frog	50.00
3. Mottled green, mythological turtle	100.00
3½". Green color or dragon	75.00
Rabbits. Carved on teakwood stand. 4¾" long. Ch'ien Lung period	500.00
Rhinoceros. 5" long	400.00
Snuff Bottle. Shape of pear, on stand, white jade. Ch'ien Lung period . . .	350.00
Tablet. Green, birds, lotus flowers, foliage. Mounted on carved teakwood stand. 25" high	5000.00
Tree. Jade, in Cloisonne planter. 11" high, 7¼" wide. Amethyst, turquoise and coral blossoms and buds, green leaves	500.00
Vase. Carved, mutton-fat type, on teakwood stand. Lettuce carved on one side with cricket and grasshopper. Greenish-white jade. 7" high. Ch'ien Lung period .	1000.00

JASPERWARE

Josiah Wedgwood described Jasperware as "a fine Terra Cotta of great beauty and delicacy proper for cameos." The background of the ware is predominantly blue; however, green, yellow, red and lavender shades were also used. The figures are often done in the Grecian classical tradition and decorations are usually white.

The product was first made at the Wedgwood Etruria Works in 1775. Probably 90% of the ware sold in shops today was made after 1890. Much of it has been brought into the U.S. within the past 20 years by importers and, in turn, sold by unscrupulous or ignorant dealers as old to new collectors or unsuspecting customers.

Biscuit Jars

5" high, blue with acorn finial and leaf decor on cover	175.00

5" high, 4¼" diam. Green, with silver cover and handle. Impressed "Wedgwood, England" . . .	195.00
5½" high, 4" diam. Silhouettes of Washington, Lafayette, Franklin . . Wedgwood. Classical blue and	350.00
white. Silverplated lid and rim . . .	225.00

Bowls

5¼" diam., light blue	100.00
7" diam., light green	115.00
7½" diam., 3¾" high, classic figures, 3 white feet	135.00

Boxes

Blue, covered, white chariot in relief, scalloped edge. Impressed "Wedgwood"	92.50
Blue, covered, heart shape	67.50
Blue, round, 5" diam., 2" deep, covered. Classic figures in relief. England	75.00
Green, covered, heart shape. Raised bust of man motif	80.00

Candlesticks

5¼" high. Royal blue. Pair	150.00
7" high. Dark blue with white decor. Marked Wedgwood	150.00
Cheese Dish. 10" diam., blue	245.00
Chocolate Pot	175.00

Candleholder. Blue and white . $150.00

Creamer and Sugar. Wedgwood, dark blue and white. Late........ 100.00

Creamers
2" high, 2¾" diam., blue 65.00
4" high, dark blue 85.00

Cup and Saucer. Medium blue, classic figures, rope handles, early 125.00

Dish. Covered, 10¼" long. Rabbit handle, game figures in relief around body. Impressed "Wedgwood" 165.00

Jam Jar. With matching plate. Dark blue with classic figures 120.00

Jardinieres
7¼" diam., 6¼" high. Classic figures, lion heads and grape garlands in relief. Impressed "Wedgwood, England" 125.00
8" diam., 7" high, green with classic figures................. 150.00

Jugs
5½" high, blue. Wedgwood, medallions of Washington and Franklin...................... 275.00
6½" high, Jasper cover, light blue, classic medallions 120.00

Match Holder. Black and white with striker underneath. Marked Wedgwood, 2" high............. 75.00

Medallion. Tri-color cameo type, 1½ x2½". Impressed Wedgwood . 185.00

Mugs
Beer. Dark blue, Wedgwood, England 100.00
3½ x5½", dark green. "Fill This Cup and Drink It Up." Drape and floral designs in white relief 100.00
6" high, blue figures representing seasons 100.00

Mustard Pot with Spoon. Blue with cameo type cupids. Covered 65.00

Pitchers
4" high. Dark blue, classic figures, grape border, twisted handle 65.00
5¼" high. Yellow, bulbous....... 145.00
5½" high. Dark blue, bulbous 85.00
5½" high. Green, looped flowers and figures 100.00
7" high. Gray-green with white classic figures. Impressed Wedgwood 165.00
8" high. Brown with white classic figures 95.00
8" high. Dark blue, tankard 100.00
9" high. Blue classic figures, grape border 135.00

Plaques
4½" diam., 3" high. Green applied girl's head, not marked .. 45.00
5¾" diam. Green, numbered. Classic figures 60.00
7¼" high, 5¼" wide. Shield-shaped, green. One with girl playing bagpipes, vintage border. Pair 100.00
2¼ x7¾". Wedgwood. "The Dancing Hour." C. 1780 ...... 275.00
8". Head of Goethe. White on blue 75.00

Ring Tree. 4¼" diam., 2¾" high. Green, "Wedgwood, England" ... 55.00

Salt Shaker. Dark blue, classic white figures. White acanthus leaves and berries around top, perforated Jasper cover 65.00

Sugar Bowls
4", dark blue and white, classic figures 100.00
Green, covered. Wedgwood 125.00
Yellow, covered. Wedgwood. Rare 250.00

Sugar Shaker. Blue, classic 95.00

Syrups
5½" high. Blue with white figures, grape trim around top. Silver-plated lid...................... 130.00
7" high. Blue, classic figures. Wedgwood 145.00

Teapots
Blue, small, classic figures 75.00
Royal blue, large classic figures, early 165.00

Tea Sets
Teapot, sugar bowl and creamer. Dark blue with classic figures. Set 300.00
Teapot, sugar bowl and creamer. Green with classic figures. Set ... 350.00

Creamer. Blue and white $85.00

Toothpick Holder. Light blue, with
angel head in blue and green
medallion 48.50
Tray. 7¾ x 10". Blue, classic design.
Marked "Wedgwood, England" . . . 120.00
Urns
9¼" high. Blue, with classic
figures, square base. 13" across
handles 275.00
12" high. Black with white decor.
Impressed "Wedgwood" 375.00
Vase. 6½" high. Green with white
cupids 65.00

JEWEL BOXES

Jewel boxes listed in this section are mainly
the so-called Victorian type. The boxes were
common during the 1880-1910 period. For the
most part, they were made of white metal
similar to the type used by manufacturers for
making hollow ware. The boxes, after being
cast, were plated with either gold or silver.
The interior was then padded lightly with
cotton and lined with fabric.

Egg-shape. 2½ x 3 x 4½". Set in
footed Dore. Bronze frame,
flowers, leaves, twigs . . . . $ 165.00
French enamel. Pink, white, green
floral decor. 2½ x 2¾ x 3¾" high . . 125.00
Kidney-shaped. Pink lining. Gold
color worn 18.50
Large. Footed, lined, ornate design.
Gold color 30.00
Medium. Floral design, lined. Gold
color worn 22.50
Pedestal-type. Metal, gold plated.
Green velvet lining. 2½ x 2½ x 3½" 28.50
Small. Lined, silver color 16.50
Victorian. Gilt worn. Embossed rose . 18.50

Victorian-type. Rogers Silverplate.
2¼ x 3 x 7". Satin lined $28.50

White metal, painted gold. Art
Nouveau $25.00

Victorian. Metal, gold plated. Satin
lining 27.50
Victorian. Pin cushion top in purple.
Blue silk lining 22.50
Victorian. Pin cushion top in shape of
heart. Green velvet 25.00

JEWELRY

Jewelry has been used since ancient times as
personal adornment or as symbols of wealth
and status. Primitive people used bone, iron,
wood, seeds, animal teeth, pebbles and shells
for jewelry. Bronze was utilized until gold and
silver were discovered. At a still later date,
precious gems were added to enhance the
appearance and value of an ornament.
In ancient Greece, gold was mainly used and
designs were usually based on animal and
human figures.
In Rome, jewelry was more splendid and
heavier than Greek jewelry. During the days
of the Roman Empire, finger rings were very
popular and people wore then on every finger
and often two rings to a finger.
In the Renaissance period, design became
more elaborate and jewelry was richly
decorated with enamel, pearls and gems. In
this period, earrings were considered an
important item of a gentleman's costume.
Also, elaborate chains and collars were worn
by the wealthy and the powerful.

In the Victorian period, the common man was able to buy a variety of items in jewelry as they became readily available through manufacturers who issued catalogues to small store owners, all over the country.

Victorian jewelry is popular among collectors today as much of it is still readily available.

Ring. Victorian mounting. Brazilian sapphire surrounded with rose cut diamonds.................. $450.00

Beads

15". 14K gold plated. Amethyst. 10mm. Siberian deep transparent purple. 14K gold clasp .... $ 275.00

15". 14K gold plated. Tiger Eye, 4mm 30.00

16". 14K gold plated. Burma Jade. 8mm., round beads, light seafoam green....................... 65.00

16". 14K gold plated. Faceted garnets, graduated 17.50

16". 14K gold plated. Biwas. 5-6mm., "Rice Pearls" 30.00

16". 14K gold plated. White Baroque pearls. 8-8½mm 49.50

18". ½ to 5/8" square cut Rock Crystal 35.00

18". Cabochon garnet, with slight graduation and 14K clasp 85.00

22". Graduated strand on GF chain, amber, shades of kumquat . 65.00

24". Angel Skin Coral. 68-graduated round from 5½ to 11mm., restrung 125.00

36". 14K gold Chinese plated. Turquoise, green to blue green ... 65.00

39". Afghanistan Lapis Lazuli. 47 gems, ½ x ¾", in blue with 16 gold balls, marked 14, goldsmithed clasp 650.00

Peking Glass. Mandarin. 107 large round opaque aqua, interspaced with 4 large medium blue opaque, center front is blue "gourd," long flat piece of silk and pink, opaque "pancake" bead; dangling on each side are strings of green semi-opaque round beads ending with clear, blue, rose and green "drops" with old butterfly wing fittings. Chinese ... 100.00

Venetian. 26 large clear with gold leaf overall, pink roses and tiny blue and pink buds and green leaves sprinkled over each bead. Cut crystal between 35.00

Victorian. 223 faceted garnet stones in goldplated mounting ... 125.00

Bracelets

Art Nouveau. Floral links alternate with links set with ¾ Ct. 4 aquamarines, 14K white and yellow gold 85.00

Chinese. Silver, ¾" wide with

Cross with anchor. Gutta Percha. C. 1850 .... $68.00

long panorama of hand carved, high relief figures in various postures. Artist signed in Chinese characters 75.00

Hair. 5/8" hank of hair is woven to expand to fit any wrist, ornate and movable fittings in front are heavy 14K GF 35.00

Snake. 14K ornately sculptured head has garnet mounted on top, round woven wires form the body. Hallmarked 150.00

Victorian. GF mesh, slide to adjust for size through 14K GF fittings with seed pearls. Fancy ends with dangling mesh tassels ending in gold balls. 5/8" wide fittings, 1" wide. Pair 150.00

Brooches

2¼" high. Art Deco. Sterling, heavy. Turbanned head of black slave 25.00

Garnet. Star, six-pointed, gold-plated. 70 flat and faceted garnets 50.00

Chains

14". 14K, heavy 298.00

16". Russian. Silver with blue enamel trim. Three ½ x 2" panels with designs. Links between and on each end. Hallmarked, 84 and St. George and the Dragon. Handmade 125.00

17". 14K 265.00

22". 14K 350.00

24". 18K heavy link, over 1 oz. . . . 295.00

25". Heavy square sterling links. Art Deco 100.00

Braided link. 14K. Unusual fittings 295.00

Cuff Pins, collection, 10K gold $7.00
Sterling $4.00

Braided link. 14K. Heavy, double, with large hinged Masonic fob . . . 500.00

Elongated link. 14K. Large and heavy 350.00

Flat link. 14K, heavy 250.00

White gold, 14K 135.00

Necklace. Victorian. Crystal. Green onyx beads $85.00

Chains, Slide

60". GF 65.00

60". 14K, with 14K precious stone slide 250.00

Charms. 14K. Approx. 1" long. Various figures or items . . . . 35.00 to 55.00

Cross. 14K. 1¼" long, ¾" wide. Faberge, 56, BC. Workmaster Vladimir Soloviev 150.00

Earrings

Diamond:

White gold. 1.00Ct. weight 500.00
White gold. 3.20Cts. weight 2250.00
Emerald 0.90Ct., diamonds
3.35Cts. 3000.00
Drop. 1½" long, 18K. 3 turquoise
stones and 6 white sapphires,
etruscan work, 2 ribbon-like
folded over and joined. New post
backs 225.00
Opal. Pierced-ear type. Diamond
chips on top. Pair 225.00

Wedgwood, Jasper

Black and white round buttons,
gold-filled mounting 27.50
Blue and white oval drop on
gold-filled mounting 27.50
Green and white buttons on
silver mountings 25.00

Lockets

Heart-shaped, 1¼" wide. Sterling
925. Floral etching............. 45.00
Round. 14K. Etched heart and
flowers on 14K chain........... 50.00
Tree of Life. Large heavy 18 Dwt.
14K. Decorated small stones 125.00
Lorgnette. French enamel gold on
silver. Handle is all blue enamel
with gold flowers.............. 135.00
Necklace. Lapis Lazuli. Large teardrop shaped, set with fluted silver
cap, 1-5/8" long, silver chain..... 45.00

Jewelry. Chatelaine $175.00

Pins

Art Deco. 14K. Amethyst, hand
constructed of horizontal bars
superimposed one on the other;
circular, approx. 8Ct. amethyst,
encircled with tiny seed pearls.
1¾" long, 5/8" high. C. 1905..... 375.00
Bowknot. 2½" wide, 84SAP, KL ... 185.00
French. 1½". Pastel pansy, blue,
orange, green, silver gilt.
Plique-A-Jour" 50.00
Watch, Lady's Lapel. 3-leaf clover
shape. Large cultured pearl on
each leaf, garnet in center. 1"
high, 14K GF.................. 15.00

Rings

Cameo with 2 diamonds around
neck, 1 diamond in hair. Set in
yellow gold 125.00

Diamond:

10pt. Surrounded by garnets 55.00
⅓Kt. Filigree sol. with 2 blue
sapphires. 18Kt. white gold 150.00
1K. Yellow gold eng. 14K with 4
side diamonds 500.00
Man's Diamond Cluster. App.
½Kt., 14Kt 175.00
Emerald in drop mount. Russian,
½" wide band with ¼Ct. deep
green, square cut emerald.
Marked 56 and workman's mark . 145.00
Hair. English 18th century.
Memorial, with hair and initials
HB under crystal................ 250.00
Opal, Adomooka Black. 1.68Ct.
Lady's yellow gold, 14K. Blues
with emerald green fires. One
gold roping below and Persian
Gulf seed pearls, each attached
by gold wire into gold of ring..... 450.00
Pearl. 3 in Tiffany setting. 14K.... 50.00
Poison. Silver, ornate, round
hinged top has tiny hole "hidden"
in design to drop its deadly
contents secretly. Band is hall-
marked and adjustable. C. 1870 .. 65.00

Watches, See "Watches."

JEWELRY [INDIAN]

Beads, Trade

Dutch. 28" on straw. Ceramic ....$ 12.50
Heische shell. 28". Sterling
spacers. Amber bead drop....... 40.00
Heische shell. 30". On straw 20.00
Millefiori. 28". Amber drop 28.50
Belt Buckle. Zuni. 3¼" sandcast with
11 skyblue Lone Mtn. nuggets and
silver snake winding between
stones. Turquoise eyes 200.00

Belt, Concha. Silver with coral in 6 silver butterfly separators, 6 scalloped Conchas. Buckle has 2 coral stones. All on genuine leather. 44" long 950.00

Bracelets

Blue turquoise. 2 stones in seafoam type turquoise, 2" widest part. Artist design 125.00

Child's. Green dot turquoise set in thunderbird 20.00

Navajo. Three turquoise stones, about size of quarter............ 275.00

Heavy silver and turquoise. Large stone of royal blue, gem turquoise with no matrix. Signed by Allen Kee.......................... 1000.00

Zuni. Antelope. Inlay of MOP, jet, turquoise and coral 375.00

Zuni. "Old Pawn." Petit pt. 41 blue gem stones, 2¼" high.......... 450.00

Earrings

1½". Pierced. Silver hoop, birds suspended on turquoise. Heische . 65.00

2" long. 4 pieces, coral on each. Set in 4 circles. Pierced 75.00

2" long, 7 pieces of turquoise set in solid teardrop. Pierced 45.00

2¼" long. 4 diamond-shaped pieces turquoise with one coral in each. Pierced 60.00

3¼" long. Zuni. Sterling silver, 13 pettipoint turquoise stones each, 4 bangles 75.00

3½" long. Pierced. Sterling silver. 5 teardrop, turquoise stones 70.00

Chanel. Screw-on. 24 pieces turquoise. Each flower with hoop . 75.00

Pierced on ear flowers. 7 pieces turquoise..................... 40.00

Pierced. 2 hoops with 3 small triangles of turquoise in each 40.00

Bracelet. Zuni. Old $750.00

Squash Blossom Necklace. 17 deep blue turquoise stones and silver
$1650.00

Necklaces

Choker. Navajo. "Gorget." 4 large light blue turquoise stones set in scalloped silver shadow boxes. 10½" long drop. Natural brown matrix 375.00

Choker. Zuni. Inlay work of coral MOP and turquoise 400.00

Gorget. 21" overall, approx. 118 sterling silver beads, 3 large turquoise stones, 1 in center each side of ornate silver settings 575.00

Heische. Shell with 14 green serpentine hand carved birds. 16 pieces of red coral interwoven. Silver clasp 300.00

Heische. Double strand, 21" long. Small, highly polished discs with interlaced black Heische 50.00

Navajo. Shadow box square blossoms. 6 blossoms on each side. 7 stones in Naja, 1 dangle, 38" overall length 600.00

Santo Domingo. Hand carved, double strand of birds, bears, turtles, serpentine, MOP, jet abalone and turquoise. Silver clasp 450.00

Squash Blossom. Navajo. 40" overall. C. 1910. 94 large handmade and hand-engraved silver beads strung on fox tail. About 500K of green, chief's turquoise, highly polished stones. 10 squash blossoms with large pieces of turquoise bordering each. Naja is 3½" across and 3¾" high, one large and 5 medium turquoise stones. 1 dangle in center 2250.00

Squash Blossom [Old Pawn]. Heirloom. 36" overall. Blue with matrix, blue gem turquoise. Large stones graduating to medium. 6 stones in Naja, 10 in necklace 2000.00

Sun Bonnet. Zuni. Inlay of MOP jet and turquoise 65.00

Turquoise Bird Fetish. Zuni. Turquoise. MOP birds, double strand with shell Heische 650.00

Zuni. Bird Fetish. 48 handcarved tortoise shell birds. Strung with golden melon heische. Silver clasp 1500.00

Pendant. Navajo. Signed by "Linda Arrowsmith." 5½" long, 3½" wide. Overall length, 35". Double strands on melon mushroom and ball silver beads............... 625.00

Rings
Blue diamond-turquoise stone. Silver rope setting, black matrix .. 125.00
Inlaid silver strips, 1¾" with pieces of oxblood coral.......... 75.00
Navajo. Turquoise stone, leaf design, 30K.................. 150.00
Navajo. Silver, leaf design, 1 coral and 1 turquoise stone 125.00
Navajo. Silver with 2 Lone Mtn. blue turquoise stones 100.00
Navajo. Deep blue stone with silver chain around stone. 1-7/8" long 100.00
Zuni. Lady's. Coral cluster, 10 oxblood coral stones............ 65.00
Zuni. Man's. "Sun God" inlay. Jet MOP coral and turquoise 100.00
Zuni. Silver snake encircles skyblue nugget. Size 10¼ 145.00

Tie, Bola. Sandcast silver, 3" long. Blue spider web, turquoise stone. Long silver tips 200.00

JUGTOWN POTTERY

Jugtown Pottery began its colorful and somewhat off-beat operation in 1920. Jacques and Juliana Bushbee decided to leave their cosmopolitan world and return to North Carolina to revive the dying craft of pottery making in their native state. They located in Moore County, miles away from any large city and accessible only "if mud permits."

They employed a talented young potter, Ben Owens, to turn all the wares. Jacques Bushbee did most of the designing and glazing. Juliana busied herself in promoting and selling the wares in Greenwich Village, New York.

From 1922 until 1962, with only a few years excepted, "Jugtown Ware" was made by Ben Owens under the operation of the founders, Jacques and Juliana Bushbee.

Utilitarian and decorative items were produced. Although many colorful glazes were used, orange predominated. The various shades of orange came either from the glaze or the color of the clay. The later decorative pieces are oriental in design. A Chinese blue glaze that ranges from light blue to deep turquoise was a prized glaze reserved for the very finest pieces.

Pottery is still being made in North Carolina and marked "Jugtown." At last report, Ben Owens, the original potter with the Bushbees, is still turning pottery under his own mark, "Ben Owens, Master Potter."

The early "Jugtown Ware," especially that made by Owens, is being sought by collectors. The recent wares of Ben Owens are also in demand.

Plate. 7". Orange. Signed $20.00

Bowls
3" diam. Dark green to blue. Rose bowl type .... $ 30.00
4½" diam. Blue, aqua iridescent.. 35.00
6" diam. Brown 25.00
Candleholder. 7" diam., finger loop. Gold........................ 30.00

Cup. Red, signed 8.50
Pitchers
  4x6½". Mottled brown, handled,
    covered 37.50
  5x5". Green 27.50
  12". Orange, bulbous 27.50
Platter. Game set, 5 pieces 150.00
Pot. 2-handled, 2 pieces. Frog-shaped 25.00
Vases
  6" high. Rose outside, brown
    inside 17.50
  7" high. Rose brown, speckled
    with white drips 20.00
  7½" high. Blue to green 20.00
  8" high. Green to tan. 3 handles .. 29.50
  8" high. Rose shading to green.
    Large handles 22.50
  9" high. Square base, green
    mottled finish 30.00
  9¼" high. Light green to aqua,
    dragon handles 35.00

KPM CHINA

Meissen originally used this mark but only for
a brief period of time. In the 1830's KPM china
was manufactured at the Royal Factory, Berlin,
Germany. In the late 19th century other
factories in Germany also produced this ware
but it is not certain whether they were
sanctioned by the ruling royal families.

Box, Jewel. All original, ornate brass
  work. Signed Wagner. $1450.00
Cup and Saucer. White ground with
  painted flowers and heavy gold
  work, ¼" from ground. Set 45.00

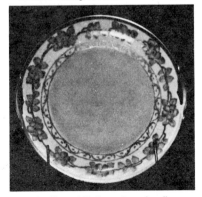

Cake Plate. 10" diam. Open handles,
handpainted floral decor, pink center,
gold trim $35.00

Dishes
  9x12". Handled, 2-part, wide pink
    edge, pink flowers 35.00
  2 sections. Center handle. Pale
    green with pink, orange and
    lavender carnations 55.00
Figurine. Man. 9¼" high. Porcelain.
  Decorated colors 325.00
Paintings
  8½x11". Magdelaine 1950.00
  Porcelain. Detail of mother and
    child. Bronze frame. Signed 750.00
Plaques
  3½x4" with black wooden frame,
  5x6". Portrait of musician holding
    music. Spanish guitar and piano in
    background 275.00
  5x7". Grecian lady with flowers in
    hair. Artist signed 450.00
Plate. 9". Christmas 1930. Flight into
  Egypt 65.00
Vase. 10½" high. Porcelain. Painted
  with portrait, gold and blue
  beading 375.00

KATE GREENAWAY

Kate Greenaway, born in 1846, was the
daughter of an English artist. In her early 20's,
she started illustrating Christmas cards. Later,
she illustrated books. Her drawings were in
vogue in the 1880's-90's. Staffordshire and
German potteries used her illustrations of
children on mugs, tea sets, plates, etc., all of
which are in great demand by collectors.

Almanacs
  1884. Geo. Routledge and Sons,
    London .... $ 45.00
  1886 .... 42.00
Books
  Alphabet. 1885. London 48.00
  "A Apple Pie." F. Warne Co. Publ.
    20 colored scenes 50.00
  "A Day in a Child's Life." 1881 .... 60.00
  Birthday 48.50
  Book of Games. 24 colored illus-
    trations 50.00
  Mother Goose. Engraved and
    printed by Edmund Evans, illus-
    trated by Kate Greenaway 60.00
  "Pictures for Painting" 50.00
  "The English Spelling Book" by
    Wm. Mavor. Illustrated by Kate
    Greenaway. 1885 .... 55.00
  "Toyland." 1882 .... 50.00
Bowl. Oval. Figures cover large
  divided bowl, handle in center.
  German. C. 1900 .... 55.00

Box. 5" across. China. Brass collared, hinged lid 65.00
Butter Pat. Boy and girl 20.00
Buttons
   "Pussycat where have you been?" . 18.50
   "Ring-A-Rosie" 18.50
Child's Set. Plate, cup and saucer ... 65.00
Coffee Pot. With figures 145.00
Cup and Saucer. With boy and girl .. 55.00
Decanter. Olive green. Kate Greenaway figures 145.00
Dinner Service. Child's. Serves six... 250.00

Tile. 6" square. "May." Wedgwood
$75.00

Dish. 8¼". Feeding, 7 scenes 55.00
Figurines
   5¾" high. Bisque. Boy and girl in
   blue and pink outfits. Pair 150.00
   6" high. Staffordshire. Boy with
   huge top hat, boots, umbrella.
   White and gold 60.00
Hot Plate, Baby's. Made in Germany. 85.00
Mug. 2½" high. Child's. Pink shows
   two children 55.00
Napkin Ring. See "Napkin Rings"
Pin Trays
   "See-Saw" 55.00
   "Ten O'clock Scholar" 55.00
Plates
   Blowing bubbles, skipping rope,
   learning to walk, etc. 8½". Each .. 85.00
Print. 6x8". Colorful outdoor tea
   party, 15 girls. Signed 70.00
Salt Shaker. Girl in yellow coat 65.00
Salt and Pepper Shakers
   3" high. Boy and girl in period
   clothing. Pair 150.00
   Girl and boy in basket. Pair 150.00

Meriden. Resilvered, girls with
   muff. Pair 175.00
Shams. "Good Night" and "Good
   Morning" with 72" matching
   spread. Greenaway figures in
   squares. Late 125.00
Tea Set. 15". Open handled round
   tray. 2 cups and saucers, teapot
   and sugar 250.00
Toothpick Holder. Boy wearing
   ruffled shirt, wide brimmed hat.
   3¼" high 65.00
   Boy on one side, girl on other in
   blue glass 60.00
Vases
   4½" high. Green coloring halfway
   up vase with soft ivorine tones
   above with 2 little girls at play.
   Sterling silver rim 75.00
   4x7". Porcelain, painting of
   children in front, irises on back ... 85.00
   8" high. Handpainted, children
   playing with hoops and dancing .. 85.00

KAUFFMANN, ANGELICA

Marie Angelique Catherine Kauffmann was an artist for Adam Brothers in England during the latter 18th century. Her paintings were adapted to decorate many porcelains of the 19th century. Most of her designs were classical.

Bowl. 10" diam. Portrait scene.
   Green and beige. Austrian ......$ 95.00
Box. 1¾x2¾". Classical scene 55.00

Hanging Plate. 11". Multicolored center of two females, green rim, gold trim. Signed $65.00

Candleholder. 5½" high. Classical
   scene, gold trim 50.00
Coffee Set. 7-pcs. Coffee pot,
   creamer, sugar on tray, 4 mugs.
   Classical decorations, gold trim.
   Signed 400.00
Figurine. 9½" high. Warrior and
   Maiden. Pink with gold 45.00
Plates
   9½". Classical scene 45.00
   11". Portrait center, dark green
   rim 65.00
Urn. 10½" high. Deep red 72.50
Vase. 11" high. Dark green with
   beige, double gold handles.
   Portrait decor. Austria 70.00

KEW BLAS GLASS

A type of novelty glass made by the Union
Glass Works, Somerville, Mass., in the late
1890s. It can best be described as an opal or
milk glass, flashed or stained with color, then
coated with a clear glass. Items are usually
marked "Kew Blas" on the bottom of the vase.

Vase. 8". Teardrop-shaped or pre-
formed. Gold iridescent $475.00

Candlestick. Signed . . . . $ 425.00
Creamer. 3¼" high. Signed 285.00
Dish. 4" diam.   175.00
Vases
   5" high. Gold iridescent 300.00
   6½" high. Opal dark blue glass
   body with pulled up opal light
   blue loopings 335.00
   7½" high. Creamy pearl with light
   green highlights, scalloped top,
   gold lining 450.00
   10" high. 3¾" base, 2¼" center
   diam. Opening 2¾". Burnished
   gold interior. Signed 600.00
   11" high. Iridescent deep blue,
   silver and gold outer surface,
   bronze colored lining. Signed 625.00
   12" high. Gold iridescent with
   brilliant highlights of rose, blue
   and green. Signed "Kew Blas" 650.00
Wine. Tall. Signed 195.00

KING'S ROSE PATTERN

Soft paste chinaware of the 1820-30 era
produced in the Staffordshire district of
England for the Pennsylvania (Dutch) German
trade. The enamel decorations are usually in
soft pinks, dark brick reds, yellows and
greens. The colors often flaked off with use.
Some people refer to the small rose as
"Queen's Rose."

Teapot $450.00

Coffee Biggin. 10½" high, pine tree
   border . . . . $ 995.00
Cups and Saucers
   Large size, King's Rose 285.00
   Regular size 235.00
Plates
   Dinner 275.00
   Luncheon. 7½" 240.00

Toddy	150.00
Sugar Bowl. Queen's Rose	**325.00**
Sugar Bowl and Creamer. Queen's	
Rose. Set	**695.00**
Teapot. Queen's Rose. 5" high	**440.00**

KUTANI WARE

The ware was produced in Japan about the middle of the 17th century. It is a heavy, porcelain paste and has purple-black or light yellow glazes, and occasionally greens which were similar to Imari ware. In the 18th and 19th centuries, the designs became more elaborate and colors of blue, green, pale yellow and purple were used to imitate enamel designs of other Oriental wares of the period.

Berry Set. 5-pcs. 10¼" diam. bowl, 4 matching 5½" bowls. Orange and red decor. Large framed picture Japanese ladies and flowers on all. Late. Set .... $ 65.00

Bowls
3½" high, 7" diam. Melon ribbed with scalloped top and four curved feet. Garden-type scene of kimonoed ladies 45.00
4" high, 5½" diam. Footed 95.00
9½" diam. Shallow, scalloped rim. Signed 75.00

Burner. Incense. 2x2½x3". Diamond shaped, green. Foo Dogs on lid. 19th century 35.00

Cups and Saucers
Dinner. Pagoda decor 25.00
Mustache. 19th century. Scenes in reserve with much gold. Melon ribbed cup and 6½" scalloped underplate 40.00
Demitasse Set. 6 ball shaped cups, stand up edge saucers, covered sugar, creamer, white ground. Bamboo pattern, green and gold. 12-pcs. Late. Set 75.00

Plates
10¾". Excellent design. No mark . 50.00
12". No mark 70.00

Sugar Shaker. 4" high, 3" diam. Swirl molded, decorated. Late 40.00
Teapot. 5½" high. Dai Kutani mark. Classic design 85.00
Tea Set. 3-pcs. Large pot, creamer and covered sugar. Rust-red borders with garden scene. Kutani mark in red on bases. Late 19th century. Set 138.00

Vases
5½" high. Marked. Ko-Kutani. Purple lotus blossoms and green leaves on yellow ochre ground speckled with black 175.00
6¼" high. Decorated with birds and flowers in burnt orange, yellows, white and gold. No mark 75.00
8¼" high. Early 19th century. 4 rectangular panels decorated with figures and flowers. 2" neck, 2½" square base. Late. Pair 150.00
12" high. Akaji King designs in a brown and honey comb pattern with gold stylized dragons in medallions 155.00

LALIQUE GLASS

A fine type of late art glass first made by Rene Lalique, a Paris artisan, about 1905. The glass is a combination of pressing, blowing, frosting and cutting. The ware remained in vogue until about 1930.

Atomizers
5" high. "Made in France" on metal top. 6 nudes in sculptured relief on frosty background ...... $ 85.00
5½" high. Gilded top, light amber base with posed nude female figures. Signed in script 125.00

Birds
2¼" high. Frosted. Stands on pedestal in middle of a 3¾" diam. clear glass, round pin tray. Signed 45.00

Vases. 12" high. Floral decor, butterflies, gold trim. Pair $250.00

3½". Signed 55.00
4x2½". Lemon yellow sparrow
sitting on pedestal in dish. Signed 145.00
"The Little Sparrows" 100.00
Bottles, Perfume
3¾" high. Square, flat shape.
Knotted vine decor. Dome-type
stopper 65.00
5" high. "La Parisien" on top. 6
nudes in sculptured relief on
background. In original leather
case 95.00
5½" high. Large, square sides
beveled toward center. Woman's
profile in center with leaves.
Square stopper................. 100.00
Frosted with bird on top. Late 35.00
Bowls
5" diam., 6" high. Blue florals and
leaves 95.00
Rose bowl. 7" diam. Fantail fish
decor 125.00
7" diam. Red, with fish decor.
Signed "R. Lalique" 175.00
8½" diam. 6 lovebirds in center
with deep opalescence. Signed "R.
Lalique" in block letters 175.00
9½" diam. Opalescent. Signed.
Raised decor. 3 molded roses
form feet 150.00
10" diam. Clear glass. Shallow
with wild swirl of bubbles. Signed.. 95.00
10½" diam. Art Deco, 8-sided.
Frosted 1½" border design.
Signed 95.00
11" diam. Shallow with swirling
fish, bubbles in bottom and blue
highlights. Marked "R. Lalique"... 250.00
11" diam. Swimming fish in relief.
Milky blue opalescent. C. 1925 ... 175.00
Boxes
1¾ x3¼ x4¼" glass. Rectangular,
frosted, design of blossoms and
leaves on lid, sides in vertical
herringbone. Signed 85.00
2½ x4". Covered, swan decor.
Signed Lalique France in script ... 55.00
5" diam. Covered, floral. Red
wash, molded signature 125.00
Cherub. Holding bowl. 4" high 125.00
Decanters. 14½" high. Decorated
with nudes at corner of each side.
Stoppers are full female figures.
Pair 400.00
Dishes
4" diam., 2" deep. Ribbon and
Bull's Eye. Script signed 40.00
8½" diam., 1½" high. Dragon fly
design 80.00
Cheese. Covered 150.00

Cologne Bottle. 5½" high $125.00
Powder Jar. 2½ x3¼" $125.00

Figurines
8x8" long. Dragonfly. Signed..... 150.00
8" high. Girl standing, holding
basket of fruit in frog flower
holder. Blue frosted glass. Signed
"R. Lalique" in block letters 185.00
8" high. Young girl holding grapes
in center of frog with holes for
flowers. 2 pieces. Transparent
pale blue frosted. Signed 175.00
Woman holding basket of fruit,
with other hand on hair. Powder
translucent blue. Signed......... 175.00
Goblet. 6" high. Figural stem.
Flattened, cut to shape of proud
rooster with details in frosted
lines. Signed 55.00
Hair Receiver. 3" high, 3¾" diam.
Acid finish, molded thistle
pattern. Round, script signed and
numbered 95.00

Jars
Covered, 6" diam., clear glass
petal-formed cover, petal edges
around base 95.00
Powder. Frosted cherubs in high
relief. Signed 65.00

Knife Rests
3" long. Blue glass with clover leaf
shape ends 20.00
3½" long. French, silverplate
animals. Fox, dog, rabbit, peacock
figures. Each................. 20.00
Crystal center posts with camphor
satin baby heads at ends 35.00
Paperweight. Shape of eagle's head.
4" high, 5" wide. Signed 225.00
Pendant. 2" long. Gold loop,
semi-doughnut shape with em-

bossed alligators. Purple glass.
Signed 225.00

Pitcher. 10" high. Clear amber. Band
of molded and cut berries, leaves.
applied handle. Signed 185.00

Plates
8½". Sailboat design. Signed 37.50
10¾". Frosted florals, urns,
foliage motifs. Signed. R. Lalique 85.00

Plaque. 4" diam. Signed R. Lalique
with raised head of Louis Pasteur 100.00

Shade. 6x10". Glass, opalescent
swirled and notched ribs. Signed
R. Lalique 250.00

Toothpick Holder. Frosted cherubs
and grapes. Signed 55.00

Trays
Pin. Approx. 4½" long. Frosted
opalescent glass, with nudes in
relief 65.00
Round. 4" diam. Female figure,
hair to feet in center holding
water lily...................... 75.00

Tumbler. Frosted, gold band at top .. 55.00

Vases
4¾" high. High shoulders, small
squat neck, frosted with eight
vertical panels of clear leaves.
Signed 85.00
5" high. Footed, flaring shape.
Ringed with narrow bands of
stylized fern leaf, opalescent with
foot almost white, body toned to
pale ice blue 145.00
6½" high. Swirling oriental fish,
blue wash. Signed block letters... 275.00
7" high. Iridescent leaf decor.
Signed 130.00
7½" high. Frosted opaline, open
fan design, signed R. Lalique 155.00
8½" high. Cased opalescent,
thistle pattern. 7½" widest diam.,
flat round base 4½". Collared
opening 4¼". Blown, molded,
detailed from top to base. Script
signed 500.00
9½" high. Bottle shaped.
Brambles pattern, script signed .. 750.00
9½" high. Approx. 10" wide
shoulder. 1¾" rim at top.
Heart-shaped except flat on
bottom. Charcoal gray. Signed 1000.00

Wine. Figural stem. Flattened, cut in
shape of crowing rooster. Signed . 45.00

LAMPS
EARLY LIGHTING DEVICES

The candle was the primary source of light at
night until the invention of the fluid lamp. One
of the first was the "Betty" lamp - a small
device which used lard oil or whale oil. The
invention of the Argand lamp by the Swiss
scientist of the same name utilized a round
wick which produced a draft both inside and
outside the burner, thus improving the lighting
quality of lamps.

Aladdin
Model B-27. Alacite. Gold lustre .. $ 175.00
Model B-39. Clear crystal 39.00
Model B-54. Clear green with
burner 45.00
Model B-75. Alacite Lincoln Drape 75.00
Model B-77. Red, tall Lincoln
Drape, kerosene 330.00
Model B-83. Red. "Beehive" 225.00
Model B-104. Clear font, black
base 49.00
French, not electrified 140.00
Lincoln Drape pattern. Cobalt. Pair 800.00

Table Lamp. Handel. Autumn leaf
design on shade. Signed base and
shade $450.00

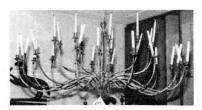

Hanging Ceiling Lamp. 18th century.
Paper-covered candles $1800.00

Angle

Double. Complete with milk glass
shades....................... 125.00
Double, early, brass. Opalescent
shades, brass rope hanging loop.
Burnished, lacquered, electrified.. 165.00
Single. Brass, embossed with
flowers. 16" overall height with
globes 75.00
Single. Frosted bowl. Wall-type.
Milk glass shade, wired N.Y. Co... 45.00

Astral Lamps

26" high, 9" prism, brass stem,
dated 1873. Cut clear and frosted.
Tulip shade. Electified.......... 275.00
All brass, original shades and
prisms. Pair.................... 400.00
Brass stem. Marble base. Early
shades and prisms.............. 225.00

Banquet Lamps

22" high. Pink satin glass, brass
base with satin glass and brass
connecting large floral embossed
pink satin font 200.00
23" high. Red satin glass, lion's
face. All original brass band
around top shade. Base is pewter
decorated with cherub faces and
lattice. Dated 4-30-95 .... 500.00
29" high. Cherub standing with
butterfly in hand. Square base,
ornate font. burnished and electrified. Large frosted ball shade .. 225.00
33" high. Gold mottled Sandstone
in brass designed band and
base-cut-out head cover oil font.
Deep yellow ball shade covered
with gold leaf fleur-de-lis. Electrified 295.00
Britannia metal, brass plated,
marble stem 175.00
Brass, painted ball shade.
Electrified 250.00

Betty Lamps

3¾" high, 3¾" long. 18th century,
small wrought iron 95.00

Colonial New England. Double
wrought iron, wall spike......... 75.00
Bicycle Oil Lamp. "M & W 97" 26.50

Bracket Lamps

Iron, lacy frame, mercury glass
reflector 50.00
*Frame only. Double 35.00
*Frame only. Single............. 25.00
Tin. Tin reflector. Shield motif,
rosettes, stars on glass. Patd. Feb.
11, 1866 .... 140.00

Bradley and Hubbard Lamps

18" high, 13" wide. 8-panelled
shade, caramel to green glass,
floral filigree over glass. Brass
base. Signed.................. 450.00
28" high, 22" wide shade. Dark
red allover floral pink background
on large tree trunk base, ripple
glass inside shade 1500.00
Brass. 13¼" high. Fluted acid etched
glass shade. Signed P & A Mfg. Co.
Victor........................ 125.00

Carriage Lamps

20". Pair 275.00
Brass, beveled lens, red lens in
black. Pair.................... 275.00
Chandeliers. Lacy iron, clear fonts,
bulbous etched chimneys
2-arm....................... 75.00
3-arm....................... 100.00
4-arm....................... 125.00
Cresolene Lamp. Milk glass chimney 25.00
Cruisie. Early.................. 75.00

Single Student Lamp. Brass, 10x21".
Green shade. Electrified $350.00

Desk Lamps

9" high. Tiffany brass. Curved arm holding orig. signed shade 575.00

Tiffany Signed. Completely counter balance, green, orange, brown. Decorated shade on green, brown patina base 750.00

Floor Lamp. 54" high, cameo cut, 6-panel shade, 11" wide, yellow on white trellis on brass and spelter base 795.00

Gone With the Wind Lamps

20½" high. Green ground, pink & red roses on font & shade. Wired . 225.00

23" high. Lion's heads on base & shade. All original green with desert scenes in lighter colors ... 500.00

24" high. Courting, 8.5" globe, satin finish with hand painted magnolia blossoms 400.00

26" high. Red Satin. Matching ball shade. Electrified 475.00

28½" high to top of chimney. Parlor. Red satin glass ground with red convex Bull's Eye 500.00

29½" high. Red cosmos flowers & green leaves. Brass base 300.00

Camel scene, burnished. Not electrified 350.00

Green, dark with Renaissance figures. Electrified 240.00

Pink MOP satin glass. Brass mountings, ruffled open top shade. Electrified 600.00

Thistle design, all orig. Not electrified 300.00

Hall Lamps

6½" high. Pink oval hobnail, hanging. Brass fittings 185.00

8½" high. Hanging, white milk glass with hand painted floral decor. Ball shade with burnished brass frame 150.00

12" high, 7" wide. Cranberry, hanging. 4-panelled square sides. Burnished lacy brass frame 235.00

Cranberry D.Q., burnished 200.00

Cranberry with sharp hobnails ... 200.00

Hand Lamps, Colored

Amber. 9" 65.00

Bull's Eye & Fleur-de-lis, emerald green 95.00

Cranberry. 11½" high, clear base, striped bowl 85.00

Loop. Emerald green, on pedestal. Milk glass. 17" stem. Floral decor under glass 95.00

Plume, blue................... 65.00

Vaseline. 10" 70.00

Handel Lamps

9½" diam. shade. Signed. Red & pink flowers, yellow inside, blue & green leaves, irregular border, base with lacy work 300.00

13" high. Floral on citron and green ground 350.00

14" high. Reversed painted shade, country scene, marked 450.00

16" high. Completely leaded shade of many subtle shadings on a bronze patina base, acorn pulls . 1200.00

17" wide shade. Dark red wild cherry, triple band floral green, gold background. Signed tag on felt bottom of bronze Dore base .. 1250.00

18" wide shade. 10". Deep red dogwood, green and gold on tree trunk. Signed base............. 1450.00

23" high, 20" diam. shade. Art Nouveau with fish back upper pattern, caramel bkgd., greens, golds on signed Handel base 800.00

26" high. 16" diam shade. Red dogwood floral border, green & gold bkgd., Signed on base 875.00

36" high. Lily Pad. Rare, hugh, fully signed. Art Nouveau 1450.00

Boudoir, ribbed chipped ice shade with blue to orange coloring dec. of orange, red & green leaves with red berries, bronze base. Double signed 300.00

Hanging Lamps

13". Bristol canopy shade, for kitchen. Up and down type with iron circle weight. Electrified..... 135.00

14". Cranberry Bull's Eye shade, brass font, prisms. Burnished & electrified 400.00

14". Sharp Cranberry Hobnail brass font, prisms. Burnished & electrified 425.00

Country store, emb. brass font, tin shade. Complete & all original ... 185.00

Cranberry. Hall lamp............ 195.00

Lard Lamp. Flattened tin, oval font & stem, openwork iron base 65.00

Lily Lamp. Tiffany. Signed completely, 3-lite, telescopic gold Dore base, 3 reddish gold iridescent signed shades 1500.00

Marriage Lamp. 13" high. Signed Ripley. Twin font with match holder. Translucent blue fonts with clambroth match holder, metal connector, dome base. Feb. 1, 1870 .... 550.00

Milk Glass

One piece matchholder combination. Ribbed lamp font.
Sena 50.00
Nutmeg 60.00
White. Colorful blossoms in relief, umbrella shade. Electrified 175.00

Oil Lamps

8½" high. Wooden, turned from maple 175.00
9½" high. Sandwich Glass. Harp pattern. Original rush burner with flame caps. C. 1860 .... 150.00
9¾" high to collar. To burners, 11¼". Excelsior pattern with Maltese Cross Flint Glass. Two-pronged burner. Pair............ 195.00
10" high. Brass. Mt. Washington satin shade in burmese coloring. Pastel enameled sunflowers, gold trim 500.00

Table Lamp. Small, with orange glass shade. Art Nouveau-type $135.00

10" high. Whale oil. Flint. Sawtooth on concave hexagonal base, 2 brass burners 95.00
12" high. Blue Acanthus leaf, on brass reeded stem, marble base. Rare grease finish 295.00
12" high. Tin whale, pedestal with original tin shade............... 450.00
Pair. Canary Whale "Loop" on hex base. [McKearin 199-23]. Original burners 595.00

Peg Lamps

Blue, melon-ribbed bubbly glass in fine brass candlesticks, with tall burners. Mkd. Rorstrand. Pair 250.00
Green opaque in brass candlestick 85.00
Tin with hook in wooden block ... 58.50

Piano Lamps

Bell-shaped shade in a harp. 7" diam. approx. 63" high. Bradley & Hubbard 300.00
2-onyx shelves, ornate brass font; turned brass legs, handpainted bail shade. Burnished & electrified 350.00

Rayo Lamps

10" shade. Nickel wired, original yellow, white lily decor.......... 60.00
Brass, burnished, no shade 75.00
Painted shade, electrified 85.00
Rush Light. Iron, wood base. Early .. 85.00

Sandwich Glass

14" high. Pressed glass font with shield and scrolls. Opaque starch blue base 395.00
17" high. Parlor lamp. Ruby cut to crystal font, deep sapphire stem, cut to clear, double marble base with brass trim. C. 1860-70 ...... 650.00
Sheffield. Early. Pair 500.00
Store Lamp. Tin shade, brass font, burnished 95.00

Student Lamps

7" shades, double 245.00
7" shades, double. Electrified 350.00
8" shades, dbl., buffed, electrified 400.00
10" shade. Hanging, double, fonts, electrified. Green shades with white linings. 40" long, pulls up or down to 40", burnished 600.00
24" high. Double, orig., brass with copper wash. Green overlay shades, gold trim............... 325.00
Brass base marked Post & Co. 7/22/77, electrified, pink cased glass shade, white scene 500.00

Table Lamps

14" shade. Pairpoint Puffy. Roses, butterflies. Reds, blues, yellows. Signed base and shade 2000.00

16" high. Reverse painted, unusual matching base. Scene, palm tree with landscape. Signed "Revere" 325.00

17" high. Filigree, 3 color slag glass, 8 sides, matching base 275.00

18" high. Completely original, reverse painting. Signed Jefferson 395.00

22" high, 14" diam. Green, six-panelled, beaded fringe. Original 175.00

23" high. Daum Nancy. Deep pink, green and white mottled glass. Signed base and shade 2200.00

23" high, 16" diam. 4-footed, green bkgd. allover flowers. "Pairpoint," signed base 795.00

28½" high. Cut glass. Harvard with Russian, cane, diamond and cut corn flowers with long cut prisms, matching shade, base 1000.00

Telephone Lamp. Old desk-type telephone. Electrified 95.00

Torch Light. Political 75.00

Vigil Lamp. Steigel-type. Cobalt glass in D.Q. pattern. Late 18th century 350.00

*Reproduced Item

Student Lamp. Single, electrified
$135.00

LAMPS, MINIATURE

Lamps, often referred to in the "old days" as night lamps, are now known as miniature lamps. The devices were modeled after the regular lamps of the day but were considerably smaller.

Aladdin. Crystal. 32" high......... $ 290.00

Brass

2" high. Sauce Lamp. Nutmeg burner 50.00

7½" high. Bristol shade, hinged stem........................ 40.00

Bristol

4½" high. White, blue and green floral band, gold 70.00

6½" high, Blue, enameled flowers, white shade 72.50

Cased Glass

7" high. Satin. Pink. Nutmeg burner 355.00

8" high. Butterscotch. Embossed floral design 315.00

8¾" high. Pink. Embossed design. Hornet burner 325.00

8½" high. Red, with enameled flowers 350.00

9" high. Red Satin Glass. Petal-type shade outlined with beading. Embossed design on base. Nutmeg burner.................... $295.00

400

Cranberry
7½" high. Embossed swirl 415.00
8½" high. Diamond pattern.
Applied clear feet 465.00
Cosmos. 7½" high. Pink top and
bottom 182.50
End-of-Day
8½" high. Swirled pattern. Applied clear glass feet 465.00
9½" high. Overlay. Clear glass feet 465.00
Glass, Blue
6¾" high. Honeycomb pattern . . . 300.00
7" high. Embossed twinkle. Acorn
burner 260.00
Glass, Clear
6¾" high. Grecian Key pattern . . . 70.00

Acanthus. 8¼" high. Nutmeg burner.
Milk glass, ribbed swirl with embossed
leaf decor $275.00

7" high. Diamond pattern 105.00
8" high. Embossed flowers, scrolls 95.00
Glass, Green. 5½" high. Beaded
heart pattern 72.00
Harry's Night Lamp." 6" high, blue . . 165.00
Mary Gregory. 8" high. Cranberry . . 300.00
Milk Glass
7" high. "Apple Blossom" 205.00
7½" high. Block and Dot pattern.
Acorn burner 148.50
7½" high. Plume pattern, gilted . . 247.50
8½" high. Scrolled, painted.
Hornet burner 165.00
9¼" high to top of chimney.
Reclining elephant 495.00
Milk Glass, Blue
5¼" high. Handled 215.00
7" high. Beaded panels 105.00
Porcelain. Turtle, 5½" high. Brown,
green and yellow 385.00
Santa Claus. Red shade forms head
and body. Milk glass base forms
legs and feet. Rare 935.00
Satin Glass
6½" high. Pink. Enameled floral
decor 215.00
8½" high. Drape pattern. Light
Nutmeg burner 300.00
8½" high. Tulip shape. Red.
Overshot glass 300.00
9½" high. Pink, embossed petal
design. Nutmeg burner 357.50
9½" high. Red. Panel pattern.
Nutmeg burner. Brass pedestal . . . 325.00
School House. 3¾" high. Clear glass 137.50
Shoe. 3½" high. Clear glass. Hornet
burner 165.00

LANTERNS

A lantern may be defined as an enclosed, portable candleholder, attached to a bracket or pole to illuminate an area after dark. It allegedly derived its name from early times when candles were placed in thin animal horns and were called "Lantern Horns." Later they were developed into portable lighting devices with glass sides or chimneys as we know them today.

Auto. Brass, small . . . . $ 55.00
Auto Oil Lamp. 14½" high. Brass . . . 100.00
Barn. Small, rectangular shape,
polished reflector. Original glass
side. Marked "Peter Gray, Boston." 14" high 85.00
Bicycle Lantern. 6" 48.00

Candle Lanterns

Copper, pierced. 17½" high. Rare.	140.00
Tin. Square. 5x5x16". 4 rows wire window guards	125.00
Wood. 4 glass panes, rectangular. Scarce	140.00
Carriage Lanterns. 15" high, beveled lenses. Pair	275.00

Dietz Lanterns

Auto Driving Lamp. 10¼" high, 5½" diam. Red reflector in back. Dated May 10, 1908. Painted black	95.00
Auto Lamp. 1907	55.00
Inspector's Hooded Lantern. With bail and handle	35.00
Hearse Lamps. 31", silverplated. Pair	500.00
Magic Lantern, See "Magic Lanterns"	
Miner's. English	45.00
Miner's Safety. U.S.A.	37.50
Paul Revere. Large, 4 glass panels ..	100.00
*Pierced Tin	75.00
Policeman's Hand Lanterns. Pair ...	40.00

13½" high, 6-sided hexagon. White metal with bronze finish. Caramel Slag panels. Electrified .... !95.00

Skater's. Triangular-shaped. Tin with glass inserts. Candle-type $40.00

Railroad Lanterns

Adlake. 5-3/8" high. B&M clear, etched, marked	40.00
Adlake Railway Switch. Red, blue. Original Bull's Eye lenses ...	48.50
B&O. 15" to top of handle	25.00
Burlington RR. "Adams & West," red globe.....................	37.50
Caboose Lamp. Electrified	60.00
CNW. Adlake Reliable. Clear globe, 5¼" high...............	35.00
CRR of N.J. Dietz #39, clear globe, 5¼" high.....................	35.00
French Lanterns. Pair	128.00
Pennsylvania RR. "Dietz #39 Vulcan," clear globe	40.00
Pennsylvania RR. Loco. Dept., "Armspear." Clear raised letters. "P.R." on globe	35.00
Pullman. Unmarked. Altered oil font. Adlake. Nickleplated "P	

402

Globe" on oil font 100.00
Rock Island RR on frame. "Hanian"
on globe 35.00
Southern Pacific RR on frame.
"Adams and West," clear globe .. 35.00
Western Maryland. "Hamm,"
Rochester, N.Y. on frame, red
globe 40.00
Ship Lanterns
Brass, small size, with red and
blue lenses. Wired for battery use.
Late. Pair..................... 125.00
Captain's. Copper reflector 120.00
Masthead. Galvanized iron with
old red paint. 12¼" high. Clear,
thick, beveled cylindrical lense.
Kerosene burner 85.00
Skater Lanterns
Brass, with chain 65.00
Tin with glass 40.00
Street Post Lanterns. 22" high, 13"
canopy. Opalescent globes, 11"
high, 8" wide. Matching pair 250.00
U. S. Ex. Co. Tin with clear globe.
Kerosene, 10½" high 50.00
U. S. Navy. Copper, fitted inside for
candle. 8x11". C. 1880 .... 85.00
*Reproduced Item

LEEDS WARE

This ware was first made at a factory in Leeds, Yorkshire, England, established by Charles Green in 1758. In the 1780's Queensware was made in competition with Wedgwood - the quality and style being as good as the products of the Wedgwood establishment.

Plate. 9½". Creamware. Feather edge, pierced rim..................$75.00

Bowl. Reticulated, footed, oval .....$ 65.00
Creamers
4¼" high. Yellow, blue and green
decor 100.00
Helmet-shaped................. 110.00
Cup and Saucer. Handleless, floral
decor, pink lustre.............. 72.50
Mug. "Watchful Eye, Etc." 80.00
Pepper Pot. Blue feather stitch decor 65.00
Pitcher. 6" high, colorful floral decor 160.00
Plates
7½". Green border, peafowl in
brown and yellow in center 45.00
7¾". Creamware, pierced, green
edge. C. 1800 .... 65.00
9". Cream with raised flowers.... 55.00
9". Wheat border in green 50.00
9½". Soft paste Queensware,
open edge..................... 75.00
13½". Cream, feather edge...... 85.00
Platters
13x16¾". Green comb edge 125.00
Large blue feather border 75.00
Open edge, black transfer center . 125.00
Sugar Shaker. Green.............. 95.00
Teapot. 7½" high. Red and green
decor, shell pattern in body 185.00
Tureen. 16" long, 25" high. White
body, blue comb decor 195.00

LENOX CHINA

Lenox was a fine American Belleek china produced in the Trenton, New Jersey area in the late 1800's and early 1900's.
Walter Scott Lenox was the founder of Lenox, Inc. His dream was to produce a fine American-made porcelain and he did. At first only decorative pieces and art objects were made. Then, in 1918, the first American dinnerware ever to grace the dining tables in the White House bore the Lenox mark.
On undecorated pieces the mark is an artist's palette, script L in a circle and Belleek. On all other items, the mark is a script L, encircled with a green wreath, Lenox, U.S.A. Lenox china produced today is marked in gold.

Birds
3½" long, Pink, green mark. Pair $ 30.00
3¾" long from beak to tall head
down. Tail up, white, green wreath
mark 15.00
Bouillon. 2-handled. Gold trim
garlands, green gold trim. Signed,
green mark.................... 15.00
Bowls
6" long, 4" wide. Nautilus-shape.
Fluting and beading. Drip edge of
coin gold, green wreath 27.50

Covered, brown ware, sterling
overlay 50.00
Chocolate Pot 65.00
Cup and Saucer. Chocolate. Pedestal, gold trim, gold handles. Made
for Tiffany, N.Y. 25.00
Demitasse Cups and Saucers
"Golden Gate" 15.00
Greek Key handle, green wreath
mark 7.50
Lenox liners, sterling holders and
monogrammed saucers. Set of 8 .. 175.00
"Washington-Wakefield" pattern.
Green mark 18.50
Figurine. Head of woman. 4" high.
Art Deco-style, white 40.00
Mug. Shrine. 59th Imperial Council
Session, Atlantic City, July 9 - July
14, 1933 .... 48.50
Pen Holder. 4" wide, 2" high. Pink,
white ruffled top, gold-trimmed
Schaeffer desk fountain pen.
Marked Lenox 35.00
Pitcher. Mask spout, hammered
finish, white. Green mark 75.00
Plates
5¾". Bread and butter. Enamel
decor. Set of 6 .... 35.00

7½". Sandwich Ming pattern.
Inserts for regular pedestal cups.
Set of 12 .... 120.00
Pot, Honey. Golden bees, green mark 35.00
Salt Dips
3" long, 2¼" wide. Scallop shell
and coral design. Green mark ... 7.50
Handpainted roses. Set of 6 ...... 40.00
Swans
3" long. Green 20.00
4½" long, 3¼" high. Green
wreath mark 25.00
9" long, 6" high. Green wreath
mark 52.50
Tobacco Humidor. 5½" high. Belleek. Shades of tan coloring,
decor of hanging corn, leaves,
palette mark 130.00
Teapot. Brown ware, sterling overlay 50.00
Toby Jug. William Penn. 6" high,
indian handle. Green mark 125.00
Tray, Pin. Round, gold edge. Green
mark 30.00
Urn. 11" high. Swan handles, square
pedestal base. Rose pattern,
green mark 85.00
Vases
4½" high. Cornucopia. Pair 28.50
5½" high, 7" long. Double,
half-moon shape, center ring
handle. Green wreath 25.00
8½" high. Fluted, white on rose
color base 45.00
8½" high. Silver overlay. Etched
silver, trumpet shape, white. Four
handpainted ovals of pink roses
on 4 sides 135.00
10" high. Art Nouveau-type,
purple decor. Artist signed 130.00
10¼" high. Soft green, white
wheat heads embossed decor.
Green wreath mark 45.00
11¼" high. Handpainted Edna
Brown 1906. Green, yellow
daffodils. Palette mark 85.00
11¾" high, 27½" circumference.
Handpainted, five large peacocks
on limb. Black on ivory 100.00
12" high. Belleek. Yellow ground,
green tendrils, wide black band at
shoulder, large sweet peas 165.00
15¾" high. Belleek. Pink and
yellow roses, green foliage.
Palette mark 185.00

Cup and Saucer. Cobalt with silver
overlay $95.00

LIBBEY GLASS

The New England Glass Company passed into
the control of W. L. Libbey in 1878. In 1888 the
factory was moved to Toledo, Ohio.

Glass produced by Libbey is of the highest quality. They were masters in fine cut glass and intaglio cut glass. Libbey never used pressed blanks. Some of their most popular designs are Columbia, Imperial, Comet and Drape.

While employed by Libbey, Joseph Locke invented Amberina, Peachblow, Agata and Pomona glass.

Bowls
3¼" high, 8" diam. Deep cut, heavy. Notched prisms, hobstars and fans. Signed Libbey . . . . $ 85.00
Topaz with blue spiraled lines. Unsigned 115.00

Champagnes
4". Clear with thumbprint pattern on bowl. Clear, knobbed stem. Signed 100.00
Silhouette, squirrel 135.00
Goblet. Silhouette. Signed 165.00
Rose Bowl. 8x8". Clear, swirl 35.00
Sherbet. 2¼" high. Knickerbocker pattern. Clear lead crystal bowl, heavy square base. Art Deco style. Unsigned 40.00
Sugar and Creamer. Unsigned 125.00
Wine. Opalescent monkey stem 165.00

LIMOGES CHINA

For information concerning the factories which produced chinaware at Limoges, France, see "Haviland China."

Bowls
Punch. 5¾" high, 13" diam. H/P, pink scalloped border. Grapes . . . $ 300.00
Punch. H/P, allover decor of outside, roses and green leaves inside, heavy gold trim, 8 cups. Set 750.00
Boxes
Patch. Hinged, yellow flowers 40.00

Dresser Set. 6 pieces. Pink apple blossom. Gold rims, Limoges. Signed J. P. L. France $145.00

White heart-shaped. Beaded design on top 20.00
Candlesticks. 8" high, blue enameled floral decor. Pair 65.00
Chocolate Pot. White, tall, gold bands 50.00
Chocolate Set. French. 25 pieces. Covered pot, sugar, creamer, 11 each cups, saucers. Gold leaves, flowers on creamy buff ground. Gold edges and handles. Set 250.00
Cups and Saucers
Demitasse. Pastel pink, gold trim . 17.50
Green band with tea rose decor surrounded by gold bands. Hand-painted 20.00
Dinner Set. 80 pieces. A Lanternier. Decorated with small orchid flowers and leaves 650.00
Dishes
Relish. 7". Pink and gold flowers, heavy gold handle. Marked LS & S Limoges, France 20.00
Vegetable. 7x9". Covered, roses and green scroll decor. Pattern #318 . . . . 35.00

Sugar and Creamer. Dark green bases to white ground. Red roses, gold handles and trim. "Venice." Dec. 22, 1896. Set $65.00
Dresser Sets
3 Pieces. Shaped, handled tray, powder bowl, hair receiver. Embossed with gold, rope trim. H/P violet decor 100.00
5 Pieces. Tray, ring tree, 2 round covered boxes, oblong covered 7½x2x1½". Blue forget-me-not decor 135.00
Hair Receiver. Handpainted, pale blue ground, pink roses. Artist signed 17.50
Hat Pin Holder. Blue forget-me-nots and gold decor. 4" high 20.00
Perfume Bottle. "Narbonne," green and gold 25.00
Pin Holder and Cover. White with pink and yellow flowers, gold trim. Marked W. Green wreath, Pouyou, Limoges 15.00

Pitchers

7½" high to top of gold handle. Bulbous. H/P strawberries, blossoms. Heavy gold trim 125.00

7¾" high. H/P cherry decor. Marked "Limoges" on bottom 95.00

15" high. 2 matching mugs. Lilac and leaf design. Signed Woodrow. Set 150.00

Cider. Red fruit on shaded green. Dated 1907 by artist 85.00

Plaque, Wall. French porcelain. Gold trim, 3 large roses, red, pink and yellow. 9½x13½" 95.00

Plates

9½". Handpainted red and yellow roses, green and yellow background. Marked "LRL" below crown. "Limoges" in frame....... 45.00

10". "Coronet." Bust of indian. Gold edge. Artist signed. LUC 75.00

12". Chop. Cream ground, 2" pink roses outlined in gold. Green leaves, gold border 75.00

12". Game plate. Scalloped, beaded, embossed border, hanging pheasant. Rich fall colors. Pierced for hanging 85.00

Dessert. Cupid center, gold. Set of 6 .... 75.00

Oyster. "France, Depose' Ahrenfeldt Limoges." White, pink and gold edging. With clear glass sauce dish. Set of 6 .... 120.00

Platters

10½x18½". Hunting scene on white ground 85.00

16½". Green and tan border, gold trim 50.00

Ramekin. Red roses. Marked "C. Arenfeld" 19.50

Spitoon. Squatty, scalloped rim. Handpainted floral decor 42.50

Sugar and Creamer. Oval shapes, pastel ground, small pink roses on curled gold feet 60.00

Tea Service. Sugar, creamer, teapot and large turtleback tray. Handpainted. Set 145.00

Tea Tile. 6½". Small pink and green florals 15.00

Trays

6½x13". Celery "GD." Lavender and yellow flowers inside and out. Scalloped edge, gold touches 32.50

13x16". Scalloped edge, pastel white flowers, gold centers, soft green leaves, shading on white .. 37.50

Tureen. 14" across handles. 8" wide, 6½" high, oval. Green band with tea rose decor surrounded by gold bands........................ 75.00

U.S. Presidentials

Grant, U.S. Dessert Plate. 8½". 1869-1877.................... 375.00

Harrison, Benjamin. Dessert plate. 8½". 1889-1893............... 350.00

McKinley, William. Dessert plate. 8½". 1897.................... 300.00

Urns

3½" high. Handpainted roses, three-footed 19.50

6" high. Enameled, depicting Sara Burnhardt in full Art Nouveau costume after Gustav Mucha. 6". Pair 65.00

12½" high. Gold ball feet, applied gold handles. Wide gold scroll top, handpainted red roses. Signed by artist 175.00

LINENS

Many people have collected and treasured quilts, coverlets, fashions and other domestic linens that were a part of the elegant and comfortable ways of homelife in the past. Now, with the new period of collecting known as "Nostalgia," more people than ever are seeking out the textiles of years gone by.

Battenburg Lace Items

Handkerchief. 12" square .... $ 15.00

Luncheon Set. 26" cloth, 8 napkins, linen centers 75.00

Scarves:

17x70" 25.00

18x54" 20.00

Table Covers, Round:

28½" diam. 30.00

49" diam. 50.00

60" 75.00

Bedspread and Pillow Cover. Linen. White, embroidered cut work .. $50.00

Bedspreads

72x102". Handmade with large center medallion of embroidered roses, daisies, bowknots, woven border. Pair 150.00

72x80". Fringed, hand crocheted . 60.00

Brussels net, embroidered with long matching sham 120.00

Marseilles, heavy, white, full size . 55.00

Coverlets

74x92". Signed and dated "Made by C. Fehr in Emaus for A. R. Weber 1842." Navy, green, red, fringed...................... 275.00

78x90". Reversible floral pattern. Signed and dated "1854 Eliza Vanderbilt. Woven at Palmyra, N.Y. by Ira Hadsell." Red and white 275.00

84x92". Chintz. Dated 1790. Brown, red, cream reverses to tiny red pineapple 175.00

Eagle Willow and Rose. C. 1835. Red and white jacquard hand knotted, fringed 325.00

Lace

3 yards, 2½" wide. Banding with scalloped edges on either side ... 20.00

3 yards, 7" wide. Small scalloped edge, fully covered with lustrous darned floral design on fine net .. 30.00

Napkins. Red and white. Fringed. Set of six 22.00

Pillow Shams

Embroidered, with ruffled eyelet borders. Pair.................. 12.50

Embroidered red wreath encircling "Sweet Lilies Close Their Eyes at Night" and "Open With the Morning Light." Each 12.00

Muslin, ruffled edge. Pair 10.00

White with embroidered wreath and crocheted edge. Pair 10.00

Quilts

¾ size. Double Irish Chain pattern. Blue calico with white 125.00

60x72". Wedding Ring pattern. Flowered percale on white background, scalloped edge, fancy quilting. Never used 175.00

62x62". Child's. Old Star pattern. Pale blue on white 35.00

67x67". Patchwork squares on yellow calico background........ 95.00

70x75". Old patchwork "Ribbon" . 95.00

74x78". Star. 4 large stars with star in center. Red and pink. Machine stitching and tied off 125.00

77x79". Appliqued, dated 1858. 4 large eagles and star center with

small stars. Yellow, light blue and pink on white 195.00

82x86". Irish. Stair steps of pink and green on muslin 55.00

Double bed size, red design on white background, fine stitching. New 150.00

Shawls, Paisley

5'5" square. Scotland. Wool. C. 1860........................... 80.00

62x63". Self fringed 75.00

Sheets

68x90". Homespun, fine condition 28.50

72x100". Linen, hemstitching 15.00

Paisley Shawl. Black center. Reds, blacks, etc. $75.00

Stockings. Hand knit. Lacy pattern. Pair 10.00

Tablecloths

42x90". Lined Cluncy lace 14.00

52x56". Dark blue, red, allover flower and leaf design 27.50

56x56". Red, white, lily design ... 30.00

56x64". Red, white striped, pansy design 30.00

60x90". Flower design in red and natural, fringed 45.00

60x90". Solid red damask, fringed 50.00

66x104". Irish linen. 12 napkins, hand hemstitched 85.00

68x88". Handmade 45.00

70x70". Satin damask, 12 matching napkins, 26" square.... 65.00

70x72". Holly pattern. 6 matching napkins, handhemmed 65.00

72x90". Cloverleaf center circles connected with diamond designs. Lace, not crocheted 55.00

84x32". Handmade filet lace. Close work, scalloped border edge 75.00

88x90". Irish linen, damask 50.00

Towels
22x35". Red and white with 4"
knotted fringe. Pair 10.00
25x43". Wide end border in red
and white with narrow side stripe.
4" knotted fringe. 4.00

LITHOPHANES

Lithophanes are highly translucent porcelains with impressed designs. The picture is formed by the difference in thickness of the plaque. Thin parts transmit an abundance of light while thicker parts represent shadows. They were first made by the Royal Berlin Porcelain Works in 1828. Other factories in Germany, France and England later produced the items. The majority on the market today was probably made between 1850 and 1900. Watch out for reproductions!

Candle Shields
5" high. Flowered and scrolled
pewter holder, candle insert . . . . . $ 115.00
19½" high. "Petraca." K.P.M. 225.00
Fairy Lamp. 2 scenes of child 165.00
Hall Lamp. 7½" square. Cut corners,
4 panels, 4x6". Brass bound, brass
fixture 400.00
Lamp Shades
5 panels, metal frame 595.00
5 panels. Colored. Rare 1500.00

3-7/8x4¾". Scene of child with dog on leash. Germany $65.00

Plaques. Marked "K.P.M."
Child on father's shoulders.
6¾x7¾" 85.00
Child reading a book, seated at
table, 7" diam. 90.00
Couple in woodland setting, with
dog. #173 . . . .   65.00
Dog flushing bird, trees in back-
ground. 3¼x4¼". #172-G 80.00
Girl with rose. 6x7½". #308-G 85.00
Man, woman in woodlawn.
4¼x5¼" 60.00
Mosque-type bldg., man kneeling.
4¾x6½". #110-ST 87.50
Queen Yasdwiga. 9½x12" 110.00
Semi-nude in front of fireplace.
5½x6¼". #761 . . . .   90.00
Woman and child. 4¼x5¼" 67.50
Women, three with child, rakes
and pasture. Blue glass frame,
10x11" 110.00
Young lovers in boat, hills and
church in background. 9x13" 195.00
Plaques. Marked "P. R. Sickle."
4-1/5x5-1/10"
Cupid and girl fishing. #1849 . . . . .   65.00
Girl at well, boy on wall 65.00
Lovers in a boat 65.00
Monk and girl. #1788 . . . .   65.00
Nymph and flowers. #1803 . . . . . .   65.00
Woman gazing at ocean. #894 . . .   65.00
Woman in flowing robe. #1422 . . .   65.00
Woman picking flowers 65.00
Young boy and girl ringing bell at
house entrance 65.00

Plaques, Unmarked
Children at play. Leaded frame.
6x7" 87.50
Girl with cat. 7¼x9" 80.00
Horses, riders at sunset. 6½x8½" .   95.00
Madonna and child. 6x7½" 75.00
People in forest. 4x4½" 50.00
Woman, semi-nude, reclining.
Lead frame, 6x8½" 87.50
Woman. "The Tempest." 4½x6" . .   65.00
Tea Warmers
4" high, 5" square. Nickleplated
holder, 4 scenic panels. All
original 150.00
7" square top. 4 scenic panels.
Original burner 160.00
Brass holder. 4 scenic panels 165.00
Brass holder, round. Pewter feet .   100.00

LIVERPOOL POTTERY

A name applied to wares made at various potters located in Liverpool, England, from about 1750 to 1840. The leading pottery was that of Sadler and Green [1790 to 1815] which decorated pottery with line drawings by a new process in black on white or cream-colored pitchers, mugs, punch bowls, plates, etc. The decorations were often designed for the American trade and consisted of prominent men, eagles, ships and scenes from daily life.

Coffee Biggin. Miniature. Transfer in black. 5" high. Scarce	$ 165.00
Creamer. 6½" long, white with black transfer of Temperance Society insignia	135.00
Cups and Saucers	
Handled cup, black transfer	82.50
Transfer, pink lustre borders	80.00
Jugs	
4½". Obverse, bust over cannon. "Decator." Reverse, similar medallion bust of Laurence	185.00
8". Obverse, medallion bust of Madison surrounded by wreath names of states. Reverse, frigate with American flag. Eagle under spout	450.00
8". Obverse, white with black transfer eagle with name of states. "Peace and Prosperity to America." American flag and Miss Liberty. C. 1800	450.00
9½". Obverse, medallion bust of Washington surrounded by wreath with names of states. Reverse, Independence inscription with eagle and liberty cap. Eagle under spout	650.00
11½". Masonic. Dated 1817	375.00
Marriage Jug. Courtship and Marriage. Trick picture with verse	225.00
Mug. 5½" high, ceramic frog inside. Outside scene "A West View of the Iron Bridge at Sunderland"	185.00
Plate. 10". Black transfer of British frigate. C. 1785	100.00
Tea Set. Teapot, sugar bowl and creamer. Queen Anne shape. Henna on white	300.00

LOCKS

The general use of locks is to keep persons from handling or pilfering private goods and property. Various types were made through previous centuries, however, in 1848, the Yale lock, a cylinder type, was introduced and is considered to be one of the most successful in retarding intruders and vandals. Later, in the 19th century, padlocks were introduced for use in insuring privacy of one's goods and buildings.

Gun Lock. C. 1890 . . . . $12.50

Door Locks	
4". Hand forged, spring spiral key	$ 35.00
With key. New England. 18th century	75.00
Gate Lock. 7½ x8". With key. Iron	62.50
Padlocks, Brass	
Adlake. R.R.	25.00
Baltimore & Ohio. With key	35.00
Corbin. Pin tumbler	7.00
Dudley. Combination	2.00
L. and Nash	35.00
Mailbag	3.50

Masonic Jug. 11½" high. Dated 1817
$375.00

Railroad switch, with chain	30.00
Yale. Lever tumbler	4.50
Padlocks, Miscellaneous	
Armory. 8-lever	4.50
Belknap. 6-lever	3.50
Champion. 6-lever	3.50
Hex	2.00
Hurd. Pin tumbler	2.00
Sargent. Push key	3.00
Winchester	6.50
Yale, Fidelity. 4-lever	3.50

LOETZ GLASS

The product was made in Austria just before the turn of the present century. It is similar in appearance to Tiffany glass. Loetz was a contemporary of Mr. L. C. Tiffany and worked in the Tiffany factory before returning to Austria to establish his own operation. The pieces are signed "Loetz, Austria."

Atomizer. Amethyst highlights, deeply colored threading ....$ 65.00

Bowls

3" high, 8½" diam. Crimped top, turned in applied threading, rose-lavender with iridescence. Signed "Loetz, Austria" 225.00

4" high, 7" diam. King Tut pattern. Green, aqua on amber irid., five pinched sides. Signed "Loetz, Austria" 275.00

Rose bowl. Brown irid. ground, bulbous, crimped top tapering to expanding foot base. 6 peacock feathers over wavy pattern. Signed 285.00

Pitchers

5½" high. Iridescent green, swirls 225.00

7½" high. Blue ground, gold Silver rim 300.00

Water. Green color, panelled ruffled top, applied handle 450.00

Sugar and Creamer. Purple metallic blue irid. with crosshatch pattern in opalescent blue, silver rims. Set 165.00

Tumbler. Green irid. "veined" design 65.00

Vases

3½" high. Miniature, blue irid. Signed "Loetz, Austria" 275.00

4-3/8" high. Pinched shape, silver overlay, flowers, leaves, silver rim and base 245.00

6" high. Five-finger. Red interior, metallic blue, mottled exterior. Fully signed 375.00

6" high. Blue irid. footed, crimped top, 4 panels, silver overlay in floral design. Unsigned 200.00

Vase. 11" high. Bulbous base, stick top. Ribboned decor. Iridescent amber
$275.00

7½" high. Damascene coloring at base. Signed 400.00

8½" high. Decorated blue allover damascene pattern over red base glass 550.00

11" high. Amethyst, irid. silver overlay. Unsigned 250.00

11" high. Emerald green, blue. Irid. gold tones. Scalloped rim pattern. Signed 400.00

12" high. Elephant Ear. Applied leaf at base. Iridescent. Rare 595.00

12" high. Signed. Heavy sterling overlay 675.00

13" high. Coinspot interior,

twisted, perforated top and sides. Color shades into amber at bottom. Signed 500.00

LOTUS WARE

A type of fine, lightweight porcelain with a warm, white color and rich glossy glaze, made by the Knowles, Taylor & Knowles Pottery Co., in East Liverpool, Ohio, between 1890 and 1900. It was named "Lotus Ware" by Mr. Knowles because it resembled the bloom of the lily. The first mark was "KTK." This was later changed to a special mark, the firm name in a circle enclosing a crescent and star, a lotus flower above and the name "Lotus Ware" below. It is now considered scarce and commands a good price, depending on the item, its size and elaborateness of design.

Bowl. 5½ x 11" diam. White coral decor
$400.00

Bonbon Dishes
  4x5½". 4 twig feet .... $ 75.00
  5x5½". Shell-shape, pure white porcelain, designed by Joshua Poole. "KTK" 150.00
Bowls
  4" high. Leaves and berries in high relief. Leaf ends form rim. Footed 300.00
  4½ x 3½ x 5". White and gold floral decor. Beaded, fluted rim, medallion-type handles 400.00
  4½ x 6½". Handpainted lovers scene. Ruffled top, pierced medallion handles. Signed 400.00
  6¾ x 4¼". Ruffled edge, ornate handles 375.00

7½". Boat-shape. KTK mark. Pink and gold openwork. Pink cherry blossoms on front and back. Artist A.L. and 1895 on base 425.00
Rose bowl. Large, dated 1895. Raised apple blossoms in gold, along with small pink, blue flowers 425.00
Cup and Saucer. Blue with gold trim, wreath molded flowers 175.00
Dishes
  7½". Branch base, light ground, pink rose in center. Gold trim 300.00
  Leaf-shaped, small. Turned-in handle 225.00
Pitchers
  3" high. Net pattern, gold panels . 365.00
  Floral decor with gold. Handle, bamboo design, with old decor ... 450.00
  Milk. Pink roses, green leaves, Scroll. Gold trim. Signed 400.00
Sugar Bowl. 6" wide at handles. 4" high, feather design. Marked KTK 400.00
Teapot. All white, embossed flowers 225.00
Tea Service. Teapot, lid, sugar and creamer. Raised pink blossoms, much gold 750.00
Vases
  7½" high. Pitcher-type. Bulbous, single handle. Colorful floral decor with gold. Painted by "J.E.B." Dated 2/92. Marked KTK . 500.00
  8" high, 5" diam. Ball feet, white with turquoise, heavy gold. Net pattern 550.00

LOWESTOFT

The term Lowestoft, when applied to chinaware, has been called "A Famous Blunder." The name is reported to have been derived from the fact that Chinese porcelain was imported into Lowestoft, England, and decorated there. It was then exported to the United States. The decorating factory operated in Lowestoft from 1757 to 1802. The ware originated from the ports of Canton, Nanking and other shipping centers of China and should be designated as "Chinese Porcelain."

Bowls
  4½" diam., blue decor. C. 1780 ... $ 135.00
  5½" diam., 2½" high. Armorial, blue with gold star decor on top of inside edge 295.00
  8¾" diam. Pink decorations on white background 275.00
  10" diam., pink and yellow florals in large medallions on front and back; sepia landscapes on other 2

small medallions. Surrounded by blue allover decoraton; blue border on inside. Early 450.00
11x14½", deep. Pink and greens. Sepia border with stripings of gold through the sepia. Arms of the Renny family. C. 1775 .... 750.00
Creamer. Helmet-type. 4". C. 1760 .. 175.00

Cups and Saucers

Demitasse.................... 75.00
Handleless. Horn-of-plenty decor, wide pink diaper border......... 87.50
Handleless. Decorated elk, fighting dogs and rabbit. Iron gray. C. 1770......................... 125.00

Dog. 10" high. Bright terra cotta, green collar with blue charms. Rare 750.00
Hot Water Jug. 5½" high, covered .. 200.00
Mug. "Mourning." Diaper design top and bottom. Black and gold side florals 80.00
Pitcher. 4¼" high. Helmet-type 200.00

Plates

8½" diam. White ground, pink, blue and green floral decor 85.00
9" diam. Armorial, floral border .. 225.00
12" diam. Blue decor............ 125.00

14½" diam. Chop plate. Plain 150.00
Platter. 8½ x12". Coat-of-Arms, decorated in pink, blues, lavenders and gold. C. 1780.............. 425.00

Teapots

4" high. Floral design and lotus pattern on bottom. C. 1780 ...... 245.00
6" high. Blue and white. Chinese landscape. C. 1760 .... 295.00
White, small gold decor. Berry finials, entwined strap handle.... 225.00
Vase. 4" high, 4" diam. 2 handles, floral decor 125.00

LUSTRES, MANTEL

Lustres are vase-shaped mantel garnitures with glass pendants or prisms hanging from the bowls. The glass is of a Bristol type and is usually colored and decorated with enamel flowers or designs.

Bristol. 8½" prisms. Top and base 5" diam. Scarce pastel green color. Pair ....$ 350.00
Bristol. 10" high. Gray ground, white and orange floral decor. 5 cut glass prisms. Pair............... 300.00
Bristol. 11½" high, 6½" across. Pink, lined with white, 2 rows of cut prisms. Pair 350.00
Bristol. 14½" high. Smoke color, ten 9½" cut crystals. Pair 300.00
Bristol. 15" high. Cased glass. Pink outside, white inside. Original enamel decor, double row of prisms. Pair.................... 400.00
Bristol. Duck-egg blue, with prisms. Pair 300.00

Cup and Saucer. Handleless ...$75.00

Bristol-type. 10" high, 5 cut glass prisms. Grey ground, white, orange floral decor. Pair $300.00

Bristol. Light smoke color. "V" cut
with painted floral decor. Cut
prisms. Pair.................... 300.00

Red-colored glass with white enameled dots. Cut glass prisms. 11"
high. Pair..................... 300.00

Ruby-color. 11" high, one row of
prisms. Pair................... 300.00

LUTZ GLASS

The name is derived from a type of glass made
by Nicholas Lutz, a Frenchman by birth, who
came to this country to ply the trade of glass
blowing. He was noted for two types - striped
[or cane] and threaded glass. He worked at
the Boston and Sandwich Glass Co. from about
1870 until it closed in 1888. He then worked
for the Mt. Washington Glass Co., and was
later employed by the Union Glass Works in
Somerville, Mass. This style of glass should be
designated as "Lutz-Type" for other workmen
in the previously mentioned glass houses also
made glass of this nature.

Bonbon Dish. 3" high, 4" diam.
Crimped, flared rim, amethyst
shaded to clear. Amber threading,
clear stem and base .... $ 45.00

Bottles
3" high. Perfume. Pink thread 75.00

Bowl. 14" to top of sterling handle.
Sterling base. Iridescent $375.00

11" long. Bellows. Pink threading,
clear rigaree trim 185.00

Bowls, Finger
6¼" diam. Clear glass with red,
white and green stripings 125.00
Clear, square on low foot. White
latticino stripes outlined in goldstone 60.00
Cranberry with bands of gold
thread. With plate. Set 85.00
Gold with wide green and rose
stripes. With plate. Set 85.00
Rose on clear, vertical ribbing 80.00

Candy Dish. Threaded 95.00

Creamer. Miniature. Latticino and
blue threads 100.00

Cruet. Heart-shaped mouth, reeded
handle, emerald, teal, goldstone . 300.00

Cups and Saucers
Clear applied handle, filigree
panels of white, blue with gold,
white and yellow 100.00
Miniature. 1¾" high cup, ruffled
edge. Blue, gold and white....... 125.00
Rainbow pattern 150.00

Ewers
8½" high. Pink ribbon panels
laced with goldstone and white
filigree. 3-pour lip, handle and
base......................... 250.00
Alternating stripes of opaque
yellow, opaque white and goldstone on clear crystal ground.
Same color combination of canes
in hollow reeded handle. Rare ... 475.00

Liqueur. Alternating stripes of
opaque yellow, white, goldstone
on clear crystal ground 85.00

Pitcher, Water. Gold threading,
applied rigaree trim 250.00

Plates
6½". Filigree canes in pink, blue,
yellow, green and adventurine ... 115.00
7". Spiral design in green, white .. 95.00
7¼". 1" deep. Gold swirls in
spiral threading 125.00

Slipper. Threaded, pink rigaree on
clear. Scarce 135.00

Sugar and Creamer. Threaded pale
blue. Set 225.00

Tumblers
3¼" high, 2½" diam., footed.
Blackberry knobs around lower
part, white and gold threading ... 100.00
Blue threading 75.00
Whiskey. 2½" high. Stripings of
pink, white and goldstone 75.00

Vases
3½" high. Clear with white
diagonal threads 85.00

7" high. Diagonal ribbing. Irid., purple base color, fluted top, unsigned 65.00

8½" high. Pink threads around top and bottom. Scroddled middle 85.00

MAASTRICHT WARE

Maastricht ware was made in Holland from about 1835 to near the end of the 19th century. English workmen and methods were employed. The product found a ready market in the United States and sold in competition with the popular English ware of the period.

Bowls

7¼" diam., 4½" high. Black and tan transfer design on white ground. Pajong pattern.......... $ 18.00

7½" diam., 4¼" high. Black and tan transfer on white ground. Pajong pattern 18.00

8½" diam., 4" high. Hong pattern . 22.50

Breakfast Set. 3-pieces. P. Regout & Co. 20.00

Cup and Saucer. Red, blue, green decor on white ground 10.00

Plates

7¾". Quilted rims edged with gold; bird and floral centers in deep blue. Set of six 50.00

Cup and Saucer $12.00

8". Souvenir. Blue and white. Commemorates the Allied Liberation of Holland. Depicts American soldiers, flags 15.00

8¼". Butterflies in red, green, blue, black decor 15.00

9". Early, blue on white.......... 35.00

Fruit. Blue and white edged in gold. Different blue center decor on each plate. Set of six 48.50

Red, blue, green decor on white ground 10.00

Platter. 11½" long. White ground, red, green, yellow flowers 30.00

MAGAZINES, See CATALOGUES & MAGAZINES

MAGIC LANTERNS

Magic Lanterns were the forerunners of the home movie machines. The period between 1890 and 1910 was the time of their greatest popularity. The earlier ones used kerosene lanterns which were housed inside the machine, hence the name "Magic Lantern." The majority was manufactured in Germany. Colored glass slides were inserted between the lantern and a lens, reproducing pictures on a wall or sheet.

Prices for the machines vary from $40.00 to $65.00, with size and condition being taken into consideration. Colored slides range from $2.00 to $4.00 depending on subject material.

"Germany. E.P." Original box, 12 scenes $50.00

MAJOLICA

The ware is classified as "soft pottery" or "faience." It is covered with a glassy coating made opaque by tin oxide.

The name is derived from the Island of Majorca, located between Italy and Spain, where the first history of the ware was recorded in the 12th century. It was later made in Italy, Germany, France and England. Wedgwood & Co. manufactured it in England from the 1850s to about 1900. The first production in the United States was credited to E. & W. Bennett Co., Baltimore, Maryland in the 1850s. Their ware is marked E. & W. Bennett, Canton Ave., Baltimore, Maryland. After 1856, the initial form was changed to E. B., when William, one of the brothers retired. The best known ware in this country was made by Griffen, Smith & Hill Co., at Phoenixville, Pa., and was marked "Etruscan Majolica" or bore the monogram "G.S.H." Beginning in 1880, the product of this plant was used by The Atlantic & Pacific Tea Co., as premiums for baking powder. The factory was destroyed by fire in 1892 and the ware was discontinued.

Asparagus Dish & Platter. 12½" Top pierced for drain, 4 feet. Asparagus stalks form semi-circular oblong dish in natural colors. Bottom represents fanned out stalks tied with blue ribbon. Imprinted "V.B.S." Set . . . . $ 85.00

Asparagus Plate. 16½" long in blue, green, white. Unmarked 65.00

Basket. 5½ x 8½". Yellow sanded ground, applied gold flowers 60.00

Biscuit Barrel. Blue ground, green scrolled medallions, rose colored flowers. Brass collar, bail. Brass lid has finial which reads "Biscuits" 100.00

Bottles
Rabbit. Head is removable stopper 140.00
Shape of ear of corn 50.00

Bowls
9¼" diam., 5" high, footed. Multicolored daisy decor, pink interior 60.00
10" diam. Shape of maple leaf, raised maple leaf in center. Unmarked 25.00
Shell shape, blue outside, orchid inside, 3 brown shell feet 60.00

Bread Plates
11" diam. Represents basket with folded white bread cloth, lavender border & fringe. Pierced brown handles. Harker imprint . . . 50.00
13" long. Green ground, white flowers, tinge of pink 40.00

11x13". Wheat and leaf design surround cobalt center. Wide turned-down edge, inscribed "Eat Bread with Joy and Thankfulness" 55.00

Butter Dish. Raised flower decor, green, yellow predominating 65.00

Butter Pats
Flower-shaped. Incised monogram. Rare, 5 different colored petals on each. Set of six 45.00
Green, floral center 6.00
Leaf shape 7.50

Cake Stands
5" high, 9" diam. 50.00
5½" high, 10" diam. Raised water lilies, green ground 65.00

Cheese Dish. 2-pc. 11" diam at base. 9½" high top. Brown picket design, red, white flowers, green leaves. Set 100.00

Creamers
4" high. Etruscan. Shell and Seaweed pattern 100.00
Small, bulbous, overall grayish blue basketweave, brown leaf on either side 28.50

Cups and Saucers
Etruscan. Shell and Seaweed pattern 85.00
Sunflower pattern. Pinks, green, yellow 35.00

Cuspidor. 6¼" high. Raised pink flowers, green leaves, brown stems on yellow stippled ground . 45.00

Dishes
6½" diam. Leaf shape, green leaf center. Signed Etruscan 35.00

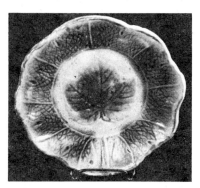

Dish. 7" diam. Leaf pattern. Cream, green and pink, scalloped edges. Franciscan $22.50

9" long. Deep, leaf shape. Brown pierced stemlike handle. Green center shading to blue, lavender, yellow & brown toward edge 35.00

9½" boat-shaped, 6¾" wide. Green background and leaves, small yellow, red pansies 55.00

9½" long. Shallow 25.00

11" long. Double, bird handle 30.00

Egg Server. Hen center 55.00

Elephant with clock 150.00

Figurines. Fighting cocks. "Italina." 7x11". Artist signed. Pair 65.00

Flask. Book-shape. 3½x4¾". "Coming Through The Rye" on back strip. Pint size, cork on top 40.00

Incense Burner. Odd shape, elflike figure with pipe 30.00

Jardiniere with Stand. Bowl has 3 dolphins entwined water lilies. 35" overall height 85.00

Lamp. Gourd-shaped, pierced 40.00

Match Holder and Striker. Center bowl 3½" high, base dish 4½" diam. Glaze, green, brown, yellow 75.00

Money Pouch. 3¼" high, 3½" long. Bone white, yellow, blue & rust forget-me-nots, gold tie cord, tassels 65.00

Mug. 5" high. Yellow, blue flowers .. 26.50

Pitchers

4¼" high. Blackberry branches, pink blossoms on 2 sides, barklike ground 35.00

4½" high. Basketweave design on lower part and band, daisies on cream ground. Butterfly forms spout 40.00

4½" high. Ear of corn in green, yellow 36.50

6" high. Etruscan Shell & Seaweed 135.00

6¼" high. Overall design of light green foliage, 2 brown lilies on either side, pink interior......... 45.00

6½" high. Green fish, white belly, brown fins on one side. Reverse shows descending fish. Eel-shaped handle. Dark blue ground, narrow yellow band, spout 60.00

7" high. Stags grazing under over hanging branches of oak & acorns. Brown and green on cream; brown handle, pink interior 50.00

7½" high. Yellow, green fern decor 38.50

8" high. Square. Brown oak leaves, blue and pink roses on cream ground. Basketweave 50.00

9" high. Ear of corn in green, yellow 60.00

9" high. Parrot, 5½" wide, rose lining. Ivory-rose head, gray beak, black claws, brown handle, green, brown bottom................. 70.00

9" high. Raised flower & leaf decor, green & yellow predominating 55.00

11" high. Ear of corn in green, yellow 70.00

Plates

8". Deer in center 25.00

8". Oyster plate. Marked Wedgwood 30.00

8". Pink center, yellow cord band, greenish-blue to scalloped edge .. 25.00

8". Shell & Seaweed. Etruscan 45.00

9". Cauliflower. Etruscan 45.00

9½". Footed, green leaf center on white basketweave, yellow edge . 37.50

11". Center has seated shaggy dog, doghouse in background. Raised green & brown floral border, brown scroll handles 50.00

Platters

9½x12". Leaf shape, brilliant green, yellow & pink, pond lily buds by handle. Sgnd. Etruscan ... 50.00

9½x12". Pink flowers & green ferns. English diamond registry mark 45.00

9½x12¼". Rococo handle, unusual coloring. Signed Etruscan... 60.00

12" long. Wedgwood. Basketweave, butterflies, floral design .. 55.00

13" long. Dark blue ground, pink blossoms 50.00

Salt & Pepper. Cauliflower pattern. White, green leaves stem. Set 35.00

Sardine Dish. Cover & underplate. Lavender lined. Set 75.00

Sauce Dish. 5½" diam., shallow. Overall leaf design in green on brown 21.00

Smoke Set. Black man strumming guitar. Basket on each side for cigarettes and matches, tray in front 48.50

Sugar Bowls

Pineapple. Covered. Green, with pink interior 75.00

Raised pink, white flowers, green leaves on basketweave. Light blue & white bottom 60.00

Sugar and Creamer. English registry mark 135.00

Syrups

6" high. Sunflower, conical body, metal top...................... 55.00

Sugar Bowl. Cauliflower pattern
$110.00

8½" high, 4½" diam. Metal hinged top	65.00
Yellow basket design on bottom half, blue top portion, raised green leaf, brown handle, pewter lid	60.00

Teapots
4½" high. Design on 2 sides. Open fan with bluebird, flowers on blue ground	65.00
Etruscan. Bamboo pattern	100.00
Shell and Seaweed	150.00

Tea Set. 3 pieces. Etruscan, Shell &
Seaweed	350.00
Umbrella Stand	75.00

Vases
4" high. Pig-shaped. Blue lining . . .	35.00
6" high. Raised flowers, leaves . . .	40.00
6" high. Sand finish, applied stem, flowers, leaves in white and gold. Pair	85.00
9" high. Sanded, yellow	65.00

Wall Pocket. Flower holder, yellow
basketweave, brown entwined branches in blue	40.00

MAPS, ANTIQUE

Maps and charts have been used through the centuries as guides to mariners and travelers. Many of the earlier ones were inaccurate but were of some use to adventurers and scholars. Today the science of map making is very accurate and trustworthy. Today most people who travel by land or air can depend on arriving at their destination promptly with the use of maps.

New Continent. 10½ x 12½" framed. Hand colored. J. Gibson. Century Magazine, May, 1758, p. 584 . $125.00

ATLASES

Drake, Edward Cavendish, Esq., London, 1770. "Travel." Contains 8 maps of voyages and travels . . .	$ 650.00
Guyot, A., 1870. "Johnson's Family Atlas of the World." Maps are colored in pastels. Contents: 71 maps of North America, 59 Dbl. pages. Others are Europe, Asia and Africa. "Dictionary of Religious Denominations, Sects, Parties, & Associations" also Treaties on Physical Geography. Double pages measure 16½ x 22½". Gilt page edges	250.00
Mitchel's. "New School Atlas." 44 copper plate maps, the U.S. is double page. Philadelphia, 1880. Quarte Maps, pastel tinted	45.00

NORTH AMERICA

Cary, John, 1806. "New Map of North America." Continents from Baffins Bay to the northern tip of South America. U.S. extends west to the Mississippi River. Mountains, the 'Stony Mountains' extend from Slave Lake [Canada] into Central Mexico. California is named New Albion. 18 x 20".	225.00

Kitchen, 1787. "North America." colored post-Revolution depiction of the original 13 states, the southern states extending to the Mississippi. Unfinished land mass above California is marked parts unknown. 13x15" 75.00

STATES AND REGIONS OF AMERICA

Carry & Lea, 1823. "Arkansas and Territories of the United States." By Major S.H. Long dedicated to John C. Calhoun depicts the Midwest from Lake Michigan to the Rockies, south to the Red River. 16½x20½" 75.00

Colton, J.H., 1855. California. Delineation marking place, names, railroads, lakes, rivers, countries, with a tinted inset plan of San Francisco. 12½x16" 50.00

Dewing, Fra. "Town Map of Boston." Framed. Dated 1722, gilted 10x13" wooden frame, carved. Engr. and Ptd. 5½x10" 20.00

Hinton, C. 1833. "States of Massachusetts, Conneticut and Rhode Island." Detailed and colored with inset plan of Boston. 7½x10" 15.00

Kitchen, 1777. Seat of War in the Environs of Philadelphia. Revolutionary War plan of the area from Somerset, N.J. to Reading, south to Chesapeake Bay, tinted with a floral title piece and compass star. 7½x10" 50.00

Luffman, 1802. "Philadelphia." Miniature of Phila., and the Delaware from Chester to Kensington. 4½x6½" 15.00

S.D.U.K. New York 1840. Colored city plan with vignettes of City Hall and Trinity Church. 15x22" .. 45.00

Sanson, 1683. "Florida." Areas from Mexico to Lake Erie to French Florida (Carolina), a Dutch edition. French cartographer. 7x10". 75.00

THE NEW WORLD

Bowen, Eman. "General Map of America." London, 1760. Map of North & South America. English colonies are named. California is named New Albion & the Baja Peninsula is called California.

Australia, New Zealand & Alaska are missing, apparently unknown to Bowen. Colored by hand. 14 x 17" 115.00

Mannert, C. "America." Nurnberg, 1812. United States extending as far west as Colorado and areas from the Rocky Mountains to the west coast are unknown territories. Locations of Indian Nations are given. In eastern America the principal cities are named & located. 20½x23½" plus margins 140.00

Sanson, N. "Atlantis Insula." 1769, from Northern Canada to the Straits of Magellan. Alaska is absent, California is an island. Hand-colored. 15x22" plus margins 75.00

THE WORLD

Cary, J. "United States of America." 1819. Large scale map marking Alabama, Indiana, Illinois & Michigan territories. 18x20" 40.00

Chatelain. C. 1730. "Carte de la Nouvelle." Early trans Mississippi map with the St. Lawrence, strange great lakes, records of LaSalle. Detail of the coast of Louisiana & colored view and plan of Quebec. 16½x19" 275.00

Sanson, N. "L'Hydrographic Ou Description De L'Eau." Paris 1652. Double hemisphere map. Shows California as an island, Alaska is absent, Australia is a huge, nearly unformed land mass. 15x21" plus margins 75.00

MISCELLANEOUS

De L'Isle, 1717. Argentina & Chili. Carte du Paraguay, du Chili, du Detroit de Magellan. Depicts all of Argentina and Chili with "Perou" and "Bresil" at the upper borders. Argentina is labeled Terre Magellanique. Uncolored. 18x24" plus margins .. 90.00

Moll. 1740. Hungary and Transilvania. Colored plan from the Carpathians to the Iron Gate Mountains. 8x10" 25.00

Salmon. Germany. 1769. Colored miniature including Bohemia, Moravia, Austria. 7x9" 25.00

Senex. Ireland, 1744. Detailed plan in green outline, towns in red 6x8" 25.00

Senex. 1744. Map of the Holy Land and the countries adjacent. Picturesque view from Cairo to Armenia with Cyprus off the coast 30.00

MARBLEHEAD POTTERY

Marblehead pottery had its beginning in 1905 at Marblehead, Massachusetts. Dr. J. Hall introduced pottery-making to the patients at the sanitarium as a rehabilitation program. A few years later, it was removed from the sanitarium, but production continued until 1936.

Vase. 8½" high $65.00

Bowls

3" .... $	40.00
5½" diam. Inverted lip	55.00
Tile. 4¾" square. Three-mast ship sailing over waves.............	95.00

Vases

4½" high. Shaded greens........	35.00
4¾" high. Beveled. Beige with aqua. Original paper label	40.00
5¾" high. Green. Marked and labeled	60.00
7¼" high. Bullet-shape. Matte glaze	65.00
8" high. Blue	65.00

MARBLES

Large glass marbles were produced by several glass houses in Ohio and Pennsylvania from about 1900 to 1920. Some had animals shaped from sulphide in the centers while others were made with colored stripes. Sizes varied from about 1¾" to 2½".

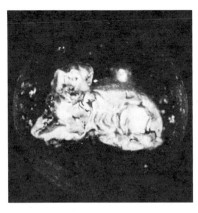

Sulphite. Dog. 1¼" diam. $45.00

Sulphides

7/8" diam. Bear, rearing ....$	50.00
1" diam. Anteater	40.00
1¼" diam. Bird................	45.00
1¼" diam. Cat, lying	45.00
1¼" diam. Dog................	45.00
1-3/8" diam. Poodle	45.00
1-3/8" diam. Rabbit, running	45.00
1½" diam. Horse, running	50.00
1½" diam. Porcupine	50.00
2" diam. Cow	55.00
2" diam. Dog..................	55.00
2" diam. Goat.................	55.00
2" diam. Lamb	55.00
2" diam. Lion	55.00
2" diam. Rooster	55.00
2½" diam. Dog................	60.00
2½" diam. Horse	60.00

Swirls

Latticino. 1-3/8". Red, white, green.........................	35.00
Latticino. Red and blue ribbons ...	35.00
Onionskin. 1-5/8" diam. Blue and white	35.00
Ribbon. Orange, green, white	35.00
Ribbon. Red, white, blue, green ..	38.50
Solid cloud core. Red and blue ribbon	40.00
Swirl with cane center. 2½" diam.	60.00

Marine Items is a general term used to cover a range of items or parts taken from dismantled or destroyed ships. It also includes model ships.

Azimuth Circle. Brass. WW II vintage, boxed. Pattern 1152 . . . .$ 100.00
Bell. Solid brass. 10" diam., 10" high. 19th century English 300.00
Chest, Medicine. Complete with 20 bottles and stoppers. Old labels, small drawer with glass mortar and pestle. Mahogany, 7½x6¾". C. 1820 . . . . 400.00

Clock. Strikes the watch, marked "Waterbury," mounted on wooden plaque. In working condition 200.00
Compass. Alcohol. Pat. No. 1153H . . 175.00
Lantern. Ship's. Brass, 18½" high to top of handle 150.00

Models
    Half-hull. American Merchant Ship. Hull, 7x49", painted green and white. Mounted on natural finish backboard, 9x59". C. 1910 . 500.00
    Shadow Box, half-model. American 3-masted ship. Carved wooden sails painted white. Diamond Line, Boston, 1820. Glass-fronted case, 5x14x26", covered with blue paper with gilded wood frame. Original paint 600.00
    Half-hull. American Tug Boat. Hull, 5x34" natural wood mounted on brown, painted backboard, 7x37". Plain design, original finish. C. 1890 . . . . 575.00
    Half-hull, American Tugboat. Hull 9x44", natural wood finish with gold decor at bow. Mounted on black painted wood backboard, 11x52". Original finish. C. 1870 . . . 650.00
    Half-hull, English Tugboat. 1914 Steel Screw Tug "Marksman" built and engined by J. P. Rennoldson & Sons, Ltd., South Shields. 8'6"x-17'6"x75', hull 3x19", painted black and brown. Mounted on backboard. 350.00
    Half-hull Canadian Working Ship. Built in Nova Scotia. Natural wood hull, 6x42", mounted on natural backboard, 9x46". Excellent detail. Fine craftsmanship. Original finish. C. 1900 . . . . 650.00

Ship's Clock. 12" diam. Walnut base, no strike. Seth Thomas $195.00

Octant. American. Fitted with brass swing arms, screws. Decorative ivory inlay in center and also ivory scale. Triangular, mahogany case. 3x12x12". C. 1800 . . . . 600.00
Sextant. English. Fitted with colored filters, additional long lenses. Mirrors stored in special, built-in box on bottom of case. USSB, Heath & Co. Ltd., New Eltham, London. Mahogany case and hardware. Brass handle for carrying. 3½x10x10" 595.00

Ship in Bottle. English. 3-masted, hull painted black, paper sails white. All rigging intact. Flying 4 multicolored flags. Fancy bottle marked "From Rigby's. Liverpool." All original. C. 1870 . . . . 395.00

Spy Glass. Wood bound, 19" to 33" extended. Complete with lens cover and working 150.00
Spy Glass. Early brass. 3 dram. Large end partly leather covered. Newton & Co., London. Closed 10", fully extended 30". Leather cover both ends 135.00

Telegraph. Brass, 40½", marked "Jos. Harper & Son, Inc., N.Y." Mint condition 350.00
Wheel. Mahogany, brass bound, approx. 27" diam. 675.00

Whistle. Mounted on wooden plaque. Pump-action type 175.00

MARY GREGORY GLASS

Mary Gregory glass is a type of clear or colored glass decorated mainly with figures of active children. The glass was named for the artist Mary Gregory who worked as a decorator at the Boston and Sandwich Glass Company in the third quarter of the 1800's. Examples of this glass originated in Europe, especially Bohemia, France and England. The European glass is more intricately decorated and more colorful. 'True' Mary Gregory glass is always decorated in white enamels and simply done. Mary Gregory-type glass is copiously reproduced.

Atomizers
Blue with boy decor . . . . $ 87.50
Cranberry, white figures 95.00
Basket, Fruit. Amethyst, in silver frame 150.00
Biscuit Jars
5" high, 3½" diam. Sapphire blue glass, decor of white enamel winged cherub, florals, leaves. Silverplated cover 85.00
7" high. Cranberry glass. Crystal finial on self covered, 4" diam. white enamel. Cherub surrounded by florals, hand blown 135.00

Pitcher. 9" high. Blown, bulbous, crimped top. White enamel on clear
$135.00

8" high to top of original glass enamel cover, 5" diam. Green, decor of white enamel cherub, flowers. Blown 110.00
Bottles
Barber:
Amethyst with girl decor 125.00
Blue with girl decor 120.00
Cobalt, 7" high, all white child scene. Lady's leg neck, rough pontil, stopper 125.00
Pale olive green. Girl picking flowers 115.00
Liqueur. 9" high. Green, boy, girl and trees. Clear handles, blown stoppers. Pair 200.00
Perfume:
Clear, gold hinged top, chain and ring. Girl decor 100.00
Cranberry. Brass-hinged top, clear stopper 110.00
Green, enameled boy. Faceted stopper 90.00
Bowl. 10" diam., 4" deep. Azure blue, white decor 165.00
Boxes
2½ x 3½ x 4". Hinged, sapphire blue glass. White enamel girl with kite in hand. Brass bound flowered base 175.00
4", hinged top, girl, flower decor . 150.00
Jewel. Large, blue, white decor . . 175.00
Butter Dish. Covered, tinted girl decor 120.00
Candy Jar. Clear glass, 6" high, girl in tree in white enamel 85.00
Claret. Blue, figure of boy 55.00
Cordial. Apple green, all white boy . 47.50
Creamers
Green, boy decor 90.00
Sapphire blue. Tankard shape, white boy decor 90.00
Cruets
Cranberry 140.00
Emerald green 130.00
Cup and Saucer. Cranberry 120.00
Decanters
7¾" high, 2¾" expanded base diam. Sapphire blue, matching handle, original stopper. 4" diam. bulbous body squared with 4 dimples. Two front dimples with boy, other two with girl. Ground pontil, gold on base and rim 235.00
8¾" high. Clear ITP. Girl in white enamel 160.00
10" high. Electric blue, crystal stopper, decor of white enamel and flowers. Tinted-face girl throwing ball. Blown. Late 100.00

Emerald green. Late 125.00
Light green. Boy's face on one,
girl's face on other. Bell-shaped,
original stoppers. Pair 275.00

Ewers
10" high. Cranberry 160.00
Emerald green. Boy in white
enamel on garden seat. Crystal
handles 145.00
Goblet. Cranberry with tinted boy or
girl. Late 40.00

Lamps
11" high to collar. Oil. Skyblue,
boy decor in white. Converted to
electric burner 175.00
14½" high to top burner, 23½" to
top of chimney. Black amethyst by
Sandwich Glass. Drummer boy in
white enamel. Font lifts out
leaving gold rim vase 650.00
Hand. Clear bowl, 8" metal
standard 100.00

Liqueur Set. 5 pieces. Bottle with
crystal stopper, 10" high. Decorated white enamel girl with
tinted face, amid white florals. 4
matching glasses, heavy-weighted
base 2½" high, 1¼" diam. 2 with
girl decor, 2 with boy. Late. Set . . . 125.00

Mugs
Clear handle. Girl with arms
stretched. Etched "Mildred 1892" . 65.00
Cranberry. Girl decor 75.00
Paperweight. 2" square black glass,
girl in white enamel on white
grass 175.00

Pickle Castors
12" high. Silverplated frame,
cranberry with white decor, gold
trim 275.00
Clear with boy decor. Silverplated
frame, cover and tongs 165.00
Double. Opaque, blue, enamel
decor, in silverplated frame 425.00

Pitchers
6" high. Milk. Clear with girl in
white. Twisted, clear rope handle . 85.00
7" high. Green with white enamel
decor 135.00
8½" high. Tankard shape, smoke
color. Girl with hoop 150.00
9" high. Girl, flora, fauna in
white. Ribbed handle, early pontil . 165.00
11" high. Lipped top, bulbous
body, applied green arched
handle. Decor of white enamel
girl, white foliage. Low pedestal
base, blown panel glass 175.00

11½" high. Gold rim edge at top,
3½" diam., 5½" diam. at base.
Tankard shape, enamel white girl,
tinted face, surrounded by foliage
and trees. Late 125.00
11½" high. Sapphire blue, white
enamel figure of boy playing ball.
Bulbous 165.00
12" high. Tankard-type. Blue with
boy decor 200.00
Water. Amber with white girl
figures. Pontil mark 150.00
Water. Clear with 2 girls, flowers.
Late 115.00
Water. Cranberry, girl, boy 185.00
Plaque. 10½". Cranberry, girl and
scenery. In brass hanger 150.00

Rose Bowls
2¾" high. Cranberry. Boy holding
leaf spray. Scalloped top 175.00
3x3¼". Cranberry. Turned in,
6-crimp rim. Paneled body, white
enamel boy picking flowers 165.00
3¾" high. Little girl in white.
Turned down scalloped rim 125.00
Blue 110.00

Steins
5½" high. Blue, girl decor 135.00
9½" high. Cobalt, white painted
boy figure with rake in garden . . . 150.00
14¾" high. Blue, white enamel
girl decor. Pewter top with
thumbrest 245.00

Vase. 7" high. Mottled cranberry.
White enameled figure of female
child. 4-footed base $395.00

Sugar Shaker. Clear, girl, butterfly .. 95.00
Tea Strainer. One piece cranberry
  inset in silver holder. 3 scenes of
  children in white enamel. Original
  burner, cover and handle 135.00
Trays
  6½ x9". Amber, 2 girls, 1 with doll 175.00
  Pin. Amber, girl decor in white ... 65.00
Tumblers
  3¼" high. White enamel decor,
  boy, gold rim, green panelled 45.00
  3¾" high, 2¼" diam. White
  enamel girl and flowers 55.00
  3¾" high. Amber, white decor ... 65.00
  4½" high. Green. Boy with out-
  stretched arms 65.00
  6½" high. Clear with enameled
  boy, tinted face. Late 30.00
  7" high. Green, boy in white
  enamel with flowers 75.00
  8½" high. Tumble-up. Emerald
  green, figures of boy and girl 200.00

Vases
  3" high, 3½" diam. Small,
  cranberry. Girl with watering can,
  other girl rolling hoop and both
  with trees and foliage in white
  enamel. Bulbous shape, narrow
  neck, top edged in gold. Pair 225.00
  5½" high. Blue with girl on one,
  boy on other. Pair 150.00
  5½" high. Cranberry with girl
  carrying basket 95.00
  6½" high. Bud. Boy, tinted face,
  carrying flowers. Late 75.00
  7¼" high. White enamel boy in
  blue suit. Blue-green, covered
  with coraline beading 165.00
  6½" high. Stick. Cranberry. Girl
  holding leaf sprays. Clear, 2½"
  round base 175.00
  8¼" high. Amethyst. Girl with
  hat, sashed dress, holding balloon 395.00
  9" high. Cranberry, figural. Pair .. 285.00
  9" high. Green, girl decor 145.00
  9½" high. Cranberry, man and
  woman in colonial costumes. Gold
  band around base, center and top
  rim. Pair 295.00
  11" high. Blue, enamel figures of
  boy, girl. Rigaree sides. Pair 250.00
  12" high. Cranberry, tinted
  features 100.00
  12" high. Ice blue, blown, with
  white enamel figure 135.00
  12" high. Sea green satin glass.
  White figures of girl, boy. White
  beading top, floral edge. Pair 150.00

12½" high. Green, white decor.
  Clear shell decor on sides.
  European origin. Late 165.00
14" high. Electric blue, white
  figures of boy, girl flying kite. Pair 325.00
Wine Glasses
  Clear with enamel figure 42.50
  Cranberry 50.00
Wine Set. Cranberry. 10½" tray,
  decanter, 2 wines. Set 350.00

MASONIC ITEMS

Collecting Masonic items is comparatively
new compared with collecting china and glass.
The majority of collectible items is of the
commemorative or souvenir type - national
conventions, etc. Most were made of glass but
a few were of pottery and metal.

Bottle. Camel. Celveland, Ohio 1931 $ 150.00
Cane. Ivory handle 75.00
Chalices
  Glass, gold decor. Dated June
  1905, Pittsburgh, Pa. 65.00
  Glass, gold, enamel decor. St.
  Paul, Minn., 1908 . . . . 65.00
Champagnes
  Dated May 1912. New Orleans.
  Alligator decor on sides 85.00
  "New Orleans 1910." Alligators
  climbing sides of glass 85.00
Coverlet. Double woven, reversible
  blue and white 265.00
  Cup and Saucer. Orange. Pitts-
  burgh, Pa. 1906 . . . . 75.00
Gavel. Wood, hand carved 28.50

Plate. 8". Pittsburgh Commandery No.
1 K.T. Twenty-Eighth Triennial. Louis-
ville-1901-Kentucky. Liverpool . $38.00

Cup and Saucer. Los Angeles, Pittsburgh 1906..................$75.00

Goblets
Pittsburgh, Pa., May 22, 1900. 5" . 65.00
St. Paul, Minn. 1908. Round base . 60.00
Shrine, Pittsburgh, Pa. 1909. With
2 sword handles................ 65.00
Mugs
Atlantic City, July 13, 1904 ...... 45.00
Pittsburgh, Pa. 1898. 3 handles... 65.00
Pittsburgh, 1903. 3". Indian in relief 50.00
Pittsburgh, 1904. Fish handle 50.00
Pittsburgh, 1905. 2 sword handles 60.00
Paperweights
4" high. Shape of iron Bible 50.00
Blown, round glass. Floral and
Masonic emblems 55.00
Pitchers
3" high. Creamer. Compliments of
Pilgrim Commandery No. 55, East
Liverpool, Ohio. "In Hoc Signo
Vinces" 75.00
5¼" high. Sunderland Lustre.
Masonic symbols and seven-line
verse 185.00
9" high. Early. Color transfer and
pink lustre decor. Pilgrim Com-
mandery #55, East Liverpool, Ohio 275.00
Ceramic with lid and handle.
Black and white transfer on
Victorian shape. 90th Anniversary
Camden Lodge No. 15. 1911. Silver
lustre gilding. Made by and
marked Maddock & Sons, Trenton . 85.00

Plates
6", Los Angeles, May 1906....... 48.50
8½". Shrine 55.00
10". 54th Annual Conclave Grand
Commandery, Knight Templar,
Harrisburg, 1909 .... 75.00

Razor. Straight. Tortoise-shell handle
with Masonic symbols one side,
pictures of women of period other
side. Pat. date Nov. 1879 .... 35.00
Shelf, Hanging 50.00
Slipper, Degree. Blue leather....... 48.00
Spooner. Shrine 75.00
Sword. Old Colony Commandery.... 120.00
Tumbler. China, souvenir of Louis-
ville. Scene of Confederate Monu-
ment, City Hall, Masonic Temple.. 75.00
Watch Fob with Chain. 32nd Degree
Masonic Knights Templar 85.00

MATCH HOLDERS

In the days of the so-called "barnburner"
matches, match holders were a household
necessity. Many styles, types and shapes were
made.

Brass
Banjo. 5" high, 2 compartments ..$ 40.00
Beetle, hinged lid 30.00
Devil's Head. Grapes and leaves.
Wall safe 35.00
China
Hanging-type, in shape of girl's
head......................... 18.50
Man with cane by old tree stump
which holds matches. 6½" high .. 20.00

Iron $28.50

Peacock. 6" high, majolica-type ..	40.00
Clear Glass	
Bear Head	45.00
Charlie Chaplin	50.00
Elephant	30.00
Jenny Lind. Wall-type	50.00
Iron	
Bacchus	27.50
Barrel-shaped on board fence. 5" high, 4" wide	20.00
Bird. Mechanical, 4" high	35.00
Boy on tree stump, with hat. 2x4x4"	25.00
Boxer dog with paw on tail of rat. 6½" long. Basket for matches	55.00
D.M.&Co. New Haven, Conn. Pat. Dec. 20, 1864	40.00
Grape decoration	25.00
Hunting scene. Deer head, hunters at side, emblem, leaves, bugle. Twin pockets	35.00
Hunting scene. Rabbit and bird each side. Hunting horn in center. 8¼" high. Hanging-type	35.00
Ornate scroll design. 7½" long . . .	27.50
Rabbit and duck. Child holds matches. Large	32.50
Remer Bros. Coal and Wood. Wall-type, open coal scuttle, 4x5"	15.00
Single. Open pocket, lacy back . . .	17.50
Wall Safe. Rectangular, decorated lift-up cover	40.00
Wellington's boots. Red tops	19.50
Milk Glass	
Butterfly. White, decorated, wall-type	25.00
Grape and Leaf	18.50
Indian Head. 5" high, standing-type. Stippled surface on back for striking	35.00
Jester, Black. 4¼" high. Pat. date, June 13, '76. Rare	55.00
Little Jack Horner. Wall-type, in shape of bellows. 5¼" high	35.00
Uncle Sam Hat. With stars	37.50
Soapstone. Hand carved. Approx. 3¼" long	20.00
Sterling. Cracked egg shape. On sheaf of wheat base	45.00
Terra Cotta. 5½" diam. Wreath design around edge. Bucket holder	15.00
Tin. Old Judson Whiskey	16.50
Wooden. Hawk's feet [2]. Middle claw has striker	28.50

MATCH SAFES - POCKET

In the period before safety matches became common, many people carried matches in safes.

There were two main reasons for this use. First, the convenience of having matches in a handy container and, secondly, as a safety feature. A number of instances have been recorded about friction matches being ignited accidentally and burning clothing, sometimes the bodies of the carriers. Wholesale jewelry catalogues of the 1890's and early 1900's offered these items.

Sterling. Embossed. Art Nouveau
$32.50

Advertising and Commemorative	
"Elk Brewing Co." Kittanning, Pa. Cutter on bottom, silverplated . . . $	40.00
"Masonic." Design includes apron, Bible, eye, etc. Pat. Jan. 1904	32.50
"Pan Am Expo, Souvenir of Buffalo, 1901"	30.00
"St. Louis World's Fair, 1904, Electric City." Reverse, Jefferson and Napoleon. Sterling	35.00
Brass	
Birds in jungle	50.00
Horseman	55.00
Sterling Silver	
Art Nouveau Face	37.50
Bull Dog. "Your Match"	60.00
Fisherman	45.00
Flower and Leaf. Germany	25.00
Flowers, leaves, scrolls. Hand wrought open work	45.00
Golfer, porcelain medallion. Embossed clubs, all on sterling silver	48.50
Hunter with dogs	55.00
Plain. Monogrammed	25.00
Snakes and cattails, with striker . .	40.00
Water nymphs and cupids. Striker	50.00
Miscellaneous	
Floral design. Silverplate	22.50

Honeycomb pattern. 9Kt. Bur-
mingham, England, 1918 ....   22.50
Mother-of-Pearl on white metal ..   25.00
Woman with flowers. Silverplated   45.00

MECHANICAL BANKS, See BANKS

McCOY POTTERY

McCoy pottery was made in Roseville, Ohio. In
1967 the firm was taken over by Mt. Clements
Pottery Co. of Michigan. Early McCoy is now
collectible.

Baskets
    9" to top of handle. 7" opening.
    Yellow at bottom, green, border,
    brown handle ....$ 14.50
    Green. Basketweave design 10.00
Cookie Jars
    Aunt Jemima 30.00
    Bear..........................   25.00
    Black Cook Stove. 5x9"..........   25.00
    Cocker Puppy in Basket 24.00
    Mr. and Mrs. Owl 25.00
    Rocking Horse 27.50
    Stagecoach 19.50
Ewers. High gloss. Pink wild flowers,
    green leaves in high relief. Pair ..   30.00
Flower Holder. "Under the Spread-
    ing Chestnut Tree"..............   12.00
Head. Uncle Sam with hat..........   15.00
Pitcher and Bowl. White. Set 28.50
Planters
    8" turtle. Green with yellow toes
    and flowers....................   15.00
    Wishing Well. Bennington-type
    brown green glaze with motto
    "Grant Me a Wish" 15.00
    Yellow duck 10.00
Teapot. Pine cone 15.00
Tea Set. 3 pieces. Pine cone pattern .   28.50

Tea Set. 3 pieces. Teapot, creamer and
sugar. Chrysanthemum pattern. Shadings of pink, green and white. Signed
$28.50

Vases
    6¾" high. Yellow lily, green
    leaves, brown base 18.50
    14½" high, 6½" diam. White with
    green leaves, bunches of purple
    grapes 25.00

MEDICAL ITEMS

Old medical instruments and bottles are of
interest to a special category of collectors,
especially doctors and persons closely
associated with the medical profession.

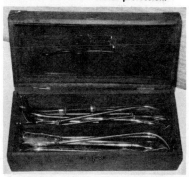

Surgeon's Tools. Original wooden
    chest $75.00

Bleeding Cup. Early blown glass ....$ 15.00
Bleeding Lance. Triggered 25.00
Bottles
    Glass measure on top. Amber ...   40.00
    Nursing. Glass nipple. Early blown
    glass 25.00
Breast Pump. Early blown glass 15.00
Cup, Wooden. "Quasio" 8.50
Dental Cabinet. Old 75.00
Doctor's Box. 6x6½x8½". Mahog-
    any wood with compartments
    holding original bottles, pull-out
    tray with other medical
    implements....................   165.00
Drill. Treadle driven 100.00
Eye Cups
    Clear glass 3.00
    Cobalt 7.00
    Milk glass 5.00
Rinsing Curettes. Original box. Set of
    two...........................   25.00
Surgical Scarifier. Mechanical. With
    several knives for blood letting or
    lancing. Brass, spring-driven 75.00

MEISSEN, See DRESDEN

MEISSEN, ONION PATTERN

A white ware with cobalt blue decorations, its original designation being the "Bulb Pattern." Common usage has determined the name to be "Onion Pattern." It was made in the latter part of the 19th century. The first European china factory at Dresden started in 1710. The words Dresden and Meissen are often used for the same ware because the factory first operated in Meissen and later moved to Dresden. Recent European reproductions of the various items have flooded the market and caused a considerable break in the price of both the new and old wares. Complete dinner services and accessories are available in reproductions.

Tureen. 11¼" long, including handles.
C. 1880 . . . . $125.00

"ONION MEISSEN"
[With Crossed Swords]

Bottles. Vinegar and oil. Pair . . . . $	60.00
Bouillon Cup. Matching saucer. Set . .	35.00
Bowls	
6" diam.	32.50
7½" diam. Lacy border	50.00
8½" square, handled	55.00
9" square	60.00
10" diam.	52.50
11" diam.	55.00
Bread Board	22.50
Butter Dish. Covered	100.00
Candlesticks. 10½" high. Matching	
bobeches. Pair	100.00
Cheese Dish. Covered	100.00
Chocolate Pot. Rose finial	110.00

Coffee Pots	
9" high. Finial	110.00
10" high. Cobalt, marked Meissen.	
Full figure finial, blue rosebud . . .	125.00
Creamers	
3½" high. Individual	30.00
5½" high	38.00
Cups and Saucers	
Coffee	32.50
Demitasse	35.00
Tea	25.00

Dishes	
5½" diam. Sauce	16.50
6x8". Covered	42.50
7½" diam. Leaf-shaped	40.00
8" diam. Leaf-shaped	45.00
8½" diam. Covered	85.00
11" square. Covered	125.00
13" diam. Divided, covered	145.00
Egg Cup	15.00
Fish Mold. 4" long, 12" fish-shaped	
handles, pierced for hanging	40.00
Flour Scoop. 9" long, 2" wide. Onion	
decor on bowl and handle	27.50
Grater. Vegetable. 5x9"	25.00
Gravy Boat. On tray. Set	60.00
Meal Box. Hanging, covered	37.50
Meat Drainer	20.00
Meat Tenderizer. Long wooden	
handle	26.50
Melon Mold. Handled	24.50
Mug. Extract. Finger handles,	
double, ¼ gill top, ½ gill bottom .	35.00
Mustard. 4¾" high, with ladle. Set . .	25.00
Pancake Turner. Long wood handle . .	28.50
Pie Crust Crimper. 2", with wooden	
handle	17.50

Plates	
6¼"	20.00
8½"	27.50
9"	28.50
9½". Soup	30.00
10"	38.50
12". Sandwich	50.00
14". Chop	85.00
14". With hot water jacket	95.00
Platters	
11½" long	95.0
13" long	110.00
17" long	125.00
20½" long. Crossed sword mark .	150.00
Pot de Creme	45.00
Potato Masher. Large ball, long	
wooden handle	35.00
Ramekin. With handles	35.00
Rolling Pin	30.00
Salt Box. With cover	50.00
Sugar Bowl and Creamer	95.00

Swizel or Cream Whip. Fluted,
   bulbous end, long wooden handle   22.50
Teapot. 5¼" high. Matching footed
   tea tile. Set 95.00
Teapot. 2-cup, rose finial. Covered
   sugar with finial, creamer, tile
   with 4 knob ball feet. Early
   crossed sword mark. Set 185.00
Tea Strainer. Wooden handle.......   18.50
Tureen or Vegetable Bowl. Oval 125.00
Tureen; Soup. 10½x14". Finial on
   lid, handles 275.00
Utensil Rack. Large 72.00
Vase. Spill-type. 5½" high, flowers
   and bugs on 3 scroll feet.........   55.00

MERCURY GLASS

A type of thin glass, usually in the form of
vases, lined on the interior with a flashing of
mercury which gives the article an allover,
silverlike appearance.

Ball. 5½" diam. ....$ 32.50
Bowl. 5" diam. 42.50
Candlesticks
   13" high, 5" base diam. White
   enamel decor 60.00
   Chamber-type. Pewter holder for
   candle. 3" high 45.00
Compotes
   5½" high. Gold interior, decorated with flowers and birds 55.00
   8" high, 5½" wide, 4" base.
   Pedestalled, cut to clear flower.
   Scroll and leaf design 65.00

Rose Bowl. Round, 5½" high. Melon-
ribbed $50.00

Gold lined, handpainted white
   enamel flowers outside. Ringed
   pedestal base. Large...........   75.00
Creamer 60.00
Door Knobs. Pair 40.00
Flower Holders. For auto. Pair 40.00
Goblet 60.00
*Lamp Reflector 18.50
Lamps. 10" high. Single marble
   pewter connections. Vintage de-
   sign on bowls. Pair 250.00
   design on bowls. Pair 250.00
Match Holder 25.00
Pitcher, Milk. Applied handle.......   95.00
Rose Bowl. 5" high 50.00
Salt. 1¾", open 30.00
Spooner........................   47.50
Sugar Bowl. Covered 85.00
Sugar Shaker. 5½" high. Pear-
   shaped on standard, original
   pewter screw-on top, leaves and
   flowers encircle bottom 45.00
Tie Backs. Rose. Pair 40.00
Toothpick.......................   28.50
Urn. Pedestal base, 3" high, gold
   lining 70.00
Vases
   4¼" high. Bud vase. Horizontal
   ribbing......................   10.00
   7½" high. Bird decor...........   20.00
   9½" high. Decorated. Pair 60.00
   10" high. Bulbous bottom, footed.
   Painted floral decor............   40.00
Wig Stand. 10" high 60.00
Wine. Etched, stemmed...........   45.00
            *Reproduced Item

METTLACH, See STEINS; also
See VILLEROY & BOCH

MICKEY MOUSE ITEMS, See
COLLECTIBLE CHARACTER &
PERSONALITY ITEMS

MILK GLASS

Milk Glass, an opaque-white glass, was
invented in the 18th century to fulfill the
demand for a less-expensive ware that
resembled porcelain. It was not new because
a fine opaque-white glass was made in
Murano, Italy as early as the 15th century.
Milk glass of the 19th century was a poor
imitation of the original in regards to
character, form and decoration.
Today's reproductions of some of the better
patterns and forms of that period are indeed
inferior. They serve a purpose but not for the
true milk glass collector.

Bowl. 10" diam. Lattice rim. Apple blossoms $50.00

Animal Dishes, Covered. See "Animal Dishes, Covered."
Bottles
  Bear. Sitting. 11" high ....$ 140.00
  Satin finish, stoppered 27.50
  Toilet. Glazed finish, original stopper 37.50
  Toilet. Satin finish, original stopper 40.00
Bowls
  7" diam. Lacy edge 22.00
  7½" diam. Lacy. Scroll with Eye .. 70.00
  8" diam. Lacy. Deep............. 72.50
  8½" diam. Lacy. Lattice, ground base pebbled bottom 80.00
  9" diam. Lattice edge. Trumpet vine decor. Atterbury 75.00
  9½" diam. Lacy. Lattice, flower spray 65.00
  10" diam. Acanthus Leaf flint 60.00
  10" diam. Shallow, scalloped oval 60.00
  10½" diam. Flared Lace 85.00
  12" diam. Beaded Rib, oval. Flint . 80.00
  Portland made "Daisy" 58.00
  Portland made "Tree of Life." All white 80.00
  Box, Glove. 10½" long, 4" wide 35.00
Butter Dish. Covered. Swan finial. Short pedestal base............. 90.00
Celery. Blue Jewel 95.00
Compotes
  9" high, 9" diam. Flint "Atlas" 75.00
  Matched "C"scroll 115.00
  Open. Sawtooth pattern. 8½" diam., 10" high................ 125.00
Creamer. Satin glass, small 35.00

Dish. Round, covered. Yellow with portrait 35.00
Egg Cup. Birch Leaf. Flint........... 25.00
Goblet. Cane.................... 50.00
Match Holder. Early flint, hanging .. 32.00
Mug. Large, footed, molded robins .. 30.00
Mustard Jar. 4" high. Hexagonal Dutch figures and background scenes 35.00
Plates
  5½". Gothic, blue 24.00
  5½". Peg border, black 22.50
  5½". Peg border, white 20.00
  5½". Star 18.50
  7". Battleship Maine. Shell and Club rim...................... 16.00
  7¼". Gothic, white 20.00
  7½". Forget-me-not 22.50
  7½". Wicket, black 24.00
  7½". Wicket, white 20.00
  8". Scroll with Eye, green 36.50
  9". Angel Head................. 26.00
  9½". Lattice. Floral spray 65.00
  11". Atterbury lattice edge, trumpet vine decor 75.00
Platter. 13½". Dog swimming to retrieve bird 145.00
Salt & Pepper Shakers
  6" high. Owl. White M.G. Birds standing on round base. Original metal tops 150.00
  White M.G. with "Columbian Exposition 1893." Pair 75.00

Sugar Bowls
  Covered. Swan finial 85.00
  Lacy edge 48.50
Syrup Jug. 8½" high. Pewter top ... 65.00
Trays
  4½ x 8½". "World's Fair. St. Louis, 1904." 30.00
  9" diam. Dresser. Floral souvenir of Wall Lake, Iowa 30.00
  Actress head. Large 60.00
Tumbler. Louisiana Purchase 14.50

Covered Dish. Hand and dove. Atterbury, dated August 1889 .....$125.00

Vases
  7" high. Raised roses............ 29.50
  9½" high. Thin, fiery opal, ruffled
  top 32.00
  11" high. Thin, fiery opal 35.00

MILLEFIORI GLASS

An ornamental glass consisting of slender canes or rods of colored glass fused together and then cut directly across into small sections and imbedded into the glass. Millefiori translates as "a thousand colors."

Basket. Small, blues & greens ......$ 135.00
Bowls
  3½" diam., 2" deep, 2 handles ... 100.00
  4½" diam. Handled with pulled
  paperweights, canes in blues,
  greens, yellow 100.00

Goblet. 7½" high. Unusual colored canes in glass bowl. Clear stem, base
$150.00

  5½" diam. Handled 125.00
Boxes
  3" high. Covered 140.00
  4" high. Knob on cover 150.00
  4½" high. Covered, round 150.00
Candy Dish. Applied green handle .. 120.00
Creamer 160.00
Cruet. Cut stopper 295.00
Dish. 3" diam., ¾" high, ruffled 100.00
Jug. 2½" 90.00
Lamp Shade. 6".................. 180.00
Lamps
  15" high. Complete with shade ... 500.00
  18½" high. Electrified, complete . 600.00
Salt. Open 70.00
Slipper. 5½" long, high heel 180.00
Toothpick. 4 pinched sides, yellow,
  gold 100.00
Tumbler. 4" high................. 150.00
Vases
  3" high. Miniature. Green & blue
  with white flowers............. 100.00
  4" high. Scalloped top 112.50
  5" high 124.50
  7½" high. Urn. Colored canes in
  red, orange, blue, yellow, white,
  green, purple, brown, 3 applied
  handles 250.00
  11" high, 31" diam. Urn type 750.00

MINIATURE LAMPS, See LAMPS

MINIATURE PAINTINGS

The art of miniature paintings began in the 16th century and was no doubt inspired by illuminated manuscript paintings. Most authorities on the subject are of the opinion that they began in Italy, then moved to France and England and later to America.

The majority were painted on porcelain, placed in a small frame with a cover which made them easy to carry. Many a soldier or officer in the days before photography carried a likeness of a loved one in this manner.

Painting on Ivory. Bust of young man
  in oval brass frame, h/p, French,
  dated 1836. Benezit artist-Cros ...$ 150.00
Painting on Ivory. H/P. Complete
  info on back dated 1825. Bust of
  man. Signed M. Surrey, alias
  Stewart 125.00
Painting on Ivory. Portrait of woman,
  wide-brimmed hat, pearls. Oval
  metal frame. 2½" high. Unsigned 125.00
Painting on Ivory. Lady, ornate
  frame. 19th century. Signed...... 148.00

Painting on Ivory. 3" diam. "Jean Guy." Bronze frame. Signed ..$195.00

Painting on Ivory. Man with long curly black hair, wearing vest, coat and bow tie. Mother-of-Pearl case. From area of Philadelphia, Pa. Unsigned 160.00

Painting on Ivory. Mother and children. 2¼x3½", gold leaf frame 150.00

Painting on Ivory. Napoleon's sister, 3¼x4"....................... 125.00

Painting on Ivory. Nude. 2x6½", ivory frame. Signed 175.00

Painting on Ivory. Set of four, oval shape, folding book-type frame, 3½x4½"..................... 475.00

Painting on Ivory. Young Napoleon, oval, about 2" 75.00

Painting on Ivory. Young woman with blonde hair, wearing white and red high empire style dress. French, 2" wide, 3" high. Frame has loop for hanging 125.00

Painting on Ivory. Young woman, bonneted and lacy. "Adelaide d' Orleans" on back. Signed Dorces. 2½x3", in hanging brass frame .. 175.00

Painting on Porcelain. Member of Prussian Royal Family. 1¾x2".... 165.00

Painting on Porcelain. Mme. Lady with brown ringlets 3¾" long. H/P, Lavalliere. Signed 150.00

Painting on Porcelain. Lady in bonnet. 4x5¼"................. 150.00

Painting on Porcelain. Princess Louise. Set on papier-mache, in gilt frame 65.00

Painting on Porcelain. Oval shape, 1½" high. Portrait of woman in square frame 75.00

MINIATURES

Collecting miniatures is a popular hobby because the field is broad. Examples are plentiful for miniatures have been made of most items produced for everyday use. Their popularity can be attributed to one of the traits of human nature, love of small things especially children. This trait extends into other phases of human exixtence and creates a love or desire to possess models or miniatures of larger things.

Bed. Canopy top. 4½x6x7". Walnut . $ 65.00
Bell, School. 1¼" 12.50
Bird. Brass. 1½" high............. 12.50
Bird Cage. Pewter, with singing bird. 2¾" high 25.00
Blanket Chest, Pine. 3x4½x7¼". 19th century New England. Six-plank style. Hinges and drawer knobs replaced. Honey color......................... 35.00

Parlor Set. 7 miniatures in box. Limoges $145.00

431

Butter. Covered. Oval. Star......... 15.00
Candlesticks
   Brass. Pair 15.00
   Milk glass, ring handle. Pair 17.50
Castor Set. 4 bottles, 4½" high 40.00
Cauldron. Iron.................... 10.00
Chair. 3½" high, 1½" wide. Walnut,
   upholstered 22.50
Clocks
   Cuckoo. Model, cast iron 10.00
   Grandfather's................. 25.00
Cocoa Set. Akro Agate Chiquita
   pattern. Cobalt, 12-pcs. Set 60.00
Coffee Mill. 1½ x 1½". Brass. Drawer
   opens, handle turns, mkd. "China" 20.00
Coffee Urn. 3-footed. 9" high, 7"
   from spout to handle. Brass 75.00
Condiment Set. M.G. No tops,
   mustard pot, salt & pepper
   shakers on leaf shaped tray. Set .. 45.00
Creamer. Sweetheart 10.50
Decanters
   1½" high. Brass 12.00
   2" high, screw top and 4 matching
   ¾" stemmed goblets. Brass. Set .. 35.00
Desk. Victorian. 2¼ x 4"......... 30.00
Dishes. See "Children's Items"
Dog. Brass 1½" high 12.00
Door Knocker. 2½" high, 1½" wide.
   Dated 1880. Shape of lion's head
   with ring in mouth. Original...... 12.50
Dresser. 7x7". 3 drawers, red velvet
   lined, wood handles 40.00

Stein. 3" high. Grey and blue with
pewter lid. Germany $25.00

Dustpan. Tin 2.50
Egg Beater. 4" diam. Glass bowl,
   wheel on top, pierced disc. beater 8.00
Flower Pot. Brass 1½" high 7.50
Goblets
   5/8" diam. Stemmed, ivory 12.50
   1½" high. Brass 5.00

Grill. Signed Wagner 22.50
Hatchet. Iron. 4" long 7.50
Iron. Swan-type with trivet 17.50
Jug. 1" high. "How Dry I Am" 7.50
Kettle. Brass 22.50
Knife and Fork Set. Brass with
   porcelain handles. Austria 10.00
Lowboy. Queen Anne. Walnut, 4"
   long, 3" high, 2¼" wide 75.00
Meat Grinder. Tin with wooden
   pusher 18.50
Milk Can....................... 7.50
Mortar & Pestle. Brass, 2" high 20.00
Parlour Set. 3 pieces. Silver filagree,
   French 250.00
Parlour Set. 2 pieces. Gold and
   handpainted porcelain 450.00
Plate. ¾" diam. Ivory 15.00
Playing Cards. With gold edges.
   2x2½" in leather case. Old 10.00
Radiator. Iron 10.00
Salt & Pepper Shakers
   ¾" high on tray. Copper. Set 15.00
   Milk Glass 14.50
Samovar. Brass, 7" high. Russian
   mark 40.00
Scale. Grocer's. Counter top-type,
   brass pan. 2x4" 20.00
Sideboard. Victorian. Oak. Shelf and
   mirror. 2½ x 5½ x 8" 30.00
Skillet. Iron 7.00

Sofa with two matching chairs. Cast
   iron, heart-shaped back, gilded.
   Set 100.00
Stove, Gas. 4½" high, 3¼" wide.
   Cast iron cutouts and trim 30.00
Tables
   Gateleg...................... 25.00
   Hutch. 3½ x 3¾ x 5¾". Maple. Seat
   has lift lid. Top folds back 35.00
Tea Kettles
   Brass. 1" high 15.00
   Iron. ½-cup size, swinging lid 12.00

Tea Sets
   Pewter, 9-pcs. 3½", melon ribbed
   Art Nouveau. Teapot, cov. sugar
   and creamer. 3 cups and saucers.
   C. 1800s American. Set.......... 125.00
   Sterling. 5-pcs. Tray 4" long. J.E.
   Caldwell, Phila., Pa. 175.00

Tea Tray. 4" long, oval with handles.
English silver gilt, with green
enamel border 30.00
Wash Sets
6½" high. Blue on white with soft
cream and pink roses. Unmarked .   55.00
Dark blue, spongeware-type with
wide bands of flowers 70.00

MINTON CHINA

Minton china was first made by Thomas
Minton in the Staffordshire district of England.
His original occupation was that of an
engraver. Later, about 1793, he began making
transfer pottery. Later he produced porcelain
with a stippled design. He retired in 1821 and
the firm was taken over by his sons and
continued to operate for more than two
decades.

Cup and Saucer. White ground with
polychrome flower. C. 1840 . . . $45.00

Bowl. 11½" diam. Multicolored
rooster center. Green, blue, gold
rim . . . . $ 110.00
Butter Dish. 2-pcs. Bottom bowl and
handled dome cover decorated
with floral Festoons and ovals
with raised turquoise bows and
jewels. Made for Davis Collamore
& Co., New York. Set 65.00
Cup and Saucer. Formed, painted
butterfly is cup handle. Gold
edge, H/P flowers on white
ground 60.00
Dinnerware "Malta" pattern #4901,
8 dinner plates, 8 salads, 8 bread
and butters, 8 cups and saucers, 8
bouillons, 7 saucers. Set 650.00
Pitchers
8" high. Cobalt with yellow mask
under pour spout and yellow
rosettes. C. 1867 . . . .   100.00
9" high. Salt glaze. Embossed.
Vehicles of past and present

Pitcher. 7" high. Raised blue decor,
cream-colored body $115.00

showing stagecoach, train travel-
lers rest. Dated 1840 . . . .   150.00
Plates
5". Lustreware with assorted fruit
in center 50.00
7½ x 9". Asparagus. Scalloped
sauce holder center, asparagus in
relief 20.00
7½ x 9". Oyster 35.00
7¾". Salad. White, gold bands.
Set of 12 . . . .   125.00
9". Burnished gold decor of
butterflies and flowers on a deep
mazarin blue ground 45.00
Tiles. King Lear. Much Ado About
Nothing, Temptress, Timon of
Athens, Twelfth Night. Late 25.00
Vase. 8½" high. English porcelain,
painted scenes of birds, flowers
and insects. Jewelled decor 200.00

MOCHA WARE

Mocha is a soft-bodied pottery similar to Leeds
ware. It is normally cream-colored and
decorated with seaweed, earthworms, tree
silhouettes or other dipped-brush patterns,
applied in various colors on bands of black,
blue, green, tan, red or terra cotta.

It was first made in Tunstall, England, by William Adams, from 1787 to 1805, and by his son, William Adams, until 1831. According to Edwin Atlee Barber, it was still being made by the descendants of the family in 1903. It appears that the two William Adamses did not mark their ware.

Mocha was also made at the Cambria Pottery in Swansea, England between 1831 and 1850, and at South Wales Pottery at Llanelly.

Mug. 5" high. Tree pattern decor. Blue bands $135.00

Bowls

4½" diam., Yelloware. Beige band and green seaweed decor. 10¼" rim. C. 1875...............$ 158.00

5½" high, 12" diam. Yellow, large lip............................ 160.00

6½" diam. Blue and brown decor. Footed....................... 175.00

8½" diam. Earthworm pattern, gray ground with black and white decor........................ 175.00

9" diam. Blue seaweed.......... 165.00

With matching lid. Earthworm pattern, in gray, green, brown and white........................ 300.00

Chamber Pot. 5½" high, 9½" diam. White band with blue decor on tan ground 150.00

Cup. 4½" diam. Cat's Eye pattern ... 110.00

Jugs

5" high. Seaweed. Signed........ 195.00

5¾" high. Blue, black and white mottling on red ground 225.00

6½" high. Combination of Earthworm, Cat's Eye and Seaweed patterns in green, blue and brown 250.00

Muffineer. 4½" high. Gray with tan band. Seaweed pattern 100.00

Mugs

2¾" high. Banded in yellow ware with white and black bands. Applied handle. C. 1845......... 60.00

3¾" high. Seaweed pattern in black on brown ground, green band at top 125.00

6" high. Earthworm pattern in dark brown and black on light brown ground.................. 135.00

6" high. Twig pattern in black, brown and white on blue ground, black bands 150.00

Mustard. ¼ pint, handled. Blue with lustre bands, orig. ladle 125.00

Pitchers

6" high. White with blue center band, leaf decoration 175.00

6½" high. Earthworm pattern 195.00

6½" high. Seaweed pattern, brown, blue and white decor..... 195.00

7¼" high. Wide brown band, narrow blue bands and white decor. White spout and handle ... 200.00

7½" high. Earthworm pattern in tan, gray and black on white ground 225.00

Pitcher. 8" high. Cat's Eye & Snail. Green, blue, grey and white ..$265.00

Salt Master. Pumpkin squat pedestal. One narrow band, 7 white
bands, black and white lines top .. 60.00
Salt Shaker. Earthworm pattern 75.00
Sugar Bowl. Covered, 5" high, tree
pattern. Tan ground, black trees,
green band. Rare 250.00

MOLDS [FOOD]

Old food molds are used primarily for
decorative purposes to create a "homey"
atmosphere in the kitchen.

CANDY MOLDS
[Tin, Tin and Copper, Etc.]

Basket. 3½x6" ....$	25.00
Bridge Club. Heart, spade, diamond, club. Set.......................	50.00
Duck	22.00
Frog. 5" long	25.00
Fruit. Fluted.....................	12.50
Groom. 3½" high.................	15.00
Jenny Lind. 3 pieces..............	50.00
Lion.............................	25.00
Pineapple	25.00
Rabbit. 5¾" high	25.00
Rabbit. 7½" high	30.00
Rooster. 5½" high	25.00
Rose	20.00
Santa Claus. 6¼"	35.00
Snowman. 4" high	28.50
Witch on Broom. 6" high	20.00

ICE CREAM MOLDS
[Pewter, Iron, Etc.]

Artichoke	25.00
Bell	35.00

Ice Cream Mold. Pansies. 6½x8"
$45.00

Rabbit. Iron. 10½" long $45.00

Bride and Groom	40.00
Camel. 2¼x6¼"	28.50
Champagne Bottle in Ice Bucket	50.00
Corn	25.00
Eagle, American.................	60.00
Fire Engine. 4½" long	35.00
Fish. 4" long	27.50
Flowers. 2" high	35.00
Football. 3" long.................	20.00
Grapes. 5" high	28.50
Hatchet. "G.W."	35.00
Heart	25.00
Heart and Cupid	30.00
Hen. Small......................	20.00
Hen on Basket...................	30.00
Hobby Horse	35.00
Leaf	25.00
Lincoln	55.00
Pumpkin	30.00
Rooster	25.00
Santa Claus	45.00
Sea Shell	30.00
Shield with Stars and Stripes	45.00
Star............................	25.00
Stork...........................	28.50
Strawberry	25.00
Tulip. 3" high....................	20.00
Turkey. 4" high	30.00
Uncle Sam	35.00
Vintage Car.....................	50.00
Washington, George. Bust	45.00
Watermelon	25.00

POTTERY MOLDS
[For Puddings, Custards, Etc.]

Asparagus. 3½x6x8"	30.00
Melon	25.00
Pea Pods	35.00
Rabbit. 6x9"	40.00

MISCELLANEOUS

Cigar. 9 sections	40.00
Fish. Copper	35.00
Lamb. Iron. 9x14"	50.00
Rabbit. Copper. 4½" high	20.00

MONART GLASS

The glass is of the Art Deco period, 1920-30. It was made in Scotland, however, the name of its maker has not been determined. The glass is heavy with the body showing small pieces of imbedded colored glass through a clear outside layer.

Bowl. 4½x10" diam. Dark amethyst, pink and green swirls $95.00

Bowl. 1¼" high, 3¾" diam. Swirled blue, pink and green with gold ... $	65.00
Lamp. 9¾" high. Electrified, originally a gas light. Green at top, pink bottom with multicolors	250.00
Vases	
5½" high. Mottled reddish-brown base shading to green rim	85.00
10" high. Tortoise to orange	150.00
11x7"	160.00

MOORCROFT POTTERY

William Moorcroft established the Moorcroft factory in 1913, in Burslem, England. Practically all items were handcrafted on the potter's wheel and no two pieces were made exactly alike. The founder died in 1945. The business is now operated by his son, Walter.

Bowls	
3" diam. Iris motif. Signed .... $	40.00
5¾". Dark blue with red, blue, green flower and leaf	48.00
6". Covered, green, Amaryllis design	50.00
9" diam. Red, yellow blossoms on green ground. W.M. in script	65.00
Boxes	
3x5". Covered. Gladiolus, floral design. Script signed	55.00

3½x4½". Covered. Blue with large flowers	50.00
4x5". Floral decor. Signed	60.00
Candle Holders	
3½" high. 5" saucer bobeche atop 5" domed foot. 1" tube socket. Red, purple poppies, green leaves, cobalt ground. C. 1925. Impressed mark and signed W.M. Pair	125.00
5" high. Light blue ground, blue, yellow floral decor	50.00
Candlestick. 10" high, yellow, blue firs, dark blue ground, mustard leaves. Script signed, impressed "Moorcroft Burslem"	75.00
Chocolate Cups and Saucers. Green script signature, grapes and pomegranates. Set of four	175.00
Cup and Saucer. Mushroom pattern. Script signed	35.00
Dishes	
Candy. 1½x5½". Blue, fruit decor inside and out	50.00
Nut. 3½" diam. Pedestalled. Dark green, dark red flower in center	40.00
Inkwell. 3" square. Blue ground with reserves of flowers. Old mark	60.00
Jam Jar. Covered, silver rim. Burslem, hallmarked	75.00

Biscuit Jar. Pale blue base with cobalt top. McIntyre period [first period] $250.00

Lamp. 14" overall height, 6" wide. Scenic trees, red, yellows on olive, deep blue. Original finial 300.00
Pitcher. 16½" high, 6" diam. base. Green branches, pink almond blossoms, lustre glaze, green script signature 200.00

Vases

1¾" high, miniature. Flaring sides, 3 tiny handles. Blue violets against white. Signed W.M. with McIntyre mark 65.00
3" high. Blue ground with flowers . . 75.00
3¼" high. Signed in script and "Potter to the Queen" 85.00
4½" high. Bulbous shape, cobalt pomea. W.M. blue script 75.00
5" high. Ovid shape, peacock feather design. Blue, green, yellow. Signed W.M. and marked Florian Ware, McIntyre 80.00
5¾" high. Blue to green with pink, yellow, purple flowers. Script "Potter to the Queen" 100.00
6" high. Dark blue with pomegranates. Script signed 62.50
6¼" high. Multicolored. Irid. lustre, green script W.M. incised with Moorcroft and Royal mark . . . 90.00
7" high. Double gourd, white ground, blue cornflowers with green. Green script signature and McIntyre mark 175.00
7" high. tree pattern in muted colors of brown, red and green . . . 85.00
7½" high. Scenic of trees in front of hills, script signature 200.00
12" high. Decorated with blooming purple orchids against blue-green ground. Script signature . . . 275.00
12½" high. Pansies in purples, pale yellow with leaves on cobalt to tan ground. Impressed Moorcroft Burslem England and script signature in green underglaze . . . 275.00

MORIAGA CHINA

This china was made in Japan before the turn of the present century. It was reputedly made to imitate a certain issue of European enameled porcelain. The body of the various pieces is painted turquoise blue. Beige beading and scroll work encircle white medallions with floral decorations in the center.

Box, Trinket. Covered . . . . $ 40.00
Creamer and Covered Sugar 75.00

Basket. 4¼" diam. 4-footed, handled, mixed floral decor $60.00

Dish, Dresser. 3-5/8". Green, 4 pinched-in areas, 4 accent circles . 45.00
Mug. 5½" high. Scenic 95.00
Pitcher. 13½" high. Tankard 150.00
Plate. 7". Long-tailed bird 60.00
Tray, Pin. Scalloped, 8 petals 45.00

Vases

4½" high, 2¾" wide. 2 handles, 4 panels 45.00
5" high, 5¾" diam. Bulbous, side handles. Ovals of roses. Matt finish 50.00
8½" high. Green and white trim with flowered insert. Handles, pedestaled, fluted collar 100.00
10" high. Bulbous base with dragon 125.00
12" high. 3 handles. Light green, enameled 135.00
15" high. Two handles, with peacock and flowers 150.00

MOSER GLASS

A type of Art Nouveau art glass made in Europe in the early 1900's by Kolomon Moser at Carlsbad. The principal colors were amethyst and green. Much of it was intaglio cut; other items were enameled, while some pieces were both cut and enameled.

Atomizers

8" high. Panel cut amethyst. Gold band, cameo-cut warriors . . . . . . $ 75.00
11" high, 4" diam. Lacy gold enameled foliage and designs, original metal top fittings, rubber bulb. Circular mark "Moser Glasfabrik Karlsbad" 95.00

Bowls

4" high, 5¾" diam. Cranberry glass with heavy gold band. Signed 65.00

4x5". Footed, blue with mint enameled fish, crawfish and turtle. Signed 185.00

7" high, 7½" diam. Amber crackle glass ground, applied enamel. 2 large fish, gold lily pads, seaweeds underwater scene. Low pedestal base 350.00

14x6x5". Intaglio cut, clear to green, ½" thick cut flowers. Signed 400.00

Finger Bowls:

Bowl and underplate. Intaglio forest picture. Signed. Set 125.00

Bowl and underplate. Each piece signed. Wide gold band, enameling in blue, green, yellow, rose and purple. Clear glass. Set 150.00

Box. Covered. 4" diam., crystal. Rose and fern decor. Intaglio style, fully signed 55.00

Compote. 9" high, 5" diam., 4" base. Purple with gold band, Egyptian scene. Signed Moser Karlsbad.... 225.00

Cruet. Blue with blackberry enameling. Signed 250.00

Cups and Saucers

Amber. Enameled flowers. Signed   175.00

Cranberry. White floral enamel ..   95.00

Demitasse. Emerald to clear. Gold trim 125.00

Emerald with gold enameling 150.00

Decanters

7½" high. Green, stopper and bottle nod. Signed 175.00

9½" high. Yellow decor, bees. Signed 195.00

Dishes

2x4". Honey. Enameled green glass with heavy overlay in silver and gold. Gilded handle 75.00

2x6". Jam. Cranberry glass with gold enamel. Pink and blue forget-me-nots, sawtoothed edging on gold feet 135.00

Ewers

4" high. Miniature. Cranberry glass with heavy gold enameling and floral decor 55.00

12" high. Smoky topaz ground with enameled flowers and berries. Blue handle 125.00

Goblets

8" high. Intaglio cut. Signed 95.00

8½" high. Panel cut amethyst, gold band around edge. Signed... 135.00

Box. 7" diam. Turquoise blue, white floral enamel, gold trim. 3-footed, ring handles, metal base $150.00

Vase. 17" high. Ivory ground, applied gold and silver decor. Metal handles and 3-footed base $265.00

Perfume Bottle. 5" high, 3¼" long. Cranberry with enameled oak leaves, 6 applied lustered glass acorns. Original clear ball stopper. Unmarked 350.00

Pitcher. Large. Crystal, intaglio cut with gold bugs and entwined vine 500.00

Plate. 9". Intaglio cut, green to clear. Signed 225.00

Plaque. 7" square, on low rim base. Sapphire blue, covered with pink, blue, gold flowers and berries. Signed 225.00

Sherbet. 3¾" high, 4" wide. Clear base to lavender bowl. Wheel cut design leaves, buds, flowers. Matching plate. Signed. Set 160.00

Tumblers

3¾" high. Cranberry, enameled flowers, rim and base in gold. Signed 65.00

4" high. Plum color with gold foliage and flowers. Signed 85.00

4" high. Caramel, green and white opaque glass, enamel work forming swags and cartouches in silver and gold gilt. Raised jewel beading 100.00

4½" high. Cranberry glass, gold and yellow enamel, gold border around rim and foot 75.00

Vases

3" high. Cranberry glass on three gold gilted feet. Enamel decor 85.00

4½" high. Cranberry glass. gold and yellow enamel 95.00

6½" high. Cranberry glass on gilted feet, heavy white and gold enamel. Signed 100.00

6½" high. Cased glass, yellow at top, graduating to blue gray base, lavender enamel. Pair 325.00

8½" high. Cranberry glass, pilgrim-shape, colored enamels . . 250.00

11½" high. Topaz glass. African scene in gold, green enamel. Double signed 275.00

15"high. Jack-in-the-Pulpit. Signed 250.00

19" high. Jack-in-the-Pulpit. Amethyst heavy enameling 325.00

Water Set. 7 pieces. Cranberry. Pitcher 9" high including handle. Etched and engraved squirrels and plants. 6 glasses, each with different squirrel scene. Set 400.00

Wine Sets

Decanter. Blue glass with enameled flowers in shades of white and green. Tray and 5 glasses 430.00

Cranberry. Bottle, 6 cordials 345.00

Cranberry and Clear Panel. Gold enamel decorations. Decanter and 6 wines 450.00

MOSS ROSE PATTERN CHINA

The Moss Rose was a popular garden flower in English gardens. Around the 1840's potters adopted the flower's form to decorate their wares. The Moss Rose pattern was widely accepted and retained its popularity until the 1900's.

Pitcher. 6" high $40.00

Box. Covered, 6½", oval shape . . . . . $ 18.00

Coffee Pot. Porcelain, 9" high. E. C. & Co. Gold trim 65.00

Creamer 32.50

Cup and Saucer. Edwards 22.50

Dresser Set. 3 covered boxes, pair of candlesticks, tray. Rose border . . . 100.00

Pitcher. Ironstone. 7¼" high. J. M. Co. 50.00

Plates

Cake. Open handles 25.00

7½". Red rim. Ironstone 15.00

8½". Knowles, Taylor & Knowles [U.S.]. Ironstone 18.50

Salad 7.50

Platter. 12x18" 35.00

Sauce Dish. Old type 8.50

Shaving Mug 25.00

Sugar Bowl. Covered, blue edge 38.50

Syrup Jug. 8" high 39.50

Teapots

Tall, bulbous 65.00

8½" high 55.00

Toilet Chamber. Covered. Meakin . . . 35.00

MUFFINEERS

These are containers, usually glass or silver, used for sifting sugar or a mixture of sugar and cinnamon on muffins. They are about two to three times larger than the ordinary salt shaker. They enjoyed their greatest popularity in England before the turn of the present century.

China. Cobalt bands, floral decor ...$	28.50
China. Stoke-on-Trent. Decorated, sterling top	35.00
Glass. Blue, 5" high, ribbed sides, milk glass, crisscross pattern, original metal top	37.50
Glass. Cut. Clear, plated top	55.00
Glass. Cranberry, 5" high, panelled .	55.00
Glass. Green, 5" high, panelled. Sterling top	60.00
Milk Glass. Oak leaf	65.00
Sheffield Silver. 7" high	75.00

Cranberry. 5½" high. Ribbed .. $55.00

Silver on Brass. Vase-shaped, 3" top diam., 7" high. Marked with crown, embossed keys and lion ..	40.00
Silverplated......................	30.00
Spanish Lace. Cranberry, 6" high....	65.00
Sterling Silver. 6" high............	75.00

MUGS, GLASS

Glass mugs, from childrens' to he-man sizes, were produced in a variety of patterns in the past. They were as humble as pressed glass with molded handles to the most exquisite hand-blown variety which usually had an applied handle. Many blown glass mugs were further enchanced by cuttings, etchings or engravings. Colored glass as well as crystal glass mugs were produced. Today old glass mugs are being collected. Some collectors specialize or concentrate only on acquiring a collection of glass mugs.

Blown Glass, Applied Handles

Amber. Enameled decor. Small ...$	25.00
Blue. Bristol. Gold trim	30.00
Blue. Enameled decor	35.00
Blue. Geometric design. Small ...	28.50
Clear. Enameled decor	30.00
Green. Geneva-type. 2¾" high ..	100.00
Red. Bohemian. Etched design, "Hunter"	48.50
Red. Bohemian-type. Etched, "Remember Me"	30.00

Pressed Glass, Molded Handles

Amber. Enameled decor. Small ...	18.50

5¼" high. Strap handle, rough pontil. Threaded design on top and bottom
$65.00

Blue, Deep. Classic head in
medallion 25.00
Clear:
"By Jingo" 16.50
Cats Fighting 17.00
Dog on drum, cat on basket 29.50
"God Speed the Plough" 25.00
Heart with grapes. 2½" high 16.50
"Humpty-Dumpty" 25.00
Lambs around body 18.50
Rabbits around body 18.50
"Red Riding Hood" 25.00
Green. Gold trim. Small 22.50
Milk, Blue. Enameled floral decor . 28.50
Pressed Glass, Molded Handles
For specific patterns such as
Basketweave, Daisy and Button,
Etc., refer to Section I, "Clear
Glass Patterns," and Section Two,
"Colored Glass Patterns."

MULBERRY CHINA

The ware derives its name from the coloring of
the applied decoration or scene. Pieces
decorated in this color were made mainly in
the Staffordshire pottery center in England, C.
1830-1850. It is called mulberry because it
resembles the color of the juice from the
berries of the mulberry tree.

Bowl. 4x5-5/8". "Rose" ....$ 28.00
Butter Dish. Covered. "Vincennes" ..   65.00
Candy Dish. Brown. "Leipsic." J.
Clementson 28.50
Creamer. "Corean" 38.50
Cups and Saucers
Chocolate size. "Corean" 27.50
Handleless. "Corean" 35.00
Dishes
Nut. Brown. "Leipsic" 37.50

Platter. 10" $35.00

Vegetable. Covered, 10½" diam.
"Balmoral." Wins Adams 1855.
Double acorn finial 75.00
Vegetable. Covered. "Corean" ... 65.00
Vegetable. Deep. "Leipsic." J.
Clementson 60.00
Gravy Tureen. Covered, with ladle
and tray. "Corean." Set 55.00
Mug. 3¾" high. Transfer of archery
hunting scene 40.00
Pitcher. Large. Ironstone. Grecian
figure 60.00
Plates
7". "Corean" 20.00
7½". "Foliage" 18.50
8¾". Ironstone. "Corean" 30.00
8¾". "The Temple." Pearl
Stoneware 25.00
9". "Cypress." Davenport 35.00
10½". "Corean." Marked J.
Clementson 35.00
10½". "Unina" by J. Clementson . 30.00
Cup plate. Country scene 15.00
Cup plate. "Corean." Ironstone ... 22.00
Platters
10". Ironstone. "Corean" 35.00
11¼x15". "Vincennes" 45.00
Sauce dish. 5½" diam. "Corean" 15.00
Sugar Bowl. Covered. "Vincennes" .. 55.00
Toothbrush Holder. Covered. 8"
long, 2½" wide 28.50
Tureen. 4½", open, with underplate.
"Cypress." Marked Davenport. Set 75.00

MUSIC BOXES

Music boxes, as we refer to them today, were
invented in Switzerland around 1825. The
instrument contained cylinder teeth [pin
barrel] and a sounding board encased in a
wooden enclosure. Later instruments used
metal records; still later ones had paper rolls
resembling player piano rolls.

Artison Disc Organ ....$ 750.00
Artison Paper Disc Organ 600.00
Brass Bedplate. 13" cylinder, 8 tunes . 1250.00
Bremond. 6" cylinder 895.00
Bremond. 10¾" cylinder, 8 tunes ... 1500.00
Celesta. 8" 550.00
Columbia. 13" long, 7¼" wide, 5"
high. Six selections 450.00
Dawkins. 8" cylinder, 6 tunes 850.00
Dawkins. Interchangeable. Three
13" cylinders 1600.00
Ducommon Girod. 11" cylinder, 6
tunes 1000.00
Empress Concert Grand Disk. 18½" . 2000.00
Fortuna. 10" with 6 bells 975.00

Regina. Mahogany case. Double comb.
Mandolin attachment.......$1700.00

Close-up view of Regina music box lid

Guitarre Tremelo. 17½", two section comb	2000.00
Herophone Paper Disc Organ	600.00
Kalliope. 7" with bells	750.00
Kalliope. 8, single comb	500.00
Kalliope. 9", with bells	850.00
Kalliope. 10", single comb	850.00
Kalliope. 13", with bells	1200.00
Kalliope. 13½", single comb	950.00
Kalliope. 15" with bells	1450.00
Komet. 10", single comb	800.00
Lokarts. D/C Christmas Tree Stand ..	350.00

Mandolinata Metal Disc Organ	950.00
Mandoline Expressure. 13" cylinder, 8 tunes........................	1350.00
Mira Table Model. 15½"...........	1250.00
Monopol. 5" vertical	450.00
Monopol. 7½"	500.00
Nicole Fieres. 6 bells, 6 tunes	1500.00
Orphenion. 13½", two-part comb ...	1000.00
Palliard. 6" cylinder, 8 tunes	800.00
Palliard. 13" clylinder, interchangeable with cabinet	3000.00
Palliard. 13" cylinder, 12 tunes, bell box............................	1650.00
Polyphone. 9", single comb	750.00
Polyphone. 10", single comb	750.00
Polyphone. 11"	800.00
Polyphone. 15½", double comb	1600.00
Polyphone. 15½", single comb	1100.00
Polyphone. 25" upright with bells ...	4000.00
Regina. 8x10x12". Oak case. 8 discs	425.00
Regina. 11", ornate case...........	1200.00
Regina. 15½". Double comb disk. Coin operated. Oak.............	1750.00
Stella. 15½"	1500.00
Swiss Cabinet. 8 tunes.............	2500.00
Swiss. 5", 4 tunes	395.00
Swiss. 6" cylinder	395.00
Swiss. 6" cylinder, 8 tunes	450.00
Swiss. 7½" cylinder, 24 tunes	1250.00
Swiss. 8" cylinder	900.00
Swiss. 9" cylinder, 12 tunes	1000.00
Swiss. 11" cylinder, 6 tunes	850.00
Swiss. 11" cylinder, 10 tunes	1000.00
Swiss. 12¾" cylinder, 4 tunes	700.00
Swiss. 13" cylinder, 6 tunes	850.00
Swiss. 13" cylinder, 12 tunes	1000.00
Swiss. 14" cylinder, 8 tunes with hidden bells	1500.00
Swiss. 21½", hidden bells, drum	2750.00
Symphonion. 5" double comb.......	750.00
Symphonion. 7", single comb	600.00
Symphonion. 8", double comb	800.00
Symphonion. 8", single comb	650.00
Symphonion. 9" cylinder, with bells .	950.00
Symphonion. 10", double comb	1200.00
Symphonion. 13", with bells........	1500.00
Symphonion. 13½", double comb ...	1500.00
Symphonion. 15½", double	1650.00
Ullman, Charles. 12 tunes, 5 bells ...	1000.00
Vertical Paper Disc Organ	600.00
Victoria Commeratice Cab. 6" cylinder, 6 bells	950.00

MUSICAL INSTRUMENTS

Down through the ages people have stamped their feet, clapped their hands or were compelled to sit quietly while some form of music was being played.

Musical instruments have changed very little since the different forms were originated. Perhaps the case design, the material used or ornamentation has changed, but a flute will always be a flute.

Palace Pump Organ. "Loring and Blake Organ Co." $500.00

Accordions
Adolphus Special. 10 ivory keys on right, 4 on left ....$ 65.00
Early. Small size, pearl keys, stenciled. Good playing condition   75.00
Germany. Beaver Brand 85.00
Banjo. Marked "Vega" and "Vegaphone Professional." Complete with velvet lined case and Tenor Banjo Tuner No. 1742 ....   165.00
Dulcimer. 15x38". Rosewood 85.00
Glockenspiel. Similar to zylophone. 2 rows of steel bars supported by gut string on brass posts. Also, tubular brass harp on which 14 bars can be hung and struck while being carried. Produces bell-like sound........................   100.00
Harp. Miniature. 6½" high. Wood, carved shamrocks 75.00

Organs
32" high, 26" wide. Pump. Mason-Hamlin, top closes, in working order 400.00
Pump. "Adler." Dark oak, in working order 450.00

Violin. Primitive-type. 7x21" ...$25.00

Piano, Grand. New strings, pins, ivories, dampers. C. 1875........   1500.00
Piano, Steinway. Square grand. 100 years old, carved legs, ebony black 3000.00
Tuba. Brass. 30", Conn-Helleberg ...   100.00
Violins
Signed. "Lopf" burned into wood on interior. C. 1890 ....   125.00
With paper label inside. Name "Stradivarus, Cremona." A Sears, Roebuck importation in early 1890-1900 period. A cheap imitation of the old master.......   35.00
Zithers
Menzenhauers. Dated 1894......   75.00
U.S.A. No. 2, Patd. May 29, 1894..   65.00

MUSTACHE CUPS & SAUCERS

Mustache cups were popular in the late Victorian period [1880-1900]. The majority was made and decorated by the transfer method in Germany. The rarest items of this group are the "lefthanded" cups which were especially made for lefthanded men. Prices on these scarce cups range from $250.00 to double the amount quoted. At the present time lefthanded mustache cups are being reproduced so the collector should buy from a reputable dealer with a return guarantee arranged in advance.

Austrian. Turquoise, gold, pink roses $ 50.00
Bavarian. Lavender, magenta and orange floral design on white. Gold trim 38.50
Floral decor. Green, rococo shape. German porcelain 40.00
Floral decor. Lavender, asters, green rim 35.00

Pink with deep pink floral decor. Gold trim $350.00

Floral decor. Pink roses, blue
forget-me-nots 45.00
Floral decor. Pink roses on white ... 35.00
Floral decor. Purple leaves, gold
beading 40.00
Floral decor. Red roses, gold trim ... 40.00
Floral. Haviland 40.00
"Papa." Ornate decor. Gold lettering. 45.00
"Present." White with gold. Mis-
matched saucer 35.00
"John Sumner, 1883," inscribed in
white panel.................... 55.00
"Think of Me." Gold and red........ 40.00
"Think of Me." White, pink and gold.
Raised flowers 45.00

NAILSEA GLASS

Glass produced at Nailsea, England, between
1788 and 1883. A characteristic of the glass is
the loopings and swirlings of colored glass
combined with clear or opal glass. Common
color combinations are green and white, and
red and white.

Atomizer. 7" high. Clear glass with
white loopings .... $ 75.00
Basket. Art Glass. Pink, blue and
white, clear handle 185.00
Bell. English, white to clear loopings 100.00
Bottles
Bellows. 8¾" high. Clear with
white striations 185.00
Cologne. 6½", silver top 125.00
Gemel. 7½" high. White and
clear. Blue rim 110.00
Gemel. 10" high, clear glass with
pink and white loopings 145.00
Perfume
2½" high, 1½" wide. Gold and
orange loopings on blue........ 45.00
5¾" long. Pistol-type 20.00
6" long. Dagger-type........... 20.00
11¾" high. Clear glass with
loopings 95.00
Finger Bowl. 5½", scalloped edge,
light blue with white loopings 75.00
Flasks
6" long. Reclining. Opaque white
with blue, red green speckling ... 95.00
7" long, 3" wide. Reclining. White
loops and red stripes........... 75.00
Globe. For Gone with the Wind
Lamp. Rose with white loopings .. 265.00
Lamps, Fairy
5½" high, 8" diam. Blue, clear
lacy marked holder 240.00
5½" high, 8" diam. Opaque white
and frosted 240.00

Cranberry with loopings, clear
pressed glass shade holder and
candle cup marked "Samuel
Clarke, Fairy, Patented" 260.00
Pink. Double tiered. Clarke's base 250.00
Vaseline. Clark base satin with
white loopings 250.00
Paperweights
6½" high. Four flowers, Berg-
strom, #44..................... 150.00
Green with floral sprays......... 135.00
Pipes
10½" long. Curved stem, clear
with white loopings 45.00
15" long. Glass curved. English
cranberry and white. Rare 150.00
Pitchers
8" high. Blue and white with clear
applied handle 175.00
10" high. White loopings, applied
handle 195.00
Rolling Pin. 9" long 65.00
Rose Bowls
5½" high, 6" diam. Cranberry
satin glass, ruffled top, applied
Camphor satin ribbon edge 150.00
Citron background with white
loopings. Ruffled top 150.00

Cologne Bottle. 7" high. Cranberry
with sterling top. English $275.00

Gemel. 8½" high. Clear with white stripes. Early American $130.00

Green with maroon and white
  striping, crimped edge 135.00
Tumbler. Green with silver loops ... 50.00
Vases
  2½" high. Miniature, blown. Red
    on white 60.00
  7" high, 10" diam. Light green
    opalescent, ruffled top 135.00
  8½" high. Gold, yellow and white 165.00
  14½" high. "Bellows." Cranberry
    with white loops 195.00
Wine Jug. 9" high. White loopings on
  electric blue ground. Crystal
  handle and stopper 175.00
Witch Ball. See "Witch Balls"

NAKARA, See WAVECREST

NAPKIN RINGS

The period from 1875 to 1915 was one in which the catalogues of jewelers and silverplating companies featured numerous types and styles of napkin rings. Some were plain and inexpensive while others were ornate and rather expensive.

Alligator. Signed ....$ 110.00
Angel hiding from large butterfly ... 95.00
Barrel with branches and leaves on
  each side 30.00
Barrel-shaped ring sits in chair
  fashioned from tree limbs 145.00
Bird perched on the end of a leaf ... 100.00
Boy kneeling with bowl of eggs 50.00
Bulldog looking out of house 50.00
Butterflies on a fan support ring 65.00
Camel. Rogers Bros. Engraved
  "Olive" 70.00
Cherub reading a book 150.00
Chick on wishbone. Simpson Hall
  and Miller 35.00
Chick looks over ring 85.00
Child with ring on back 80.00
Cupid on sled 100.00
Dog chasing cat 100.00
Dog, harnesses pulling napkin ring,
  on moving wheels 200.00
Dog, chasing squirrel on top,
  engraved "Maude" on side 65.00
Eagle on each side with outstretched
  wings. Engraved "Jessie" on top .. 40.00
Eagles, double 55.00
Easel with book, footed.......... 50.00
Elephant, ivory carved in relief. 25.00
Fans holding ring. Butterfly on base . 65.00
Fans, oriental, on either side hold
  ring above ball footed square
  base......................... 125.00
Grecian clad boy holding ring 95.00

Figural. Eagle on each side. Meriden
$40.00

Horseshoe base, silver plate, embossed and engraved	25.00
Horseshoe is crown for ring on circular footed base. Engraved "bonheur" (good luck) Dated Oct. 21, 1881. James W. Tufts 1540 ...	85.00
Horseshoe leans against ring.......	45.00

Kate Greenaway

Boy smiling, hands behind large sailor hat. Ruffled collar	125.00
Boy. Cookie in hand for dog, Rogers & Smith Co. Old mark, rectangular base 3½". Ring 1½" wide, 3-3/8" high to boy's head ...	140.00
Girl. Hat, old-fashioned costume, hands on ring base	125.00
Girl holding gun	145.00
Girl feeding a yearling	75.00
Girl with hand on bulldog, 3" long, 2½" high	125.00
Knights with armor	75.00
Leaf base with strawberry on double ring	45.00
Mother bird on ring, looking down at 3 baby birds	100.00
Pansy on a delicate leaf	100.00
Ring and toothpick	65.00
School boy	75.00
Stag and ring on sculptured base, etched and place for engraving. 3½" diam., 2½" high	55.00
Soldier holding shield on base. Bailey and Brainard	65.00
Squirrel with nut. Simpson, Hall, Miller initials M.W.	55.00
Squirrel with big fluffy tail on footed base with ring attached	36.50
Swan floating on oval base........	110.00
Turtles, two with ring on backs	85.00

NASH GLASS

Nash glass was made in Corona, New York by Nash and his sons after 1919. Nash was formerly employed by the Tiffany Glass Co., in the United States and the Webb factory in England.

Candleholders

4½" high. Blue, highlighted with gold tint #b sgnd. Nash. Pair .....$	500.00
12" high. Signed. Pair	750.00
Plate. 6½". #115 "Chintz." Clear with spirals in orchid and chartreuse from center to edge ..	120.00

Stemware, "Chintz"

4" high	65.00
5¼" high	75.00
6½" high	85.00

Vase. 8¼" high. Fuchsia blend. Gold iridescent	$550.00
Vase. 6¼" high, 3¼" diam., at top. "Chintz." Trumpet-shaped, footed with blue stripes. Signed	250.00

NAZI ITEMS

In recent years a large number of collectors, interested in World War II items, are gathering various items of Hitler's lost cause.

Armband. Cloth, red, black swastika on white ground................$	10.00
Ammo Carrier. World War II........	18.50
Arm Band. Deutscher Volkssturm Wehrmacht with issue stamp.....	15.00
Badge. Nazi Crimea. Brass shield with zinc backs. 1941-1942	12.50
Banner. Wind. Triangle. 18" long. 1940. Red with black swastika ...	15.00
Bayonet. Nazi Police Eagle's head dress, with bone-type grips and police eagle in center. Complete with frogs, etc..................	85.00
Bayonet. Nazi etched blade with black plastic grips	65.00

Motorcyclist's Hat $45.00

Belt and Buckle. Wermacht.........	27.50
Cross. Mother's. Blue and white enamel with swastika center. Dated Dec. 16, 1938. Original matching blue and white ribbon saying: "Der Deuchen Mutter." Size 1½ x 1¾"..................	35.00
Daggers	
Navy Officer Dress with etched blade	95.00
Nazi Youth. World War II	55.00
Scabbard	75.00
Eagle. Staff Car. Alloy with fixing bolt...........................	25.00
Emblem. Swastika. 7¾" diam. Sewn onto a red banner	17.50
Flags	
2x3". Swastika and German Cross	75.00
2x3". Battle Kriegsflagger, for Navy motor launch, with halyards and markings	65.00
30x48"	95.00
Flare Gun. Nazi Paratroopers	30.00
Fork. Luftwaffe	7.00
Goggles. German Tankers, Amber lens, type used in Africa	8.50
Helmet. SS. Large issue type	75.00
Holsters	
German Lugar. Dated 1910	25.00
German Lugar. WW II	15.00
Knives	
Nazi Labour Corps. With motto blade, contractor's name and stag grips........................	120.00
Youth-type in sheath. Swastika on handle. "Blut und ehre" [blood and honor] on blade	55.00

Medals

German Cross. Swastika center, silverplated	25.00
Serpents death head, swastika ...	20.00
Plaque. Hitler. 1933 Officer's mess, with famous motto underneath...	85.00
Plate. Nazi. With German eagle and swastika emblem. Rosenthal China dated 1941	225.00
Stickpin. Red, white and black swastika	22.50
Transfers	
For Nazi helmets. SS, army, Luftwaffe, etc., 14 per sheet	10.00
Massive Luftwaffe staff car eagle with 2 matching smaller types. Set of three	15.00

NETSUKES

Netsukes are fasteners or buttons for clothing. Carved of ivory, jade or other materials, they are a domestic product of past generations in Japan.

Boy bending over fishbowl. 1½" .... $	50.00
Crab. Dark shading	45.00
Chicken in Egg. Ivory, hand carved ..	45.00
Devil Mask. 1¼". Wood	50.00
Double figure. 1¾"	60.00
Elephant. 1½", ivory, signed	50.00
Elephant. 2" high. With three men ..	60.00
Face. Oriental lady. Signed	75.00
Face, Revolving. 2", happy face, sad face	50.00
Foo dogs. Entwined, ivory. 1¾"	65.00
Frog. 2¼" high. Sitting on woman's head.........................	55.00
Frogs. Group. 1¾"	50.00
God of Wisdom. Bone	45.00
Hare. Riding on back of turtle. 2¼" high	45.00

Man with musical instrument. Ivory
$55.00
Man with fish. Ivory $55.00

Horse. Ebony	65.00
House Boat. 1½" high, 2¼" long	68.50
Kabuki Dancer. 2¼" high. Face revolves from comedy to tragedy. Ivory. Sugiyami 54	75.00
Man, Crouching. 1½"	50.00
Man sharpening saw. Signed	60.00
Man with bag over shoulder. Ivory . .	50.00
Man with basket. 1½" long	50.00
Man with can and dog. 1¾"	50.00
Man with fish. Ivory, 2" high	55.00
Man with monkey on his back	85.00
Man with woven basket. 1½" long . .	50.00
Monkey	48.50
Mouse "Baisho"	90.00
Owl	47.50
Pearl Diver	50.00
Popping Eye. Ivory. Hand carved	48.00
Potter and Wheel. 1½"	50.00
Reaper. 1½"	55.00
Skeleton. 2", seated, ivory	55.00
Skull. Ivory, gold snake on top. 1¾" high, 1-3/16" wide, 1½" deep. Signed	75.00
Snail. Wood. 1½"	45.00
Tiger. Ivory. Signed	50.00
Woman, Old. Apple vendor	45.00
Woman playing flute. 1¾"	50.00
Worriers [3] with cask. 2"	90.00

NEWCOMB POTTERY
[Newcomb College]

Newcomb pottery was first made in conjunction with the Art Department at Sophie Newcomb Memorial College for Women in New Orleans, Louisiana in 1896. Ellsworth and William Woodward were the founders. This art pottery is of good quality and highly collectible.

Bowls

2½" high, 5" diam. Black and high glaze decor which flows irregularly from rim over orange body . . . . $	120.00
3x5½". Morning glories painted in light yellow & blue. Sgnd.	200.00
4". Signed	150.00

Vases

4"high. Bulbous, 4½" diam. Sgnd.	125.00
5" high, 4½" diam. Rounded. Misty blue, massed flowers, blue, yellow and green	195.00
5½" high. Moon shining through the trees hung with Spanish Moss. Henrietta Bailey	235.00
5½" high. Oak trees and mountains in bkgd. Pink, blue and	

Vase. 6" high. Blue-green, incised with pine cone design $240.00

green. Signed. Original paper label	250.00
6" high. Scenic, moon shining through oak trees. Shades of blue and green. Signed. J. Meyer & S. Irving	240.00
6¼" high. Forest green, ribbed with cream colored flowers. 3½" diam., 2¼" lip. Signed, AFS-EQ85	250.00
6¼" high. Scenic of moon shining through trees covered with Spanish Moss. Artist Henrietta Bailey	250.00
8½" high. Pink, cream and blue stylized tulip decor. Artist signed .	265.00

NEWHALL CHINA

Made at the Newhall Factory, Shelton, Staffordshire, England, it is reputed to be the first true English china. Until 1810 it was hard-paste china with a "composition" glaze. The factory later produced bone china. It closed in 1825 and reopened in 1826. In 1842 it moved to Joiner Square under another name.

Creamer. Pink lustre decor . . . . $	75.00

Cups and Saucers

Blossom band decor	50.00
Family scene in pink, blue, green and brown	65.00
Flower decor in green, red, yellow	60.00
Oriental figures, flowers	60.00
Pat. 195. Early	70.00

Creamer. 5½" high..........$75.00

Mug. Small. Oriental decor........ 45.00
Plates
    7¼". Rose decor 60.00
    8". Deep with center bouquet and
    single floral motifs at intervals
    around border. C. 1790. Marked.. 125.00
Platter. 16½ x 21". Two scenes - one
    with sailboat, other with stream
    and trees 135.00
Sugar Bowl. Pink lustre decor 100.00
Tea Bowl and Saucer. Pat. 195. Set .. 45.00
Tea Pots
    Chinese pattern 150.00
    Flower spray.................. 150.00
    Pink lustre decor 165.00

NILOAK POTTERY

The pottery was located in Benton, Arkansas.
It began operations before 1920 and finally
ceased manufacturing with the end of World
War II in the middle 1940s. One of the main
characteristics of Niloak is the marblized
finish.

Bowls
    4½" diam. Marblized ....$ 14.50

Vase. 7" high. 5 holes, mauve .. $35.00

5½" diam., 6" high. Rose. Ovid
    shape with blue, beige, wine red
    and brown..................... 24.00
Creamer. Small, brown 12.00
Cup & Saucer. Square, yellow. Sgnd.. 20.00
Ewer. 10", blue matt glaze.
    Embossed eagle & star 22.00
Lamp Base. Signed, paper label 40.00
Pitcher. 5½ x 5¼". Maroon 17.50
Planters
    Dutch Shoe 9.50
    Elephant on Drum, 6". Blue 10.00
    Swan. Blue 12.00
Vases
    4" high. Basket-shape, white,
    edged in green. Signed 18.50
    4½" high. Signed 25.00
    4½" high. Swirled turquoise,
    brown cream. Signed 28.50
    5½" high. Marblized. Signed 32.50
    8" high, 5" wide. Marblized blue,
    brown, beige. Signed 40.00

NIPPON CHINA

Much of the Nippon porcelain seen today was
manufactured by the Noritake Company, Ltd.
in Nagoya, Japan.

In 1891, when congress passed that all imported articles must be marked as to country of origin, Japan chose to use their own name for Japan, "Nippon."

In 1921, it was decided "Nippon" was no longer acceptable and all Japanese wares must be marked with the English word Japan, thus the end of the "Nippon" period.

There is quite a controversy over the many marks used on Nippon wares. (over 50, some identical except colored differently). The most agreeable explanation and perhaps the most logical is that the different marks indicate the quality of the porcelain and the decorative workmanship. Other marks may identify the importer, artist or maker. Serious collectors of Nippon should familiarize themselves with these marks.

All Japanese porcelains are not Nippon and all Nippon is not fine Japanese porcelain.

Ash Tray. 5" sq., jeweled, ship decor $	45.00
Basket. 4x7½". Boat-shaped. 6¼" to top of handle. Handpainted	50.00

Bowls

7¼" diam. Blue with turned in ruffled top. 2 swans in lake in center of bowl	85.00
7½" diam. Basketweave with blownout peanuts	75.00
Chocolate Set. Handpainted, pot 9½" to top of lid. 4 chocolate cups, saucers, 2" gold decor around top with small pink roses. Set........	75.00
Chocolate & Tea Set. 29-pcs. All over pink cherry blossom with green wreath mark. Set	350.00
Cigarette Box. Covered. Bisque finish, enameled horse head, riding crop, horseshoe	45.00
Cracker Jar. Covered. Mat finish with floral gold	65.00

Covered Dish. 5½" diam. Handpainted pink roses, gold trim on white. Gold handles $40.00

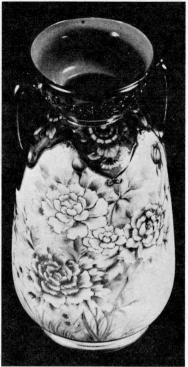

Vase. 10" high. Pale green with multicolored flowers. Gold handles and trim $85.00

Mug. 5½" long. Marked, 4 moriye, scenic.........................	95.00
Peanut Set. Bowl 8¼" long. Decor of peanuts and vines. Shell-like exterior, small peanut feet, 5 matching individual bowls. Set ...	65.00
Pitcher. 9½" high. C. 1870. Bulbous base, landscape scene, middle area creamy, sky with thunder-clouds. Superimposed sparrow in flight thru blossoms, enameling, brown line around upper rim, white inside	65.00
Planter. 7¼" sq. Footed. Jeweled around top. Ship decor on all 4 sides. Nippon in green wreath ...	95.00
Plate. 10". Red roses. Narrow green border beaded gold loops	15.00

Tray. 9½" sq., 2 handles, yellow
ground with flowers & parrot on
tree limb. Nippon in green wreath   55.00
Vases
7" high. Bulbous, decorated 75.00
8½" high. 2-handled. Dull green &
stippled gold ground with flowers
and leaves 30.00
10" high. Deep blue, handpainted.
Green mark M 1880-1910 ....   65.00
10¾" high. Yellow iris, long gold
side handles and bands 50.00
11½'" high, 2-handled. Flowers
and leaves in pastels, edges and
veining traced in gold 65.00

NODDERS

Nodders are porcelain figures with heads and
arms attached to the bodies with wires. The
slightest movements makes them "come to
life." Most of them were made in the 19th
century and are being collected today.

Clown. Boy, 7" high, Staffordshire...$ 75.00
Clown. Girl, 7" high, Staffordshire ..   75.00
Lady. Old, sleeping in chair 39.50
Lady. 5½" high, blue cape over pink
dress 65.00
Lady. Professor, holding book and
quill pen 68.50
Woman. 6½" high, blue and white
clothing, holding umbrella.
Staffordshire 75.00

NORITAKE CHINA

The ware is of Japanese origin and is
considered "late" when compared to most
European china. The bulk of the ware was
imported sometime after 1900.
The best known pattern is "Azalea" and it
received wide distribution in the eastern part
of the United States when the Larkin Tea and
Coffee Company gave it as premiums. Dinner
sets of finer china were also made and
exported to this country.

Creamer and Sugar. Azalea pattern
$37.50

Plate. 7¼". Child's birthday scene
$10.00

AZALEA PATTERN

Basket. 4½" long, 2½" wide ....$ 75.00
Bowls
9½" diam. 22.50
10½", oval 25.00
11½" diam. 27.50
Child's Set. 15 pieces 285.00
Coffee Pot. Demitasse. Rare 325.00
Compote. 2¼" high, 6½" diam. 40.00
Creamer 12.50
Dishes
Bonbon. 6¼". Handled 25.00
Celery. 12½" 30.00
Relish. 2 sections 25.00
Shell. 7¾" long. Rare 165.00
Egg Cup 25.00
Gravy Boat. Attached tray 28.50
Jam Jar. 3 pieces. Set 65.00
Pancake Set. Sugar shaker, pitcher..   68.50
Pitcher, Milk. 1-qt. size 100.00
Plates
6½" 5.00
7½" 7.00
8½" 10.00
9¾" 13.50
Platters
12" 27.50
14" 35.00
16". Rare 275.00
Salt and Pepper Shakers. 3" high. Pr.   18.50
Sugar, Covered, and Creamer. Set ..   25.00
Sugar, Open and Creamer. Small
size. Rare 75.00
Teapot. Regular finial. 4½" high 50.00
Tile 25.00
Toothpick Holder. Rare 75.00

MISCELLANEOUS

Bowls

3x7". Nuts in relief	25.00
6" diam. "Tree at Lake"	18.00
7¾" diam. 2 handles. Yellow, floral decor	18.50
8½" diam. Handled. Blue rim, orange and white flowers	20.00

Butter Dish. Covered, 7¼" diam., with insert. Yellow on white. "Rengold" **29.50**

Candy Dish. Ring handle. Orange flowers **7.50**

Celery. Red with blue, gold trim **12.50**

Chocolate Set. 13 pieces **60.00**

Creamer. "Sahara" **12.00**

Dinner Sets

"Hanover." 64 pieces	250.00
Unidentified pattern. 12 place settings, including serving pieces .	450.00

Plate. 6". "Tree at Lake" **18.00**

Sugar. "Sahara" **15.00**

Sugar and Creamer. "Aldive" **32.50**

Tobacco Jar. Owl motif, red, black . . . **30.00**

Trays

6¼x14¼". "Tree at Lake"	15.00
8x12". Crimson and gold bands on white	15.00

NUT CRACKERS

Since primitive man first cracked nuts with his teeth or with stones, inventors have been devising ways to make the task simpler and easier. Examples listed below are the fruits of some of their ingenuity.

Alligator. Brass, 7½" long. Late . . . . $	17.50
Alligator. Brass. 14" long	50.00
Bear's Head. Wood, glass eyes. 7" long. C. 1850	45.00
Bear's Head. Wood, 9" long, 4½" high	50.00

Dog. 11" long. Brass, wooden base
$45.00

Bowl. Turned, 9¾" diam. Squirrel nut cracker attached **30.00**

Chicken Head. Brass. Late **25.00**

*Dog. Iron. 10½" long, 5½" high. Name "Renz" on top of base **25.00**

Dog on base. Brass **45.00**

Dragon. Brass **45.00**

Parrot. Brass. 5½" long **40.00**

Rooster. Brass, 2 handles **35.00**

Rooster. Bronze **75.00**

*Squirrel. Iron **29.50**

Wolf's Head. Iron. "Pat. June, 1920." 4½" high **32.50**

*Reproduced Item

OCCUPIED JAPAN CHINA

Items marked "Occupied Japan" were made after the surrender of Japan in World War II and during the occupation by the Allied Forces.

Ash Tray. 2 black boys throwing dice. "Come Seven" . . . . $ **8.50**

Box. 4½x5½". Green ground, gold leaves, brown birds **12.00**

Candy Dish. Petaled leaf, curled edges, raised flowers. Marked Chuby China, O.J. **12.00**

Chocolate Set. Victorian style floral. Pot, 6 cups and saucers. Set **35.00**

Cigarette Lighter **6.50**

Planter-type Figurine. 5x7". Man pulling cart. Painted in bright colors
$8.00

Cups and Saucers

Demitasse:
Cobalt and white	10.00
Handpainted	7.50
Raised figures, gold handle	5.00
Tulip decor. Regular size	6.50

Dolls
Bisque Ballerina. Tall, glazed	7.50
Celluloid	4.50

Figurines
Elephant. 5" carved base. Ivory	7.50
Gents. 5½" high, 18th century. Pr.	12.50
Man and woman. 8" high. Pair . . .	15.00
Football Player. Boy, movable limbs	4.50
Victorian Lady	8.50
Humidor. Covered, rust color with mums. Foo Dog finial	25.00
Lamp Base. 8½" high. Male mandolin player in multicolored dress, gold trim	20.00
Mugs. Toby-type. 4" high	8.50
Planter. 3" high, 2½" wide. Goose in front	6.50

Plates
7". Blue Willow, with gold	6.00
9¼". White ground, blue, floral decor with red, blossoms in center	8.50
Cake. Square shape, decorated with large flower in center	7.50
Salt and Pepper Shakers. With mustard jar. Floral, woman's head as cover. Set	15.00
Spoon Rest. Blue-green seascape . . .	3.50
Sugar and Creamer. "Orchard." Fuji China	17.50

Tea Sets

Cottage shapes. Teapot, creamer, sugar, mustard with spoon, salt,
pepper, tray. Marked. Set	45.00
Gray with raised gold and green design. Teapot, sugar, 6 cups and saucers. Set	35.00
Tile. 4" square. Rose decor	6.50
Toothpick Holder. Burro	7.50
Vases. Bud-type. White porcelain painted with roses. Pair	15.00

OLD IVORY CHINA

This china derives its name from the ground color of the ware. The difference in patterns is indicated by a number on the base. It was made in Silesia, Germany in the latter part of the 1800's. Marked pieces usually bear the Crown Silesia mark,

Berry Set. #7. 9½" bowl, six sauces . **$**	**75.00**
Bowls	
6½" diam. #16. Signed Silesian . .	30.00
7" diam. #21	35.00
9¼" diam. #200	45.00
9½" diam. #28, #73, #84. Each . . .	45.00
Butter Dish. Covered. #16	95.00
Cake Plate. 11" diam., open handles.	
#10, #15, #16, #28, #78, #84. Each	65.00
Celery Dish. #7, #10, #11, #16, #84.	
Each	37.50
Chocolate Pot. #15	150.00
Chocolate Set. Pot, 6 cups, saucers . .	275.00
Coffee Pot. #84	175.00
Creamer. #15, #84. Each	50.00
Cup and Saucer. #15, #16, #84,	
#121, #200. Each	35.00

Cigarette Lighter. 3¼" high. Tray, 4¾" diam. Handpainted, cobalt and white ground, red and gold $15.00

Plate. 8½". #75 . . . . $45.00

Hair Receiver. Thistle pattern, ivory,
    pink and lavender flowers 40.00
Pickle Dish. Oval. #75 . . . .   25.00
Plates
    6". #5 . . . .   22.50
    6¼". #16 . . . .   22.50
    6½". #118 . . . .   25.00
    7½". #7, #16, #22. Each 32.50
    8½". #75, #125, #202. Each 45.00
    12". #78 . . . .   60.00
    13". #32 . . . .   60.00
Platter. 11½" long, 8¼" wide.
    Painted rose decor, gold trim. #78   65.00
Salt and Pepper Shakers. #16. Pair . .   95.00
Sauce Dish. 5". #84 . . . .   18.00
Sugar Bowl. Covered. #84, #200,
    #202. Each 60.00
Sugar Bowl and Creamer. #16, #84.
    Each set 125.00
Tea Tile. Round, 6½". #55 . . . .   22.50
Teapots
    Pot only. #16 . . . .   150.00
    Pot with 6 cups. #200. Set 275.00
Toothpick. #16 . . . .   60.00

OLD PARIS CHINA

A number of French pottery and porcelain
factories were situated in Paris during the
18th and 19th centuries. The finer porcelain
products bore the generic name of Old Paris.
The difference in the ware can be
distinguished by the marks appearing under
the glaze.

Box. With matching tray. 5x6".
    Handpainted flowers on entire top
    of lid. Set . . . .$ 65.00
Cake Plate. White and gold trim 42.00
Cups and Saucers
    Hot chocolate. Scenic design on
    both pieces. Gold inside cup 65.00

Vases. 12" high. Urn-type. Scenic
decor on red, gold trim. Pair . .$400.00

Cream Jug. 7½" high. White with gold
    trim. Late $27.50

Plates
    7". Floral decor in center,
    scalloped border wth gilt scrolls.
    C. 1820 . . . .   37.50
    10". Painted fruit decor in center.
    C. 1840 . . . .   55.00

Teapot. White with gold trim 75.00
Tea Service. Miniature. Teapot,
    covered sugar bowl, cup and two
    plates. Set 125.00

Figurines
    3½" high. Boy and girl with boats,
    pastel colors, oval bases. Pair 295.00

    6x6". Animals, embracing Oran-
    gutans, one gray, one white. Porce-
    lainedeParis.sgd.E.Sandoz.C.1910   125.00

Mug. Red background 50.00
Pitcher, Water. White with gold trim .   75.00
Plaque. 12½" diam. Birds on hut,
    foliage, gilt border 135.00

Maroon and gold border, colorful flowers	50.00
Tall, decorated with pink rose garland, green leaves, gold stems. Tall gilt handle and wide gilt border	60.00
White with gold trim	35.00
Dessert Set. White. 2 cake plates, eight 7" plates. Set	195.00
Dinner Set. 63 pieces. "Wedding Ring"	750.00

Tea Sets

3 pieces. Teapot, covered sugar bowl and creamer. Pink with blue forget-me-nots, gilt handles. C. 1840	195.00
5 pieces. Miniature. Cream, blue, forget-me-nots, burgundy, gold trim	250.00
Tureen. No. 128800. Brown decor, water scenes	125.00
Urns. 24" high. Painted flower decor, gold trim. Pair	750.00

Vases

12" high. Handled, gold trim. Painted scene on bowls. Pair	500.00
12½" high. Robed maiden filling urn from fountain	195.00
13" high. Blue with rose decor. C. 1855	250.00
24" high. Handpainted flowers, gold trim. C. 1840. Pair	795.00
24" high. Horse and Italian scenery, gold trim. C. 1840	300.00

OLD SLEEPY EYE

In the early 1900's, Sleepy Eye, Minnesota was the milling center of the world for production of flour in barrels. The town was named for Chief Sleepy Eye, a Sioux indian.

Along with their many fine products, the Sleepy Eye Milling Company offered premiums which are now considered collectible.

In 1972, Sleepy Eye celebrated its centennial with a gala, nine-day festival. Many items were produced to mark the occasion, such as plates, medals, spoons, etc. They are also considered collectible for those interested in Sleepy Eye.

| Bowl, Salt. 4" high, 6½" diam. Grey stoneware with blue. Embossed indian head with war bonnet. Vine-like decor on reverse side. Marked "Old Sleepy Eye." Impressed "E" on bottom | $ 100.00 |

Centennial Items

| Calendar | 3.00 |

Vase. 8½" high $95.00

Coin. Official centennial issue	4.50
Newspaper. Sleepy Eye Herald Dispatch. 114 pages	5.00
Trivet. 1872-1972	6.50
Creamer	65.00

Pitchers

7" high. Cobalt and cream. Indian head on handle. Marked Monmouth	85.00
8" high. Cobalt and white	95.00
11" high	135.00
Stein. 7½" high. Indian head on handle. Signed "Old Sleepy Eye"	100.00

Vases

| 8" high | 85.00 |
| 8½" high. Indian head, rushes, dragonfly, frog | 95.00 |

ONYX GLASS [SILVER INLAY]

Onyx glass was made in the 1890's by the Findlay Glass Co., Findlay, Ohio. It is a multi-layer of white ivory color with floral designs covered with real silver which has the appearance of being imbedded in the body of the item. When held to the light, a fiery opalescence appears. The glass was made for only a short time because of the high cost of production and slack demand.

Bowl .... $	365.00
Butter Dish. Covered	450.00
Celery Vase. 6½" high	350.00
Condiment Set. Cruet, original stopper. Salt and pepper shakers in matching tray. Set	795.00
Creamer	400.00
Pitchers	
Milk	500.00
Water.......................	750.00
Salt and Pepper Shakers. 3" high. Pair	275.00
Spooner. 4½" high, fluted rim	375.00
Sugar Bowl. Covered	475.00
Sugar Shaker	295.00
Syrup Jug. 7" to top of lid	375.00
Toothpick Holder	175.00

Celery. 6½" high............$350.00

OPALINE GLASS

Tumblers

Barrel shape	300.00
Regular	250.00

This glass derives its name from the opal - a gem with a milky iridescence. When held to the light it exhibits a play of colors like the opal. It should not, however, be confused with milk glass.

Basket. Small, with deep blue and gold trim .... $	125.00
Bottles	
Perfume. 5" high, jade green, enamel decor	85.00
Perfume. 5½" high, gold trim around neck. Pair	150.00
Bowls	
6" diam. Low	80.00
Finger. Light blue..............	50.00
Box, Trinket. 2" diam, raised enamel flowers	47.50
Cheese Dish. White with enamel....	175.00
Cruet. Applied handle, soft aqua trim	85.00
Cup and Saucer. Jade green color ...	69.50
Hen on Basket. 7". English	55.00
Jar. Covered. Red, gold leaf trim	55.00
Lamp. French origin. 12½" high	80.00
Mug. 4" high. Handled, decorated...	60.00
Pitcher. 7" high. French. Ground pontil. Soft pink ground. Signed by "Anne"	200.00
Toothpick Holder. Lavender color, on small ball feet	50.00
Vases	
5½" high. Globular body, slender neck, pink, yellow flowers, green leaves	95.00
6" high. Plain, no decor..........	85.00
6¾" high. French. Mauve with gold trim. Pair	150.00
10" high. Bud vase. Pink with gold enamel decor	100.00

Bowl. Flat, 1½ x 10". Pink $65.00

11" high. White with pale green,
turned-down rim 125.00
11½" high. Gold decor. C. 1840.
Pair 200.00
12" high. Mint green. Pair 220.00
16" high. Quilted. Blue 165.00

ORIENTAL ITEMS

The term "oriental" applies to articles which originated in or were manufactured in China and/or Japan.

Bowls
   3½x8" diam. Peking glass. Yellow
   with high relief carving allover ... $ 295.00
   *Rice. Blue, set of 6 with
   different design on each 42.50
Boxes
   Cigarette. With match holder.
   Brass and Soapstone 39.50
   Cosmetic. 3" diam. Black and
   green enamel with dragon on
   cover. Late 18th century 85.00
   Gold-lacquered. 8x17x17". Chin-
   ese scene on lid. C. 1850 .... 145.00
Burner. Open, 5½", soapstone
   burner 45.00
Cake Mold. 13½" long, 2" wide,
   1½" deep. Wooden, for rice 78.50
Candlesticks. Cobra bronze. Pair.... 175.00
Carving. Jade, in shape of lock 95.00
Chest. 20½x21½x39". Black lacquered, brass bands, handles,
   shell figures 600.00
Chocolate Pot. With 2 cups, saucers.
   Phoenix Bird. Set 55.00
Chopsticks. Ivory, carved decor, in
   turquoise holder 45.00
Compass. Set in black lacquered
   holder, 2" square 47.50
Desk Set. Brass. Hand-decorated
   tray, letter opener, blotter cover.
   3½" lined wooden box, hinged ... 65.00
Figurines
   6½" high. Lady, carved in
   amethyst quartz. Flowing draped
   robe, holding pot of flowers.
   Attached to footed teakwood stand 650.00
   6½x6½". Foo Dog. Porcelain.
   Aborigine, green tail and mane .. 250.00
   8½". Goose. Porcelain. Wings
   spread, peacock blue glaze 75.00
   12½". Lady and priest. Chalkware, handpainted costumes,
   each standing on platform in front
   of tall, curved bamboo fence. Pair 250.00
Incense Burners
   Brass. 9½". On 4 legs, animal
   decorations 150.00

Plate. 8¼". Goldfish decor $30.00

Bronze:
   1¾x2½". Green Foo Dog finial . 35.00
   4x4". Handled, footed 40.00
   5x5". With Foo Dog 50.00
   Pottery. Camel 25.00
Jars
   4½" high. Horses 65.00
   5" high. White porcelain. Handpainted ladies, gentlemen, horse,
   coolie, 4 Chinese characters on
   bottom 85.00
   9" high. Yellow ground with
   insects and flowers in reds and
   blues 150.00
   13" high. Chinese Hawthorne 300.00
Mug. 6" high. Four panels, paintings
   and birds perched on trees. Four
   figures in garden of the Elders
   teaching young boy lessons. Early 300.00
Pillow. 8x14". Porcelain. Shape of
   reclining cat. Ivorine with lustre
   spots 165.00
Plate. "Broken Bamboo." Small,
   handpainted blue on white 50.00
Platter. Chinese Export period. Oval
   with scalloped rim, blue and
   white. Deer and pine tree in
   center. 18th century 300.00
Pot. With handle and lid. 6x10".
   Eight different scenes, people at
   work, birds among trees. Blues,
   greens, yellow. Chinese Export ... 395.00
Printing Set. Hand carved Chinese
   characters. Over 100 pieces 150.00
Purse. 5¼" wide, 3½" deep.
   Leather. Tooled dragon in color,
   brass dragon catch, ivory netsuke
   button, brass dragon in center ... 200.00

Bowl. 9¼" diam. White ground, painted figures and scenes. Chinese Export $300.00

Rabbit. Bronze. 4¼" long. Signed ... 195.00
Saucer. Ming. 6" diam. Lotus blossoms, foliage. On bottom, calligraph "YA" 65.00
Sword. Samaurai. In metal scabbard. Detailed work in copper and brass on Tsuba and other mounts 220.00
Tea Caddy. Chinese porcelain. Pink floral on green. 8½" high. C. 1830 95.00
Teapots
  2¼". Chinese porcelain 50.00
  4". Chinese porcelain 65.00
  8". Yi-Hsing. Brown unglazed stoneware in form of Buddha's hand citron. C. 1800 .... 200.00
  Pewter overlay stoneware. Dragon design. Chinese corn on lid.
  Late 35.00
  Terra Cotta 37.50
Urn. Chinese. Bronze, 11" high. Flowers, tree branch design. Signed 300.00
Vases
  4¼" high. Japanese bronze. Elephant head handles, dolphin, mountains, foliage 150.00
  6½" high. Chinese. Pair 12.50
  7½" high. Pottery. Tz'uchow-type. Brown glaze of leaves 150.00
  8" high. Cinnabar-type. Red, overall carving. Marked "China".. 185.00
Also See "Jade"

*Reproduced Item

ORIENTAL RUGS, See RUGS

OWENS POTTERY

The J. B. Owens Pottery Company operated in Zanesville, Ohio from 1885 into 1892. Their products bear the marks "Owens Utopian," "Henri/Deux" and "Owens Feroza."

Vase. 11" high. Floral decor. High glaze.......................$95.00

Mug. 5" high. Utopia. Red cherries on vine with green foliage ....$ 95.00
Pitchers
  5" high. Lefthanded. Yellow florals on standard brown glaze .. 65.00
  6" high. Bulbous footed body forms handle. High glaze, floral decor 75.00
  12" high. High gloss, shaded brown, green. Long side handle, yellow berry decor 95.00
Urn. Utopian. 3½" high, 6" wide. Mat glaze, clover decor. Signed .. 65.00
Vases
  4" high. Lotus line, green shamrocks on shaded pale green to pink background. High glaze ... 68.50

4½" high. Utopian teapot shape.
Brown and greens, high gloss 85.00
5" high. Bulbous. Matte green.
Free-form design 60.00
7" high. Brown glaze, floral 68.50
10" high. Pansy decor. Matched
pair 145.00
11½" high. Glazed rose decor ... 75.00
Water Set. Tankard pitcher, six
tumblers 395.00

PAIRPOINT GLASS

The Pairpoint Company was primarily a silverplating concern but for a number of years offered specialty glass items, as well as sterling silverplated designs on glass objects. The firm was located in New Bedford, Massachusetts and began operations around 1880.

Bell, Table. 5" high, cut crystal .....$ 35.00
Biscuit Barrel. Moss Rose decor 150.00
Bowls
  Finger. Overlay, clear to amethyst 60.00
  Sweetmeat. Bryden Burmese.
  Signed 55.00
Box. Round 6½" diam., 4" high.
Hinged cover, decor of blue and
purple violets with green leaves.
White lusterless ground. Signed
P.M.C. in diamond 225.00
Butter Dish. Covered. With knife
rest. Silverplated. Set 65.00
Candlestick. Clear, paperweight
base......................... 60.00
Champagne. 5½". "Flambo" 50.00
Compotes
  6x6" high. Cut leaf and floral
  decor on underside 55.00
  7" high. Amber, bubble ball in
  stem 55.00
  8" diam. Cut tulip design, ball
  stem 90.00
Console Set. Bowl, 9½" diam.
Lamps, 16¾" high, with coralene
shades. C. 1900-20. Sgnd. 350.00
Cracker Jar. Signature on glass.
Pansies with gold scrolls, puffy
base. Metal bail and lid 365.00
Creamer and Sugar. Silvered pattern
on green with white tops. Gothic
shape. Set 40.00
Figurine. Peachblow hat with
enameled sprig of flowers 45.00
Inkwell. Paperweight type 60.00
Ladles
  14". Hobstar handle 300.00
  16". Hobstar handle. Teardrop ... 325.00

Vase. 13½" high, pedestal base.
Copperwheel. Decor of leaves and
flowers $175.00

Lamps
  14" diam. Shade shows clipper
  ships, waves, sea gulls, sea
  horses. Signed 1000.00
  21" high. Table. Art Nouveau
  base. Iris decor on globe 800.00
  Rose, blownout, puffy. Signed.
  Small shade, red roses on green
  background. Unsigned base 450.00
Napkin Ring. Figural and leaves,
domed base 27.50
Paperweights
  3" diam. Bubbles, alternating red
  and blue swirls 65.00

3" diam., 3½" high. Glass dome
shape. Blue center, bubble design.
Paper label on base............. 60.00
3" diam., 3¾" high. Clear, tall
dome shape, large suspended
teardrop, pin center surrounded
by rows of tiny bubbles 50.00
3½" high. Egg-shaped. Clear 55.00
Red and blue swirls within a clear
bubbled ground. Original label ... 65.00
Pitchers
3" high. Burmese 55.00
Water. Signed.................. 65.00
Plate. 10". Silver, embossed, grapes
& leaves, footed. Signed W.M.
Mounts 95.00
Salt Shakers. Molded green line
outlining panels of pastel flowers.
3¼" high. Pair 100.00
Shaving Mug. Quad silverplate.
Heavy floral, gold lines. Lift-out
soap rest 40.00
Sherbet. 4" high. Flambo with
underplate. Set 60.00
Swan. Opalescent and pink. Paper
label......................... 125.00
Vases
3½" high. Delft Mini. Melon-ribbed. White glossy ground, windmill scene on one side, sailboat on
reverse. Signed 155.00
10". Trumpet-shape. Deep blue,
bubble base 95.00
Wine. Red bowl, black glass base ... 65.00

PAISLEY SHAWLS,See LINENS

PAPERWEIGHTS

The term "paperweight" in the antique trade
usually refers to a small object of glass used
on a desk or table for holding papers in place.
Glass paperweights are often highly decorative in that they contain colored flowers,
canes, thread twists and/or air bubbles.

Advertising
"Brown Wright & Co., N.Y." Flat
bottom. Amber-red glass. 3"
diam., color on bottom, balance in
clear glass.....................$ 28.50
"National Lead Co." Dutch boy.
Brush in hand, bucket beside him.
Weighs nearly 2 pounds 30.00
"New England Glass Co." Scrambled, many diverse canes 135.00
"Prudential Insurance Co." Solid
bronze, Fiftieth Anniversary,
1875-1925.................... 65.00

Advertising-type. "Chatauqua Lake Ice
Co." Pittsburgh, Pa. Pure Ice Distilled
Water $32.00

"Plume & Atwood Mfg. Co." 24.50
Anvil-shape. Small, brass 15.00
Baccarat
"Cog" design of wheels in dark
blue, rose red, white and green,
set on lace bkgd. 3¾" diam. 2500.00
Geometric setup of jewel-like
canes of white, blue, rose, set in
wheels 2250.00
Multicane close-set design. Ani-
mal silhouettes in some canes,
also date B1848 indicating year of
manufacture. Nearly 100 canes
form the design. 3½" diam. 2500.00
Baccarat - Modern
Eisenhower. 1952, sulphide 250.00
Hoover, Herbert 125.00
Kennedy, John. Sulphide 195.00
Monroe, James. Green overlay .. 295.00
Monroe, James. Sulphide 150.00
Pope John. Ruby star base.
Sulphide 195.00
Roosevelt, Eleanor.............. 75.00
Roosevelt, Theodore. Sulphide ... 175.00
Stevenson, Adlai 100.00
Truman, Harry S. Sulphide 100.00
Virgin of Lourdes. 1958. Sulphide . 200.00
Wilson, Woodrow. Sulphide 75.00
Bell. Cobalt to frosted clear top 275.00
Bohemian. 3" diam. Ruby glass.
Etching of deer in forest 100.00
Brass. Nude baby on stomach. 6"
long, 2½" high. Signed "Fonderia
Giorgio." Sommer Napoli 40.00
Choko. 2½". Orange, yellow striped
lizard, clusters of goldstone and
plant in ground. Signed.......... 200.00
"Christ in Glory." Emblem, sur-
rounded by laurel wreath and five
stars. Red, white and blue scatter
field 45.00

Chicago World's Fair Hall of Science.
Glass 30.00

Clichy
Canes on lace bed, multicolors of
brilliant tints, set on white thread
twist bits. 3¼" diam. 1750.00
Rare flower on stem over latticino
ground. Rose petals, tipped with
yellow, green leaves. 3¼" diam. . . 2000.00
Scattered "Fleurettes" or canes of
brilliant multicolors set in crystal
clear glass. 3" diam. 1500.00

d'Albert Weights - Modern
Astronaut Magnum, regular 90.00
Columbus Overlay. Royal blue . . . 195.00
Leonardo da Vinci, overlay 150.00
Hemingway, overlay 150.00
Kennedy. Overlay 175.00
J.F. Kennedy and wife, sulphide . . 65.00
King of Sweden. Overlay 150.00
Lind, Jenny. Sulphide 72.50
MacArthur. Overlay 170.00
Paul Revere. Overlay 150.00
F.D. Roosevelt. Sulphide 75.00
F.D. Roosevelt. Overlay 175.00
Mark Twain. Sulphide 65.00
"Don't Forget Your Father." Lincoln
photo on pillow background.
"Good Luck" with horseshoe
center 75.00

Door Stops
4" high, 4" diam., 3 tiers of flower
sprays 85.00
F.O.E. Red, white, blue eagle 45.00
Dragonfly. Faceted and signed 200.00
Fish Aquarium. Fish among seaweed 35.00

Gilliland (Brooklyn, N.Y.), geometric
setup of canes, suspended ¼"
above latticino bkgd. Soft blues,
lavender, yellow and white.
Probably made by a worker
trained in French glass works who
emigrated to the United States . . . 1200.00
"God Bless Our Home." 3½" diam.
Made by Daggenhart of Union
Glass Works 67.50
Hand. Camphor glass 55.00
Hanson, Ron. Signed. Facet-cut
yellow flowers weight. Shaded
leaves and yellow flowers on
velvety bkgd. 155.00
Indiana Centennial. 1966 - Zim-
merman 25.00

Iorio. Single cane and blown.
Pendant in sterling with 18" chain 25.00
Iron. Camel reclining 18.00
Kazium
Blue Rose 295.00
Lily and green leaves 275.00

Purple pansy with gold bee on
green leaf on white ground.
Signed 2" diam. 300.00
Labino. 4-petal flower. Signed 125.00
Lalique. Carved boar. 3½" smoky
gray color 95.00
Lewis, Pete. 2¼", crimped red rose
in clear crystal 295.00
Lighthouse in Snow. 4" high 27.50
Lion. Reclining. Frosted. Centennial
Exposition. Gillinder & Son, 5¾" x
2½" high 95.00
Masonic
"Grand Master" inscribed inside . 55.00
Holy Bible. Brass. 3½ x4" 25.00
Slipper, bronze 28.50
Millefiori-type with multicolored
canes. Unsigned 300.00
Millville
Mushroom, footed. 4" high 375.00
New Jersey Rose. 3¼ x4". Signed
Oscar "Skip" Woods 350.00
Moses in Bull Rushes. 1876. Frosted
oval shape 75.00
Nailsea. Green with silvery white
petals, long bubbles. 4½" high . . . 135.00

Bird in Flight. Green pedestal, clear
ball. "Hawkes." Signed $75.00

Pairpoint

Amethyst glass with swan on top. 6½" high. Original paper label of Pairpoint Glass Co., Sagamore, Mass. 135.00

Silverplated. Bee sitting on top ... 65.00

Snake pedestal 5¾" high. Coiled coral snake around an opal glass globe 75.00

Spiral threads 65.00

Pear. Irid. On black onyx base 165.00

Pittsburgh Exposition 40.00

Plymouth Rock. 1876 .... 75.00

Ray, Ron. 1½", yellow crimped rose tipped in, blue feet 150.00

"Remember Father and Mother" 50.00

"Remember the Maine" 50.00

St Louis

2¼". Camomile. White flower with yellow center, white bud, green leaves and stem. Pink spiral background 1250.00

2½"diam. Bouquet. 3 flowers and green leaves surrounded by alternatings of white and blue canes 1250.00

3½" diam. Dark red, 25-petal dahlia-like flower, green cane forms center, flat 1500.00

3½" diam. Fruit, cluster over latticino basket. Bright yellow, apricot and red cherries, green leaves 1500.00

"Crown Weight," hollow, ribbons twist up to central cane at top center. Red, green, edged with white, lace bkgd. 1500.00

Hawaiian millefiori limited edition of 1975. Signed 225.00

Yellow flower. 1970 .... 200.00

Sandwich. Floral, blue pin stripe 275.00

Somerville. Blue, white, black chips. 1884 .... 80.00

Spatter. Pestle, blue and green roses. Opaque white ground 80.00

Statue of Liberty. Bronze-type 5.00

Steuben

3½". Pear, clear and signed 80.00

4½". Apple with berry pontil. Signed 95.00

Venetian. Scrambled, red and white rods. White filigree plus goldstone 90.00

West Virginia weight 65.00

Whittefriars. Canes in rows of white red and blue. Window cut 2"diam. Signed, dated 75.00

Whittemore

2¼". Three flower bouquet on cobalt ground. Signed 250.00

2¾" high. Pedestal. Nosegay on white ground. Signed and numbered 275.00

Double rose Perfume bottle. Blue. Signed 350.00

Tilted yellow rose, green leaves on pedestal. Signed 285.00

Ysart Weights

Dragonfly on blue, white jasper .. 250.00

Millefiori on green muslin 200.00

Orange-red butterfly on latticino 250.00

Red flower on latticino 250.00

Single swimming fish over sand .. 285.00

PAPIER-MACHE

A literal translation of the French means "chewed paper." Paper is soaked in water and then ground. The resulting mass is molded into forms where they are japanned and dried at a temperature of about 300 degrees F. The finished product is tough, durable and capable of withstanding great heat. So-called Chippendale trays, tilt tops for tables, boxes and daguerreotype cases were made of this material and decorated.

Artist's Folder. 9½x12". H/P gilded and set with MOP .... $ 100.00

Bowl. 3x5½"diam. Marked. "Made in Soviet Union." Colorful 25.00

Box. Russian. 3½x5½". Horses pulling sled with riders 55.00

Case for folding glasses, velvet lined 9.00

Case for Spectacles. Inlaid With MOP . 25.00

Dish. 14" diam. Decorated with tropical birds and foliage 25.00

Dog. 22" long. "The Bryant Pup" $45.00

Eagle. 11" high, 15" wingspread 150.00
Funnel. 11", red 17.50
Glove Box. With lock and key.
2¾x4x11½" 17.50
Handkerchief Box. 3x4x10". Hinged,
MOP inlay 35.00
Hen on Nest 17.50
Lap Desk. Victorian. Black, gold
designs, MOP floral decor. Red
velvet inside. 9½x11½" 120.00
Pail, Water. Dated 1883 .... 35.00
Pitcher. 5½". Red 28.00
Plaque. Hanging type, 20" diam.
Painting of St. Bernard 30.00
Plate. 6½". Geisha girls, oriental
bkgd., red & gold. Scalloped edge 30.00
Santa Claus. 11½" high. Red, gold
black and white 50.00
Shelf, Wall. Oriental, gold trim 30.00
Snuff Boxes
French print 22.50
Oval. Plain case, hinged lid.
1¾x2¾" 18.50
Round, 3¾". Hunting scene on lid 28.50
Round, colored print on lid 22.50
Spill Holder. Floral & scenic
decorations, collared feet 25.00
Tables
Tier. 2 round trays, 12" top, 14"
bottom, 3 bamboo-style legs.

Owl. 16" high $125.00

Painted black, with chrysanthemum decorations 175.00
Victorian tilt-top. 22x26". 28"
MOP inlay 200.00
Trays
8" diam. Painting of dog 75.00
10x12". Handled, Grape 125.00
10x17". Black with floral decor ... 65.00
11x25". Black with floral decor ... 150.00
12"diam. Chippendale edges 100.00
Large, Chippendale. Exotic bird,
lush flowers, MOP inlay 175.00

PARIAN WARE

Parian ware is a true hard-paste, white
porcelain known as biscuit ware, so-called
because of the absence of a glaze. The effect
is similar to marble which it was intended to
simulate. Many of the figurines and groups
are of religious or classical subjects. Tea sets,
plaques, pitchers, vases and jewelry were
made of this ware which originated in England
about 1845. It became popular in the United
States about 1860 and continued in public
favor until around 1900.

Basket. 5x5". Cupid sitting at the
side, open-top egg, rope of roses
entwined around handle ....$ 55.00
Bowl. 4½" diam. Pond Lily 35.00
Boxes
Round, raised strawberry leaf
decor 52.50
Trinket. Casket shape, with
applied grapes 40.00
Trinket. Sleeping baby on cover .. 40.00
Busts
Andrew, John A. 9x13". Pedestal
base 85.00
Apollo. 9½" high 60.00
Beethoven. 8" high 60.00
Bennington. Marked. "Spring &
Autumn." 8" high. Pair 120.00
Cromwell. 8" high 60.00
Dante. 5" high 60.00
Dickens. 6¼" high 60.00
Enid. 11" high. Rampart lion on
her vest. Signed Copeland 165.00
Enid. I. Miller. Crystal Ice Palace .. 250.00
Garfield. 10" high 75.00
Garfield. 12½" high, 8" wide.
Pedestal base 85.00
Goethe. 11½" high 75.00
Grant, Ulysses S. 125.00
Juliet-type woman. 8" high. C.
1860-70 .... 65.00
Lincoln. 5½" high 85.00
Napoleon 85.00

Schiller	60.00
Scott, Sir Walter. 12" high	75.00
Shakespeare. 4½" high. Blue eagle mark	65.00
Shakespeare. 7½" high	95.00
Sumner, Charles. 12½" high	85.00
Sunflower Maiden. 11" high	75.00
Venus De Milo. 8" high. Sgnd.	75.00
Washington, George. 9" high	95.00
Wellington. 11½" high	120.00
Worcester. 8½" high. Signed	90.00

Creamers

Cow, in white	30.00
Lily pad pattern	50.00
Cup & Saucer. Lily pad pattern	75.00
Cupid. 9½" long. Holding torch. Loop on back for hanging	75.00

Dishes

Oval. 8x10½". Raspberry & white	75.00
Sweetmeat dish on plate. Covered. Lily pad pattern	100.00

Statue. 18" high. "Maidenhood."
Copeland. Dated 1868 ......$250.00

Sweetmeat dish without plate. Covered. Lily pad pattern	85.00
Ewer. 8½" high. Ring handles with small masks. Beading and leaves over body ....$	95.00

Figurines

5" "Heubach." Schnauzer sitting on haunches. Signed	65.00
8½". Ear of corn, with 2 girls	57.50
9". Boy and girl, white. Pair	100.00
9". Girl wearing hat, cape, gun at side, 2 pistols in belt. Standing on oval base. Pair	125.00
9". Girl with long hair, kneeling in prayer on pillow, with open book. Pair	135.00
9". Man and maiden in colonial attire. Pair	125.00
10". Boy eating fruit, short jacket, hat, 2 baskets	85.00
10". Girl in plumed hat, fancy gown. Urn and bird	55.00
11". Girl with dog	75.00
13". Girls, one holding sheaf of wheat, other holding pitcher. Pair	150.00
13". Rock of Ages. 2 girls clinging to cross	85.00
14". Nude woman, hands chained	150.00
19". Woman, wearing draped gown, holding rose garland in one hand, tambourine in other	135.00

Hands

4" high. Ring holder	55.00
6" high. Holding urn	75.00
Hen. 7"	120.00
Horses. 5" high, on 3x6" base. Pair	75.00
Jug. 7½" high. White with classic figures	60.00

Pitchers

4". Flowers, vines and leaves in relief	27.50
4". Squirrel	30.00
4½". Birds, berries, leaf decor	35.00
6½". Embossed birds	38.50
8½". Lily-of-the-valley decor	125.00
9". Daffodil and leaf decor around neck	135.00
11½". White with American shield and flag. Geo. Washington in uniform on one side, words "American Independence" and "Mother" on other	200.00

Plate. 8". Raised water lilies	60.00
Platter. 13". Deep collared rim. Old English lettering "Give Us This Day, Our Daly Bread," wheat heads form handles	75.00

Snuff Box. American, round with
portrait of Lafayette. Early 19th
century 135.00
Sugar Bowl. Lily pad pattern........ 85.00
Syrup Jug. 9" high, bulbous base.
Panelled with embossed ovals,
dotted stripes on pebbled white
ground. Silver hinged lid, applied
head of Norseman, silverplated
handle 85.00
Tray, Bread. Round, 13" diam. "Get
Thy Bread with Joy and Thank-
fulness"...................... 60.00
Tumbler. 4". Classic figures 30.00
Vases
    4½x7". Cornucopia. 2 cherubs
    standing on pillow base 75.00
    6½". Decor of grape leaves, two
    bands........................ 60.00
Tumbler. 4". Classic figures 30.00
Vases
    4½x7". Cornucopia. 2 cherubs
    standing on pillow base 75.00
    6½". Decor of grape leaves, two
    bands........................ 65.00
    7½". Grape decor, spots of blue .. 75.00

PASTILLE BURNERS, See STAFFORDSHIRE SECTION

PATE DE VERRE

Pate de Verre can be translated simply as
"glass paste." More precisely it is a molded
glass form. The process is to grind lead glass
into a powder or crystal form. The ground
glass is then made into a paste by adding a
two or three percent solution of sodium
silicate. The resulting mixture can be molded,
fired and carved. This type of molded glass
was known to be Egyptian as early as 1500
B.C. It had its "on and off" periods of
popularity during the centuries that followed.
In the late 19th and early 20th centuries Pate
de Verre was again revived by advanced glass
makers in France. Cros, Dammouse and the
Daum Brothers were active in leading this
movement. Within the past ten years,
contemporary artists have rediscovered Pate
de Verre as a medium for sculpturing.

Bowl. 5-5/8". Signed A. Walter
Nancy ....$ 375.00
Box. 3x3", round. Violet decor.
Signed G. Argy Rousseau 950.00
Dish. Leaf-shaped. 2x5¼". Blue and
green. Signed A. Walter Nancy ... 465.00
Figurine. Monkey sitting on stump.
3¾" high. Light amber to green.
Second signature of "A. Mercie" .. 385.00

Inkwell. 1½" diam., ½" high. Large
bee cover. Yellow to russet, twig
and berry trim. Signed A. Walter . 500.00
Plaque. 2". Yellow daisy, silk cord
attached. Signed A.W. 160.00

PATE-SUR-PATE

Pate-Sur-pate [paste on paste], an outstanding
nineteenth century porcelain, has become
unmistakably synonymous with Marc Louis
Solon. About 1863 Solon and other artists
employed at the Sevres manufactory in France
experimented with this process of porcelain
decoration, inspired by a Chinese Celadon
vase in the Ceramic Museum at Sevres.
Just prior to the outbreak of the Franco-
Prussian War in 1870, Solon suffered a severe
illness and ultimately was unable to aid in the
defense of his country. Together with the
other inhabitants who were routed from the
villages, he soon became virtually homeless.
Given an opportunity to accompany an artist
friend to England, Solon obtained employment
at the Minton factory, at Stoke-on-Trent and
worked there for 35 years, during which time
he made most of his masterpieces in this
ware.

Lamp Base. 22½" high. Semi-
translucent floral design on tinted
grey-green ground ....$ 500.00

Vase. 5" high. Celadon with white
blossoms, butterfly, gold leaves,
4-footed base in gold $245.00

Plaque. 8x9". 5 reclining nudes with swan. Scalloped border with foliage, blue-green 300.00

Plate. Blue, figures in white, gold borders. Each panel different figures. Signed Tiffany & Co. 395.00

Vases

4½" high. White floral with butterflies on dark brown ground. Signed Geo. Jones & Sons 200.00

5" high. Celadon green with panel of children playing, silver deposit in floral design 250.00

6" high. Emerald green with fernery, on ball feet with gold. Pair 350.00

7" high. Sea green with mauve medallion depicting dancing lady. Garland of 14K gold on body 295.00

8¼" high. Blue with lavender ground. Nude-top maiden holding large shell filled with four cherubs 600.00

11½" high. Blue ground with white decor. Gold band around top and base 700.00

Pilgrim-shaped. Brown with white decor. Marked "Schenck" 275.00

PEACHBLOW GLASS

A type of art glass which derived its name from the coloring of fine Chinese porcelain of the same name. It was produced first at Wheeling, W.Va., in 1886. The New England firms followed with their ware a year or two later.

There are three existing types of this glass. Wheeling Peachblow, which is a red-rose color at the top, shading to a bright yellow at the bottom. The inside of the ware is cased or lined with white. Most of the items have a glossy finish; however, some were completed with an acid or satin surface.

New England Peachblow is a red-rose color at the top, shading to white at the bottom. The glass is not cased or lined with white on the interior. The majority of items has a satin finish.

A third type, Mt. Washington Peachblow, is a smoky-pink at the top, shading to a bluish-white at the base.

During the past twenty years, reproductions have come onto the market. These include goblets [not originally made], rose bowls, cruets, plates and baskets.

The new items are of the New England variety but are off-color and can be "spotted" by anyone remotely familiar with the product.

Baskets

8½" diam. Twisted amber handle, yellow shading to pink $2400.00

Gundersen-type, small 565.00

Bowls

5¼" diam. Ruffled top 450.00

7" diam. Gundersen-type. Round, three triangular leaf-like feet, cream colored. Berry applied over pontil 675.00

9" diam., 4" high. Sandwich. Crimped, ruffled 4-scallop edge. Satin finish 850.00

Finger bowl. Wheeling 500.00

Rose bowl. New England 550.00

Butter Dish. Wheeling. Glossy finish . 1200.00

Celery Vase. Wheeling 750.00

Vase. 10" high. "Wheeling." Separate amber [4 gargoyles] base ... $1250.00

Creamers

4¼" high. Light yellow into dark
red. Applied amber handle 875.00
5¼" high. Deep mahogany to
fuchsia below shoulder. Lemon
yellow to base, square top, 5"
widest diam. Applied amber
handle 895.00
Cruet. Wheeling. Yellow with amber
handle and stopper 1000.00
Cup and Saucer. Gundersen. Deep
raspberry color, white reeded
handle 375.00
Darner. New England 155.00
Decanter. Wheeling. 9" high 1750.00
Lamp. Hanging, for hall. 15" high, 9"
diam. Candle burner. Brass 1000.00
Lamp Shade. For banquet lamp. New
England-type. Ruffled top 795.00
Muffineer. Wheeling. 5½" high.
Shades from deep red into yellow.
Original metal top 750.00
Mustard. Fuchsia coloring, re-
silvered top 300.00

Pitchers

Syrup. Pink shading to white 975.00
Water. Wheeling. Deep pink to
yellow. Applied amber handle ... 1500.00
Punch Cup. Applied handle 425.00
Salt. Wheeling. Glossy finish 250.00
Salt and Pepper Shakers. Pair 550.00
Spooner. 4½" high, base 3¼".
Scalloped edge, 2¾" diam. 395.00
Sugar Bowl. New England, deep wild
rose color. Applied white handles 650.00
Toothpick Holder. Wheeling. Glossy
finish 350.00

Tumblers

New England. Dull finish 425.00
New England. Glossy finish, deep
pink to yellow 425.00
Wheeling. Acid. Deep mahogany
fuchsia, into dusky yellow at
halfway mark 450.00
Wild Rose 295.00

Vases

4¾" high, Sandwich. Turned down
top 400.00
7" high. Gundersen-type. Banjo.
Pair 750.00
7¼" high. Wheeling. Bulbous 1000.00
7¾" high. New England. Acid
3-petal lily vase. Raspberry to
pink to white 700.00
10" high. New England. White
shading to deep rose with gold
tracery design on body 900.00
10" high, 5" wide. Mt. Washington. Light blue at base shading to
deep rose with shades of
lavender. Typical Mt. Washington
style decor of shasta daisies in
raised enamel dots of yellow and
white. Coin gold stems and
centers, powder blue leaves, jade
green dots..................... 2200.00
Dull finish, applied handle, applied decor around base of long,
narrow neck 1300.00
15½" high with long neck. Deep
red at top shading to peach at
base. Wheeling 1500.00
Water Set. Wheeling. Finest coloring, glossy finish. Bulbous pitcher
with 6 tumblers 3500.00
Whiskey. New England. Glossy finish 275.00

PEKING GLASS

Peking glass is a type of cameo glass, in that
the designs are carved into the glass. Its
production began in the 1700's and continued
well into the late 1880's.
Reproductions are now showing up in the
market, but are readily identified if you know
the original ware.

Bowl. 7" diam. White with blue decor
$295.00

Bowls

6" diam. Flowers, birds. Imperial
yellow. Black ornate teakwood
stand ....$ 325.00
8" diam. Red birds and leaves on
white 300.00
12" diam. Red over white, carved,
cranes and rushes 325.00
Snuff Bottle. 3" blue overlay. Horse
beneath trees.................. 90.00

Vases

2½"high, 2½"diam., 2"deep base . 125.00
5¾" high. red on yellow.
Leopards, florals. C. 1800........ 420.00

7" high. Blue, red floral on white . 500.00
10" high. Turquoise on white.
Figures, sea gulls 500.00
Stick. Carved red overlay on
mandarin yellow. Foo dogs [4]
playing with ball. C. 1850. Pair . . . 500.00

PELOTON GLASS

Peloton glass was made in Germany in the late Victorian period. Threads of glass in a different color were applied to the body in spaghetti-like fashion.

Pitchers
6½" high. Tankard-type. White
spaghetti-like decor on clear . . . . . $ 85.00
7½" high. Water, bulbous, white
on clear 85.00
8" high, 2" diam. Bulbous body.
Irid. ground, gold, purple high-
lights. Green handle 145.00
8" high. Water, bulbous, blue on
clear 95.00
Water. Collar neck 2½" high, 3½"
diam. Smooth rimmed opening,
handle attached to neck. 6¾"
body diam., ground pontil 235.00
Tumbler. Iced tea. 5½" high, blue
fragments on clear 65.00
Vases
4¾" high. Fan-shaped top, ribbed,
bulbous body 150.00

Biscuit Jar. Multicolored threads.
Sterling bail and top $350.00

7" high. Blue, pink, yellow
spaghetti-like decor 125.00
7" high. Bulbous, clear, cranberry
strings 135.00
11½" high. Green, two handles . . 165.00

PENNSYLVANIA DUTCH ITEMS

One of the most interesting and individual forms of American Folk Art developed in the Southeastern countries of Pennsylvania during the 18th and 19th centuries.

Pennsylvania Dutch [or German] arts and crafts have a "peasant" quality about them. The people used gay, colored paints and forms on almost all their wares, namely, furniture, china, quilts, etc. Some of the most popular designs were the tulip, heart, angel, peafowl and fruits.

Cabbage Slicer. 18". Made into a
kitchen hanging . . . . $ 47.50
Cookie Boards. Gingerbread man
and woman. Indented early
figures. 20" long, 7½" wide. Pair . 40.00
Coverlet. One piece. Red, white,
blue and green. H. Stager, Mount
Joy, Lancaster Co., Pa. 350.00
Fractur. 12x15". Hand drawn. C.
1836. . . . . 950.00
Gun, Fowling. 45" barrel, .75 cal.,
with horn. Carved designs, en-
graved lock 450.00
Trivets
8", cast iron, heart handle, 2
tulips, side bird heads 22.00
9", cast iron, heart design,
handled 18.00
Platter, Bread. Oval 17.50

Jewel Chest. "Hattie Brunner." Penna.
Dutch graining $145.00

PEWTER

Pewter is an alloy of the metals tin and lead. It was used for tableware and utensils prior to the general use of chinaware. Pewter ware made by early American craftsmen is now relatively scarce. According to earlier writers, it was melted and used to make bullets during the American Revolution War and again in the War of 1812.

Pieces marked "Jas. Dixon & Son, Sheffield" or "Dixon," have the appearance of being pewter but in reality are made of Britannia metal, known as the hard pewter of the late 1800's. Although technically there is a difference in the formula of the two, dealers and collectors in America over the years have accepted pieces with the above marks as late pewter. Contemporary brides and homemakers have re-established 'new' pewter flatware, hollow ware and accessories to a prominent place in their homes.

Basins

6½". Unmarked	$ 150.00
8". Austin, R.	300.00
8". Boardman	325.00
8". Danforth, S.	300.00
8". Pierce	300.00
10½". Unmarked	185.00

Beakers

Dixon & Son. Pint	150.00
Griswold, A.	165.00
Bed Pan. Boardman	175.00

Bowls

2½ x 8½". Heavy. 3 ridges, design on rim. Marked K.S. Co.	35.00
8". Boardman, T.	325.00
8". Compton & Leonard	200.00
8". Danforth, S.	300.00
Baptismal. Unsigned	185.00

Boxes

Powder. Chinese. 6" diam.	35.00
Snuff:	
Round, incised lines	55.00
Shape of 18th century watch	72.00

Candlesticks

6". Dunham	165.00
6". J. B.	150.00
8". Saucer-type. Gleason	175.00
9". Unmarked. Pair	150.00
9¾". Sellew-type. Pair	225.00
10". Unmarked. American, baluster turned. Pair	170.00
12". Bobeches. Unmarked. Pair	250.00

Chalice. 7½" high, 3" across top, 3¾" base. Boardman & Co., Hartford, Conn.	250.00

Coffee Pot. 12" high. American. "A. Porter"	$395.00

Chamberstick. 11" long, 5½" wide. Kayserzinn. Art Nouveau flowers, raised handle	75.00

Chargers

12". Unmarked	125.00
12". Townsend	135.00
13½". Rose mark	150.00
17". English	225.00
18". English	250.00
20". English	275.00

Chocolate Pot. 18th century, Swiss. Black, Engle & Zinn	175.00

Coffee Pots

Boardman	225.00
Danforth, Josiah. 11"	285.00
Dixon & Son. 10½". Wood handle.	140.00
Dunham	300.00
Dunham & Sons	260.00
Gleason	250.00
Leonard, Reed & Barton. 9"	145.00
Morey & Sons	150.00
Richardson. 11½"	200.00
Savage	200.00
Sellens & Co., Cincinnati	150.00
Smith & Co. 10"	135.00
Trask. 9", domed top	275.00
Ward & Co.	175.00
Whitehouse	250.00

Coffee Urn. 14" high, footed base. Reed & Barton	200.00
Compote. 3¼" high, 6" diam. Flagg & Hoffman	30.00

Creamers
Sheldon & Feltman. 5½" high 125.00
Yale, H. 4" high. C. 1830 .... 135.00
Cuspidor. Derby 165.00
Dishes, Deep
B. Barns 275.00
Calder 300.00
Danforth. 11" 285.00
Kayserzinn. 8". Late 50.00
Richardson, G. 300.00
Flagons
9¾". Jas. Dixon & Son, Sheffield .. 135.00
10". Gleason 360.00
10". With platter. Gleason. Set ... 420.00
11". Calder 300.00
11". With platter. Calder. Set 400.00
Unmarked 195.00
Foot Warmer. Oval 130.00
Funnel. For decanter. Unmarked 95.00
Goblet. Late 40.00
Jug. 11" high, 6-sided with screw cap
and free swinging handle 145.00
Ladles
12". Yates 100.00
13". Wooden handle 100.00
14½" 125.00
Dated 1792 .... 150.00
Lamps
Nursing. 2". T.B.M. Co. Pair 200.00
Peg. 7". J. Newells. Pair 300.00
Ship. Unmarked. Pair 375.00
Whale Oil:
Gleason 400.00
"Morey & Ober" 395.00
Porter, F..................... 400.00
Wildes 350.00
Loving Cup. Kayserzinn 50.00
Master Salt. Low foot. Marked James
Dixon 65.00
Measures
½ pint. Dandre hallmarked 75.00
½ pint. Yates 85.00
1 pt. Yates 125.00
Mugs
Handled. English. C. 1825 .... 85.00
Handled. 5" high. Morey & Smith . 95.00
Mustard Pot. Blue china liner 75.00
Pitchers
Dunham, R. 6½" 395.00
Gleason. Covered 265.00
Kayserzinn. Late 100.00
McQuilkin 265.00
"Old Colonial." 6". Late 45.00
Porter, F. 6" 300.00
Unmarked. Covered 225.00
Vaughn, Taunton, Mass. 5" 250.00
Plates
Austin, N. 8" 215.00
Austin, Richard. 8" 215.00

Badger, Thomas:
7½" 200.00
7¾" 225.00
8½" 235.00
Barns, B.
7-7/8" 190.00
8" 190.00
9" 225.00
Bassett, Fred. 9 .... 200.00
Boardman:
8" 195.00
12". Flat, eagle touchmark 250.00
Calder, William:
8" 198.50
11½" 250.00
Danforth, E. 8" 225.00
Danforth, S. 8" 200.00
Danforth, Thos. 3rd. 8" 200.00
Danforth, William:
7¾" 225.00
8" 240.00
Griswold, Ashbel. 7-7/8" 185.00
Kayserzinn. 10". Late 75.00
Kilbourn, S. 8" 215.00
King, Richard, Jr. 8¾". London ... 120.00
Marked. Maker unknown:
7½", 8". Each 85.00
9¾" 95.00
12". Deep 125.00
Pierce, S. 8" 200.00
Smith & Feltman, Albany. 10" 150.00
Unmarked:
8¼" 70.00
9½" 100.00
13½" 115.00
Platters
Badger, Thomas. 12" 295.00
Calder. 11½". Deep 335.00
Kayserzinn. 12½ x 20". Late 145.00
Plaque. 5x6". Oval, Napoleon 75.00
Porringers
2-1/16". R. Lee 325.00
3". Unmarked 95.00
3¼". Heart handle. Lee 300.00
3-3/8". R. Lee 350.00
4-1/8". Crown handle 140.00
4¼". 2 handles, H.K. on handle ... 150.00
4¼". Pierced handle. Late Reed &
Barton 60.00
4½". Heart handle. Marked I.C. .. 175.00
5". Boardman 195.00
5". Crown handle. Marked I.C. ... 195.00
5". Crown handle. Lee 300.00
5¼". Crown handle. Unmarked .. 135.00
5¼". Hamlin 295.00
Shaving Mug. Richardson 185.00
Spoon Mold 75.00
Spoons
Tablespoon. Yates, England 45.00

Inkwell for quill pens. 7¾" diam. base
$95.00

Teaspoons:

Fiddle shape	25.00
Holland, crown and rose. Marked J.M.	35.00
Shell back. Early. Set of 4	75.00
Sugar Bowl. 2¾" diam. Manning & Bowman	95.00

Sugars and Creamers

4 feet. Marked Winthrop. Pair	50.00
"Brewster"	135.00
Nesting-type. Marked "Pilgrim 764." Late. Set	39.50
Syrup Jug. Horn handle. 6" high. Jas. Dixon	75.00

Tankards

1 Litre	127.50
8½" high, 4¾" diam. Manning Bowman & Co., Middletown, Conn. C. 1865	250.00
14". Unmarked	150.00

Teapots

Boardman. 8"	195.00
Boardman & Hart:	
7½"	220.00
8"	240.00
Dixon, James	150.00
Dunham, R. 7½"	165.00
Gleason, R. 7"	185.00
Morey & Ober. Boston	145.00
Old Colony. 5¼". Late	65.00
Porter, F. Westbrook	175.00
Putnam. 8"	285.00
Richardson, G.:	
7½"	250.00
11"	325.00
Savage. 10"	175.00
Shaw & Fisher, Suffolk, England. 5¾"	120.00
Smith & Co. 7½". Wood handle	150.00

Unmarked	150.00
Wilcox. Signed	165.00
Tea Set. Teapot, sugar bowl, creamer, round tray. Marked "Genuine." Late. Set	100.00
Vase. Footed, Art Nouveau-type decor. Leaves, berries, swimming fish. 7" high	135.00
Whistle. 1¾" long. Late	15.00
Wine Taster. 2-1/8". Pierced handle. Taunton	60.00

PHOENIX GLASS

The Phoenix glass firm was established in 1880 in Pennsylvania. Although Phoenix glass was known primarily for commercial glasswares, they produced a very fine sculptured, decorative, gift-type glassware in the 1930's. This sculptured glassware design was dropped in the early 1950's, after World War II. It is this product of Phoenix that is being collected today by knowledgable collectors.

Bowls

4x5½x10". Leaves, branches, birds. Amethyst	$ 12.50
14" long. Oval. Diving girl	80.00
Box. Covered, 6", raised floral, blue decor	50.00
Candlesticks. 2½" high, 5" diam. Angular pattern. "The Phoenix." Pair	60.00
Cigarette Box. 7 ash trays. Green, white flowers. Set	50.00

Lamps

13" high. Table-type, sculptured with pale yellow roses, aqua foliage against white ground	95.00

Plate. 6¾". "Dancing Nudes" ..$35.00

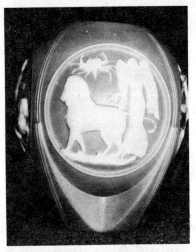

Vase. "Zodiac" pattern. Blue and white
$135.00

22" high. White, orange honey-suckle, green leaves	145.00
Table Lamp. Sculptured glass. White, blue berries, green leaves, no shades. Pair	195.00
Pitcher, Water	65.00
Planter. 3¼ x 8½". Green lion motif	32.50
Plates	
8". Cherry pattern. C. 1925	32.00
10". Nude frolicking figure	47.50
14". Pale blue, frosted white daffodils in relief	60.00
Shade. Small, frosted to clear. Signed	55.00
Vases	
6" high. Dragonflies, leaves. Matching pair	85.00
7" high. Rectangular. Yellow birds, brown detail on either side. Background pink flowers, green foliage on custard	65.00
7¼" high. Brown sculptured ferns, cream ground	55.00
8" high. Praying Mantis. Cone-shape. Raised satin finish, clear on white frosted	55.00
8" high. Pillow-shape. Blue with white blossoms	75.00
10" high. Cream ground, blue-berries, brown pods, green stems	85.00
10" high. Madonna MOP finish on grey ground. Original sculptured Artware paper label	95.00
11¼" high. Teal blue, opalescent. philodendron leaf	100.00
12" high. Yellow peonies, green vines	100.00
Madonna. Persimmon-colored ground, pearly irid., profile	95.00
Pale blue, two embossed women's heads in white. Paper sticker	95.00
Pillow-shape. White flying geese on blue ground	100.00

PHONOGRAPHS

This instrument was commonly known as the "talking machine" by old timers. Thomas A. Edison invented the first successful machine in the 1880's and placed it on the market. It was manufactured by numerous firms in later years.

Columbia Gramaphone. Pat. 1885, 25 cylinders	$ 250.00
Edison Cylinder. Morning glory decor on horn	325.00
Edison Cylinder-type, spring wind, with horn	250.00
Edison. Disc type. Horn in bottom	195.00
Edison. Record cylinder	4.00
Edison Cylinder. Outside horn	325.00
Edison Standard. Morning glory horn	275.00
English Disc-type. Robeyphone, with large green horn	230.00
Horn. Decorated with flowers	75.00
Kameraphone. Portable, folding. 4½ x 6½"	65.00

Edison. Cylinder-type with morning glory horn. $325.00

Keeno-Lo-Phone. Double doors con-
ceal 2 drawers with record
pockets. Bonnet is amplifier. C.
1815 .... 200.00
O'Neil James Co., Chicago.
Miniature, with horn 195.00
Victor. Early, small horn. 6½"
square cast iron base 185.00
Victor. Spring-driven. Oak case, 2
sound baffles. Model VV-IV. Pat.
1904. Circa WWI 145.00

PHONOGRAPH RECORDS - 78 RPM

With the advent of more sophisticated
recording materials, such as 33-1/3 RPM long
playing albums, 8-track tapes and cassettes,
the older 78 RPM phonograph records have
become collectors' items. These records are
also sought by collectors of memorabilia
because of the artists who once recorded on
the different labels.

Bluebird
   Martin, Freddy. 10" .... $ 2.00
   Monroe, Vaughn. 10" 2.00
Brunswick
   Capitol Grand Orchestra. 12" 3.50
   Leopold Godowsky. 12" 3.50
   New York String Quartet. 12" 3.50
   R. Strauss & Symphony Orchestra.
   12" 3.50
   Virginia Rea. 12" 3.50
Capitol
   Anthony, Ray. 10" 2.50
   Miller, Eddie. 10" 2.00
   Paul, Les. 10" 2.00
   Stafford, Jo. 10" 2.50
Columbia
   Griffen, Ken. 10" 2.50
   James, Harry. 10" 2.50
   Kyser, Kay. 10" 2.50
   Lane, Frankie, Stafford, Jo. 10" ...   2.50
   Lombardo, Guy. 10" 2.50
   Prince's Orchestra. 12" 3.50
   Shore, Dinah. 10" 2.00
   Sinatra, Frank. 10" 2.50
   Stevens, Rise. 12" 3.50
   Coral. Ames Brothers. 10" 2.50
Decca
   Andrews Sisters. 10" 3.50
   Andrews Sister, Bing Crosby. 10" .   3.50
   Andrews Sisters, Dick Haymes. 10"   4.00
   Dorsey, Jimmy. 10" 2.50
   Dorsey, Tommy. 10" 2.50
   Hampton, Lionel. 10" 2.50
   Herman, Woody. 10" 2.00
   Lombardo, Guy. 10" 2.50
   Noble, Ray. 10" 2.00

78 RPM. "Columbia." Glenn Ford. 10"
$2.50

"Good Time Jazz"
   Firehouse Five Plus Two. 10" 3.00
   Murphy, Turk. 10" 3.00
   Scobey's Frisco Band. 10" 3.00
   Watters, Lu. 10" 3.00
Hi Tone. Barry, Jim. 10" 2.00
London. Arman, Kay. 10" 2.00
Majestic. Prima, Louis. 10" 2.50
Mercury
   Laine, Frankie. 10" 2.00
   Page, Patti. 10" 2.00
Okeh. Autrey, Gene. 10" 2.50
RCA Victor, 10"
   Cougat, Xavier 2.00
   Day, Dennis 2.00
   Dorsey, Tommy 2.50
   Hampton, Lionel 2.50
   Martin, Freddie 2.50
   Monroe, Vaughn 2.50
RCA Victor, 12"
   Emilio de Gegorza 3.00
   McKee's Orchestra 3.50
   Victor Concert Orchestra 3.50
   Victor Light Opera Company 3.50
   Victor Military Band 3.50
RCA Victor. Red Seal, 12"
   London Philharmonic Orchestra ..   3.50
   Minneapolis Symphony Orchestra   3.50
   Paris Conservatory Orchestra 3.50
   Phila. Orchestra, Ormandy 3.50
Royale, 12". Symphony Orchestra ...   3.50
Victrola, 12"
   Farrar, Geraldine 3.00
   Galli-Curci, A. 3.50
   McCormick, John 3.50
   Powell, Maud 3.50
   Williams, Evan 3.50

PICKARD CHINA

The Pickard China Company was founded by Wilder Pickard in Chicago, Illinois in the late 1890's and was noted for its handpainted china. Although they first acquired blanks from other manufacturers such as Haviland, they now produce their own. The firm is presently located in Antioch.

Bowls

5½" diam. Nuts in bottom, sides. Signed ....$	38.50
7" diam. Shallow with side handle, scalloped border. H/P scenic in pastels................	48.00
10" diam. Berry, with 6 small 5¼" diam. bowls. Large tulips in yellow, orange, gold outlines. Signed Arno	195.00
11" diam. Punch. Footed, Aura Argenta Liniar design. C. 1912 ...	150.00
Candleholders. Pink roses, gold base. 1905, signed "Arno." Pair ..	45.00
Candlesticks. 9" high, 4" diam. Raised floral design. Limoges, shield mark. Pair	65.00

Candy Dishes

7" diam. Pierced handles, allover gold stippled florals	32.50
8" diam. Tall center handle, divided, 3 sections, stippled gold .	45.00
Chocolate Pot. 11½" high, white pearlized background, H/P tall green leaves, orchids	145.00

Compotes

9½" diam. Raised foot, gold handles. Artist signed Miller	78.50
Low, footed, handled. Decor of lilac/purple violets, gold trim. Signed Fisher and Pickard	65.00
Cup and Saucer. Nasturtiums	35.00

Hatpin Holders

1905. Florals, gold band, top. Rare red mark. Signed M. Hille	40.00
1925 year mark. Allover gold etched florals	32.50
Marmalade Jar. 6" high. Covered, with separate underplate. Blackberries, gold trim. Signed Vesche, J. & C. "Louise" Bavaria, W. A. Pickard. Set...................	85.00
Nut Set. Painted nuts, foliage in shades of brown, wide gold borders. Large bowl, 6 small matching bowls. Signed "Valhal" .	150.00

Pitchers

5" high. H/P orange poppies, gold. Signed Fuchs	35.00

Vase. 5" high. Gold..........$45.00

6" high. Tankard. Art Nouveau design, Limoges blank. Signed Passon	125.00
7½" high. Tankard. Lily pads, flowers, 5 colors, gold. Signed Leach	135.00
Cider. 5½" high, 9" from spout to handle. Multicolored enameled floral bank. Leaf mark	75.00
Water. Golden pheasant, helmet-shaped........................	150.00

Plates

5½". Acid etched design in gold ..	22.50
6½".'h1p florals, gold scroll, bands	17.50
8". 2" embossed gold border, center humming birds, orchids. Hutschenreuther blank, gold leaf mark. Signed E. Challinor	75.00
8". Red poinsettia, gold scalloped edge. Signed	35.00
8½". Art Nouveau design, gold border, green leaves. Artist signed	45.00

8½". Scalloped with gold. Strawberries and white blossoms. 1905
mark, artist Challinor 75.00
8½". Oak leaves, acorns with
raised gold work, wide gold,
scalloped border. 1898 . . . .   48.50
11¾". Cake. Leaf clover design,
gold. C. 1912 . . . .   35.00
Relish Tray. 8½" long, 5" wide.
Purple violets, green leaves 50.00
Salt and Pepper Shakers
1912. Silver design, gold tops,
stylized floral decor. Signed
Podlaha 28.00
Gilt tops, enamel floral decor.
Signed 28.00
Service Plates. Green decor with
floral centers. Set of 12 . . . .   650.00
Stein. 7" high. Tankard shape. Red
poinsettias on irid. pearlized
ground. 1898-1904 mark. Signed
N. R. Coutall 125.00
Swan. 3" long, heavy allover gold
inside and out. Signed 22.00
Tea Sets

3 pieces. H/P, gold and platinum.
All signed. A. Richter 250.00
4 pieces. Teapot, creamer, sugar,
16" tray. Pierced handles. Allover
gold stippled florals 185.00
Vases
5¾" high. Gold top, purple violets
on green leaves 50.00
7" high. Urn-shaped with gold
neck, gold basket-type handle.
Orange poppies on black ground.
Double circle mark, signed LOH . .   85.00
7" high. H/P scenic. Signed Marke   60.00
7" high. Scenic, gold rimmed.
Autumn trees bordering lake,
hills, shaded blue bisque ground.
1905-10 mark, signed E. Challinor   200.00
15" high. Large peonies, pastel
ground, gold scalloped rim, base.
Signed Rean 175.00

PICKLE CASTORS

A novelty of the 1880-1900 period consisting
of a silverplated frame with a clear or colored
glass insert and metal tongs. The primary use
was for decorative or ornamental purposes in
a china closet or on a sideboard.

Amber. Cane pattern. In holder, with
tongs . . . . $ 135.00
Amber. Sprig pattern 125.00
Amber. Waffle pattern. American
Silver Co. Triple-plated frame 145.00

Amberina. IVT with ribbed swirling.
Gold and silver enamel decor of
peach branch. SP Wilcox frame,
silverplated tongs 245.00
Amethyst. Enamel decor 125.00
Blue
Daisy & Button. In holder with fork   150.00
Fine Cut. 12" 150.00
Inverted Thumbprint. Enameled
flowers 165.00
Clear
Button pattern. Silverplated
holder with fork. Small 95.00
Daisy insert with ornate silver-
plate frame, tongs 75.00
Double. 12" 100.00
Pressed, cut jar, with holder, tongs .   75.00
Swirled Zipper pattern insert. S/P
frame with tongs. Southington
Quad. 90.00

Blue glass liner, yellow flowers.
Resilvered holder and tongs . . $195.00

Venus and Cupid insert. Quad. plate, with tongs 95.00

Cranberry
  9½" 160.00
  11", enamel decor 175.00
  12", enamel decor 200.00
  12", plain 135.00
  Diamond Quilted. Resilvered holder 95.00
  IVT insert. Enameled daisies. Ornate frame on high base 200.00
  Melon-shaped 195.00
Green. Zipper pattern. With tongs .. 135.00
Mother-of-Pearl.D.Q. Fuchsia to pale pink. White satin lining 185.00
Opalescent base, shading to pink at top. Heavy printed Hobnail. Silverplated holder with lid, tongs 150.00
Red Satin Glass. Silver frame, tongs . 165.00
Rubina. Melon-ribbed with pattern on alternating panels. Fork included. Resilvered frame 165.00
Rubina Verde. Frosted, with enamel decor. Resilvered frame, tongs ... 250.00

Vaseline
  Daisy and Button, with V pattern . 135.00
  Footed frame, resilvered 165.0

PIGEON'S BLOOD GLASS

Pigeon's Blood glass is an orange-red glass produced around the turn of the 19th century. Do not confuse it with any red-colored glass. Pigeon's Blood glass definitely has an orange glow.

Bottle. 4½" to top of stopper .... $ 42.50
Bowl. 8" diam. Beaded top, grilled triangular design on sides 135.00
Bride's Basket. 4" high, 11" across. Ruffled rim, silver-handled holder 245.00
Butter Dish. Covered, 7" 135.00

Candlesticks
  4". Red with flowers, fish handles. 85.00
  7½". Twisted stem 95.00
Castor Set 185.00
Champagnes. Knob stem. Set of six . 175.00

Compotes
  7½" high, 9½" diam. Open scalloped edge 150.00
  16" high. Cut 225.00
Cracker Jar. Vertical ribbed, top resilvered 195.00
Creamer. 4½" high, petal top, clear applied handle 85.00
Dish. Deep, 10¼" long. Beading around edge 75.00
Lamp. 9". Teakwood base.......... 125.00
Muffineer. Flame pattern, open bubble 75.00

Vases. 10½" high. Floral decor of lavender, green and gold. Pair $300.00

Pitchers
  8" high. Clear applied handle 230.00
  9" high. Bulging loop, clear handle. 295.00
Sugar Shaker. Ribbed Eight. Consolidated Lamp & Glass Product. 1880s 95.00
Syrup Jug. Tin top 110.00
Toothpick Holder. bulging Loop pattern 45.00
Tumbler 40.00

Vases
  4½" high. 2 clear loop handles ... 45.00
  7¼" high. Birds, bamboo decor... 120.00
  11¾" high. Pedestal base, applied clear glass scallop on top edge. Pair 225.00

PINK LUSTRE CHINA

Pink Lustre China derives its name from the pink decoration used on the ware. The china is normally of the Staffordshire variety. It is believed to have become popular in the 1840's.

Biscuit Barrel. 4½" high. With lid and verse. C. 1860 ....$ 135.00
Bowl. Shallow. 7¾" long. House pattern 60.00

Creamers
  5-petal flowers, green leaves 50.00
  House pattern 65.00

Cups and Saucers
  Schoolhouse pattern 55.00
  Small. Child with lamb 37.50
  Sunderland. Demi. Mottled pink .. 55.00
Mug. 3½" high. C. 1850 .... 65.00

Pitcher. 7" high. House pattern $120.00

Dessert Plate. 8½". Strawberry decor
$30.00

Pitchers

3½" high. House pattern	57.50
6" high. House pattern	100.00
6" high. Sunderland. Inscription both sides. "Sailors Farewell, etc."	125.00
Plaque. 8½x9½". Sunderland. Inscription both sides. "May Peace and Plenty on our Nation Smile," and "Trade with commerce bless the British Isle"	140.00

Plates

6"	27.50
8½". House pattern	50.00
9¼". Soup	35.00

Sauce Boat. Vintage pattern decor	45.00
Sugar Bowl. House pattern	115.00
Teapots	
Floral medallion decor. 5½" high	110.00
House pattern	155.00

PINK SLAG

The molded pattern regarded as true Pink Slag is that of an Inverted Fan and Feather. Recently pieces have come onto the market in the Inverted Strawberry and Inverted Thistle. The two patterns were made from molds of the now defunct Cambridge Glass Co. and are Not considered 'true' Pink Slag. The price of these late patterns are only a fraction of the original Pink Slag. Quality pieces shade from pink at the top to white at the bottom. This is the most sought after of the slag wares. The glass is extremely scarce and commands a good price from advanced collectors.

Berry Bowl	$ 600.00
Butter Dish. Covered	825.00
Compote. Jelly	625.00
Creamer	500.00
Cruet	650.00
Jam Jar	950.00
Lamp Base.Miniature	600.00
Lamp, Miniature. In shape of swan. Rare	800.00
Punch Cup	375.00

Jelly Compote. 5" high. "Feather and Fan" $625.00

Sauce	200.00
Sugar	550.00
Syrup	600.00
Toothpick Holder	425.00
Tumbler. Inverted Fan and Feather. 4" high	375.00

PIPES

According to history, tobacco was introduced in England by Sir Walter Raleigh. The use of the "vile weed" quickly became popular on the continent and the need for pipes developed. Many were produced in Holland in the Gouda vicinity and were exported throughout the world.

Meerschaum. Floral carved, in silk-lined leather case $75.00

5". Meerschaum. Running horse. Amber stem .... $ 55.00
5". Meerschaum. Two dogs carved on bowl. Amber stem	65.00
5". Bird devouring bug	55.00
5". Lioness on amber stem	70.00
5". Large bowl, tree stump with two wolves	75.00
5". Italian. Steer head with horns	32.50
5½". Bear head carved from walrus tusk. Wood stem	35.00
5½". Ivory carved bear head bowl. Wood stem	60.00
5½". Meerschaum. Wolf in relief. Amber stem	85.00
6". Meerschaum. Plain bowl with claw decoration	60.00
7". Meerschaum. Deer pursued by dog	115.00
9". Painted porcelain bowl. Wood stem	42.00
10". Lion and tree stump	85.00

Meerschaum. 12" long. Plain bowl $65.00

10". Painting of Kaiser Wilhelm First. Silver cover	125.00
11". Meerschaum. Fancy carved bowl, wood base, metal cover	60.00
11". Majolica barrel-shaped bowl with dog at base. Bright colors, wood stem	55.00
12". Meerschaum bowl, silver ribs, briar bottom. Regimented pipe, dated 1862	95.00
12". Meerschaum. Gold cover	85.00
12". Regimental pipe. Meerschaum bowl, briar bottom, metal cover, wood stem	85.00
14". Deer carved all around bowl	75.00
14". Face carved all around bowl	75.00
14". Meerschaum bowl with large carved dog	115.00
15". Meerschaum bowl. Girl by fence	75.00
15". Meerschaum bowl. Large dog	115.00
15". Porcelain bowl with Meissen mark, cherry wood stem. Green leaf decor on porcelain	100.00
16". Porcelain bowl, painted decor	50.00
17". Indian head bowl, size of baseball	95.00
17". Plain bowl, metal cover. Wood stem	65.00
17". Devil's head bowl of porcelain	65.00
18". Meerschaum bowl with carved house, fence and men. 5" high, dated 1800	145.00
28". Deer painted on bowl, wood stem, horn bottom	75.00
32". Painted porcelain bowl. Horn stem	85.00
34". Painted porcelain bowl	95.00
34". Porcelain bowl. Painted landscape decor	95.00
40". Prussian soldier and girl. Horn bottom, dated 1856	100.00
48". Porcelain bowl, cherry wood stem, gold trim	95.00
Horse's head bowl. Made in Italy	32.50
Meerschaum. Suede-covered, leather case	55.00

Meerschaum. Gold bands on pipe. In
velvet-lined case 75.00
Meerschaum. Original leather, velvet case. Carved horse on top 95.00
Opium. Cloisonne base, black background with blue and white water
lilies and white crane with blue
feathers...................... 85.00

PLATES, See
PORTRAIT AND SOUVENIR PLATES

PLAYER PIANO ROLLS

Vocalstyle Song Roll. "Shows You How
to Sing Correctly"

QRS Word Roll. "Mexicali Rose."

Player pianos were first introduced at the turn
of the 20th century. These first pianos were a
65-note player, i.e., the piano rolls had 65
notes punched across the 11¼" wide paper
roll.

In 1901 the Melville and Clark Piano Company
of New York manufactured the first 88-note
player...88 notes were punched in the roll. It
was not until 1908 that the 88-note piano roll
was universally accepted as the standard size.

Within the next few years there was a
controversy involving the publishers of sheet
music and piano-roll producers. The sheet
music publishers claimed that their copyrights
were being violated by the piano-roll people.
The piano-roll manufacturers explained that
their products were recordings. The courts
decided in favor of the piano-roll firms and
classified the rolls as 'sound recordings'.

There were several piano-roll companies in
the beginning, U. S., Imperial, Vocalstyle,
Recordo, Cannonized, and International to
name a few. The largest was QRS, who issued
over 1000 new titles a year. In 1920, QRS
acquired many of the smaller companies.

Piano-roll sales diminished to practically zero
when people began to move out of their
homes for entertainment. The first step in
"Modernizing any parlour" was to remove the
bulky player piano from the decor.

When the "do-it-yourself" craze swept the
country in 1951, old player pianos were
retrieved, restored and returned to the
recreational or family room. A new, smaller
spinet-type player piano was introduced. Two
new piano-roll companies, Aeolian and
Melodee, began producing new rolls until
1967 when they were dissolved.

Music rolls are still being made today but it is
the earlier ones that music collectors seek.
The average-price range of these older rolls is
between $2.00 and $5.00, depending on
condition, title and producer.

POCKET KNIVES

Over the years a wide variety of pocket knives
has appeared on the market. Each had its use
or mis-use, especially by young boys.

Boy Scout. Pal Cutlery Co. 4-blade...$ 12.50
Boy Scout. Remington. Bone handle,
emblem on side. 4" long 16.50
Coin Silver. 2½" blade, nail cleaner.
Ornate case, elongated figure 8
with lily-of-the-valley 15.00

Advertising-type. Two blades. "Wood-
worker's Tools" $10.00

Coin Silver. 3¼" long, 2 blades.
Fancy engraving with medallion
head each side 22.00
Gold. Gold-filled. One blade 14.00
Imperial
1 blade. MOP silver fish on handle 15.00
2 blades. Rough black 10.00
2 blades. MOP. Moose head on blue 25.00

3 blades. MOP, grey	18.50
Switch blade. 4¼" long	14.00
Jackknife. Carved, ivory, shaped like fish. Serrated blade............	15.00
Jackknife. Popeye	8.00
L. F. & C.N.B. Conn. 2 blades........	9.50
Pewter. Early 1800's	27.50
Providence, R.I. 3 blades. Rough black on white	10.00
Sheffield. G. Wostenholm. "Eng. IXL" on 3" blade, 2" blade, horn handle, 3½" long	20.00
Sterling, Hammered. 1 blade, 1 pick .	20.00

POMONA GLASS

Pomona glass was invented by Joseph Locke in 1884 and first produced by the New England Glass Co. It has two distinct surfaces. The etched portion has a pebbled surface, while the other part is flashed or tinted glass. A pattern is sometimes present but many times the ware is plain.

Bowls
4½" diam. Diamond Quilted
pattern ....$ 125.00

Cruet. 6" to top of stopper $225.00

5" diam., 3" high	225.00
8" diam. New England. Second grind, cornflower, leaf decor, frilled rim	325.00
9½" diam.	350.00
Finger Bowls	
5" diam. Second grind, diamond quilted, gold-washed rim	135.00
Blue. Cornflower decor.........	150.00
Light amber with frosted base...	125.00
Rose Bowl. 5½" high. Cornflowers, 10-toe base, D.Q. body. Second grind	350.00
Jug. 12" high. Lambrequin. Honey amber rim, handle	295.00
Lamp. Hanging. Strawflower decor on shade. Brass font and frame...	850.00
Pickle Castor. 11½" high. Cornflower pattern. Quad. plate holder with tongs	425.00
Pitchers	
5½" high. Bulbous, cornflowers ..	350.00
7" high. Amber-stained top, blue, amber cornflower design in center	500.00
7½" high. IVT, enameled green fern, pink flowers, blue cornflowers, tulips. Amber band, handle	450.00
8" high, 6" widest diam., 2" scalloped amber-tint band around collar. Band of blue cornflowers at mid section, undecorated portions are stippled, applied crystal handle	550.00
8½" high. Second grind. Undecorated...................	350.00
Plate. 6½" diam., straw color, ruffled edge	225.00
Punch Cups	
Acanthus Leaf. First grind	295.00
Blue cornflowers. First grind	175.00
New England. Diamond Quilted. Hand engraved	165.00
Ramekin Set. New England. Second grind, undecorated. D.Q., pale amber rim on plate and dish	150.00
Salt and Pepper Shakers. 4" high, pale amber leaves, cornflowers. Original tops. 2nd grind. Pair	245.00
Spoon Holder. 5½" high. Blue cornflowers, applied amber base .	175.00
Toothpick Holder	175.00
Tray, Ice Cream. 7½ x 12½". Cornflower decor in center	185.00
Tumblers	
Acorn decor. ITP................	110.00
Cornflower decor	110.00
Pansy and butterfly decor. D.Q. body, second grind	150.00
Plain. First grind...............	75.00

Vases

3" high.Fan-shaped, pinched top, second grind	130.00
1¾ x4x7". Amber top, inverted thumbprint	180.00
5" high. New England. Footed, pale blue cornflowers	225.00
10"high.Irid. green, stemmed	365.00
10" high. New England. Lily-shaped, sandy finish	250.00
15½" high. Lily-shaped, amber D.Q. top, blue cornflower border below. Clear base	300.00

PORTO BELLO WARE

This is an early ware issued by John & Thomas Astbury about 1739 commemorating the capture of Porto Bello on the Isthmus of Panama. It is usually a brownish-red pottery type of product with a glaze and figures of fortifications, ships and other scenes. Designs on the first ware were in white. Its popularity continued until 1860. Other designs and colors were applied.

Deep Dish. 7½ x11½" long. 2 handles, octagon-shape, ochre on dark brown. Signed. Impressed "Scott Bros." $145.00

Bowls

4" diam.	$ 85.00
5" diam.	95.00
Flower Pot. 6½" high. Black, ochre foliage decor	125.00
Jug. J. & T. Astbury. Shelton. C. 1760	175.00

Pitchers

5-3/8" high	100.00
6½" high. Reddish-brown ground with design in yellow	135.00

PORTRAIT PLATES

During the latter part of the Victorian era it was the fashion of the day to have portrait plates, primarily of female subjects, hanging in the hall or Sunday parlor. Produced commercially, the subjects were not of members of the family.

9½". Dark green rim, gold trim. Lady in black hat and blue flowers. Signed. "Copyright 1909 by Phillip Boleau" $45.00

5". Center of classic figures, gold borders. Signed Kaufmann. Pair	$ 175.00
8". Pittsburgh Commandery Plate. Girl with roses, blue border, gold trim	28.50
8¼". Transfer picture of lady and cherub	25.00
8½". Signed Madam Sans. Gene	55.00
8¾". Limoges. Queen Louise	30.00
9". Madam LeBrun and Daughter. Gold border	28.50
9¼". Woman with rose in hair, dark brown rim, gold trim. Signed G. Bonfits	38.50
9½". Brunette woman. Decorated in deep rose and gold	35.00
9½". Madonna and Child. Brown to tan tints	30.00
9½". Marie Louise. Royal and embossed white and royal gold	45.00
9¾". Woman with brown hair, yellow background, brown rim. Signed"Innocence." Cress Wiollett	29.50
9-5/8". Tin. "Dresden Art #201 Ariadne." Lady border	28.50

10". Farmer, dog, cows. Irregular edge. Deep, rich shading. Gold, reliefs. Marked Z.S.Bavaria 47.50

10". Girl's head in center with gold band surrounding it. Marked D. & C. France 45.00

10". Portrait of lady 48.00

10". Portrait of lady on gray background. Red hair, yellow ribbon, light pink dress. Red border with fine gold decor 36.50

10". Queen Louise, with scarf 35.00

11½". Art Nouveau design. Brunette, iridescent border. Wired to hang.......................... 42.50

11½". Lady's head and shoulders on Bavarian china 65.00

Military figures "Miles and Hobson." Cobalt and gold trim 35.00

POST CARDS
(Before 1915)

Airplanes. Early ....$	2.50
Angels	.50
Autos	1.25
Boats, Naval	1.00

May the toys of your liking fill your Christmas stocking

Santa. Gibson Art Co., Cinn., Ohio. Copyright 1910 ....$1.50

Boats, Sailing	1.00
Bridges..........................	.50
Bunnies	.50
California (before 1900)	1.00
Capitols [U.S.State]	.50
Chicks	.50
Christmas, children	2.50
Churches	.50
Comics	.50
Coney Island, N.Y.	.50
Courthouses	.50
Crosses	.25
Disasters (floods, tornadoes, etc.) ..	1.25
Easter Chicks	.50
Easter, Children	3.00
Easter Crosses	.25
Embossed and Airbrush Types	1.25
Expositions (to 1900)	2.00
Fairs (before 1900)	1.25
Flags, 1918. Silk woven. "Loving Sister"	6.50
Florals (mixed flowers, etc.!)	.45
Florals, Letters	.45
Foreign, Colored	.35
Gelatin (processed type)	1.00
Greetings, Birds	.50
Greetings, Children	.75
Greetings, General type	.75
Hall Mfg. July 4th, St. Patrick, etc. ..	1.00
Horseshoes	.50
Indians	1.00
*Kewpie Christmas Postcards. Each .	12.50
Leather	1.75
Newspaper Comics	2.00
New York Views..................	.35
Old New England	.50
Parades (before 1900)	.75
Patriotic	.50
Presidents (before 1915)	3.50
Roses (only)	.35
Rotograph Views (colored)	.35
Santas	1.25
States..........................	.50
*Sunbonnet Baby. 7 cards..........	50.00
Thanksgiving (General)	.75
Thanksgiving Turkeys	1.00
Tinselled	1.50
Tucks Mfg. Greetings	5.00
Tucks Mfg. Halloween	4.00
Tucks Mfg. Oilettes...............	3.50
Tucks Mfg. Santa	7.50

*Reproduced Item

POT LIDS

Tha majority of these lids for containers of hair oil (bear grease), shaving soaps, etc., was made by the Pratt Works at Fenton, Staffordshire between 1845 and 1880. The various designs were placed under glaze by a multicolor transfer method.

Alas. Poor Bruin ....$	82.50
Blue Boy. Framed	90.00
Contrast	65.00
Crystal Palace. Framed	110.00
Dr. Johnson	65.00
Fallen Tree, with river in bkgd.	60.00
Farriers, The. Signed J. Austin, complete	95.00
Fisherman in boat on turbulent sea .	72.50
Garibaldi	75.00
Golden. Hour. Constantinople, framed	95.00
Harbor at Hong Kong	65.00
Hide and Seek...................	75.00
International Exposition, 1862......	75.00
Landing the Fare, Pegwell Bay......	55.00
Letter from the Diggins, A	75.00
Master of the Hound, complete	85.00
Ning Po River	72.50
Pair, A	65.00
Queen standing on balcony. 7" square frame	110.00
Racing Scene at Fair..............	80.00
Rifle Contest. Wimbledon	80.00
Second Appeal. Framed	95.00
Shapespeare's Home, complete	70.00
Shepherdess with Dog, 3 sheep. Framed	110.00

"A Pair"....................$65.00

Shrimpers, The	65.00
Soldier's Dancing Before Villiagers ..	75.00
Village Wedding	75.00
Uncle Toby......................	75.00

POTTERY, EARLY

Pottery has been made since ancient times. This category mainly covers items made in the United States, especially in New York, New Jersey, Pennsylvania and Virginia, from 1800 to 1900.

Pottery with decorations such as swans, ducks, flowers, people, etc., commands a higher price than pottery with only the manufacturer's name. Eagle decorations bring the highest prices.

Crock. 3-gallon. 3 coggle wheel lines around top. Cobalt decor $195.00

Bank. Turnip. Mkd. "Charity" ......$	25.00
Bowls	
Milk. 2¾ x9½" diam.	35.00
Pennsylvania Redware. 10¼" diam. Deep red color...........	145.00
Chimney Pot. 25½" high. Jos. Eneix Evans, New Geneva, Pa. Scarce ..	500.00
Crocks	
2-gallon. Jas. H. Hamilton & Co. Greensboro, Pa...............	110.00
3-gallon. 12" high, blue swan "Cowden & Wilcox," Harrisburg, Pa.	175.00
3-gallon. A. P. Donaghho, Parkersburg, W. Va.	95.00
3-gallon. C. W. Braum, Buffalo, N. Y. Bird decor	300.00

Crock. 8-gallon. Incised marked J. Hamilton, Beaver Co. Cobalt decor, grey ground, coggle wheelmarks
$350.00

Close up of J. Hamilton, Beaver

3-gallon. Gray with blue flowers	95.00
4-gallon. 14" high. Blue eagle on gray ground. By T. F. Reppert in Greensboro, Penna.	375.00
4-gallon. 14" high. Blue floral decor on gray ground. By Jas. Hamilton & Co., Greensboro, Penna.	175.00
4-gallon. Williams & Reppert, Greensboro, Pa.	175.00
5-gallon. Williams, New Geneva, Penna.	195.00
10-gallon. Williams & Reppert. Greensboro, Penna. Eagle decor .	600.00
16-gallon. Gray ground, dark blue decor & stenciled "Hamilton & Jones, Greensboro, Pa."	450.00

Lard Crock. By T. F. Reppert, Greensboro, Pa.	500.00

Foot Warmers

Shape of pig	75.00
Shape of suitcase. 4½" high, 9½" long. Mkd. "Bourne, Denby, England"	75.00

Jugs

1-gallon. 8" high. Impressed "John Bell." Celadon-type glaze	195.00
1-gallon. "Hamilton & Jones." Gray body with cobalt decor	60.00

Molds

Fish	28.50
Pudding. 9" diam. Redware	95.00
Rabbit. Large	45.00
Turk Head. Pennsylvania Redware	75.00
Wheat	35.00
Pie Plate. 9". Pennsylvania Redware	75.00

Pitchers

New Geneve, Pa. Tan Ware:

5½" high	225.00
6¾" high	275.00
Redware. 4" high. Green glaze ...	195.00
Water. 2-gallon. Made at Greensboro, Pa. by James Hamilton, Potter	300.00

Crock. 4-gallon. Grey with cobalt decor. Woman, two trees $650.00

Pitcher. 8" high. Penna. Tan Ware
$350.00

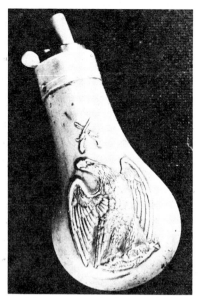

4" long. Brass eagle decor on both
sides $67.50

Roof Tile. 7" wide, 14½" long, ¾"
thick. Early American, red clay
with rain funnel 40.00
Salt Box. Hanging-type with tin
cover. Blue decor with "Salt" on
front 40.00
Tobacco Jar. Pebbled gray with blue
rose and leaves, matching metal
handle. 4½ x 6-1/8" high 60.00

POWDER FLASKS AND HORNS

Containers for gun powder were made in a
variety of shapes and sizes. The most common
types were cow and buffalo horns and were
sometimes engraved. Patented containers
were later produced in brass and pewter.

Brass. 9½" long. U.S. .... $ 87.50
Brass. European 55.00
Civil War. 2x4½" long. Pistol flask,
with eagle holding a pistol and
flask in each claw on obverse and
reverse 95.00
Copper. Brass fittings 25.00

"Dead Game." 8½" long, brass.
James Dixon Co. 60.00
"Eagle." 5" long. Coat-of-Arms,
decorated on front and back.
Copper with brass top 65.00
"Fleur-de-lis." Brass 65.00
Flower with vines. 7½" high. Patent
dispenser. Copper 55.00
Flora and Fauna." 9". Leather
tooled 50.00
Gunstock-type. Copper. C. 1850s.
"Dixon" 85.00
Horn, Carved
5" long. Hunter 95.00
6" long. Leather strap 27.00
7" long. Carved dog, tree 85.00
16" long. Hunter's metal name
plate 45.00
"R. Ritter, 1842" 30.00
Horn, Plain
8" 22.50
9" 24.50
13" 30.00
15", pewter spout 45.00
16" 40.00
"Hunter and Dog." 7½" high. Patent
dispenser. Brass 65.00

8" high. Brass, leather strap. Shell design $55.00

Leather with brass fitting. 9" long ... 30.00
Petal designs
  5" long. Brass 50.00
  7" long. Pewter with brass
    dispenser 50.00
Rabbit. 8" high. Brass. Patent
  dispenser 55.00
Ribbed center. Patent dispenser.
  Copper........................ 55.00
"Shell" Pewter. Brass nozzle 65.00
"Stag and Dogs." 8" high. Patent
  dispenser. Copper 60.00
Scrimshaw Scenes
  Alamo under attack by Mexicans,
    flag of Texas, dated March 6,
    1836.......................... 350.00

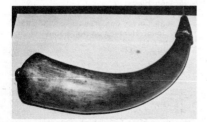

Plain with wood plug. 10" $38.00

Carved decor of a knight and lion.
  European origin, dated 1600 ..... 395.00
War of 1812. American ship
  attacking British at Delaware Bay.
  June 12, 1813 .... 395.00
"Wreath and Shield." American
  Brass and Cap Co. 50.00

PRATT WARE

Pratt ware was made at the Fenton Factory in the Staffordshire district of England, C. 1775-1805. Characteristics of the ware are the raised figures and decorations which are highly colored in green, blue, black, purple and orange. Transfer pictures were also used in dinner services and other items.

Candlestick. 7-3/8". Marked "Pratt
  Fenton Old Greek." People and
  motifs on background ....$ 45.00
Compotes
  9¼" diam., 5" high. English castle
    scene 125.00
  Colorful transfer picture in center 125.00
Creamer. 3" black basalt ground,
  Grecian figures 55.00
Cup and Saucer. Scenic 35.00
Dessert Set. Eight 5½" plates. Oval,
  handled bowl 350.00
Drinking Vessels, Satyr Mask
  4¼" high. Multicolored. C. 1790 .. 165.00
  5" high. Frog inside, bright glazes,
    brown, yellow predominating.
    C. 1790 .... 150.00
Figural. 3½" high. Man on white
  base, in white pantaloons, green
  over-garment, long black coat,
  yellow hat..................... 55.00
Humidor. 5½" high, 4" diam.
  "Pratt Fenton Old Greek." People
  and motifs on background 75.00
Jug. Tavern scene, raised figures.
  Olive-green, yellow, blue, brown . 150.00
Lids, See "Pot Lids"
Pipe. 9¾" long. 4 human masks in
  relief on bowl. Mottled black
  dog's head stem, blue, ochre
  glazes. 18th century 165.00
Pitchers
  4¾" high. Dove of Peace design in
    Pink Lustre. Early 265.00
  5" high. Illustrated with picture of
    Admiral Nelson on one side,
    Captain Berry on other. Silvered
    spout 250.00
  5¼" high. Lustre, Wellington..... 130.00
  11" high. Pewter cover, beige
    background, colorful seashells. C.
    1800......................... 275.00

Plates

7". Animals, people in front of Rust-colored border. Colorful, signed J.A. 50.00

7". Cattle and Ruins. White, gray and gold border 50.00

7". Center transfer of man reading newspaper, "The Times" . 55.00

7". Transfer, with apple green border. Pair 80.00

8½". Red Bull Inn. Lilac border ... 60.00

8½". Ruined Temple. Tan border . 60.00

8½". Rustic Laundrywoman. Tan border 60.00

8½". The Picnic. Maroon border .. 60.00

8½". View of Phila. Expo. 1876. Lavender band 55.00

8½". Waterfalls, people. Maroon border 55.00

8¾". Market scene. Center turquoise border, gold decorated rim. Late 50.00

9¼". Transfer, gold border. Pair ... 165.00

9½". The Cavalier. Basketweave with white border 62.00

9½". Fording the Stream. White border 65.00

9½". Game Bag. Basketweave with white border 65.00

9½". Scene, two boys peeping through doorway into school room. Acorn and leaf border 65.00

9½". Shakespeare's Birthplace. Basketweave with white border .. 70.00

9½". The Trooper. Basketweave with white border 65.00

9½". Wimbledon, 1860. Basketweave with white border 65.00

9¾". Battle of the Nile 65.00

Pot Lids, See "Pot 'lids"

Snuff Jar. 4" high, blue with tan and black transfer of men, animals ... 25.00

Sugar and Creamer. Etruscan. Grecian figure. C. 1850 .... 110.00

Sugar Bowl. Covered, black body with white classical figures 90.00

Teapot. Large 185.00

PRIMITIVE PAINTINGS

The term is used in the United States to denote Folk art — amateur art, beginning art or untrained art.

The majority was done in the 1800-1900 period. Folk art from the 1825-1850 era is considered best as itinerant artists taught the subject and it was "fashionable" to have painting as a hobby. Most primitive paintings are unsigned.

Water Color. 5x6½". Painting of woman in blue dress, pink shawl and collar. Early. Penna. $195.00

Boy and Dog. Boy standing, with hand on dog's head. In gold leaf frame, 4½' high, 3½' wide $2000.00

Farm Scene. Farm house with children on porch, barn, cattle and buggy....................... 850.00

Pitcher. Children playing, within ear-shaped decoration $295.00

Farm Scene. House, barn, horses in field, cat on porch, rider. Approx. 20x30", in walnut frame. ... 750.00

Girl. In blue dress, red background, brown hair and eyes, with brown dog ... 2500.00

Girl, Young. 37½x50", including gold-gilt frame ... 1750.00

Girl. Pouring tea. 26x30" gold leaf frame ... 2500.00

Girl. Small, in red dress, brown eyes, black shoes ... 1250.00

Girl, Young. With dog. 20x25¾", gold frame ... 1650.00

Man. Seining for fish. Bridge nearby. Trees and mountains in background. 30½x38½" ... 500.00

Portrait of a judge's children, Erie, Penna. ... 3000.00

Woman in red. Tiverton, R.I. 33½x40" gold leaf frame ... 1250.00

PRINTS

Prints are intended reproductions of an artist's original painting, drawings, designs, etc.

Recently, prints have come into their own because of the surging interest in the arts, and the almost "untouchable" prices of good original works. It is still possible today to gather good works of art at a fraction of the cost of the originals through prints, but do be careful of the 'reproductions' of the 'reproductions.' Know your prints or know your dealer!

The following list is a guide to the prints of some artists of the 20th century, mainly Parrish and Nutting.

For the most complete, comprehensive and up-to-date prices on Currier and Ives and other printmakers, consult the 1976 edition of "4th Print Price Guide" by Edwin G. Warman.

Christy, Howard Chandler
Four in Hand, 1901 ... $ 12.00
Gold is Not All ... 12.00
Poaching, 1903 ... 12.00

Nutting, Wallace
Berkshire Cross Road, A ... 12.00
Birch Approach, A. 13x16", framed ... 18.00
Cliff Clingers ... 10.00
Jane. 4½x9½", stands on steps, etc. Framed 12x17" ... 35.00
Larkspur. 17½x20½", Signed, old frame ... 30.00
Life of the Golden Age, The. Large, framed ... 25.00
Pomperacing Water ... 12.50
Purity ... 10.00
Road to Far Away, The ... 12.00

Maxfield Parrish. 17x18½", including highly carved frame. "Ye Royall Recepcioun" ... $30.00

Roadside Grace. Framed ... 18.50
Rock Bound Coast, The ... 17.00
Swimming Pool, The . 12½x15½". Signed, framed ... 32.50
Very Satisfactory. 14x17". Signed, framed, copyright #C9106 ... 27.50
Where the Road Turns ... 10.00

Parrish, Maxfield
Cleopatra. 12x14" ... 6.50
Contentment. 5x7" ... 5.00
Daybreak. 18x30" ... 20.00
Dreaming. 9x15" ... 7.50
Ecstasy. 5x7" ... 5.00
Old King Cole. 7x25½". In Art Nouveau solid oak frame, on handcut mat frame, 13½x32" ... 22.50
Reveries. 5x7" ... 5.00
Stars. 5x7" ... 5.00

QUEZAL GLASS

A fine type of art glass produced at Maspeth, L.I., New York from 1901 to 1920 by Martin Bach, Sr., a former Tiffany Glass Company employee. The glass was of the Tiffany-type but generally improved in design. It is an overlay glass with a colored or opaque white over a pure transparent color. The outer layer of glass was drawn into various designs or shapes, often having a drape with a peacock eye at the end of the feather.

The glass was named for the Central American bird. All pieces are reported to have been signed with the word "Quezal."

After the death of Mr. Bach in 1920 his son-in-law, Conrad Vahlsing, opened a small shop near Elmhurst, L.I., New York, where he produced the same types of ware until 1929 when the glass lost its popularity. In later years Vahlsing marked his glass "Lustre Art Glass."

Candleholder. 7" high. Iridescent. Shade on old base $150.00

Bell. Large. Green pulled feather on white calcite, glass ball clapper and cut jewel top . . . . $ 495.00

Bowls

3" diam., 8" high. Green and white. 4½" stem ends in 5 white leaves outlined green on gold. 3" diam bowl, 2¼" opening 300.00

10" diam., 3½" high. Blue, with matching 11" plate, purple and green iridescent. Set 500.00

Rose Bowl. Footed, 4¼" wide. Deep gold with purple and red iridescence 285.00

Compotes

6" diam., 8" high. Golden iridescence. Signed 350.00

7½" diam., 4½" high. Deep blue bowl with gold feet. Signed 575.00

Bonbon. Small, shallow. Gold amethyst, scalloped top. Signed . . 145.00

Nut. 4" diam. 175.00

Glass, Juice. Signed 175.00

Lamps

Hanging. Byzantine motif in white with feathers 1000.00

Night Light. 13" high, 5" diam. Green, gold and white feathered. Signed 1250.00

Table. Metal base with 13" shade. 3 lily-shaped lights beneath shade in same pattern 1500.00

Lamp Shades

5" diam., 5½" high. Gold and white, with gold irid. threading, green and gold leaves. Signed . . . 85.00

5¾" diam. Gold iridescent with King Tut designs. Signed 95.00

6¼" high. Gas. Green veining on calcite. Gold irid. Signed 85.00

6½" diam., 4½" neck. Mushroom-shaped. Signed 85.00

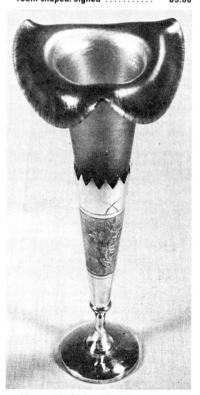

Vase. 9" high. Lily. Two parts, quadruple plate holder $265.00

23" diam., 11¼" high. Vine and
leaf decor, with milkmaid and
bucket 395.00
Plate. 11¼". Iridescent with rainbow
rim 250.00

Salts

Master. 1½" base, 3" diam. top,
1¼" high, irid. gold, purple. Signed   175.00
Ribbed body. Signed 100.00

Vases

3" high. Dimpled sides, gold irid.
Signed 175.00
4" high. Iridescent blue, gold and
green with red stripes 300.00
5" high. Silver overlay, irid.
Signed 625.00
5" high, 5" wide. Melon-shaped
and colored in deep grass-green
with lighter green and rose.
Opalescent pearl colored lining.
Signed 500.00
5" high. Opaque, scroddled in
gray, brown, yellow, peacock
green, lavender and blue 375.00
6" high. Gold pulled feathers to
cream. Gold neck 875.00
7" high. Green and gold hearts
with gold applied webbing. Signed   525.00
9" high. Iridescent gold, green
blue, purple and bronze in feather
design on emerald background...   775.00
9½" high. Burnished coin-gold
above green and gold feather
ends at shoulder. Feathers are
iridized yellow. 2½" base diam.
Signed 800.00
9½" high. Gold color. Signed 800.00
10" high. Gold, yellow-green
lustre swirl decoration. Signed
A369 ....   1000.00
12" high. Green and white, bold
stripes outside, gold iridescence
inside. Signed 1200.00

QUILTS, See LINENS

QUIMPER

A type of pottery produced by Henry Quimper
of Finistere, France, after 1900. It is usually
decorated in bright colors with provincial
scenes of the country. It was imported into the
United States as a gift shop item until the
beginning of World War II.
The marks "Henriot Quimper, France" or
"Quimper" appear on most articles.
A number of items have been reproduced
recently, including various sizes of plates,
cups and saucers.

Cup and Saucer. Flower and leaf
decor. Signed. "Henriot" Quimper.
France $18.50

Bagpipe. Hanging................$ 27.50
Bell. 3", yellow ground, blue florals .   22.50

Bowls

6½" diam. Cereal. Signed 10.00
9" square. Yellow 15.00
10". Woman 24.50
10½". Pink and blue 27.50
12". Holes for hanging 35.00
Box, Covered. Deer decor.
2½ x 4½ x 6"...................   30.00
Butter Dish. Covered. Marked "Hen-
riot Quimper, France"...........   37.00
Butter Tub. Covered. 4½" diam.,
2½" high.....................   27.50
Candleholder. 5¼" high. Chamber-
type, handled 32.00
Candlestick. Boy with jar on head.
Marked 25.00
Creamer. Character shaped,
woman's head 28.50
Cruet Set. Yellow around floral
design holder, two bottles 38.50
Cup and Saucer. Square 20.00
Egg Cup 18.50
Figurals
2¼" high, 4" wide. Provincial.
Man. Green, yellow, blue on
white. Double handled. Signed
Henriot 28.50
5¼". Goose. Marked France 30.00
5¼" high. Stock Peasant carrying
basket. Blue smock, plaid pants,
#759. Signed..................   28.50

5½" high. Man in Breton costume. Signed	28.50
Flower Holder. Floral decor with pheasant. Henriot-Violin	30.00
Inkwells	
8" long, 4½" wide. Pen tray, round covered well. Marked	30.00
12" long, double, decorated	50.00
14" long, 7" high. Portrait of girl in costume	55.00
Shape of peasant's hat	45.00
Knife Rest. Peasant scene	20.00
Mug. Dancers	17.50
Nappie. 5¾" diam.	12.50
Pitchers	
3½" high	20.00
6½" high. Woman	28.50
8" high. Pinched spout. Marked	32.50
Water	55.00

Plates	
5". Signed. Pair	38.50
6½". Decorated in yellow, blue, green and orange	20.00
7". Portrait center	20.00
7½". Flowers	22.50
8". Hexagonal, with portrait of girl with rope in center, floral border	25.00
9½". Irregular shaped rim. Peasant man blowing pipe. Signed.	28.50
9¾". Floral center, peasant-type decor. Border	28.50
10". Man with staff. White with green, yellow and blue	30.00
Platter. 12", dragonfly center	45.00
Porringer. Double, signed	25.00
Salts	
Double. Diamond shape, peasants	27.50
Open. Two swans	22.50
Oval	10.00
Single. Diamond shape. Woman	12.00
Saucer	8.50
Shoes. 3¼". Figure of woman. Pr.	30.00
Sugar Bowl. Yellow background, man and flowers	40.00
Sugar Bowl and Creamer. Marked	75.00
Sweetmeat Dish. 12" square. Large, snake handle. Peasant pictures, scalloped	24.50
Tea Plate. Fluted rim. Man and woman with floral decor	22.50
Tea Tile. Four feet, peasant decor	20.00
Teapot. Small, red and white with yellow bands	75.00
Tray. 8½x15". Open handles, boy, girl center. Marked	45.00
Tumbler. 4½" high. Marked	18.00
Tureen. 9x14". Large, covered	85.00

R. S. GERMANY

The china was made in Tillowitz in lower Silesia. It is approximately the same quality as R. S. Prussia china, since a member of that firm left the company in Prussia and started a new operation.

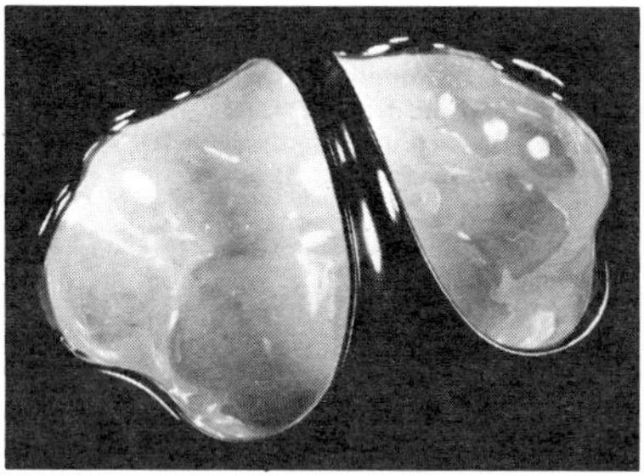

Candy Dish. 7" long. Handled, pearlized interior. Silver lustre exterior
$45.00

Ash Tray. 5¼" oblong. Handles, gray ground, allover figured gold and gold leaves. White iris center. Signed	$ 15.00
Basket. Small, handled. Blue, cream-colored center, small pink flowers	25.00
Bowls	
6¾x9¼". Footed. Elipse with border folded out. 4 embossed feet. Satin greens, gold tracery floral decor. Signed	62.50
7¼" diam. Pedestaled. H/P orange, white flowers, green ground	25.00
8¼" diam. Hexagonally rounded. Underplate 9½". Gold trim, floral, signed. Set	65.00
9" diam. "Poppy" pattern. With 5 berry bowls. Set	60.00
9" diam., 2½" high. 8-sided wreath and star, high open handles	45.00
10" diam. Floral satin finish. Molded rim sides. Green mark	50.00
Candle Holder. 5" high. Lilies of the valley on beige, green ground. Widens toward bottom	28.50
Chocolate Cup and Saucer. Diagonal, melon-ribbed, white dogwood. mauve iridescence. Raised gold. Signed	28.50

Chocolate Pot. 5" high. Blue, pink
Nouveau florals, light green
ground, gold handle 38.50
Chocolate Set. Pot, 6 cups, saucers.
Colored ground, florals. Set 195.00
Compote. White with silver design.
Tillowitz-Silesia 29.50
Cookie Jars
5" high. White lustre, handpainted
roses, gold trim. Signed 78.50
Covered. 2 handles. Acorn finial,
gold and gold tracery. Geometric
decor in aqua and black with
floral medallions 75.00
Creamers
Calla Lily. Eggshell 26.50
Mossy caramels to off-white.
White flowers, caramel bud
center, long stems, leaves. Signed .   26.50
Orange poppies and buds 17.50
Crumber and Scraper. Apricot edge,
scroll and gold decor, roses 20.00
Cups and Saucers, Demitasse
Gold with black, green stems.
Mauve and pink flowers. Signed . .   24.50
Roses, shades of bown, greens
fading to whtie. Signed 25.00
Dishes
Candy. Shell-shaped. Scalloped,
gold border, pastel roses. Green
mark 37.50
Cheese and Cracker. 9" diam., 2"
high. Bisque finish, white
hydrangea 75.00
Pickle. 9". Rising sides, gold
border. Mossy apricot, mustard
flowers, roses, snowballs, leaves.
Signed 22.50
Relish. 7½". Boat-shape. Handled,
light blue-turquoise ground, to
mauve, pansy roses, gold leaves,
stems. Signed 25.00
Hatpin Holders
Green mark. Closed bottom, pale
green poppies 24.00
Green with white flowers 25.00
Large. Green mark only. White
and yellow roses 50.00
Pale green with handpainted
yellow jonquils. Signed 24.00
Mustard Pot and Ladle. 3" high, rose
decor, pink and gold trim. Set 22.50
Nappies
5½". Green mark. H/P daisies,
much gold, handled 17.50
Triangular-shaped. 6¾" long,
including round handle. Pink roses,
green to beige background,
scalloped, satin finish 19.50

Plate. 6½". White tulips on shaded
green ground $16.50
Pitchers
Cider. Large, yellow crysanthe-
mums, blue-green ground. Signed
in red 50.00
Syrup. Pale green to white, white
hydrangea, gold trim. Bisque 35.00

Plates
7½". Scenic, shepherd boy,
farmhouse, tree 35.00
7-5/8". Scenic. Forest scene of
man in wagon talking to woman
with basket. Signed Rein 35.00
9". Gold rim, yellow turquoise.
Floral decor, fronds and stems.
Signed 35.00
11½". Gardenias, daisies. Brown,
green, open handles 45.00
Powder Box. Round, pink rose decor   30.00
Sugar. Covered. 2 handles, green
and pastel moss, floral decor.
Signed 30.00
Sugars and Creamers
Floral on shaded beige ground . . .   60.00
Footed. Red flowers, gold handles
and finial 75.00
Tea Set. 4 cups, saucers, four 7½"
plates, creamer, covered sugar,
3x7½". Bowl not marked. Tan and
brown lustre. Pink roses. Set 195.00
Toothpick Holders
2 handles. Roses, 14K gold 30.00
3 handles, gold trim. Pansies over
pastel body. Signed 35.00
Trays
3¼x5½". Pin. White and yellow
roses. Scalloped 25.00

5x14". Handled, tan shading, white flowers with gold centers, green leaves.................... 26.50
Bread. 12½" long, 5¾" wide. Pink, roses, gold 20.00

R. S. PRUSSIA CHINA

A type of china made the latter part of the 19th century in Prussia, one of the German states. The quality is similar to Haviland and Limoges. The majority of it was factory decorated, however, a piece turns up occasionally bearing the name of a decorator. The ware bears the letters "R.S." with a green wreath and red star.

Berry Sets
7 pieces. Heavy gold and floating water lilies in center .... $ 250.00
Bowl with 5 dishes. Daisy pattern, enameled, green and gold trim. Red mark..................... 350.00
Bowl and 6 dishes. Pastel poppies on tinted ground, gold scalloped edge......................... 200.00
Bowl, large, with 6 small bowls. Pale roses on cream ground. Erdmann Schlegelmilch Thuringin mark 225.00

Bowls
5" diam. Green ground, white, yellow poppies................. 45.00
5½" diam. Springtime portrait ... 75.00
8½" diam. Green on white ground, gold decor, floral center . 125.00
9x14". Bluebirds and cottage 500.00
10" diam. Green ground, scalloped, beaded edge, white, pink, yellow poppies........... 125.00
10" diam. Raised orchid border, rose in center, gold scalloped edge......................... 135.00

Bowl. 9½" diam. Green, multicolored flowers. Gold trim $125.00

11" diam. Baroque-type, large roses 150.00
12" diam. Double scallop, gold edge, flowers, pink orchid and white poppies.................. 150.00
13½" diam. Oval 175.00

Boxes
2½x4¼". Covered. Scroll embossed beaded top, scalloped, scrolled. Tea roses, buds, leaves.. 95.00
Powder. Rose decor............ 68.50
Jewel. Small, covered, small pink and white flowers 85.00
Celery Holder. Pink roses. Red mark 100.00

Chocolate Pots
10" high. White ground shading to green, pink wild rose finial. Crimped top, ornate handle. Unmarked.................... 125.00
Red roses on green background. Red mark..................... 175.00
Swans, birds, satin. Red mark..... 275.00

Chocolate Sets
Dogwood pattern. 6 cups, saucers 350.00
Pot, 8 cups, saucers. Green on white with gold trim 300.00
Coffee Pot. Footed, 9½" high. Intricate leaf finial on lid. Ornate handle with gold trim. Floral decor. Feet splayed out and embossed over ecru, turquoise ... 225.00
Compote. Pedestal-type. 7" high, 6½" diam. Green ground, decorated with shaded roses. Red mark 125.00
Cookie Jar. Covered. Red mark. Base scallops form feet. White and caramel, lilac flowers, gold. Flower finial, floral decor in cerise, yellow and green leaves .. 150.00

Cracker Jars
6½" to top of finial. Green decor with gold sprays................ 135.00
7¼" high, 6" diam. Footed, paneled with pink, yellow roses, green decor 145.00
Covered. Bulbous. Pink rose decor with green wreath, red mark..... 185.00
Creamer. Swirled, pearl-lustre body with daffodils outlined in gold ... 75.00

Cups and Saucers
Demitasse. Green & white floral decor 45.00
Mustache. Flower decor on yellow ground. Gold handle 115.00
Swans and trees................ 75.00
Tea. Flower decor, red mark 75.00

Dishes
Bonbon. Satinized, pink, white roses 50.00

Candy. 7". Pale orange, roses on soft green ground 98.50

Celery. 7x14". Red roses, white mums, gold 100.00

Olive. 4½x9½". Pink roses, gold trim 48.50

Sauce
  5". Yellow floral, wheat shafts in relief 25.00
  Gold scalloped edge, pastel poppies on tinted background. Set of six 150.00

Vegetable. 8x13". White lilies, silver resist 95.00

Hair Receiver. Diamond-shaped 78.50

Hatpin Holders
  Gold, shading with yellow roses .. 75.00
  Poppies 85.00

Muffineer. Panelled, green & white flowers, gold sprays and trim, scalloped...................... 100.00

Mustard 65.00

Pitcher. 6¼" high, 6½" diam.
Lemonade. White & green ground, gloss finish. Lilies on both sides .. 225.00

Planter. With insert. Red mark 150.00

Plates
  6½". Rose decor. Set of six 85.00
  7". "Lily-of-the-Valley" 35.00
  7½". Rose decor, raised border .. 70.00
  8". Blue and gold 60.00
  8½". Pink poppies & white lilies of the valley. Irregular edge........ 75.00
  8¾". Rose flowers, heavy gold. Signed 62.00
  9". Scenic, boats, castle. Open handles 125.00
  9¾". 2-handled, 5 large roses shading to salmon to white 45.00
  10". Open handles.............. 100.00
  10½". Melon boys, browns 395.00
  10¾". Handled, white ground in center, lavender poppies, violets . 65.00
  11". Shepherd, sheep on path to house. Rust floral. Handpainted. Marked, signed 65.00
  11". Ship scene, red mark 150.00
  11". Swans swimming, gold border with blue, yellow, green background 125.00
  11". With 5 matching serving plates, 7½". Pink carnations. Set . 175.00
  11¼". Handled with large scalloped edge, gold, handpainted lavender flowers 110.00
  Floral decor, handled 115.00
  Large. Deep pink flowers on green, white ground. Signed 99.00

Powder Box. Rose decor 68.50

Ring Tree 62.00

Salt & Pepper Shakers. Melon twist ribs in glossy ferns, white shadow flowers. Pair 70.00

Shaving Mugs
  3" high. Pink, lavender on white, green bkgd., gold 95.00
  Footed, floral decor. Red mark ... 145.00
  Pink flowers, gold trim, green leaves 120.00

Sugar Bowl. Covered, pink roses & green leaves with gold 125.00

Sugar Bowls and Creamers
  Ball shaped. Dark green shading with ferns, yellow roses and pond lilies........................ 125.00
  Bluebird pedestal. Jeweled and pearlized...................... 425.00
  Dogwood pattern 145.00
  Footed, red rose decor 145.00
  Mill scene on creamer. Cottage scene on sugar with white background. Ornate 275.00

Sugar Shakers
  Red roses, white mums 75.00
  Satin finish. Roses around base, three handles 85.00

Syrups
  Green & yellow, pink roses 85.00
  Petalled feet, intricate handle. Embossed, floral decor, gold 90.00

Teapot. Footed, red rose & green leaf decor with gold trim 145.00

Tea Set. Pot, sugar & creamer. Green and white 225.00

Tea Strainer. Handled, depressed center with holes. Star within star

Plate. 6½". White ground with roses, gold trim. Red mark $18.00

pattern. Aqua embossing, small
gold and lavender flowers, green
leaves 60.00
Toothpick Holders
3-handled 125.00
Swirl pattern................. 75.00
Trays
7x11". Pale green ground, white
blossoms with pink centers. Gold
edge. Red mark 145.00
Bread. 6x12". Irregular border,
fuchsia on green ground........ 100.00
Dresser. 7½x11½". Green with
pink roses 110.00
Vases
6½" high. Cobalt 165.00
8" high. Pink & white flowers on
yellow ground 95.00
8¼" high. Portrait, winter season,
purple & gold 265.00
9½" high. Swans, pine trees, open
handles 165.00
10" high. Mill, cobalt. Handled,
gold decor 575.00
10" high. Two handles, melon
boys. Jeweled 350.00
10½" high. Handled. Spring
Season. Red mark 500.00
11" high. Pitcher-type, footed.
Pink flowers, gold decor 275.00

R. S. TILLOWITZ

The china was made in Tillowitz, Germany in
the 1870s and 1880s. R.S. Germany and R.S.
Prussia china were also made in the same
town. The ware could be purchased factory
decorated or sold as blanks to amateur
painters.

Basket. 5" diam., 2½" high,
handpainted. Gold handle 4",
multicolor florals around body,
gold rim, octagon shape ....$ 40.00
Bowl. 7½" diam. Shallow, two
handles. Poinsettias. Signed 55.00

Creamer and Sugar. 3" high. Poinsettia
decor on white ground. Set $30.00

Cake Plate. 10" with open handles,
orange poppies, marked "Tillowitz Silesia" 40.00
Cake Set. 7-pcs. Blue handpainted
roses, gold decor edges. Sgnd. .. 125.00
Tea Tile. Orange, white sweetpeas.
Silesia, Germany 30.00
Vase. 6" high. Ovid, large tea roses,
shaded cream to caramel ground . 30.00

RADIOS (OLD)

Recently a growing number of collectors have
taken an interest in early items in the
electronics field. At present old radios are one
of their favorites.

Eveready. Table model. Metal
cabinet. Speaker separate. C.
1932..........................$ 65.00
Grebe Radio. Table model with
separate speakers. Type CR-9.
Serial No. 578.................. 125.00
Imperial. Steeple-type 60.00
Peerless. Steeple-type............. 60.00
Phantom. Steeple-type 70.00
Philco. Beehive-type 65.00
RCA Radiola III. Small, box shape
with earphones, 5¼x6½x8".
Bakelite top with controls and 2
small tubes. Complete. 1924 ..... 75.00
Scott. Floor model 325.00
Silvertone. Wire recorder 115.00
Traveler. Portable antique battery
RCA Victor. Intact, antennae on
inside cover. C. 1925 .... 60.00
Westinghouse. Early battery-type.
Pat. 1921. Aeriola Sr. Receiver.
Type RF style................... 75.00

Beehive shape $65.00

RAILROAD ITEMS

With the passing of railroads for transportation of people for business and pleasure, many of the items used on and for the maintenance of the trains have become collectible, especially the china and tableware that graced the well appointed dining cars of the past.

Airbrake & Signal Instructions. June 1892 ....$	15.00
Back-Up Whistle. Compressed air, brass. Sherburne Co., Boston, Mass.	35.00

Bells

5-3/8" high globe. Lant-LV, g & f mkd. globe, clear raised letters ..	55.00
5-3/8" high. DL & W. Dietz 39, stand frame unmarked. Clear globe	40.00
5-3/8" high globe. Erie. Rel g & f clear marked	40.00
5-3/8" high. Southern RR marked. Frame unmarked. Red globe	40.00
5½" high. Westlake. PRR mkd. g & f. Clear globe, 1895	70.00
10¾" high. Usual bail smoke stack, clear globe etched. "Capt. Mills US Army - Wreath" #39, bottom lant Kero	150.00
Armspear. PRR. Bell, clear etched globe, g & f mkd.	60.00
Dressel. PRR. mkd. frame squat green, unmkd. globe	30.00

Buckles. TOP: "Central Union Pacific R.R." Loading cattle. . . $48.00; BOTTOM:Wells Fargo & Co. "Texas Central." Train $48.00

Bonds

Baltimore & Ohio RR, 1890s detailed cert. with engine engraving	4.00
Baltimore & Ohio Southwestern RR, ornate, engine engravings ...	2.00
Bay City & Saginaw RR, old cert. with engine engraving	2.00
Blue Ridge R.R. $1000 Bond with 40 coupons ornate, 1869, engr. ..	15.00
Canal Revenue Certificate, 1867 .	10.00
Cedar Falls & Minn. R.R. Unissued cert. dated 1860s, engines	2.00
Chester Street RR, issued in Pa. in 1930s, trolley car vignette	3.00
Cincinnati, Washington & Baltimore RR, large eng. engravings .	2.00
Denver & Rio Grande RR, 1880s ..	30.00
Dubuque & Pacific RR, black cert. 1850s, unusual high stack engine .	3.00
Illinois Central RR, two engine engravings, contemporary 1940s .	2.00
Iowa Falls & Sioux City RR, western cert. 1880s, brown	2.00
Jackson & Eastern RR (Miss.) not issued but attractive engraving ..	2.00
K. C., St. Louis & Chicago RR common cert. engraving on engine	4.00
Lawrenceburg & Indianapolis RR, 1836 cert. with engine engr.	2.00
Mississippi Central RR, large ornate bond with engine and river boat	12.00
Wells Fargo - American Express Co. Signature item sgnd. by the famed H. Wells & Wm. Fargo in 1860s. Am. Exp. Trade-mk. Classic	85.00
Western RR, original line, certificates dated 1840s, simple engr.	2.00
Buttons. PRR Locomotive. Dated 1910. Set of 8	16.00
Lantern. 16" high. Signal, Arlington, N.J. Daessel	115.00
Lock, Chain. Two brass keys. PRR. J. L. Howard & Co. Wooten's Pat. Dec. 11, 1866. Set	32.50
Map of Railroads of N.Y. State. Dated 1861	17.50
Oil Can. Engineer's	30.00

Passes

Burlington RR., 1898	12.00
Civil War Soldiers	15.00
Grand Trunk, 1892	12.00
Long Island R.R. Co., 1893	10.00
Miss., Kansas & Topeka, 1897	12.00
Missouri Pacific Railway Co., 1892	10.00
Southern Pacific, 1898	10.00
St. Louis, South-west, 1897.......	12.00

Paper Fan. Advertisement for excursions of "Chicago & Northwestern RR"
$5.00

Texas Pacific, R.R., 1896	10.00
Photo. First train entering New Harmony, Ind., 1885. 12x14" frame	25.00
Pin. PRR Conductor's. White enamel inlay	10.00
Playing Cards	
Mobile & Ohio	7.00
Ogden & Shasta Routes. C. 1915 ..	15.00
Ring. Conductor's PRR. 10K gold, enamel inlay...................	28.00
Rules for Ticket Agents and Conductor's of NL,NH & Hart. R.R., 1905	16.50
Tableware	
Coffee Pot. Large 1402. Silverware. PRR. Keystone herald on front	47.50
Creamer. PRR. Reed & Barton. Quad. plated, hinged lid	35.00
Cup. N & W	8.50
Cup & Saucer. B. & O. Dark blue train scene	35.00
Plate. 6½". B. & O..............	19.50
Platters	
6x9". "Gould" pattern	15.00
B. & O. Large.................	50.00
Tablespoons	
B. & O.	7.50
PRR	6.50
Teaspoon, Knife, fork. Each	6.50
Trays. Relish. Gould or Starrueen pattern. Each	15.00

Tickets	
B. & O., 1876	12.00
Grand Trunk, 1888	12.00
Sunbury & Erie Railroad. Dated Mar. 9, 1861...................	10.00
Texas Pacific, 1896	10.00
Union Pacific, 1898	12.50
Timetables	
Erie R.R., 1940	3.50
Pennsylvania R.R., 1899	13.50

RAZORS (STRAIGHT EDGE)

Razors date back several thousand years. The Egyptians, Greeks and Romans all had razors of metal. Earlier man used sharpened stones for the purpose of shaving.

Early metal razors were made of hand-hammered steel such as Damascus steel. Later, in the 19th century, razors were made of machine steel and hard tempered to hold their edges. The best known in this country were those made by the various companies in the Sheffield area of England. Razors of equal quality were also imported from Germany.

The invention of the safety razor has practically edged out the straight-edge razor. Today the electric shaver is fast replacing the safety razor.

The average straight-edge razor normally sells from $5.00 to $10.00. Fancy razors, especially those with sterling silver or mother-of-pearl handles, are valued from $25.00 to $35.00.

Beau Brummel. Amber, brass ......$		7.50
Columbian Expo. Sheffield engraved Expo. Bldg's on blades, dated 1893. Orig. case...............		15.00
English. Rolls, folding, metal case ...		10.00

F. Forestier Tour De Lile Geneve. Leatherette case $25.00

Handle inlaid with MOP floral decor.
Hamburg ground. Wadsworth
Razor Co. 30.00
Horticultural Building World's Fair
1893 on blade 12.00
Straight. Seven, in original barber's
box 25.00
"The Razor That Fits Your Face."
Black with nickelplate trim. Blade
marked 5.00
Victorian. Sterling, ornate 32.00

REDWING POTTERY

The Redwing Pottery was located in Redwing,
Minnesota. It was founded in the 1880s and
continued until 1967. Their art pottery of the
1920s is now collectible.

Cookie Jars, Figural
Apple .... $ 12.50
Chef 17.50
Dutch Girl 18.50
Cornucopia. 8½". White, brown trim 12.00
Planter. 4x4x8". Red decor in relief . 10.00

Vase. 12" high, light green glaze, two-
handled $19.50

Vases
7" high. Soft pink 7.50
7½" high. Red, scalloped top..... 10.00
9½" high. Greyish-blue, star
shaped....................... 10.00

RELIGIOUS ITEMS

Items in this category were made of many
different materials, such as glass, stone,
silver, gold, wood, etc. Most are known to
everyone and need not be enumerated here.

Statue. "St. Joseph." 6½" high. Pottery
$95.00

Holy Water Font. 6¾" high, white,
blue, gold trim. Porcelain .... $ 7.50

REVERSE PAINTINGS ON GLASS

The work was done in a manner to be
observed through a pane of glass-the painting
being executed on the back. This type of art
was in demand in the 1820-1850 period. The
popular subjects were men of national
prominence, ladies of fashion and children.

18¼ x 22½". Basket of flowers, birds. Pastel shades of red, blue, green and yellow $275.00

Building in color. Gold frame.
5¾ x 6½" ....$ 125.00
Clipper Ship. With American flag ... 275.00
Country Scenery
   11½ x 13". Wood frame 95.00
   21x25"........................ 125.00
Fire Screen. Tole frame with reverse painting on glass of bird and flowers, 23x23". English......... 250.00
Floral with birds. Reds, blues, greens, yellows. Red painted frame. 18¼ x 22½" 265.00
Lafayette. 12½ x 15½" framed...... 325.00
Oriental Scene. 7¾ x 10" mother-of-pearl. Framed................... 65.00
"Sweet Little Dear." 6¾ x 10", full length portrait of girl 200.00
"The Jersey Beauty." Primitive type, bust of girl. 10¾ x 11¾" 200.00
"The Young Cavalier." 8x10", framed....................... 200.00
Washington. 7x10" portrait 325.00
Washington. 9¾ x 12". Standing at table with scroll in hand, eagle decoration in background 400.00
Washington. 17x18½" 450.00
Woman in blue gown. 7½ x 10" 195.00

REVOLVERS, See GUNS

RIFLES, See GUNS

RING TREES

Small tree-like objects of glass, metal or china, with branches for hanging or storing finger rings are known as "ring trees."

China
   2¼" high. In shape of hand. Painted flowers on base ....$ 19.50
   2¾" high. H/P blue forget-me-nots, gold trim. Signed R.S. Germany 35.00
   3½" high. Green decor.......... 25.00
   Bavarian China. Gold trim, floral decor 24.50
   Copeland China. Morning glory and bee decor 28.00
   Limoges. Hand with gold ring, bracelet. Pink roses, gold trim.... 25.00
   Wedgwood-type............... 45.00
Cobalt Glass. Gold decor of leaves and flowers.................... 35.00
Cut Glass. Blue 75.00
Leprechaun. Green with red hat 18.50
Metal. Marble base and 6" porcelain figure of man. Ornate 65.00
Milk Glass. Pink roses, green leaves. 3" high 30.00
Parian. Hand 38.50
Shape of Hand. Mounted on heart-shaped goldplated metal tray 30.00
Shape of Pear. Clear crystal with large blue rose in center 75.00
Tiffany Silver. 3½" diam. Post 2½" high 60.00

Tree with attached hatpin holder. White, pink roses, gold trim. Austria
$37.50

ROCKINGHAM WARE

The original Rockingham pottery was situated in the Staffordshire district of England and began operations before 1800. It is heavy and has a brown or chocolate colored glaze. The English type of table service is in white with or without decoration and gold trim. The product was made at many potteries in the United States, including the Ohio River establishments and Bennington, Vermont.

Bank. Turtle.......................$	45.00
Bed Pan	45.00
Bird Whistle. 3" long	40.00
Bottle. Shape of potato	55.00
Bowls	
9" diam., 4¼" high	35.00
10½" diam., mottled brown	50.00
Cat. 5½" high. Early	60.00
Coffee Pot. Dome top, acorn finial ..	225.00
Compote. Low, turquoise flower border	55.00
Creamers	
Cow	65.00
Squat, silver lustre with fluted fan decor	48.50
Cups and Saucers	
Plain white with rose and gold decor	45.00

Plate. 6". Green rim, gold trim. Red flower in center. English $28.50

Tea. Green and gold with flower sprays	45.00
Toy. Rose decor	22.50
Cuspidor. 8" diam., 3½" high. Scalloped shell with embossed ribbing	60.00
Foot Warmer	75.00
Inkwell. Sanded surface, pastel color. Birds and snake..........	72.00
Lions. Pair	250.00
Man sitting, brown glaze	85.00
Pastille Burner. 18th century. Encrusted with mossy porcelain grass and pastel flowers. 4 columns, 5x5¼"	325.00
Pitchers	
7½" high. Hound handle, stag, hounds on body	175.00
9" high. Hound handle	195.00
Plate, Pie. Brown, 11" diam.	40.00
Poodles. 2 dogs at foot of tree on each base. Pair.................	185.00
Spill Holder. Bird medallions	35.00
Teapots	
8-cup size. White and gold	75.00
7¾" high. 10½" from handle to end of spout	85.00
Tea Set. Teapot, sugar bowl, creamer, 6 cups and saucers	400.00
Tureen. 6" high, 6½" diam., covered. Flowers and panels of gilt and buff, scroll feet and handles. C. 1825	150.00
Vase, Wall. 8½" long, 3" top	40.00
Window Stops. Lion head, high glaze. 4x4½x5"	75.00

Dog. 10½" high............$110.00

ROGERS' STATUARY

John Rogers, born in America in 1829, studied sculpturing in Europe and produced his first plaster-of-paris statue, "The Checker Players" in 1859, followed by "The Slave Auction" in 1860.

His works were popular parlor pieces of the Victorian era. He published at least 80 different subjects and the total number of groups produced from the originals is estimated to be over 100,000.

One of his best and largest pieces is "The Council of War" which shows President Abraham Lincoln, Gen. U.S. Grant and Edwin M. Stanton. Rogers' groups are not classified as works of art but are fine genre' items showing the life and times of the people of the Victorian period.

It has been determined recently that "Romeo & Juliet," "Is That You Tommy?" and "A Capital Joke," were never listed in Rogers' catalogue. Some authorities attribute them to Casper Henneke, one of Rogers' contemporaries.

Balcony	$ 425.00
Bath	450.00
Beecher, Henry Ward	450.00
Bubbles	425.00
Bushwhacker	400.00
Camp Fire	475.00
Camp Life	475.00
Challenging the Union Vote	600.00
Charity Patient	500.00
Checker Players	550.00
Checkers up at the Farm	550.00
Chess	600.00
Coming to the Parson	550.00
Council of War (hands behind head)	900.00
Council of War (hands at side)	950.00
Council of War (hands forward of head)	1000.00
Country Post office	550.00
Courtship Sleepy Hollow	500.00
Elder's Daughter	400.00
Fairy's Whisper	375.00
Faust & Marguerite: Leaving the Garden	400.00
Faust & Marguerite: Their First Meeting	400.00
Favored Scholar	500.00
Fetching the Doctor	700.00
Fighting Bob	475.00
First Love	350.00
First Ride	550.00
Football	850.00
Foundling	400.00
Frolic at the Old Homestead	500.00
Fugitive Story	700.00

Going for the Cows	450.00
"Ha! I Like Not That!"	400.00
Hide and Seek	600.00
Hide and Seek:Whoop!	625.00
Home Guard	650.00
"Is It So Nominated in the Bond?	395.00
"Madam, Your Mother Craves a Word with You"	450.00
Mail Day	600.00
Marguerite & Martha: Trying on the Jewels	500.00
Matter of Opinion	525.00
Mock Trial	600.00
Neighboring Pews	450.00
One More Shot	575.00
"Othello-Ha! I Like Not That!"	350.00
Parting Promises (young man)	400.00

"Bubbles" $425.00

Parting Promise (older man)	400.00
Peddler at the Fair	600.00
Photographer and Sitter	650.00
Phrenology at the Fancy Ball	400.00
Picket Guard (with veil)	450.00
Picket Guard (without veil)	450.00
Playing Doctor	625.00
Politics	475.00
Polo	600.00
Private Theatricals	600.00
Referee	650.00
Returned Volunteer	625.00
Rip Van Winkle at Home	500.00
Rip Van Winkle on the Mountain	500.00
Rip Van Winkle Returned	500.00
School Days	650.00
School Examinations	650.00
Sharp Shooters	700.00
Shaughram and "Tatters"	395.00
Slave Auction	1250.00
Taking the Oath	650.00
Tap on the Window	450.00
Town Pump (canteen in front)	500.00
Town Pump (canteen at side)	500.00
Traveling Magician	400.00
Uncle Ned's School	500.00
Union Refugees (short-sleeved)	750.00
Union Refugees (long sleeved)	750.00
Village Schoolmaster	650.00
Washington	850.00
Watch on the Santa Maria	475.00
We Boys (head down)	400.00
We Boys [head up]	400.00
Weighing the Baby	850.00
"Why Don't You Speak for Yourself, John?"	450.00
Wounded Scout	800.00
Wrestler	850.00
"You Are a Spirit, I Know, When Did You Die?"	550.00

ROOKWOOD POTTERY

Rookwood is art pottery and was first made in 1880 by Mrs. Maria Longworth Storer, daughter of a wealthy family from Cincinnati, Ohio. The name was derived from the family estate "Rookwood," which was so named because of 'rooks' or 'crows' which inhabited the wooded grounds.

The underglaze background colors are usually in soft tints of brown and yellow. The decorations are also underglaze. In the period 1880-1882, the name "Rookwood" and the year of manufacture were incised or painted on the base. Between 1881 and 1886, the firm name, address and date appeared in the oval frame. The date was changed each year.

Vase. 6½" high. Yellow-green background, pink-purple flowers . . $145.00

Ash Trays
4½" high, 8" long. Large gray rook, extended wings on side . . . . $ 45.00
Green alligator shape. Dated 1922 45.00
Basket. 11¼" long. Folded sides, 2 handles. Footed. Brown and green glaze with cream flowers. Aliza D. Sohok 250.00
Bookends
6" high. Dutch boy, girl standing behind brick wall, tulips blooming in front. Pair 150.00
6½" high. Large ivory-colored elephants. Matte glaze, dated 1920. Pair 150.00
Baby sitting on floor. Light brown. 1921. Pair 110.00
Rooks. High glazed brown. Signed. Pair 125.00
Bowls
12" diam. Floral interior, cobalt drip exterior. Signed LE 1924 . . . . 150.00
Bird. Bamboo decor, yellow on yellow. "Y. Rookwood 1885." Matte Daly 75.00
Flower bowl. Small, yellow 65.00
Punch bowl. Flame mark 450.00
Rose bowl. 4x6½". Beige with rust drip pattern. Flames 1916 . . . 75.00
Box. Covered. 7" deep, leaf green, vintage motif. 1824 . . . . 125.00
Candleholder. Chamber-type. 7" square, handled. Floral spray and leaf decor 85.00

Candlesticks. 3½", seahorse design.
Pair 135.00
Chalice. 3-handled 125.00
Chocolate Pot. 9" high. Floral
decor. C. 1890 .... 140.00
Cookie Jar. 6x9". Brown, high glaze.
Dated 1885. Signed A.R.V.
Marked with separate "S" 350.00
Creamer. Small, signed. 1890 ...... 85.00
Cruet. Blue top, brown body.
Butterflies and grass decor. 1884 . 125.00
Cup and Saucer. Demitasse. Sailing
vessel in light blue on white
ground. 1896 mark 72.50

Statue. 15" high. "Sacred Heart"
$85.00

Ewers
4½x4½". Yellow, orange, green
gooseberries on brown ground.
1901. Signed Howard Altman 175.00
6" high. Brown glazed with pansy
decor. Signed Caroline Steinle.
1897 .... 195.00
6½" high. Christmas rose, brown,
green glaze. HEW, 1894 .... 195.00
9½" high. Deep brown glaze.
S.E.C. 1894 .... 225.00
11" high. White clay, large
poppies underglaze. Dated 1898.
Signed Anna Valentien. No. 642 .. 250.00

Figurines
Doe. 4½" high. oblong base. White 80.00
Dog. 5" high. Brown. XLVI 85.00
Duck. ¾" high, 3" long. Cream.
1933 .... 50.00
Frog. Green, open mouth 85.00
Rabbit. 3¼" high, 3½" long.
White, 1910 .... 90.00
Font. 9" high, wall-type. Figure of St.
Francis. Light tan color. 1947 ..... 65.00
Humidors
Cigar. 5" wide, 9" high. Yellow
glaze. 1940 .... 85.00
Tobacco. 6-flame mark 225.00
Inkwell. 3½" high, 6" diam. Molded,
dated 1903. Green with incised
geometric design. 3 pieces 65.00

Jardinieres
8" diam. Gold with chrysanthe-
mum spray. Signed "LTF" 135.00
8¾" diam., 7¾" high. Yellow
roses, buds. Done by Artus Van
Briggle, 1889 .... 350.00
Jugs
Brown. Dated 1884 .... 200.00
Brown glaze, currants, leaves.
Dated 1898, R.F................. 175.00
Corn. 8". Dated 1892............ 295.00
Lamp. 22" high. Electrified, brass
fittings 275.00
Lamp Base. 24" high, green standard
glaze with flowers in high relief.
XXIII. 2613 .... 125.00
Letter Holder. Blueberry, leaf.
Signed HA. SBG 1901 .... 150.00
Mugs
4½" high 85.00
7½" high. Barrel-shaped, banner
over group of drinking dwarfs
inscribed "Cincinnati Cooperage
Co." C. 1885 .... 125.00
Chestnuts. C. 1890. H.E.W. 175.00
High glaze. E. T. Hurly. St. Bernard
1900 .... 450.00

Paperweights
3x4x3" high. Ivory-colored with
crisscross lattice pattern 85.00
Pitchers
3" high. Miniature. Iris glaze, pink
ground with white clover, green
leaves. 1901 C.S. 150.00
6-5/8" high. 1897 standard glaze.
Gold and amber, brown near top . 125.00
9½" high. Pinched sides 145.00
10" high. C. 1891 .... 165.00
10" high. Green, 1903 mark 135.00
Plaques
5¼x8¼". "Evening," by E. F.
McDermott. In original 9½x12½"
frame........................ 350.00
9x12". "The Frozen Mirror" 350.00
Plates
8¼". Pastel floral design. 4
flames, signed H.E.W. 135.00
8½". No flames, blue ships 35.00
Sugar and Creamer. Sprigs of
cherries and berries. 1901 ...... 190.00
Teapot. 7" high. Dark mat-green
handle over top 95.00
Tea Set. Teapot, sugar bowl and
creamer...................... 350.00
Tea Tile. 5½" square. Matt ivory and
blue ground, slate blue rook. 1945 40.00

Trays
10½x16½". Corn cob pipes,
matches. Brown glaze. Ed Diers
1898......................... 350.00
11¾". Three angels abound by
shaped clouds. Standard glaze by
H.E.W. 1891 .... 1250.00
Trivet. 5¾" square. 4 feet, sculptured design in blue, red, purple,
yellow. Artist Wm. E. Hentschel.
Signed 130.00
Vases
3" high. Cream, pastel flowers.
L.A. 1926.................... 95.00
3½" high. Bulbous. Dark, light
brown glaze with wild rose decor.
Artist signed [impressed C.S.]
Carrie Steinie, dated 1893 .... 165.00
4¾" high. Running deer in green.
Dated 1932 .... 85.00
4¾" high. Two turtles among
marsh grass, swirls of sand. C.
1885. Signed Matthew A. Daly ... 385.00
5" high. Orange nasturtiums.
Artist signed. Katherine Hickman.
1898......................... 185.00
5" high. Shape of bag with
drawstring. Standard glaze,
yellow, brown, green. A.B.S.1888. 225.00
5¼" high. Brown glaze with

orange, yellow blossoms. Signed
Clara C. Lindeman 150.00
6" high. Tan mantle. L. Epply 1907 100.00
7" high. Daffodils under high
glaze on soft tan, yellow ground.
Artist signed. Clara Lindeman 1907 185.00
7" high. Goldstone, dragonflies.
Dated 1924.................. 150.00
7" high. Yellow. Japanese decor.
Iris 1906. Edith Noonan. 160.00
8" high. Brown, handpainted
flowers. Signed, dated 1892 ..... 225.00
8" high. Iris glaze, pink flowers by
O.G. Reed 1903 .... 175.00
8½" high. Parchment or vellum
finish. Blue, gray, light pink.
Oriental style decor. Flame mark . 225.00
8½" high. Vellum. Daisies in
groups of three, from base to 1"
from upper rim. Blue, yellow-gold
Signed Louise Abel 1920 .... 150.00
9½" high. Dogwood. Sara Saxe.
1906......................... 195.00
10" high. Pear-shaped, green,
gold glaze. Floral decor in gold.
Marked, 4 flames, 1890 .... 250.00
10¼" high. "Vellum" Nasturtium.
Dated 1904. Signed Mary Nourse . 185.00
10½" high. Brown with yellow to
brown autumn leaves. 1898.
Signed 235.00
12" high. Heavy green foliage and
fruit. 1891, by Katro Shiraua-
madani 450.00
12½" high. Madonna 175.00
12½" high. Pear-shaped, fruit
decor. 1930................... 135.00
Fish. Green glaze. Seven fishes,
dated 1909 and signed 625.00

ROSALINE GLASS

Rosaline is a form of rose-colored jade glass
[colored alabaster glass]. However, due to its
popularity, it has been separated into a color
group. It was a product of the Steuben factory.

Basket. 8" high, 9" long. Clouded
clamsbroth with heavy Rosaline
handle .... $ 275.00
Bowl. 3" high, 4¾" diam. Signed
"Carder" 250.00
Cologne. 7¾" diam. Slender-type
alabaster stopper and base 300.00
Compotes
2¾" high, 4¼" wide. Brass base... 300.00
5" high, 6" wide, 10" long. Fades
to alabaster base. Boat-shaped,
unsigned 250.00

Rose Bowls. 3½" high. Pair . . . $400.00

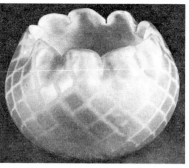

Yellow MOP satin glass. 5" diam.
$95.00

8". Alabaster stem. Steuben	275.00
12". Alabaster foot	350.00
Cordial. 3½" high. Conical Rosaline cup supported by slender alabaster stem, round base. Signed "Carder"	250.00
Dipper. Miniature cup with alabaster handle. Steuben	95.00
Garniture. 2¾" high, 4¼" wide. Small, footed	165.00
Goblet, Water	275.00
Plate. 8½". Steuben signed "S"	150.00
Sherbet. Alabaster stem and underplate	300.00
Tazza. 8" diam., baluster stem	450.00

Vases

8" high. Bud. White base, pink stem. Steuben	145.00
9" high, 5½" diam. Fades to alabaster base. Amphora-shaped. Signed Steuben	375.00

4"	75.00
5" diam. Ruffled, fluted rim. D.Q. pattern	120.00
7" diam. Enameled "Moser"	175.00
Durand. 3½ x 4". Gold irid. Signed Durand 1995	375.00
Optic Rib. 3½ x 4¾". Translucent cased. Glass floral decor. Ruffled top	55.00
Peachblow. 4½". New England	550.00
Sandwich. 3¾ x 4". Pink with enamel decor	75.00

ROSE BOWLS

The term "rose bowl" is a general one covering a variety of crimped and pinched-edge bowls. Their primary use was for decoration, however, in season, rose petals were placed in them and the pleasing aroma permeated the air. Most of them are of the art glass type which was first made about 1880.

Amberina. 6". Honeycomb pattern . . $ 225.00	
Amethyst glass. 8½" high, edged in gold with enameled flowers	95.00
Bristol. 4¼" high. Turquoise, gold decor of drapes, tassels	65.00
Carnival Glass-Type. 5"	75.00
Clear with gold intaglio, floral design. 3¾ x 4½"	25.00
Cranberry	
3¼". Crimped top, white enamel decor	65.00

Carnival. Purple, footed, rose decor.
Marked Northwood $75.00

Satin Glass

Blue. 4" high. Herringbone.......	125.00
Blue. White enamel floral decor ..	135.00
Light green with purple flowers and gold decor................	85.00
Pink to rose. 3¼". Orange enameled shell pattern	125.00
Salmon colored, 5". Herringbone .	130.00
Yellow. 4", crimped top	85.00
Yellow Satin Shell and Seaweed. Pink enameling	135.00
Yellow top, fading to white. 4½" .	95.00

Spanish Lace

Clear. 3½"	45.00
Blue. 4½"	55.00

Spangled Glass. 7¾". Egg-shaped. Shaded from bottom to top white to rose pink. Ruffled top 150.00

Tiffany. Decorated and signed 450.00

Tiffin Glass. Black Satin. Poppy. 5" .. 35.00

Vasa Murrhina 85.00

Vaseline

3" high. Clear, spattered with white	55.00
5". Ribbed, opalescent	65.00

Webb

3½" diam., 2¼" high. Low rim base, leaf and vine enamel decor. Signed Webb Queens	325.00
3½" diam. Vaseline to amber. Pedestal base..................	200.00
5". Floral decor on white background, pink lining	275.00

ROSE MEDALLION CHINA

Rose Medallion was produced in China. It was decorated in Canton and exported from there. The name generally applies to pieces of glazed china or pottery having medallions with figures of people, alternating with panels of pink flowers showing birds and butterflies. The ware is called "Rose Canton" if all the panels are filled with flowers. The smaller pieces usually have four panels, however, large platters often contain six.
Rose Medallion china is now being reproduced.

Basket. 4" diam., 10½" long. Reticulated pattern ....$	400.00
Bottle. 16" high. Butterfly, with stopper	425.00

Bowls

4¾" diam., 2½" high. Rice.......	65.00
7¼" diam. Flanged, 1½" deep ...	85.00
8" diam. Marked China. Late	65.00
8¼" diam. Shallow, 4 panels.....	125.00
9" diam. Round.................	150.00

Cup and Saucer. Shallow, scalloped edges	$35.00
9½"x10¾". Fruit, with tray, openwork sides, flared rim. Set ..	450.00
10" diam., 4" high. Panels with roses and people. Gold trim	195.00
10¾" wide, oval	350.00

Punch Bowls

11¾" diam.	350.00
14½" diam., 4" deep	500.00
15½" diam., 7½" deep. Canton. Large	600.00
16" diam.	600.00

Box. Covered, 3½ x7½" 75.00

Candleholders

8" high. Pair	450.00
8" high. Pair	450.00
10" high. C. 1870. Pair	550.00

Coffee Set. 6 pieces. Decor of roses, birds, Chinese medallions. Gold trimmed. Late.................. 250.00

Creamers

Helmet-type	95.00
Squatty, bulbous	125.00

Cups and Saucers

Demitasse.....................	40.00
Handleless	60.00
Heavy, with thorn handle	65.00
Mixed marks, well-matched designs. Set of three	100.00

Cuspidor. Scarce.................. 300.00

Dishes

7¼", leaf-shaped	60.00

Vegetable. Covered, oblong, cantered corners, gold nut handle. Artist signed 275.00
Vegetable. Covered, oval, gold finial 165.00
Flower Pot. Crocus. Melon-shape. C. 1870 . . . . 450.00
Ginger Jar. 3½", covered 150.00
Gravy Boat. 3¼" high, 8" long. Medallion inside boat. Marked China 75.00
Jug. 5" high. C. 1820 . . . . 250.00
Mugs
    4¼" high 75.00
    Strap handle 95.00
Pitchers
    6½" high. Water. Octagonal 200.00
    8½" high 260.00
Plates
    6", scalloped edge 42.50
    6½" 45.00
    7" 60.00
    8". Octagonal. Late 30.00
    9½" 75.00

Water Bottle. 15" high $395.00

12" 125.00
16". C. 1840 . . . . 300.00
Platters
    7½ x 10½" 100.00
    8½ x 11" 110.00
    9½ x 12" 150.00
    12¼ x 17½" 195.00
    14½ x 17½", oval 220.00
    16½" long 260.00
Powder Jar 60.00
Soap Dish. 4¼ x 5½". Covered. 3" high to large gold finial on cover. Inner drip dish covered with pink and gold roses 160.00
Spill. 4¼" high. C. 1850 . . . . 100.00
Spoons, Rice 18.50
Sugar Bowl. 5½" high. Covered. Berry finial, 2 handles 200.00
Teapots
    5" high, 5" diam. 150.00
    6" high, 5" diam. White spout and twisted twig handle. Finial lid. China mark 135.00
    7" high. China handle 260.00
Teapot and Cup. In original wicker basket 240.00
Teapot and Cups [2]. In wicker basket. 350.00
Tea Set. 3 pieces. 7¼" teapot, 4½" creamer, 5" covered sugar bowl . . 500.00
Vases
    3½" high. Miniature. C. 1820 . . . . 55.00
    6" high. Gold handles. C. 1820 . . . 150.00
    8" high. Late 175.00
    8½" high. Wine bottle shape with panels showing people at various tasks 275.00
    9¼" high 250.00
    10¼" high. Late 195.00
    12" high. Early 300.00
    13½" high, 8½" diam. 325.00
    14" high. Pair 650.00
    36" high. Temple vase 850.00

ROSE O'NEILL ITEMS

Rose O'Neill was a decorator who used Kewpie dolls as illustrations. China bearing her name was made in Germany about 1900.

ABC Plate. 1½ x 7" . . . . $ 125.00
Bank. 3", glass 75.00
Book. "Titans and Kewpies." Life of Rose O'Neill 25.00
Bowl. Eight action kewpies. Signed O'Neill Royal Rudolstadt 85.00
Boxes
    Candy. Black. 2 kewpies 35.00
    Jewelry. Kewpies crawling atop . . 275.00

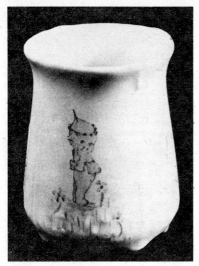

Kewpie. Toothpick holder. 2½" high.
Porcelain $65.00

Candleholder. 4" high. Kewpie on
 holder. Floral, base 3x3" 85.00
Christmas Card. Foldback-type.
 Kewpie rolling out dough 17.50
Clocks
 4x4½" 250.00
 Blue Jasper, running. Signed 195.00
Cups and Saucers
 Green and orange, impressed
 fern design with kewpie decor-
 ation 85.00
 Ornate gilt decor. Signed Rose
 O'Neill 65.00
Dish, Feeding. Signed O'Neill.
 Kewpie bouncing on tight rope ... 125.00
Doll. Bisque. 5½" high. Sticker,
 marked 65.00
Figures: Kewpie
 6¼". Action-type. "The Thinker."
 Orig. sticker with name O'Neill .. 65.00
 With large umbrella 75.00
Hair Receiver. Kewpies and flowers
 allover. Two handles 80.00
Handkerchief. 10½" square. Action
 "K", "Kewpie." Copyrighted 25.00
Inkwell. With kewpie, ... 220.00
Jar. Kewpie. Green jasper. Pale
 pink, mkd. Rose O'Neill Wilson .. 185.00
Mug. Kewpie 55.00
Napkin Ring. Kewpie. Sterling 50.00
Paperweight. 1¼x2". Iron 20.00

Pitcher, Cream. Green Jasperware . 100.00
Plates
 5". 2 Kewpies. Mkd. Copyrighted.
 Rose O'Neill Wilson Kewpie,
 Germany Royal Rudolstadt 50.00
 6". Six action kewpies. Royal
 Rudolstadt................... 75.00
 7½". Green and orange. Im-
 pressed fern design, kewpie
 decoration 75.00
 8". 9 kewpies in different poses .. 120.00
Post Card. Kewpie Romeo & Juliet.
 Signed 12.50
Salt Shakers. Kewpie decor. Pair .. 175.00
Shaker, Powder. 7" high. Compo.
 body, painted features, 3 stickers.
 Rose O'Neill 1913 .... 60.00
Sugar Bowl. Covered 95.00
Sugars and Creamers
 2½" high, 5" diam. Lustre on
 white 120.00
 Six action kewpies. Rose O'Neill.
 Signed, covered sugar 150.00
Table Set. Salt, pepper, toothpick.
 Klondyke 150.00
Tea Set. Teapot, sugar bowl and
 creamer, 6 cups and saucers, blue
 coloring, decorated with kewpies.
 Signed 500.00
Toothpick Holder. Glass, kewpie
 decor 65.00
Trays
 Bisque, large with kewpie. "With
 Love from Rose O'Neill" 250.00

Sand Bucket. 3" high. Tin. "Kewpie
Beach" $40.00

Ice Cream 60.00
Trunk. Advertising Hendlers Ice
  Cream 165.00
Vase. 6½" high. Blue and white
  Jasperware with four kewpies .. 90.00

ROSE TAPESTRY,See
ROYAL BAYREUTH

ROSENTHAL CHINA

Rosenthal Porcelain Factory began operating at Selb, Bavaria in 1880. Its specialties were tablewares and figurines. According to recent reports, the manufactory is still in operation.

Bowls
3½" high, 4" diam. Fluted, scalloped rim. Front has painting of girl kneeling on rock. Back, girl sitting in grass ....$ 48.50
4" high, 10" diam. Pedestaled, embossed fruit around bowl. H/P interior florals 65.00
10½" diam. "Doratello." Windmill, 2 maids, sailboat 50.00
Candlestick. 2¾" high. Porcelain. 3 legs, white with gold trim........ 20.00
Chocolate Pot. "Donatello" 28.50
Chocolate Set. Pot, 5 cups, saucers. Light green, gold lining in cups ... 175.00
Coffee Pot. Cream ground, blue leaves, gold vines, trim.......... 55.00

Pitcher. 5" high. White ground, pink roses on front and edge. Signed $29.50

Coffee Set. Demitasse. Blue and white decor. Ornate. Service for 6 175.00
Cookie Jar. Pate-sur-Pate-type decor 125.00
Cups. For melted butter. Ivory and gold band. Set of 12............ 45.00
Cups and Saucers
Blue and gold 18.00
Blue and white. Footed. Selb, Germany..................... 18.00
Demitasse. Ivory with wide band of gold inside cup and on handle. Set of six 125.00
Silver Overlay in Art Nouveau style 25.00
Dish. Bonbon. Scenic in muted greens 20.00

Figurines
Butterfly. H/P, resting on banch. 3¾" base 50.00
Dancer. 8" high, white and gold. C. 1905 .... 75.00
Dog. 5" 38.50
Girl. 9" high. Nude top, flowing skirt, gold trim. Old mark 95.00
Kingfisher. 4½" high. Brown and white accents on blue, sitting on stump. Green mark 35.00
Mother Deer. 6" high, 3½ x 6" oval base. Germany 60.00
Rooster. 4½" high. White with red comb and wattles. Green mark. Signed F. Heidenreich 50.00
Wren. On branch. Yellow and brown. Marked 35.00
Fish Set. Scalloped gold rim. Fish and water scene. Set of six 9" plates .. 160.00
Mustache Cup. Hydrangeas, gold decor. Signed 25.00

Plates
8½". Fruit. "Handmaleret." Scalloped, embossed border........ 30.00
8¾". H/P gold and black with pink roses. Selb-Bavarian. Signed "Aigie" 22.50
10¾". "Secession." H/P pink roses. Early 60.00
Chop-type. Greek Key design 37.50
Christmas 1940. Scene of "Marienkirche in Danzig"........ 85.00
Luncheon. Birds, flowers, leaves. 24K gold trim. Set of six 150.00
Portrait. Hanging-type. Bust of young woman with red hair 47.50
Urn. Lady gazing into mirror. Reverse has cherubs. Bavarian. C. 1880........................ 35.00
Vase. 8" high. H/P with pink roses 55.00

ROSEVILLE POTTERY

Roseville pottery was made in Zanesville, Ohio after 1900. Much of it bears the mark "Rozane."

Baskets

8½".Iris ....$	25.00
10" high. Green with rust-colored flowers	40.00
10" high. Soft blue, gray colors with white roses	40.00
Hanging. Suspended on 3 chains, raised flower design	42.50

Bowls

4x5". Handled. "Holly"	45.00
8" diam. 2 handles. Fuchsia flowers on blue ground..........	30.00
8¾" diam. "Donatello." Matching frog holder	35.00
11½" diam. Handled. "Imperial" .	50.00
12" diam. "Magnolia." Blue	50.00
Rose Bowl. 4½" high, 2 handles ..	15.00

Candlesticks. 3" high. Carnelian.

Pair	28.50

Cigarette Holder. Table-type. 3" high, green & beige color with pine cone and needle decor ..... | 18.50

Console Set. 10" footed bowl and pair of candlesticks .... | 55.00

Cookie Jar. 2 handles. Dark green ground, "White Magnolias." 9" diam., 10½" high.............. | 45.00

Dish, Feeding. 4 rabbits in center ..	28.00
Ewer. 8¼" high. "Dogwood" on blue	25.00
Ferner. 8". "Green poinsettia" decor	25.00
Frog. Handled	18.00

Jardinieres

6x6". "Rozane"................	35.00
7x8". "Pine" cone, twig handle, orange to brown	42.50
8" high. Blue, green ferns, handles	45.00
32" overall height, with stand	145.00

Jug. 7" high, 4½" diam. Handled, H/P grapes & blossoms. Signed ... | 65.00

Planter, Hanging. 5½"x6". Tapered bowl, rose ground, green & white leaves. Original bracket, triple chain .... | 25.00

Sugar and Creamer. Blue with yellow-white flowers .... | 35.00

Teapot. Blue with white berries, leaves .... | 28.00

Trivet. Footed, signed	12.50

Tumbler. 5½" high. Two handles. "Sunflower" .... | 26.50

Vases

4¼" high, 7½" diam. "Donatello." Double with cherubs	25.00

Bowl. 2-handled, 4½x5". Yellow, brown and green. Pine cone pattern
$35.00

7" high. Egypto. "Rozane"	48.50
7½" high. Bud. Light green shading to dark green at base. Pair	40.00
7½" high. Two handles. "Cherry Blossom"	32.00
8" high. "Mostique".............	30.00
8½" high. Blue with white flowers. Handled	35.00
8½" high. Gourd-shaped. Two handles. "Jonquils"	25.00
9" high. Handled, orange to brown raised acorns, original R.V. Roseville label	40.00
9" high. Wide type. Blue with pine cone design, twig handles. Impressed "Roseville 1148"	38.00
10½" high. Carnelian. Green	40.00
12" high. Green, handles, indented top, raised berries and leaves	50.00
15½" high. Brown to amber, yellow lilies, green branches beside them. Two handles, flared collar	50.00
15½" high. Peach color, brown base. "Hyacinths." Two handles ..	60.00
Wall Pocket. "R.V." mark	18.00

ROYAL BAYREUTH

A late type of novelty porcelain made in Germany. The tapestry type, which has the appearance of woven tapestry, is considered the most desirable. Creamers and other items were made in a variety of designs. The following list is representative of the ware.

Ash Trays

Cavaliers. 3-cornered ....$	50.00

Clown holding hat. Pearlized, gray
feet and hair 75.00
Deer in field. 4½" 35.00
Devil. Arms extended over top,
legs around base. Small curled
tail 85.00
Moose head, antler's form edges .. 45.00
Basket. Rose Tapestry. Ruffled edge . 375.00
Bell. Children at play 65.00
Bowls
5¾" diam. Four feet. Sheep
grazing in mtn. scene. Scalloped
top 125.00
5¾" diam. White Poppy (BM) 65.00
9½" diam., 2½" deep. Dutch girl,
house scene, blue sky, white
clouds 130.00
Rose. Cigar holder. Black Corinthian 100.00
Vegetable. Tomatoes on pastel
green, 9½" diam. 110.00

Boxes
4x5". Covered. Black and tan with
pink roses 55.00
5¾" diam., 3¾" high. Covered
with domed lid. Rose Tapestry.... 250.00
6" long, covered. Kidney-shape.
Rose Tapestry 250.00
Card. Dark green ground, footed.
Hole in base to push out cards.
Tavern scene of men playing
cards 95.00
Large, covered. Rose Tapestry
with portrait 300.00
"Little Bo Peep." Green BM 95.00
Pin. Covered. Rose Tapestry 125.00
Spade-shape with peasant and
turkey decor 65.00
Breakfast Set. Nursery decor 85.00
Candleholders
5½" high. Handled, H/P violets
with gold trim 65.00
Cape Cod scene with sunbonnet
babies fishing 150.00
Chamber-type. Pink roses on blue
ground 50.00
Clown holding hat 90.00
Santa Claus. Saucer-type with ring
holder 145.00
With shield 135.00
Celery Vase..................... 60.00
Chocolate Pot. 8½" high. Rose
Tapestry 375.00
Compote. 2½x4", pastoral scene ... 50.00
Creamers
Alligator 95.00
Apple 58.00
Bear......................... 65.00
Black Eagle 70.00

Crab Dish. 6" long. Orange $48.50
Buffalo, Water. Black 75.00
Bullhead. Black 72.00
Cat. Black. 5" high, red glaze
interior 50.00
Cavalier. 3¾" high. Tapestry..... 175.00
Cavalier. 4" high 47.50
Children running 60.00
Children sliding downhill 60.00
Clam Digger 60.00
Clown. BM 100.00
Coal Hod. 3½" high. Rose
Tapestry 150.00
Conch Shell 48.50
Corinthian pattern. 2 pouring
spouts 80.00
Corn......................... 60.00
Cow decoration 45.00
Crab 55.00
Crow. Black................... 75.00
Devil and Card. BM 65.00
Dog's head 55.00
Donkeys. Scenic. 4" high 72.50
Ducks on green ground.......... 65.00
Eagle. Gray 75.00
Elk 68.00
Geranium 45.00
Goats, Mountain 50.00
Goose Girl. Rose Tapestry 135.00
Horses in pasture 45.00
Lamplighter 125.00
Lemon 50.00
Little Boy Blue decor 50.00
Little Jack Horner 55.00
Lobsters
3½" 50.00
4½" 60.00
Moose Head 68.00
Oak Leaf 65.00
Orange. 4¼" high 45.00
Pansy 52.00
Pig 85.00
Poppy. 4¼" high. Red 75.00
Ram's Head 70.00
Shell. Conch. Mother-of-Pearl-type
glaze 65.00

Strawberry	75.00
Tomato	55.00
Town Crier. 4½" high	100.00
Cups and Saucers	
Chocolate size. Rose Tapestry	120.00
Demitasse. Tomato-shaped, leaf saucer	50.00
Corinthian pattern. Dinner size	75.00
Dresser Set. 3-pcs. Rose Tapestry	400.00
Gravy Boat. Tomato, leaf under-plate	85.00
Hair Receivers	
Barnyard Scene. Blue mark	60.00
Handpainted. Ivory. Artist signed. Blue mark	50.00
Rose Tapestry. 3 gold feet	165.00
Rose Tapestry. Turkey decor	175.00
Hatpin Holders	
Poppy Red	45.00
Rose Tapestry, with portrait	150.00
Humidor. 7" high. Covered, bar-rel shape	100.00
Inkwell. 4" diam., covered. Girl holding dog on leash	60.00
Jugs	
Toby. Coachman. 4½" high	75.00
Turkey, pheasant. 3¼" high. Tapestry	125.00
Match Holders	
Devil and cards. Blue mark	75.00
Snow Babies	100.00
Mayonnaise Set. Poppy	55.00
Mugs	
3¼" high. "Little Miss Muffet"	65.00
"Ye Old Belle" scene. Cavaliers drinking. Green ground	85.00
Mustard Jars	
Farm scene. Attached tray	45.00
Lobster. Covered, with original leaf spoon	60.00
Orange BM, no spoon	40.00
Tomato, covered	60.00
Pitchers	
Alligator	95.00
Apple	45.00
Castle in canyon	65.00
Cat handle, black body	75.00
Clown. In bright red. Spout forms face. Large	135.00
Corinthian. Large, with portrait	80.00
Cow. Black	85.00
Crow. Black	95.00
Hunting scene. 7½" high	60.00
Legal advice scene. 5" high. Green ground	145.00
Lobster. Large, with bowl (Cra-cker Set)	165.00
Milk. Rose Tapestry. Pinched spout	180.00

Moose. Milk size	120.00
Pansy	100.00
Polar Bear	85.00
Poodle. Gray	80.00
Poppy. Quart	90.00
Portrait of ladies. 4" high	75.00
Robin. Milk Pitcher	75.00

Tea Set. Teapot, creamer and sugar.
"Strawberry" $225.00

Sailing Ship scene, 7¼" high	175.00
Seal. Gray	75.00
Shell. Conch. Mother-of-Pearl type glaze	100.00
Tavern scene. 6" high. (man lighting pipe). Brown, green purple at mouth	95.00
Plaque. 9" diam. Ring around Rosie	95.00
Plates	
5½". Leaf, with handles	60.00
6". Rose Tapestry	145.00
7". Card and devil. Signed	85.00
7". Leaf, with handles	75.00
7½". Pastoral scene, raised shell border	70.00
7½". Rose Tapestry. Gold decor on edge	160.00
9". Black Corinthian	72.50
9¾". Rose Tapestry. Gold decor on edge	185.00
10". Rose Tapestry. Hanging-type, deep, with scalloped border, gold trim	225.00
12". Cavaliers. Signed Dixon	120.00
Powder Jars	
Handpainted	60.00
Rose Tapestry. Covered. 3 gold feet	165.00
Relish. 8". Rose Tapestry. Scalloped edge	150.00
Salt. Open, lobster claw	20.00
Salt and Pepper Shakers	
Devil and Cards	95.00
Lobster	85.00
Rose Tapestry	165.00
Shell, Conch	65.00
Tomatoes on green leaf	65.00
Sauce Dish. Rose Tapestry	75.00

Shoe. Man's brown oxford, laces ...	65.00
String Holder. Hanging, rooster	60.00

Sugar Bowls

Apple, covered..................	60.00
Corinthian pattern. Red ground ..	60.00
Lobster. Small..................	45.00
Poppy. Open	65.00
Red devil handle. Open	55.00
Tomato. Covered	50.00

Sugar Bowls and Creamers

Footed. 5" high. Lime green body decorated with flowers, finial and handles with gold trim	62.50
Lobster	100.00
Pheasant.....................	95.00
Rose Tapestry	200.00
Tomato	95.00

Sunbonnet. See "Sunbonnet Babies"

Tea Sets

Apple. Teapot, covered sugar bowl and creamer	225.00
Tomato. Teapot, covered sugar bowl and creamer	225.00

Teapots

Apple	125.00
Rose Tapestry	350.00

Vase. 5½" high. Dutch scene . . $55.00

Tomato	125.00

Toothpick Holders

Boy and donkey, 3 handles	55.00
Coal Hod. Rose Tapestry	150.00
Deer head	50.00
Footed. Conventional type. Rose Tapestry	140.00

Trays

Celery. 12" long. Conch shell design, tinted edges	85.00
Dresser. 7¾ x 11". Hunting scene .	75.00
Dresser. 8x11". white ground with pink roses, gold border..........	65.00
Pin. 3x5". Gold leaves, rose garlands in center. BM	45.00

Tumbler. Mountain scenery	45.00

Vases

2½". "Little Bo Peep." Handles ...	75.00
3¾". Scenic. Swans on lake. BM ..	55.00
4" high. Castle scene. Tapestry ...	135.00
4¼". Ball shape. Deep blue with doll seated on log with frog	70.00
5" high. Tapestry. Beiges & browns, maiden in meadow......	175.00
5½" high. Rose Tapestry	185.00
6½" high. Cows grazing, green ..	50.00
6½" high. Rose Tapestry. Farm boy and turkeys	195.00
8½" high. Urn-shaped. Inn scene .	65.00
10" high. "Don Quixote".........	85.00

ROYAL BERLIN

This porcelain was made under the patronage of Frederick the Great from 1763 until his death in 1786. It was known as the Royal Factory until 1918. In 1832 the mark KPM [Royal Porcelain Manufacture] was used as a trademark. From 1870 thru 1918, the letters K.P.M. were printed under a sceptre.

Figurine. 8½" high. Man with goat under arm as a bagpipe, decorated with blue, coat, pale pants, red coloring "Aires" ....$	175.00
Tea Cup and Saucer. Handpainted in multicolored florals, gold handle. C. 1820-40	100.00
Teapot. 6½" high. Painted flowers and gold gilt	125.00
Tray. 12½ x 12½". Porcelain. Floral and butterfly decor. Gold border. Early Baton mark	145.00

ROYAL BONN

The factory was established in the latter part of the 18th century by Clemers August. The majority of the ware found in antique shops today is from the Victorian period.

Bowl. 9½" diam. Wild rose and heart decoration ....$	45.00
Celery Tray. Floral decor...........	35.00
Clocks	
11" high, 12" long. China	195.00
Pink and red roses. Ansonia works with outside escapement, chime stroke. Running	250.00
Cracker Jar. Daisies and gold decor .	95.00
Dishes	
10" diam., 3 sections, handled. Floral and gold decor	75.00
Bone. "Rosenguirland." Blue and gold. Set of four	50.00
Cheese. Covered, roses, gold edge	85.00
Ewers	
10½" high. Delft-type decor	120.00
12" high. Lavender, pink and green florals..................	150.00
Jam Jar. 5" high. Silverplated top and bail. Floral decor on beige ground........................	45.00
Jardiniere. 6½ x 7½". Blues and gold. Persian Cashmere pattern ..	85.00
Pitcher. Narrow neck, H/P bird and flowers	55.00
Plates	
7¾". Blue decor. Late	20.00
9". Handpainted...............	45.00
9½". Portrait	55.00
Soup. 9". Wild rose	35.00
Punch Bowl or Deep Salad Bowl. 10" diam., 5" high. Pink with yellow roses inside and out, gold decorated top	155.00
Stein. Large pouring size. Masked spout, blue and white body, raised circle of old men's heads, with grape decor	350.00
Tray, Dresser. Floral decor. Late	45.00
Vases	
4" high, green with red roses, gold trim	85.00
6½ x 12½". Gold and portrait. Signed A. Wichaz...............	125.00
7" high. Cream ground with floral and leaf decor. Gold decorated handle and trim	85.00
7½" high. Yellow roses, green on brown background	75.00
8" high, 14" diam. Yellow ground with red roses	85.00

Plate. 8". Wild Rose pattern ... $35.00

9½" high. Pastel floral, raised gold. Animal head handles in gold .	125.00
12¼" high. Gold and enameled decor. Handled. Germany	75.00
15" high. Portrait, leaf stem handles. Bust of girl on shaded green base, green leaves, pink lilacs	150.00
16" high. Portrait of lady. Footed, 2 handles. Signed	175.00
18" high	220.00

ROYAL COPENHAGEN

Royal Copenhagen has been produced continuously since the factory was established in 1771. It was under royal management in 1799. Much of the ware was imported into the United States from 1875 to 1900.

Bottle, Wine. 10" high. Oval picture of Fredercksborg Castle on front, crown on back ....$	50.00
Chocolate Pot. Blue and white, spring-type lid	100.00
Coffee Pot. Underglaze decor in cobalt. Gold edge and handles traced in gold	135.00
Compote. Muschel pattern, triangular, early mark	110.00
Cruet. Blue and white, original stopper	80.00
Cup and Saucer with Plate. Blue with white floral decor. Set...........	45.00

Tray. 6x11". Floral decor. Blue and white $20.00

Dinner Service. "Dagmar." Twelve
  8-piece place settings and six
  cigarette urns. Set 695.00
Dishes
  Bonbon 28.50
  9½" diam. Shape of seashell with
  crab sitting on one edge 95.00
  Oval, blue and white 30.00
Figurines
  3¼" high, 4" long. Dachshund
  laying down 55.00
  3½" high. Puppy, Pug. Sitting with
  legs askew in tan and brown 50.00
  6" high. Cat, sitting. Grey porcelain, white glaze on chest, green
  eyes 60.00
  7" high. Girl carrying sheaf of
  wheat 95.00
Inkwell with Tray. 6" wide, 8½" long .   85.00
Plaques
  5½" diam. Zodiac signs around
  angel 75.00
  5¾" diam. White marked "B&G"
  with 5 different subjects, including
  "Night"and "Day." Set of 5 . . . .   200.00
  13¼" diam. Mythological figures
  of winged woman and children
  with flowers and owl. Pair 350.00
  Cherubs making wine. C.1815. Pair   175.00
Plates
  4½". "Charity" 50.00
  8½". Deep, flower in brown,
  black and green leaves 30.00
  9½". White with blue decor 25.00
  Bread and Butter. Blue and white .   15.00
  Soup. 7¾". Open-chain edge, blue
  decoration, green mark 25.00
  Soup. Blue and white 22.50
Platters
  8x10". Blue and white 55.00
  9x12". Blue and white 65.00
  12x16". Blue and white 85.00
Teapot. Blue and white 95.00
Tureen, Vegetable. Covered 128.50

Vases
  7½" high, 4½" wide. Flagon-
  shape. Female head, front and
  back. Silver deposit 85.00
  8" high. Ship decor 75.00
  9½" high. Fuchsia flowers, leaves   85.00
  11" high. Decorated with light blue
  and white flowers 95.00

ROYAL CROWN DERBY

The factory now in existence was established
in England between 1875 and 1880 and had
no connection with an earlier factory which
operated around the turn of the 19th century.
It is estimated that 99% of the ware found
today in antique shops is from the later
factory.

Bowl. 11" diam., 3¾" deep. Floral
  cobalt rim, H/P floral interior and
  exterior . . . . $ 50.00
Candlesticks. 10" high, 5¼" diam.
  Cobalt, floral medallions. Pair . . .   135.00
Cups and Saucers
  Demitasse. Flowered, with blue,
  gold and green decor 37.50
  Mustache. Blue and gold 60.00
  Pink and blue decor inside and
  out. Deep saucer, impressed and
  stamped 45.00
  Tea Cup. Blue chinoiserie decor . .   48.00
Dish. Kidney-shaped, 7½x10½".
  Cobalt blue border, rose center,
  gilt trim 75.00
Eagle. 5" high, spread wings 120.00
Egg Cup. 2" 30.00
Ginger Jar. 7½" diam., red mark.
  Gold and green, red embossed
  flowers. Signed Tiffany & Co., N.Y. .   375.00

Box. Covered. Octagonal, 3" diam.
$65.00

Mug. Child's. 2¼", double gold handles, gold, blue and henna colors 65.00
Pill Box 35.00

Pitchers
Neptune's Mask. Dolphin tail. C. 1769 .... 225.00
Satyr's Mask. C. 1790 .... 200.00
White body with blue and gold. Pink, purple and white flowers. C. 1810 .... 175.00
Salt and Pepper Shakers. In silver-plated holder 85.00
Sugar and Creamer. Miniature 95.00
Teapot 140.00
Tray. 13x17". White body with blue flowers in swag design. Gold edge. Handled 135.00
Tureen. 7" long, covered, oval. Lion's mask, claw feet, handles. Multi-colored painted floral groups 175.00
Urn. Footed, 9¾" high. Blue color with gold, looped handles 325.00

Vases
7½" high. Cobalt, red, gold on white 120.00
10" high. Blue, white, gold trim ... 145.00

ROYAL DOULTON

A type of decorated hard porcelain pottery manufactured in England. It is often decorated with drawings of scenes from daily life and usually was finished with a dark brown glaze. The type mainly found in antique shops today was made after 1890.
Some of this ware is still being manufactured and imported into the United States.

Bank. 8½" high. Rabbit in costume, drum .... $ 20.00
Bottle. Zorro. 10½" high 50.00

Bowls
6½" diam. "Queen Elizabeth I at Old Moreton." Dark colors 25.00
8" diam., 4" deep. Forest scene with girl walking with basket 35.00
9½" diam., 2" high. In Gaffer's series 37.50
Punch Bowls:
10" diam., 4" high. H/P in blue and white hunting scenes, leaf, grape rim. Gold handles, artist signed 100.00
12" diam., 7" high. Gallon capacity. Dark blue, gold decor on foot. Bowl decorated inside and out in lighter shades of blue and white with gold 135.00

17" diam. Blue ground with hops decor. Grecian Key border in blue, gold at top and base 195.00
Salad bowl. With 12 matching 8½" plate. Pink and green poppy decor. Set 90.00
Butter Pat. 3¾" diam. Dickens Ware. "Tony Weller," signed Noke...... 19.00
Cake Set. 5 pieces. 10" diam. handled plate, four serving plates, 7½". Castle scenes in yellow and brown 55.00
Cake Stand. 9½" diam., 4¼" high. Pastel florals on top, gold scalloped edge................. 67.50
Candle Holder. With portrait 87.50
Charger. 13" diam. Green border, decor of trees and village........ 60.00
Compote 57.50
Creamer. 3½" high. Brown ground with Egyptian head spout 32.00
Cruet Set. 4 pieces, with stand. 1881 74.00

Cups and Saucers
Canterbury Pilgrims 21.50
Cream with pink and red roses ... 50.00
Demitasse. Flambe' mark........ 29.50
Demitasse. Fox in relief, riding crop handle.................... 20.00
Two-handled. Blue, silver rim 18.00
Cuspidor. 9" diam. at bottom. 8" high 29.50
Decanter. Whiskey. Marked "King George IV Scotch Whiskey" 27.50
Dinner Service. "Old Leed Spray." Octagonal. Service for 12 .... 450.00

Dishes
Cheese. Base 6½x7½". White ground with blue and yellow decor. Top 4½x5½" 55.00
Child's. 8½". "There Was a Little Man and He Had a Little Gun" 18.50
Deep. Scallop shape, floral. Pat. 1902 mark. Pair 48.00

Figurines
Afternoon Tea 75.00
Beagle, Sitting. Yawning, 4½" ... 35.00
Bunnies. Miniature. Ears up or down. Each 7.50
Drake, Standing. 6½". Flambe ... 60.00
Duck, Standing. 6½". Flambe 55.00
Duck, Swimming. 2x3". Flambe... 20.00
Falconer. 4½" 12.00
Fox, Sitting. 4½" 35.00
Fox. 6½" long, set on onyx base pen holder. Flambe 75.00
Gardener, The. 4½" 12.00
Granny's Heritage 125.00
Hare, Sitting. 4" 28.00
"Lady Charmain," 8". Blue dress .. 145.00
Lily 47.50

"Little Jack Horner"	58.00
Old Balloon Seller. #1315, old mk.	85.00
Rabbit. 3". One ear raised. Flambe	20.00
Rabbit, Running. 5½"	16.50
Shepherd, The. #1975, disc.	85.00
Tall Story. #2248. Disc.	70.00

Humidors

6" high, 5" diam. Barrel-shape, clamp on cover, blue, green with swags of flowers, fruits	35.00
Sailing ships on blue ground, blue and brown border	50.00

Jardinieres

6¼ x 7½", 24" circum. Fully marked. Also initials of decorator, F.J. Glazed multicolors	75.00
8" high, 8" diam. White with dark blue floral decor	40.00

Jugs, Character

1¼". Arry	65.00
1¼". Sam Weller	65.00

2½" - Miniatures:

Arry	37.50
Baccus	25.00
Fat Boy "A"	45.00
Gardener	18.50
John Barleycorn	40.00
John Peel "A"	40.00
Mr. Miscawber	45.00
Mr. Pickwick "A"	45.00
Paddy "A"	40.00
Toby. Filpots "A"	40.00
Town Crier	37.50

3½" - Small:

Ard of Earing	125.00
Fortune Teller	55.00
Gladiator	85.00
Gondolier	80.00
Gardsman	28.50
Lawyer	27.50
Lobsterman	27.50
Paddy "A"	45.00
Parson Brown "A"	50.00
Sarry Gamp "A"	50.00
Ugly Duchess	55.00
4½". Special size - only 6 characters made. Very rare 50.00 to	75.00

6" - Large:

Auld Mack "A"	70.00
Boot Maker	40.00
Captain Hook	62.50
Drake	85.00
Falconer	45.00
Jockey	47.50
John Barleycorn	135.00
Johnny Appleseed	145.00
Mr. Pickwick "A"	100.00
Pied Piper	45.00
Sarry Gamp "A"	70.00

Sleuth	40.00
Touchstone "A"	165.00

Pitchers

4" high. Lamplighter, embossed on brown glass. "More Than Enough, Is Too Much." Signed and marked	58.00
4½" high. Woman and child in fields. Marked "The Gleaners" . . .	25.00
5½" high. Square. Oliver Twist . . .	95.00
5¾" high. With Tudor rose	65.00
6¼" high. Milk. "Rosalind." C. 1920's	42.50
7¼" high. Milk. Dickens Ware. "Artful Dodger"	75.00

Vase. 7¾ x 8". Scene of children, trees
in background $45.00

Plates

6½". Monk's plate. "And He Peers in the Face of His Lordship's Grace"	28.50
8½". "Battle of Hastings"	27.50
9". Monk in wine cellar	35.00
9". "Mr. Micawber Delivers Some Valedictory Remarks." Dickens character	40.00
9½". Center H/P dog. Burslem. Rd. 72067	37.00
10". "The Admiral"	37.50
10". Bone background with wide borders of roses in basket, medallions deep blue and gold allover with gilt edge. Set of 12 . . .	295.00
10". "The Hunting Man"	26.50
10¼". Portrait of Shakespeare . . .	35.00
10½". Arab on Camel	32.00
10½". Dickens "Old Peggoty"	40.00

10½". Dickens "Mr. Squeers." Signed Noke	40.00
10½". Spaniel dog portrait	30.00
10½". Golfing scene	37.50
10½". Horseless Carriage Series. "Itch Yer On Guvenor?"	42.00
10½". Portrait of Isaac Walton in center	40.00
10½". "The Gypsies"	37.50
10½". "Solington Tournament," dueling knights	39.50
10½". Two men in red coats drinking	39.50
11". Dickens "Fagin"	42.00
Platter. Turkey. Painted turkey in center	95.00
Soap Dish. With drain, rose and gold decor	27.50
Syrup Jug. 7" high, hinged pewter lid. Mottled blue borders, center decor of gold tapestry, enameled flowers	55.00

Teapots

4½" high. Squatty, rose decor	65.00
Stoneware. Brown with tan decor in relief	75.00
Tobacco Jar. Dickensware	65.00

Tureens

8x12". Covered, allover hunt scene	135.00
Soup, with ladle	150.00

Vases

5½". Man and woman in house. Marked "Sir Rogu De Coverley."	28.00
6". Flambe, woodcut	40.00
7½". Woods, house scene. Rouge Flambe	115.00
8". Raised decor in blue, brown. Signed, dated 1887. Pair	125.00
10". Orange and blue	48.00
12½". 2 handles, brown with monk decor	65.00
16¼". Incised mules grazing among slip-painted thistles	195.00
Santa Claus. Miniature, rare	95.00
Small. Iris decor	50.00

ROYAL DUX

Items of this company were first manufactured in Bohemia in the late 1800s. Large quantities were brought to the United States in the early 1900s. Recently new items with this mark have come onto the market.

Basket. 2¾x4x4½". Creamy satin bkgd. with brown basketweave pattern, leaves and stemmed cherries	$ 85.00

Bowls

5x9½". Applied leaves over body, with handles	75.00
6x9½". Green bkgd., rose spray decor. Small open twig handles	75.00
7" long. Lady, reclining on edge of bowl	115.00
Box. 5¼x7½". Covered, elephant finial. Red panels, gold border	125.00

Figurines

*6½" high, 8" long. Nude, in semi-reclining position	95.00
7" high. Stalking lioness on oval base. 5¼x13¾". Pink, triangle mark	200.00
7¾" high x 3 x 10¾". Deer pottery, rect. base. Beige, tan satin finish. Signed Tarl. Pink triangle mark on base	150.00

Pitcher Vase. Art Nouveau-type. White, fine black and gold lines
$125.00

8". Man & woman decorating jugs
in gold. 4x6" base. Pair.......... 350.00
9" high, 21" long. Fish among the
reeds 125.00
10" high. Boy driving ox and cow
in harness 150.00
11" high. Woman in Grecian
clothing, holding basket......... 120.00
12" high. Sea Gull. Blue & white .. 75.00
13½" high. Young girl holding
doll, pink, green, beige. Signed .. 295.00
14" high. Girl & boy with little
animals, pink triangle mark. Pair . 375.00
14" high. Lady holding large shell 220.00
14" high. Man & woman tango
dancing, bisque skin & hair. Blue
and white china costumes & base,
gold trim. Art Deco 125.00
14" high. Woman in Greek classic
pink gown, standing against
pedestal with hand on water jug.
Artists initials on bottom 125.00
14½" high, 12" long. Maiden at
pool. Triangle mark 175.00
17" high. Statues. Carrying fruit &
water. Green & flesh color.
Signed. Pair 350.00
17½" high. Camel with rider on
6½x14" base 350.00
18" high. Girl with water jug 220.00
Mirror. Art Nouveau. Figure of
woman in pond removing shoes.
9x13" 225.00
Planter. 7x11". Woman in Grecian
costume holding vase. Ivory with
gold trim 165.00

Vases
6" high. Yellow with green and
pink 45.00
7" high. Mermaid. Art Nouveau .. 60.00
9½" high. Horizontal semi-clad
female figures. 19" long at base .. 150.00
10" high. Boy spraying flowers
from tank on back. Beige & brown
coloring 135.00
10" high. Ewer-shaped pitcher
vase. Applied flowers, cherries
and peaches 140.00
11½" high. Ivory painted ground
with pink flowers & green leaves.
Pair 250.00
12" high. 2 handles. Bulbous with
long neck and flared top. Green
and gold foliage. Boy playing flute
and girl holding lamb. Pink Dux
Triangle, Bohemia. Pair 295.00
14" high. Ladies' heads (2) in
relief at top, 2 handles ending in
heads. Triangle mark. Pair 250.00

16" high. Ornate handles, bun-
ches of cherries in relief. Marked.
Pair 325.00
*Reproduced Item

ROYAL FLEMISH GLASS

Royal Flemish glass was made by the Mt.
Washington Glass Works at New Bedford,
Mass., in the late 1880s. This same factory
produced Burmese, Crown Milano and other
art glass. The glass is russet brown with a
satin finish and is decorated with gold.

Cookie Jar. Mt. Washington. Gold
coin medallions, silver top and
handles $1250.00
Pitcher 1400.00
Sugar Shaker. Fig-shape, frosted in
white with bark look 650.00
Sweetmeat Dish. Turtle on cover.
Signed 750.00
Vases
4" high. Handled. Opaque enamel
decor in russet, tan and brown
with enamel gold decor. Gold
dragon in medallions with initials
"R.F." 1125.00
5" high. Four medallions separated by shaded, stained glass
sections. Gold handles and gold
detailed collar 1375.00
11" high. Stick-type, 7½" high
neck. Bulbous base 1500.00
13" high. Guba ducks. Tan and
brown coloring. Signed. Pair 3000.00

Vase. 7" high. Round, collared. Latin
inscriptions on coin decor ...$1750.00

ROYAL RUDOLSTADT

The factory was established in 1758 at Volkstedt and later moved to Rudolstadt in Schwartzburg. The early mark was the letter "R". Later a mark representing a hayfork, part of the arms of Schwartzburg, was used. Still later, crossed two-pronged hayforks were utilized to imitate the Dresden or Meissen mark.

The majority of the items appearing in shops today is of the late 19th and early 20th century period.

The late marks show a shield with the letters "RW", a crown on top, with the word "Crown" above and the name "Rudolstadt" below the shield. Another mark has the word "Germany" in place of the word "Crown" which indicated that ware so marked was definitely made after 1891.

Tray. Shallow, 10" diam. Corn pattern, ochre shading, gold trim. Signed
$45.00

Basket. 4½ x6¾". Creamy ground, floral design, gold handle. Old mark .... $	65.00
Bowls	
8½" high, 9" long. Centerpiece. Large shell with a cupid sitting on the edge	125.00
10". Berry. Decorated with small pink peonies	70.00
11" diam. Cream ground, pink and yellow roses, green foliage	75.00
Cake Set. 7 pieces	120.00
Celery. Painted violet decor, gold edge.........................	35.00
Cheese Dish. Small, slant top, decorated with roses	65.00
Chocolate Set. Pot, four cups, saucers, handpainted roses on cream ground, gold trim, mark incised & stamped. Set	200.00
Compote. Small, covered. Large raised yellow enameled roses, gold trim	50.00
Cup and Saucer. Newport Belle pattern	35.00
Dresser Set. Large & small trays, hatpin holder, hair receiver, ring tree, covered jar. Rose decor. Marked	200.00
Dresser Tray. Ovid shape, gold edge and touches , open roses in pale yellow with pink. Signed T. Kahn .	52.00
Ewer. 8" high. Face on spout, mums on creamy white	65.00
Hatpin Holder. Decorated with roses and lavender	29.50
Lamp. 10" high. Dresden-like coloring in pastel pink, blue and gold ..	225.00

Pitchers	
4½" high. Cream, pink pansies, gold trim	35.00
4½" high. Flower spray medallions with gold decor, serpent handle	58.50
Cream. 3¾" high. Scalloped edge and gold trim at top, satin finish. Floral spray on cream bkgd.	45.00
Syrup. Covered. German chestnuts on white ground. Heavy gold on handle and finial. Matching oval tray. Sgnd. "Armand"	65.00
Plates	
6". Multicolored roses, blue and gold trim	30.00
8½". 3 poppies, white, pink & salmon coloring	37.50
10½". Cake. Roses with buds, foliage, pierced handles	50.00
11". Rose decor. Mkd. "Prussia" .	55.00
Beethoven portrait. Marked	45.00
Platter. Fish. 15", green base color with fish decor	60.00
Salt and Pepper Shakers. H/P floral decor. Pair	35.00
Sugar and Creamer. Violet and gold on cream ground. Set	65.00
Vases	
8¼" high. RW handpainted cupids on front, detailed fancy handles, fluted top	85.00
8¼" high. Cornucopia with flying dragon. Beige with mocha	85.00
9" high, 5½" widest diam. Cream colored, floral decor. Gold applied handles. Mkd. R.V. Crown	85.00

9½" high. Floral decor, gold handles 65.00

10" high. Bulbous, long, thin neck. H/P floral on cream. Stamp mark and sticker 75.00

14" high. Ornate, beige with pastel flowers and gold decor, gold handles 135.00

16¼" high. Grecian motif, light pastel colors 165.00

ROYAL VIENNA

The factory was founded in 1720 in Vienna, Austria, by a runaway foreman from the Meissen Works. In 1744, Empress Maria Theresa brought it under royal patronage. The wares were of the Meissen type and noted for their brilliant colors and technical excellence. The factory closed in 1864. The so-called "Beehive" mark on the ware was one of its distinguishing features. The majority of the ware on the market today has been produced by other factories which have made modern reproductions. Items made after 1891 have the country of origin, Austria, as well as the "Beehive" mark.

Basket. Porcelain, green body, handles, applied red cherries, green leaves.................. $ 135.00

Bowl, Berry. 9¾" diam. Light pink shading to red, decorated with pink poppies, leaves, bouquet of lilies in center, gold trim on edge . 95.00

Portrait Plate. 11" diam. "Lady Harcourt." Beehive mark $250.00

Chocolate Pot. 10" high. Decorated with cupids on purple ground 150.00

Compote. 8¼" diam., 4½" high. Floral decor in blue and green.... 115.00

Cracker Jar. Covered.............. 185.00

Cups and Saucers
Blue. Beehive mark 60.00
Gold on cobalt. Greek woman decor, gold lined cup. Artist signed 85.00

Dinner Set. Service for 12. Dark red, gray and gold colors 1250.00

Dish. 11" long. Open lattice, rectangular, "Beehive" mark 165.00

Figurines. Porcelain lady dancers. 10" high, 4" bases, colorful costumes. Pair 500.00

Perfume Cruet. Cobalt, gold trim, medallion of woman and cupid ... 85.00

Pitchers
10" high. Tankard-type. Beehive mark 185.00
12" high. Red ground, with gilt sprays. Large picture panel, gilt handle. "Die Hochzeit" (The Wedding) depicting 19 figures, horses and chariot. Signed Huber. C. 1815 .... 245.00

Plaque, Wall. 13¾". Green and red border with gold trim. Classical scene "Pearl" by Carl Larson 275.00

Plates
9¼". Portrait of Queen Louise ... 195.00
9½". Classic figures in center. Red band border with a gold edge 140.00
9½". Portrait. C. 1840. Gold and blue, white rock lady in center. Signed Wagner................. 250.00
9½". Portrait. Young lady and three cherubs, cobalt border and ½" gold border around center scene. Beehive mark 235.00
9½". Scalloped edge, H/P roses in pink, yellow & white, gold edge. Marked with crown and Royal Vienna on back 45.00
10". Bathing scene, blue and gold border, maiden, cupid and swan.. 155.00
10". Dark green with gold tracery, mythological figures. Beehive mark 245.00
14". Nude with three cupids. Heavy gold. Signed "Frichling" on back 275.00
15". Hanging-type. Blue border, colorful classic scene, gold scroll decor on border 280.00

Dutch mother and children look-
ing out to sea. Green border.
Signed 75.00
Rose Jar. With lid. Dark red ground,
gold decor. Portrait of woman, by
Wagner, outlined in jewels 250.00
Tea Caddy. 7" high. Red and cream
ground with gilt sprays. Two large
panels of courting lovers, "Amor
Und Cephiste" and "Rinaldo Und
Almeido." Sgnd. C. Herr. C. 1820 . 275.00
Tea Set. Pot, creamer, sugar bowl, 2
cups and saucers 450.00
Toothbrush Holder. Canary yellow
with red scroll design, gold decor . 45.00
Trays, Dresser
8¼x12". Handpainted violet decor on pale green ground, gold
trim 100.00
Pin. Small, round. Cherubs on lid.
Beehive, Austria 45.00
Urns
6" high. Green decor with gold
including handles and knob. H/P
panels on sides 195.00
8x13". Covered, square pedestal
bases. Sgnd. "Kaufman." Pair 575.00
11¼" high. Covered. Ann Gitana.
Firemarked. Signed "Wagner" . . . 395.00
15" high. Covered, flower and
figure panels 275.00
18" high. Green bkgd. with three
H/P ladies on front, two handles
and covered. Beehive under glaze 450.00
19" high. Underglaze. Three H/P
ladies. Deep green, gold back-
ground. Beehive. 600.00
20" high. Pedestal. Square base,
signed "Kaufman" 495.00
Vases
7" high. Portrait of girl. Signed
"Wagner" 195.00
8½" high, 9¼" circum. Scene
depicts story of Moses. Mother
holding child, children riding lions 250.00
10" high. Portrait (Klysti). Iridescent blue and gold. Signed
"Schieslneer" 295.00

ROYAL WORCESTER

The porcelain works was established in 1751
by Dr. John Wall and 14 partners. Dr. Wall
died in 1776 and the entire business was sold
to Thomas Flight in 1783. Martin Barr was
admitted as a partner in 1793 and the firm
was known as Flight & Barr. In 1807 the name
was changed to Flight, Barr & Barr. It was

changed again in 1813 to Barr, Flight & Barr,or
"B.F.B." and continued as such until 1840 at
which time Chamberlin & Son and Barr, Flight
& Barr were consolidated. The works was
moved to Dighlis, the home of Chamberlain &
Son. The company was sold to Kerr & Binn in
1852 and it is still in existence. Most of the
ware encountered in the United States is of
the 1870-1900 variety, although an occasional
piece of the Dr. Wall or Flight & Barr is found.

Plate. 9", multicolored floral decor
$35.00

Biscuit Barrel. H/P Locke Worcester.
Pheasant silverplate handle & lid . $ 195.00
Bone Dish. Blue flower decor 25.00
Bowls
9" square. 19th century. Butterfly
and sprig decorations 195.00
Berry. 7½x9". Woven basket
pattern, cream shading to tan.
Open gold handles, H/P orchid
and gold flowers inside 145.00
Medium size. Dr. Wall period. 300.00
Rose. 3" high, with blue bird and
leaves, gold branches 95.00
Butter Dish. Dr. Wall period. C. 1770.
Blue and white 350.00
Cache Pot. 2¼" high, 2½" diam.
White porcelain with decor of
roses, blue bells, berries, dragon-
fly, etc. Gold trim, three gold feet 125.00

Caddy. 4½". Globe-shape with
gilded gold fernery on ivorine
background 90.00
Cake Stand. 10¼" diam., base 5¼",
2¾" high. Solid lilac with narrow
gold band at top & bottom.
Scalloped edge. Purple mark 125.00

Candleholder. Bright gold mouse nibbling on dull gold tallow, sitting on simulated wood platform. Handled 6" long, 2¼" high . 185.00

Candle Snuffers
   3¾" high. Old gent wearing night cap, bathrobe. Has toothache 125.00
   "Toby and Punch." C. 1882. Pair .. 250.00

Chocolate Pot. Cream background .. 195.00

Cracker Jar. Covered, with matching plate, floral decor 200.00

Creamer. Florals with green decor .. 95.00

Cups and Saucers
   Decorated. C. 1888 .... 55.00
   Demitasse. Cream ground, rust flowers. C. 1890 .... 35.00
   "Flight." White and gold 135.00
   Ivory ground with gold paste, bronze leaves and berries. C. 1886......................... 55.00

Dessert Set, 1877. 2 low compotes 9" high with six plates. Each plate has a different center, gold borders, raised enameling. Set ... 350.00

Vase. 12" high. Pink roses, reptile handle $295.00

Dish. Small. 5" long, 2¼" wide. Simulating an oyster shell. Date mark 1883. Cray fish on edge forms handle 58.50

Ewers
   6" high. Handpainted blossom. 1885......................... 75.00
   8½" high. Cream ground, purple flowers, raised faces, animal heads. Ornate, purple mark 275.00
   11¾" high. Rose pink bkgd. Decor in medallions, firs and geometric pattern. Dark green/gold lizard wound around neck forms handle. Green mark. C. 1883............ 150.00
   11½" high. Serpent forming handle. Flowers in lavender, red, blue, green, brown and gold. Purple mark 395.00
   12" high. Quilted texture of ivorine ground with painted floral work & butterflies. Chinese dragon forms handle........... 395.00

Flower Holder. Horn-shaped 75.00

Ginger Jar. 12½" high, with reticulated cover 200.00

Hands. 6½" high. Pair 195.00

Menu Holder. 7½" high. Tree trunk, frog sitting on base. Purple mark . 125.00

Statue. 15½" high. Woman holding urn on head 195.00

Sugar Shaker. Signed 75.00

Tea Caddy. 5½" high, gold and blue spatter. Marked............... 125.00

Tea Set. Teapot, sugar bowl and creamer. Leaf and floral decor, brown twig finials on blue leaf covers 300.00

Teapots
   5¾" high. Floral decor 175.00
   7¼" high. Chinese style painted decor. Dr. Wall. C. 1790 .... 375.00
   Shakespeare's house on front. Reverse, scenic mountains. Bamboo gold trim handle and spout... 125.00
   Squat. 5-cup size. Satin finish, floral decor.................... 185.00

Thimble. Roses and shamrock decor. Signed 50.00

Tray. 7½ x 10½". Floral decor on edge 100.00

Tumble-Up. 4½" high, leaves, fern .. 145.00

Tureens
   4½" high, 9½" long. Blue, white oriental decor. Covered, gold, white finial, resting on gold feet. Gold elephant heads and trunks as handles.................... 125.00
   11½" high. Blue and gold decor in oriental style, with platter and ladle. Set 300.00

| Miniature. Covered. Melon-shaped with stalks on yellow base | 90.00 |
| Urn. 9" high, floral decor with green lizard forming handles | 165.00 |

Vases

7" high. Sabrina ware. Gourd-shaped. Mottled avacado green	100.00
8" high. Reticulated pink and cream, pedestaled. [Locke]	250.00
10½" high. C. 1760. Blue and relief molded cabbage leaves, leaf band at top. Old mark	395.00
11" high. Floral decor and gold. Applied handles	200.00
11½" high. White with tan, gold acorn design	325.00
13½" high. Soft ivorine ground with decor of fernery and flowers, enameling	395.00
Wine Jug. 9½" high. Cream-colored ground with allover floral decor	195.00

ROYCROFT ITEMS

Elbert Hubbard, founder of the Roycrofters in East Aurora, New York, was considered a genius in his day. He was an author, lecturer, manufacturer, salesman and philosopher. His philosophy paralleled that of Wm. Morris, English philosopher and inventor of the Morris chair.

Hubbard established a campus, including a printing plant where he published "The Philistine," "The Fra" and "The Roycrofter." His most famous book was "A Message to Garcia" in 1899. The campus also included a furniture manufacturing plant where heavy oak furniture was produced; a metal shop and a leather shop. Workmen were hired to produce the items.

| Ash Tray. 3-7/8". Copper. Marked Elbert Hubbard's Work Shops".... $ | 12.00 |

Books

American Bible, An. 1911. Leather bound	8.00
Dictionary, 1914	5.00
Message to Garcia, 1908. Leather bound	7.00
Myth in Marriage, 1912. Leather bound	5.00
Note Book, 1927. Dust cover	8.00
Scrap Book, 1923. Dust cover	8.00
Bookends. L-shaped, hammered copper. Signed. Pair	10.00
Bowl. Hammered copper, brass-toned, crimped top. Signed	12.50

| Wastebasket. 11½x13". Weathered oak | $40.00 |

Candleholders

2x3½". Hammered copper. Footed and handled	12.00
2¼" high. Copperware	25.00
8" high. Pair	50.00
Jug. 5½" high. Mottled brown. Marked	16.50
Tray. 10" diam. Hammered copper, handled, octagon shape	40.00
Vase. 4¾" high. Hammered metal	17.50

RUBINA GLASS

The glass appears to have first been made by the Geo. A. Duncan & Sons Co. at Pittsburgh, Pa., in 1885.

Part of the item was made of ruby glass which gradually "melted" into a clear body. Some objects were then frosted which produced a beautiful effect.

| Bonbon Tricorn. 6" wide, diamond quilted. Deep pie-crust edge. Applied handle | $ 65.00 |

Bottles

4½" high, 1½" square. Perfume. Clear cut stopper	65.00
7" high. Perfume. Three-footed, decorated	125.00
8" high. Arrow shape, sterling top	75.00
Atomizer. Swirl design. Marked Baccarat	75.00

Bowls

| Finger. Plain | 45.00 |

Hobnail. 5½" high, 5" diam. In two-handled silver holder 165.00
Rose. 4" high, clear to red at top . . 70.00
Rose. 5" high, ribbed, with green and gold enamel decor 85.00
Rose. 6" high, 7" diam. Ribbed . . . 75.00
Square. Petal edges, sparkling fern pattern in bottom 85.00
Cookie Jar. Crystal base to deep cranberry glass. 6½" high. Silver cover and handles 160.00
Cracker Jar. Allover floral decor. Silverplated cover 175.00
Creamer. 5¾" high, 4½" diam. Overshot, cranberry to clear applied, reeded handle. Bulbous bottom 125.00

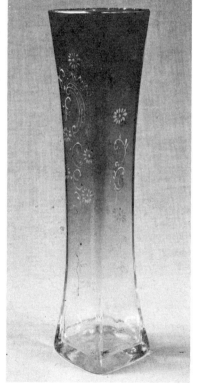

Vase. 7¼" high. Square top and bottom $55.00

Cruets
7½" high. Hobnail 115.00
IVT. Cranberry, clear faceted stopper 95.00
Muffineer. Shading from clear to cranberry. 4" high, square shape. Resilvered top. 85.00
Mustard Jar. Enameled blue daisies. Plated lid and underplate 60.00
Pickle Castor. Decorated enamel spots 175.00
Pitchers
5" high. Applied, reeded handle. IVT design. Tri-cornered lip 55.00
7" high. Water. Hobnail, clear applied handle 165.00
9" high. Clear handle 195.00
10" high. IVT with enameled flowers 250.00
Salt and Pepper Shakers. Enamel floral decor. Pair 95.00
Sugar and Creamer. Fuchsia to clear. Silver tops and handles. Pair 200.00
Sugar Shaker. 6" high 75.00
Syrups
6" high 115.00
Acid-etched flower decor 115.00
Tumblers
Plain 50.00
Pointed Hobnail. [Not opal]. Cranberry. Hobs to near top 65.00
Vases
6" high 60.00
8" high. Footed, swirled, heavy crystal, sterling rings. Pair 165.00
10" high. Enameled flowers 110.00
Whiskey Glasses. Decorated. Pair . . 55.00

RUBINA VERDE GLASS

A type of colored glass which is now considered to be in the field of art glass. The first of this ware was made by Hobbs, Brockunier & Co., Wheeling, W.Va. around 1890. The glass shades from yellow-green to a cranberry color.

Bowls
4" high, 5" diam. Rose. Ribbed. Garnet-crimped top . . . . $ 85.00
4½" high, 8½" long. Fuchsia to green at bottom. Decor of enameled flowers, white and yellow, gold leaves, applied glass bead flowers in blue 175.00
9" high, 4" deep. Rounded down, scalloped rim 150.00
9¾ x6¾", crimped top 185.00
Finger. Inverted Thumbprint 75.00

Fruit. 8" square top. 3½" deep,
diamond quilted............... 150.00
Rose. Large.................... 125.00
Butter Dish. Daisy and Button
clear base, domed thumbprint
cover 225.00

Candlesticks. Pair 200.00
Compote. 9½" across, 6" high, on
silverplated pedestal base....... 140.00
Creamer. 3¼" high, 2¼" wide at top 120.00

Cruets
6½" high. Pale yellow-green at
base shading to cranberry in the
necks. Inverted Thumbprint,
applied clear crystal handles, cut
crystal stopper. Pair 295.00
8" high. Floral decor, green cut
stopper 225.00
Cup, Punch. Enamel decor 70.00

Jack-in-the-Pulpit Vase. 13" high
$275.00

Epergnes
8½" diam., 1½" deep base.
Single. Cranberry glass top with
green glass petals twisted around
stem. Blown 125.00
13" high, 8½" diam. Ruffled and
fluted with clear glass edge...... 150.00
3 horns with hanging baskets 295.00
Mustard Pot. ITP 80.00
Pickle Castor. Resilvered frame and
lid.......................... 250.00
Pitchers
5½" high. Applied handles. IVT.
Square top and shading from
cranberry to vaseline, green at
base..........................$ 180.00
5¾" high. Quart. Bulbous melon-
ribbed. Blue with polished pontil . 135.00
7" high. Cranberry to canary.
Canary handle 260.00
Water. 8" high, 8" diam. Pointed
Hobnail. Cranberry to bulbous,
greenish-vaseline base. Claw
handle 275.00
Water. Hobnail, clear applied
handle 285.00
Sauce Dish. 4½" square. Pointed
Hobnail, ruffled top 60.00
Shade. Large, hall lamp-type 275.00
Vases
5½" high. Ruffled top, opalescent coin spots, clusters of gold
and pastel flowers 145.00
7" high. Ribbed green base
shading to ruffled cranberry top.
Applied green glass rigaree
around body 175.00
8¾" diam. Trumpet-shaped with 8
scallops at top 185.00
9½" high. Flared top, 6-pointed
petals, gold scrolls and flowers... 195.00
11" high. Drapery pattern. Pair... 240.00
12" high. Jack-in-the-Pulpit, with
applied clear ribbons 250.00

RUGS, ORIENTAL

The early history of oriental rugs is obscure for
they have only been preserved since the 16th
century. The largest number were probably
made in Persia, now Iran, while others are
attributed to Central Asia, Caucasia and
Afghanistan. They became popular in this
country during the Victorian era. However,
some were in use prior to that time.
The origin of certain rugs may be determined
by the style of weave. Some examples are
Bijar, Cabistan, Kazak, Kurd, Mir, Royal
Bokhara, etc.

Kerman. 3'x4'2" $350.00

Afshar. 2'3"x3'	$ 200.00
Ardebil. 5'6"x8'5"	1250.00
Ardebil. 6'6"x10"	725.00
Baktiary. 12"x16'7"	3600.00
Belouj. 2'x3'	125.00
Belouj Ivory. 3'x4'6"	250.00
Cabistan-Prayer. 3'5"x5'	200.00
Chindia. 6'x9'	575.00
Chinese. 9'x11'8"	250.00
Dargazin. 2'6"x4'	150.00
Fereghan. 5'3"x9'	1000.00
Fereghan. 14'x20'	275.00
Hamadan. 3'5"x4'5"	250.00
Hamadan. 9'3"x15'10"	375.00
Hamadan. 12'3"x23'6"	3750.00
Herez. 8'1"x11'3"	1750.00
Isfahan. 3'6"x5'4"	4000.00
Isfahan. 10'4"x16'9"	6000.00
Kandahar. 10'9"x14'3"	1350.00
Kasha. 4'7"x7'2"	1350.00
Kashan. 9'8"x18'3"	8000.00
Kerman. 3'x5'	400.00
Kerman. 4'x7'	600.00
Keyseri. 3'x4'5"	400.00
Kum Solk. 7'2"x4'9"	7000.00
Lilihan. 6'10"x9'3"	160.00
Lilihan. 6'10"x13'	650.00
Lilihan. 8'7"x10'8"	425.00
Meshkin. 2'3"x3'6"	150.00
Meshkin. 3'x17'	800.00
Meshkin. 5'3"x9'3"	700.00
Meshkin. 9'4"x14'	2000.00
Milas. 4'x6'3"	600.00

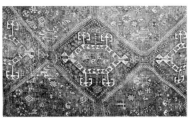

Shiraz. 7'6"x10'11" $650.00

Nain. 5'x7'7"	5000.00
Pakistan. 2'x3'	100.00
Pakistan. 2'x6'	200.00
Pakistan Bukara. 5'1"x7'8"	500.00
Pakistan Bukara. 10'3"x13'3"	2200.00
Pakistan Ivory. 6'2"x9'5"	1000.00
Sarouk. 2'x3'	150.00
Sarouk. 2'x4'	200.00
Sarouk Medallion. 8'7"x12'8"	3500.00
Sarouk, Red Ivory. 8'9"x12'3"	2250.00
Sarouk, Red. 9'3"x13'3"	1600.00
Sarouk, Med. Green. 10'3"x13'6" ...	3000.00
Serapi. 9'9"x12'10"	3500.00
Serapi. 9'9"x13'5"	4000.00
Tabriz. 11'x17'2"	12500.00
Tabriz. 12'8"x19'2"	9500.00
Tabriz. 12'10"x19'5"	10500.00
Tabriz Ivory. 6'7"x9'6"	1500.00
Tabriz Ivory. 9'9"x15'5"	5000.00
Tabriz Rust. 12'7"x19'9"	8000.00
Yalameh. 2'6"x2'6"	150.00
Yezd. 9'8"x12'5"	1000.00

RUSSIAN ENAMELS, ETC.

Works of Russian artists and craftsmen are highly regarded by collectors.

Russian enamels are one of the most exquisite examples of the Russian arts during the Czarist period. The items were fashioned of precious metal and then elaborately enameled. Many were encrusted with previous and semi-precious stones.

Russian enamels are not too plentiful and, therefore, they command a good price.

Enamels

Blotter. Rocker-type, knob holder ...	$ 450.00
Bottle, Scent. Perfume compartment at both ends with black enamel and silver caps. Opening in center	650.00
Bowl. Sloped sides, beaded rim, 2½" across. Signed	1200.00
Brandy Taster. Signed	1000.00

Cigarette Case. 2¾x4". Amethyst
clasp $1500.00

Candleholders
   7" high. Ornate marble base. Pair   1250.00
   Spoon-type. With bobeches 750.00
Cane Head......................   375.00
Cigarette Case 1500.00

Cups
   3-3/8" long. Bird decor. Borsch ...   700.00
   3½". Demitasse. Faberge work,
   master multicolored. 84 Worn, St.
   George and Dragon mark. H.C.
   Helen Skishkina 175.00

Eggs, Easter
   2½x4". Hanging-type, close
   enameling 1250.00
   3". Silver gilt, Kuzmitchev. C. 1890   2500.00
Glass Holder. Vodka. Miniature,
   shape of tea glass holder. Multicolored 88 Kokoshnik with ml 325.00
Inkwell and Pen Holder...........   600.00
Letter Opener. 3" handle on 12"
   wood opener. Number on handle .   375.00
Salt Dip. 1-7/8" diam., 1" high.
   Silver gilt. Signed F.R. 88 ....   395.00
Salt Master. 2¾" diam. Multi-
   colored. Mkd. 84, maker's mark ...   375.00
Salt, Open. Colored, ornate. Russian
   hand marks....................   150.00
Scoop. 4½" long, 5-colored. Cobalt,
   lavender, white, red and turquoise   1850.00

Spoons
   2½" long. Salt 225.00
   4½". Teaspoon. Pastels, 84
   Kokoshnik, 11 Attel 185.00
   7". Gold over silver. Marked 75.00
   Transparent enamel bowl with
   poison container at top 400.00
Tea Strainer. Round, post war ermine
   tails mark, 925 ....   375.00
Tie Pin. 1x2¼". Signed 84 AA 295.00
Tongs. Silver gilt, blue enamel in
   wire twist cloisons, white beading. 5" long 425.00

Napkin Ring. Oval, 2" long ... $550.00

Tumbler. Enamel on tin, Coronation
   of Czar Nicholas II. May 1896 ....   185.00
Vase. 4¾" high. Cream ground,
   mauve bands. Sterling overlay
   garlands. Faberge' 950.00
Vodka Cup. Signed...............   1250.00
Russian Silver
Dish. Shallow, 3½" diam. Outer rim
   decorated with concentric raised
   ribs bound with X's at six points.
   Signed Faberge' 400.00
Napkin Ring. 1-3/8". Floral design ...   65.00
Salt Dip. Etched floral, 2 ball feet.
   Marked 84 ....   75.00
Spoons. 4¼" long. Goldwashed, in
   original box. Twisted handles,
   engraved bowls, dated 1886.
   Set of six 165.00

Sugar Tongs. 4¼" long. Bright-cut
   type engraving, pineapple motif.
   Dated 1842 ....   125.00
Miscellaneous
Bread Plate. Wood. 11" diam.
   Carved with sickle, plow and
   wheat. Russian lettering 75.00

SABINO GLASS

Sabino opalescent glass figurines are a
modern ceation of the artist "Sabino," the
"Sculptor in Crystal."

Sabino models each figure by hand. A mold
is then made. Each piece is labeled "Sabino,
Made in France."

Because of the fine workmanship and beauty
of Sabino figurines, they are considered quite
collectible.

Turtle	$16.50
Rabbit	$14.00
Squirrel	$25.00

Ash Trays

3½" diam. Small swallow	$ 15.00
3½ x 5½". Small shell	18.00
4" wide, 7" long. Large shell	35.00
4½" diam. Violet	22.00
4¾" diam. Large swallow	25.00

Birds

Baby. 1½"	15.00
Cluster of 2. 4½" long, 3½" high .	75.00
Cluster of 3. 5" long, 5" high	100.00
Feeding. 2" high, 2" wide	22.00
Fighting. 2¾" wide, 2" long	22.00
Kingfisher. 4" high	47.50
Mini. ½" high, wings out	12.50
Mocking. 3¾" high, 4" long	45.00
Mocking. 6" high, 4½" long	55.00
Perched. 3¾" high, 4" long	42.50
Teasing. 3" high, 3½" wide. Wings down	45.00
Wren. 1½" high	15.00
Bottle, Perfume. 6½" high. 5 dancing nudes	55.00
Butterfly. 2¾" high. Wings open	30.00
Cat. 2" high	17.00
Cherub. 2" high	15.00

Dogs

German Shepherd. 2" high	17.50
Pekinese. 2" high	17.50
Dragonfly. 6" high, 5¼" long	50.00
Elephant. 2" high	16.50
Fish. 2" high, 2½" long	25.00
Fish Bowl. 5" diam.	40.00
Fish Vase. 5" high	95.00
Gazelle	60.00
Knife Rest, Poodle. 3½" high, 4" long	15.00
Madonna. 3" high	20.00
Madonna. 5" high	45.00
Mouse. Large	65.00
Napkin Ring of Birds. 2¼" diam.	15.00
Owl. 4½" high	55.00
Panthers. 6x8". Pair	250.00
Pheasant. 3½" high	20.00
Pigeon. 1¾" high. Head up	15.00
Rabbit	14.00

Rooster. 3½" high	22.50
Snail. 2" long, 1" high	17.50
Snail Shell. 2" high, 4" long	37.50
Squirrel. 3" high	25.00
Statue. Nude. 6¾" high	100.00
Stork. 7¼" high	90.00
Swan. 2" high	20.00
Turkey. 2" high	20.00
Turtle. ¾" high, 2" long	16.50

SALOPIAN WARE

A type of decorated pottery made at the Caughley Pot-Works, Salop, Strophshire, on the Severn River in England. In 1772 Thomas Turner took over the works and produced fine porcelain.

In 1780 Turner opened his Salopian warehouse on Portugal St., Lincoln Inn Fields, London. His mark was "Salopian" or the letter "S" impressed or painted in blue underglaze, and occasionally an impressed 8-point star. He is noted for the famous "Willow" pattern which he originated.

Turner retired in 1799 and the works was sold to John Rose and Co. In 1815 the establishment was moved across the river to Coalport where the plant is still in production under the name of Coalport.

Cup and Saucer. Double Deer pattern
$295.00

Bowl and Jug. Black transfer with blue edging. Man and woman taking tea in garden with blackamoor pouring from pot. Bowl 3½" high, 6¾" diam. Jug 5¼" high	$ 575.00
Creamer. House pattern	350.00

Cups and Saucers

Chintz pattern. Deep blue and white	85.00
Deer pattern	240.00
Double deer	295.00
House pattern	195.00

Plates

6-1/8". Farm scene, sheep, two shepherds	265.00
8½". Pastoral scene, yellow border	300.00
Saucer. 4-7/8" diam. 2 birds and cottage	125.00
Tea Set. Covered teapot, covered sugar and creamer, 4 handleless cups and saucers. Blue and white decor. Some pieces marked "Caughley"	1250.00
Teapot. House pattern	450.00

SALT GLAZE

The Staffordshire district of England was considered the center for salt-glazed pottery. The ware has a hard glaze which resulted from throwing regular table salt into the hot kiln. The salt vaporized and fixed itself, in fine drops, to the items. It is reported that Salt Glaze is still being produced in England today.

Bowl. 4x8½" diam. Plain	$ 75.00
Butter. Covered	185.00
Dish. Olive. 7" long, 5¾" wide. Late .	45.00

Jugs

6" high. Bulbous, wide-necked. Light grey with raised jewels. Pewter lid, signed. Broadhead	75.00
6" high. Pewter lid with thumbrest. Registration mark on bottom, 1870	125.00
7" high. White raised berry & leaf design on a fabric texture. Handled, pewter lid	60.00
7¼" high. Melon-shaped with alternating blue and white strips, pewter top. Marked "W.B. Flouger, Cobridge"	100.00
7½" high. Tournament, light gray, signed, dated. Ridgway, 1840	145.00
8½" high. Cherubs in relief. C. 1845	145.00
9¼" high. Pewter-type cover, Bacchus design in relief	165.00
10" high. Pewter lid, figures of apostles by Chas. Meigh, dated Mar. 17, 1842	350.00
10¼" high. White pewter top. Baccanalian theme in raised decor. Made by Chas. Meigh & dated 1843	295.00

Pitchers

4" high. Good Samaritan scene, raised lavender figures in white forest. British Royal Arms. Mark	135.00

Syrup Pitcher. 8½" high. Pewter lid. Argus pattern. Cobridge. C. 1864
$110.00

7½" high. Raised lily & leaves decor. No mark. England	55.00
8" high. Raised fern, flowers, thorn handle. Dated 1835	130.00
8¼" high. Raised tulips, leaves	125.00
8½" high. Stork in lily pads, bearded man spout	135.00
8¾" high. Pale green, hanging birds. Enville	120.00
11½" high. Muenster. Dated Nov. 12, 1846. #33063	395.00
Teapot. 8" high. White, Neptune's face framed with shells, scrolls & cane-like birds. Shell finial. C. 1835. Unmarked	145.00
Vase. 7½" high. Decorated with raised ferns, grapes in blue and white	100.00

SAMPLERS

Examples of samplers date back to the late 1700s. The earliest ones were made in a rectangular shape, being higher than they were wide. Later examples were square. Before the fad died out about 1900, the shape had changed again and they became longer and narrower. A typical sampler was made by embroidering colored thread in a cross stitch design onto a piece of material. The usual design included flowers, the alphabet, the maker's name and age, and the date.

Dated 1779 (birth date), Hannah
   Eaton Hunt. Mahogany frame,
   18x23"......................$ 200.00
Dated 1805. Small, never framed ...   100.00
Dated 1812. Alphabet, numbers,
   poems, flowers and crowns.
   13x16".......................   150.00
Dated 1812. Small, name, age 12 ...   95.00
Dated 1813. Made by Hannah Marie
   Nash. Strawberry, vine border,
   15x19".......................   225.00
Dated 1818. Alphabet, trees, birds,
   house, name of maker, "Elizabeth
   Voorhees," 12x20" 165.00
Dated 1818. February 24. Alphabet
   repeated 3 times, numbers once.
   Ursula Ann Taft of Upton. 13x16".   95.00
Dated 1825. Medium, name, date.
   Framed 135.00
Dated 1829. "Wrought By", name,
   age 11, town and state. Wide
   embossed border of flowers and
   vines. Framed..................   150.00
Dated 1830. American. Free form
   strawberry border with colonial
   house, pink roses on either side,
   alphabet & verse flanked by two
   satin stitch birds. Signed Julian
   Clark 275.00
Dated 1831. Alphabet and name of
   maker. "Christine Bauman," 8x17"   120.00

Dated 1834. Unfinished, unframed.
   15½" square 100.00
Dated 1835. Alphabet verse, Flowers. Framed, 21" square 150.00
Dated 1836. April 21. Name,
   Monongalia, Va. 13x17"..........   165.00
Dated 1837, Dec. Sara Jane West.
   House, birds, flowers. Religious
   theme, 17x18" 150.00
Dated 1838. Alphabet and em-
   bossed pictures below with flower
   pots and trees. Name, age 11 ....   145.00
Dated 1848. Alphabet and numbers.
   12x13".......................   125.00
Dated 1848. Birds, flowers, lions,
   buildings, verse. Framed 23"
   square 195.00
Dated 1949, April. Roseanna I.
   Spohn. House, church, flowers,
   fruit baskets. 20½" sq...........   325.00
Genealogical. Listing husband, wife
   and their children as born, with
   dates. 14" square handspun linen
   cloth. Black, green and red colors .   175.00
Lord's Prayer. Framed, 14x17" 65.00
Welcome Poem. Framed 13x18" 75.00

SANDWICH GLASS

The term Sandwich glass applies to the large variety of lead-type glass made in lacy patterns by the Boston and Sandwich Glass Co. from 1825 to the factory's closing in 1888. The Pittsburgh glass factories also made lacy glass patterns and much of this stippled-type glass is erroneously attributed to Sandwich.

Dated 1834. 14½ x 15" including
frame. Dorothy Kirtlan $175.00

Plate. 8¼". Horn of Plenty or Eye and
Tail of Comet. C. 1836 ....$85.00

Basket. Overshot, deep cranberry shading to pink. Twisted thorn handle . . . . $ 225.00

Bottles

2½" high. Blue, pewter top 55.00
2½" high. Emerald, pewter top . . . 75.00
Toilet Water. Emerald green, original stopper 90.00

Bowls

5¼x8". Overshot, reeded feet . . . 135.00
6¼" diam. Flat lacy. Princess pattern 95.00
6¼" diam. Flat, lacy. Tulip and acanthus leaf 95.00
Industry. Lacy, with scalloped edge. 165.00

Candlesticks

7" high. Blown candle cups, flaring six-sided stem and heavy flint glass bases. Clear glass. Pair 180.00
9½" high. Clear. Pair 195.00
Canary yellow, fluted column. Pair 250.00
Carafe. 9½" high, 5" diam. Overlay blue to white to clear. Star-cut stopper. Enamel decor in panels . . 185.00

Cheese Dish. Covered 195.00
Creamer. Individual-type 48.50

Cup Plates

Bunker Hill 22.00
Eagle design 25.00
Heart pattern 20.00
Opalescent 37.50
Star and forget-me-nots 22.00
Waffle pattern, loop border 20.00

Decanter. Blown and engraved. Applied reeded handle 95.00
Ewer. 12½" high, amber thorn handle, deep pink at top shading into white at bottom 250.00
Finger Bowl. Overshot-type. 5" diam. 60.00
Goblet. Star and Punty 65.00

Lamps

8½" high. Amethyst 325.00
9" high. Pewter rim, clear glass . . 125.00
10" high. Pewter tops, clear glass. Pair 250.00
10½" high. Whale oil. Clear Star and Punty 195.00
11" high. Canary 250.00
11½" high. Flint glass. Oil, two-prong burner 175.00
Electric blue, 8-panel. 265.00

Paperweight. Scrambled-type 110.00

Pitchers

5½" high. Milk, tankard-shape . . . 65.00
7" high. Blue overshot glass, square mouth, bulbous body, applied amber handle in ribbed shell. Blown 135.00

8½" high, 5" diam. Overshot amber glass. Clover leaf-shape top, amber, ribbed shell, applied handle. Blown 120.00
10½" high. Overshot, with a metal lid 195.00
11" high. Overshot cranberry glass. Tankard-shape. Applied crystal ribbed shell handle 195.00
11½" high. Overshot white glass with bladder for ice. C. 1865 . . . . . 185.00
13" high. Overshot, with bladder, naturalistic handle 245.00

Plates

5¼". Peacock Eye 45.00
6". Leaf and Scroll 35.00
6". Washington variant (acorn) . . 45.00
7¼". Roman Rosette 65.00
9". Octagonal lacy 65.00
9 ¾". Beehive pattern 85.00
Octagonal. Thistle & Star pattern with scroll and leaf border 120.00

Pomade. 3¾" high. Black Muzzled Bear. 150.00

Salts

Eagle. Early, 13 stars & shield 80.00
Footed. Rayed base, 3" high, 3" diam. Flint 45.00
Master
3" long, 2" wide, 1¾" high. Diamond pattern with leaf band . 65.00
Clear, open lacy design 50.00
Lacy Lyre 75.00
Purple-blue shades. Crown pattern 185.00

Sauces

4½". Lacy, Peacock Eye Scroll 35.00
Oak Leaf pattern 35.00

Spill Holder. "Sandwich Star" 65.00
Spill Vases. Hairpin loop. Tall, ribbed stem. Clear flint glass. Pair 110.00

Sugar Bowls

Covered, Acanthus pattern 150.00
Covered. Clear and lacy. Gothic pattern 110.00
Open. Acanthus pattern 95.00

Sugar Shaker. Diamond Quilted, original top 125.00
Syrup. 7" high. Clear. Star & Buckle. Blown molded. Tin lid and large hollow, applied handle, hexagonal body 135.00

Tie Backs

3" diam. Opalescent, lacy, pewter screws. Pair 50.00
4½" diam. Pair. 65.00

Toddy Plate. Prince of Wales. Feather with crown an thistle 50.00

Tumblers
Toy. Panelled sides with plain rim 30.00
Water, overshot, rainbow colors . 65.00

Vases
3½" high. Fireglow and coquille.
Squatty, pouch-shape. Outer surface allover coquille finish. Rose
color at rim 125.00
5½" high. Fireglow. Pair 140.00
7½" high. Amethyst. Pair........ 260.00
9" high. Amethyst. Pair.......... 295.00
11¾" high. Canary. Pair 350.00
15" high. Mottled red and
aventurine, with applied amber
rim and feet 240.00

Whiskey Taster 45.00

SARREGUEMINES CHINA

The factory was established in Germany in
1770 and operated by Utzchneider & Co. Later
a factory was put into operation at Degoin,
France. They made sets of chinaware,
novelties and cameo ware of the quality of
Wedgwood.

Asparagus Set. Celadon green,
embossed asparagus on 12
plates. Platter with drain ....$ 150.00

Bowl. 10x11". Shape of scalloped
shell. Pink 38.50

Coffee Pot. Yellow, pink, purple
roses. Gold trim 65.00

Dishes
Covered. 5½" diam., 4-leaf clover
shape........................ 50.00

Plate. 7½", strawberry leaves and
fruit. Lead glaze $28.00

Fruit. Blue floral china, in wire
frame........................ 30.00

Jam Jar. Covered. Mustard color,
basketweave, molded apricot on
cover with stem for handle 28.00

Jug, Character. 7" high, 1½ qt. Head
of a rosy cheeked, smiling man ... 50.00

Pitchers
4¾" high. Cream. Pink interior,
greenish-yellow exterior 25.00
6¼" high. Originally had pewter
lid. Transfer pictures of children .. 35.00
7" high. Inside turquoise. French,
before 1825 .... 75.00
8¼" high. Pewter top, cherub
decor 48.50
8½" high. Dark green, picnic
scene in relief 48.00
9¾" high. Tankard. Green exterior, aqua interior. Figural scene
in high relief. "Villagers, Dancing,
Drinking, Partying" 95.00
13" high. Figural, fierce dog with
gaping mouth as spout. Cobalt
handle, blue and white porcelain,
impressed block signature,
w/903A 85.00

Plates
7¼". "Songs of Roland" 22.00
7½". Black transfer. "Qui Aime
Bien Chatie Bien"............... 20.00
7½". Hanging-type. Strawberries
on deep gold background........ 28.00
8". Monk scene on white and pink
background 22.50
8". Varicolored flowers 19.50
8½". Napoleonic military plate
with French captions under picture 25.00
12". Fruit decor 30.00
Music Plate. Picture of Knight and
Wagner. Music from Rienzi 25.00
Napoleonic military plate with
French captions. Set of 8 .... 115.00
Oyster. Shell decor, gray-green to
pink on white ground 28.50

Vases
13¼" high. Blue ground, decor in
tan and green slip portraying
flowers and geometric design 65.00
14" high. Colorful. Pair 125.00

Wine Jug. 11" high. "Hanoi" pattern.
Pewter top, thumbrest, country
chintz effect. Cream ground with
aqua, brown, dull rose, blue floral
motifs 60.00

SATIN GLASS

The glass was brought to perfection in 1886 by Joseph Webb, an Englishman by birth, who patented the process while working for the Phoenix Glass Co., Beaver, Penna.

The object was first blown into a mold with diamond, circular or square-shaped depressions, usually opal or milk glass was employed. Next, a colored transparent coating of glass was applied over the core. The third step in the manufacture was the application of a colorless transparent covering of glass. The object was then annealed or tempered by heat. The final step was to treat the item with hydrofluoric acid vapor which produced a satin finish to the surface. It was always acid finished, never polished or frosted by sandblasting or grinding. The range of colors is broad but pink and blue are the most prominent.

Bobeches. Swirled rose pattern with applied camphor rim. Scalloped, fluted rim. 5" diam. Pair . . . . $ 65.00

Bonbon Dish. 4¼" high, body 6x7". White MOP, D.Q. Ribbon-crimped rim, folded down on two sides. 4 applied camphor feet, berry pontil   225.00

Bowls
   5" diam. Cloverleaf MOP swirl of golden brown on olive green. Cased in robin-egg blue. Ribbon crimped edge 425.00
   6" diam. MOP, deep blue with applied thorny feet in crystal 500.00
   7" diam., 5" high. Signed Thos. Webb & Sons. MOP, blue D.Q. coin gold flowers, leaves 500.00
   10" diam., 3½" high. Ribbed. Red to pink. For bride's basket 175.00

Boxes
   5¼" square. Embossed and enameled with pink and blue flower clusters 150.00
   7½" square. White with pink lustre scrolls, blue forget-me-nots, pink lustre scrolled edge 195.00

Compote. 9¼" diam. Blue, ruffled, fluted, frosted white edge. Silver-plated base 300.00

Creamer. Blue MOP scalloped top, threaded handle 185.00

Dish. 8½" diam., in RARE rainbow satin glass. Delicate shades of blue, yellow and pink with fine scroll decor in gold 525.00

Egg. 3½" high. Robin-egg blue, on metal stand 95.00

Ewers
   7" high. Melon-ribbed, deep rose to pink, herringbone, camphor glass handle and stopper 265.00
   8" high. Raspberry pink shading at top to light base. Jewelled butterfly in center front of beaded sprigs [cased] 135.00
   8½" high. Shading from coral at top to pale pink. Pair 285.00
   9½" high, 3" diam. Scalloped, turned-down top edged with camphor satin ribbon. H/P enamel florals on shaded pink and apricot color background. Satin twisted handle 150.00
   10" high. White MOP in raindrop pattern. Camphor glass handles . .   275.00

Finger Bowls
   Blue and pink 145.00
   With plate. Bowl 5" diam., 4¾" high, plate 6" diam. Chartreuse to cream. Each has folded-down, crimped rim with applied frosted edging 195.00

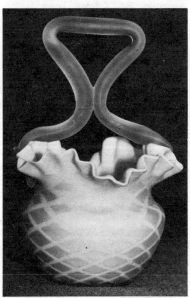

Basket. 6½" high, clear frosted handle, yellow ruffled top to frosted white at base. MOP $95.00

Cologne Bottle. Metal cap with chained Peacock Eye pattern . $135.00

Jars, Cracker

Green with pink floral H/P decor. Silver top	125.00
Orange shading to yellow with painted flower decor and silverplated lid	165.00
Pink, 7¾" enamel. Satin glass embossed shell and floral decor, white case. Silverplated rim, cover and bail	250.00
Pink and white with lilac decor. Plated bail and cover	125.00
Pink, shell pattern with enamel decor. Top and handle resilvered .	225.00
Ribbon pattern in pink. Silverplated bail and top	325.00
Rose, Diamond Quilted MOP, with silverplated lid and bail. Bulbous .	225.00

Lamps

Hall. Blue MOP, diamond quilted shade and brass frame	395.00
Hall. Hanging. Deep pink shading to lighter pink. Raised pattern on shade	300.00
Red Satin. Maple leaf design. Gone with the Wind. Electrified . .	600.00
Table. 12" high. Pink with enameled flowers, gold butterfly. Metal base. Webb	650.00

Mustard Pot. 3" high. White ribbed satin with blue enamel flowers and dots. Resilvered top and handle	110.00
Perfume Bottles. Melon-shape, lime yellow with floral decor. Pair	175.00

Pickle Castors

Blue, diamond quilted, in resilvered frame	295.00
MOP, diamond quilted. Light to deep pink insert, ornate holder. Resilvered frame	300.00

Pitchers

9" high. Diamond Quilted	395.00
10" high. Blue, D.Q. with ruffled, fluted top	425.00
10½" high. MOP Rainbow. Coinspot design, soft pink and blues, frosted handle	600.00
12¾" high, 6½" widest diam. Rainbow MOP, applied camphor glass handle. RARE	1000.00
Plate. 6", rainbow MOP, ruffled edge	400.00
Puff Jar. 4x5", open, rose decor	115.00

Rose Bowls

3" high. Pink to deep rose with white casing. Shell and seaweed embossing	85.00
3½" high, 4½" diam. MOP, diamond quilted pattern. Blue color, scalloped top	125.00
4" high. Pink shading to blue	110.00
4" high. Pink with yellow and green enamel decor	100.00
5" high, 5" diam. Blue, footed, crimped top. Enamel flowers, coralene stems and leaves. 6 applied feet, lined white	155.00
5½" high. White MOP, egg-shaped. Venetina diamond pattern, applied camphor thorn feet, amber stems with canary yellow flowers on three sides	195.00
Salt and Pepper Shakers. Enameled flower decor. Pair	100.00

Sugars and Creamers

Red with silver lid on bowl	375.00
Ribbon stripe, MOP, chartreuse ..	950.00
Enameled daisies, silver lids and top rims	500.00
Sugar Bowl. Ivory shading to rose. Diamond quilted, MOP	250.00

Sugar Shakers

Blue. Plain	110.00
Melon-shaped. Cream shading to blue, floral decor, silver top	145.00

Tumblers

Apricot color, diamond quilted ...	145.00
Blue. Herringbone pattern	95.00
Yellow swirl	115.00

Vase. 9" high. Diamond Quilted pattern, pink. Signed Webb "Patent"
$395.00

Vases

5" high. Green shading to white with applied white flowers with rose-amber center, amber leaves and handle 225.00
5" high. MOP, turned-down top, bulbous body. D.Q. pattern, vaseline 165.00
5½" high. Blue raindrop. Mt. Washington 250.00

6" high. Blue, D.Q., ruffled top . . . 250.00
6" high. Rose shading to pale pink with hobnail. MOP pattern 275.00
6½" high. Bulbous bottom. MOP pink. Signed Webb 350.00

6½" high. Jack-in-the-Pulpit. White body with applied camphor petal feet. Apple green lining 300.00
6½" high. Rose to yellow. MOP crimped, indented top 275.00
8¼" high. Rainbow satin. Decorated with gold enamel. Delicate pastel blue, pink and yellow vertical strippings, sprays of small leaves, berries and clusters of blue and red blossoms, light cream casing 750.00
8½" high. Enamel decor of two black birds perched on brown branches with white and beige florals. Blown 165.00
9" high. Shaded apricot to salmon pink. MOP with gold and silver decor of birds and flowers. Applied frosted crystal handles . . 500.00
10½" high, 5½" widest diam. Yellow quilted MOP 300.00
12" high. Raspberry and light salmon color 250.00
14" high. Lavender, red and blue stripes. Bulbous base, slender neck 365.00
15" high, 4" diam. MOP, ruffled top. D.Q. pattern. Ornate footed brass frame, twisted brass handle 365.00
15¼" high. coin pattern. Rainbow. English 575.00

SATSUMA WARE

This ware was named for a Japanese war lord, Satsuma, who brought skilled ceramic workers to Japan from Korea after a victorious campaign about the year 1600. Much of the ware on the antique market today was produced by mass production methods during the past 80 years and cannot be compared with the finer handmade items of the previous centuries.

Basket. 9" long, 6" wide, 4" high. Decor of flowers and butterflies in red, blue and black. Gold trim on ivory ground . . . . $ 145.00

Bottle, Saki. 6¼" high. 4 panels depicting family life. Rich blue ground with gold decor 150.00

Bowls
5½" diam. Scalloped. People in center, scenic border 175.00
6½" diam. 185.00
8" diam. 6-sided 195.00

Bowl. 7½" diam., 3" deep. Heavy gold,
Geisha girls $250.00

Boxes
    1½" high. Satsuma. Ivory ground,
    green leaves, pink flowers, small
    bird on lid with gold tracery.
    Footed 225.00

    2¼ x5". Fan-shaped. Oriental char-
    acter markings under lid. Figural
    and floral decor. Late 45.00

    Cricket. Round, footed, decorated
    with birds and bamboo on body,
    round lid. Openwork decor. Foo
    doghead handles, black color 120.00
Brush Holder. 5" high. Decor of
    colorful flowers and butterflies on
    cream-colored ground 45.00
Buddha. Seated, small 100.00
Buttons
    ¾" diam. Purple wisteria, gold
    rims. Set of 6 . . . .   15.00
    1½" diam. Floral motif. Early 45.00
Cake Plate. 1½" flower border.
    Marked "B.C.&W." 100.00
Candy Dish. Handled 55.00
Coffee Pot. Peacock among vines
    and branches with gold scrolls, etc.   185.00
Creamer. 4¾" high. Cream ground
    with red and white flowers, green
    leaves and gold decor 96.00
Cups and Saucers
    Demitasse 50.00
    Gilt faces on men and women.
    Edges decorated in blue and gold   70.00
    Two-handled 65.00
Figurine. 6½" high. Woman sitting
    on tree trunk 425.00
Ginger Jar. Covered, square, 6"
    high. Figures over body 145.00
Hat Pin 40.00
Incense Burner. White, known as
    Awata Satsuma. C. 1790 . . . .   125.00

Inkwell. Butterfly, bird and floral
    decor. Dimpled, hinged top 115.00
Jardiniere. 7" high. Resembles
    1000-face pattern in blue, green
    and yellow. Embossed red figures,
    gold scrolls 195.00
Jug. Wine. Bamboo and mums
    design 65.00
Lamp 250.00
Mustard Jar. Covered, gold en-
    crusted design 75.00
Pitchers
    3½" high. Imperial signed. 7
    panels of people, scenery
    culture of Japan 95.00
    Large 175.00
Plaque. Scenic, small 38.50
Plate. 7". Oriental woman in center,
    surrounded by 7 male faces 48.50
Pot Pourri Jar. 3¾" high 120.00
Pot Sauce. 3¾" high. Cylindrical
    with bamboo handle, spout.
    Multicolored. Scholars under
    bamboo trees 160.00
Rose Jar. 4". Signed 125.00
Salts. Open, set of six 85.00
Sugar Bowl, 5½" high, creamer,
    4½" high. Set 200.00

Tea Sets
    15 pieces. Original wood box,
    padded and lined with blue silk.
    Rogal Satsuma 1200.00
    15 pieces. Teapot, creamer and
    sugar bowl, 6 cups and saucers.
    Gold and typical color decor.
    Crackle, glaze, signed 750.00
Teapots
    5½" high. Cream background, red
    and white flowers, green leaves
    and gold decor 175.00
    Miniature. Cream ground with
    male and female Noh players 85.00
Urn. Large, 3 Foo dogs 750.00

Vases
    2" high. Miniature. Flowers with
    gold trim 28.50
    4¼" high. On teakwood stand.
    "Ladies and the Warriors" 180.00
    6" high, 4" diam. for buds.
    Decorations on 4 sides depicting
    groups of figures 195.00
    6" high. Orange ground with
    figure in blue green. Relief dragon
    in gold. Late 65.00
    6" high. Thousand-face panels on
    glossy cobalt ground 195.00
    6½" high. Decorative panel of
    scholar and student 185.00

6½" high. Ten people seated, overlooking mtns. Fish, flying crane on sides, reverse, scenic of ten women in flower garden 135.00
7¼" high. Green crackle ground, colorful battling warriors 235.00
7½" high. Jeweled. Pair 500.00
8" high. Royal blue ground, ladies and child decor 75.00
9" high. Heads of Immortals. Gold dragon in high relief 250.00
12" high. Bolted base, green with red and gold chrysanthemums . . . 275.00
12½" high. 2 decorated panels on blue and gilt 285.00
13½" high. War lord on white elephant surrounded by warriors. Much gold 295.00
19½" high. Thousand faces 375.00

SCALES

Prior to 1900 the balance scale was commonly used for measuring weight. A variety of styles and types were used by druggists, farmers and storekeepers.

Photographer's Scale. Complete with weights. German silver pans . . $75.00

Beam. 5-150 lbs. x ¼ lbs. Steel. Two weights . . . . $ 20.00
Druggist. Enclosed in glass dome. 12 weights 100.00
Jeweler's. Brass pans, marble-top base with drawer 80.00
Platform. Floor model-type. Single or double beam 95.00
Platform. Counter top-type
  50 lbs. x 2 oz., 11x14" platform. Iron, used in markets 60.00
  240 lbs. x ½ oz. 10x13" platform. Tin scoop. Used in hardware stores 50.00
  250 lbs. x 1 oz., 12x21" platform. Brass scoop 85.00

Spring Balance
  10 lbs. x oz. Painted dial, tin scoop, family-type 30.00
  25 lbs. x oz. Hanging-type, with tray. Brass dial 45.00
  Brass. Polished. C. 1850 . . . . 150.00
  Hanging-type, with ring and hook. Brass dial 10.00
  Iron base, brass trays. 19½" long . 95.00

SCHNEIDER GLASS

Charles and Ernest Schneider founded the Schneider Glassworks in Epinay-sur-Siene, France in the late 19th century.

Their fine, collectible art glass, which can be identified by the distinctive mottled colors and usually signed "Schneider," was made in the early 1900's.

According to the latest reports, the firm is still operating but producing only crystal glassware.

Vase. 5¼" high. Molded orange to white to clear. Signed $95.00

Compotes
  5" high, 14" diam. Shades of mottled rose. Amethyst disc. base, stem . . . . $ 175.00
  5½" high, 8" wide. Purple base, with orange bowl, shading to blue. Signed 135.00
  8" high, 7" diam. Ribbed. Blown into wrought-iron stand, orange

coned base into deep red flared
top. Signed 225.00
Dishes. 4" diam. Mottled glass,
shallow. One bright blue and
gray. Other, red and gray. Signed.
Pair 100.00
Lamp. On teak base. Wired, with
harp. Signed 175.00
Pitcher. 11" high. Shaped art glass,
yellow streaked with bubbles,
amethyst base and handle. Signed 165.00
Vases
5" high, 4½" diam. Cuspidor-
shaped, mottled colors, taffy at
bottom, reddish, wispy white
above. 140.00
23½" high. Mauve and white.
Signed 300.00

SCHOENHUT TOYS

Albert Schoenhut came to America from
Germany in 1865. In 1872, at Philadelphia, he
established the firm of A. Schoenhut Company
which made standard size and toy pianos.
In 1903 the firm introduced a Humpty Dumpty
Circus which was an immediate success. It had
patented steel spring hinges and swivel joints.
The wood heads were not handcarved but
were made on a multiple carving machine.
Then, in December of 1913, a walking doll was
marketed. The manufacture of dolls was
abandoned in 1924 due to the importation of
cheap German and Japanese dolls.
Albert Schoenhut died in 1912 but the firm is
still being operated by members of the family.

Alphabet Blocks . . . .$ 60.00
Blocks, Building. Large, in original
box dated 1927. Complete. 65.00
Chimes, Trinity. Working 110.00
Circus. In original box. Mule,
elephant, 3 clowns, 2 chairs, 2
2 ladders, barrel. Pamphlets
dated 1902. Imcomplete set 500.00

Dolls, See "Dolls"

Pianos
8½ x 9½ x 16". 15 keys 75.00
11 x 21 x 23". 3 brass pedals. 125.00
17 x 29 x 31". 29 keys. Matching
bench. 150.00
Schoenhut Circus Figures and Others
Acrobats, girl or man. Each 45.00
Buffalo 50.00
Clown 48.50
Donkey. Small, molded hair. 55.00
Elephant 50.00
Giraffe. 50.00

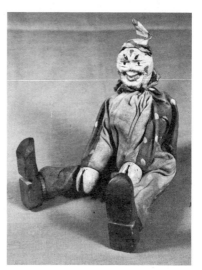

Clown $48.50

Goat. Glass eyes, horns, leather
beard 75.00
Hippopotamus 50.00
Horse 65.00
Lion. Small 45.00
Mule. 55.00
Poodle. Glass eyes 85.00
Ringmaster 65.00
Sheep. 45.00
Tiger 50.00
Zebra 50.00

SCONCES, WALL

2-Arm Candleholders. Beveled mirrors,
ornate brass frames. Pair $250.00

A sconce is a lighting device of the wall bracket type, usually ornamental in design, used for holding candles or lamp fonts.

Brass
2-arm. American. Pair	$ 150.00
2-arm burner. Pair	135.00
3-arm. French, lacy design. Pair	275.00

Iron
2-arm, with candleholder. Pair	95.00
Early Florentine-type. 10" high, removable holders. Pair	150.00
Tole. 14" high, candle-type. Early and scarce. Pair	250.00

SCRIMSHAW

Scrimshaw is a true form of American folk art dating back over 150 years ago. During the 19th century, when whaling was an important industry, sailors whiled away their idle hours by hand carving and engraving walrus and whale tusks and bits of discarded bones and ivory.Most of these items were decorated with intricate designs of ships, nautical adventures, likenesses of loved ones and were purely ornamental. A few articles were carved for utilitarian purposes. Scrimshaws were usually presented as homecoming gifts.

Like so many primitive arts, scrimshaw disappeared. Today, with modern technology, the almost forgotten art is being revived. Reproductions of past designs are being introduced to the public. The only acceptable modern scrimshaw is that of the new forms created for tomorrow's treasures and heirlooms.

Whale's Tooth. 4½" high. Carved eagle and flag $325.00

Busk or Corset Stay. From whale bone. 1½" wide, 14" long. Heart-shaped top with geometric design and scene of baby birds being fed in a nest . . . . $	35.00
Buttons, Ivory. Set of 7. Incised in typical sailor-type geometric design. Average size under 1"	65.00

Clothes Pin	30.00
Elephant's Tusks. Carved. Pair	1500.00
Etched figures of girl, boy and woman. Pair	275.00
Hammer. 6½" long, dolphin-head handle	150.00
Indians [2] by Tree. Carved on 6¼" walrus tusk	375.00
Lady raising flag over fort. 6½" walrus tusk	425.00
Ostrich egg-shape with portrait, compass, etc.	400.00
Pie Crimper. From whale bone, rosewood handle. 6½" long, star decor	110.00
Primitive carving on walrus tusk. 14" long	300.00
Punch	30.00
Trinket Box. Small, hinged lid	100.00
Victorian Lady	350.00
View of Sag Harbor, L.I., N.Y. Waterfront with ships, 1stCustoms House in U.S. and firehouse. Reverse, heart and clasped hands. Border star design. 13½" long . . .	750.00
War of 1812. American ship attacking British at Delaware Bay, June 11, 1813	650.00
Whale's Tooth	
"The Ship Carpenter"	350.00
Woman carved on front and back. 6" high, mounted on black lacquered base	375.00
Woman. Holding eagle aloft. Reverse, holds leaves aloft.	400.00
Women. Mounted on lacquered bases. Pair	500.00

SEWING ITEMS

A variety of sewing items were found in practically every home as late as 40 years ago. Sewing and dressmaking were two of the arts almost every woman learned.

Among the interesting items used was the sewing bird. They were usually made of iron or brass with a screw-type fixture for attaching them to a table or shelf. The beak or mouth was used to hold cloth while sewing was accomplished. Later models had a pin cushion for holding pins and needles.

Chatelaine. 19th century English sterling. Scissors in case, note pad with 5 ivory inserts for sewing notes. Thimble case with thimble and button hook. All working . . . . $	450.00
Clamp with Gage. Ivory	25.00

Thread Holder. 3½" high. Wooden, beehive shape, 3-footed $55.00

Darning Eggs
3¾" long. Black with sterling handle	15.00
6" long. Mushroom-type, walnut ..	10.00
Red and gold glass	30.00

Needle Box. One drawer, divided,
11" diam., 2¾" high	30.00

Needle Cases
Barrel. Mechanical	20.00
Gavel. Carved ivory	15.00
Sterling. Hallmarked	25.00
Sterling	15.00
Umbrella. Ivory	18.50
Urn. Mechanical	28.00

Pin Cushion. Advertising-type.
"Kemp & Burpee Mfg. Co.," 2¼" ..	6.00

Sewing Birds
Brass. One cushion	37.50
Brass. Two cushions	55.00
German Silver. 5½" high. Pin cushion top	37.50
Iron. 5¼" high, 3½" bird. 2 pin cushions. Gold lacquered	35.00
Iron. 6½" high. One cushion	25.00
Iron. New red cushion	25.00
Silver. 2 pin cushions	39.50

Shuttle, Sewing. 2 embroidery
punches, crochet hook. Ivory. Set .	17.50

Spool and Thimble Holder. 3 tiers of wood topped by large pin cushion, on 4 button legs. Holds 16 spools,
5 thimbles. Walnut	50.00

Tape Measure. Alarm clock. Hands
turn when tape is pulled	65.00

Thimbles
Birds	12.00
German. Band of enameled roses on blue ribbon	50.00
Gold. Plain	45.00
Gold. Set with jewels	75.00
Miniature. ½" high	20.00
Persian. Pierced	15.00
Silver enameled with bird on two sides. Birmingham, England......	22.50

Thread Holders
Sterling. Cherub heads around top	55.00
Sterling. Embossed	28.50

SHAVING MUGS

[Fraternal and Miscellaneous]

A.O.U.W. Colorful ....$	40.00
Anchor and Chain. No name	35.00
B.P.O.E.	45.00
Cat's Eye. 3½" high	24.00
Deer's Head	26.50
Dog...........................	35.00
Dogs, Hunting	40.00
Eye. Large, 3 links	37.50
F.L.T. Limoges. White, gold trim.....	35.00
F.O.E.	45.00
Flags, Crossed. United States.......	55.00
Gibson Girls [2]	50.00
Horse's Head. Large, gold horseshoe	45.00
I.O.O.F.	45.00
K. of C. [Knights of Columbus]	45.00
K. of L. [Knights of Labor]	45.00
K. of P. [Knights of Pythias]	45.00
K. T. [Knights Templar]	47.50
L. O.O.M.	45.00

Scuttle Mug. 4¾" high. White, crest in multicolors. "A Present from Walsall"
$60.00

M.W.A.	45.00
Masonic, Square and Compass	60.00
O.W.M.	45.00
Odd Fellow. "R. E. Adams"	65.00
Rooster	36.00
Scuttle-type. Soap holder, brush rest, pink poppy decor	55.00
Shriner, "C. M. Sible," Bavarian	95.00
Theatrical Drape. Name on side, colored	85.00
Viking. 3½" high	25.00
W.O.W. [with leaf]	38.50

SHAVING MUGS, OCCUPATIONAL

During the period of 1870 to 1910, shaving mugs of chinaware were manufactured and decorated with the owner's name and occupation. They were usually kept at the owner's favorite barber shop and were for his exclusive use.

Motorcycle transfer. J. B. Levy $135.00

Accordion	$ 125.00
Anchor, with name	75.00
Anvil, Hammer and Tongs	100.00
Architect's Emblem	95.00
Arc Light	110.00
Athlete. High jump	130.00
Athlete. Track runner	130.00
Automobile. Early	135.00
Baggage Car	120.00
Baggage Master, Truck and Car	125.00
Baker Working	125.00
Bakers at Work	125.00
Baker Wagon, Horse with Driver	130.00
Bar. Men drinking	110.00
Barber	110.00
Barber Shop	115.00

Bartender	110.00
Baseball Player	155.00
Baseball and Bats	125.00
Beer Barrel, Bottle, Glasses	90.00
Beer Bottle and Glasses	85.00
Beer Mug	85.00
Beer Wagon, Horses with Driver	140.00
Bicycle	125.00
Bicyclist	125.00
Billiard Players	140.00
Bill Poster	145.00
Blacksmith and Anvil	100.00
Blacksmith Shoeing Horse	110.00
Boiler Maker Working	110.00
Bookbinder Working	125.00
Bookkeeper	95.00
Boot and Shoe	85.00
Brakeman Turning Brakes	115.00
Brewmaster	160.00
Bricklayer Working	100.00
Bridge, Steel	120.00
Buggy, Horse and Driver	90.00
Buggy Maker, The	125.00
Butcher's Emblem [Knife, Cleaver, Steel and Saw]	85.00
Butcher in shop with customer. "Guiseppi Monteroseo, 1912"	125.00
Butcher Slaughtering Steer	95.00
Butcher Store	100.00
Cabinet Maker	135.00
Camera	150.00
Cannon and Gun Carriage	125.00
Captain of sailing vessel	125.00
Carriage, Horses and Driver	95.00
Cigar Store	100.00
Clothing Store	95.00
Coal Miner at Work	125.00
Coal Wagon, Horse and Driver	115.00
Cooper Making Barrels	135.00
Cowboy Lassoing Steer	120.00
Dentist Pulling Teeth	165.00
Dentist, with False Teeth	150.00
Doctor Tending Patient	225.00
Dray and Driver with Horses	85.00
Drug Store	100.00
Druggist Working	110.00
Drum	85.00
Engine. Stationary	95.00
Express Wagon, Horse and Driver	95.00
Farmer taking grain to market	95.00
Farmer Plowing	95.00
Fire Engine. Motorized	150.00
Fire Engine. Steam	170.00
Fisherman	95.00
Flour and Feed Store	95.00
Flute	85.00
Forest Scene. With deer and dog	95.00
Freight Car	95.00
Furniture Store	100.00

Grist Mill Operator	135.00		Tug Boat	160.00
Grocery Store and Clerk	100.00		Umbrella	85.00
Grocery Wagon and Horse	110.00		Undertaker	395.00
Guns, Crossed Rifles and Target	100.00		Watch and Chain	100.00
Hardware Store	100.00		Whiskey Wagon	135.00
Harness Maker	125.00			
Hatter Working	125.00			

Grist Mill Operator 135.00
Grocery Store and Clerk 100.00
Grocery Wagon and Horse 110.00
Guns, Crossed Rifles and Target 100.00
Hardware Store 100.00
Harness Maker 125.00
Hatter Working 125.00
Hod Carrier 90.00
Hotel Register 95.00
Ice Wagon, Horse and Driver 115.00
Jewelry Store 100.00
Jeweler's Design, Watch Sign 100.00
Jockey 130.00
Judge 175.00
Letter Carrier, Mail Wagon 100.00
Livery Stable 130.00
Locomotive 125.00
Locomotive. Wood-burning type 135.00
Machinist at Lathe 95.00
Mail Wagon 95.00
Marble Cutter at Work 100.00
Milk Can Maker 140.00
Milk Wagon, Horse and Driver 100.00
Miner with Tools 125.00
Minister in Pulpit 175.00
Motorman and Conductor 110.00
Musicians 85.00
Notary, Hand and Pen 100.00
Oil Derrick 120.00
Painter Working 95.00
Passenger Car. Railroad 85.00
Photographer 150.00
Pianist, Concert 150.00
Piano Player 95.00
Plasterer Working 85.00
Plumber 100.00
Policeman 145.00
Printer Setting Type 100.00
Printing Press 100.00
Prizefighter 300.00
Restaurant and Bar 95.00
Roller Skater 85.00
Saloon, Bartender 110.00
Sawmill 120.00
Sheep Shearer 85.00
Shoe 75.00
Shoe Dealer 85.00
Soldier on Guard 125.00
State Senator 125.00
Steamship 110.00
Sulky 120.00
Surveyor 125.00
Tailor, Sewing 125.00
Tailor, with assistants, working 130.00
Taxi Driver 115.00
Telegrapher 95.00
Telegrapher's Key 90.00
Telephone 100.00
Tobacco Store 100.00
Tow Truck and Driver 125.00

Tug Boat 160.00
Umbrella 85.00
Undertaker 395.00
Watch and Chain 100.00
Whiskey Wagon 135.00

SHIRLEY TEMPLE ITEMS, See
COLLECTIBLE CHARACTER AND
PERSONALITY ITEMS

SHEET MUSIC

Even if you can't play a note or sing on key, collecting sheet music can be an informative and rewarding experience. Much of our history is recorded in music...times of war, depressions, fashions and even glimpses of our romantic trends.

Some people collect sheet music by composers, others by favorite stars, musicals, movies, colorful covers or just for memories. A few years ago old sheet music could be bought for a "song." Today prices range from one dollar for the ordinary to several dollars for the earlier lithographed covers.

"The American Flag" by J. R. Drake.
Phila. $3.00

All American Girl. 1932. Picture of
  Milton Slosser . . . . $ 3.50
All By Myself. 1921. By Irving Berlin . 8.50
Anchors Aweigh. 1943 . . . . 2.50

Anniversary Song. 1946. From "The
Jolson Story" 2.50
Auf Wiedersehn, Sweetheart. 1952 . 2.50
Beer Barrel Polka. 1936 .... 2.00
Bicycle Built for Two, A. 1935.
Picture of Eddie Duchin 3.00
Billets Doux. 1921. French 3.50
Children's Christmas Carol, The. 1957 2.50
Come Along. 1922. From the
"Ziegfeld Follies" 2.50
Dance-O-Mania. French. 1920 ...... 3.00
Darktown Strutters' Ball. 1945. By
Shelton Brooks 2.00
De Gal I Dream About. Bromo
Seltzer Collection. Black and
white. Pre-1900 .... 2.50
Dream Faces. Bromo Seltzer Col-
lection. Color. Pre-1900 .... 3.00
Father of the Land We Love. 1931. By
George M. Cohan. To Commemo-
rate 200th Anniversary of George
Washington's Birth. Cover by
George Montgomery Flagg 8.50
Girl of My Dreams. 1927. Picture of
Perry Como................... 3.00
Goodnight Irene. 1950. Picture of
Frank Sinatra 2.00
Green Palms. Bromo Seltzer Col-
lection. Color. Pre-1900 .... 3.00
Here Comes the Bride. 1937. Inset
picture of Kay Kyser 2.50
Home Again [Quartette]. Bromo
Seltzer Collection. Black and
white. Pre-1900 .... 2.50
If You Forget. Music supplements
from the Sunday Examiner.
Color. Pre-1900 .... 2.00
I'm Just a Vagabond Lover. 1929.
Picture of Rudy Vallee.......... 3.50
J'en Ai Moire. 1921. French 3.00
Just a Little Sunshine Waltz. Bromo
Seltzer Collection. Color. Pre-1900 3.00
La Paloma [The Dove.] 1935. By
Jerry Costillo and Sebastion
Yradier. Picture of Gene Krupa ... 2.00
Let Me Dream Again. Bromo Seltzer
Collection. Color. Pre-1900 ...... 3.00
Liechtensteiner Polka. 1957. By Ed
Kotscher & R. Lindt 2.50
Lili Marlene. 1943. By Mack David .. 3.50
Loin Du Pays. Waltz. 1899. French... 3.00
Love, I Will Love You Ever. Bromo
Seltzer Collection. Black and
white. Pre-1900 .... 2.50
Moonlight Serenade. 1939. By
Mitchell Parish and Glenn Miller.. 2.00
My Christmas Rosary. 1957. By Lee
David. Picture of Teresa Brewer .. 2.50
My Heart is There. Music supple-
ments from the Sunday Examiner.

Color. Pre-1900 .... 2.00
My New York. 1927. By Irving Berlin,
from "Ziegfeld Follies" 5.00
Old Fashioned Garden. 1919. By
Cole Porter 4.00
Pennies From Heaven. 1936. By John
Burke and Arthur Johnston, from
show of same name. Picture of
Bing Crosby................... 3.50
Ragtime Mixes My Brain. Music
supplements from the Sunday
Examiner. Color. Pre-1900 ...... 2.50
Si-Vous Aimez Les Fleurs. 1923.
French 3.00
Strawberry Roan, The. 1931. By Fred
Howard and Nat Vincent 2.00
Swedish Rhapsody. 1953 .... 3.50
Sweet One. 1923. By Al Jolson and
Louis Silvers. Picture of Jolson 1.50
There is a Tavern in the Town. 1934 . 3.50
Three O'clock in the Morning. 1922 . 2.50
What Are the Wild Waves Saying
[Duet.] Bromo Seltzer Collection.
Black and white. Pre-1900 .... 2.50
When Irish Eyes Are Smiling. 1912 .. 7.50
Wisconsin Evermore. 1921 .... 5.00

SILHOUETTES

Silhouettes are shadow profiles, cut,
mechanically drawn, or painted.

A. Lincoln, T. Roosevelt. Black
frames, 4x5". Signed "Gutte-
namy." Pair....................$ 175.00
Andrew Jackson. Facsimile,
signature...................... 85.00
Bonneted lady in full skirt, leg-o-
mutton sleeves. 10½" high, in
frame......................... 95.00
Colonial Gentleman. 5x6" wood
frame. Wax bust 75.00
Daniel Hayworth. Old Massachusetts man 75.00
George & Martha Washington.
5¼x6". Reverse painted on glass.
Oval brass lined black frame..... 39.50
James Monroe. Oval, 4¾" long,
3¾" wide 90.00
Man. Early, in gold leaf frame.
3¼'x3¾" 95.00
Man. Full-length silhouette in
original gold leaf frame. 6x9" 150.00
Man and woman. Papier-mache
frames, woman touched with gold 125.00
Revolutionary General. 3¼" long ... 110.00
Woman. In 5" round frame. C. 1820 . 95.00

7x8½" framed in gold-leafed gesso.
Gentleman and Lady. Matched pair
$295.00

Woman. Not a silhouette but in pen
and ink. Difficult to detect the
difference 64.00
Young man in frock coat, holding
book. 9½x13½". Signed Aug.
Edouard 1810. Framed 250.00

SILK PICTURES, See STEVENGRAPHS

SILVER

Pure metallic silver is too soft for practical use. A spoon of unalloyed pure silver would bend and finally break in normal use. To overcome this ductility of the metal, a small portion of copper is added or alloyed to the pure metal before the craftsman starts to work on it. However, only 75 parts of copper need be added to every 925 parts of pure silver. Silver of this quality is known as Sterling.

The word "sterling" is believed to be a contraction of the word "Easterlings" which was the name of a band of traders of the 12th century, during the reign of Richard I. They came from the eastern part of Germany and, in trading, offered tokens in exchange for goods. These tokens were made of a silver alloy with a standard of 925/1000 fine.

SILVER, COIN

"Coin Silver" was made by melting coins from circulation during the early years of our country, about 1796 to 1850. It appeared that silversmiths were able to obtain this type of silver more readily than sterling. Coin silver consists of approximately 9 parts silver and I part copper or other alloy.

Butter Knives
  Bacon & Co. Large, grape pattern.
  C. 1850 .... $ 22.00
  Bailey & Co., Phila. Flat, shell
  design top of handle. C. 1848-50 . . 19.50
  Mills, New York, N.Y. Large,
  C. 1834-37 .... 25.00
  Smith, Samuel N. Large, C. 1845 . . 25.00
Cups
  Boyce, G. C. 1835. Marked 145.00
  Christening, Child's. Gold wash
  interior. Marked 135.00

Dessert Spoon. Hand-forged. R. & W.
Wilson $35.00

545

Dish. Sweetmeat. Pedestal base, beaded trim, 2 handles. Marked Boston and Pure Coin 175.00

Dessert Forks
Palmer & Bachelder, Boston. Marked Pure Coin and initialed. Set of three 45.00
S. Kirk & Son, Baltimore, 1846-61. Mayflower pattern. Marked "10.15". Set of eleven 250.00

Dessert Spoon. King's pattern. Bailey & Co. 30.00

Forks
Bacon & Co. Small, Grape pattern, 6" long. C. 1850 .... 15.00
R.&W.Wilson.Small,King's pattern 15.00
S. Kirk & Son. Luncheon. 7¼", Mayflower pattern. Set of four ... 100.00
Tiffany & Co. Serving. Large, rare, with flared tines. 8¼". Marked ... 75.00

Goblet. Embossed floral, beaded trim 125.00

Ladles
B. R. Jenkins. Sauce, 6½". Mkd. .. 35.00
Geissler & Delang, impressed. Punch, 12"..................... 185.00
Hewson & Brower, Albany, N.Y. Soup, 13" long, 4" wide bowl. Straight fiddle handle. Family name "Koffman" on handle. C. 1845......................... 110.00
Lincoln & Reed, Boston. Soup, 12" long, bowl 3½ x4", plain fiddle-shaped handle, tipped at end. C. 1835......................... 120.00
N.&T.Foster. Mustard, 5½", mkd. 19.50
Palmer & Batchelder, Boston, Mustard. Oval bowl, simple tipped. Marked. C. 1835 .... 20.00
S. Kirk & Son. Baltimore, 1846-61. Gravy, 7½". Mayflower pattern. Marked "10.15" 65.00

Napkin Rings
C. 1850. Unmarked, initialed 15.00
Engraved Jan. 1, 1851. Unmarked 20.00

Salt Spoons
Bailey & Co. King's pattern 15.00
Henry B. Stanwood, Boston. Master. C. 1850 .... 18.50
P. & G. Pangborn & Brimsmaid. 3½" Fiddle Thread. Marked P. & G. Coin 15.00
S. T. Crosby. Master, 4". Beaded handle, shell bowl. Pure Coin, marked 18.50

Servers
N. Harding & Co. Dessert. Olive pattern, engraved spatula. Pure Coin, marked 50.00
N. Harding & Co., Boston, 1830-60, marked. Pie 55.00

Stauffer & Harley. Berry, 7¼", shell bowl. Pure Coin, marked.... 39.50

Sugar Shells
Farrington & Hunnewell 25.00
O. D. Seymour 25.00

Sugar Tongs. King's pattern. Bailey & Co. 45.00

Tablespoons
A. Cutler, Boston. C. 1820-50..... 18.00
A. C. Collier. C. 1820-24 .... 20.00
Albany. Set of six 150.00
J. Moulton, Newberry, Mass. 8½", pointed handle upturned and tip at end. Engraved W. on back. C. 1820......................... 25.00
Joel Curtis & Co., Cairo, N.Y. Fiddle Thread pattern. Name "Emily" on handle. C. 1840 ...... 18.00
Sherwood & Whatley. Fiddle shape 22.50

Tea Caddy. S. Kirk & Son. 5½" high. Allover repousse' and American Coin Silver 325.00

Teapot. Christopher Griffing, New York City Silversmith. C. 1820 .... 1200.00

Teaspoons
A. Sanborn, Lowell, Mass. C. 1850, set of seven 125.00
Albert Coles, N.Y. Jenny Lind pattern. C. 1860. Set of six 95.00
D. Laverack. C. 1838-40 .... 16.50
E. D. Tisdale, C. 1850. Set of six ... 100.00
Fiddle-back. C. 1835. Set of six ... 110.00
Harris & Stanwood. C. 1835. Set of four 50.00
Jenkins & Clark, Auburn, N. Y. C. 1820 .... 15.00
John Tanguy, Phila. Fiddle, with rounded end. Engraved T.E.B. C. 1801-22 .... 20.00
N. Harding, Boston. Set of four ... 50.00
S. A. Brown, New York. Set of 5... 75.00
S. Kirk & Son, Baltimore, 1846-61. Engraved MP, 5¾", mkd. "10-15" . 17.50

SILVER, SHEFFIELD

Sheffield silver is a type of silverplating that was made by sandwiching a heavy sheet of copper between two thin sheets of silver. The layered sheets of metal were pressed and rolled. The usual standard was two pounds of silver to eight pounds of copper. However, some silversmiths used as little as six ounces of silver to eight pounds of copper.

The method was in use from the middle of the 18th century [1740-1750] until the 1840's-1850's when the electro-chemical process of silverplating replaced it.

Most of the silverplated items found today and marked "Sheffield" are not the early, authenticated Sheffield plate. They are wares made in Sheffield, England. Even this later silverplate is collectible because it was electroplated silver on copper. Copper is seldom used as a base for silverplating today.

Candle Snuffer and Tray $110.00

Candelabra. 3 candles. C. 1850. Pair	$1200.00
Candle Snuffer & Tray. Set	110.00
Candlesticks	
Fluted, square base. C. 1860. Pair	400.00
Georgian design. C. 1810. Pair ...	500.00
Shell-cornered. C. 1800. Pair	650.00
Coffee and Tea Maker. 21" high. 1785-90	2500.00
Coffee Pot. Large. C. 1850	500.00
Dish, Souffle. C. 1833	400.00
Epergne. Cut crystal bowls. C. 1830 .	1000.00
Jam Pot. 3½" high, 4 feet and cobalt glass liner	50.00
Kettles	
14" high. Swinging. Repousse grapes and leaves on pot and base. Hallmarked	195.00
18" high. Swinging. Marked with eagle in a square and the word double over the top. Ornate ivory handle	250.00
Muffineer. 8¼" high. Octagonal shape	65.00
Syrup Jug. 8½" high. 2-gill size	225.00
Teapot. Marked Walker & Hall. Emblem on side. "Stewart & Co." .	135.00
Tea Services	
4 pieces. C. 1821	3000.00
5 pieces. Tray, 15x26"	500.00
Tea Urns	
C. 1760	750.00
C. 1780	700.00
C. 1800	650.00
C. 1820	600.00
Trays	
16x25". Late	275.00
19" diam. Pierced edge, 3-footed base. Late	250.00

Tureens	
Adam design. C. 1790	1500.00
Soup. Baroque design. C. 1840 ...	1000.00
Wine Coolers	
C. 1810	1000.00
C. 1816	950.00
C. 1830	850.00

SILVER, STERLING

Sterling silver is a highly refined metal which derived its name from English Coin of the same name.

Animals	
Bear. Walking, 2x3" .... $	85.00
Bear. Walking, 3½x5½"	150.00
Poodle. Sitting up, 3½" [127 gr.] .	135.00
Rabbit. Crouching, 2½x3"	85.00
Asparagus Server. Fret work, engraved "B"	100.00
Basket. 8", openwork border, handle .	50.00
Bell. Peruvian. Woman with side skirt	55.00
Bookmark	10.00
Bowls	
9" diam. Pierced, scalloped top ...	165.00
10½ oz. Gorham	85.00
11x2¼" deep. Gorham "Marie Antoinette"....................	95.00
12" diam. Flowers, leaves in "Tiffany"	250.00
22" overall length, 8½" wide. Footed, marked "Louvre"	650.00
Boxes	
Book-shaped. 2x2x¾". "Biblia" ..	55.00
Heart-shaped. Repousse' flowers cover sides. Shell and scroll design on top. 2¾" long, 2½" wide. Marcus & Co.	45.00
Round. 3½" high, 3" deep. Marked Tiffany & Co.	65.00
Stamp. With inside divider. 2½x¾"	18.50
Bread Tray. 6½x12". Kirk	65.00
Butter Pick. Embossed scroll and floral design. Marked sterling and Keystone	18.50
Button Hook	16.00
Cake Servers	
Repousse'. Kirk	75.00
Shell design, hollow handle. Marked with an anchor in a shield and Gorham	75.00
Candlesticks. 7" high. Pair	265.00
Child's Set. Fork and teaspoon. "Arabesque," dated 1875. Whiting	30.00
Chop Dish. 14½" diam. Kirk	200.00
Cream Jug. 4¼" high. Kirk	150.00

Tea Set. 3 pieces. Signed. Tiffany & Co.
$250.00

Cups
    Baby. 2" diam. 25.00
    Demitasse. Lenox china cup in
    silver-pierced holder, saucer. Set . 15.00
Dinner Set. Service for 12. 72 pieces.
    6-piece place settings. "Gothic" .. 550.00
Forks
    Cake Server. 4-prong. Tiffany 65.00
    Cold Meat. Pat. 1885. Tiffany..... 52.50
    Dessert. Marked anchor, lion, G.
    Sterling. Roses and beading on
    handle 38.50
    Dinner. Large, set of six. Marked
    ship 90/45, Wellner 125.00
    Sweetmeat. Small, 2-tined, shell
    on end of handles. Set of six.
    Marked 1889, Towle Mfg. Co. 85.00
Goblets
    Water. 6¾ x 3½". Bell-shaped,
    gold washed inside 120.00
Grape Shears. Grape design on
    handles 60.00
Gravy Boat. 7¾" long, 2¾" high. On
    3 dolphin-shell feet. Kirk 145.00
Hairpin. Surmounted with 1½"
    engraved and openwork, crown
    design with flowers 25.00
Hat Pin. Flower top 20.00
Ice Bucket. 6" diam., 4½" high.
    Three ball feet with two handles.

1" openwork at top, gold washed
    liner. Tiffany & Co. 195.00
Ice Tongs. 6½" long. Alvin 35.00

Knives
    Butter. Hollow silver handles,
    bright cut. Designs on blade with
    shell pattern on end of handle. E.
    P. Juichiya & Co................. 35.00
    Fruit. Dot in circle. Hollow sterling
    handles, flower festoon on
    handle. Set of six. Rogers Bros. 95.00
    Fruit. Sterling fittings, pearl
    handles. Set of 12 .... 95.00
    Steak. German steel blades.
    Twins trademark, plain beading
    on hollow silver handles. Set of
    six. J.A.Henckels, Swillingswerk .. 120.00
Ladles
    Gravy. Shell design. Eagle within
    a circle. Griffin 110.00
    Punch. 15" long. Cut glass handle . 265.00

Nut Server. 1912, 225/10000.
    Pierced, square, flat bowl, simple
    handle. English.................. 55.00
Paper Clip. Shield-shaped back,
    1½ x 2¾". Fluer-de-lis 45.00
Pen/Pencil Set. C. 1920. Waterman . 95.00
Pin Cushion. Elephant 35.00
Plates
    6". Bread and butter. Beaded
    rims. Scrolled monogram. Signed.
    Set of 12 .... 225.00
    13½". Strawberry. Reed & Barton . 145.00
    Bread and Butter. Triple mono-
    gram. Set of six. Gorham 85.00
    Bread and Butter. Set of eight.
    Monogram ALM 120.00
Porringer. Large, 5½" diam., 2"
    deep, pierced handle. Weighs 12
    ounces. Bigelow, Kennard & Co. .. 95.00

Fish Fork. "Lily." Flatware. Whiting
Division of Gorham $30.00

Cream Soup. "Lily." Flatware. Whiting
Division of Gorham $28.50

Goblet. "Repousse'. S. Kirk, Baltimore
$200.00

Spoons

Berry. Large, deep bowl. Marked
eagle's head, hand full of arrows,
3 links and Towle Mfg. Co. 55.00
Bouillon or Soup. Chrysanthe-
mums on top, and reverse sides of
handle and around bowl. Set of
six. Marked, sterling, lion and
anchor, G 135.00
Demitasse. Gold-washed bowls,
embossed on both sides of handle
with scroll work and shell design.
Set of six 115.00
Salt, Master. 3 7/7" Old English
pattern with large gold-washed
bowl. Richard Crossley, London,
1812. . . . .   36.00
Serving. Pierced gold-washed
bowl. Scalloped shell on front.
Marked CB., lion, sterling and
anchor 125.00
Zodiac. Aquarius, Leo, Taurus, etc.
Each 18.00
Statue. Knight. 10" high, ivory face,
sword, shield 375.00
Sugar Shaker. Urn-shape on round
base. C. 1910. S. Kirk & Son Co. . . .   75.00
Sugar Tongs
James Young. #1775 . . . .   70.00

Plain 45.00
Tea Ball. Round, with chain 25.00
Tea Strainers
6½" overall length. Openwork
handle, round bowl 22.50
Relief flower design on wide,
flaring border, slender wood
handle. "Tiffany" 25.00
"Repousse'. Kirk 37.50
Teapot. 11" high. American made,
Georgian style 850.00
Trays
6½" diam. Hammered, round 25.00
11" diam. Kirk 600.00
12" diam. Initial P. 15½ oz.
International 145.00
Wine Cooler. Loving cup style. 16"
high, 8" top diam. C. 1890 . . . .   350.00

SILVER, VICTORIAN PLATED

Plated silver production began in the period
1840-1850. By 1855, in the United states, a
number of companies were producing the
ware in large quantities. The base was usually
Britannia metal - 10 parts tin and 1 part
antimony. After being shaped, articles were
plated by an electrolytic method which placed
a thin coating of silver over the base metal.
Considerably less silver was used when
compared with the Sheffield method and
consequently the ware was inexpensive
enough to find a place in almost every home.

Baskets

10" diam. 10" high. Resilvered . . . $ 65.00
10¼" diam. Ornate edge and
etching inside. 4 ornate feet and
bail. Marked Victor Silver Plate.
Needs resilvering 40.00

Grape Shears. Germany $50.00

Gallery Tray. 10½x16". Hallmarked
"Kentshire" $95.00

Butter Dishes
    Ornate, engraved flowers and
    birds on lid, horse finial, 4 feet.
    Needs resilvering 35.00
    Ornate 4-footed base, handles,
    beaded rim, etchings and finial.
    Needs resilvering 40.00
Castor Sets, See "Castor Sets"
Champagne Bucket. 8½" high, 2
    handles. Reed and Barton 125.00
Coffee Pot. 13½" high, 7¼" diam.
    Porcelain liner. Quadruple plate
    by Simpson Hall & Miller, dated
    1893. Bird mounted on handle,
    four panels circle the girth, each
    with polar bear on ice floe, seal in
    water. Ornate 128.50
Cracker Jar. Covered, 6" diam., 7½"
    high. Ornate etching on front,
    ornate bail and finial. "Crackers"
    engraved on front. Needs
    resilvering 40.00
Cup and Saucer. Marked Meridian
    Quadruple Plate 28.50
Dish, Nut. Pairpont silver. 6" long,
    3½" high. Deep cranberry glass
    liner........................ 115.00
Egg Cooker. 11" high. Insert for 4
    eggs. Hen finial 85.00
Goblets
    Meriden Co. 6¾" high. Resilvered 40.00
    Ornate, 6½" high, marked "Mfg.
    and plated by Reed & Barton" 35.00
Pickle Castor, See "Pickle Castors"
Services
    5-piece set. Teapot, 8½" coffee
    pot, sugar bowl, creamer,
    spooner. "Acme Silver Plate,
    Quadruple." Resilvered 295.00
    4-piece set. 6½" teapot, sugar
    bowl, spooner, creamer. Floral

etchings, ornamental spout, finial
    and handles. "G. Uher Silver Co.,
    Quadruple Plate." Needs Resil-
    vering 60.00
Spoon Holder and Dinner Gong.
    10½" high. Holds twelve spoons.
    Petaled standard extends from
    holder. 2 soldiers and 2 dogs
    stand by handle to guard silver.
    Marked Wallingford Triple Plate .. 75.00
Spreaders. 8" long, bone twisted
    handles, floral engraved blades.
    Leather box, padded and lined in
    purple velvet and silk 62.50
Sugar Bowl. Covered, 7½" high.
    Ornate handles and finial, 4 feet.
    Marked "Queen City Silver Co." .. 45.00
Syrup Jug. Ornate handle and lid,
    ornamental band at bottom and
    top. Marked "Kan & Co."......... 55.00
Teapots
    7½" high, quart capacity. Ribbed
    bowl rests on base, rose band in
    relief, ornamental spout and
    heat-resistant handle. Needs re-
    silvering 35.00
    14" high. Reed & Barton, classic
    style........................ 125.00
Vegetable Dish. Covered, 8½" diam.
    Ornate band around base. Mar-
    ked "Barbour Bros. Quadruple
    Plate" 60.00
Water Cooler. "Meridian" plate.
    Porcelain lined, on holder with
    two goblets, with tray. Set 200.00

SILVER DEPOSIT GLASS

Silver Deposit glass gained popularity around
the turn of the present century. As the name
indicates, silver was deposited on the glass by
using a current of electricity while the glass
and a piece of silver were placed in a solution
which caused the silver to decompose and
pass through the solution to the part of the
glass which had previously been outlined into
a pattern.

Bonbon Dish. 8" diam. ....$ 50.00
Bottle. 5½" high. Crystal bottle and
    stopper with concentric lines of
    silver deposit. Liberty Bell shape . 65.00
Bowls
    4¼" diam. 35.00
    5½" diam., 3" high, clear glass ... 42.50
    8" diam. 75.00
    9" diam., 2" high. Flared sides.... 82.50
Box, Puff. 4¼" diam., 3½" high..... 47.50
Cologne. Green glass, 3½" high 75.00

Plate. 12", crystal, mixed fruit decor
$67.50

Creamer and Sugar. 2¾" high
   creamer, 2½" high sugar bowl.
   Set 45.00
Cruet. 6¾" high, with fluted steeple
   stopper 50.00
Decanter. 8½" high 85.00
Marmalade Jar. 4¾" high 55.00
Mustard Pot. 3¾" high 38.50
Perfume Bottle. With stopper, 3¾"
   high 29.50
Plate. 6½" diam. 35.00
Sherbet and Plate Set. 6 sherbet
   cups, 3½" high and 3" diam., 6
   plates, 5¼" diam. Set 250.00
Toothpick Holders
   2" high 22.50
   2½" high 25.00
Tumbler. 5½" flared top. Bottom has
   narrow flutes with silver lines in
   block pattern 10.00
Vases
   4¼" high. Emerald green glass,
   leaf design 32.50
   6" high. Bud 35.00
   8" high. Bud 40.00
   8" high. Bulbous bottom, long
   neck, flared top 50.00

SILVER LUSTRE WARE

The ware was made in large quantities in the
Staffordshire district of England between 1805
and 1840. After 1840, electroplating of metal
items brought about a decline in the demand
for metal-surfaced earthenware.

Bowl. 6", Festoon and Shell motif. C.
   1840...........................$ 60.00

Teapot. 3½ x 5½". C. 1830 .... $225.00

Bowl. Open, footed. Handled 75.00
Candleholder. Late, chamber-type,
   6" diam., embossed scroll decor at
   edge. Candle cup is gold lustre ... 45.00
Coffee Pot. 10½" high............. 225.00
Creamers
   4½" high to top of handle. Fine
   ribbed design 97.50
   Dolphin handle 120.00
Goblets
   3¾" high 45.00
   4" high, 3½" diam. bowl with
   copper lustre lining 48.50
   4½" high...................... 55.00
Jug. Canary ground, mask spout 400.00
Mug. 4½" high, 4" diam. Marked
   Wade. C. 1830 .... 85.00
Pitchers
   "Hanover." Porcelain lined,
   hinged pewter lid with porcelain
   knob, ribbed base, black handle .. 150.00
   "Harlequin." White quilted body
   with silver lustre at top. 2-quart
   capacity....................... 250.00
   7" high. Medium grey-brown
   ground, black scenic transfer.
   Monogrammed "G.G. 1812" in gold 265.00
Sugar Bowls
   Scroll design on body and cover .. 150.00
   With lid. Small open handles. Fine
   ribbed pattern 160.00
Sugars and Creamers
   3" high. Queen Anne pattern. Set . 125.00
   4" high creamer, 5" high sugar ... 150.00
Teapots
   5½" high 195.00
   8½" high. Footed 235.00
   11" high. Footed, domed lid 295.00
Toby Jug 225.00

SILVER RESIST WARE

The ware, first produced about 1805, is similar to Silver Lustre in respect to the process of silvering. However, it differs in that a pattern appears on the surface.

The outline of the pattern was drawn or stenciled over the body of the item to be silvered. A glue or sugar-glycerin adhesive was brushed over the part which was not to be lustred. The lustreing solution was applied and allowed to dry; then the glue or adhesive was washed off. This glue or adhesive had caused the drawing or pattern to "resist" the lustreing solution; and, when fired in a kiln, the lustre-like glaze covered the entire surface, except for the pattern.

Pitcher. 6" high, yellow with silver resist decor $500.00

Cups and Saucers
  Berry and leaf design .... $ 85.00
  Late 40.00
Jug. 4¾" high 195.00
Mug. 2½" high. White with tiny red roses, silver decor 45.00
Pitchers
  4¾" high. Tan ground with grape and vine decor 145.00
  5" high. Leaf and foliage design. Applied handle, bulbous shape. C. 1815......................... 150.00
  5¼" high. Vintage decor 165.00
  6¼" high. Colorful floral medallion. Flutes and flowering vine decor on body.................. 185.00
  7" high. Vine and leaf decor 195.00
Plate. 7" diam. Vine decor 68.50

Tea Set. Miniature. 6 cups and saucers, covered sugar and creamer......................   65.00
Teapot. 5½" high. Vine and flower decor 265.00
Toothpick Holder 18.00

SINCLAIRE GLASS

H. P. Sinclaire and Company was founded in 1904. They were the twelfth glass works to locate in the "Crystal City," Corning, New York.

In 1920. H. P. Sinclaire began his own glass blowing factory in Bath, N.Y. Prior to this, Sinclaire's cut and engraved designs were done on other glass makers' blanks.

Sinclaire produced some of the most beautiful glass of the "Brilliant Period." Many of his designs were based on nature...fruits, flowers and foliage...and he approached them from an architectural viewpoint.

Bowls
  12" diam. Green, amber foot..... $ 75.00
  13" diam. Rolled rim, canary yellow, etched florals. Signed 85.00
  Blue crystal, center bowl. Signed . 125.00
Candlesticks. 9" high, black and white trim. Signed. Pair 80.00
Console Set. 5 pieces. Green etched, 4 candlesticks, 3¼" high, bowl 14¼" diam., 6" high 325.00
Lamp. 17" high, cut glass. "Flower Basket" pattern 650.00
Vase. Fan. 6" high, gold ruby and flint. Farrar 85.00

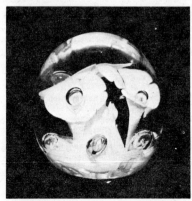

Paperweight. Trumpet design in clear glass $65.00

SMITH BROS. GLASS

Two brothers, Alfred and Harry Smith, worked at the Mt. Washington Glass Co. decorating glass for about four years, beginning in 1871. In 1875 they began their own operation in New Bedford, Mass.

The brothers made a line of fancy, decorated tableware. Their claim to fame was the popular Smith vase, which later was copied and sold in mail order catalogues and 5 and 10-cent stores in the eastern United States.

Bowls

   4¼". Melon-ribbed, handpainted
   aster. Signed .... $ 160.00
   4½". Opaque glass, handpainted
   flowers in 2-handled silverplated
   holder. Signed 200.00
   9". Shasta. Daisy decor, dotted
   top. Signed 350.00
   Miniature. Burmese-colored, decorated with pansies outlined in
   gold, white beading on rim,
   melon-ribbed 200.00

Boxes

   3½ x 4". Covered. Bluebells,
   leaves on pink, white ground 150.00
   Open, round, with floral decor.
   Mt. Washington. Signed with
   rampant lion 125.00
   Dish. Sweetmeat. Raised gold and
   enamel on pansies. Signed with
   rampant lion 275.00

Rose Bowl. 4" high. Satin finish with floral decor. Rampant lion trademark
$175.00

Fernery. 10" wide, melon-ribbed, 3
   shades of brown pansies, metal
   rim 350.00
Fingerbowl, Glass. Opaque with H/P
   flowers in handle. S/P holder. Sgd. 125.00
Jars
   Cookie. Mt. Washington, melon-
   ribbed. Acorns and oak leaves
   allover. Signed red lion 395.00
   Cracker. Cream shade with blue
   wisteria trailing on all sides.
   Signed with rampant lion 375.00
   Cracker. Ivory melon with blue,
   grey pansies outlined in red 285.00
Mustard. Barrel-shape. Deep blue
   violets on a china blue, high glaze
   background 95.00
Mustard. Handled, pansy decor. Sgd. 125.00
Pitcher. Cream. Raised gold and
   enamel on pansies. Signed with
   rampant lion 225.00
Plate. 7". Santa Maria ship decor.
   Signed 500.00
Rose Bowls
   4" diam. Melon-ribbed, cream
   ground. H/P asters. Signed 175.00
   Gold inscribed with "Compliments
   of the Season." Signed with
   rampant lion 195.00
Salt 35.00
Sugar and Creamer. Silver tops,
   melon-ribbed, pansy decor 500.00
Vases
   4¼" high. Cylindrical, one pale
   pink body; other, greenish-grey
   painted and enameled cranes. Pr. 250.00
   5" high. Tri-sided, blue asters,
   white beading. Signed 240.00
   6" high. Pastel foliage decor 250.00
   8½" high. Flask. Pink roses, blue,
   gold on white 275.00
   8½" high. Santa Maria ship decor.
   Flask-shaped. Signed 950.00
   8½" high. Gold pattern over
   mottled on green ground. Branches
   of red and yellow roses. Gold
   tracery. Bulbous body, tapered
   neck. Script signed 295.00
   9½" high, 6" diam. Signed
   trademark with rampant lion 500.00

SNOW BABIES

It appears there are now two theories on the origin of snow babies, the small German bisque figures which came on the American market after the turn of the present century. The first theory is that German doll makers copied Christmas candy figures and, the

1" high. Germany $15.00

second, that they originated with the daughter of Admiral Robert E. Peary, discoverer of the North Pole. She was born on the northwestern coast of Greenland in September 1893 and was called the "snow baby" by the eskimos. In 1901 an illustrated book showed her in a parka [snowsuit]. This seems to be the more logical theory on the origin of the snow babies.

1" high. Germany ....$	15.00
2" high. Pulling sled	25.00
2" high. Seated. Germany	25.00
3" high. On skis	28.50
4½" high. Back pack	30.00
5½" long. On sled, snow baby with stick	55.00
Double. One on stomach sliding down roof. Other, hands out in front. Germany	75.00
On sleigh pulled by huskies	45.00
Playing Accordion	40.00
Playing Drums	40.00
Playing Trumpet	40.00
Polar Bear	30.00
Seated	34.00
Seated. Teeny	16.00
Sheep	30.00
Standing	25.00
Teddy Bear. Green top hat	30.00
Two Girls. Hugging	48.00

SOAPSTONE

Soapstone is a mineral called steatite, also known as potstone. Found in Vermont, Massachusetts and the Delaware River area, it was extensively used for table tops and for carvings. Carved figures and vases marked "China" are often encountered on the antique market.

Ash Tray. Polar bear ....$	15.00
Bear. 3¾" high	28.50
Bookends	
Carved oriental dogs. Gray	60.00
Flower pot and flowers on each ..	50.00
Bottle. Carved, with immortals	55.00
Box. 3½ x5". Carved oriental scene .	42.50
Buddha. 4-3/8" high. Yellow	30.00
Candle/Flower Holder. 3 holes, 9" long, 4½" wide	40.00
Chicken. 4" high	32.00
Elephant, Seated. 5½" high, dog at base	50.00
Elephant with trunk up	32.00
Flower Holder. 9½" high, 6" wide. Maroon, carved mums, 4 legs	45.00
Foo Dog. 7", "Han," old and heavy ..	60.00
Match Holder. With monkey, 4½" long	26.50
Monkey. 6" high, with two birds and small vase....................	48.50
Monkeys, Three. 1½" high, 2" long .	22.00
Oriental Man. 9½" high. Marked "China"	65.00
Oriental Woman. Holding vase. Marked "China"	95.00
Toothpick Holder. With two sections, decor of birds and leaves	25.00
Urn. 11" high. Covered with two small vases on sides, three birds,	

Vase. 6½" high, carved flowers. China......................$67.50

flowers and urn with flowers
on front of urn. 5 colors 195.00
Vases
7" high. Carved birds and flowers . 65.00
7" high. Carved vines and leaves . 65.00
7½" high. Flower decor. 2 colors . 70.00
8" high. Carved flowers, leaves .. 75.00
9" high, 5" base width. Tinted
daisies and leaves. Double 95.00
9½ x6". Carvings, rose to ivory ... 85.00
9½" high. Carved chrysanthe-
mums and leaves 80.00
Wine Cups. Soft, pale gray-green
color. Straight cylindrical sides,
2½" high, 2" diam. Set of 4 ...... 60.00

SOUVENIR AND COMMEMORATIVE PLATES

The plates referred to in this section had their
beginning at about the time of the
Philadelphia Centennial in 1876 and were still
popular at the New York World's Fair in 1938.
They should not be confused with the earlier
Staffordshire historical and pictorial plates
which went out of vogue in the 1850-1860
period.

Capitol at Washington, D.C. Dark
blue. Marked "R. & M. Co." in
diamond. Staffordshire, England. . $ 40.00
DeSoto's Discovery of the Mississ-
ippi. 10", marked R&M 35.00
Faneuil Inn. Late Wedgwood, blue .. 37.50
Fort Ticonderoga, Lake Champlain.
Wedgwood. 9¼" 36.00

Plate. 9½". "Souvenir of Delaware
Water Gap from Winona Cliff."
Staffordshire England. Blue $38.00

Gov. Yates House, Schenectady, N.Y.
7½", blue 32.00
Independence Hall, Phila., Pa. 10",
marked R&M................... 42.00
Indian Hunter Menotomy. Wedg-
wood, blue 40.00
Keokuk, Iowa 40.00
Library of Congress. Wedgwood,
blue 37.50
Longfellow's Home, Portland, Maine.
9", Wedgwood, blue 38.00
Mt. Vernon. Late Wedgwood, blue .. 35.00
Niagara Falls. Greenish-brown.
Ridgeway, 9" 34.50
"Old Northchurch." Marked Wedg-
wood 35.00
"Old South Church," Boston. Re-
introduced by Shreve, Crump,
Low. Tea party met here in 1771 .. 40.00
Pilgrim Memorial Monument. Late
Wedgwood, blue 37.50
Portland, Oregon. Blue and white
Staffordshire, 1905 .... 40.00
Portraictuer of Captayne John Smith,
Admiral of New England, by the
Rowland and Marcellus Co.,
Staffordshire, England 35.00
Public Library, Boston. Late Wedg-
wood, blue 35.00
The McKinley Home. Late Wedg-
wood, blue 36.00
The Witch House. Roger Williams'
House. Deep blue Wedgwood 35.00
"Views of Chicago." Federal Building
in center surrounded by other
well-known structures. 9" 42.00

The following late plates, made by
Rowland & Marcellus, Staffordshire
England list at $15.00 to $18.00
each: Atlantic City, Detroit, Independence Hall, New London, Philadelphia City Hall, Plymouth and
Richmond.

SOUVENIR GLASS, See
FLASHED GLASS

SOUVENIR SPOONS, See SPOONS

SPANGLE GLASS, See
END-OF-DAY GLASS

SPANISH LACE GLASS

The glass derives its name from the lacy
patterns which run through the glass. The
design is found in clear, blue, yellow and
cranberry-colored glass.

Bottles. 7" high, slender neck. Pair .. $ 65.00

Pitcher and 5 tumblers. Cranberry and white. Set $295.00

Bowls

4½" high, 11" wide. Ruffled, cranberry to clear 85.00
4¾" high, 10¾" wide. Ruffled. Pink to clear, flower decor 70.00
Fruit. Opalescent with electric blue stylized flowers. Footed, with flared, fluted rim 85.00
Celery. 6" high, 4½" wide. Yellow with ruffled top 55.00
Lamp. Oil-type. Skyblue with lace decor. Panelled, square font of clear glass. 11" high 125.00
Muffineer. Raspberry 75.00

Pitchers

8" high. Light translucent blue, blue handle 95.00
10" high. Blue opalescent, fluted edge, clear reeded handle 125.00
10" high. Cranberry, opalescent . . 100.00

Rose Bowls

4" high. White on clear 45.00
Canary 60.00

Salt Shakers

Blue 22.00
White 18.00

Syrup Jugs

Blue opalescent. Original top and applied handle 65.00
Cranberry 75.00
Tumbler. Pink 40.00

Vases

4" high. Jar-shaped, pale vaseline with white lace, ruffled rim 45.00
6" high. Opalescent and clear ruffled edge, bulbous bottom 48.50
6" high. Yellow 65.00

SPATTER GLASS, See
END-OF-DAY GLASS

SPATTERWARE

The origin and exact period of Spatterware is one of the intriguing mysteries of the antiques world.

It appears that the majority of the ware, which is a heavy, soft-paste Staffordshire type, has been found among the Pennsylvania [Dutch] Germans. However, some have been found in Ohio, Maryland and New England.

The period of manufacture is believed to have been between 1820 and 1860. A piece impressed "Adams" is occasionally found.

The process of spattering was elementary. A fine sponge was dipped into paint and dabbed evenly around the borders and inner surface, or around a previously outlined decoration. After the colors dried a glaze was applied and the item fired in a kiln.

Bowls

5½" diam., 3¼" high. House. Green and blue . . . . $ 175.00
6½" diam., 3½" high. Peafowl . . . 185.00
6½" diam. Rainbow, in red and blue 195.00
Cats. 12½" high. White ground with purple decor, green eyes. Pair . . . 275.00

Creamers

3¼" high. Peafowl. Blue 110.00
6" high. Blue with pink flowers . . . 197.00
Cup Plate. 4" diam. Blue 90.00

Cups and Saucers

Fort. Blue 195.00
Peafowl. Child's, green 115.00
Peafowl. Handleless. Blue 185.00
Peafowl. Light green 185.00
Peafowl. Red 185.00

Pitcher. Tulip pattern, yellow . $265.00

Rainbow. Red, green 175.00
Rainbow. Red, purple 165.00
Pitchers
  7" high. Rainbow. Red, blue 250.00
  8" high. Peafowl. Blue 265.00
  10" high. Fort or Castle 320.00
Plates
  8". Tulip, blue spatter around edge 215.00
  8¼". Tulip 225.00
  8½". Rose. Purple border 200.00
  9". Peafowl. Red 245.00
  9". Rainbow. Red, blue 195.00
  9". Thistle. Red 260.00
  9½". House. Red house, red
  border, green, black background . . 300.00
  9¾". Thistle or Cock's Comb.
  Yellow border, green leaves and
  red thistle 265.00
  Peafowl. Blue border 200.00
  10¼". Soup. Rainbow 275.00
Platters
  10¼ x 13½". Peafowl. Cut corners 365.00
  10¼ x 13½". Rainbow. Cut corners 350.00
  11x14". Rainbow 350.00
  14x17¾". Rainbow. Blue and red . 395.00
Sugar Bowls
  "Cock's Comb" or "Thistle." 5½"
  high 275.00
  "Peafowl," blue 225.00
  "Rose" 250.00
  "Tulip," blue 235.00
Teapots
  "Fort" or "Castle" 360.00
  "Rainbow" 325.00
  "Thistle". 9" high 350.00
  "Tulip," red, blue 350.00
  Yellow and red, squat, bulbous
  type. Scarce color combination . . . 395.00
Wash Set. "Rainbow" pattern. 13½"
  diam. bowl, 11½" high pitcher . . . 695.00

SPODE CHINA,
See COPELAND SPODE CHINA

SPONGEWARE

Although Spongeware is similar to Spatterware in design, they should not be classified
together. Seasoned collectors can differ-
entiate between the two without any
difficulty.
Spongeware derived its name from the
method of dabbing the decorative color to the
ware with what might appear to have been a
sponge.

Bowl. 3 high, 4" diam. Late . . . . $ 12.00
Cup and Saucer. Large, blue, with
  handle 60.00

Casserole. Covered, 7½" diam. Green
and brown on cream ground . . . $35.00

Pitcher. 9" high. Blue sponge on buff
  base 68.00
Platter. Oval, 12" long. Blue 50.00
Spitoon. Green and white, embossed
  with gold 45.00

SPOONS, SOUVENIR

Souvenir spoons were made especially as
mementos of events, personalities and
places. Their period of greatest popularity was
between 1880 and 1900.
Spoons of this type are still being produced
and feature present day activities. The spoons
are finding favor among collectors today. The
late Albert Stutzenberger, author of "The
American Story in Spoons," in a letter to the
writer, stated, "They are rapidly being
transformed from ugly ducklings into swans,
from 'Aschenpudel' into 'Cinderella' of the
antique trade."

"Washington Court House." M. E.
Church. Sterling $18.50

ACTOR'S FUND FAIR. A much sought
  after spoon. Pictures 5 actresses
  and 5 actors of the early theatre . . $ 35.00

ACTRESS. Poli Neari 10.00
AMPERSAND. Fraternal. Sterling 15.00
ATLANTA, ILL. June 30, 1892 . . . . 10.00

BERGEN, 1891. Fancy handle, tiny ringlets on handle, scene of deer pulling sleigh, fish. Silverplate ... 12.50

BOSTON. Old South Church 15.00

BUFFALO. 1897. 31st. National Encampment. Silverplate 12.50

BUTTE, MONTANA. Indian face. All copper 15.00

CADILLAC. Pictures the founder of Detroit who is better known for the auto named after him........ 24.00

CALIFORNIA 10.00

CANADA. Plain handle with enameled shield, gold-washed bowl. Early Quebec scene 12.00

CAPITOL, RICHMOND, VA. State seal. Sterling 18.00

CHAPLIN, CHAS. Rogers silverplate . 16.50

CHARLESTON,S.C. 10.00

CHICAGO. Embossed handle, shield, corn, "Illinois" bowl enameled ship "U.S.S. Chicago" 20.00

CHICAGO. World's Fair 15.00

CHIEF SEATTLE. An indian orator for whom the City of Seattle, Washington was named 15.00

CINCINNATI FOUNTAIN. A heavy spoon of early vintage, with floral design, commemorating a famous Cincinnati landmark 12.50

COLORADO SPRINGS. Prospector Panning Gold. Sterling 18.00

COLUMBIAN EXPOSITION. Chicago, 1893. Columbus Taking Possession of the New World. Portrait of Columbus on handle 20.00

COMPLIMENTS OF THE SEASON. Cupid ringing bell, Easter Bunny, Christmas stocking. Sterling 25.00

DAYTONA, FLORIDA. Sterling. Palm tree on handle 12.00

DELAWARE WATER GAP, PA. "The Kittatinny." Sterling............ 13.50

DETROIT. With vine and flowers 12.00

DIONNE QUINTS. Silverplate 10.00

DELUTH,MINNESOTA. Skyline handle. Sterling 12.50

FERNBANK LOCK & DAM, Cinn., Ohio. Garfield Mon. Corn, Etc..... 10.00

FLORIDA. Handle embossed front and reverse. Bowl embossed "Over Sea Railroad, Key West" ... 14.50

FORTRESS, MONROE,AT OLD POINT COMFORT. The Moat 12.50

FORT SUMTER. Charleston, S.C. Picture...................... 12.50

FREEMONT, NEBRASKA 9.50

GRAND RAPIDS, MICHIGAN. Flowered handle. Sterling 20.00

GRAND UNION TEA CO. 6.00

HOT SPRINGS. Ornate openwork handle 15.00

IDAHO, STATE SEAL FINIAL 16.50

INDIANA. Old fort embossed in bowl 12.00

INDIANA. West Baden Springs Hotel 12.00

IRISH BRIGADE. Commemorates the courageous action of the Irish born soldiers from New York City at the battle of Gettysburg....... 17.50

ITHACA, N.Y. Cornell University Library. Sterling 15.00

JUAREZ, MEXICO. Sterling 15.00

KANSAS STATE. "Colby" in bowl 12.50

KNICKERBOCKER. Personification of the jovial New Yorker 22.00

LAKE CHAMPLAIN. With head of indian at top 8.00

LANCASTER. Gorham sterling. Beaded rim handle with raised roses . 17.50

LAST SACRIFICE, NIAGARA. Shows Niagara Falls and the Indian maiden who, according to legend, was sacrificed by her tribe to propitiate the gods 17.50

LAW BLDG. Univ. of Michigan. Sterling 16.00

LEWIS-CLARK EXPOSITION. Forestry Building. Demitasse 10.00

LONGFELLOW. The spoon honored the American poet.............. 15.00

LOS ANGELES. Sterling, embossed .. 22.50

LOUISVILLE. Old Kentucky Home ... 7.50

LUDINGTON, MICHIGAN 8.00

LUTHER, MARTIN. Sterling 20.00

MACKINAC ISLAND. "Indian Head Landmarks." Sterling 20.00

MAINE. Feb. 13, 1898. "50,000.000 for defense." Silverplate 11.50

MANDAN, N.D. Indianhead handle, plain bowl 12.00

MARYLAND STATE. Seal finial 12.50

MCKINLEY. Sterling and enamel 15.00

MILES STANDISH. "Ruby '91." Sterling 17.50

MILES STANDISH MONUMENT. Sterling 17.50

MILWAUKEE. City Hall. Sterling 12.50

MISSOURI. Enameled state spoon. Sterling 15.00

MOLLY PITCHER. An unusual spoon in that it commemorates 2 women of the same name: a heroine of the Revolution and the "last of the witches" [Lynn, Mass.] 22.50

MONTICELLO. Ornate leaf handle. Sterling 18.50

MONTREAL. Enameled crest handle . 16.50

MOUNT VERNON. Sterling 17.50

MOUNT WASHINGTON. "Tip-Top
House." 1953. Sterling 12.50
MUSKOGUE. With indian head
medallion 14.00
NASHVILLE. With open lettering and
heart-shaped bowl with twist
handle 12.00
NEW HAMPSHIRE. "Fabyan House."
Sterling 12.00
NEW ORLEANS. Sterling 12.00
NEW YORK SKYLINE. Shows Statue of
Liberty in harbor and skyline of
New York City 15.00
NIAGARA FALLS. Sterling 15.00
NORTH PLATTE, NEB. Steer roping.
Sterling 12.50

OLD POINT COMFORT. "Entrance to
Fort Monroe" (military). Sterling . 14.50
OSCEOLA, A "soffkee" spoon similar
to those used by Seminole indians
in Florida. Bowl pictures their
Chief Osceola 18.50
PALERMO. Jester handle. Demitasse 9.50
PICKFORD, MARY. Rogers Silverplate 12.50
PORTLAND. Twisted, ornate cutout
handle 14.50
QUEEN ELIZABETH CORONATION.
Enamel and sterling 18.00

RETURN OF COLUMBUS. Celebrates
the discoverer of America. Put out
for the Chicago World's Fair in
1893......................... 22.50
ROCHESTER 12.00
ROCKY MOUNT, DENVER. Skyline
handle; train going over a trestle
(in bowl). Sterling 15.00
ST. PAUL, MINNESOTA. State capital.
Silverplate 12.00
SALEM WITCH. One of the earliest of
souvenir spoons, manufactured by
Gorham for Daniel Low of Salem . 25.00
SALT LAKE, UTAH. Landmarks of the
Mormons. Sterling 16.50
SAN ANTONIO. With enameled
woman on handle 12.00
SAN DIEGO. With 2 palm trees and
marked. Sterling 14.00
SHAKESPEARE. Enameled 13.50
SOUTHERN PINES, N.C. Sterling 12.50

STAGE COACH. Shows a coach and
horses, fishing rod, rifle and creel 18.50
STATE HOUSE, BOSTON. 4" long,
picture in bowl 14.50
STATE REFORM SCHOOL. Mandan,
N.D. Picture in bowl 16.00
STATE TRAINING SCHOOL. Red
Wing, Minn. Picture in bowl 16.00
STATUE OF LIBERTY. Sterling 18.50

STEAMSHIP LANDING. Petroskey,
Mich. 12.00
STEWART, ANITA. Actress, silver-
plate 12.00
THOUSAND ISLANDS. "Lachine Ra-
pids." Sterling................. 16.50
TORONTO, CANADA. Maple leaf
handle, silverplate 12.00
VANCOUVER, CANADA. Enamel
coat of arms. Sterling 15.00
VASSAR COLLEGE. Gold bowl, R.L.G.
Sterling 18.50
VICTOR HERBERT. 4" long, picture in
bowl. 15.00
WASHINGTON, D.C. Capitol 12.50
WASHINGTON, D.C. Congress 12.50
WASHINGTON PORTRAIT. Sterling .. 18.50
WASHINGTON'S HATCHET. Pictures
the hatchet; also on reverse side
is the cherry tree which Washing-
ton is reputed to have chopped
down 20.00
WASHINGTON'S TOMB. Shows
burial place and home of George
Washington at Mount Vernon 17.50
WILLIAMSBURG, VA. Sterling 14.50
WORLD'S COLUMBIAN EXPOSITION,
Columbus at top of handle, ship
on bowl 25.00
WORLD'S FAIR, CHICAGO. 1892.
Sterling 20.00
WORLD'S FAIR, ST. LOUIS, 1904.
Handle ornately embossed front
and back. Bowl, fair scene, "Inside
Inn" 24.00
YALE. Twisted handle, monogram,
1893. Sterling 15.00
YELLOWSTONE ELK AND DEER. A
rare spoon of fine craftsmanship . 22.00
YELLOWSTONE PARK. Ornate moose
head in high relief. Sterling 20.00
YOSEMITE BEAR. The spoon has an
unusual rattail handle........... 22.50
ZODIAC. February. Sterling 17.50

STAFFORDSHIRE

The Staffordshire district had an abundance of
fine clay for pottery making. There were 80
different establishments operating there in
1786; by 1802 the number increased to 149.
The district included Burslem, Cobridge,
Etruria, Fenton, Foley, Hanley, Lane Delph,
Lane End, Longport, Shelton, Stoke and
Tunstall. Among the many famous potters
located there were Adams, Davenport, Spode,
Stevenson, Wedgwood and Wood.

WILLIAM ADAMS

William Adams of Stoke-upon-Trent produced American views of blue china. Two of his cousins, both of whom were named William Adams, were also potters. One operated at Greengates, Tunstall, and the other at The Brick House Works, Burslem and Cobridge. Neither of the cousins is reported to have made American historical views.

Cup and Saucer. Pink. "Columbus." Larsen 351	\$ 95.00
Pitcher. 7½", dark blue. American eagle	375.00

Plates

6". Deep pink. "New York City"	200.00
7", pink. "Montevideo, Conn."	150.00
9", pink. "View Near Conway, N. Y."	175.00
10", dark blue. "Mitchell and Freeman's China and Glass Warehouse"	350.00
10½", pink. "Catskill Mountain House"	235.00
10½", soup, pink. "Headwaters of the Juniata"	185.00
10¾", black. "Landing of Columbus." Larsen 348	150.00

Platters

9-7/8", pink. "Schenectady on the Mohawk"	325.00
15", medium black. Columbus and indian scene. Larsen 356	300.00

WILLIAM ADAMS & SONS

In 1819 a fourth William Adams, son of William Adams of Stoke, became a partner with his father and was later joined by three brothers to form the firm of William Adams & Sons. In 1829 the father died and William, the eldest of the sons, became manager. The company operated four potteries at Stoke and one at Tunstall. American views were produced at Tunstall in black, light blue, brown, pink and green in the 1830-40 period. William Adams died in 1865 and all operations were moved to Tunstall where the pottery is reportedly still being operated by the Adams family.

Creamer, pink. "Palestine"	\$ 85.00
Cup and Saucer. Handleless. "Garden Sports"	65.00
Pitcher. 10", pink. "Bologna"	95.00

Platter. 16x21". "Lyme Castle Kent." Adams	\$450.00

Plates

5¾", pink. "New York, U.S."	145.00
6", medium blue. "Palestine"	50.00
6¾", deep pink. "Monte Video, Conn."	80.00
7¼", red center, green border. "Columbus"	100.00
7½", deep pink. "Caledonia"	50.00
7½", deep pink. "Palestine"	50.00
7-7/8", dark blue. "St. Paul's School London." Impressed Adams & Sons	95.00
8", black. "Shannondale Springs, Va."	110.00
8", rose pink. "Andalusia"	45.00
8½", blue and white. "Caledonia"	95.00
8½", deep purple. "Columbus", camp scene. Larsen 317	120.00
9", dark blue. "Boston Glass House"	375.00
9¼", pink. "View Near Conway, N.H., U.S."	150.00
10¼", dark blue. "Mitchell and Freeman's China & Glass Warehouse"	420.00
10½", deep pink. "Caledonia"	65.00
10½", soup, brown. "Headwaters of the Juniata"	150.00
10¾", black. "Catskill Mountain House, U.S."	200.00

Platters

12½x15½". Black. "Harper's Ferry, U.S."	425.00
16". Pink. Same as above	450.00
17". Pink. "Landing of Columbus".	325.00

Sugar Bowl. Brown, "Log Cabin" with Harrison medallions on lid	225.00

Vegetable Dishes

8x10". Pink, "Bologna"	95.00
9½x13". Black. Open handles. "Lake George, U.S."	250.00
Athens. Round, covered	110.00

From sketchy historical accounts that are available it appears that James Clews took over the closed plant of A. Stevenson in 1819, with his brother Ralph entering the business a little later. The firm continued until about 1836 when James Clews came to America to enter the pottery business at Troy, Indiana. The venture was a failure because of the lack of skilled workmen and the proper type of clay. He returned to England but did not re-enter the pottery business.

Bowl. 5½", dark blue. "Christmas
   Eve." Wilkie .... $ 200.00
Creamers
   4½", "Landing of Lafayette" 225.00
   5½". "Eagle on Urn" 195.00
   Dark blue. "Christmas Eve."
   Wilkie 220.00
Cup Plates
   4½", dark blue. "Peace and
   Plenty"...................... 250.00
   4½", dark blue. "Pittsfield Elm" .. 200.00
Cups and Saucers
   Dark blue. "Eagle" on Urn 225.00
   Dark blue. "Landing of Lafayette" 175.00
Gravy Boat with Tray. Open type,
   blue. "Landing of Gen. Lafayette
   at Castle Gardens, N.Y., Aug. 16,
   1824" 400.00
Gravy Tureen with Lid and Tray.
   "Landing of Lafayette" 435.00
Plates
   6½", light blue. "Dr. Syntax, The
   Garden Trio" 150.00
   6½", dark blue. "Dr. Syntax and a
   Blue Stocking Beauty" 150.00
   6¾", dark blue. "Pittsfield Elm" .. 140.00
   7", pink. "Rapids Above Hadley
   Falls" 200.00
   7¼", dark blue. "Dr. Syntax
   Turned Nurse" 165.00
   7¾", dark blue. "Landing of
   Lafayette".................... 175.00
   8", dark blue. "Pittsfield Elm" 200.00
   8", dark blue. "States Bldg." and
   driveway..................... 195.00
   8", sepia. "Baker Falls" 95.00
   8¾", dark blue. "Christmas Eve."
   Wilkie 210.00
   8¾", dark blue. "Dr. Syntax
   Returned from His tour" 250.00
   8¾", dark blue. "Dr. Syntax Star
   Gazing"...................... 225.00
   8-7/8", dark blue. "Landing of
   Lafayette".................... 185.00

"States' Plate." 9", dark blue. Clews
$195.00

9", dark blue. "Hobart Town" 150.00
9", dark blue. "States." Building in
center, sheep grazing on lawn in
foreground 195.00
9", light blue. "Near Fort Miller,
Hudson River" 175.00
9". "Peace and Plenty" 195.00
9¾", dark blue, soup. "Dr. Syntax
Mistakes a Gentleman's House for
an Inn" 235.00
10", blue. "Harvard College" 150.00
10", dark blue. "Dr. Syntax Bound
to a Tree by Highwaymen" 235.00
10", dark blue. "Dr. Syntax and
the Bees"..................... 240.00
10", dark blue. "Knighthood
Conferred on Don Quixote."
Wilkie 200.00
10", dark blue. "Landing of
Lafayette".................... 225.00
10", dark blue, soup. "Peace and
Plenty"....................... 175.00
10", dark blue. "The Valentine."
Wilkie 175.00
10", purple and white. "Peace and
Plenty"....................... 225.00
10-1/8", dark blue. "Dr. Syntax
Disputing His Bill with the
Landlady" 250.00
10½", purple. "Near Fishkill" 200.00
10½", black. "Pittsburgh, Pa." ... 220.00
10½", dark blue. "Winter View of
Pittsfield, Mass." 265.00
10¾", dark blue. "States" 225.00
11", dark blue. "Escape of the
Mouse." Wilkie series 235.00

Platters

10½ x 13", dark blue. "Winter View of Pittsfield, Mass."	500.00
11 x 13½", black transfer. "Hudson River"	300.00
12 x 15½", lavender. "Penitentiary in Allegheny near Pittsburgh"	450.00
13 x 15½", brown. "Newburg, Hudson River"	350.00
14¼", dark blue. "Columbus, Ohio"	850.00
14½ x 19½", blue. "Dr. Syntax Amused with Pat in the Pond"	350.00
15", dark blue. "Landing of Lafayette"	600.00
15 x 15½", blue. "Dr. Syntax Advertising for a Wife"	350.00
16 x 19¼", black. "Hudson River"	400.00
17". Dr. Syntax, "A Noble Hunting Party"	375.00
17", dark blue. "Landing of Lafayette"	650.00
17", sepia. "Little Falls of Luzerne, N.Y."	325.00
18½", dark blue. "Detroit, Mich.".	1800.00
19", dark blue. "Landing of Lafayette"	750.00
Vegetable Dish. 10", black, rectangular. "New Hudson, Hudson River"	230.00
Vegetable Dish. 12½", dark blue. "The Escape of the Mouse." Wilkie	325.00

7¾", blue. "Race Bridge, Philadelphia"	250.00
8", black. "Battery, N.Y."	195.00
8", brown. "Battery & C., N.Y."	200.00
8", pink. "Battery & C., N.Y."	200.00
8", purple. "Battery & C., N.Y."	230.00
9", purple. "Battle Monument, Philadelphia"	225.00
9", purple. Shannondale Springs	230.00
9", blue. Water Works, Phila."	250.00
9", brown. "Water Works, Phila."	225.00
9¼", pink. "Race Bridge, Phila."	225.00
10-1/8", black. "Hartford, Conn."	245.00
10¼". "Boston State House"	245.00
10¼", black. "Hartford, Conn."	240.00
10¼", brown. "The President's House, Washington"	250.00
10¼", black, soup. "View of Canal, Little Falls, Mohawk River"	250.00
10½", green. "The President's House, Washington"	225.00
10½", medium blue. "The President's House, Washington"	265.00

Platters

15½", purple. "Clyde Scenery" [England]	165.00
17½", black. "Newburgh, New York"	450.00
Tureen. Green, open handles. 6¼ x 9". "Lake George"	400.00
Vegetable Dish. Black, 8 x 9½". "Upper Ferry Bridge"	400.00

J. & J. JACKSON

Job and John Jackson began operations at the Churchyard Works, Burslem, about 1830. The works had formerly been owned by the Wedgwood family. The firm did not produce dark blue china but made black, light blue, pink, brown, green, maroon and purple. In all, approximately 40 different American views of Connecticut, Massachusetts, Pennsylvania, New York and Ohio were issued. The firm is believed to have closed about 1844.

Basket. 9" long, 3½" high, oval. Medium blue, openwork, "Fort Ticonderoga"	$ 400.00
Dish, Sauce. 5" black. "University Hall, Harvard"	135.00
Plates	
6", pink. "Girard's Bank, Philadelphia"	195.00
7", black. "Ay Richmond, Va."	195.00
7", medium blue. "At Richmond, Va."	225.00
7", brown. "At Richmond, Va."	200.00
7¾", pink. "Hancock House, Boston"	200.00

THOS. MAYER

Thos. Mayer operated a pottery at Stoke, Staffordshire in 1829, where he produced the coats-of-arms of the thirteen original colonies. Teapots and sugar bowls, showing Lafayette at the Tomb of Franklin and at the Tomb of Washington, were also products of the pottery. In 1829 Thomas and his brothers, John and Joshua, bought the Stubbs Works at Burslem where they continued to produce a superior grade of chinaware.

Bowl. 12½" diam. "Arms of Maryland"	$3000.00
Fruit Dish. 8¾". "Arms of Mass."	1500.00
Plate. 8¾". Dark blue. "Arms of Rhode Island"	2000.00
Platter. "Arms of Pennsylvania." Rare	7500.00
Vegetable Dish. "Arms of Virginia"	2500.00

J. & W. RIDGWAY

John and William Ridgway operated a pottery firm from 1814 until 1830 at which time it was dissolved. Previously their father, Job

Ridgway and his brother George had operated the Bell Bank Works at Hanley since 1792. In 1813 Job built the Cauldon Place Works near Stoke-on-Trent, with his sons as partners. The firm operated under the name of Ridgway & Sons. After Job's death in 1814, his sons operated the business as J. & W. Ridgway. The establishment was known for its "Beauties of America Series" which included buildings of historic or scenic importance rather than natural views, such as Niagara Falls or the Hudson River.

Cup and Saucer. Light blue. Catskill Moss series. Saucer, "Near Troy, N.Y." Outside cup, "Valley of Wyoming, Pa." Inside cup, condensed "Near Troy, N.Y." 250.00

Custard Cup. 2½", handled. Dark blue, "Boston State House" 265.00

Gravy Boat. Handled. "Boston State House" 395.00

Plates
6", light blue. "Valley of the Shenandoah from Jefferson's Rock" 200.00
6-1/8", dark blue. "Antheneum, Boston" 350.00
7-1/8", dark blue. "Insane Hospital, Boston" 365.00
7-3/8", rose pink. Log cabin, "Columbus Star." Harrison souvenir. Larsen 179 . . . . 275.00
8", dark blue. "Library, Philadelphia" 340.00
8¼", dark blue. "Straughton's Church, Philadelphia" 375.00
9", light blue, soup. "Harper's Ferry from the Potomac Side" 300.00
10", dark blue. "City Hall, N.Y." . . 385.00

Platters
9½", dark blue. "St. Paul's Church, Boston" 450.00
10¼", dark blue. "Court House, Boston" 550.00
12½", dark blue. "Hospital, Boston" 650.00
15½x21", dark blue. "Capitol, Washington" 750.00

Relish Dish. Leaf-shaped. "Boston State House" 450.00

Vegetable Dish. Covered. 10½", dark blue, "Hospital, Boston" 475.00

WILLIAM RIDGWAY & CO.
NARROW LACE ORDER

Cup and Saucer. Light blue, "Crow's Nest from Bull Hill" and "Valley of Shenandoah from Jefferson Rock" $ 200.00

Custard Cup. 2¾", footed, light blue. "Narrows from Staten Island" 165.00

Plate. 8", light blue. "Washington's Tomb." Mt. Vernon 215.00

Platters
10", light blue. "Peekskill Landing. Hudson River" 350.00
15", black, without border. "View from Fort Putnam" 365.00

Sugar Bowl. Light blue. "Narrows from Staten Island" on cover. "Undercliff near Coolspring" on bowl 325.00

Vegetable Dish. Covered. 7¼", light blue, rectangular, cut corners. "President's House, Washington" . 375.00

JOHN ROGERS & SON

John Rogers and his brother, George, built a pottery near Longport about 1782. George died in 1815. John's son, Spencer, then became a partner in the firm which operated under the name of John Rogers & Son. In 1816 John died but Spencer continued to use the name of John Rogers & Son until he disposed of the business in 1842. The firm produced only four American views of which three were of the Boston State House. The other was the battle between the U. S. Frigate Chesapeake and the British Frigate Shannon. The Shannon was victorious, consequently the subject was not popular in the United States.

Pitcher. 5¼" high. "Boston State House." "City Hall, N.Y." on reverse. Blue and white. Rogers & Son . $650.00

Cup and Saucer. Blue. "Boston State House" . . . . $ 300.00

Plates

7½", medium dark blue. "Boston State House" 325.00

8½", medium blue. "Boston State House" 350.00

9¾", medium dark blue, soup. "Boston State House" 365.00

10", medium dark blue. "Shannon." Companion to "Chesapeake and Shannon" platter 400.00

10", dark blue, soup. Frigate "Chesapeake" 375.00

Platters

13", dark blue. "Boston State House" 500.00

18¾", dark blue. "Boston State House" 650.00

21½", dark blue. "Chesapeake and Shannon" 750.00

Teapot. Medium blue. "Boston State House" 750.00

RALPH STEVENSON

Ralph Stevenson was operating a pottery at Cobridge, Staffordshire, England, in 1802. It is believed that Williams was probably Stevenson's New York agent. The marks on the ware were R.S.W. or R.S.&W., with an occasional piece being marked "Stevenson" or "R. Stevenson and Williams, Cobridge, Staffordshire." In 1834 the name was changed to "R. Stevenson & Sons." The firm was discontinued in 1840. Most of the views were of the Boston and New York areas.

Coffee Pot. 11" high. Black transfer "Vale of Wyoming" [Wilkes Barre, Pa.] ....$ 625.00

Jug. 10", dark blue. "Hartford Deaf and dumb Asylum" and "Alms House, N.Y." 700.00

Plates

6", dark blue, "Columbia College, New York" 235.00

7", dark blue. "Battery, N.Y." 320.00

8½", dark blue. "City Hotels, N.Y." 345.00

10", dark blue. "Capitiol, Washington" 350.00

10", dark blue. "Harvard College" 400.00

10¼", dark blue. "Park Theatre, N.Y." 225.00

Platters

10½", dark blue. "Brooklyn Ferry." Embossed white edge. Rare New York view 1200.00

16½", dark blue. "Alms House, Boston" 850.00

Teapot. Dark blue. "State House, Hartford." Scarce 975.00

Soup Tureen. "View of the Deaf & Dumb Asylum." Stevenson . .$2850.00

Tureen, Soup. 15½". "Philadelphia Hospital, Phila., Pa." 2650.00

RALPH STEVENSON & WILLIAMS

Plates

6¾", dark blue. "Harvard College." Scarce ....$ 500.00

8", dark blue. "Columbia College, N.Y." 295.00

8½", dark blue. With tree. "Nahant Hotel near Boston" 285.00

8½", dark blue. "City Hotel, N.Y." 295.00

8½", dark blue. "Harvard College" 345.00

9", dark blue, vine border. "Hospital, Boston" 300.00

10", dark blue. "Capitol, Washington." Vine border 395.00

10", dark blue. "Park Theatre, N.Y." 400.00

10", dark blue. "Water Works, Phila." Acorn and Oak Leaf border . 425.00

Platter. 17", dark blue, Acorn and Oak Leaf border. "Boston State House" 750.00

JOSEPH STUBBS

In 1790 Stubbs established a pottery works at Burslem, England, which he operated until 1829 when he retired and sold his works to Mayer Bros. It is believed that he produced his views of America about 1825. Many of his scenes were from Boston, New York, New Jersey and Philadelphia. He died in 1836.

Creamers

4½" high, dark blue. "Boston State House" ....$ 285.00

5½" high, dark blue. "City Hall, N.Y." 300.00

Cup Plate. 3¼". "Woodlands near
Phila." 165.00
Cups and Saucers
Dark blue. "City Hall, N.Y." 225.00
Rose border. "Boston State House" 200.00
Mug. 3½" high, 3½" diam., dark
blue, rose border. "Boston State
House and New York" 350.00
Plates
6¾", dark blue. "City Hall, N.Y.".. 245.00
6¾", dark blue. "Woodlands near
Phila." 250.00
7", dark blue. "Hoboken in New
Jersey" 275.00
8¼", dark blue. "Nahant Hotel
near Boston" 295.00
8¾", dark blue. "Upper Ferry
Bridge" 275.00
9", dark blue. "Nahant Hotel near
Boston" 325.00
9¾", dark blue. "Fairmont near
Phila." 275.00
10", dark blue. "Dam and Water-
works, Phila." 295.00
10", dark blue. "Exchange, Baltimore" 325.00
10-1/8", dark blue. "Fairmont
near Phila.".................... 300.00
10¼", dark blue. "Bank of the
U.S., Phila." 375.00
Platters
10x18". "Upper Ferry Bridge" 395.00
13½ x 16½", dark blue. "Menden-
hall Ferry" 325.00
21", dark blue. "Fairmont near
Phila." 550.00
Teapot. Covered, dark blue. 10"
high, rose border. "N.Y. City Hall" 600.00

JOHN TAMS & CO.

John Tams, a potter, operated the Longton
Crown Works in Staffordshire, England, in
1840. During the same year James Tams from
Philadelphia, who was an importer and
relative, sent him an order for plates bearing
the portraits of Gen. Wm. Henry Harrison and
Henry Clay. The two portrait plates were
made with three different borders and are
known in blue or black. The mark is "James
Tams and Co., Importers, Philadelphia."

Plate. 9". Cream background with
blue decor. Made for Harrison's
campaign in 1840. Scarce........$ 750.00

S. TAMS & CO.

The firm operated at Longton, England. The
exact date of its beginning is not known but is
believed to be around 1810-1815. The
company produced a number of American
views including the United States Hotel,
Philadelphia, the Capitol, Harrisburg, Pa., and
the Capitol, Washington, D.C. About 1830 the
firm became Tams, Anderson and Tams.

Bowl. 11¾" diam., dark blue.
"Capitol, Washington" ....$ 950.00
Soup Plate. 10¼", dark blue.
"United States Hotel, Phila." Rare . 650.00

ENOCH WOOD & SONS

The pottery was located at Burslem, in the
Staffordshire district of England and ran under
the name of Enoch Wood & Sons from 1819 to
1846. Wood began business in 1783 at
Fountain Place, Burslem. His cousin, Ralph
Wood, was associated with him. James
Caldwell became a partner in 1790 and the
firm was then known as Wood & Caldwell-
until Enoch obtained full control in 1819 and
admitted his sons as partners. He died in 1840
but his sons continued the business until 1846
under the same name. The establishment was
then sold to the firm of Pinder, Bourne & Hope.
During the period 1819 to 1840, the pottery
produced more marked American historical
views than any other Staffordshire firm.

ENOCH WOOD & SONS
SHELL BORDER, CIRCULAR CENTER

Cup Plate. 3½", creamware with
rust red transfer. "Jackson, Hero
of New Orleans" ....$ 265.00

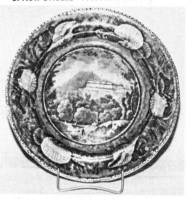

Plate. 10". "Pine Orchard House,
Catskill Mts." Shell border, circular
center. Wood & Sons.........$325.00

Plates

6½", dark blue. "Highlands near
Newburg" 235.00
7½", dark blue. "Erie Canal,
Aqueduct Bridge at Rochester" ... 265.00
7", dark blue. "Pass in the Catskill
Mountains" 275.00
7½", dark blue. "The Capitol,
Washington" 265.00
7½", dark blue. "View of Trenton
Falls" 225.00
8½", dark blue. "B.& O. Railroad
Incline" 300.00
8½", dark blue. "City of Albany" . 275.00
8½", light blue. "Landing of the
Fathers" 200.00
8¾", dark blue, soup. "Fall of
Montmorenci, near Quebec" 145.00
9", mulberry. "Natural Bridge,
Va." 245.00
9-1/8", dark blue. "Gilpins Mills
on Brandywine Creek" 300.00
9-1/8", dark blue. "Transylvania
University" 300.00
9¼", medium blue. "Boston State
House" 260.00
9¼", dark blue. "B. & O. Railroad
Incline" 345.00
9¼", dark blue. "Fall of Montmorenci, near Quebec" 155.00
9¼", dark blue, soup. "Pine
Orchard House. Catskill Mountains" 295.00
9¾", dark blue. "Marine Hospital,
Louisville, Ky." 275.00
10", dark blue. "City of Albany" .. 225.00
10", dark blue. "Pine Orchard
House" 325.00
10¼", dark blue, soup. "The B. &
O. Railroad." Level view 385.00

Plate. 10". "Table Rock Niagara." Shell
border, blue. Wood & Sons ...$350.00

10¼", dark blue. "Table Rock
Niagara" 350.00
Platters
9¼x12", dark blue. "Military
Academy, West Point" 950.00
12½x16½", dark blue. "Lake
George" 750.00
15", dark blue. "Niagara from the
American Side" 800.00
16x20", dark blue. "Castle Gardens" and "Battery, N.Y." 950.00

Platter. 20½" long. "Capitol of
Washington." Beauties of America
Series. Ridgway $750.00

ENOCH WOOD & SONS

SHELL BORDER, IRREGULAR CENTER

Cup Plate. 3½", dark blue. "Cadmus" .... $ 250.00
Cup and Saucer, dark blue. "Wadsworth Tower" 295.00
Plates
6½", dark blue. "MacDonough's
Victory" 155.00
7¼", medium blue. "Boston State
House" 195.00
7½", dark blue. "Southampton,
Hampshire" 135.00
7¾", dark blue. "MacDonough's
Victory" 175.00
8", dark blue. "Chief Justice
Marshall. Troy Line" 275.00
9¼". Dartmouth 150.00
9-1/8", dark blue. "MacDonough's
Victory" 210.00
9-1/8", dark blue. "Marine Hospital, Louisville" 240.00
9¾", dark blue, fruit. "The Union
Line" 265.00

10", dark blue. "Cadmus." So called ship flying American flag .. 375.00
10". "Union Line" 285.00
10", dark blue. "View of Liverpool" 120.00
10¼", dark blue. "MacDonough's Victory" 260.00

Platters
8½x11", dark blue. "East Cowes Isle of Wight." Sloop with American flag in foreground 325.00
18½", dark blue, shell border, "Christianburg, Danish Settlement on the Gold Coast of Africa" 800.00
Vegetable Dish. 7½x9¾", dark blue. "East Cowes, Isle of Wight" . 185.00

ENOCH WOOD & SON

VARIED BORDER

Bowl. Dark blue, 12". "Lafayette at Franklin's Tomb" ....$ 350.00
Cup and Saucer. Dark blue, flower border. "Lafayette at Washington's Tomb" 195.00

Plates
8½", dark blue. "Vesuvius" 75.00
10½", medium blue. "Landing of Fathers of Plymouth." C. 1820 .... 175.00

STAFFORDSHIRE FIGURINES

Baden Powell standing in front of cannon....................... 95.00
English Queen. Crown and ermine, 16" high...................... 130.00
Equestrian figures. C. 1840. Pair 250.00
Farmer and Wife. Jug and wheat. 13½" high.................... 90.00
Garibaldi. Orange shirt, white trousers. 9" high 110.00
Going to Market. Returning Home. Polychrome colors. 8½" high. Pair 175.00
Hunter and Dog. White background. Green clothes with brown and orange trim................... 95.00
King John Signing the Magna Charta 175.00
Milk Maid with Suckling Calf. 5" 85.00
Moody. Black and white. 15½" high . 130.00
Pastoral scene. Grazing lambs. 7½" high 95.00
"Peace on Earth, Good Will Toward Men." 12¾" high 150.00
Rivals. 3 figures in bower. 15" 90.00
Sankey. Black and white. 15½" high 135.00

Statue. 18" high. Prince of Wales. Edward VII. C. 1875. White ground, painted face, orange robe $175.00

Scot hunter and dog. Leaning on tree trunk. 12½" high, greens, reds and black on white 95.00
Shakespeare. Standing figure. 18" .. 125.00
"The Huntsman." Orange coat and cap, blue leggings. 15" high...... 115.00
Wolseley on horse 110.00

STAFFORDSHIRE ITEMS

Boxes, Trinket
Anchor and hooks. 2¾" ....$ 52.50
Angel, winged, and boy dressed in blue coat looking at book...... 55.00
Books and Vase. 2" 55.00
Children (2) and lamb 48.50
Child, pitcher and cup 60.00

Child sitting on couch, pulling on
socks 47.50
Clock and vase. 2" 55.00
Lamb and baby lamb. White with
green, oval, footed. 2x2½x2"
high 52.00
Red Riding Hood and Wolf on
cover. 2½" 55.00
Spaniel reclining on cover 50.00
Table and chairs on lid 55.00
Three children sitting on bench
atop lid. 4¾" high 55.00
Wash Stand, Miniature. Cover has
bowl, pitcher and mug in front of
mirror frame. Footed gold decor
on edges. 1½x1¾x2¼"......... 50.00
Watch and ring on cover 52.50
White with brown and white shell
decor. Crossed dolphin tails in
back. Green with edge lines in
gold. 4-7/8" high 60.00
White with green and gold. Large
watch on lid. 3¾" high 52.00
Candle Holder. Small, leaf-shaped .. 18.00

Cats
7¼" high. Sitting on cobalt
cushions. Pair.................. 125.00
Large. Dark and light gray, white
chests and noses, gold collars
tied in bow knots. Pair 175.00
White, green and red hearts 60.00

Dogs
5" high. Poodles. White, gold
collars. Numbered. Pair 75.00
9½" high. White, some original
gold decor. Pair 120.00
10" high. Sitting. Pair 135.00
12" high. White with gold lustre
decor. Pair 150.00
13" high. C. 1850. Pair 225.00

Spaniels. 8" high. Decorated with red
and black. Pair $135.00

Cottage Pastille Burner. 5" high.
White, blue roof, green shrubbery
$95.00

Hens
2½", miniature 60.00
6½", brilliant coloring, caramel
nest 135.00
7", yellow nest with green interior 165.00
7½", on base. Typical Staffordshire coloring 150.00
8", white Staffordshire, brown
nest 130.00
8¾", hen on nest. Light brown
base, black and white hen 150.00
Inkwell. Girl and dog on top 85.00
Lions. 10½x14". Standing with one
foot on ball. Pair 175.00

Marriage Bed Series
"Last in bed to put out the light" .. 50.00
"Three o'clock in the morning" ... 50.00
"Will we sleep first or now?" 55.00

Pastille Burners
Figure of woman with dog seated
on pedestal. 4¾" high, 2½" diam. 100.00
White castle with two towers and
center turret 125.00

Slippers
High-heeled, white with colored
flowers. Heel rests on 4" pillow .. 55.00
5½" long, fluted top. Gold sanded
rose on front 40.00
Spill Holders. Boy and girl, 5½" high.
Pair 85.00
Swan. 6" 165.00

STAINED GLASS WINDOWS

An artist-craftsman creates a stained glass panel by taking colored glass of various shapes and sizes, outlines them in lead cames and attaches them together, usually with a lead solder, to form either a simple design or to produce an easel-type painting.

The Egyptians are credited with using the first stained glass windows in their architecture. With the advent of Christianity, stained glass windows became a major form of religious art.

Perhaps the best known stained glass artist of the 19th century was Louis C. Tiffany.

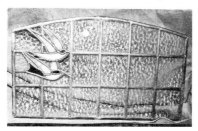

Stained glass. Opalescent panels, with two birds. Lead cames $85.00

2½'x4'. Landing-Type Window. Center has rectangular pattern showing birds in nest, flowers and leaves, in blues, green, orange and yellow glass . . . . $ 475.00
3'x3½', overall, 15x20" oval center section says CAFE in white letters on red background 175.00
Transom Window. Circular geometric design surrounded by leaves and bold-type decorations in blues, greens, orange and yellow glass. In good, used condition without cracked sections 225.00

STANGL POTTERY

Stangl pottery acquired Fulper Pottery in the late 1920's. Stangl birds are their most collectible items but other objects such as planters, vases and bowls are now considered collectible. These wares are readily available at reasonable prices.

Birds
Bird of Paradise . . . . $ 45.00

Blue Bird $18.50

Bluebird. Yellow belly	18.50
Bluejay on Stump	37.50
Cardinal on Stump	35.00
Cockatoo. 9" high. #3580. Signed .	55.00
Hen and Rooster. 9¾". Pair	65.00
Hummingbird. Allen	35.00
Kingfisher. 3½"	20.00
Parakeets, Double. 7½". Green . .	60.00
Parrot. 9" high	35.00
Pheasant, Ringneck. #3491 [Old mark]	90.00
Quail Dove. #3454 [old mark]	90.00

Vase. 5½" high. Low pedestal base, flared top $5.00

Warbler, Prothnaty. #3447 [Old	
mark]..........................	40.00
Woodpeckers. Double...........	47.50
Wrens, Three. Signed B.F........	65.00

Miscellaneous

Ashtray. 9" square. Deep yellow .	15.00
Bowl. Covered, 3¼x7½", divided	12.00
Console Set. 9½" bowl, 3½" high	
candleholders. Black and gold.	
Signed #2064	35.00
Mug. 4". FDR "Happy Days, Etc."	37.50
Pitcher. 4". Green, pink lining	7.50
Plate. 9", western scene. Signed	25.00

Vases

7" high. Cornucopia.............	8.50
8½" high. Dancing lady	9.50
9½" high. Leaping Eland. Yellow	
and green	10.00

STATUES

Classical, mythological female	
figure. 36" high ....$	695.00
Satan. Bronze. 12" high. C. 1500	600.00
Wild Horses of Mallet. Man in loin	

Saint Joseph with Christ Child. Wood,
approx. 5' high $250.00

cloth holding rearing horses.
French, bronze, signed 500.00
Woman. 13½" high, semi-nude.
Ivory head, hands and bust.
Bronze skirt, washed in gold,
marble base. Tiara in gold with
rubies, pearl earrings. Serpent
decoration. French, signed by
artist 1250.00
Woman. 22" high. Signed Moreau... 650.00
Wood carving. 16" high, ivory insets.
Italian, 19th century 450.00
For additional listings, see "Bronze"

STEINS

Steins are vessels of German origin for
drinking ale and beer, usually made of
pottery, although some are made of glass and
various kinds of metal. The surfaces are
generally decorated with a painted picture, a
reproduction of a print, or a design in relief.
The steins usually have a hinged, pewter top
or other types such as porcelain, silver, etc.,
with a thumblift.

METTLACH

#1052 - ½ L ....$	325.00
#1100 - ¼ L	175.00
#1164 - ½ L	345.00
#1180 - ½ L	200.00
#1395 - ½ L	325.00
#1396 - ½ L	400.00
#1397 - ½ L	375.00
#1403 - ½ L	350.00
#1471 - ½ L	325.00
#1492 - ½ L	375.00
#1645 - ½ L	295.00
#1649 - 1L	365.00
#1675 - ½ L	425.00
#1725 - ½ L	375.00
#1779 - ½ L	240.00
#1786 - ½ L	400.00
#1796 - ½ L	375.00
#1799 - ½ L	350.00
#1863 - ½ L	325.00
#1909/1179 - ½ L	195.00
#1932 - ½ L	375.00
#1940 - 3L	850.00
#1946 - ½ L	350.00
#1983 - ½ L	300.00
#1998 - ½ L	350.00
#2002 - ½ L	400.00
#2005 - ½ L	375.00
#2025 - ½ L	395.00
#2035 - ½ L	350.00
#2044 - ½ L	425.00

#2922 - 1L	425.00
#3099 - 5L	2500.00
#3384 - 5L	750.00
#5020 - 4L	500.00

MISCELLANEOUS

5½" high. Enamel. French	350.00
6" high. Royal Vienna. Monk scene	595.00
6" high. Threaded Glass. Rubina coloring, pewter top with bail thumbrest, crystal handle	150.00
6½" high. Lithophane bottom showing portrait of woman. German bridge and town scene. Pewter top. No maker's name. ½L	225.00
6½" high. "V. B. Gwawhutzt," forerunner of Mettlach. Gnomes at wine keg. 1L	275.00

Mettlach #2765. ½L. Knight sitting on white horse. Blue, white and amber. Signed H. Sch. $700.00

#2051 - ½L	375.00
#2086 - ¼L	225.00
#2086 - ½L	250.00
#2090 - ½L	400.00
#2090 - 1L	450.00
#2100 - ½L	375.00
#2182 - ½L	325.00
#2194 - 3⅓L	600.00
#2210 - 3L	450.00
#2246 - ¼L	150.00
#2277 - 3/10L	250.00
#2323 - ½L	395.00
#2382 - ½L	475.00
#2383 - 1L	600.00
#2402 - ½L	395.00
#2428 - 4L	1400.00
#2482 - 1L	650.00
#2764 - 6L	2500.00
#2893 - 3L	400.00

Regimental-type. Bullet-type pewter lid. Franco-Prussian War scenes
$250.00

7" high. Capo-di-Monte	375.00
7" high. Clown. Lithophane	350.00
7" high. King, Jack, 2 Queens in relief on sides. Dark green	145.00
8" high. Owl head cover. Marked "Hanke, Germany"	175.00
9½" high. Man, blowing bugle, with horse. Lithophane bottom. No maker's name. 1L	215.00
10" high. Contemporary. Rozart. Pewter lid, handpainted horse's head. Signed	75.00
10" high. Dresden. White with orange stripes. View of monument in park at Rolandbrunnen. Lithophane scene in bottom	275.00
10" high. Firefighting scene. Pewter. Lithophane scene in bottom. ½L	250.00
10½" high. Blue and gray. Raised figure of seated man being served by maid. 1L	195.00
11½" high. Field Artillery. 1903-05. Regimental lithophane	225.00
11½" high. Sheffield silver. Bacchus design	550.00
17" high. Serving stein, dark blue and gray. Bulbous, high neck. Four medallions of frolicking cupids in garlands	295.00
17" high. Three panels showing frolicking monks	275.00
20" high. Lovers drinking a toast in bold relief medallion. Bright colors. 4L	395.00
Brown with cameo picture of young couple. Pewter top with eagle thumb rest	150.00
Monk with stein with word "Munchen." "Gesetzlicht," ½L	135.00
Monkey Character. Drunken. Mustershutz	325.00
Nun. ½L. Lithophane scene of woman on bottom. No mark	225.00
Regimental 18th Infantry	250.00
Regimental stein with lithophane	225.00
"Sad Turnip." ½L. Mustershutz	300.00
Shape of flower. 1L. Gray, with pewter top. "Gesetzlicht" on bottom	250.00

STEREOSCOPE VIEWERS AND CARDS

VIEWERS

The stereoscope came into use in America about 1850, having been invented in England a dozen years earlier. The picture is taken with a dual lens camera and the scene is reproduced as two pictures. Upon being seen through a viewer the pictures blend into one with the scene in three dimensions.

Viewer. Base 13x26". Ornate . $250.00

Double-type. Made of wood. 18" high, 10" wide. "Pat. date 1859, Alex Beckers, N.Y."	$ 120.00
Double-type. French. Approx. 10½ x 6½". Wood	95.00
Hand-type. With sliding adjustment	35.00
Junior. Keystone	30.00
Mirroscope. Buckeye Stereoscope Co.	45.00
Stereosconse. 100 WW I cards, 100 world tour cards, tele binoculars. Set	85.00

Hand-type $35.00

CARDS

Sets

Denmark. 100	25.00
Egypt. With map and book. 100	40.00

Germany. 100	25.00
Greece. With map and book. 100 .	40.00
Holland. 100	25.00
Italy. With maps and book. 100 ...	40.00
Japan and Russia. Battle at Port Arthur. 82	25.00
Norway. With maps and book. 100	35.00
Panama. 100	28.50
San Francisco Earthquake and Fire. 55	35.00
Sears, Roebuck. 50	20.00
World War I. 100	50.00

Singles. Prices quoted are for cards in good condition. Folded, mutilated or badly soiled cards are of little or no value to collectors.

Alaska Gold Rush. Each ......$	2.00 to	5.00
American Scenic	1.00 to	2.00
Anthony. Brady photographer Civil War.................	5.00 to	10.00
Anthony, E...................	3.00 to	5.00
Anthony, E.H. & T.	2.50 to	5.00
Autos.......................	2.00 to	5.00
City Scenes	.75 to	1.50
Comics	.50 to	1.25
Commercial Advertising Cards .	.75 to	2.00
Disasters....................	1.00 to	2.00
Expositions	1.00 to	1.50
Indians	1.50 to	3.50
Langheim. Light cardboard	5.00 to	10.00
Lithographed cards. Some in color. Late	.50 to	1.00
Oil Wells	2.50 to	4.00
Panama Canal	1.15 to	2.50
Pan Handle R.R.	1.00 to	2.00
Presidents	2.50 to	5.00
Railroad War. Pittsburgh	1.50 to	2.50
Rogers' Statuary	1.50 to	3.50
Sentimentals	.75 to	2.00
Ships	2.00 to	4.00
Spanish American War	1.00 to	2.00
Tissues. American and French .	3.00 to	5.00
Trains	2.50 to	5.00
Transportation. Wagons, buggies, etc..................	1.50 to	3.50
United States Views	.50 to	1.00
Western scenery, etc.	2.00 to	4.00
Whaling	1.50 to	3.00
World War I	.50 to	1.50

STERLING, See SILVER

STEUBEN GLASS

The Steuben Glass Works was started in 1904 by Frederick Carder, a native of England and Thomas G. Hawkes of Corning, New York. In 1918, the Corning Glass Company purchased the Steuben Works. Carder remained with the company and designed many of the pieces bearing the Steuben mark.

Ring Tree. Candleholder, 5½" high. Blue iridescent, calcite trim on top and bottom edges $325.00

Bobeches. Approx. 4". Topaz, cerise ruby rigaree. Signed. Pair ....$	100.00
Bottles	
3½" high. Blue Aurene. Signed...	575.00
7" high. Colognes. Venetian-style, flemish blue. D.Q. gilt dusting. Original ribbed stoppers with berry prunts. Unsigned. Pair	150.00
15". Fish-shape with stoppers. Green. Pair....................	500.00
Bowls	
3" high, 9" diam. Blue Aurene. No. 2852. Signed..................	395.00
3" high. Grotesque design. Shaded amethyst to crystal	150.00
4" high, 12" wide. Cluthra. Green to white. Signed	600.00
4½" high. Yellow jade. Alabaster stem and foot. #6252	200.00
7" diam. Clear, spiral foot	125.00
7" high. Irregular fluted sides, cerise to clear. 6x12" diam.......	345.00
9" diam. 5" high. Ivorine, flared top, ruffled. Signed	275.00
9½" diam. Aurene and calcite. Gold	400.00
9½" diam. Light blue, bittersweet. Signed Cintra	425.00
Boxes	
Letter. 9" long, 3¼" wide, 5¾" high. Green jade acid-cut back. Pine cone decor	260.00
Puff. Rosaline and alabaster	275.00

Candleholders. 12" high. Light green
glass. Pair 295.00
Candleholder. 10" high. Topaz,
twisted stem, signed with fleur-
de-lis. Pair 250.00

Champagne
5½" high. Set of 8. Van Dyke
pattern. Clear foot and top. Sgnd. 600.00
Jade. Alabaster twisted stem,
alabaster foot, 5½" high 85.00

Claret. Celeste blue. Crystal stem
and blue foot. 4¾" high 75.00

Compotes
3½" high. Rosaline with alabaster
stem and base. Bowl 7¾" x 1½".
Round, flat base, 3¾" diam. 350.00
8". Jade green base and bowl,
creamy white stem. Signed 450.00

Cup and Saucer. Rosaline with
alabaster handle 225.00

Decanter. 9½" high. Amethyst.
Blown stopper, original paper
label. 250.00

Dessert Set. Pink, eight 8½" plates,
one 14" plate. Floral motif on
borders. Set 500.00

Flower Pots
5" high. With matching base.
Signed "Steuben Aurene." Set . . . 275.00
5¼" high. Jade green with two
heavy alabaster threads around
top edge. Signed "F. Carder" 400.00

Goblets
6¼" high. Topaz, contr. bubbles
threading, hollow stem, prunts.
Signed 100.00
7¼" high. Alabaster trumpet and
disc foot. Pink and blue cintra
twist stem 200.00
Red, vintage pattern. Signed . . . . . ·125.00
Teardrop 100.00

Lamp. 12" high. Acid-cut. Gold
aurene cut to alabaster in an
oriental poppy design 1750.00

Mug. 2-5/8" high. Clear glass with
applied handle. Applied blue-black
threading. Signed with fleur-de-lis
mark 85.00

Plates
8¼". Deep center with swirled
rim. Emerald green, signed with
fleur-de-lis 165.00
8¾". Jade. Signed "Steuben" 195.00

Salt. Pedestaled, green jade and
alabaster. 120.00

Shades
Calcite. Signed 125.00
Gas. Pearl white with green
looping. Signed 150.00

Console Set. Footed bowl, 13½" diam.
Underplate, 14" diam., 2 candleholders, 3" high. Signed $500.00

Sherbets
Adventurine. 5" high, 3½" diam.
2¼" base diam. 50.00
Rosaline & alabaster. Ped. stem
and underplate. Set of 6 sherbets
and 6 plates 750.00
With underplate. Green jade.
Signed. Set 130.00

Tumblers
Amethyst. Unsigned 40.00
Selenium red. Pedestaled, octag-
onal top 50.00

Vases
3" high, 3½" diam. Small, rolled
over top edge, alabaster base.
Unmarked 165.00
5½" high. Footed, clear with
cerise ruby threading 1½" wide
around base of bowl. Concave
sides with 3-5/8" top diam. Signed
with fleur-de-lis 275.00
6" high. Clutha. Sgnd. # 2683. . . . . 400.00
6" high. Jade, alabaster base.
Signed. Pair 650.00
6½" high. Clutha. Lavender.
Signed 495.00
7½" high. Ovoid body, short neck,
flared rim. Rosaline 375.00
7½" high. Peacock blue, irides-
cent, 4½" rolled top diam.
Spreads to 7" diam. then tapers
down from 6" to 3¾" bottom
diam. 500.00
8" high. Bud vase. Rosaline, flared
tricorn top, short neck, elongated
ovoid body overcased with alabaster which forms stem and foot.
2 applied alabaster handles 395.00
8" high. Alabaster acid-cut back
fan vase, carved allover with

chrysanthemums and leaves. Rim
and pedestal carved with leaves . 650.00
8¾" high. Diamond Quilted,
crystal neck and flared top. Blue
threaded. Signed 145.00
8½" high. Amber, pinched top on
green foot. Signed 145.00
9½" high. Trefoil, shaded green
crystal. Signed 295.00
10" high. Alabaster to rose clutha.
3-prong, crystal base 800.00
10" high. Ivory. Straight panelled
sides. Signed F. Carder 500.00
10½" high. Clutha. Solid yellow,
green 850.00
10½" high. Jade, amphora,
shaped with 2 applied inverted W
alabaster handles. Expanded 3¼"
base, widest diam. 7". Neck 2½"
with 4" smooth rim opening.
Signed with fleur-de-lis 500.00
10½" high. Jade, alabaster
handles 475.00
11" high. Amethyst Clutha. Sgnd. . 850.00
12" high. Amethyst flared top.
Body and scalloped base joined by
clear swirled ball 295.00
14" high. Stick vase, fully signed . 245.00
Wine. Bowl and foot blue. Stem has
mica flecks encased 95.00

STEVENGRAPHS

All miniature silk weavings should not be
classified as "Stevengraphs."

Thomas Stevens of Coventry, Warwickshire,
England established his business to produce
woven silk designs in 1854. He produced his
first bookmark in 1862 and introduced his first
Stevengraph in 1874.

Stevens' bookmarks are relatively longer than
they are wide and have mitred corners at one
end and finished with a tassel. Stevens' name
is ALWAYS woven into the silk at a mitred
corner.

True Stevengraphs are miniature silk pictures,
matted, framed, and produced by Stevens.
Stevens' name was NEVER woven into a
Stevengraph. His name may appear on the
mat, along with the title of the picture.

Contrary to past information, Stevens'
bookmarks were never sold at the New York
Crystal Palace Exposition in 1853, simply
because they did not exist at that time.

Bookmarks

"Birthday Blessings" . . . . $ 60.00
*Centennial. George Washington   135.00
Coach scene, Christmas verse 75.00

"Full Cry." Framed $225.00

"Home Sweet Home" 120.00
"Pharaoh's daughter finding
Moses in the bullrushes." Woven
silk. Marked T. Stevens, Coventry.
13" long, 2" wide 95.00
Ye Ladye Godiva 125.00

Stevengraphs

Buffalo Bill (W.F. Cody) 500.00
Called to the Rescue 235.00
Crystal Palace, The (Exterior) 275.00
Death, The 225.00
Death of Nelson, The 275.00
Dick Turpin's Last Ride 295.00
Finish, The 135.00
First Touch, The 350.00
For Life or Death 250.00
Fourth Bridge, The 350.00
Full Cry 225.00
Good Old Days, The 295.00
Grace, W. G. (Dr.) 500.00
Lady Godiva Procession 165.00
Last Lap, The 250.00
Madonna and Child 500.00
Meet, The 220.00
Mrs. Cleveland 285.00
Present Time, The 350.00
Water Jump, The 135.00

*Reproduced Item

STEVENS AND WILLIAMS

In the late 19th century, the firm of Stevens
and Williams, Stourbridge, England, became
one of the pioneers in producing a less
expensive and commercial cameo glass.

The original or earlier cameo glass was
handcarved. It was produced mainly for
exhibition purposes or for the wealthy. But as
the demand increased, Stevens and Williams
revised the method by employing the wheel
and acid for the engraving. This hastened the
production and subsequently made the glass
available to more people.

While the earlier cameo glass was of the classical design, Stevens and Williams' designs were influenced by the Orient. One of their foremost artists was also a botanist, which accounts for the many beautiful nature designs.

Vase. 5¾" high. Blown-out. Butterscotch coloring $650.00

Bowls
    5" diam. Footed. "Rainbow," tricorn shape .... $ 475.00
    7" diam. Tortoise shell glass. Gold gilded decor of flying birds and flowers, scalloped and fluted top .   145.00
    Ice Blue with three ormulu legs and a cluster of applied fruit and berries. Matsunoki 275.00
    Rose Bowls:
        3" high, 3¼" diam. Cranberry and white Arabesque. Crimped top, white crackle surface 75.00
        6" high, 10" diam., at center. Applied green leaves and stems and hanging brown glass pear and apple against crystal glass bkgd. Blown, large, polished pontil 245.00
        7" high. Crimped top, decorated .   140.00
Compote. 7" high, 6½" diam. Gold apples, pears, leaves and stems ..   145.00
Dish, Jam. Double, shaded vaseline to pink, white. Silverplated holder   125.00
Epergne. 17" high. Ribbed Diamond Puff. Center bowl 10" diam., ruffled. Silverplated stand with deer in forest 195.00

Ewer. 8" high. Applied glass, wild rose color, lined white, ruffled, turned down rim. Amber leaf and branch form handle. Cased and blown 85.00
Lamp. 7x14". Acid-cut back shade. Raspberry and white ornate silver base, rose panels. Three baroque handles 1650.00
Parfaits. 5½" high. Green jade with alabaster foot and stem. Signed. Set of 10 ....   500.00
Vases
    1-7/8" high, 1-1/8" diam. Chartreuse green satin, white carved flowers and leaves. Signed 350.00
    4½" high. Satin glass. Pink and green swirl stripes 145.00
    5" high, 3½" diam. Applied blue alligators on panelled amber. Urn-shaped, signed S&W and Stourbridge 195.00
    5¼" high. Sunshine yellow glass with pastel enamel flowers, lady bugs and dragonflies. Pair 150.00
    6" high, 12" diam. Applique, blue with crystal blossoms, stems, leaves. Applied amber rim and three feet 250.00
    7" high. Blue & brown swirl satin. Yellow interior 850.00
    7¾" high. Off white interior 750.00
    12" high. Intaglio cut, dragonfly, frog and other species. Lake and cattails, cut toward bottom. Handles are rich blue shells. Signed 1195.00
    12" high. Applied pears and vines, four feet 350.00
    15" high. Blue. Four applied amber legs, flowing up and into leaves and applied handles. Signed 395.00

STIEGEL-TYPE GLASS

America's first flint glass factory was founded by "Barron" Henry Stiegel at Manheim, Pennsylvania in the middle 1760s. Business thrived for a number of years but extravagant living by Stiegel and the import of cheap European glass caused the enterprise to fail. Decorated bar and tableware were the main products of the establishment.

Bottle. 7" high. Blown half-post enameled with distel fink birds, hearts and flowers in blue, red, yellow, white and green. Rough pontil. 18th century .... $ 295.00

Pot. 4" high. Diamond and Daisy. Amethyst $4000.00

Case Bottle. Clear soda lime, glass
applied neck with cut decorations.
Penna. C. 1767 .... 450.00
Flip Glass. 27 rib panels around
lower half, engraved leaf pattern,
3¾" high. C. 1767 .... 350.00
Mug. Applied strap handle. Etched in
floral design 750.00
Salt, Master. Cobalt blue glass in
diamond-quilted pattern. Applied
foot. C. 1768 .... 300.00

STORE ITEMS (OLD)

Old store items consist mainly of large metal
containers for various products sold by
measure or weight, or certain individual items
pre-packaged in tin containers, namely,
coffee, chocolate, tea and tobacco.

Candy Containers
Bunte Diana 'Stuft" Confections.
Tin and cardboard. Round, 10"
high .... $ 15.00
Hershey's Chocolate Perfecto Ci-
gars. 3x5" 12.50
Chewing Gum Containers
Adams Tutti Fruiti. Cardboard box 12.00
Sen Sen Chewing Gum. Book-
shaped cardboard 12.00

Cocoa Containers
Walter Baker Breakfast Cocoa. ½
pound 9.50
W.H. Baker Best Cocoa. 4", oval
embossed lid 8.50
Hershey Chocolate and Cocoa.
12" diam. 22.50
Huyler's Cocoa. Cocoa pod design
Iona Cocoa. A&P. 2lb. tin and
cardboard 7.50
Larkin Cocoa. ½ lb., paper label .. 6.00
Monarch Cocoa. 16oz........... 6.00
Our Mother's Cocoa. Cardboard
and tin. 1lb................... 6.50
Coffee Containers
Battleship Coffee. 1lb. 6.50
Flint's Coffee. 2 lb., red and white
paper label 10.00
Forbes Golden Cup Coffee. 3 lb.
"Delt" design................. 15.00
Franco-American Coffee. Friction
lid on bottom 8.00
Java Coffee. Special Christmas
present 1936 from Manhattan
Rubber Company 10.00

Nabisco Premium Saltine Container.
Tin $7.50

Cough Drop Containers

Lutted's Cough Drops. Hinged lid .	18.50
Moses Celebrated Cough Drops. 8½" high	22.50

Dispensers, Coffee

Johnson Coffee. Log Cabin	135.00
Johnson Coffee. Litho picture of factory, rounded base delivery	95.00

Dispensers, Tobacco

Bagley's Game Fine Cut Tobacco .	75.00
Polar Bear Tobacco	90.00
Sure Shot Chewing Tobacco	115.00
Ribbon Cabinet. Large	195.00

Store Bins

Beech-Nut. Blue	55.00
Eveready. Tin	65.00
Nector Coffee. Blue, orange and white	95.00
Old English. Curve Cut	225.00

Tea Containers

Banquet Tea. Candelabra design. ½ lb.	5.50
Columbia Tea. Trunk shape. 3x3½x5"	10.00
English Breakfast. Bulk tea shelf caddy. 13x16", black and gold, picture of Chinese lady and gardener	85.00
Golden Rule Tea. 3 lb. Red and white	16.50
Golden Rule Tea. 5 lb. Red and gold	25.00
Monarch Tea. 8-oz. Lion trade mark	6.00
Richlieu Tea. ½ lb.	6.00
Ridgeway Tea. Tea merchant to Queen Victoria. 1 lb.	6.50

Tobacco Containers

Bagley Co. Trunk-style. Tax stamp	30.00
Brownie. Storekeeper, Red Indian Div. American Tobacco Co. Name on pocket and picture of R.I. Cut Plug package on back	125.00

"Pastime. Plug Tobacco." Tin. John Finzer & Bros. $48.00

Dixie Queen Tobacco. Lunch box, with portrait	50.00
Gibson Girl. Cigarettes	22.00
Lix-All Cut Plug. Blue paper package. 1926 tax stamp	6.00
Mayo's Cut Plug. Large	18.00
New Bachelor. Round tin, multi-colored. 1902 tax stamp	9.50
Old Gold Smoking Tobacco. Yellow and red, hinged lid, 5" high	26.50
Union Leader. Lunch Box	18.50
Winner Tobacco, Race Car. Lunch box	55.00

Miscellaneous

Corticelli Spool Silk. 5¼"	3.00
Diamond Dye	2.50
Fairy Soap. Oval bar	1.00
Hat Pins. Elite brand. Pkg. of 3	5.00
Jumbo Salted Peanuts. 10" high	25.00
Log Cabin Syrup. Small	22.00
Mammy Coffee Pail	45.00
Needle Chest. 5¼x7½x13". 2 drawers "Crowley Needles"	75.00
Ribbon Cabinet. Large	195.00

STRAWBERRY CHINA

Strawberry china derives its name from the decoration of the ware. It is an early soft-paste china and a contemporary of Gaudy Dutch and eagerly sought by collectors.

Bowl. 6½" top, 3½" high $300.00

Creamer	$ 300.00
Cup and Saucer	225.00

Plates

7¼"	225.00
8½"	250.00
10"	285.00
Sugar Bowl. Covered	325.00

Teapots

4¼" high, 9½" long	350.00
6" high, 9½" long	395.00

STRETCH GLASS

Stretch glass was produced by many glass manufacturers in nearly every mold, from 1915 through the 1920's. The most prominent makers were located in Ohio, namely, Cambridge, Fenton (who probably manufactured more Stretch glass than any others), Imperial, Northwood and even Steuben.

Stretch glass can be identified by its iridescent, onionskin-like effect. Always look for the mold marks. The so-called imports that are blown and show a pontil mark are not true American Stretch Glass.

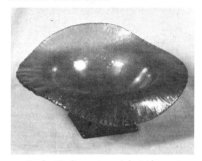

Bowl. 9" diam. Imperial. Iridescent
blue $65.00

Ashtray. 4¾". Art Deco. Amethyst
and white, blown and contoured,
polished pontil .... $ 18.00
Bowls
8¾". Blue, turned up and down
rim 65.00
10" diam., 4½" high. Yellow
iridescent. Imperial 60.00
12" diam. Pink 55.00
Footed, blue iridescent 60.00
Candlesticks
8" high. Peacock blue 20.00
Green, blown. Pair 25.00
Compote. 6½" diam. White iridescent 35.00
Console Set. White, blue flowers 50.00
Dish, Candy. 6½", on standard 18.50
Plates
12". Light green, reticulated
border 35.00
Luncheon. Green. Set of five 60.00

STRING HOLDERS

Grocery and dry goods stores found string holders to be useful items. Usually made of iron, there were two common types - the hanging holder, and the beehive which was placed on the floor or counter.

Flint-type glass. 4½" high $25.00

Apple .... $ 10.00
Glass. Beehive, 5" high 25.00
Iron
Beehive 28.00
"Bullman," attaches to counter.
Marked 18.00
Hanging-type. 4½" high 25.00
Man in top hat, smoking pipe.
Wall-type 15.00
Pottery. 9¾" high. Cone-shaped,
glazed interior 18.50

SUGAR SHAKERS

Sugar shakers, or sifters as they are sometimes called, came into general use in the 1870-80 period. The majority was made of opaque white glass, while some of a later period were made in colors of cranberry, green and blue.

Acorn shape. Metal top, opaque
white .... $ 38.50
Clear. Flower mold 18.00
Cranberry. Craquelle glass......... 75.00
Cranberry. Cut panels 65.00
Cranberry. Diamond Quilted. Original top 85.00
Emerald Green. Outside ribs with
enameled flowers 60.00
Emerald Green. Quilted Phlox. Old
top 75.00
Flowered panel. 4" high, white milk
glass 38.00
Green-blue. Ribbed with opalescent
lattice 40.00

4½" high. Ivory ground, pale green top, handpainted gold floral design $22.50

Handpainted. Artist signed	22.50
Limoges. Handpainted with gold	75.00

Milk Glass

4½" high. Apple Blossom pattern	37.50
4½" high. White. Double-tooth band. Tin lid	25.00
5¼" high. Painted flowers on body, shell pattern base, tin lid	35.00
Satin Glass. Pewter-type top. Orange coloring at top shading to yellow at bottom	115.00
Single Ring. Tin top, opaque white	28.50

SUNBONNET BABIES

Molly and Mae, the Sunbonnet babies, appeared in the early 1900's. Their "mother" was Bertha Corbett. The main characteristic of these irresistable darlings was the large bonnet covering their faces.

Primers, or first readers, were illustrated with them. Porcelains, post cards and prints were decorated with them. The Royal Bayreuth China Company made most of the china bowls, dishes and vases with the Sunbonnet Babies' decor.

Print. "Baking Day." 9x11" framed. Signed $55.00

Books

Primer. Eulalie Osgood Grover. 109 pages, 1902	$ 140.00
"The Sunbonnet Babies in Holland." Grover. 1915	75.00

Bowls

Cereal. "Ironing," R.B. BM	100.00
Footed. 8¼" diam. "Ironing"	185.00
Candlestick. Ring handle, saucer. "Sweeping."R.B.	225.00

Cups

2½" high. "Ironing." Germany	37.50
"Sweeping"	85.00

Cups and Saucers

"Cleaning." Printed on back in gold, "Joseph Horne Co. Dolls' Tea Party"	140.00
"Fishing." Gold handle	165.00

Plate. 7", boy and girl. "Kiss and Make Up" in transfer. K.T.&D.Co. Late $45.00

Feeding Dish, Child's. "Washing" ... 160.00
Nappie. 5", "Washing" 145.00
Pitchers
  3½". "Fishing." R.B. 145.00
  3¾". "Cleaning." R.B. 145.00
Plates
  7¼". "Ironing." R.B. BM 115.00
  7-5/8". "Ironing." R.B. 135.00
  7-5/8". "Washing." R.B.......... 135.00
  10½". Cake. Open handles.
  "Ironing" 195.00
  10½". Cake. Open handles.
  "Washing" 195.00
Post Cards
  Dixon. Last Day of Summer 12.00
  Peek-A-Boo................... 15.00
  The Lovers................... 10.00
  6 A.M. to 6 P.M. Ullman Mfg. Co.
  Set of six 75.00
Relish Dish. 4x9½". "Fishing."
  R.B. BM 145.00
Tea Set. Child's. 6 pieces. "Ironing"
  and "Washing." Set 500.00
Vases
  3½" high. "Washing." Footed. R.B. 185.00
  4x4½". "Cleaning." Wall-type.
  Cup for flowers 225.00
  "Cleaning." Two handles 185.00

SUNDERLAND LUSTRE

A type of lustre ware with marbled or spotted decorations which shade from pink to purple. A solution of gold compound applied over a white body developed the many shades of pink lustre, the shade being determined by the metallic film's thickness. The ware was made by many potters, including Adams, Bailey & Batkin, Copeland & Garrett, Wedgwood, Enoch Wood and many others.

Box. 2½x3½x5". Comic black
  transfer on top of cover and in
  bottom ....$ 85.00
Box. 2½x4x6". Separate lid. Black
  transfer of old-time English people 100.00
Bowls
  10". "Sailor's Farewell" and
  "Sailor's Return" verses inside and
  out 265.00
  10" diam., 4½" high. View from
  the cast iron bridge 235.00
  Waste 45.00
Cake Plate 125.00
Chalice. 4½" high 85.00
Cups and Saucers
  "Babes in the Woods" 75.00
  Black and white transfer com-
  memorating death of Princess
  Charlotte 75.00

Jug. 5½" high. "Sailor's Departure"
$225.00

"Cloud" 75.00
Handled. Allerton & Son 65.00
Mustache. Black transfer of ship
  on front, sailor's poem on back.
  Late 90.00
Goblet. Allover lustre decor........ 110.00
Jugs [Pitchers]
  3¾" high, white ground. "Christ is
  my pilot-wise, etc." 135.00
  5" high. "Home is a name of more
  than, etc." 250.00
  5½" high. "Sailor's Departure" ... 225.00
  5½" high. Ship with caption
  "Success to the Tars of Old
  England" 350.00
  6" high. Hunting scene in black,
  allover pink lustre 145.00
  6½" high. Wilkie comic. Mottling
  inside and out................. 275.00
  Pink lustre trim with raised figures. 195.00
  Quart. Allover lustre decor, 2 light
  green bands and three verses
  around bowl 245.00
  Shell. Hunting scene. Medium 195.00
Mugs
  "Cloud" 55.00
  "Faith, Hope" 135.00
  Frog. 5" high, 3" diam. English,
  pink with mariner's compass and
  figures of John Bull and Britannia
  in colors. Large green frog looking
  up from bottom 165.00
  Iron bridge. With black transfer,
  ships and peace and plenty on
  reverse. 4½" high 135.00
  "Sailor's Tears" and ship flying
  British flag. 4" high 125.00
Plaques
  "Farmer's Prayer" 95.00

"Prepare to Meet Thy God"	95.00
"Thou God, See'st Me." Late	35.00
Plates	
7". Pink and floral decor	47.50
8". Deep. Lady with harp, trees	
and child	75.00
9". "Babes in the Woods"	95.00
Platter. 7½ x 8½". Picture of Adam	
Clark, Wesleyan minister	165.00
Shakers	
Pepper	75.00
Salt. Round, footed	65.00
Sugar	65.00
Teapots	
Large. "Cloud"	245.00
Medium. "Cloud"	175.00
Water Set. Bowl 10" diam. Pitcher,	
7" high. "Ship Caroline"	275.00

TAFFETA GLASS, See CARNIVAL GLASS

TEA LEAF LUSTRE

A type of gold lustre decoration on late ironstone chinaware which is more or less a form of the oriental tea leaf. It was also known as "Lustre Band with Sprig." The ware was an inexpensive type produced by a number of English and American potteries.

Relish Dish. 8½" long $25.00

Bone Dish . . . . $	10.00
Bowls	
3x5". Rectangular	12.50
15" diam. Covered	50.00
Vegetable. Covered	45.00
Vegetable. Open	20.00
Butter Dish. Covered	50.00
Butter Pat	6.00
Coffee Pot	65.00
Cups and Saucers	
Coffee	22.00
Handleless	28.50
Gravy Boat	37.50
Pickle Dish. Handled	25.00

Pitchers	
Milk	40.00
Water. 12" high	60.00
Plates	
7½"	10.00
8"	12.00
8¾"	14.00
9". Soup	15.00
9½"	16.00
10"	20.00
Cake. Meakin	42.00
Cup.	8.50
Platters	
12" long	30.00
13" long	35.00
14" long	37.50
16" long	40.00
Sauce Dish. Meakin, round	8.00
Shaving Mug. Ribbed, embossed	
berries on handle	32.50
Soap Dish. Square, covered, handled	
and removable insert	40.00
Sugar Bowl	45.00
Tea Service. Teapot, sugar bowl,	
creamer, four 6" plates, 4 cups	
and saucers	195.00
Teapot	65.00
Tureens	
Sauce. Covered, with tray, ladle . .	75.00
Soup. Covered, round, with ladle .	125.00
Wash Bowl and Pitcher. "Alfred	
Meakin Royal Ironstone China" . . .	175.00

TEA WAGONS, See FURNITURE

TELEPHONES

Alexander Graham Bell patented the first telephone in 1876. Since that time a variety of instruments have been designed. One of the most common is the wooden case wall-type which collectors seek today, mainly for decorative purposes.

Magneto Box. Western Electric. C. 1920 . . . . $95.00

Wall-type. Wood, 20" long $175.00

Desk-type. American. C. 1930 . . . . . . $ 30.00
Desk-type. Western Electric Co.
    Patented 1915 . . . .   75.00
French. Cradle-type 130.00
Wall. Oak case, crank-type, with
    shelf. 175.00

TEPLITZ

Teplitz wares were manufactured in the Bohemian province of Czechoslovakia, the location of the city of Teplitz. They reached their peak of production when this area was part of the Austrian-Hungarian Empire. An early 1900 industrial directory lists 26 ceramic manufacturers in Teplitz.

Teplitz wares consisted of four main bodies - pottery, low-fired stoneware, true vitreous stoneware, and porcelain. The wares were molded, cast and hand decorated. Transfer decorations were not used. The general shapes and decor have an Art Nouveau or Art Deco style with an influence of the Viennese School of Sezession.

There may be an exception but all the wares were marked "Teplitz" or some variation such as "Turn-Teplitz" or "Turn" [a city near Teplitz].

As in any of the arts, superior and inferior grades of work exist. However, the majority of the existing Teplitz is of high quality.

Basket. 5½x8". Woven, 2 handles,
    applied flowers and leaves.
    Multicolored . . . . $ 135.00
Bowls
    Art Deco. Gold, reticulated,
    footed, ornate, 4 oval panels 125.00
    Rose bowl. Cream ground with
    pink flowers 45.00
Candleholder. 13" high, 7" diam.
    Single, blue-grey with gold outline
    on flowers. Marked "Teplitz" 95.00
Candlestick. 12". Etruscan. Moorish
    and Masonic decor 75.00
Ewer. 7", oval-shaped. Gold handle
    and trim. Decorated with colorful
    flowers 72.50
Figurines
    Boy and girl. Pair 150.00
    Golf Caddy. 7" high. Signed 85.00
    "Tom, Tom the Piper's Son."
    5½x8". 5" front to back 95.00
    Woman. Bust. 12". Victorian-style   125.00
Lamp. 13" high. Art Nouveau with
    matching decorated base. 1895
    decor with woman's head in
    multicolors 125.00
Mug. Arab on stallion. Olive green
    background 45.00
Vases
    3½" high. Green, figure of boy . . .   40.00
    5¼" high, ¾ of body in brown,
    purple at top, with woman and
    cherub, simulated pearls 50.00

Vase. 6" high. Grey-green, with
berries in relief $35.00

6" high. Blue-grey ground, boy with owl on lap, looking at moon. Bulbous base, flared top 55.00
6" high. Pale yellow roses, gold trim 75.00
7" high. Art Nouveau. Handled, yellow and pink flowers on green and white background 55.00
8" high. Alabaster white, woman's face. Amphora......... 95.00
8" high. White ground, orange, purple floral decor. Trimmed in brown and gold 85.00
9" high. Green iridescence with incised design. Bird heads form three handles 95.00
9" high. 2 dragon handles 85.00
9¾" high. Flower effect, open-work top and handles. Gold decorated base 85.00
11" high. Footed and handled, scalloped, openwork top 95.00
12¾" high. Egyptian urn-shape. Marked "Bohemia" 135.00
13½" high, 2½" diam. Pedestal base, 2¼" high. Cream-colored with gold in beaded design, scrolls and Greek Key. Oval white medallions, heart-shaped with child's sober face 135.00
15" high, 7" diam. Art Nouveau. Maroon with gold trim, silver jewel teardrops. Marked "Teplitz Turn" 150.00
19½" high. Cream ground, red floral arrangement, green leaves, gold trim 275.00

TERRA COTTA WARE

Terra Cotta is another name applied to wares made of a hard, semi-fired ceramic clay. The color of the pottery ranges from a light orange-brown to a deep brownish red.

Art objects, utilitarian wares and architectural elements were made of this material. The finished products were usually left unglazed, but they may be found partially or completely glazed and/or decorated with slip designs, incised or carved.

Creamer. Royal Terra Cotta Porce-
lain with colorful Chinese panels . $ 45.00
Cup and Saucer.................. 35.00
Mug. 6½" high. Raised dragon and
other symbols. Dragon tail handle 65.00
Plaque. Cupids and dog, hunting 37.50
Statues. 9½" high. Chinese subjects,
enameled fronts. Pair 175.00

Vase. 11½" high. Dragon decor $95.00

Tea Sets
3 pieces...................... 160.00
Child's. Tray, teapot, 3 cups 35.00
Teapots
3-1/8". Tan ground with green and yellow enamel decor. "Made in China" impressed on bottom ... 35.00
Individual. Enamel decor. Oriental 20.00
Tobacco Jar. 10" high. Man in swallowtail coat, white vest, skull cap, sideburns 80.00
Vases
5" high. Flying dragons in relief .. 45.00
10" high. Flying dragons in relief . 85.00

THREADED GLASS

The glass was originally made in this country at the Sandwich factory. The threading is not impressed but applied to the outside of the object. The early examples were hand threaded while later pieces were done by machine.

Vases. 4" high. Blue threads on clear glass, ruffled top. Pair $55.00

Atomizer. Swirled, red .... $	45.00
Basket	65.00
Biscuit Jar. 5" high, 3¾" across. Applied white feet, rose threading, clear trim..................	95.00
Ewer. Cranberry. 7½" high. Large crystal leaf across front, forming handle. 6 crystal, petal-shaped feet	75.00

Finger Bowls

Cranberry. Ruffled, gold edged with original matching plate. Set .	65.00
Cranberry. Sandwich threaded, fluted edge, matching plate. Set ..	85.00
Rose threaded. Opaque lining, 14 scallops at top	95.00
Vaseline	50.00
Venetian. Diamond pattern with ruffled edge. Teal blue	50.00
Jam Jar. Pink glass. Silverplated lid and handle	75.00
Juice glass with Peridot green-colored threads on clear.........	18.50
Juice Set. Pitcher and 4 glasses	150.00
Lemonade Glass. Sandwich. Deep pink threads on crystal ground. Engraved with pond flowers and leaves. 5" high, applied handle...	85.00

Pitchers

5¼" high. Milk. Cranberry on clear. Tankard-shape, threads applied from the pontil mark on the bottom to the rim. Clear applied handle	120.00
11½" high. Cranberry with white floral decor. Applied clear glass handle.......................	165.00
Sugar Bowl. Medium blue color	85.00
Tumbler. Cranberry. Sandwich glass	60.00

Vases

3" high. Cranberry with green shading, bulbous base. Diamond pattern in threadng, crystal rigaree top. Pair...............	95.00
4" high. Clear, on brass leaflet stand. 2 pieces	55.00

TIFFANY ITEMS

Louis Comfort Tiffany, the son of a wealthy New York jeweler, established his own glass house in 1878 to make stained glass for windows.

Around 1890 he began to make vases, lamp shades, tableware, etc., in a gold iridescent or lustred glass. Most of the items bore the name "L. C. Tiffany," or the initials "L.C.T." However, in sets such as goblets, lamp shades, salts or finger bowls, only one item was marked. Some items also carried a number, while others, in addition to the name or initials, were inscribed with "Favrille," the French word for color. The ware was discontinued about 1910. Tiffany died in 1933 at the age of 85.

Pitcher. 10" high. Intaglio cut, grape cluster. Signed L. C. Tiffany. Favrille
$875.00

Bobeches. Blown, gilt rims. Set of six $ 350.00

Bowls
   4¾". Ruffled top, gold iridescent .   275.00
   5½". Gold 200.00
   6" diam., 2½" high. Gold and blue
   iridescent. Signed "L.C.T." 295.00
   8¼". Blue and rose. Signed
   Favrille #1404 . . . .   650.00
   9". Ribbed, blue, ruffled edge.
   Signed 750.00
   12". Centerpiece. With flower
   holder 2" deep. 5 green lily pads
   and vines. Signed 950.00
   12". Etched leaves on bronze
   base. 5" high. Signed 1250.00
   Rose bowl. Verre Moire 450.00

Candle Lamps. 9½" high, 5" shade
   diam. 3 pieces, shade, candletube
   and base. Favrille, gold iridescent.
   Brass fixtures, push-up type.
   Signed "L.C.Tiffany." Pair 2000.00

Candlesticks
   3x4½". Carved rock crystal. Art
   Nouveau style, flowers and
   occlusion inside crystal 650.00
   4½". Gold and blue. Signed
   "L.C.T." Pair 950.00
   7½". Signed 395.00
   7½", 3¼" top diam., 15½" base
   circum. Signed. Pair 1250.00
   8½". Gold dore finish, 3 ball feet.
   #1202 . . . .   350.00
   10". Blue, gold. Signed 400.00
   11½". Signed 500.00
   13½". Signed 650.00
   19". Bronze. Tiffany Studios. Pair .   500.00

Champagnes
   5½". #1197. All signed and
   numbered. Intaglio cut. Set of 8 . .   2200.00
   7". Hollow stem. Signed 300.00

Chandelier. Ivory, yellow swirled,
   feather and chain pattern. Original
   metal rim and chains. Signed 2375.00

Clocks
   Carriage. Repeater with alarm.
   Beveled glass, brass case, porce-
   lain face, French works 450.00
   Mantel. Tiffany & Co. Marble and
   ormolu. C. 1860 . . . .   600.00
   Regulator. Crystal, heavy bronze
   case. Merc. pendulum 750.00

Compotes
   3" high. Gold and purple
   iridescent stretch glass. Signed . . .   495.00
   11½" high. Gold iridescent. Signed   700.00
   14½" high, 6½" diam. Feather
   design. Signed 950.00
Cordial. Gold iridescent. Signed 225.00

Desk Sets
   3 pieces. Bronze. Indian pattern
   owls' heads. 3-tiered letter holder, pen tray and rocking blotter.
   Dark patina 300.00
   7 pieces. Zodiac. Two blotter
   ends, note pad holder, inkwell,
   calendar holder, rolling blotter,
   pencil tray, stamp box. All signed
   and numbered 600.00
Dish. Square, in 4-legged metal frame   350.00

Finger Bowls and Plates
   Brown, Light. Translucent, irides-
   cent. Millefiori decor of white
   flowers, green leaves. Signed LCT
   and numbered 400.00
   Gold. Iridescent, fluted edge. Sgd.   350.00
   Pink. Signed 300.00
Glass, Juice. Lily pad decor 250.00

Parfait or Champagne. 8" high.
Turquoise, opalescent $325.00

Goblet. Clear, blue and opalescent.
Signed 350.00
Inkwell. By Tiffany Studios. Beige
mottled panels 275.00
Liquer Set. Gold and blue iridescent.
Decanter and 8 glasses, threaded.
Paper label and numbered 2500.00
Magnifying Glass. Lacy handle.
Signed "Venetian" 150.00
Nut Dish. Gold iridescent. Signed L.
C. Tiffany Inc. Favrille. 3" diam. . . . 150.00
Nut Set. Bowl, 6 dishes. Signed 500.00
Parfait. 5" high, gold iridescent.
Signed LCT Favrille 185.00
Perfume Bottle. Peacock blue.
Original stopper 275.00
Picture Frame. Zodiac bronze.
12x14". All signs of the Zodiac in
border. Holds 8x10" picture.
Signed Tiffany Studios, New
York 920 . . . . 350.00

Pitcher, Water. Border etched with
grapes and leaves. Signed "L. C.
Tiffany" and "Favrille" 875.00
Plates
4-3/8". ¼" high, 2" base. Minia-
ture. Gold with rainbow iri-
descent. Scalloped border. Signed 150.00
6". Gold iridescent. Signed 395.00
6½". Pastel MOP with white to
pink border.Signed 220.00
8½". Pastel aqua blue and white.
Signed 250.00
Rummer. 11¼" high, 6¼" diam.
Gold iridescent. Signed 300.00
Salts
Blue. Pedestal base 175.00
Footed 150.00
Gold iridescent. 2½" diam.
Ruffled edge. Signed 100.00
Master 225.00
Sconces, Wall. 3 green feathers.
Signed. Pair 1500.00
Shade, Gas. 7" top diam., 2½" base.
Signed 250.00

Sherbets
Leaf band in gold lustre around
bowl. Gold iridescent, ingaglio
cut. "L.C.T." 250.00
Lily pad design. Signed 300.00
Tazza. 6" diam. Morning glory blue.
Signed 1250.00
Toothpick Holder 250.00
Urn. 2" high, amethyst and gold.
Signed "L.C.T." 400.00
Vases
3¾" high. Butterfly, blue and
green with allover swirls 400.00

5¼" high, 1½" diam. Green
glaze. Pottery. RARE 1200.00
6" high. Iridescent dull blue with
white, gold and green loopings . . . 750.00
6" high, 4" diam. Twisted, gold.
L. C. Tiffany #547 . . . . 500.00
6½" high. Gold iridescent 500.00
8¼" high. Bud. Pastel white with
gold flame decor. Fully signed and
numbered 450.00
9½" high. Light green iridescent,
applied gold bands and four ap-
plied flowers. Gold swirls. Sgd. . . . 895.00
10½" high. Urn-shape, handled.
Iridescent gold 950.00
11" high, 5½" diam. Cream
opalescent, green iris leaves,
bronze base. "L.C.T." 1850.00
12" high. Lotus leaf decor, metal
base. Signed 1250.00
13½" high. Trumpet vase, gold
iridescent with green leaves.
Signed and numbered 1500.00
15½" high. Trumpet-shaped, with
large leaves in iridescent amber
and green. Gilded metal base 2250.00
18" high. Amber and pink color
with brass base. Stems form
flower-shaped opening 2500.00
Wines
6" high. Opalescent to green. Sgd. 195.00
6½" high. Amethyst with opales-
cent striping 235.00

TIFFIN GLASS

The Tiffin Glass Company, a subsidiary of U. S.
Glass Company, is located in Tiffin, Ohio.
Although they continue to produce fine
glassware and other colors were made, it is
their black satin glass made between 1923
and 1926 that is considered the most
collectible. Tiffin also manufactured blanks for
other concerns and did a limited amount of cut
glass themselves.

Basket. 11" high . . . . $ 38.00
Bottle, Perfume 20.00
Bowls
5". Black Satin. "Poppy" 30.00
5½". Black Satin. "Poppy" 35.00
7". Black Satin. "Poppy" 37.50
9". Black Satin. "Poppy" 45.00
11". Black Satin. "Poppy" 50.00
Box, Powder. Covered. Black Satin . .   20.00
Candleholder. Saucer-type 25.00
Candlesticks. Pair 50.00
Compote. 5" high, 7" diam. Crystal.
Paper label 15.00

Console Set. 4 pieces. Bowl, 9½"
diam., with base. 2 candleholders 8½"
high. Yellow $72.50

Dog, Seated. 7" high. Amber jeweled eyes	95.00
Stemware. Blue and crystal. Paper label. 36 pieces	185.00

TILES

Tiles fall roughly into two categories,
decorative and table. Decorative tiles were
used for fireplace fronts, floors, benches and
furniture. Table tiles were used to hold hot
dishes and thus protect the table.

Advertisement. "Jello." Roaring lion. Signed Robertson . . . .$	25.00
Calendar	
1895. "Boston State House"	45.00
1911. Jones McDuffee & Stratton. Wedgwood	15.00
1913. Jones McDuffee & Stratton. Wedgwood	15.00

Biblical scene. Framed $39.50

6¾" diam. Transfer of George
Washington. Gold trim $25.00

1914. Commonwealth Docks, Boston	28.50
1917. Jones McDuffee & Stratton. Wedgwood. Framed	20.00
1925. "Flying Cloud." Wedgwood .	30.00
Castle. Blue. 5x5¼"	15.00
Cat. 6" square. Blue and white	14.50
Coolidge Homestead. 1926	30.00
Delft. 7" hexagonal. Windmill scene .	28.50
Dutch Children. 5¾" square	15.00
Elk in Woods. Blue and white. 1870 Reg. mark	25.00
Floral decor. Round	14.00
Floral decor. Square	12.00
Gibson Girl-Type	19.00
Minton. Children in black and white .	20.00
Mosaic. 6" square. Rabbit on green and red. Scaffito. M.T.C.	85.00
Mosaic. "Lincoln"	35.00
Old Hancock House. 6" square. Stoke-on-Trent	25.00
Owl. 5x5¼". Polychromed	20.00
Snake 1x4½x6½". Black	12.50
Tiffany. 4" square. Raised medal-lions, orange and black	75.00
Villeroy and Boch. 5¾" square	26.50
Wedgwood. Month tiles. Blue and white. Each	50.00

TINSEL PICTURES

A form of primitive art made by housewives
and children from colored tinsel paper. The
pictures mainly depicted flowers, birds, Bible
scenes, landscapes and costume subjects. The
art enjoyed its greatest popularity from about
1825 to 1875.

Floral arrangement on black background. 15½x20". C. 1820-1830
$95.00

Bowl of Flowers. 9½x12" ....$ 75.00
Bowl of flowers in center. Black
background, in molded walnut
frame, gold liner. 26x36" 150.00
Floral. Walnut frame. 12x14"....... 125.00
Flowers and Birds. Original pine
frame with applied grapes.
13½x14"...................... 150.00
Jacob's Dream. Bible scene. 9½x12" 135.00
Peacock on porch rail. Outlined with
roses. 22½" wide, 27½" high,
including gold finished frame 150.00
Roses, buds and leaves. Framed.
8x10"........................ 95.00
Roses. On black background, in gold
frame. 12½x16½" 110.00
Roses. Wild, with buds and leaves,
white background, narrow gilt
frame. 10¼x22½" 100.00

TINWARE, See TOLE

TOBACCO CUTTERS

Plug tobacco and snuff were the popular types
of tobacco before the cigarette came into
vogue. Chewing tobacco was received in
"sheets" by the merchant and was cut into
small squares with a tobacco cutter before
being sold to the public.

*Black Beauty...................$ 32.50

John Finzer & Bros., Louisville, Ky.
$35.00

Brown Mule Cutter. Iron. R.J.R. 24.50
Climax Plug. Cast iron 24.50
*Drummond. Drummond Tobacco
Co., St. Louis 28.00
Five Brothers Tobacco Co., Louisville,
Kentucky 35.00
Griswold Tobacco Cutter. Ordinary
type 25.00
*Imp thumbing nose on blade. Iron.. 65.00
P. Lorillard & Co. 19", original paint
and stripping 35.00
*Reproduced Item

TOBACCO JARS

The tobacco jar was, in most cases, a
combination holder and humidor for cigars or
pipe tobaccos. The containers were made of
pottery, china, wood, metals, etc.

Arab. 7".........................$ 50.00
Bag. 5" high. Draw string with pipe
attached to side. Blue and red 48.50
Bisque. 6¾" high. Young boy with
cossack-type hat 75.00
Bulldog. "Old Sport." Bristol, light
brown with pipe on reverse 65.00
Cut Glass. Silver cover 135.00
Devil's Head 85.00
Egyptian Queen. 4" high, colorful .. 75.00
Gnome on top of barrel. Woodlike
texture 60.00
Handpainted. 6" high. Floral, pipe
handle 55.00

4½" high. Press inside $85.00

Human Skull	85.00
Indian Girl Head. Small, colorful	60.00
Iron. Round with fluted sides, tall finial on lid	40.00
Jasperware. Blue, 5" high, 4¼" diam. Adams, C. 1892	95.00
Lion's Head. 4". Ivory, beige	35.00
Lion Head. Austrian	65.00
Maiden's Head. Art Nouveau, with flowers	135.00
Majolica	
Elephant	85.00
Girl's Face. Blonde hair, purple tam cover	80.00
Indian. 10" to top of feathers	95.00
Indian Chief. 5" high, dark gray . .	75.00
Monkey Head. Pipe & sports hat, green with pink at base	85.00
Negro Jockey. 4½" high. Pink and yellow cap with white beak, white collar and green bow tie	95.00
Pipe on lid. Green and pink	75.00
Pirate with green hat, black hair, blue shirt	80.00
Ram's Head	75.00
Sea Captain. Pipe in mouth	85.00
Male figures on grey ground. 4". Lid, embossed. Spode pottery	35.00
Man with derby hat, pipe in mouth. 6½". Vest, black buttons. Austrian	35.00
Man with English hunting cap. Terra Cotta	85.00

Man seated in chair, with gout. 8½" high. Staffordshire-type	125.00
Man with skull cap. England	85.00
Owl on branch. Handel, hand-painted. Signed	295.00
Papier-Mache. 3 monkeys on lid. 10 faces around base	125.00
Pewter. 7" to top of round finial on cover. 16½" circum. Mkd. "Copenhagen Pewter 439"	95.00
Postman, French. 7" high. Reads "Posters"	65.00
Rookwood. Shades of brown with yellow. Spray of clover. 5¾" high .	150.00
Royal Bayreuth. Tapestry Ware. Cows in field	195.00
Satan head with bee on top. Red popping white eyes	85.00

TOBY JUGS

According to an historian, the term "Toby Jug" was probably secured from the character "Uncle Toby" in Sterne's "Tristram Shandy," and the following verse is connected with the jugs:

> "Old Toby Philpot,
> A Thirsty old soul,
> As e'er drank a bottle
> Or fathomed a bowl."

They were used as containers for ale and beer in England and America in the 18th and 19th centuries.

Cat Toby. 9" high, full figure . . . . $ 120.00	
Coachman. 9" high, full figure, drinking cup hat	250.00
Delft	
9" high. Man with beard, marked on lid. Early	450.00
10" high. Full figure of seated woman. Early	500.00
11" high. Full figure of man taking snuff, bug on nose. Early	550.00
English. Primitive, standing 9" woman, 8" man. Pair	500.00
Englishman. 9" high, seated figure with angel handle and tricorn hat .	350.00
George Washington Head. 9" high, patented 1892	250.00
"Great War, The 1914-1918." 9½" high. "Peace 1919"	165.00
Herbert Hoover. 7" high. Patriotic Products Assn.	85.00
King Louis. 7" high. Details in delft blue and white. Late	95.00
MacArthur, Douglas. 3¾" high. Winton, late	30.00

12" high. Blue coat, white trousers.
"Nelson"..................$175.00

Madam Philpot [so-called]. Delft-type
  in blue, white, yellow and brown.
  8¼" high. Top of hat is removable
  lid. C. 1760-1780 ....   600.00
Man in green, dark red and brown
  costume, astride barrel. Late 145.00
Napoleon. 10" high. Trenton, N.J....   265.00

Ralph Wood-type
  8" high. Seated man with tricorn
  hat 425.00
  8" high. Seated man holding cup
  almost to his mouth 425.00
Roosevelt, Franklin. 8½" high.
  Copeland-Spode. Eric Olson 85.00

Royal Doulton. See "Royal Doulton"
Santa Claus. 7" high, red and white
  color. Late.....................   100.00
Scroddle. 5½" high 285.00
Smith, Al. 7" high. Patriotic Products
  Assn. 75.00

Staffordshire. 5" high. Squat, embossed figure. Late 150.00
Staffordshire. 10" high. Man in
  sitting position with a glass in one
  hand and pitcher in other. Green
  coat, yellow trousers. Dark
  brown, green and yellow spatter
  design on top and bottom........   400.00
"Toby Philpot." Prattware. 11" high.
  Brown coat, green pants, black
  and green base 600.00
Uncle Sam. 6" high. Signed Royal
  Winton. Late 55.00

TOLE
(TINWARE, ETC.)

The term was originally used to designate
items made of sheet iron and decorated.
Usage of the term through the years has
caused it to be applied to decorated tin
articles as well.

Bathtub. 27" diam., 13" ....$ 125.00
Beater. For making whipped cream.
  8½" high 25.00
Boxes
  Book-shaped...................   25.00
  Rounded cover with handle.
  4½x5x8½", ends stenciled 165.00
Cake Pan. Angel..................   18.50
Candle Molds
  6-candle 45.00
  8-candle 55.00
  12-candle 75.00
  24-candle 120.00

Candle   Mold.   Round,   18-candle
                          $185.00

Pitcher. 4" high, hinged lid. Red and
yellow $95.00

25-candle holes. 5x5x5½". Zinc
metal, 5½x5½" top and bottom
for ½ size candles 110.00
Candle Snuffer. With 19" decorated
tray. Set 85.00
Candleholder. Wall, 18th century ... 75.00
Candlestick. Saucer-type, push-up .. 35.00
Coffee Pot. Green, with original
flowers 140.00
Comb Case 30.00
Cookie Cutters
Chick. 4" high 8.50
Dog. 3½" long 8.50

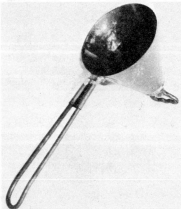

Ice Cream Scoop. Revolving release
$6.00

Dutch Man and Woman.......... 8.50
Horse. 7" long, 4" high 8.50
Rabbit. 6" long, 3½" high 8.50
Rooster. 4½" high 8.50
Star 8.50
Deed Box. 9" high, 10½" wide. Old
stenciled decor. Red, yellow,
black 165.00
Diamond Dye Cabinet 225.00
Dipper. Long handled, 26" long 18.50
Dispatch Case 25.00
Document Box. 6x9x13". Gold and
red stenciled. "Sec'y Treas. The St.
J.W.W. Co." Keys included 135.00
Ear Trumpet. With carrying case 50.00
Food Molds, See "Molds, Food"
Foot Warmer. Round, pierced 45.00
Gun Powder Container. Tin, 9x12" .. 37.50
Jack-O Lanterns. Pair 50.00
Lamp. Black, gold handle decor 50.00
Lantern. Cone-shaped, pierced, with
original snuffer and candle 85.00
Lunch Basket with Tray 35.00
Match Box. Large. Large........... 75.00
Match Box. Wall. Fluted edge....... 85.00
Match Safe. Double 20.00
Measure. Pint 18.50
Mustache Curling Set. Small, with
alcohol burner, etc. 30.00
Nutmeg Grater, 1854 .... 10.00
Pitchers
Syrup. Pint, lift lid 35.00
Water. Brown with floral decor ... 95.00
Plates
6". National cigars, portrait
center 22.00
10". Baseball scene, early 28.00
10". Woman holding water jug ... 20.00

Apple Tray. Early $225.00

10". Woodland scene, stag in foreground	25.00
Rattle, Baby's. Whistle handle, porcelain mouthpiece. Painted designs on tin rattle part	35.00
Scoop	15.00
Snuff Box. 1-oz. Murray Sons & Co., Belfast, Glasgow	8.50
Soap Bubble Pipe	5.00
Spice Boxes. 6 round boxes in open handled container. Set	45.00
Sugar Shaker. Original tole	130.00

Trays

7½" diam. English. C. 1830. Green ground, gold chinoiserie decor	75.00
19x25". Chippendale-style. Deep well, original gold leaf and scroll border, flower spray in center	135.00
Painted to fit on a high chair. Big top with circus figures	45.00
Wash Bowl and Pitcher. Set	120.00

TOOLS, HAND

Before the days of power tools and machinery, chores were carried out using hand implements.

Tradesmen and craftmen, such as carpenters and cabinetmakers, all had their specific hand tools. Today, these early examples are being collected sometimes just out of curiosity or fascination. The fine woodworking tools are sometimes used very effectively for wall decorations in game rooms, dens and offices.

Adz. Cooper's Curved ....$	22.00

Augers

Hub. 13" long. Hand-forged	17.50
Wood. 13" long with bit	45.00
Axe, Broad	25.00
Axe Heads	9.00
"C" Clamp. Hand-wrought	14.50
Chisels. 1/8" to 2". Cabinetmaker's. Round wood handles. Set	35.00

Measuring Wheel. 8" diam. Iron
$26.00

Croze

Howell combination	50.00
Sawtooth	40.00
Froe, with handle	20.00
Gauge, Marking. Wood	4.50

Knives

Chamfering. Cooper's	25.00
Crooked	28.00
Race, brass handle	40.00
Level. Wood, brass ends	13.50
Mallet. Refinished	15.00

Measures

Folding Rule. Mid 19th century	9.00
Lumber Gauge. Iron	12.50
Wheel. Wheelwright's. Wrought iron	26.00
Nail Puller. 13" long. Hand-forged	8.00

Planes

Block. 8"	14.00
Grooving	16.00
Molding	18.00
Plow Casey	25.00
Router. #77	25.00
Scorp. Two-handled	28.00
Sickle. 25" blade	25.00
Slick, Barn. 4"	45.00

Squares

21" Wooden	9.00
24" Framing	12.00
Traveler	30.00

TOOTHPICK HOLDERS

Toothpick holders, as the name implies, are small containers used to hold toothpicks for

"Colorado." Green $25.00

after dinner use. They were an important table accessory during the Victorian era.

Amethyst. Gold trim	$ 38.00
Clear Glass	
Bird with tail holder	25.00
Butterfly	20.00
Cauldron, Witch's, green eyes	30.00
Coal Hod	22.00
Trunk, snake decor	22.00
Milk Glass	
Black Boy	50.00
Monkey and Hat. 1¾x3x3¾"	39.50
Santa Claus. 2x3½"	85.00
Seashell	25.00
Shoe, Tramp's. 2" high	20.00
Silver, Plated. Porcupine on base.	
Wilcox	30.00
Silver, Sterling. With underplate.	
Late	35.00
Uncle Sam's Hat. Painted	40.00

For additional listings see "Pattern Glass Sections I and II" for particular pressed glass patterns, and "General Section" for specific wares.

TORTOISE SHELL ITEMS

Tortoise shell items, as the name indicates, are made from the shells of tortoises. The rich shading of amber brown comes from the under side of the shell.

Very few articles made today and called "tortoise shell" are made of shell. Most are made of tortoise-colored plastic. Thus, genuine tortoise shell combs, jewelry, card cases and other personal accessories delight collectors of items made of materials used in the past.

Box. 2-3/8". Georgian, with intricate sterling pique work on front, back and top. Bright cut sterling band around top. For carrying glass perfume flask. C. 1780	$ 135.00
Calling Card Case. Dark, pierced, with silk lining	25.00
Comb. 7" across. 8¾" long. Hand carved. C. 1900	35.00
Lorgnette. 11" handle. Openwork	35.00
Vase. 8¾" high, 3½" wide. Molded, pedestal base. Flaring to 4" wide at top, fluted panels	35.00

TOURAINE PATTERN CHINA

Touraine is a popular floral pattern of Flow Blue China. The rims of plates are scalloped, gilded and outlined in dark and light blue swirls. There is some embossing. The predominate decoration consists of five sprays of flowers placed around the border and extending somewhat into the well.

The pattern was made by Henry Alcock, but Touraine wares may also be stamped Stanley Pottery Co. Alcock used the "65" mark from 1880 to 1910. The Stanley Pottery Co. was

Card Case. Monogrammed "PRE"
$25.00

Soup Plate. 8" diam. $27.50

594

operated by Colclough and Company in England from 1887. The registry mark dates the design late 1898.

Bone Dish. Crescent-shape . . . . $	14.50
Bowls	
6½ x9", oval, 1¾" deep.Alcock . . .	30.00
9" diam., 2¼" deep. Stanley	35.00
Butter Pat	12.00
Creamer	25.00
Cup and Saucer.	35.00
Dishes, Vegetable	
5½". Sauce. Stanley	11.50
8½", oval	35.00
Round	35.00
Gravy Boat	40.00
Honey Dish	28.50
Pitcher, Milk	50.00
Plates	
6½"	18.50
8¼"	20.00
9"	25.00
10"	30.00
Platters	
8½ x12½". Alcock	45.00
10¼ x15". Alcock	60.00
Relish Dish. Oblong	17.50
Sauces	
Oval	12.50
Round. 5½ diam.	11.50
Soup Dish. 10"	29.00

TOYS

The subject covers a wide variety of playthings for children of past eras. The early ones were made of wood; later cast iron was used. In the past forty or fifty years, tin has been used in the manufacture of toys. Today, plastic is used mainly but it is not considered as durable as the earlier metal items.

Airplanes	
Cast Iron . . . . $	25.00
Kenton Air Mail	45.00
"Spirit of St. Louis." Kit in original box. Metalcraft	135.00
Animals	
Alligator. 10" long. Tin	35.00
Bear. 10" long. Pull-type. Bell	50.00
Bull. "Ferdinand." Mechanical, tin. Marx 1938	15.00
Cat. 15". Iron shaft. Stuffed	50.00
Cows:	
Calfskin, 7x10" on rollers, moos when head is turned	65.00
Papier-Mache. 8½ x12. Pull-type .	65.00
Donkeys:	
12" pull-type.	35.00
Wind-up.	25.00

Plush Horse. Pull-type. 12" high, horse hair body. Platform 11½" long .	$65.00
Duck. Tin. Pull-type	20.00
Elephant. Wood body covered with paper. Tin legs. "Jumbo"	75.00
Frog, Jumping. Tin, wind-up type .	55.00
Goats:	
Tin. Cast metal wheels. Bell	100.00
Tin. Wind-up type	35.00
Horse with lady. 15". Wilkin Phaeton	850.00
Horses, Two. Tin. Cast wheels. Two bells. C. 1890	135.00
Monkeys:	
7" high. Wind-up	25.00
Lindstrom. 8". Tin on string	25.00
On log. 6" long. Iron	300.00
On tricycle. Tin, wind-up.	85.00
"Zippo." Marx Mechanical, climbs string	55.00
Mules:	
Balky. German. C. 1900. Original box.	125.00
Tin. Wind-up	55.00
"Sparky." Cloth-stuffed	35.00
Autos	
Amos and Andy Fresh Air Taxi. Spring sprung, complete	200.00
"Auto Van." Tin. C. 1925	50.00
Cast Iron. 3½" long. Old and original, silver paint	30.00
Coupe. Iron	45.00
Dodge. Scale model. Pot metal. 1930's	18.50
"Leapin Lena." Tin, mechanical. C. 1920-25	55.00
Model T. Ford coupe. C. 1926	40.00
"Phaeton." Tin, 6x14". Early	85.00
Racers:	
5¼". Cast iron. Hubley	35.00
10" Tin. Thimble Drome Champion	25.00

Plush Teddy Bear. 14". Early ... $60.00

Racing Cars. Lionel. C. 1914
Complete set 250.00
Roadster. Walt Disney. Tin,
mechanical, with box 35.00
Taxi. Cast iron. 8", yellow,
unmarked spokes in wheels 45.00
Tin. 7" long, wind up-type........ 50.00
Tin and wood, friction drive. Early 85.00
Touring, 11" long. Tin, mechanical 48.00
Wyandotte. 5". Cast iron. Yellow
body, black running board,
fenders and hood. Solid wheels .. 30.00
Barnacle Bill. 6" high. Lithographed
wind-up 55.00
Battleship. 18" long. Schieble 125.00
Buck Rogers. Space ship with box.
Early......................... 275.00
Buggy. 6½". One horse and driver .. 115.00
Buses
Arcade Fageol. 8" long 72.50
Greyhound. Sightseeing. 8" long,
1934......................... 45.00

Marx Royal. 10" long. Litho-
graphed wind-up. Early.......... 85.00
12" long, Iron 85.00
Cannons
Pot metal. 5½" long, spring-shot . 10.00
Tin. Spring-shot. 4½" base. Mark
Hesse......................... 9.00
Tin. Spring-shot. 8" long. New 12.50
Circus Items
Auto. "Overland." 7½", with
hippopotamus and driver 125.00
Auto. "Overland." 7½" with lion
and driver 125.00
Clown. 5", wood on stick. Hinged
to do tricks. dated 1880 .... 75.00
Donkey and Clown. Tin. 7½" long,
wind up-type.................. 55.00
Lion Cage. Tin, 7½x12". 2 lions
and driver 125.00
Wagon. "Overland." Iron, 2 horses
with driver and lion 125.00
Wagon. Iron. 4¼x9". "Royal
Circus," bear in cage, driver and
two horses 125.00
Wagon. 15½" long, tin and wood
with lithographed scene of circus
on wagon, 2 horses 75.00
Wagon. 16" long, driver and 2
horses. Revolving head of chinaman on top 135.00
Drummer Boy. Wind-up by Marx 35.00
Dump Carts
11", cast iron. Mule-drawn, 2
wheels........................ 65.00
13", 2-wheel cast iron horse, tin
body......................... 85.00
13" long, iron with one horse.
Dated 1881 .... 95.00
Ferris Wheel. Tin, wind-up. Original
box........................... 42.50

Rocking Horse. 23x38".......$175.00

Street Car. Friction-type, 15" long
$95.00

Fire Equipment
9" long. "Buddy L." Sheet metal,
with driver. Original red paint ... 115.00
13½" long. Driver and ladders,
rubber wheels. Hubley 175.00
14". Chief's Fire Wagon. Horse
and chief 185.00
14½" long. Motorized. 2 horses
for drawing up water, eagle
ornament, 2 iron men drivers, bell
rings on back when wheels turn .. 165.00
14½". Pumper. Kenton, 2 horses,
nickel......................... 295.00
31". Hook and ladder with driver,
2 horses...................... 295.00
Garage. Tin with 2 wind-up cars 125.00
"GI Joe." Tin, with pups. Art
Newark. Working mechanism 35.00
"Happy Hooligan." Tin, mechanical.. 125.00
Ice Skates. Iron, miniature 7.50
Iron. Miniature. Flat, swan-shape ... 40.00
Jack in the Box 35.00
"Jazzbo Jim." Tin, mechanical 125.00
"Joe Penner." Wind-up, tin 85.00

Man. 5" high. Sgt., colored,
mechanical 20.00
Man playing billiards. Mechanical,
tin 95.00
Man sawing wood. Tin............ 85.00
Miner. Mechanical, with box 38.00
Mirrorscope 35.00
Motorcycles
Cycle and sidecar. 5" 150.00
Cycle, sidecar. Loose passenger.
"Champion" 125.00
Champion. 7" 85.00
Harley. 7¼" 95.00
Marx. Rider, military 85.00
Rabbit with sidecar. "Easter Bunny
Delivery." Made by Wyandotte,
U.S.A. 25.00
Negro. 5", celluloid. Wind-up 100.00
"Paddy Rides the Pig." Tin, dated
1903, mechanical 95.00
"Pinocchio." The acrobat, with box .. 110.00

Pistols
Cap. 3½" long, patd. 1887 .... 45.00
Cap. Dog 110.00
"Super." Late, C. 1920-30 .... 40.00
Mfgd. by J. D. Frary, Meriden.
Shoots corn 40.00
Popeye Roller Skater. With plate of
spinach. Tin wind-up 60.00
See Saw. "The Wizard" 135.00
Sewing Machines
5x6". Hand operated............ 50.00
Child's size, gold stencil design,
crank operated. C. 1915 .... 30.00
Sleigh. With driver and horse. Cast
iron. 14" long. Scarce 300.00

Steam Engine. Vertical.......$150.00

597

Sweeper, Child's. "Our Baby." Wood   15.00
Spurs. Signed 'Hoppy' 20.00
Steamboats
   9" long, 2-stacker with name
   "George Washington" 125.00
   12" long, 3-stacker. Wind-up 95.00
Steam Engine. 10", brass tank, 6¼"
   long by 2¼" diam. On cast iron
   base 150.00
Steam Shovel. Iron. Swivels on
   4-wheel base, weighs 8 lbs., 11½"
   to top of boiler. 14" high to top of
   boom. 20" long, 7" wide. Corru-
   gated roof 55.00
Stoves
   Coal. Iron, 6 covers, lifter, coal
   hod, shovel, kettle, frying pan and
   turning grate. Set 150.00
   Gas Range. Iron 85.00
Teaching Clock. Musical. Fisher 15.00
Tractors
   Arcade. 5", rubber tires, green . . .   30.00
   Fordson. With driver 85.00
Trains, Cast Iron
   American Flyer:
      #283. Pacific type, smokes 20.00
      #290. New Haven type, tender . .   25.00
      #322. Hudson and tender 25.00
      #4019. Std. gauge train, 4 cars.
      Repainted 365.00
   Lionel. C. 1946-1975, "O" Gauge:
      #2423. Hillside observation
      passenger car 15.00
      #6457. Caboose 5.00
      #6472. Refrigerator car. Orig. box   6.00
   Lionel "O" Gauge. C. 1920-41:
      #238E. Gray Steam Loco. Tender .   75.00
      #652. Gondola. Yellow, restored   5.00
      #653. Hopper. Green, restored . .   7.50
      #817. Caboose. Red 20.00
      #1688. Engine tender. Black 25.00

Rider on Motorcycle. Iron. Marked
"Patrol" $95.00

Train. Engine and tender. "American
   Flyer" $30.00

Standard Gauge:
   #112. Lionel. Gondola. Grey 15.00
   #390. Steam tender. Work set,
   cars complete. Original 395.00
   #3235. Ives. Elec-type, engine,
   brown, restored 95.00
   Lionel. Steam Loco. Tender.
   Green, orange stripe. Bildaloco-
   motor 250.00
Miscellaneous:
   "Buddy L." Train engine, tender,
   box car, flat car, gondola,
   caboose. Set 950.00
   Clay, H. 16½ x 27". C. 1854 . . . . . .   225.00

Trains, Tin
   Engine Tender. 4½ x 17". Friction
   type 35.00
   Marx. "Honeymoon Express" 22.50
   Marx. "Union Pacific Postal."
   Wind-up 20.00
Trolleys
   8" long, lithographed. Chein
   Broadway 175.00
   14". Kingsburg, Keane, N.H.
   Orange #784, running 110.00
Trucks
   International Harvester. 11",
   dump-type. Cast iron 135.00
   Marx Mack Partition. 1927 . . . .   95.00
Wagons
   ABC. Litho. 3¼ x 6½" 75.00
   "Brownie Farm." No driver,
   4-horse wagon 175.00
   Coal. Iron, driver, chute and
   shovel 165.00
   Dairy. 15¼" long. Tin and wood
   with horse 125.00
   Delivery. Single horse 125.00
   Special Delivery. 15¼" long. Tin
   and wood with horse on wheels . .   135.00
   Hay. 11 x 21¼". Original paint. C.
   1895 . . . .   195.00
   Hay. Wooden-type. 13½", 2 oxen
   and darky driver 225.00
   Ice Wagons:
      8". Hubley 65.00
      9½" 135.00

12½"	150.00
Kenton. Original box	165.00
Patrol:	
10" long. Iron, 2 horses	150.00
14" long. Iron, 2 horses	185.00
Sand and Gravel. Cast iron, 2 horses, driver	125.00
"Whirley Tinker." Wood	10.00
Washing Machine. 10" high, 7" diam. Metal, C. 1920's. Orig. box	45.00
"Wild Mule Jack." Pull toy. Monkey rider, hearts form wheel spokes ..	195.00
Windmill. Steel, 17" high, with tank ..	125.00

TRAMP ART

Tramp art is the term applied to a type of chip-carving to enrich the surfaces of decorative and sometimes utilitarian wooden objects.

Tradition states that this craft was executed by hoboes or tramps who wandered the country side doing odd jobs in towns and villages.

Although there is evidence that Tramp Art was practiced over an extended period of time and in many geographical areas, most items are neither signed nor dated.

Magazine Rack. Wall-type, 17x24"
$75.00

Box with porcelain knob. 4½ x9x13"
$80.00

Bird Cage. 10½ x15½ x20½". Black with gold and green trim .... $	350.00
Chest. 6x10x16". Two small drawers at top, three drawers below. Porcelain knobs ..., ...	140.00

TRIVETS

A trivet is a three-legged stand used to support hot vessels, either in an open fireplace, in workrooms or on table tops. Most were made of iron, brass or the like.

The popular collectible trivets are those that were used to hold the early hand irons. These trivets were usually very ornate, incorporating designs of animals, birds, flowers, fruits, etc.

Bar and Holes. Old iron Hankenson #55 .... $	7.50
Chevrons. Iron Hankenson #69	8.00
Club pattern. Brass, hexagonal	35.00
Colebrookdale	12.50
Crab. With legs, heart handle	22.00
Crisscross	12.00
Doves and Grapes. Brass	36.50
Eastern Star	18.50
Enterprise	10.00
Fanner	12.00
Fern	15.00
Fox and Geese Tracks. Iron	18.50
Fox and Grapes. Brass	35.00
Fox and Trees. Brass	35.00
Geometric. 5" diam. Iron	9.00
Good Luck	15.00
Harp	17.50
Harp. Brass. English	32.00
Hearts	
7½", inverted, brass	28.50
9½", three hearts design	30.00
12"	30.00
12", star center, long handle	35.00

Turtle. Iron $27.50

Beaded, flowers and scroll.
Handled. 24.00
Pennsylvania Dutch-type, with
long handle and 3 slender peg
legs. Small heart at handle end. . .   75.00
Piercing, two arrows 28.50
Horseshoes
7". Eagle and globe. K of L.
Original paint. 28.00
Masonic emblem inside 15.00
Rose center. 20.00
"I Want U Comfort." Iron, Handerson
#148. . . . .   10.00
Imperial. 12.00
Jenny Lind. Iron 26.50
Leaf and Scroll design. 8½" long.
Brass 35.00

Letters
"B." Iron, Hankensn #113 . . . .   8.50
"B." Iron, Handerson #113 . . . .   8.50
"H" in center. 8.00
"K" in center 8.00
"W" in center 8.00
Loop. Brass, English 30.00
Lyre and Berry design. Iron. 28.00

Movable. 2 heights of handles.
8½ x 23" long. Fireplace-type 100.00
Paw. Round 10.00
Pennsylvania Dutch. Hex sign,
handled. Early 65.00
Shield. Brass, English 37.50
Snake and Eagle Head. Iron 30.00
Spade center. Lacy iron 15.00
Star. Brass 25.00
Star and Sunburst. Iron 8.50
Streeter 10.00
Sunflower 12.50
Swastika center 15.00
Target. Handled. Old iron, Han-
kenson #55 . . . .   8.00
Triangular 9.50
Triple-eight pattern. Brass 40.00
Turtle. 9", brass 45.00
Washington, George. 9¼", iron 35.00
Washington, George. Brass 65.00

TUCKER CHINA

Tucker China is believed to be the first
commercial porcelain made in America.

William Ellis Tucker, son of a china merchant,
produced his first china in Philadelphia, Pa. in
1825. In 1828 Thomas Hulme joined Tucker
and the wares were marked Tucker and
Hulme. This partnership lasted for only a little
over a year.

William Tucker continued alone until 1832,
when after his death, the firm passed into the
hands of Joseph Tucker, a brother, and Judge
Joseph Hemphill. Judge Hemphill withdrew
from the firm in 1837 and Joseph Tucker
maintained the business until 1838. Thus,
Tucker china was only made for a few years
from 1825 until 1838.

Tucker porcelain is of exceptional quality and
comparable to Sevres. It was hand decorated;
no transfers were used. Although dinner
services were made, urns and vases were also
produced.

Needless to say, Tucker China, because of its
history, short production and fine quality, is
considered rare. Very few pieces can be found
outside of museums and private collections.
The prices listed below can only serve as a
guide for those fortunate enough to own or
acquire Tucker China.

Coffee Pot. Tucker and Hemphill,
Phila., 1832-1837 . . . . $ 575.00
Cups and Saucers
Demitasse. Landscape scene 250.00
Tea. Handleless 300.00
Dishes
Oval, covered 500.00
Round, covered 500.00

Plates
6¾", each with different land-
scapes in sepia. Set of six 600.00
7¼" 250.00
8¼" 300.00

Platters. Decoration of rosebuds,
arrow-shaped blue sprig, green
leaves:
7 x 10¼" 500.00
12 x 17¼" 750.00

Urns
3½" high. Flower decoration, blue
band and gold trim on white
ground. ¼" gold decoration on
base. Pair 750.00
10¼" high. Gold painted base,
floral decor, round bowl, gold
decorated handles. Pair 2000.00

VALENTINES

There are many myths and mysteries surrounding the origin of Valentine's Day and the Valentine greeting card.

Although Valentines were known to exist as early as the 15th century, the first commercially printed cards were not made until the 1800's.

Esther Howland was the first American manufacturer of lacy Valentines. As the custom of sending Valentines became more popular, other companies and artists turned their attention to designing and printing "love messages" for February 14th.

The Victorians delighted in sending and receiving these brightly hued and elaborately decorated cards. Therefore, most of the collectible Valentines found today in old homes, flea markets and antique sales will be from this era.

Antique Valentines can be bought for as little as one dollar or as high as several hundred dollars. Quite reasonable when you consider some of them originally sold for as much as ten dollars and more.

American. Comic-type . . . . . $	2.00 to	3.00
American. Handmade	5.00 to	75.00
American. Lithographed . . .	2.00 to	7.50
Artists		
Addenbrooke	35.00 to	50.00

Dobb	25.00 to 100.00
Greenaway, Kate	15.00 to 50.00
Howland, Esther	10.00 to 50.00
Mansell	10.00 to 125.00
Meek	100.00 to 150.00
English. Handmade	5.00 to 100.00
Theorems. Velvet	100.00 to 200.00

VALLERYSTAHL GLASS

The town of Vallerystahl, Lorraine, France, has been an important glassmaking center since about 1500 A.D. In 1870 the province and the factory fell into the hands of Germany as the result of the Franco-Prussia War. It was returned to France in 1918 and continued as such until 1939 when the factory was destroyed by bombs in World War II. The glass in which collectors are most interested today was imported into the United States between 1850 and 1915.

Bottle, Perfume and Powder Jar, covered. Blue bulbous, swirl ribbed, swirled stopper. Gold star decor. Set . . . . $	85.00
Box, Powder. 3x3½". Blue milk glass. Raised diamond pattern . . .	50.00
Candlestick. 11" high, carved, frosted Grecian girl, urn on head, square floral base	95.00
Compotes. 6x6¼" high. Blue milk glass. Square tops. Ornate molded designs. Unmarked. Pair	150.00
Dishes, Covered	
Bees. Honey Pot. 5" to top of finial. Ribbed base	60.00
Camel. Camphor glass. Marked . .	85.00
Cow and pasture scene on cover. 7"	60.00

Folding-type. Marked "Bestie," U.S.A.
$4.00

Covered Dish. 5" long. Squirrel finial.
Milk glass $75.00

Dog. 3½ x 5". Amber 80.00
Dog. Setter. Flowered base. Blue
milk glass. Marked 85.00
Dog. White milk glass. Signed 75.00
Dolphin feet. 5½ x 6½" high.
Large shell finial on lid, decorated
with small shells, green milk glass 100.00
Duck. 4½" high. Brown top,
painted green base 70.00
Duck. 6". Swimming, white 75.00
Duck. 8½" 85.00
Elephant. On round base. Stand-
ing 45.00
Fly on walnut. White, signed 90.00
Hen. 7", covered. 6 egg cups with
standing check bases. 2 basket
salt dips and 10" tray with wells
for each. Milk glass. Set 350.00
Hen. 7" long. Milk glass 65.00
Hen. 7½" long 70.00
Hen. Salt. Small, green 65.00
Pig. 3¼". Drum-shape. Signed
Porteux 35.00
Rabbit. Clear glass.............. 57.00
Ram's head. Salt Dip. White 35.00
Tortoise and rider. Milk glass 95.00
Egg Cup. Milk glass. Chicken decor .. 35.00
Jam Jar. 3½" high. Conical, grape
and leaf pattern 50.00
Plates
6". Thistle pattern 45.00
7". Scalloped edge. Lily-of-the-
Valley pattern. Signed 35.00
7½". Aqua, floral pattern. Set of 4 85.00
Sherbet with underplate. Blue
opalescent milk glass. Gold star
border 45.00
Tumbler. 3¼" high. Cobalt blue,
grapes & foliage decor 48.00

VAN BRIGGLE POTTERY

The Van Briggle Pottery Co. was established in
1901 at Colorado Springs, Colorado by Artus
Van Briggle who was an excellent potter. Mr.
Van Briggle was a former employee of
Rookwood Pottery for several years.

Book Ends
Bear. Dark green .... $ 65.00
Owl. Maroon 65.00
Peacock design, turquoise 65.00
Squirrels 65.00
Bowls
3" high, 5" diam. Art Nouveau.
Double A mark 60.00
3 x 5½". Acorn and oak leaves,
dated 1910 .... 85.00
5½ x 7". Green. Numbered 65.00

Bowl. Flower arranger with insert.
6½" diam. Turquoise blue and green
$38.00

10½ x 11 x 15". Frog. Kneeling
Nude. Colo. Spgs. Maroon/bl. 95.00
Candlestick. Deep blue, saucer-type.
Signed by artist 50.00
Console Set. Bowl, underplate, 2
candleholders. Maroon. Set 165.00
Creamer and Sugar. In shaded
green. Set 75.00
Figures
Dog. 2" high. Persian rose 30.00
Donkey. 3½" high 35.00
Rabbit. Double A mark 40.00
Planter. 12½" long. Persian Rose ... 45.00
Plaque. Oval head of Indian maiden,
"Little Star" in high relief.
Turquoise, signed 55.00
Plate. 8½". Green glaze. 46th
Annual Meeting National Boy
Scouts, 1956 .... 30.00
Vases
4½" high. Green to blue, leaf
decor 35.00
9¼" high. "Lorelei." Sculptured
figure of woman emerging from
water. Blue color, dated 1919 .... 55.00
9½" high. Deep maroon, daffodils
& foliage in relief. Signed 60.00
9½" high. Persian rose 65.00
10" high. Blue 65.00
11" high. Brown & green with
3-molded indian heads at top,
each with a different expression . 85.00
13" high. Maroon and blue....... 85.00

VASART

A late type of art glass made in Scotland by the Streathearn Glass Co. The usual signature is "Vasart" engraved on the base of items.

Vase. 7½" high. Pink to purple. Signed
$95.00

Basket. 4½ x 5½". Loop handle, blue
 and yellow .... $ 45.00
Bowls
  4" diam., 2" high. Yellow at
  bottom, speckled blue at top 60.00
  9¾" diam. Deep pink, flecked.
  Signed 78.50
  10½" diam., 3-3/8" high. Signed . 85.00
Jam Dish with Spoon. In EPNS frame.
  Ruffled amethyst to translucent
  white 62.50
Mug. Handled, blue 40.00
Tumblers
  White....................... 40.00
  4¼" high. Blue and white with a
  striped effect. Signed 47.50
Vase. 8¾" high. Blue at top, pink at
  bottom. Signed 95.00

VASA MURRHINA GLASS

Vasa Murrhina Glass was produced by the Vasa Murrhina Art Glass Company, Sandwich, Massachusetts in the late 1800's. The name Vasa Murrhina was derived from Roman Murrine which was a glass embedded with precious metals and stones.

Basically, Vasa Murrhina Glass was made by incorporating metallic flakes and particles of colored glass into a ball of transparent glass and heating it sufficiently to cause the mica to become embedded within the glass. Then the glass was formed into different articles.
There is some confusion in identifying Vasa Murrhina, Adventurine, Spangle and Spatter glass. Also a similar type glass was produced in England in the late 19th century. Just what can be attributed to the New England Glass Works is doubtful.

Baskets
  6½" high. Pink, white casing,
  clear looped handle .... $ 125.00
  9¼" high. Deep rose to pink with
  white, clear thorn handle 195.00
  Blue, reeded handle, small 55.00
  Pink, with dark red, silver flecks,
  ruffled top, applied clear handle . 165.00
Bowls
  3½" diam. Rose. Deep pink, cased 95.00
  4½" diam. Rose. Pink, deep
  maroon. Swirl pattern. Crimped
  top 100.00
  9" diam. Mottled, multicolors with
  mica flecks throughout, cased ... 150.00

Vase. 6½" high. Pink crimped top
$95.00

9½" diam., 3½" high. Deep pink to light. 8 fluted scallops 135.00

Rose. Pink and white with silver flecks. Artichoke pattern 85.00

Creamer and Sugar Bowl. Cobalt blue, gold flecks, melon-ribbed, amber knobs and handles 125.00

Decanter. 12½" high. Cranberry color with gold flecks, hour-glass shape. Applied ribbed handle, matching stopper, 3-lip top 130.00

Ewers

9" high. Bulbous, ruffled top with clear edge and applied handle. Pink, maroon, blue and yellow spatter 95.00

10" high. Pink with silver flecks, white lining, applied clear leaf handle, 3 rows of shells 150.00

Cruet. 8½" high. Amber with white enamel floral decor. Silver flecks
$95.00

Fairy Lamp. 4½" high. Zebra-type shade with white lining. Exterior mottling with green, red, blue, yellow and white with silver mica crystals. Pressed glass holder 250.00

Finger Bowl. Cranberry and opalescent with silver flecks 75.00

Finger Bowl and Plate. Crimped, scalloped rims iridescent colors of cranberry, gold and green. Set ... 85.00

Lamp. 8" high to top of burner. Amber and white. Amber swirl shade 145.00

Mug. Amber with gold flecks 60.00

Pitchers

5½" high, 3" widest diam. Mottled in green, red, yellow and sprinkled with silver mica dust. Applied reeded crystal handle. Cased...................... 165.00

7½" high. Bulbous, swirled, ribs. Clear handled, cased 185.00

8" high. Mottled cranberry with silver flecks, white lining, clear applied handle 200.00

8¾" high, 7" diam. Pink and white in amber. Blue enameled forget-me-nots, gold leaves 245.00

10" high. Tankard 175.00

10½" high. Opaque white lining, outer casing splashed with red, flecked all over with silver mica. Molded in cabbage rose design. Applied crystal handle 275.00

12" high. White lining, outside splashed with blue and brownish-gray, silver mica flecks. Applied clear crystal handle 295.00

Salt Shaker. White and rose with gold mica flecks. Artichoke pattern 50.00

Sugar Shaker. Pink and white with silver flecks 75.00

Syrup Jugs

5" high. Cabbage rose shape. White background with green, rose and white mottling. Applied clear crystal handle, pewter top .. 95.00

Clear and cranberry with gold flecks...................... 85.00

Toothpick. 2" high. Cobalt blue with gold flecks 50.00

Tumblers

Blue & white with silver flecks ... 80.00

Multicolored with gold flecks 135.00

Pink and maroon with silver flecks...................... 80.00

Tans, pinks, silver flecks......... 85.00

Vases

2½" high. Honey yellow, brown swirls	50.00
4½" high. Rainbow colors with gold and silver	80.00
6½" high. Cased glass mottled in red, yellow and green in a swirl design	75.00
6½" high. Rainbow striped spatter with mica flecks, clear spiral rigaree. Cased. Pair	165.00
7" high, 3½" diam. at ruffled top. Jack-in-the-pulpit. Spatter in rose and white, yellow and oxblood red. Cased and blown	95.00
7½" high. Blue glass. Applied crystal thorn, glass handles, ruffled top. Cased and blown	95.00
8" high. Tri-cornered crimped rim. Green and white with gold mica	130.00
8¼" high. Rainbow hued, silver mica. Fan-shaped, turned down top with applied clear ribbon edging, cased white lining	120.00
9" high. Soft yellow with random brown stripes, gold mica flakes, stick top, bulbous base, cased with white glass	130.00
10" high, 6½" diam. Custard and cranberry. Aventurine flecks all-over. Applied amber glass rigaree, 6 amber feet, bulbous body. Polished pontil	145.00

Scent Bottle. 4" high. Ribbons of white and gold stone $65.00

Candy Jar. Covered. 10½" high, enameled ribs, pink enamel flowers in orchid and blue, wreath	65.00
Centerpiece. Small. Oval mirror base, cornucopia center, shell sides, ribbed clear to white glass	125.00
Champagnes	
Cranberry enameled with cherubs and fruit	85.00
Dolphin-type. C. 1869	115.00

VENETIAN GLASS

Venetian glass was made on the island of Murano, near Venice, from the middle of the 13th century until around 1900. The factory was owned by the Republic. The glass is very fine and fragile. Some of it contains lace work, metal flecks, and is gold washed.

Bowls

3½ x9½". Clear with gold foot and edge . . . . $	55.00
Rose. Green, gold	45.00

Candlesticks

5". Dolphin. Clear glass flecked with gold	45.00
9¾". Cactus tail-type for one candle. Large, many petaled glass blossoms. Round cup-like base	85.00
17½". Opalescent. Elaborate	200.00
Candy Dish. 6" diam., enameled pink roses, green leaves. Gold on cover and small pink roses around wide rim	42.50

Chandeliers

5-arms. 30" diam., 34" high. Applied pink and blue decor, gold-washed, electrified, originally for candles	1200.00
6-arms and drip cups. Blown scrolls of unusual design extend from center stem. Applied decor in blue, pink and orchid, gold washed	850.00
Compotes	
4¾" diam., 2¾" high. Red with pedestal base and gold decor	75.00
7" diam., 6½" high. Cranberry bowls and fret and crystal dolphin stems. Pair	260.00
10" diam., 8" high. Blue, with gold overlay	135.00
Cordial Set. Decanter, tray, 8 hollow stem glasses, gold and enamel decor on clear	150.00
Cups and Saucers	
Demitasse. Blue, lacy	45.00
Demitasse. Pink	45.00
Punch. Green with gold decor	48.00

Ewer. Latticino striped in pink and clear, with gold. 4½" widest diam., 12" to top of handle 160.00

Figurine. Swan sitting on round base with raised wings and arched neck in gold flecked ribbed yellow glass. 2½" high, 2" long 35.00

Glass, Hoch. 7½" high, clear stem, cranberry bowl with gilt and flower decor 125.00

Goblets
8" high, 3¼" top diam. Cup and foot of latticino glass, turquoise blue and goldstone in a chaplet-bead design. Hollow knob stem with gold dustings. Applied dragon with yellow eyes and pink tongue 150.00

Cranberry stem. Cherubs around top, dance in grape vines 60.00

Pitcher, Water. Bulbous shape. Enameled lilies. Wide gold band with enameled dots. 6 gold band tumblers with standing pink lilies and leaves. Set 165.00

Salt, Master. Shape of swan. Pink body with gold decor............ 45.00

Vases
9½" high. Pale rose bottom shading to deep peach, rose pleated top, applied green leaves 120.00
10½" high. Ruby, flat center section. Applied clear ring 85.00
11" high. Urn-type. Gold washed on pink 120.00
11½" high, 7" diam. Blue and clear with gold outlining the blue . 145.00
15" high. Multicolored canes, florals, heavy gold designs 150.00
18" high. Red top blending to clear. Gold decoration with small white flowers 165.00

Wine. Cranberry stem. Cherubs and grape vines 50.00

Wine Set. 11" amber decanter, and six 5½" wines 225.00

VERLYS GLASS

The glass was originally made in France about fifty years ago. It is a semi-antique art glass made after World War I.

For a period of a few months Heisey Glass Co., Newark, Ohio produced the glass, having obtained the rights and formula from the French factory.

The French-produced glass can be distinguished from the American product as the name is molded into the base of items. American-made pieces have the name "Verlys" applied in script on the base.

Box. 3¾x5". Horse decor. Signed
$35.00

Ash Trays
3¾x4¾". Frosted doves on base, frosted floral border. Script signed $ 30.00
4x5". Penguin perched on one end. Clear bottom, hobnail design 50.00
4½", round. Camphor-colored floral center 35.00

Bowls
6" diam. Cupid with bow and arrow and hearts in the center. Script signed 55.00
11½" diam. Bird pattern, clear glass. Script signed 95.00
11¾" diam., 2-3/8" high. Frosted birds and bees in relief. Script signed 125.00
12" diam. Thistle pattern, molded signature...................... 125.00
13½" diam. Lily pad decor. Frosted and clear. Signed 110.00
13¾" diam., 3" high. Dragonfly. Etched clear crystal. Script signed 100.00

Doves. 4¼x12¾". Blue, script signed 85.00
Planter. 4¼x6¼x10-1/8". Chrysanthemum, frosted and clear. Signed 72.50
Plate, Concave. 13½" diam., clear with frosted figures of child and sheep in relief 95.00
Plaque. 9" diam., with iridescent, raised pattern of 3 swirling fish. Molded signature 85.00

Vases
5" high, 2½" diam., base. Frosted blue, butterflies 75.00

9" high. Opalescent wheat and thistle pattern. Rolled out rim. Script signed 160.00
9-3/8" high, 5-1/8" diam. Heisey Mandarin, etched and clear. Script signature...................... 195.00
9½" high. Chinese raised motif. Chinaman with umbrella, bushes with birds and urns with flowers all in relief. Script signed 165.00

VERRE DE SOIE GLASS

Verre de Soie glass was produced by the Steuben Glass Company around the 1905-10 period. Its development was reportedly under the supervision of Frederick Carder who originated Aurene glass shortly after the turn of the present century. Production was discontinued about 1930.

Verre de Soie (glass of silk) is an iridescent type of glass. This iridescence was produced by using a metallic chloride spray which caused the glass to develop a satiny finish with the appearance and feel of silk.

Some collectors and dealers who are not familiar with its original name call it White Carnival Glass.

Basket. Small, white with pink
    iridescence, blue handle ....$ 85.00
Bottle. Cologne. 7" high, with glass
    stopper 110.00
Bowls
    4¾" diam., with 6" matching dish
        underneath 85.00
    8" diam....................... 165.00
    Finger. With underplate, light
        green tinge. Steuben............ 65.00
    Rose.......................... 85.00
Candlesticks
    10" high. Steuben 85.00
    Twisted stems. Pair 145.00
Compote, Jelly. 4" high, 4¼" across
    top 65.00
Console Set. 3-pieces. Cyprian color,
    blue border. Blown Candlesticks
    and bowl to match 350.00
Cornucopia. 8¾" high. Applied
    green brushed gold, leaf feet. 8"
    diam. "Cut-petal" pastel irides-
    cent 145.00
Goblet. Large 75.00
Salt. Pedestaled. Steuben 55.00
Shade. Gas 48.50
Sherbets
    Ground pontil 30.00
    With underplate. Steuben 65.00
Sugar Bowl, Covered. Engraved..... 120.00

Tumbler. F. Carder................ 95.00
Tumble Up. Pitcher and tumbler.
    Cobalt blue handle. Set.......... 165.00

Vases
    5¾" high. Bud. Pair............. 90.00
    6" high. Jack-in-the-Pulpit 125.00
    6" high. Squat, bulbous base,
    narrow throat ending in a wide
    ruffled top 85.00

    7" high. Bulbous base, short neck
    with 3¼" diam., flaring rim 115.00
    7" high. Slender. Clear enameled
    water lilies, twining stems 45.00

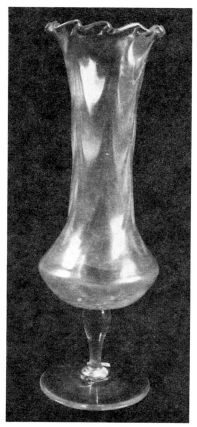

Vase. 11" high. Ruffled top, pedestaled
$95.00

7½" high. Ground pontil. Pale
green with opalescent crimped
top. Floral decor, in gold 75.00
9" high, 7½" diam. Steuben 150.00
12" high. Fan-shaped and ruffled
5½x9" top, 5" stem, 7" deep
bowl, 4" diam., flat base 165.00
Water Set. Decanter Pitcher. 12½"
high. Spray of large orchids in
shades of lavender. 6 matching
tumblers 295.00
Wine. Etched with flowers and
leaves 50.00

VILLEROY & BOCH

A firm of potters was originated by P. J. Boch
in Luxembourg before 1880. The firm was
later known as Boch and Buschmann. Still
later, N. Villeroy came in as a partner and the
firm was operated as Villeroy & Boch. This
latter firm made the famous "Mettlach" steins
and other ware bearing the name.

Beakers
4" long. Mettlach signed 2368.
Scene of 4 dwarfs . . . . $ 45.00
5" high, 2½" wide. Handled, tan
color, woman holding pitcher in
one hand, pheasant on platter in
other. "Wohlbehomm's #2327 . . . .   50.00
Bowl. 10¼" diam., two handles,
flower and fan, blue border 60.00
Bread Board. 5½x8½". Marked
"Villeroy & Boch, Dresden" 65.00
Butter Dish. Covered, design in relief   85.00
Cheese Board. 4½x7½". Marked
"Villeroy & Boch, Dresden" 60.00
Cider and Donut Set. 6 tumblers, 2
plates and tall pitcher. Dark taupe
ground with pictures of uni-
formed, handle-bar, mustached
players. Labeled "Catcher,"
"Pitcher," "Batsman" 150.00
Cruet. 8½" high. Large.Side handle,
blue and white. Signed 35.00
Cup and Saucer. Ramekin-type.
Dresden pattern 20.00
Match Holder. Frog. White crackle
glaze 45.00
Mold. Fish, 7x8", white and brown . .   40.00
Pitchers
4" high, 12" diam., 1½" white
stenciling, deep cerulean blue.
Dresden, Saxony, 6851 . . . .   30.00
7½" high. Dresden. Mercury
mark. White ground, handpainted
raised red flowers, green leaves .   50.00
9" high. Ornate. Pink and white
raised decor 75.00

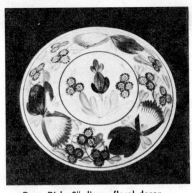

Deep Dish. 8" diam., floral decor
$35.00

Plaque
11" diam. Young maiden carrying
basket. Forest in background.
#1607 . . . .   350.00
14" diam. Pond scene in relief,
#1500 . . . .   295.00
16¼" diam. Female with wings in
relief, #1617 . . . .   300.00
Plates. Set of 6. Mercury mark. Each
different 85.00
Punch Bowls
2-quart size. Floral decor in relief.
Underplate 400.00
4-quart size. White figure, grape
vines in relief. Underplate #2602 .   550.00
Teapot. 6¼" high. White with blue
decor. Dresden 85.00
Tile. 6x6". Delft-type, blue windmill
boat scene 15.00
Vases
7½" high to 5x7½" oval top. Silver
7½" high to 5x7½" oval top.
Silver lustre trim, beige figures on
gray ground. C. 1832 . . . .   165.00
Cherubs in relief 65.00

WARWICK CHINA

Warwick China Co. was incorporated in 1887
in Wheeling, West Virginia. They were one of
the first manufacturers of vitreous or glazed
china in the United States.
Practically everything that could be made in
china was produced by Warwick. . . vases,
mugs, personal items, dinnerware, etc. Colors
were in abundance and most of the wares
were decorated with decals, including
beautiful ladies and insignias of fraternal
orders. Warwick chinaware is comparable in
quality to Haviland china.

Mug. BPOE Elk .... $	25.00
Plate, Pancake. Covered with cherry design	38.00
Syrup. Pewter top................	37.50

Vases

6¾" wide mouth. Dark brown shading to cream. Nude portrait of dark-haired lady	75.00
10" high. Portrait vase. Dark gray tones. Marked Warwick. Signed "Magnolia" underglaze	45.00
12" high. Handled. Beige to brown. Marked	65.00

WASH SETS

In the days before the advent of modern plumbing the wash set was an essential part of every bedroom. wash stands were made especially for their accommodation.

Wash Bowl and Pitcher. Royal Doulton.
Blue and white. "Willow" pattern
$350.00

Homer Laughlin. Holly decor on white ground, gold trim .... $	95.00
Homer Laughlin. Wash bowl and pitcher. Pink body with copper lustre decor. Ship scene in center of floral decor	120.00
Ironstone. English, white, undecorated	135.00
Limoges. Wash bowl and pitcher. Floral decoration	185.00
Maddock, John. English, 7-piece set. Bulbous pitcher, covered chamber. Green leaves and scrolls	350.00
Meakin. Pink hollyhocks, leaves and buds. 4-piece set	195.00
Minton China. Bowl 15½" diam. Pitcher 11½" high. Blue-white background, green decoration ...	200.00

Staffordshire. Bowl 12½" diam. Pitcher 10" high. Mulberry Bologna	225.00
Staffordshire. Wash bowl and pitcher. Names "Spring, Summer, Winter, Autumn"	185.00

2-Piece Sets

Blue and white. C. 1880	125.00
Cabbage roses, large. Small yellow roses. Devon Furnival England. Reg. number..........	175.00
White to pale blue with yellow iris decor	140.00
5-Piece Set. Brown roses, vine decor	225.00
7-Piece Set. Green ivy vines, leaves .	300.00
12-Piece Set. Begonias, leaves in natural green, illuminated with gold, gold-traced handles........	450.00

WATCH FOBS

Watch fobs were popular in the Victorian era and through the 1920's. The wrist watch replaced the pocket watch and the need for a fob. The fob was not only a decorative item but was useful in pulling the watch from a vest pocket. The earlier fobs were made of silk with metal fastenings and decorations. Later, the advertising fob appeared with a leather strap.

Allis-Chalmers Tractor Division ..... $	10.00
Baseball Player. Leather strap	8.50
Boy Scout Shoes for Boys. Dated July 1910.........................	17.50
Bucyrus Erie. "Road Machinery," leather strap...................	9.00
Caterpiller Tractor Co., Peoria, Ill. U.S.A. Leather strap	7.50
Coco-Cola, Goldstein, Vol. II. Original leather strap	75.00

R. E. Edmonds, 107 Third Ave.,
Pittsburgh, Pa. Stoves, Furnaces &
Refrigerators $9.50

Echo Springs Whiskey. Advertisement fob	9.50
English Victorian, 1x1½". Gold shield on hallmarked (B'ham 1850) silver, ship's wheel with crown at top	18.00
Halcomb Steel Co., Syracuse, N.Y. . .	15.00
Initial "P" on front, leather strap . . .	6.00
Kansas City. "The Heart of America." With eagle, covered wagon, train and red heart	10.00
Keystone Watch Case	10.00
Keystone Watch Case Co. "Columbia Exposition 1893"	25.00
Marblehead, Mass. 30th Anniversary	7.50
Motorcycle. Inscribed "Perfect Score Gypsy Jaunt." 1928	7.50
National Assn. of Ice Industries	8.00
Newport, Maine. Centennial. U.S. flag in colors on front	8.00
Ohio Power Shovel Co. Enamel decor	8.50
Quincy Mass. 1625-1925, no strap. 300th Anniversary	6.00
Rose Festival, Portland, Oregon 1913	8.50
Sailboat, Old. With strap	8.00
Silk. With gold decor. C. 1895	20.00
State of Massachusetts seal	7.50
Steward Horse Clipping	20.00
United Spanish War Veterans, Gloucester, Mass. 1921, 22nd. Annual encampment	5.50
Woodsman of the World	6.00
Woolworth Building, N.Y.	75.00

WATCHES

The watch, which was devised as a personal timepiece, first appeared in Germany in the 16th century. Since that time watchmaking has appeared the world over.

Numerous watch companies operated in America during the latter half of the 1800's into the early 1900's. Later Switzerland became the leading maker of timepieces. Lately Japan has taken much of the Swiss business because of low-production costs.

AMERICAN

Burlington, 12s, 21 jewel, 14K warranted 25y, YG, engraved . . . . $	109.00
Burlington, 16s, 21 jewel, nickel case, Montgomery dial	90.00
Burlington, 19 jewel, Montgomery dial, 25y, case yellow	110.00
Elgin, 10s, 7 jewel, 18K, case plain with engine turned rim. Gold	280.00

Pocket. "Howard." Nickel case $165.00

Elgin, 16s, 15 jewel, 14K, H.C. C. 1880's, engraved case. Plenty of gold weight	195.00
Elgin, 16s, 15 jewel, Coin Silver H.C., design engraved case. Fine movement	65.00
Elgin, 18s, 17 jewel, G.F.H.C. C. 1890's, engraved case still has original watch paper. Lever set . . .	95.00
Elgin, 18s, 21 jewel, "Father Time" G.F.O.F., Leverset RR	80.00
Elgin, 18s, 1868 BW, Raymond. Engine turned Hunting coin silver. KW	130.00
Elgin, 18s, 15 jewel, BW, Raymond, 1881, KW	100.00
Hamilton, 16s, 21 jewel, G.F.O.F. RR. Engraved case	70.00
Hamilton I 18s 992B Railway special Montgomery Dial. 10K GF case plus 12K GF round link chain. Original box	140.00
Hamilton, 18s, 21 jewel, 992. 20-year, double GF case	100.00
Hamilton, 992B Railway Special. GF case mint cond. with GF chain . . .	130.00
Hamilton, Railway Special 992B. 10K GF case	125.00
Illinois, 18s, KW, or stem wind. Engraved coin silver Hunting	120.00
Illinois, 18s, KW, silverene	65.00
New York Watch Co. 10s, 15 jewel, KW, yellow GF Hunting	140.00
Seth Thomas. Man's, closed case . . .	95.00
Seth Thomas, 18s, 7 jewel, silveroid O.F., case with engraved steam engine	55.00

Pocket. "Dudley." Masonic front
$900.00

Pocket. "Dudley." Masonic back
$900.00

Swiss, 16s, full-jeweled, Gun Metal
   Alarm. C. early 1900's 60.00
Rockford, 18s, 15 jewel, case, KW,
   4oz. case. Y. 1876, coin silver 100.00

Waltham, 12s, 17 jewel, Sterling
   Silver O.F., case with inlaid
   2-color gold stag & design 75.00
Waltham Regina, 16s, 15 jewel,
   G.F.H.C., engraved case. Dial
   trimmed in gold & royal blue 95.00
Waltham Vanguard. 18s, 23 jewel,
   10K........................... 140.00
Waltham, 18s, 15 jewel, Hunting
   coin silver. Case with shield, KW,
   1872.......................... 125.00
Wheeler, GM. 18s, 15 jewel, KW,
   silveroid case. 1874 .... 90.00

CHARACTER

Cinderella. Expansion bracelet $75.00

Bambi	85.00
Bugs Bunny	150.00
Cinderella	85.00
Dale Evans.....................	75.00
Davey Crockett	40.00
Dick Tracy	225.00
Donald Duck. '39 pocket watch	295.00
Dopey.........................	50.00
Hopalong Cassidy	75.00
Joe Palooka	250.00
*Mickey Mouse	175.00
Orphan Annie	225.00
Popeye, 1934	175.00
Robin Hood	110.00
Roy Rogers	95.00
Snow White....................	75.00

*Reproduced Item

FOREIGN

Agassiz. Chronograph. 16S O.F. 14K.
Double back case 150.00
Breitling. 16 size, 16 jewel. O.F.
Navigational Chronograph. Black
dial, chrome case, separate
seconds. Registered 95.00
Chinese Duplex. Jump second hand.
Silver open face with Chinese
signature..................... 195.00
English. George Denham. C. 1813.
Pair case fusee, intricate balance
cock. Silver base 145.00
English. Charles Frodsham. 18 size
lever escapement, chain driven.
Silver hunting presentation watch
in 1860 .... 400.00
English. John Tarts London. Hallmark
1769 pair case fusee. Silver case . 265.00
English. Tobias and Co. 4 jewel, 16
size cylinder keywind and keyset.
Engraved silver case 55.00
English. 18K gold. English-turned
face with Roman numerals.
Keywind, 2-1/8" diam., George III
type. C. 1815 .... 200.00

French. F. Berthoud. 16s, O.F. 4
jewel keywind and keyset. Thin
movement. Silver dial with bird
engraved, silver case with gold
borders 150.00
French. Diana Chronometer. Open
face, engraved silver case, stem
wind. C. 1880. Nos. 1 to 12 on
raised translucent medallions; 13
to 24, outside ring 135.00
French Lapel Button Watch. Made in
1917, dial ¼" diam., stem wind .. 75.00
French. 16s, O.F. Lepine, keywind
and keyset. Silver case 125.00

Swiss. Cylinder, 9 ligne, O.F., 11
jewels. Silver case, outside back
cover has enameled religious
scene of Mother and Child. Inside
back cover has enameled scene of
Jesus 145.00
Swiss. Cylinder, 9 ligne, O.F., 11
jewels. Gold filled, long pendant
case. Bezel of pearls surround
small dial 125.00
Swiss. Cylinder. Pendant watch, 9
ligne, O.F., 11 jewels. Silver case
with repousse portrait of woman . 100.00

WATERFORD GLASS

The factory was established at Waterford,
Ireland in 1729. Chandeliers, candelabras,
boat-shaped and turn-over bowls, drinking
vessels, etc., were produced. It was a
flint-type glass commonly decorated by
cutting. The characteristic of the glass made
before 1830 is the dark color. The color
became whiter and more brilliant after that
date. The factory closed in 1852 as the Irish
glass industry was a dying business. The last
maker of the old Irish cut glass died in 1896. In
1952, 100 years after the Waterford Glass Co.,
in Ireland closed, it was reopened and is now
in production.

Pitcher. Applied handle $135.00

Celery. 8", turned-down rim .... $ 115.00
Chalice. Covered. 16" high, long
stem, round foot, high finial. Cut
allover 285.00
Cruet. 12" high, cut. Spire stoppers.
Pair 145.00
Decanters
9" high, applied handle 100.00
10" high. Cut allover. Mushroom
stoppers. Late. Pair 195.00
With 6 matching stem wines.
Signed 200.00
Epergne. Tulip in silver standard ... 120.00
Jar. Covered. 10" high, 5½" diam. .. 150.00
Lamps, Hurricane. 27" high, cut
base, stem and bobeches. Double
button cut spear prisms. 18th
century. Pair 700.00

Lustres. Cut, 12½", 9" prisms with
cut ball on end. Pair............ 500.00
Pitcher. 10½" high............... 145.00
Plate. 8" 50.00
Salt, Master. Diamond-shape,
footed 45.00
Salts. Oval. Pair 85.00
Sugar Shaker. Crystal, silver top 75.00
Tumbler. Cut 45.00
Urn. 9½" high. 4 round, pointed
ends extend above the rim. Cut,
square base 245.00
Vases
6½" high. Diamond cut, square
base......................... 145.00
7¾" high, 6" diam. top. Late 95.00
10¾" high. Cut, footed. C. 1810 .. 275.00
12¼" high. Flared top, petal-
shaped base 225.00
15" high. Cornucopia in silver
holder 300.00
Wine Glass. 5½" high. Heavy
diamond cut pattern 39.50

WAVECREST GLASS

The glass is made of opal or milk glass and has
a satin finish. It was made in France but was
imported into the United States and decorated
in the Sevres manner by the C.F. Monroe Co.,
Meriden, Connecticut, from about 1894 to
1905. The mark is "Wavecrest" with the
initials of the company "C.F.M. Co."

Bell. 4" high, 4" diam. Ivory with
yellow raised scrolls. Pink blossoms, 4 ornate brass filigree,
splayed feet. Brass Crown finial .. $ 450.00
Bowls
2¼" high, metal rim. "The CFM
Co." on bottom 100.00
3½" diam. Three ornate legs.
Signed 145.00
7½" diam., 6" high. Brass ring and
feet 195.00
Boxes
2¾" high, 4" diam. Round, red
pennant mark. Ivory color with
pansies on top. Original satin
lining 175.00
3¾" base diam. Portrait top.
Painted Cherubs. Covered. Signed 165.00
4" square, hinged cover. Raised
blue shell, yellow floral decor,
satin lining 195.00
4" square. Powder. Round beveled glass mirror on cover. Pink
flowers on green bkgd.......... 230.00
4½" diam. Jewel. Relief enamels,
tufts. Red mark................ 240.00

Box. 3" diam. Pink decor, hinged cover
$160.00

5" high, 3¾" wide, 7" long.
Footed and jeweled............ 385.00
6" high, 4½" wide. Letter.
Enameled violet decor 225.00
6" high, 7" square. Collar and
Cuffs. Satin lining.............. 295.00
6" square. Puffy, hinged lid with
decor 375.00
7" diam. Jewel. Brass hinged
cover, pink, allover floral decor,
embossed in light blue 250.00
Card Holder. 1¾x2½x4". Goldplated collar, pink enamel flowers 65.00
Cigar Humidors
4x6". "Cigars," shell lid. Aqua,
pink flowers. Red Banner, paper
sticker 325.00
6x8" 295.00
6" high, 6½" diam. Red 300.00
Indian Chief portrait. Signed 275.00
Cracker Jars
7½" high. With lid, fully decorated 265.00
White satin ground with mum
decor. Puffed blank 250.00
Dish. 7" diam., gold ormulo rim,
baroque handles. Pink and blue
with enamel amethyst flowers ... 175.00
Flask. Floral decor 145.00
Hair Receiver. Brass top, raised
enamel decor 190.00
Jar. 2x3". Round, open, metal rim
and handles, flowers. Marked ... 145.00
Jardinieres
7x8½". Enameled, beaded rim.
Signed 275.00
10x14". Signed................. 350.00

Letter Holder. Brass band, footed ...	250.00
Pin Trays	
No handles	65.00
Ormolu handles	75.00
Planters	
3x4x9". Fern and floral decor	265.00
7½" diam., 6-sided. Brick-red color, floral decor	300.00
Salt and Pepper Shakers. Pair	150.00
Sugar Bowl and Creamer. Resilvered tops. Set	350.00
Syrup Jug	250.00
Toothbrush Holder	165.00
Tray. 7" round. Blue & pink flowers ..	165.00
Vases	
6¼" high. In footed, ormulo holder. Pink and blue pansies and raised shell, gold decor	265.00
7" high. Bulbous, low. Heavy gold ormolu butterfly side handles, running leaf, intaglio decor	295.00
7" high. Ormolu collar, 4-footed holder. Blue, enameled, scrolls. Red Banner mark	300.00
8½" high. Oval, cream, white and gold with pink apple blossoms and gold beaded rim	345.00
9" high. Metal base, cream with pink blossom decor	350.00
11" high. White and blue. Sprays of yellow cosmos front and back. Metal collar and feet	400.00
Wig Holder. Ornamental wall decoration. Banner mark	325.00

WEATHER VANES

A weather vane indicates the direction of the wind. They were often made in the shape of animals or other objects.

Auto. Open-top, driver wearing duster and goggles. Milk glass ball, copper. C. 1915 .... $	600.00
Chicken. Tin. Iron rods, word shaft. Old decorations. Pennsylvania Amish-type	500.00
Cow. 28" long, 18" high. Copper	650.00
Deer. Copper	550.00
Eagles	
Copper, on orb	750.00
Iron, Cast. On orb, directional letters	600.00
Zinc. 37" wingspread, 54" long. N.E.S.W.......................	550.00
Fish. 26" long, 9" high. Copper	600.00
Horses	
16" high, 31" long. Copper	650.00

Horse $650.00

Whirlygig. Windmill propels man sawing wood, homemade. Whimsy	250.00
Bullet hole in horse. Copper......	500.00
Ram. Copper	600.00
Roosters	
18" long, 24" high. Copper	675.00
Small, on arrow	450.00

WEDGWOOD

Josiah Wedgwood founded the famous Wedgwood Pottery at Burslem England, in 1759. Wedgwood's history is complex and confusing.

Although Wedgwood is probably associated more with Basalt and Jasperware, the factory produced many other wares including creamware, drabware, redware and a fine quality of porcelain.

In 1920 Fairyland Lustre was introduced. This porcelain is decorated with colorful, fantasy-like decals with gold detailing. Lustre-ware production ceased in 1932. Lately interest and prices on this ware has increased rapidly. The firm is still active and producing fine quality dinnerware and accessories.

Bowl. 4¾". Fairyland Lustre. Octagon-shaped. Blue inside, orange outside. Bird and Persian $195.00

Plate. 8¾". Majolica. Mottled green, brown center, pierced rim $45.00

Biscuit Jar. Jasperware. Dark blue, Wedgwood mark. Classic figure, silver lid . . . . $ 135.00

Bowls

2½" diam. Lustre Ware. Green outside, MOP inside, dragons 125.00

2½x4". Lustre Ware. Octagon shape, butterscotch exterior with six temple dogs, gold border, moss green lustre interior with scarabs 200.00

3" diam. Lustre Ware. Blue outside, MOP inside, dragons 135.00

3¼" diam., 1½" high. Lustre Ware. Mottled orange inside, blue outside. Hummingbird inside on bottom. Portl. Mk. 25942 . . . . 155.00

5" diam., 2½" high. Lustre Ware. 3 gold dragons on mottled green outside 295.00

5½" diam. Lustre Ware. Blue outside, orange inside, birds 225.00

8-5/8" diam., 5¾" high. Lustre Ware. MOP inside, mottled blue outside, dragons, lustred 395.00

9" diam. Lustre Ware. Blue, octagonal. Pearlized interior with paintings of frogs, mice, butterflies and dragonfly. Elves sitting and climbing in trees 425.00

10" diam., 2" deep. Black Basalt. Turned-in top, border of high relief grapes, leaves and twigs. Impressed England 75.00

11x9½x3" deep. Creamware. Basketweave center with green medallion. Lattice sides, applied green strapwork 145.00

15¼x4½". Creamware. Green scenic design, 1879, signed 100.00

Boxes, Jasperware

3" diam., 2" high. Blue. White cameo bust of Washington on cover in high relief. White floral border on base. English 95.00

3" diam. Lilac. Round, covered . . . 75.00

3" diam. Covered. Terra Cotta. Kidney-shaped 75.00

4¼" diam., 3" long. Heart-shaped, covered. White with green figures. English 250.00

Butter Dish. Jasperware. Metal lid and tray. Marked Wedgwood 130.00

Creamer. 4" high. Salt glaze. Pinched-in spout. Berries, leaves and vines in relief 95.00

Dessert Service. Pink. 6 scallop and shell plates, 8½" diam. Center, conch shell dish on standard, 8½" high, 11¼" long. Impressed Wedgwood 950.00

Dish, Game. 5½x6x8". Caneware. Cauliflower finial, raised leaves, base decor of grapes and leaves in high relief 250.00

Jardiniere. 6½x7". Jasperware. Blue background with five classical women and lion heads holding laurels in mouths marked Wedgwood 165.00

Medallions. Jasperware. Green and white. 2-3/8" long in pale green jasper dip, 1 with cupid holding sheaf of wheat and a sickle. Other holding floral garland. Impressed Wedgwood marks, remounted in frames 6½x7½". Pair 325.00

Mug. 2x2". Friendship. Lustre Ware. 3-handled with mottled blue exterior with humming birds. Orange interior with humming bird 175.00

Pin Tray. Terra Cotta. Coral, diamond-shape 45.00

Pitcher. 4½" high. Jasperware. Blue. White classic scenes, grape border 125.00

Planter, Wall. 7x9". Bird's Nest, bird flying into nest. C. 1873 . . . . 350.00

Plates

9". Lustre Ware. Blue ground with large butterfly in center outlined in gold. Floral gold border. Portland Vase Wedgwood, England mark 175.00

Platter. 12½" long. Creamware. Early
$40.00

9". Pearlware. Matching shell-shaped bowl. 12½ x 7½ x1¾" diam. Set 375.00

10". Commemorative of U.S. Military Academy. Blue and white scene 25.00

Sherbet. 4" diam., 3-1/8" high. Lustre Ware. Footed, orange outside, MOP inside, tiger 185.00

Tea Set. Portland vase mark #9133, high glaze, white background, decor of green, brown and yellow. Impressed Wedgwood 300.00

Teapot. Caneware. Sheaf of wheat finial on cover. Body has basket-weave pattern 175.00

Tile. Blue and white. Old Man of The Mountain 22.00

Vases
3" high, 4-3/8" diam. Lustre Ware. Squaty rare flame lustre. Background with pixies and fairies inside a soft pea-green MOP lustre with colored design 850.00

5-1/8" high. Bud. Lustre Ware. MOP inside, butterflies 195.00

8" high. Lustre Ware. Dark blue. Dragons 235.00

8" high. Lustre Ware. Humming birds flying in different directions on blue mottled ground. Borders of geese in gold, orange interior . 385.00

WELLER WARE

Weller ware was first made in Steubenville, Ohio in the early 1890's by W. A. Long and was called "Lonhuda." In 1896, S. A. Weller, Zanesville, Ohio purchased the factory. The name was changed to "Louwelsa" and it was produced in quantity. Many pieces resembled Rookwood which had floral decorations on a dark ground underglaze. Most items were marked "Weller."

Baskets
9". Hanging. "Forest" . . . . $ 40.00
10" high, 6" diam. Twig handle on top of acorn. No mark 75.00

Bowls
7" diam., 3-3/8" high. "Forest." Unsigned 35.00
7". Wedgwood, blue with red apple decor. 25.00

Candlestick. 9" high. Louwelsa 75.00

Clock. 6½", marked Louwelsa. Footed, orange floral and green leaves on glossy brown ground . . . 250.00

Console Set. 12" diam. bowl, two candlesticks and flower holder in shape of flying fish. Green with blue decor. Each piece marked. Matched set 165.00

Cruet. 7" high. Cherry blossom decor 75.00

Flower Pot. 8" top diam., 6" bottom diam., 7" high. Black with U.S. flag on obverse and reverse 80.00

Jardinieres
6x7". Etna. Unmarked. Maroon pansies around top 30.00
8" high, 9" diam. Etna. Wine-colored iris on two sides 50.00
8½" high, 9½" wide. 3-footed. Blue ware. Classic figures of

Vase. Weller-Chase. 6½" high. Pillow-shaped. Ivory figurines in relief. Pair
$130.00

women dancing, holding grapes, playing pipes. Pink, green floral band around top and bottom.

Impressed "Weller"	100.00
9" high. Apples	85.00

Floral. Orange, brown, green high
gloss	95.00

Jugs

3" high, 5½" diam. Short squat. Handled with spout on top. Floral decor. Mkd. "Aurelian Weller K".. | 110.00
5" high, 3½" diam. 2 chess players	145.00

Lamp Bases

8" high, 34" circum. Drilled for
wiring	120.00

12" high. "Blue Drapery." Marked,
no shade	75.00

19" high. Harp shades. Blue with colorful pink flower decor and
green vines. Electrified. Pair	200.00

Mugs

5½" high. Handled, Indian "Black-
bird"........................	55.00

5½" high. Handled, Indian "Tame
Wolf"	60.00

Pitchers

2½" high, 6" across flat pitcher. Brown glaze with berries and autumn-colored leaves. Marked
Louwelsa Weller	65.00

8¼" high. "Kingfisher" advertise-
ment on base	65.00
12" high. Tankard. Indian "Chief Hollow Horn Bear".............	135.00

21½" high, 7" square base. Full figure of blonde woman in relief, green and pink coloring. Signed
"Weller Art Nouveau MAT"	175.00
Plaque. Wm. McKinley. 4½" diam. ..	37.50

Planter. Bulbous, 8¾" high. Portrait of young child on side. Brown with green glaze $90.00

Compote Vases. 6½x16". Ivory ground, classical rose, wreath decor. Pair $250.00

Punch Bowl. 13" diam., 6½" high. Rich browns and green fruit decor	200.00
Tankard. 11" high. "The Hunted." Artist signed A.H.	175.00
Teapot. Tea rose pattern. Pumpkin-shape, light yellow with green stem, finial on lid. Artist signed DE	50.00
Umbrella Stand. 20" high, 10" diam. Red, green and gold tulips	95.00
Urn. 7" high. Dark brown to orange. Flower and leaf decor. High glaze	85.00

Vases

3½" high. Brown tone with cherries. Louwelsa	35.00
4½" high. Sicard. Gourd-shaped, leaves and berries decor. Irides-cent and well fired..............	125.00
5¾" high. L'Art Nouveau. Dark brown to gold glaze, 2 stylized flowers, high gloss	75.00
6" high. Hudson. Glazed, colored flowers	49.50
6¼" high. Handled, nasturium decor	85.00
7" high. Double bud vase with acorn and oak leaf decor. Signed .	85.00
7½" high. Dickensware Weller. Man playing golf. Brownish-green background	195.00
8" high. 4 handles at neck, gray background with grapes in relief .	110.00
8½" high. Louselsa, floral decor, artist's initials.................	115.00

9" high. Sicard. Bullet-shape with decor of acorn leaves and branches. Signed 195.00

9¼" high. Abstract iridescent scene 135.00

9¼" high. Green body with panels of lighter green leaves and brown stems. Pair 150.00

9¼" high. Sicard. Trumpet top, greenish-gold flower design. Signed 225.00

10½" high. Louwelsa. Indian. Signed by A. Dunlavy 125.00

11" high. Hudson. Six-sided in matt blue. Detailed iris flowers and leaves on two sides 75.00

11¼" high. Golfer. Artist signed L.M. 250.00

11½" high. Bottle-shaped vase. Dickensware Weller. "Domby & Son" 195.00

12" high. Louwelsea ware. Rose decor. Artist signed, Hester Pillsburg. Pair 265.00

12" high. Varigated green and tan ground with blue plum decor 140.00

14" high. Pale turquoise with pink blossoms 135.00

16" high. Floretta, grape decor in relief 185.00

16" high. Louwelsa, decorated with berries. High gloss 175.00

16½" high, 7¼" diam. Dickensware. Mat green, sgraffito dragon. Impressed "Weller" 425.00

17" high. Louwelsa, rose decor, signed by artist 220.00

WESTERN FRONTIER ITEMS

Western frontier items available now date from about 1850 to 1890. It was in this period that the great migration to the West took place.

Arrowheads. Old Mexican ....$ .35

Branding Iron. Massive, used for crates. AWF & Co. Ex. 80.00

Buckles

Bronze. Wells Fargo & Co. 1877 pattern, Union Pacific train with classic old iron horse on face 25.00

*Bronze. Wells Fargo & Co. 1902 pattern, with names San Francisco and Sacramento on face 17.50

Clip corners and detailed stagecoach loaded with WF mine workers 25.00

Clip corners. Part of State pattern with exact replica of famous Currier & Ives "Express Train"

Branding Iron. 23½" long. Initials "EB"
$18.00

embossed in heavy brass face, with Wells Fargo name 35.00

Wells Fargo & Co. "Alert & Faithful," with a WF guard dog protecting a strong box and safe . 25.00

Wells Fargo & Co. Bankers & Forwarders. 1886 pattern. AC & CRR gold train with full company name 30.00

Buttons. Buffalo nickel and old dime. Each 2.00

Cinch. Woven horsehair 8.50

Cup, Drinking. Copper, marked Wells Fargo & Co. Sutter Creek ... 35.00

Key. Jail or ranch. Old, large, 6" long, iron...................... 8.50

Knife. WF & Co., die set. C. 1870 .... 75.00

Lariat. 20'. Woven rawhide........ 19.50

Mail Bag. US embossed Pony Express type 95.00

Pistol, Boot. Steel. "WF & Co., Express Bldg. SF" on barrel. With under hammer 250.00

Plate. Small, heavy brass. Adams Express Co. Two loop fittings on the back, for use as buckle or badge 25.00

Reins, Pony. Woven rawhide 6.00

Rope 20'. Woven horsehair......... 15.00

Scale. Brass, enamel finish. With words "Adams Express Co." 97 Broadway New York and Great Eastern, Western & Southern Express and "London" engraved in the pans 275.00

Sign. Metal, yellow 1'x2'. Bears the words "Wells Fargo & Co. Bankers and Express Forwarders" 75.00

Spurs, Spanish. Iron, 2½" rowels. Pair 10.00

Vest, Steel. Made to fit under overcoat. Covered in soft hide and bears name "Butterfield Stage Co." Transit Overseas, W.B. & Co. 1859, Paris. Weighs 27 pounds. Smith & Tower's number 4 pattern armor........................ 1250.00

Wax Seals. Wells Fargo. Western seals 75.00

*Reproduced Item

WHIELDON

Whieldon ware was made by Thomas Whieldon from 1719 to 1795. Whieldon is considered one of the most important Staffordshire potters and probably the last craftsman to use traditional potting methods. Whieldon ware is commonly associated only with the creamware decorated with the mottled browns, greens, blues, greys and yellows resembling tortoise shell. Whieldon also produced other earthenwares in the shapes of vegetables, such as cauliflower and cabbage, with a deep green glaze.

Josiah Wedgwood worked for and was in partnership with Thomas Whieldon for a short time. Therefore, there is much confusion in identifying a particular piece as Whieldon, Whieldon-Wedgwood or very early Wedgwood.

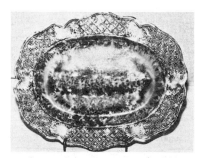

Platter. 10" diam. $375.00

Mug. Tortoise Shell decor . . . . $	425.00
Pitcher. Mottled browns	600.00
Plates	
8½". Tortoise Shell	250.00
9¾". Mottled greens, yellows, browns. Scalloped edge	265.00

WILLOW WARE

The ware derives its name from the design or pattern. The scenes are in the Chinese tradition and are usually done in medium or light blue, although some examples were made in red.

The pattern is probably one of the most popular ever used by the Staffordshire potters and by potteries located elsewhere.

Butter Pat . . . . $	4.00
Butter Tray. 5" diam., ½" deep	15.00
Cereal Bowl. Alfred Meakin	8.00

Platter. 8½ x 11" $30.00

Compote. 8½" diam., 4¾" high. Doulton, Burslem	45.00
Cups and Saucers	
Allertons	18.50
Handleless. Early Staffordshire . . .	27.50
Egg Cup. Double	10.00
Gravy Tureen. Covered, on tray	47.50
Ladle. For large tureen	47.50
Pitcher, Milk. Covered. Ridgway, England	38.50
Plates	
7". "W.R. Ridgway & Co."	12.50
8".	13.50
8½".	14.00
Platters	
12½".	35.00
12½ x 15½". England	35.00
17".	50.00
Salt Shaker	14.00
Sugar Bowl. Covered. Ridgway	45.00
Teapot. Doulton	85.00
Tea Set. Blue and white. C. 1890. 19 pieces. Set.	295.00
Tureens	
Covered, on tray. 2-quart size. Ridgway	125.00
Large, with cover and ladle	195.00
Vases. 8" high. Mason's Ironstone. Blue. Pair.	100.00
Vegetable Dish. Square sides, 5½" high, 9¼" square. Marked "Ye Olde Willow." Staffordshire, England. Late	35.00

WITCH BALLS

A witch ball is a hollow sphere of colored or multicolored glass, often with a hole at the top for attaching a string or wire. It `was supposedly hung near the fireplace to ward

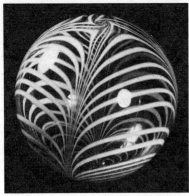

Nailsea. 5½". White on clear .. $55.00

off the evil spirits from entering the home. Witch balls were made in England during the 18th century but those found today were probably made in the 19th century.

Nailsea

3½". Cobalt blue	$ 45.00
4". Clear	40.00
4½". Amethyst	60.00
5½". Clear	55.00
Large, pink and white	95.00
Red glass. 11". Hand blown. Long pontil stem. C. 1840	250.00

WOODENWARE

A general term which serves as a "catch all" for wooden items of dairy, kitchen and general use in the 19th century.

Barber Pole. Hanging. 22" long, original decorations	$ 225.00
Bellows. Pine	50.00
Blueberry picker. Wood and tin	150.00
Boot Jack	15.00

Bed Smoothing Board. Dated 1781. Heavily carved. German $350.00

Box. Pine, 11x13x23". Handcarved eagle on top. Primitive-type ...$45.00

Bowls

7" diam. Cottage Cheese. Hole in bottom for drainage	45.00
9¼" diam., 3½" high. Maple burl .	95.00
9½" diam., 3½" deep. Cone-shaped	50.00
14x23". Original paint	85.00
15" diam. Burl. Refinished	175.00
16" diam. Maple, old	195.00
22" long, 8" deep, turned	150.00

Boxes

2½", oval, covered	12.00
Cheese. Large	55.00

Buckets

Oaken, for well	35.00
Sugar	30.00

Butcher's Block. Maple. Round 29½" diam., 33" high, three legs	200.00
Butter Molds, See "Butter Molds"	
Butter Paddle	15.00
Cabbage Cutter. Walnut, Penna. Dutch-type with heart cutout in handle	65.00
Candlestick, Hogscraper. 7" high. Hook and push-up. Penna. Dutch .	50.00
Ceiling Fan. 3-speed	195.00

Churns

Barrel, with crank	65.00
Dasher-type, with handle	135.00

Clamps. 18" heavy jaws, marked "T. B. Minor"	25.00
Cookie Roller. 15" long, grooved	18.50
Cranberry Picker. Refinished	135.00
Cream Scoop. Wood	20.00
Cutting Board. Handled	12.50
Darning Egg. With handle	10.00
Dumbbells. Pair	25.00
Eagle. Carved, on gilt ball. 7½" high, wingspread 11", good detail	275.00
Flour Scoop	20.00

Forks
11" long	20.00
Hay. 2-prong	55.00
Gambling Wheel	100.00
Grain Measure. 9" diam., 5" high	22.00
Grain Scoop	20.00
Grain Shovel, one piece	125.00
Hat Stretcher	18.00

Hay Fork. All wood, 4-tines, 1 yard 32", hickory. MB Young burned in towards tines top. Unpainted	75.00
Hobby Horse. 41" long, 33" high, in swing standard	195.00
Indian Clubs. Pair	40.00
Ink Sander	20.00
Inkwell. Glass insert, holes for quill pen	22.50
Keg. Labeled "Kentucky Rifle Gunpowder"	50.00

Candle Dryer. 20" high $75.00

Knife Boxes
Pine, refinished	55.00
Walnut, refinished	60.00
Walnut, rough	35.00

Ladles
14" long. Chinese Rice, filigree carved handle	15.00
Curly maple, refinished	25.00
With holes	15.00
Lemon Squeezer	10.00
Lignum Vitae. Rich graining natural patina. Early	55.00
Merry Go Round Horses. Allan Herchell Trojan Horses. Painted	500.00
Mortar and Pestle. 6", maple	65.00

Ox Yokes
With bows	85.00
Without bows	65.00
Pantry Box. 6½" diam.	12.00
Peck Measure. Iron band	22.00
Pepper Mill	25.00
Pie Crimper	8.50
Pie Lifter. Two-prong	8.50
Potato Masher	8.50

Rolling Pins
Curly maple, with handles	27.50
Pine, one-piece	10.00

Salt Boxes
5½ x 6¼ x 6". Pine, refinished	55.00
Hanging. Pine, Penna. Dutch-type. Refinished	85.00
Sap Bucket. 11½" diam. Handle added. Refinished	35.00

Butter Churn. Dasher-type. Penna. All original. Early $135.00

Salt Box. 10½" high $28.00

Spoons
   Refinished 10.00
   Rough 7.50
Stirring Paddle. Primitive 7.50
Sugar Bowl with lid, miniature,
   maple turned 150.00
Sugar Box, large natural stenciled
   twist lid 95.00
Sugar Nippers. Spring release. 18th
   century 65.00
Sugar Scoop 18.50
Sugar Tub. Medium 45.00
Wagon Jack. 34" high. Mainly wood . 40.00
Washboard. With rolls 35.00

ZANESVILLE

Zanesville pottery is a type of art pottery. The firm was founded in 1900 by David Schmedt, Zanesville, Ohio. They produced jardinieres, tankards, umbrella holders and vases. Production ceased in 1962.

Tankard. 15½" high. Brown, slip
   berries. LaMoro .... $ 200.00

Globe. Mosaic Tile Co. N.Y. Green
$12.50

Vases
   7" high. Clover blossoms. LaMoro.
   Artist signed 150.00
   9½" high. Pansy decor on dark
   brown. LaMoro 75.00
   12" high. 4-handled. Blends from
   dark brown base to deep blue top.
   Pair 50.00
   14" high. Standard brown, wild
   rose decor. Unmarked, unsigned . 75.00

Figurine. German Shepherd. Black
glaze $25.00

ZSOLNAY PORCELAIN

Zsolnay porcelain is a soft paste porcelain. It is usually found decorated and enameled in many brilliant colors and glazed. It was produced in Funkkirchen, Hungary after 1855. Recently figurines referred to and sometimes marked Zsolnay have been showing up on the market. These small figurines are in solid colors and are highly lustred. They are currently being made in Canada. Although they can be purchased for a reasonable price in Canada, they command a high price in the United States.

Cup and Saucer $35.00

Bowls

2¾ x5x6". Oval, open lattice
work. mauve, cream-colored flow-
ered medallions . . . . $ 75.00

3" high, 5" diam. Raised mark.
Reds and black with soap bubble
iridescence 165.00

10" diam. Enameled pink flowers
on gold crackled ground. Early
mark 145.00

Reticulated two-handled, cream
color, oval. Pink, blue and gold
flowers 95.00

Candle Holder. Iridescent blue and
green 45.00

Dish. Oval. 3" long, 2½" high.
Iridescent blue, pink and gold.
Reticulated edge. Signed 65.00

Figurines, Late

Bird. 2½". Metallic iridescent 95.00

Deer, Lying. 5x5". Iridescent blue
green 135.00

Doe, Lying. 3x6". Iridescent blue
green 135.00

Girl. Small, 3" high, with lamb.
Lustre 125.00

Hawk, Sitting. 2½". Iridescent . . .   95.00

Garniture Set. Large, one oval and
two round planters. Caramel-
colored with handpainted birds
and flowers set in bronze dore'
stands with winged dragons 450.00

Inkwell, 3½". Yellow, purple, green,
mottled. Coloring with Sgraffito
work on body. Figure of nude
woman by opening 150.00

Plate. 2½ x3¼". Pink and cream.
Cats fishing 50.00

Pot. Cache. 4½" high. Reticulated
and enameled. Marked Zsolnay
2933, gold. Five steeple castle
mark 135.00

Tea Set. 7 pieces. Signed 150.00

Vases

3x6". Crystaline. Powder blue . . .   135.00

3½" high. Metallic iridescent of
green and yellow mottled coloring. Woman's nude figure in full
relief on side. Signed 135.00

4½" high. Green and yellow.
Mermaid in relief on side.
Marked 140.00

8" high. Conical, flaring neck with
designs in ochre and green
against red ground. Iridescent,
marked on back Millennium 275.00

9" high. Pinched, gourd-shape,
iridescent glaze 325.00

13" high. Iridescent scenic in reds,
blues, green and orange. Tall
trees on side, full moon and stars
on reverse 775.00

Index

McCoy Pottery, 426
Mechanical Banks, 158-161
Medallion, 115
Medical Items, 426
Meissen, See Dresden, 301-302
Meissen, Onion Pattern, 427-428
Melrose, 115-116
Mercury Glass, 428
Metal Banks, 158-163
Mettlach, See Steins, 570-572; also See
  Villeroy & Boch, 608
Michigan, 62-63
Mickey Mouse Items, See Collectible Char-
  acter & Personality Items, 257-259
Mikado, See Daisy & Button with Cross Bars,
  103
Milk Glass, 428-430
Miffefiori Glass, 430
Minerva, 63
Miniature Lamps, 400-401
Miniature Paintings, 430-431
Miniatures, 431-433
Minnesota, 63
Minton China, 433
Mirror, See Virginia, 91
Mirrors, See Furniture, 318-344
Mocha Ware, 433-435
Molds:
  Butter, 213
  Candle, See Tole, 591-593
  Food, 435-436
Monart Glass, 436
Monkey, 116
Moon and Star, 63-64
Moorcroft Pottery, 436-437
Moriaga China, 437
Moser Glass, 437-439
Moss Rose Pattern China, 439
Muffineers, 440
Mugs:
  China, 239
  Glass, 440-441
  Shaving, Fraternal & Misc., 541-542
  Shaving, Occupational, 542-543
Mulberry China, 441
Music Boxes, 441-442
Musical Instruments, 442-443
Mustache Cups and Saucers, 443-444
                    N
Nailhead, 64
Nailhead and Panel, See Fine Cut and Panel,
  107-108
Nailsea Glass, 444-445
Nakara, See Wavecrest, 613-614
Napkin Rings, 445-446
Nash Glass, 446
Nazi Items, 446-447
Netsukes, 447-448
Nevada, 64
Newcomb College Pottery, 448

New England Pineapple, 64-65
Newhall China, 448-449
New Hampshire, 65
New Jersey, 65-66
Niagara, 66
Niloak Pottery, 449
Nippon China, 449-451
Nodders, 451
Noritake China, 451-452
North Pole, See Polar Bear, 72-73
Notched Rib, See Bamboo, 12
Nut Crackers, 452
                    O
Oak Leaf, See Ribbed Palm, 76; also See
  Willow Oak, 129-130
Oak, Royal, See Royal Oak, 121
Oats and Barley, See Wheat and Barley,
  127-128
Occupational Shaving Mugs, 542-543
Occupied Japan China, 452-453
O'Hara Diamond, See Sawtooth and Star,
  121-122
Old Ivory China, 453-454
Old Man of the Mountains, See Viking, 91;
  also See Bearded Man, 15
Old Paris China, 454-455
Old Sleepy Eye, 455
Old Store Items, See Store Items, Old, 577-578
One Hundred One, 66
Onion Meissen, 427-428
Onyx Glass [Findlay Glass, Silver Inlay], 456
Opalescent Hobnail, See Hobnail, Opalescent,
  109
Opaline Glass, 456-457
Open Basketweave, See Basketweave, Open,
  96
Open Rose, 66
Oregon, See Beaded Loop, 14
Orient, See Buckle with Star, 20
Oriental Items, 457-458
Oriental Rugs, See Rugs, Oriental, 526-527
Orion, See Cathedral, 99
Oval Medallion, See Panelled Daisy, 67-68;
  also See Daisy and Button, 101-103
Oval Mitre, 66-67
Oval Star, 67
Owens Pottery, 458-459
                    P
Paintings:
  Miniature, 430-431
  Primitive, 487-488
  Reverse on Glass, 498-499
Pairpoint Glass, 459-460
Paisley Shawls, See Linens, 406-408
Palace, See Moon and Star, 63-64
Palm, Ribbed, 76
Palmette, 67
Panelled Cherry, 67
Panelled Daisy, 67-68
Panelled Dewdrop, 68